Introduction to Engineering

Seventh Edition

Carleton University

With additional material by: M. John Hayes,
Daniel Brassard, and Tabassum Aziz

Taken from:
Introduction to Excel, Fourth Edition
by David C. Kuncicky and Ronald W. Larsen

Introduction to Professional Engineering in Canada, Third Edition
by Gordon C. Andrews, J. Dwight Aplevich, Roydon A. Fraser, and
Carolyn MacGregor

Introduction to MATLAB®, Second Edition
by Delores M. Etter

Graphics Concepts for Computer-Aided Design, Second Edition
by Richard M. Lueptow

ISBN 10: 1-256-36271-9
ISBN 13: 978-1-256-36271-5

Contents

Section 1

Welcome to Engineering

Chapter 1
An Introduction to Engineering

An engineering degree opens the door to a highly respected and highly structured profession, so graduation is a major achievement. Engineering students look forward to the happy day when they receive their engineering degrees, as shown in Figure 1.1, and their iron rings. Chapter 1 of this book introduces you to the engineering profession by exploring the following topics:

- a definition of engineering,

- the role of engineers in relation to other technical specialists,

- characteristics of some important engineering disciplines,

- engineering in Canada, including Canadian engineering accomplishments and the distribution of engineers by province,

- the talents and skills needed to become an engineer,

- some of the engineering challenges faced by society.

Figure 1.1   Two engineering graduates, diploma in hand and Ritual of the Calling of an Engineer in memory, celebrate their achievements. Graduation is the first important step to becoming a professional engineer.

The Further Study questions at the end of this chapter (Section 1.7) may help you to master the main ideas in the chapter, and also to confirm your decision to choose engineering as a career.

1.1   WHAT IS AN ENGINEER?

The term *engineer* comes to English from the Latin word *ingenium,* meaning talent, genius, cleverness, or native ability. Its first use was to describe those who had an ability to invent and operate weapons of war. Later, the word came to be associated with the design and construction of works, such as ships, roads, canals, and bridges, and the people skilled in these fields were non-military, or *civil* engineers. The meaning of the term *engineering* depends, to some degree, on the country. In England, people with practical skills have been called engineers since the time of the Industrial Revolution. In North America, more emphasis was placed on formal training, as a result of a recognized need for trained engineers during the wars of the 1700s and 1800s, and the modelling of early American engineering programs on French engineering schools [1].

In Canada, the title *Professional Engineer* is restricted by law for use by persons who have demonstrated their competence and have been licensed by a provincial licensing body, referred to in this book as a *provincial Association.* Exceptions are permitted for stationary and military engineers, who are subject to other regulations. The legal definition of engineering and the licensing of engineers are discussed in Chapter 4. Licensing is important, because the designations *engineer, engineering, professional engineer, P.Eng., consulting engineer* and their French equivalents are official marks held by Engineers Canada, and only licensed engineers may use these titles. Engineers Canada, known until 2007 as the Canadian Council of Professional Engineers (CCPE), acts on behalf of the provincial Associations of Professional Engineers and the Ordre des ingénieurs du Québec.

Although early civilizations produced significant engineering achievements, tools and techniques evolved especially rapidly in the 18th and 19th centuries during the Industrial Revolution. Advances in mathematics and science in this period permitted the prediction of strength, motion, flow, power, and other quantities with increasing accuracy. Recently, the development of computers, inexpensive electronic communication, and the Internet have placed huge amounts of information within easy reach, and the role of the engineer is rapidly evolving, together with the rest of modern society. Therefore, a modern definition of engineering must be broad enough to allow for change. The following definition is adequate for most informal discussions, although a more specific definition, as well as a legal definition, is given in the next chapter:

> An *engineer* is a person who uses science, mathematics, experience, and judgment to create, operate, manage, control, or maintain devices, mechanisms, processes, structures, or complex systems, and who does this in a rational and economic way subject to human, societal, and environmental constraints.

This definition emphasizes the rational nature and technological base of engineering, but it does not fully express the human context of the profession. An engineering career involves problem solving, designing, and building, which can give great pleasure to the engineer and others. There are many opportunities for friendship with team members, and engineering projects exercise communication, management, and leadership skills. Engineering decisions may involve societal or ethical questions. Personal experience and judgment are needed for many decisions, because complex projects sometimes affect society, and social effects are not always reducible to scientific principles or mathematical theorems.

Engineer and writer Henry Petroski emphasized the human side of engineering in *To Engineer is Human* [2]. He contends that in reaction to constantly changing requirements imposed by clients and society, it is human nature to extend design methods to their limits, where unpredicted failures sometimes occur, and to create new design methods as a result of those failures. Samuel Florman, also an engineer and prolific writer, suggests in *The Existential Pleasures of Engineering* [3] that since humankind first began to use tools, the impulse to change the world around us has been part of our nature. Thus, he argues, to be human is to engineer.

1.2   THE ROLE OF THE ENGINEER

Engineering is usually a team activity. Because of the great complexity of many projects, engineering teams often include persons with widely different abilities, interests, and education, who cooperate by contributing their particular expertise to advance the project. Although engineers are only one component of this diverse group, they contribute a vital link between theory and practical application. A typical technical team might include scientists, engineers, technologists, technicians, and skilled workers, whose activities and skills may appear at first glance to overlap. The following paragraphs describe the tasks performed by different members of a typical engineering team. These are broad categorizations, so exceptions are common.

Research scientist   The typical research scientist works in a laboratory, on problems that expand the frontiers of knowledge, but which may not have practical applications for many years. A doctorate is usually the basic educational requirement, although a master's degree is sometimes acceptable. The research scientist typically supervises research assistants and will usually be a member of several learned societies in his or her particular field of interest, but will not usually be a member of a self-regulating profession. The *raison d'être* of pure science is the understanding of natural phenomena, and in a project team, the main responsibility of the scientist is to provide scientific analysis. Although many scientists apply their knowledge to practical tasks, science does not have the same legal structure or responsibilities as engineering.

Engineer   The engineer typically provides the key link between theory and practical applications. The engineer must have a combination of extensive theoretical knowledge, the ability to think creatively, the knack for obtaining practical results, and the ability to lead a team toward a common goal. The bachelor's degree is the basic educational requirement, although the master's degree or doctorate is useful and preferred by some employers. In Canada, all work that is legally defined as engineering must be performed or supervised by a licensed professional engineer, who is required, by provincial law, to be a member or licensee of the provincial Association of Professional Engineers (or in Québec, the Ordre des ingénieurs). Membership confers the right to use the title *Professional Engineer* (P.Eng. or in Québec, ing.).

Technologist   The technologist typically works under the direction of engineers in applying engineering principles and methods to complex technical problems. The basic educational requirement is graduation from a three-year technology program at a community college or equivalent, although occasionally a technologist may have a bachelor's degree, usually in science, mathematics, or related subjects. The technologist often supervises the work of others and is encouraged to have qualifications recognized by a technical society. In Ontario, for example, the Ontario Association of Certified Engineering Technicians and Technologists (OACETT) confers the title of *Certified Engineering Technologist* (C.E.T.). This is a voluntary organization, and the title is beneficial, but not legally essential, for working as a technologist. The fundamental technical difference between technologists and engineers is usually the greater theoretical depth of the engineering education and the greater hands-on experience implied by the technology diploma.

Technician   The technician typically works under the supervision of an engineer or technologist in the practical aspects of engineering, such as making tests and maintaining equipment. The basic educational requirement is graduation from a two-year technician program at a community college or its equivalent. Associations such as OACETT may confer the title *Certified Engineering Technician* (C.Tech.) on qualified technicians, although the title is not essential to obtain work as a technician.

Skilled worker   The skilled worker typically carries out the designs and plans of others. Such a person may have great expertise acquired through formal apprenticeship, years of experience, or both. Most trades (electrician, plumber, carpenter, welder, pattern maker, machinist, and others) have a trade organization and certification procedure.

  Each of the above groups has a different task, and there are considerable differences in the skills, knowledge, and performance expected of each. In particular, a much higher level of accountability is expected from the professional engineer than from other members of the engineering team. The engineer is responsible for competent performance of the work that he or she supervises. In fact, engineers may be held legally accountable not only for their own acts but also for advice given to others. Judgment and experience are often as important as mathematics, science, and technical knowledge; liability insurance is becoming essential in the public practice of engineering. These professional aspects are discussed further in Chapter 4.

  As you begin your engineering career, you should recognize that the categories described above are not rigid. Movement from one group to another is possible, but is not always easy.

1.3   ENGINEERING DISCIPLINES

Most people can name a few branches of engineering: civil, electrical, mechanical, and chemical engineering, perhaps. However, the number of engineering disciplines is much larger than is commonly known. The Canadian Engineering Accreditation Board publishes an annual list of accredited Canadian engineering degree programs [4]. The list changes slightly from year to year as new programs are created or old ones dropped. Equating equivalent French and English names and then removing all duplicates reduces the full list of accredited programs to a smaller set of distinct specializations, illustrated in Figure 1.2. In 2008, there were 244 accredited programs and 60 specializations. The figure shows the names occurring more than once and the number of occur-

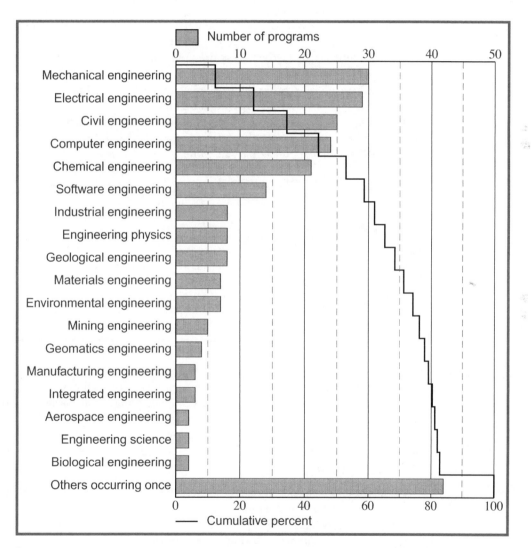

Figure 1.2   Names of accredited Canadian engineering programs in 2008. Of the 244 program names published in reference [4], those occurring more than once are listed on the left, with the bottom row showing that 42 names occur once. The most common program is mechanical engineering, which is found at 30 institutions. Although there are 60 distinctly named specializations, the cumulative percent line shows that the five most common disciplines make up more than 50 % of the total.

rences of each name on the list. The five most common branches make up more than half of the total number of accredited programs in Canada.

In the United States there are approximately eight times as many accredited engineering degree programs as in Canada, with twice as many program names, but the most common names are typically identical and in the same order as in Canada.

Choosing your program

You must choose an engineering discipline that is right for you. Many students choose before they apply for university, but if you have not made a choice or have doubts, you should get further advice from your professors, guidance counsellors, or perhaps best of all, a friend who is a practising engineer. Libraries also have many references, such as encyclopedias and university calendars showing the courses offered for each discipline. The Internet is also an important source of information and advice; see reference [5] for example.

Your choice of university program (that is, your engineering discipline) should be a conscious decision, because it will likely shape the rest of your life. It is wise to consider all relevant factors before you commit to a program. For example, typical factors to consider are the courses that really motivate or inspire you, the type of work you want to do, your preference for mathematical or applied work, your preference for the design office or field-work, or even where you want to work after graduation.

The first step is to gather information about engineering programs. Only then can you make an informed decision. To compare programs, an easy method is simply to write a list of the advantages and disadvantages for each program, based on the factors that are most important to you. You can then make a subjective, but informed, decision.

However, you might like to try the computational decision-making method. To use this method, create a chart with a column for each program, and a row for each factor that is important in your decision. Assign weights to each factor, depending on its importance to you, then rank each program according to how well it satisfies each factor. The "best" program is one that receives the largest sum from the weights that you gave the factors. The computational method sometimes yields surprising results! A spreadsheet is useful, because you may want to recalculate with different factors and weights until you are confident that you have the right result. This repetitive process ensures that all relevant factors are systematically considered before a final decision is made.

To help you confirm your knowledge of engineering disciplines, the following paragraphs describe a few well-known specializations. The basic courses are similar in many disciplines, especially in the first year or two. Consequently, switching from one discipline to another is usually easiest then.

Chemical

Chemical engineers use knowledge of chemistry, physics, biology, and mathematics to design equipment and processes for the manufacture of chemicals and chemical products. The chemical process industries are skill- and capital-intensive, and require highly specialized designers to achieve competitive manufacturing. Some chemical engineers design equipment and processes for the extraction of minerals, petroleum, and other natural resources. Others design new processes for sustaining and reclaiming the natural environment.

Civil

Civil engineers design and supervise the construction of roads, highways, bridges, dams, airports, railways, harbours, buildings, water supply systems, and sewage systems. Many civil engineers specialize in one phase of their discipline, such as highway, sanitary, soil, structural, transportation, or hydraulic engineering. The largest number of licensed engineers in private practice is in civil engineering.

Computer

Computer engineers use a combination of electrical engineering and computer science subjects to design, develop, and apply computer systems. They must understand electronic circuits, computer hardware, computer interfacing and interconnection, software development, and algorithms. Most importantly, they must be able to select the optimal combination of hardware and software components required to satisfy specified performance criteria.

Electrical   Electrical engineers design and supervise the construction of systems to generate, transmit, control, and use electrical energy. Specialists in the power field typically design and develop heavy equipment (such as generators and motors), and transmission lines and distribution systems, including the complex equipment needed to control these powerful devices. Specialists in electronics and communications design and develop devices and systems for transmitting data, solid-state switching, microwave relays, computer logic circuits, and computer hardware.

Environmental   Environmental engineers respond to needs for improved air and water quality and efficient waste management. Environmental engineering is a rapidly growing discipline, concerned with site assessment and approval, air quality in buildings, monitoring and control devices, and a host of investigative, instrumentation, and other support activities. These environmental applications require a broad engineering knowledge, including topics from chemistry, physics, soils engineering, mechanical design, fluid mechanics, and meteorology.

Geological   Geological engineers use knowledge of the origin and behaviour of geological materials to design structures, such as foundations, roads, or tunnels built on or through these materials, and to develop exploration or extraction methods for petroleum and minerals. They may also work with civil engineers in the geotechnical design or construction of roads, airports, harbours, waste disposal systems, and other civil works. Geological engineers are also in increasing demand for ground-water and environmental impact studies and for new petroleum recovery projects such as tar-sands oil recovery.

Industrial   Industrial engineers use probability, statistics, and other mathematical subjects for the design of efficient manufacturing processes. They assume responsibility for quality control, plant design, and the allocation of material, financial, and human resources for efficient production. Automation, materials handling, environmental protection, robotics, human factors, and data processing are some of the specialized subjects required.

Mechanical   Mechanical engineers enjoy a wide scope of activity, including the design, development, manufacture, sale, and maintenance of machinery, ranging from appliances to aircraft. They may be involved with engines, turbines, boilers, pressure vessels, heat exchangers, or machine tools. They may specialize in fields such as machine design, heating, ventilating and refrigeration, thermal and nuclear power generation, manufacturing, quality control, or production scheduling. There are many mechanical engineers employed in related fields, such as mining, metallurgy, transportation, oil refining, and chemical processing.

Software   Software engineering is a new discipline that combines classical engineering project-management skills with the specialized tools and knowledge that are required to design, build, analyze, and maintain complex computer software. In addition to intimate knowledge of the program-design aspects of computer science, the software engineer requires a sufficiently broad understanding of the natural sciences in order to work with specialists in other disciplines and to design correct software to be embedded in machines.

Other programs   Some engineering programs have a relatively broad set of requirements, with the opportunity to choose specialized options or projects in later years. Systems design engineering, engineering science, and génie unifié are examples of such programs. Graduates may work in interdisciplinary areas requiring computer expertise and broad problem-solving and group management abilities. Some engineering disciplines are industry-related, for example, aerospace, agricultural, biosystems, building, forest, mining, and

TABLE 1.1   Distribution of the 155 485 engineering licences in Canada by province and territory in 2006 (data from reference [6]). Many engineers (about 12%) are licensed in more than one province or territory.

Province or Territory	Association Acronym	Practising Engineers	Percentage of Total
Ontario	PEO	60 987	39.2
Québec	OIQ	35 368	22.7
Alberta	APEGGA	27 422	17.6
British Columbia	APEGBC	14 137	9.1
Saskatchewan	APEGS	3 559	2.3
Manitoba	APEGM	3 556	2.3
Nova Scotia	APENS	3 548	2.3
New Brunswick	APEGNB	3 391	2.2
Newfoundland and Labrador	PEG-NL	1 814	1.2
Northwest Territories and Nunavut	NAPEGG	894	0.6
Prince Edward Island	APEPEI	413	0.3
Yukon	APEY	396	0.3

petroleum engineering. Finally, some engineering disciplines are directly related to specific scientific knowledge: engineering physics, management engineering, mathematics and engineering, materials engineering, mechatronics engineering, and nanotechnology engineering are examples.

Other careers   An engineering degree can be excellent preparation for a career in another discipline, such as law, medicine, or business, to name only a few possibilities. If this is your intention, emphasize breadth in your choice of elective courses, since your breadth of knowledge combined with your problem-solving skills will be key future assets.

1.4   ENGINEERS ACROSS CANADA

In 2006, the annual membership survey conducted by Engineers Canada showed that 155 485 licences were held by professional engineers practising in Canada, including holders of temporary engineering licences, but not including geologists, geophysicists, or geoscientists. The distribution of engineering licences, by province and territory, is shown in Table 1.1.

Most engineers are found in the industrialized areas of Ontario and Québec, with the next largest numbers in the resource-rich provinces of Alberta and British Columbia. Comparing the coasts, the West Coast (British Columbia) has many more engineers than the four Atlantic Provinces combined (Nova Scotia, New Brunswick, Prince Edward Island, and Newfoundland and Labrador)—in fact, about half again as many. Yukon and Prince Edward Island have the fewest of Canada's engineers. Nunavut is included in the total for the Northwest Territories.

1.5   CANADIAN ENGINEERING ACHIEVEMENTS

The history of Canadian engineering is full of personalities, struggles, and achievements—too full, in fact, to describe in detail in these few pages. This section lists some important accomplishments of Canadian engineers and concludes with sources of further information on this fascinating subject.

The centennial of engineering as an organized profession in Canada was celebrated in 1987. As part of the celebration, the Engineering Institute of Canada (EIC), Engineers Canada, and the Association of Consulting Engineers of Canada (ACEC) assembled a jury to identify the top engineering achievements of the previous century. The choices were based, among other criteria, on originality, ingenuity, creativity, the importance of the contribution to engineering, and whether the accomplishment initiated significant social and economic change. The jury received many nominations and reviewed a final list of 110 engineering projects, which was then reduced to the 10 most significant achievements.

Another formal review was held in 1999 to identify the five most significant Canadian engineering achievements of the 20th century. The review was sponsored by the organizers of the 1999 National Engineering Week and was held at the National Museum of Science and Technology in Ottawa. The selection criteria included special ingenuity, Canadian content, scope, and diversity.

The centennial list is given below, followed by the five achievements selected from the 20th century and some other well-known Canadian engineering accomplishments.

Transcontinental railway
The Canadian Pacific Railway linked Canada from coast to coast in 1885, a massive project for its time.

St. Lawrence Seaway
The seaway is a series of canals and waterways that opened the Great Lakes to ocean-going ships in 1959.

Synthetic rubber plant
The synthetic rubber plant of Polymer/Polysar (later Polysar, now Bayer Rubber) at Sarnia, Ontario, was built during World War II and was of great importance to the war effort.

Athabasca oil sands
The commercial oil sands development in Northern Alberta showed the feasibility of recovering oil from the Athabasca oil sands. Canada has more oil than Saudi Arabia, but the oil must be separated from the sand.

Very-high-voltage transmission
Hydro-Québec was the first electrical utility to develop transmission lines at a very high voltage (735 kV) for long-distance power transmission.

Nuclear power
The CANDU nuclear power system is an outstanding Canadian design that produces electric power using natural uranium fuel and heavy-water cooling, avoiding the need for expensive fuel enrichment.

Beaver aircraft
The De Havilland DHC 2 Beaver aircraft was designed and built in 1947 to open and explore Canada's North. The Beaver is a robust all-metal aircraft with excellent short takeoff and landing ability with heavy loads.

Alouette satellite
With the Alouette I, Canada became the third nation with a satellite in orbit, after the Soviet Union and the United States. Alouette I was launched in 1962 for the purpose of studying the atmosphere. The satellite operated for 10 years and was one of the most successful satellites ever launched.

Snowmobile
Joseph-Armand Bombardier invented the snowmobile in 1937. The revolutionary idea provided essential winter travel for snowbound Canadians, and developed into a huge new manufacturing industry.

Trans-Canada telephone network
Completed in 1958 as the world's longest microwave network, a Canada-wide chain of microwave towers enabled the reliable transmission of rapidly increasing telecommunication traffic. The Anik satellite, launched in 1972, other geo-stationary satellites, and fibre-optic transmission have enhanced the network.

CPR Rogers Pass project
The Rogers Pass rail link through the Selkirk range of the Rocky Mountains was notorious for heavy snow and steep grades for trains to negotiate. The $500 million, 34 km

Rogers Pass project, completed in 1989, included 17 km of surface route, six bridges totalling 1.7 km, and two tunnels. The 14.7 km Mount Macdonald Tunnel, the pride of the project, is the longest railway tunnel in the western hemisphere.

Confederation Bridge The 12.9 km Confederation Bridge, linking New Brunswick and Prince Edward Island across the Northumberland Strait, is the longest bridge in the world crossing salt water and subject to winter ice hazards.

Canadarm The Canadarm remote manipulator system, one of the main Canadian contributions to the U.S. space shuttle program, was designed by Canadian engineers and built in Canada. The Canadarm deploys and retrieves satellites and other cargo from the space shuttle cargo bay. A more recent enhanced version, Canadarm2 is Canada's contribution to the International Space Station.

IMAX William Shaw, one of the early members of the IMAX Corporation, was the engineer responsible for developing an Australian patent into the "rolling loop" film-transport mechanism in the IMAX projector, which produces stable high-resolution images on an immense screen.

Pacemaker John A. Hopps, working in 1949 with medical colleagues at the Banting and Best Institute in Toronto, discovered a method for restarting a heart that had stopped beating. This led Hopps to develop the first pacemaker at Canada's National Research Council in 1950. A poll of the Canadian public identified the Hopps pacemaker as the achievement that "made them most proud to be Canadian."

Rideau Canal The Rideau Canal is the oldest continuously operated canal system in North America. It was constructed after the War of 1812 to provide a navigable route, well away from the U.S. border, from Lake Ontario to the Ottawa River. Under the direction of military engineer Colonel John By, the canal was constructed entirely by hand, employing thousands of labourers to build the 45 locks along its 200 km length.

Avro Arrow The Avro Arrow was a Canadian-designed all-weather fighter–interceptor that first flew in March 1958. Its flight performance was decades ahead of other aircraft of the time, including Mach 2 speed at 15 000 m (50 000 ft) in normal flight. Prime Minister Diefenbaker abruptly cancelled development in September 1958, and many engineers emigrated to the United States to work in the American space program.

CN Tower The CN Tower was built in 1976 as the world's tallest free-standing structure, rising to a height of 553 m. A telecommunications centre, the tower is also a popular tourist attraction. In 1995, the American Society of Civil Engineers (ASCE) listed the CN Tower as one of the seven wonders of the modern world.

Toronto domed stadium The Toronto domed stadium features a retracting roof, supported by steel arches. It was opened in 1989 as Skydome, but has since been renamed.

Winnipeg floodway In 2008, the International Association of Macro Engineering Societies added the Winnipeg floodway to its list of major engineering achievements. The floodway diverts floodwaters around the city of Winnipeg, and its construction between 1963 and 1968 required moving more earth than was moved for the construction of the Suez canal.

1.5.1   Sources related to Canadian engineering history

Many excellent books have been written on Canadian engineering history; we particularly recommend references [7–10]. The following organizations all maintain web sites, and most produce printed material on Canadian engineering history.

The Engineering Institute of Canada (EIC), the Canadian Academy of Engineering, and the Canadian Society for Civil Engineering (CSCE) are discussed in Chapter 2. The EIC lists over 70 sources for Canadian engineering history on its web site and has published a series of historical and biographical working papers on engineering topics. The Academy web site lists historical publications of interest to Canadian engineers, and the CSCE web site contains links to civil engineering history and heritage.

A search in *The Canadian Encyclopedia* [11] will lead to an explanation and discussion of almost any topic from Canadian engineering history.

The archives of the Canadian Broadcasting Corporation contain historical reports under the headings "science & technology" and "disasters & tragedies."

The University of British Columbia and other institutions host web sites that describe well-known engineering failures and disasters, most of which are not Canadian.

1.6   CHALLENGES AND OPPORTUNITIES FOR ENGINEERING

You will encounter many personal challenges in your education and in your professional life, but you are also a member of a global society, living on a fragile planet. Crises aggravated by rising world population and by increasingly rapid movement of people, goods, money, and disease may affect you during your working life. However, climate change caused by global warming is likely the most important challenge to society that you will face during your engineering career. The problem is illustrated humorously in Figure 1.3, but the reality is more serious. Canada generates most of its electric power from fossil fuel plants, which emit greenhouse gases that cause global warming and climate change.

Climate change—
A major engineering
challenge

Any doubts about global warming and climate change were set to rest in 2007, when the authoritative Intergovernmental Panel on Climate Change (IPCC) issued its comprehensive reports [12]. As a prominent British engineer stated, after reviewing the first IPCC report: "There is now virtually no doubt that climate change is directly linked to

CIVILIZATION ,
AS WE KNOW IT.

Figure 1.3   This editorial cartoon, which depicts our dependence on electric power, appeared after the massive power failure in Ontario and the northeastern United States in August 2003. Sophisticated computers and basic life support alike depend on a heavily loaded power network. Electric power generation, which currently depends largely on fossil fuels, leads to global warming and climate change. Developing sustainable electrical power is a major challenge for engineers. (Reprinted with permission from *The Globe and Mail.*)

mankind's profligate consumption of energy" [13]. The IPCC conclusions are discussedin greater detail in Chapter 9. The message to be drawn from the conclusions is that climate change in the next few decades will cause intense weather, floods, droughts, crop failures, drinking-water shortages, and mass migration that will seriously disrupt our lives unless we take immediate action to combat it.

The challenge for engineers is to aggressively reduce our greenhouse gas emissions. This requires new, intelligent efforts to conserve energy and to avoid waste, such as the invention of innovative methods to reduce, reuse or recycle materials. Engineers must also think ahead, and adapt our current infrastructure for the inevitable effects of climate change. We must design our infrastructure more robustly, to withstand the intense windstorms, hurricanes, and floods that climate change will inflict in future decades. Engineers are, or should be, becoming better informed about the consequences of climate change—we must be part of the solution, not part of the problem. Climate change is a serious challenge, but several authors have suggested ways to fight it, adapt to it, or even profit from it [14, 15].

The role of engineers in society Engineers must take a greater role in political and social debate. Canadian engineers are rarely found in the upper levels of our government, and are seldom involved in policy-making, even when the issues have an engineering content. For example, global warming is not entirely a technical problem. Wasteful practices, accepted by society for centuries, must be changed. Fighting climate change will require some effort and sacrifice, and we must ensure that the effort is rewarded, and that the sacrifice is spread evenly. Constraints that are sufficient to contain global warming will not be easily accepted. Engineers must speak out in the political and ethical debate over climate change and similar issues, so that society's attitudes, laws, and way of life change, appropriately.

Engineering opportunities More positively, Canada's engineering students live today in a world of unparalleled opportunity. The information revolution is still in its early stages, and it will continue to multiply our strength and intelligence, and help to create a world of diversity, freedom, and wealth that could not have been imagined by earlier generations.

The challenges to the engineer, and the opportunities, have never been greater.

1.7 FURTHER STUDY

1. Choose the best answer for each of the following questions.
    (a) In Canada, the title of *engineer* (implying that the holder is a professional engineer):
        i. is not restricted by law.
        ii. may be used only by people employed in technical jobs.
        iii. may be used only by graduates of accredited university engineering programs.
        iv. may be used only by people licensed under provincial or territorial laws.
    (b) Engineering projects are usually a team activity, and the engineer typically
        i. provides the key link between the theory and the practical applications.
        ii. takes responsibility when engineering work affects public safety.
        iii. sets the "factor of safety" between the system capacity and the expected load.
        iv. All of the above are correct.

(c) Technologists and technicians typically work with engineers on projects. Which of the following statements is true about their certification process?

   i. Certification as a technician or technologist is voluntary.

   ii. Certification as a technician or technologist is compulsory.

   iii. Technicians and technologists do not have a certification process.

   iv. Technicians and technologists must be certified as engineers-in-training.

(d) How many distinct names of accredited engineering programs are found in Canadian universities?

   i. fewer than 30   ii. approximately 60

   iii. more than 100   iv. more than 200

(e) Engineering decisions must be based exclusively on the objective use of logic without letting personal experience influence them.

   i. false   ii. true

(f) A professional engineer who designs hydroelectric power transmission lines and distribution systems, including the control systems for these devices, is most likely to have studied in which of the following engineering programs?

   i. civil   ii. electrical   iii. industrial   iv. geological   v. software

   vi. mechanical

(g) A professional engineer who improves the quality of rivers, lakes, and the atmosphere by monitoring air and water quality and by solid and liquid waste management and disposal is most likely to have studied in which of the following engineering programs?

   i. civil   ii. environmental   iii. industrial   iv. geological

   v. manufacturing   vi. mechanical

(h) A professional engineer who develops software for digital telephone switching systems and designs control systems for automated manufacturing production lines is most likely to have studied in which of the following engineering programs?

   i. manufacturing   ii. electrical   iii. industrial   iv. computer

   v. software   vi. environmental

(i) Of the many challenges of the future, the one described in Chapter 1 as probably the most important is

   i. the population explosion.   ii. environmental pollution.

   iii. the rapid spread of disease.   iv. climate change caused by global warming.

   v. congestion in crowded cities.

(j) According to the Engineers Canada membership survey conducted in 2006, which provinces or territories have the most and the fewest licensed engineers?

   i. Ontario has the most, and PEI and Yukon have the fewest.

   ii. Alberta has the most, and Yukon and Northwest Territories have the fewest.

   iii. Ontario has the most, and Yukon and Northwest Territories have the fewest.

   iv. Québec has the most, and PEI and Yukon have the fewest.

2. Select one of the many Canadian engineering achievements listed in Section 1.5, and write a brief summary of its development and impact.

3. If personal characteristics are important in selecting a career or, in particular, a branch of engineering, what interests, aptitudes, and experiences led you to select the particular branch of engineering in which you are currently enrolled? How do your characteristics match the characteristics that you think would be necessary in your chosen branch?

4. "An engineer is someone who can do for ten shillings what any fool can do for a pound"—Nevil Shute in *Slide Rule: The Autobiography of an Engineer*. See if you can find an equally pithy definition that could be used to interest high-school students in the profession.

5. What is the difference between a profession and a job? Your opinions may be influenced by Chapters 4 and 5, which describe the engineering profession.

6. Should the professional person be more concerned about the welfare of the general public than the average person? Should persons in positions of great trust, whose actions could cause great harm to the general public, be required to obey a more strict code of ethics with respect to that trust than the average person? You may find some hints by glancing at Chapters 4 and 5.

7. When you graduate, you will want to know how intense the competition is for career positions. The number of students enrolled in your discipline is a rough indicator of the future supply of job applicants. Search the Internet to find enrollment statistics for engineering disciplines in Canada.

8. Question 7 considers the supply of engineering graduates in your year of graduation. The demand for graduates in each discipline is more difficult to predict, but is cyclical in some industries and subject to major trends, such as the computer and communications revolution, the biological gene-modification revolution, and the demographics of birth, death, and immigration. Make a list of at least five possible jobs you might wish to do, and consider how each of them might be affected by current economic trends. Your conclusions cannot be exact, but might be very useful as you seek work-term or internship experience before graduation.

1.8   REFERENCES

[1] L. P. Grayson, *The Making of an Engineer*. New York: John Wiley & Sons, Inc., 1993.

[2] H. Petroski, *To Engineer is Human: The Role of Failure in Successful Design*. New York: St. Martin's Press, 1985.

[3] S. C. Florman, *The Existential Pleasures of Engineering*. New York: St. Martin's Press, 1976.

[4] Canadian Engineering Accreditation Board, *Accreditation Criteria and Procedures*. Ottawa: Engineers Canada, 2007. <http://www.engineerscanada.ca/e/files/report_ceab.pdf> (March 9, 2008). Pre-publication data at <http://www.engineerscanada.ca/e/acc_programs_2.cfm> (September 10, 2008).

[5] Industry Canada, *Professional Engineering in Canada: Building a Nation*. Industry Canada, 1998. <http://epe.lac-bac.gc.ca/100/205/301/ic/cdc/pec/index.html> (March 9, 2008).

[6] Engineers Canada, 2006 *Membership Survey*. Ottawa: Engineers Canada, 2007. Advance data provided to G. Andrews by S. Colasante, June 26, 2007.

[7] N. Ball, *Mind, Heart, and Vision: Professional Engineering in Canada 1877 to 1987*. Ottawa: National Museum of Science & Technology, 1988.

[8] J. J. Brown, *Ideas in Exile: A History of Canadian Invention*. Toronto: McClelland and Stewart, 1967.

[9] J. J. Brown, *The Inventors: Great Ideas in Canadian Enterprise*. Toronto: McClelland and Stewart, 1967.

[10] J. R. Millard, *The Master Spirit of the Age: Canadian Engineers and the Politics of Professionalism, 1887–1922*. Toronto: University of Toronto Press, 1988.

[11] J. H. Marsh, ed., *The Canadian Encyclopedia*. Toronto: McClelland and Stewart, 1988. <http://www.thecanadianencyclopedia.com/> (March 9, 2008).

[12] S. Solomon, D. Qin, M. Manning, Z. Chen, M. Marquis, K. B. Averyt, M. Tignor, and H. L. Miller, eds., *Climate Change 2007: The Physical Science Basis. Contribution of Working Group I to the Fourth Assessment Report of the Intergovernmental Panel on Climate Change*. New York: Cambridge University Press, 2007. <http://www.ipcc.ch/ipccreports/ar4-wg1.htm> (March 9, 2008).

[13] I. Arbon, "Quoted on the BBC news," 2007. Energy, Environment & Sustainability Group, Institute of Mechanical Engineers, <http://news.bbc.co.uk/2/hi/science/nature/6324093.stm> (March 9, 2008).

[14] G. Monbiot, *Heat: How to Stop the Planet from Burning*. Toronto: Random House Anchor Canada, 2007.

[15] T. Homer-Dixon, *The Upside of Down*. New York: Knopf, 2006.

Chapter 2
Engineering Societies

Most undergraduates learn about engineering societies through design contests held on campus. For example, the Society of Automotive Engineers (SAE) organizes an annual Formula SAE race (as shown in Figure 2.1) for students who design, build, and drive the vehicles. However, the main role of engineering societies is to develop and distribute technical and professional information, including technical standards and research results. This key role is vitally important to practising professional engineers. This chapter describes:

- the purpose and history of engineering societies,
- differences between engineering societies and licensing Associations,
- the importance of engineering societies,
- some criteria for selecting and joining engineering societies.

Figure 2.1   A Formula SAE race, in which engineering students design, build, and race cars under specified rules (Photo courtesy of Formula SAE team, University of Waterloo).

2.1   THE PURPOSE OF ENGINEERING SOCIETIES

The general term *engineering societies* includes *technical societies, engineering institutes,* or even *learned societies.* Engineering societies are voluntary organizations, but they provide technical information that is essential to most practising engineers. This information is often too specialized to be provided by the provincial licensing Associations.

To avoid confusion, it should be emphasized that engineering societies are significantly different from the provincial professional engineering licensing Associations discussed in Chapters 4 and 5. The provincial Associations are created by law and have the legal authority to license engineers and to regulate engineering practice. Membership in (or registration by) the provincial Association is not optional, because a licence is required to practise engineering in Canada. Conversely, membership in an engineering society is voluntary.

Engineering societies often advocate on behalf of their members, and this is another distinctive difference from the provincial licensing Associations. The primary goal of licensing Associations is to protect the public, so they cannot advocate for engineers–it could be a conflict of interest. The roles of engineering societies and licensing Associations are therefore different and complementary.

The role of engineering societies in Canada   Engineering societies usually focus on an engineering discipline, such as computer, electrical, or mechanical engineering; on an industry or specialization, such as the nuclear, mining, or manufacturing industries; or on a specific membership, such as engineering students, engineers in management, or consulting engineers. Some well-known engineering societies are listed in Section 2.5.

The purpose of engineering societies may vary, depending on the society, but the main goals usually involve activities of vital interest to their members, such as:

- publishing technical information,
- developing technical codes and standards,
- encouraging engineering research,
- organizing engineering meetings and conferences,
- organizing engineering design competitions for students,
- organizing short courses on specialized topics,
- advocating on behalf of their members, when appropriate.

These activities have an immense impact on the engineering profession. They stimulate the creation of knowledge and innovative new products. Codes and standards guide engineering design to assure safety and product quality. Meetings, conferences, and short courses are extremely useful for the rapid dissemination of new ideas.

In addition, all engineering societies advocate on behalf of their members, and this is the most distinctive difference from the provincial professional engineering Associations. The primary mandate of the provincial Associations is to protect the public, so the Associations would have a conflict of interest if they took a leading role in advocating for engineers.

The role of engineering societies in other countries

The role of engineering societies varies among countries. The licensing laws in other countries are less comprehensive than in Canada, so the engineering societies play a role in regulating the engineering profession. Discipline-based engineering societies assess education and training programs and evaluate the qualifications of individuals who apply to be registered or "chartered."

In the United Kingdom, for example, registration as a chartered engineer (C.Eng.) is a desirable qualification, but is not generally required by law to practise engineering. However, British regulations have started to specify the C.Eng. for some safety-related work.

2.2   THE HISTORY OF ENGINEERING SOCIETIES

The Industrial Revolution stimulated the need to disseminate technical information. Britain led the way in establishing engineering societies, with the Institute of Civil Engineers in 1818, followed by the Institution of Mechanical Engineers in 1848. In the decade following 1848, many additional societies were established [1].

In the United States, the first engineering society was the American Society of Civil Engineers, founded in 1852. Several others were established later, such as the American Society of Mechanical Engineers in 1880 and the American Society of Heating and Ventilating Engineers in 1894.

The American Institute of Electrical Engineers was established in 1884 as a national society, primarily for electric power engineers, but later electronics and communications engineers were included. In 1912, the Institute of Radio Engineers was formed as an international body for both professionals and non-professionals in the new field of radio communications. These two organizations merged in 1963 to create the Institute of Electrical and Electronics Engineers (IEEE), which is now the world's largest engineering society. Within the IEEE are about 40 specialty societies, with names ranging from aerospace electronic systems to vehicular technology, and with members in all parts of the world. The IEEE publishes over 130 specialized periodicals and magazines, and arranges or co-sponsors 450 technical conferences annually.

History of engineering societies in Canada

Several engineering societies were formed in Canada shortly after Confederation, between 1867 and 1900. Examples are the Canadian Institute of Surveying in 1882 and the Engineering Institute of Canada in 1887, originally the Canadian Society of Civil Engineers. The Canadian Institute of Mining and Metallurgy was formed in 1898.

The formation of student societies began in 1885 with the Engineering Society of the University of Toronto; surprisingly, the "Society was, indeed, a 'learned society,' and published and disseminated technical information [. . .] in addition to looking after the University undergraduates in engineering" [1].

In keeping with trends toward greater specialization, several Canadian engineering societies have recently been reorganized and new societies created. The Engineering Institute of Canada (EIC), which had served all disciplines for many years, recognized that it could not serve the many diverse specialties of engineering within a single organization; the EIC is now a federation of member societies, as listed in Section 2.5.

2.3   THE IMPORTANCE OF ENGINEERING SOCIETIES

When you leave university and begin to practise engineering, your technical ability will be enriched by participation in (one or more) engineering societies, and your competence will be maintained. Moreover, maintaining your competence—through conferences, courses, workshops and similar professional activities—is not voluntary. Every provincial and territorial law (act) defining professional engineering (and some codes of ethics) requires the practitioner to maintain professional competence, and this requirement is also stipulated in the Engineers Canada guideline on continued competency assurance [2].

The provincial Associations have begun programs to monitor the continuing professional development (CPD) of their members, starting with the Alberta Association (APEGGA) with a mandatory program in 1998 and the British Columbia Association (APEGBC) with a voluntary program in 2001. As of 2007, all provincial and territorial Associations have adopted the Engineers Canada guideline, or are in various stages of adoption. Some programs are voluntary and some are mandatory. Fortunately, whatever CPD requirements exist in your jurisdiction, engineering societies can help you to maintain your professional competence.

Engineering societies hold a vast storehouse of useful knowledge that they readily offer to members. Societies also stimulate and encourage research into new areas, and provide a wide range of conferences, publications, courses, and workshops to disseminate the information to the engineers who need it and can apply it.

2.4   THE RELATIONSHIP OF THE ENGINEER TO LAWS AND ORGANIZATIONS

The relationships between the practising engineer and the laws, agencies, and organizations that regulate and assist engineers are shown graphically in Figure 2.2. In each province, the government has passed a law to regulate the engineering profession, and under the law, an Association has been created. The council, staff, and committees of each Association enforce the relevant act and admit, regulate, and discipline members of the profession.

As described in Chapter 4, the provincial Associations are linked by Engineers Canada, which assists the Associations in establishing national policies, and represents the Associations in negotiating international issues. Engineers Canada has two key standing committees (as shown in Figure 2.2), which perform important tasks for the engineering profession. The Canadian Engineering Accreditation Board (CEAB) evaluates the quality of engineering degree programs, and the Canadian Engineering Qualifications Board (CEQB) advises the Associations on standards for admission to the profession, standards of practice, and ethical conduct.

The CEAB is particularly relevant to engineering students because it visits established engineering degree programs to verify that academic standards are met. New undergraduate engineering programs are evaluated by CEAB in the final year of the first graduating class. Although accreditation is rarely denied entirely, some programs are accredited for less than the full term of six years. This limited accreditation usually stimulates rapid remedial action by the university. The list of CEAB-accredited programs is published annually, but does not distinguish between limited and full-term accreditation.

Although the provincial Associations regulate the engineering profession, they cannot provide the lifelong learning that all engineers require to keep their knowledge up to date. The simplest way for you to keep up with the rapid changes in your profession is to join and participate in the activities of an engineering society specializing in your discipline. Most practising engineers are members of both a Canadian engineering society and an international engineering society.

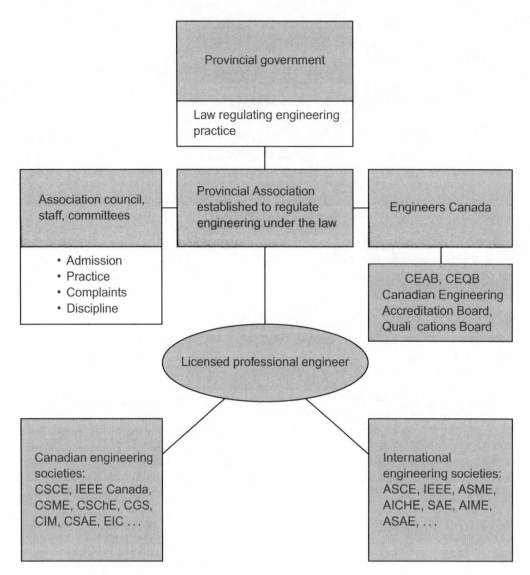

Figure 2.2   The relationship of the licensed engineer to the provincial engineering Association, Engineers Canada, and Canadian and international engineering societies.

Several Canadian societies exist to advocate for engineers in a more personal way. Although the members of these societies are licensed engineers or engineering students, the societies are not, strictly speaking, "learned" societies. These advocacy societies focus on improving the welfare of the individual, rather than the advancement of a specific discipline.

For example, the Canadian Federation of Engineering Students (CFES) is an advocacy group that works on behalf of engineering students, mainly by improving communication between students at different universities, and acting as a liaison with Engineers Canada and with the National Council of Deans of Engineering and Applied Science. The CFES is the main organizer of the Canadian Engineering Competition, a prestigious annual design competition that attracts the top engineering students from across Canada.

Similarly, the Canadian Society of Professional Engineers (CSPE) is an umbrella body for provincial societies that promote the welfare and working conditions of individual licensed engineers. The first provincial society formed to advocate for individual engineers is the Ontario Society of Professional Engineers (OSPE), which describes itself as "a member-interest society for Ontario's professional engineers." Self-employed consulting engineers have had provincial advocacy groups for many decades. A federal "umbrella" group, the Association of Consulting Engineers of Canada (ACEC), coordinates the activities of these provincial consulting advocacy groups.

In the United States, the National Society of Professional Engineers (NSPE) advocates for the welfare of individual U.S. engineers, and its web site (www.nspe.org) is of interest to Canadian engineers. Self-employed U.S. consulting engineers also have advocacy groups, coordinated by the American Council of Engineering Companies (ACEC).

Finally, honorary engineering societies exist, such as the Canadian Academy of Engineering, which was established in 1987. The academy exists to promote engineering, to recognize important service, and to speak as an independent voice for engineering. It cannot be joined; the fellows of the academy elect new members, from all disciplines, based on their record of distinguished service and contribution to society, to Canada, and to the engineering profession. The academy is distinguished and exclusive; membership is limited to a maximum of 250 fellows.

2.5   CHOOSING YOUR ENGINEERING SOCIETY

As a professional engineer in a rapidly changing world, you have an obligation to maintain your competence. Engineering societies are one of the best sources of up-to-date technical information, and the societies are as important today as they were during the Industrial Revolution. Each professional engineer should be a member of at least one society. For tax purposes, engineering society dues are deductible from personal income, for practising engineers, under Canadian income tax laws.

Your choice of society depends mainly on your engineering discipline. Most major societies have student chapters, and you should, if possible, participate in their activities to learn about the society. However, if student chapters do not exist in your area, then you can learn about engineering societies easily through the Internet or by speaking with a practising engineer.

Internet addresses are listed on page 24 for some of the larger societies, and a search of the Internet for "engineering societies" will yield thousands of organizations, but not all are equally well established and trustworthy. A good guide to societies is the *International Directory of Engineering Societies and Related Organizations* [3], published by the American Association of Engineering Societies (AAES). This directory should be in your university library. The directory lists the purpose, membership, address, dues, and other information about each society.

2.5.1   Canadian engineering societies

Engineering Institute of Canada (EIC)

As mentioned previously, the long-established EIC is now a federation of engineering member societies that cooperate to advance their common interests, such as maintaining engineering competence through continuing education courses, recognizing engineers by special awards, preserving Canadian engineering history, and creating opportunities for Canadian engineers to participate in disaster relief activities.

Table 2.1 lists the web site addresses of the EIC, its main constituent societies, and several other well-known Canadian engineering societies. The addresses were current at the time of publication of this book. In addition to the engineering societies listed in Table 2.1, several Canadian engineering societies have been established for advocacy,

TABLE 2.1 Major Canadian engineering societies

Society		Web address
EIC	Engineering Institute of Canada	www.eic-ici.ca
CGS	Canadian Geotechnical Society	www.cgs.ca
CSCE	Canadian Society for Civil Engineering	www.csce.ca
CSME	Canadian Society for Mechanical Engineering	www.csme-scgm.ca
CSChE	Canadian Society for Chemical Engineering	www.chemeng.ca
CSEM	Canadian Society for Engineering Management	www.csem-scgi.ca
IEEE	Institute of Electrical and Electronics Engineers, Canada	www.ieee.ca
CNS	Canadian Nuclear Society	www.cns-snc.ca
CIM	Canadian Institute of Mining, Metallurgy and Petroleum	www.cim.org
CSBE	Canadian Society for Bioengineering	www.bioeng.ca
CMBES	Canadian Medical and Biological Engineering Society	www.cmbes.ca
CIC	Chemical Institute of Canada	www.cheminst.ca
CSSE	Canadian Society of Safety Engineering	www.csse.org
MTS	Canadian Maritime Section of the Marine Technology Society	www.mtsociety.org
CDA	Canadian Dam Association	www.cda.ca

honorary, or charitable purposes. A sampling of these societies is given below, with their web addresses:

Advocacy societies

- Canadian Federation of Engineering Students (CFES), www.cfes.ca
- Canadian Society of Professional Engineers (CSPE), www.cspe.ca
- Ontario Society of Professional Engineers (OSPE), www.ospe.on.ca
- Canadian Military Engineers Association (CMEA), www.cmea-agmc.ca

Consulting engineering advocacy organizations

Every Canadian province and territory except Prince Edward Island and Nunavut has a voluntary advocacy organization devoted to consulting engineers. The names, locations, and web sites of these consulting advocacy organizations are available from the web site of their umbrella group: the Association of Consulting Engineers of Canada (ACEC), www.acec.ca.

Honorary society
Charitable societies

- The Canadian Academy of Engineering, www.acad-eng-gen.ca
- Engineers Without Borders (EWB), www.ewb-isf.org
- Registered Engineers for Disaster Relief (RedR), www.redr.ca

Memorial Foundation

The Canadian Engineering Memorial Foundation (CEMF) (www.cemf.ca), was created with the help of Engineers Canada, following the tragic murder of 14 young women in an engineering class at the École Polytechnique, Montréal, in 1990. CEMF is funded entirely by donations, and it awards scholarships to outstanding female engineering students.

2.5.2 American and international engineering societies

In 1904, five U.S. societies cooperated to create the United Engineering Trustees, Inc. The five founding societies have undergone changes over the years, and in 1998 the United Engineering Trustees, Inc., was reorganized as the United Engineering Foundation, Inc. More recently, some of the duties of the foundation were undertaken by the American Association of Engineering Societies, which claims a membership of over 25 organizations, most of them devoted to general disciplines.

TABLE 2.2   Major American and international engineering societies

Society		Web address
ASCE	American Society of Civil Engineers	www.asce.org
AIMBE	American Institute for Medical and Biological Engineering	www.aimbe.org
AIME	American Institute of Mining, Metallurgical and Petroleum Engineers	www.aimeny.org
ASME	American Society of Mechanical Engineers	www.asme.org
IEEE	Institute of Electrical and Electronics Engineers	www.ieee.org
AIChE	American Institute of Chemical Engineers	www.aiche.org
ASAE	American Society of Agricultural Engineers	www.asae.org
ASEE	American Society for Engineering Education	www.asee.org
AIPG	American Institute of Professional Geologists	www.aipg.org
ANS	American Nuclear Society	www.ans.org
AGMA	American Gear Manufacturers Association	www.agma.org
EAMT	European Association for Machine Translation	www.eamt.org
SAE	Society of Automotive Engineers	www.sae.org

U.S. advocacy society

The principal American advocacy organization is the National Society of Professional Engineers (NSPE), www.nspe.org.

International societies

Thousands of societies exist to develop and disseminate information about specific interests. Major American and international societies are listed in Table 2.2. Most of the large engineering societies include subgroups devoted to specialized topics. In fact, the IEEE, the world's largest engineering society, includes approximately 40 special-interest groups. The more-established organizations publish periodicals or other material that is available to members or is in your university library. However, the most convenient way to find most societies is by a simple web search. A search for the name of almost any engineering device, theory, or topic will often reveal a society devoted to the subject.

A word of caution is in order: Not all of the information obtained from the Internet is true. In particular, numerical data obtained from the Internet is not usually reliable enough to be the basis for engineering decisions. Only publications from reputable sources, such as the engineering societies listed in this chapter, may be depended upon to be accurate, because their publications must stand the test of peer review, debate, and validation. The established engineering societies, therefore, provide the extra measure of reliability needed for engineering decisions. Many American engineering societies also publish codes of ethics, although formal enforcement of these codes is extremely rare.

2.6   FURTHER STUDY

1. Choose the best answer for each of the following questions.
    (a) In Canada, engineering societies were first formed
        i. by French army engineers in Québec, prior to 1700.
        ii. shortly after Confederation, between 1867 and 1900.
        iii. during the Canadian centennial celebration, in 1967.
        iv. during the centennial of engineering in Canada, in 1987.

(b) Engineering societies are important, because they

    i. develop and publish technical codes and standards.

    ii. encourage engineering research and the exchange of results at conferences.

    iii. organize engineering design competitions for students.

    iv. assist engineers in remaining competent through specialized short courses.

    v. perform all of the above functions.

(c) The Canadian Engineering Accreditation Board (CEAB) is part of Engineers Canada, and is

    i. the committee that evaluates and accredits university engineering programs.

    ii. the national honorary engineering society, with limited membership.

    iii. a national engineering advocacy society.

    iv. the committee that advises on qualifications for admission and standards of practice.

(d) Engineering societies are distinctly different from the provincial and territorial engineering licensing bodies (the Associations and the Ordre in Québec), because the societies

    i. are created by acts of the provincial or territorial legislatures.

    ii. exist primarily to assist engineers by developing and disseminating engineering information.

    iii. exist primarily to regulate the engineering profession as required by law.

    iv. require compulsory membership in order to practise engineering.

(e) The provincial and territorial engineering licensing bodies (or Associations) have agreed to act jointly on national interests through an "umbrella" body, called

    i. the World Federation of Engineering Organisations (WFEO).

    ii. the American Association of Engineering Societies (AAES).

    iii. the Canadian Society for Professional Engineers (CSPE).

    iv. Engineers Canada.

(f) The main goal of most engineering societies is to

    i. license professional engineers.

    ii. assist practising engineers.

    iii. publish books.

    iv. advertise the engineering profession.

(g) The Canadian Academy of Engineering is

    i. a national university for engineering.

    ii. a national honorary engineering society with limited membership.

    iii. a national engineering advocacy society.

    iv. a national engineering fraternity, open to all professional engineers.

(h) The main purpose of the provincial Associations (including the Ordre in Québec) is to

    i. encourage engineers to become entrepreneurs.

    ii. regulate engineering practice and protect the public.

        iii. publish engineering standards and codes of practice.

        iv. advocate on behalf of engineers.

(i) The Engineering Institute of Canada (EIC) has a long history, but has changed roles in the past decade or so. The role of EIC is now

    i. to license engineers who satisfy the education and experience requirements.

    ii. as a national honorary society, with limited membership.

    iii. to monitor and accredit university engineering programs.

    iv. as a federation of Canadian engineering societies, with a mission to assist continuing professional development.

(j) Information is increasingly obtained through the Internet. The established engineering societies play a leading role in this revolutionary access to information, because they

    i. have Internet addresses and well-developed web sites.

    ii. encourage research in applying newly developed techniques to engineering problems.

    iii. provide engineering information that can be trusted.

    iv. perform all of the above functions.

2. Consulting engineers have an advocacy group, the Association of Consulting Engineers of Canada. What is the role of ACEC, and how does it differ from CSPE and the Ontario Society of Professional Engineers (OSPE)?

3. Find at least five student design competitions currently underway or held in the last five years, such as the Canadian Engineering Competition sponsored by CFES or the Formula SAE race sponsored by SAE.

4. Determine the purpose (mission), activities, criteria for admission, and financial support of the Canadian Academy of Engineering in more detail than described in this chapter.

5. Find and list the requirements for continuing professional development (CPD) for professional engineers licensed in your provincial or territorial Association. Is the CPD requirement voluntary or compulsory? How is the CPD activity reported, and what amounts of CPD are recommended or required?

6. A long-standing debate considers whether Canadian engineering societies are needed or whether Canadian engineers should simply join foreign-based societies that are already in existence and have a longer history, more publications, and a larger membership. Write a brief summary listing the pros and cons of these two alternatives. Does Canada need distinct engineering societies? Are engineering societies truly apolitical, or do national interests influence the research published in their journals and periodicals? Are dues paid to international engineering societies ever used to lobby governments in favour of a specific nation's interests? Are there uniquely Canadian conditions that would justify uniquely Canadian societies? What is your conclusion or recommendation?

7. Find and list the requirements, if any, of your provincial Association for engineers to demonstrate continuing professional development (CPD) after receiving a licence. Is the CPD requirement voluntary or compulsory? If no CPD program is in place, what does your act or code of ethics state about the need for continuing competence or ensuring your competence to practice?

8. Find your nearest advocacy association devoted to consulting engineers. What is its stated purpose?

9. Visit the web site (www.cemf.ca) of the Canadian Engineering Memorial Foundation (CEMF) and read the qualifications and eligibility requirements for its scholarship program. Determine if you or members of your class are eligible to apply for a CEMF scholarship.

2.7   REFERENCES

[1] L. C. Sentance, "History and development of technical and professional societies," *Engineering Digest*, vol. 18, no. 7, pp. 73–74, 1972.

[2] Canadian Engineering Qualifications Board, *Guideline on the Definition of the Practice of Professional Engineering*. Ottawa: Canadian Council of Professional Engineers, 2002. <http://www.engineerscanada.ca/e/files/guideline_definition_with.pdf> (March 9, 2008).

[3] American Association of Engineering Societies, *International Directory of Engineering Societies and Related Organizations*. Washington, D.C.: American Association of Engineering Societies, sixteenth ed., 1999.

Chapter 3

Advice on Studying, Exams, and Learning

Studying to be an engineer is not a spectator sport—success requires participation. Even if you were at the top of your class in high school, you are in a new league now, with classmates who know how to set priorities, schedule their time, take notes, and organize their studies. This chapter will help you to excel academically, but for best results, you must "read it before you need it." That is, you should read this chapter early in the academic year and apply these skills regularly. This chapter tells you:

- how much time you should expect to spend studying,

- how to organize yourself to study effectively,

- how to prepare for examinations and write them,

- what to do if things should go wrong in your studies.

Figure 3.1   Resist the urge to sit in the rear rows of large university lecture halls. Sit at the front and participate.

If you follow this advice (and a first hint is shown in Figure 3.1), you will almost certainly succeed and still have the free time to enjoy university life. However, this chapter discusses only the main strategies for university success—for more help, your university probably provides study skills workshops. To find them, start with an Internet search of your university web site, using key words such as *study skills*, *note-taking*, *time management*, *test* or *exam* or *learning strategies*, *writing techniques* or *strategies*, or *study groups*. The university groups, publications, and workshops in references [1–9] are typical. If these aids do not help, speak to someone immediately: start by speaking to your professors, but senior students are also a good source of advice, and every university has counselling staff who are hired to provide personal help and confidential guidance. Finally, many books on study skills are available in your university library, and may be found by a simple search of the library catalogue, using the key words suggested above. A few examples of such books are references [10–12].

3.1   THE GOOD AND BAD NEWS ABOUT UNIVERSITY STUDIES

The good news is that you have survived a very competitive engineering admission process, so you almost certainly have the academic ability to graduate. The bad news is that your high-school study skills probably will not be good enough for university. Professors report that in some programs, the average grade obtained in the first year by a typical engineering student is significantly below that student's high-school average. A partial explanation for this phenomenon is that university programs typically admit only the top fraction of high-school graduates, so almost everyone in your university class was a top student in high school. If you want to cope with the higher university standards, you must study effectively.

Moreover, engineering courses are difficult. This should not be surprising; courses are difficult in all professional schools, including law, medicine, optometry, accounting, and others. Professional schools cannot risk losing their accreditation because of low standards. However, there is no required quota of student failures, as some students may believe, and the greatest problem for students is not high standards; it is coping with newfound freedoms.

3.2   HOW MUCH STUDY TIME IS REQUIRED?

An informal survey of university students showed that, in addition to lectures and laboratories, students typically spent 28 to 32 hours per week completing assignments and studying. That is five hours per day for a six-day week! You might need a little more or a little less study time, depending on your capabilities. In any case, organize your timetable so that, after time is allotted for lectures, clubs, sports, and entertainment, about 30 hours per week are free for assigned work and studying.

At a university, free time tends to get lost! Universities generally treat students as responsible adults. Some students may be tempted simply to relax and to neglect their studies, with tragic consequences. There are no watchful parents or high-school teachers to worry about, and university professors do not check attendance or remind students to submit assignments. However, students who lose sight of academic priorities get a rude awakening when they learn that universities promote students only on the basis of demonstrated performance, not on future potential. Don't be tempted to skip classes, ignore assignments, or procrastinate.

3.3   MANAGING YOUR TIME

Every university student has heavy time commitments, many of which are beyond the student's control. You must attend lectures, laboratory sessions, tutorials, and meetings. Professors set deadlines for assignments and projects. However, you also need a personal life, to meet people, develop friendships, and enjoy university. Problems arise when these activities conflict or deadlines are missed. You need to manage your time!

You likely developed a technique for time management in high school. However, if not, the basic ideas of time management are very simple. Time management requires a little basic planning and discipline—but not much. Planning is simply a four-step process, from general plans to specific action, as follows:

- Term calendar: First, you need a general plan of the term. This is simply a calendar showing the dates of key events during your academic term.
- Weekly timetable: Second, you need a weekly timetable. Your classes are usually scheduled weekly, so this is a key document. Most importantly, it can be used to calculate your free time.
- "To do" list: Third, you need a master "to do" list of tasks to be done, and their deadlines, so that you can set priorities for your work.
- Synchronizing: Finally, you must synchronize these documents, usually every few days, to avoid conflicts, to set priorities, and to allocate your free time effectively.

The four steps are explained in detail below, but you may adapt these recommendations to suit your personal preferences.

Step 1:
Prepare a term
calendar

A calendar is a very useful map of the months ahead. Get a calendar that covers your academic term, and insert all key academic events, such as project due dates, field trips, mid-term tests, and final exams. Include major social events, also. If you know that you will be attending a special concert or watching the Grey Cup game or the hockey playoffs, put the event on the calendar and work around it. Keep your calendar up to date!

Every office-software program has a calendar template, and the university bookstore sells calendars of all sizes, from pocket size to huge white-board calendars that you bolt to the wall. (But don't confuse size with ease of use.) Wall calendars give you the big picture; however, they do not show routine activities, so that takes us to the next step: your weekly timetable.

Step 2: Prepare a weekly timetable

A weekly timetable shows your routine activities (like classes and labs), and you may already have this—universities usually give students a printed class schedule. Check that your lecture times and locations are correct. Your timetable is usually set for the term, but if your classes change drastically, revise your timetable. For example, when your final exams start, prepare a new weekly timetable (or exam timetable, as explained later in this chapter).

Write all your scheduled weekly courses and labs on your timetable, and block out time for normal mealtimes, regular sports or physical exercise, sleeping, social events, and spiritual attendance. The timetable should still show about 30 hours per week of "free" time. "Free" time means unscheduled time, free of lectures, labs, meals, meetings and social commitments. Most of it will likely be evenings or weekends. This is your study time. If you do not have 30 hours per week of "free" time (or fairly close to it), including evenings or weekends, then you should re-examine your timetable critically, and see if all the activities are essential.

Post a copy of your final timetable on your bulletin board with your wall calendar, and keep another copy with your notebooks, for use in class. To achieve your goals, you must apply your free time to the academic studies with top priority. However, to set priorities, you need a "task list" or "to do" list.

Step 3: Keep a "to do" list

Make a task list or "to do" list, and review it daily. Carry a pad or notebook, and when your professors assign a task, add it to the list, along with the due date. If possible, make a rough estimate of the time needed for each new assignment. Add personal tasks to the list, also. When tasks are completed, cross them off the list, or start a new list.

Step 4: Synchronize, set priorities, and schedule your "free" time

Every few days, you must "synchronize" your calendar, timetable, and "to do" list. The key purpose of synchronizing is to avoid conflicts between your calendar and your timetable, to set priorities for the tasks on your "to do" list, and to decide how to use your unscheduled "free" time.

Examine each task on your "to do" list, and decide its priority. The priority depends on urgency (or due date), time available, and work required. Number your tasks in order of priority. At this point, you can see what needs to be done first (on your "to do" list), and you can see when you can do it (from your calendar and timetable), so insert the tasks in the unscheduled "free" time on your weekly timetable. Your time is now properly managed, so get working on your tasks!

Some final advice

Time management always involves the four steps described above, but many students simplify the paperwork by buying planners. For example, many bookstores sell personal planning books, usually in leather ring binders. These planners contain all three documents in one binder (calendar, timetable sheets, and "to do" list).

Most planners also include an appointment book, and many students use the appointment book in place of (or in addition to) the calendar. This condenses the time management into a smaller format, which you can carry with you. It is usually convenient to use both an appointment book and a calendar, although it is a minor duplication. Conversely, if you condense everything (calendar, timetable sheets and "to do" list) into a single binder, it is very portable, but don't lose it!

Some students simplify the paperwork differently, by photocopying the timetable for each week of the academic term. This permits the calendar and the "to do" list to be synchronized, right on a copy of the timetable, each week. This method is simple, and works effectively. Many other modifications are possible. Use what works for you!

Other students go the electronic route, and use a Blackberry or a personal digital assistant (PDA) that fits in a pocket. However, the authors of this text recommend that students start with paper, to keep time management as simple and as cheap as possible. When you master the effective use of your time, your method will adapt easily to a computer or PDA. The four basic steps in effective time management are the same, regardless of the electronic complexity.

3.4   PREPARING FOR THE START OF LECTURES

A few simple tasks can get your term off to a good start.

Prepare a timetable   As mentioned previously, schedule your lectures, clubs, sports, and entertainment, but leave at least 30 hours per week free for reading and studying.

Buy the specified course textbooks   Many university bookstores encourage textbook orders by Internet or telephone, so that bookstore line-ups can be avoided. Obtain the texts as soon as possible; sometimes texts sell out and must be restocked. Used books might be available, but make sure that you obtain the correct edition.

Skim through the texts before lectures start   As soon as you get your texts, skim through them. If you read even a little bit about a subject before a lecture, you will be astounded how simple and logical it becomes. If you cannot do this for every subject, choose only the most difficult courses. You will be able to ask good questions, clear up doubts, and avoid panic at the end of the term.

Obtain a detailed outline for each course   Each of your professors will post a course outline on the Internet or distribute a detailed course outline in the first lecture. If no outline is provided, speak to your professor, because you need to know what to expect. In particular, the professor must define the course content, the marking scheme, and the main assignments, early in the term.

3.5   DEVELOPING A NOTE-TAKING STRATEGY

Note-taking during lectures is a personal matter and most students have their own preferences. Before the term starts, you should decide what your note-taking strategy will be for each course. The authors of this text recommend a moderate note-taking strategy that is suitable for most courses, provided that a textbook has been specified and the professor is following it. Your class notes should include headings, derivations, and quotations that can be reviewed later and compared with the textbook. For this strategy, the general rules are:

- Make notes for every lecture.
- Include the course number and date on each page of notes.
- Make your notes brief but complete, with appropriate headings, textbook page references, the topics discussed, derivations that are difficult, and points that are controversial.

Regardless of your note-taking strategy, organize your notes in a file or binder, and review them, along with the textbook or other course aids, to learn the concepts. If you have questions, raise them at the next lecture or tutorial session. Reviewing your lecture notes for a few minutes before the next lecture will greatly improve your understanding of the material. Lecture notes are also an excellent resource for review prior to examinations.

3.6   A CHECKLIST OF GOOD STUDY SKILLS

The checklist below lists 10 basic points; they are common sense but are worth repeating. The checklist is arranged in order of importance, with the most important rules first. The first six points are absolutely essential—if you are not following all of them, you will likely have academic problems.

Attend the lectures

1. Attend lectures regularly, and pay attention. This is extremely important; a few skipped lectures may seem innocuous, but in a fast-moving course, they can begin a vicious cycle of losing interest and skipping more lectures, which ends when the entire class is dropped.

Submit all assignments

2. Even if assignments are not counted as part of the term grade, the final exam will undoubtedly include topics from the assignments. Work on assignments in tutorial sessions where you have the help of a teaching assistant.

Find a place to study

3. If your residence is not suitable for studying, use the study tables in the university library or unused classrooms, or even the local coffee shop.

Don't take part-time employment

4. Outside work is a common cause of poor performance. You may have had a part-time job in high school, but time is much more limited in university. Speak to a university student-loan counsellor if you have financial problems.

Don't procrastinate

5. Major assignments can turn into disasters if left to the last minute. Even an hour spent early in the project, organizing and scheduling how and when you will complete the assignment, will pay off dramatically as the deadline gets closer.

Work weekends

6. Don't schedule every weekend for trips, parties, or travel home. Some weekend work is essential, whether it is studying, catching up, reviewing, writing reports, or preparing for examinations.

Don't stay up all night

7. Late nights, whether for work or play, disrupt your life and can lead to serious health problems. To study effectively, you need a minimum of seven to eight hours of sleep each night, or at least 50 hours per week.

Concentrate on your work

8. When you study, do it! Work will be done more quickly if you concentrate on it. Don't study in bed or try to do two things at once, such as watching TV with your books open; you're just wasting time.

Read ahead

9. A brief preview of your texts every week gives you an overview of each subject and greatly aids the learning process. If you cannot do this for every course, just preview your most difficult courses. If a recommended course text is not very readable, ask your professor, librarian, or bookstore to suggest an alternative text, or seek information on the Internet.

Reward yourself

10. When you are studying, take a five- to ten-minute break every hour. Stretch, walk, exercise, or reward yourself with coffee or a snack. If you have a deadline for a major project, promise to reward yourself with an entertaining night off when the deadline is met.

3.7   COLLABORATING ON ASSIGNMENTS

Most assigned problems are intended to apply the principles introduced in lectures, and you should submit them regularly, on time. However, avoid the extremes of spending too little or too much time on them. An engineer must strive for an optimal return for the time invested. Occasionally, enthusiastic students spend an excessive amount of time on interesting projects. Remember the "law of diminishing returns": as the time spent on a project increases, the incremental benefit decreases.

Many students collaborate when working on assignments, and this joint work is usually beneficial. However, there is a fine line between collaboration and copying. When you submit an assignment with your name on it, it is assumed that you have prepared all of the material in the assignment, except where you indicate that material has been taken from other sources and the sources are cited. To put this point in clearer terms: exchanging ideas by talking to one another is collaboration; exchanging written materials is copying, and exchanging computer files is serious copying. Although copying is easy to do, professors and teaching assistants watch closely for it.

Another word for copying is *plagiarism,* which is defined as taking any intellectual property, such as words, drawings, photos, or artwork, that was written or created by others and presenting it as your own. If you submit an assignment with your name on the front, and include material inside that has been taken from others but not cited, then you have committed plagiarism, and you may be subjected to severe disciplinary action, including dismissal from the university. Plagiarism is discussed at several places in this book.

3.8   PREPARING FOR EXAMINATIONS

Few people like exams, but they are essential in the university. Exams were originally devised, centuries ago, to prevent favouritism, and they are used today for the same purpose. Exams ensure that students are promoted on knowledge and ability, and not on apple-polishing, bribery, or luck. There are no limits on the number of students who can pass. Exams, therefore, are only an impartial metre-stick, applied to see that everyone measures up. Try to view them in a positive way, as an achievable challenge.

Examinations are also a learning experience; in fact, the effort put into summarizing and organizing the course material in preparation for an exam is usually very efficient learning.

As soon as the exam schedule is known, usually a few weeks before the end of the term, you should begin your exam routine, as described in the following paragraphs.

Make a timetable
- Prepare a personal exam schedule, showing your scheduled exam dates, plus any remaining lectures, tutorials, interviews, or important social events. Identify the uncommitted days remaining until exams begin. This is the time that you can control.

Review each subject
- Include a block of time in your exam schedule to review each subject before the exams begin. If your assignments interfere with your review schedule, talk to your professors; maybe an assignment can be delayed or shortened.

Organize your notes
- At this point you will appreciate having a course outline and dated notes for each lecture. Old exams are also very useful references; obtain them and list the topics covered by the old exams.

Review systematically
- Ideally, you should review each course in three stages: first, review the outline and purpose of the course; second, reacquaint yourself with the main topics; third, review derivations, assignments, and problems from previous exams. Prepare brief review notes as you go, containing definitions, summaries, and lists of equations. These notes will be very valuable for a final review the day before the exam.

Chemical stimulants
- Avoid the use of mood-altering drugs of any kind. Even coffee, in excess, can cause trouble. Collaborating with fellow students is useful, but avoid "all-nighters."

Final review
- Save the afternoon before the exam for a final review. You should have started studying early enough that you can spend these last few hours rereading your notes, trying old exam problems, and reviewing key points. Then relax, and make sure you get a good sleep.

3.9   WRITING EXAMINATIONS

Even if you are well prepared, it is normal to feel slightly tense before an exam. Don't let it bother you; everyone else feels the same, even if you can't see it. These suggestions may help you.

Take a walk
- Take a brisk walk before the exam to reduce anxiety and clear your mind.

Arrive early
- Arrive a little early; check your pens and pencils, and visit the toilet.

Read the questions carefully
- *Read the exam paper!* Many students give excellent answers to questions that were not asked.

Easiest question
- Always solve the easiest question first.

Defer the tough questions
- If you are faced with a really tough question, read it thoroughly and go on to the next question. Your mind will work on it subconsciously, and you may have the answer when you come back.

Write clearly
- Write clearly and solve problems in a logical order. This shows a methodical approach to problem-solving, and almost always will get you a higher grade.

Describe how to solve the problem
- If time is running out, describe how you would solve the problem if you had more time. A blank page gets a zero, but a description of how to proceed might get partial marks. Remember that the exam is a communication between you and your professor, so you may include any comments, references, or explanations that you would make orally.

3.10   WHEN THINGS GO WRONG

Everyone has bad luck occasionally: sickness, a car accident, family problems, and legal, social, or other problems. Every university has a procedure for helping students with serious personal problems at exam time. However, the student must take the initiative! If you have a serious problem that clearly interferes with your ability to write an examination, then tell someone! The appropriate person may be your medical doctor, counsellor, professor, department chair, or the exam-room supervisor (proctor). However, the earlier you speak out, the easier it is to remedy the problem. Don't wait until you receive your examination results to say that you were seriously ill, for example.

After the examination, if you feel that there is an error in your grade, it can be reviewed. This causes some inconvenience and should not be done casually. A formal letter to the university registrar explaining your reasoning (and there must be a reason) will set the process in motion. Refer to your university calendar for more information about the examination review process.

Finally, if you find that the subjects you are studying are not really the topics that you expected when you enrolled in engineering, you may have enrolled in the wrong program. Your professors and faculty counsellor may be able to help you define your career objectives more clearly. This book, particularly Chapters 1 to 5, is intended to help you clarify your career choice. However, if you still have doubts, get more advice and guidance. Every university has a counselling service available to assist students, such as shown in references [1–9]. If you are not sure how to contact your university counselling service, try searching your university web site.

3.11   YOUR PROFESSIONAL CAREER AND LIFELONG LEARNING

There are three major learning tasks in the lifetime of every engineer. The first is to succeed as a student, the second is to obtain and profit from practical experience, and the third is to maintain continuing professional competence in the fast-changing world of engineering.

Take charge of your timetable

This chapter explains how to succeed at university. Since the university demands most of your time, you must identify the free time that is left over, and use it effectively. If you apply the advice in this chapter, you will succeed as a student and still have time to enjoy the friendship, diversity, and good times of university life.

Document your work experience

Remember to document your work experience, particularly if you are in a cooperative (work–study) program or an internship program. Don't delay, or the details may slip from your mind. Your student work experience is valuable, because work-terms and internships link theory to practice. At the end of each project, or at the end of each work-term, prepare a summary of your activities, so that it can be inserted into your résumé.

Updating your résumé is a minor task, but it is very useful—it gives you a sense of pride and achievement, and an up-to-date résumé will be essential for interviews when you apply for your next job.

Documenting your work experience may shorten the time it takes to get your engineering licence. Most provincial Associations require four years of documented experience to obtain an engineering licence. However, they will typically accept up to one year of experience obtained after the midpoint of a bachelor's degree program if the work is well documented, so keep your résumé up to date.

Prepare for lifelong learning

University studies are a springboard to a professional career that involves life-long learning. As explained in Chapter 4, every provincial and territorial professional engineering act (or code of ethics) contains a clause that requires the practitioner to maintain professional competence. Every provincial and territorial licensing Association has adopted either a mandatory or voluntary continuing professional development (CPD) program. In fact, several licensing Associations monitor and audit the continuing professional development of professional engineers and geoscientists.

In summary, remember that your university engineering program is not just a set of related courses—it is an entry into an important and dynamic profession that looks to the future and builds on new developments. Your task is to prepare as an undergraduate, profit from your work experience, and maintain your competence as new knowledge becomes available.

3.12   FURTHER STUDY

1.   Choose the best answer for each of the following questions.

   (a) Engineering attracts some of the very best students. The university grades achieved by most first-year engineering students are typically

   i. much higher than their high-school grades.

   ii. about the same as their high-school grades.

   iii. much lower than their high-school grades.

(b) The informal survey of engineering students reported in this chapter revealed that engineering students typically spend how much time per week completing assignments and studying (outside of lectures and labs)?

    i. 12 to 24 hours per week

    ii. 28 to 32 hours per week

    iii. 32 to 40 hours per week

    iv. 40 to 64 hours per week

(c) The main objective in managing your time is to

    i. identify your free time and then schedule this time to achieve your goals.

    ii. prepare a term calendar.

    iii. prepare a weekly timetable.

    iv. maintain a "to do" list.

(d) In this chapter, the authors provide a strategy for writing examinations. Which of the following is *not* recommended?

    i. Take a brisk walk before the exam.

    ii. Read the exam paper.

    iii. Always solve the hardest question first.

    iv. If you are faced with a tough question, go to the next question and come back later.

(e) Studying for an examination by reviewing old exams is

    i. unfair and not recommended.

    ii. fair but not recommended.

    iii. an obvious step in a well-organized study plan.

(f) Skipping lectures

    i. is normally not permitted in universities.

    ii. has been found to be occasionally useful, since it increases student interest in the course.

    iii. can begin a vicious cycle of losing interest and skipping more lectures.

    iv. is acceptable, as long as you have paid your tuition fees.

(g) Collaboration with other students on course assignments is

    i. strictly forbidden.

    ii. allowed but not recommended.

    iii. encouraged, provided that the collaborator is identified on the assignment.

    iv. encouraged, providing that only ideas are exchanged (no written matter).

(h) If you have a serious personal problem that affects your academic performance, you should

    i. wait until examinations are over to speak to your professors.

    ii. keep the situation a secret, since problems may affect your assigned grades.

    iii. contact a counsellor or (in an exam) speak to the exam proctor.

    iv. tell a relative, as soon as possible, to put the situation on record.

    (i) Staying up all night is

        i. occasionally necessary before an examination and is recommended.

       ii. not recommended at any time and may lead to health problems.

     iii. recommended for studying but not for partying or examinations.

     iv. recommended for partying or studying but not for examinations.

    (j) Engineering, like almost every profession, involves lifelong learning. Which of the following will *not* help you to maintain and demonstrate your continuing competence?

        i. documenting your experience at the end of each project (or work-term)

       ii. joining the student branch of your engineering society (if one exists)

     iii. becoming a student member of your provincial Association (if permitted in your province)

     iv. selling your engineering textbooks to pay tuition fees

2. Using your computer, prepare a calendar for the end of your current academic term, including an end-of-term exam schedule, as suggested in Section 3.3. Insert dates of known university or class events. Compare and exchange templates with other class members to ensure that all essential events are included. When you receive your final exam schedule, insert the exam dates as suggested in Section 3.3, and schedule your exam review.

3. Search your university web site using the key word *plagiarism*. Search also using the key words *academic offence*. What is your university's policy on plagiarism? Does your university classify plagiarism as an academic offence?

4. Search your university web site for documents including the phrase *study skills*, as suggested on page 29. Compare the study skills on the web site with the suggestions in this chapter. Do the suggestions that you found on the Internet substantially agree or disagree with those in this chapter?

3.13 REFERENCES

[1] UBC Student Services, *New to UBC, Welcome*. Vancouver, BC: University of British Columbia, 2007. <http://www.students.ubc.ca/newtoubc/index.cfm> (March 9, 2008).

[2] University Student Services, *Academic Support Centre*. Edmonton, AB: University of Alberta, 2007. <http://www.uofaweb.ualberta.ca/academicsupport> (March 9, 2008).

[3] University of Manitoba, "Learning assistance centre," 2005. <http://umanitoba.ca/student/u1/lac> (March 9, 2008).

[4] Counselling Services, *Study Skills Package*. Waterloo, ON: University of Waterloo, 2005. <http://www.adm.uwaterloo.ca/infocs/study/index.html> (March 9, 2008).

[5] University of Toronto, "Counselling and learning skills service," 2007. <http://www.calss.utoronto.ca> (March 9, 2008).

[6] First Year Office, *Reading and Study Skills Workshops*. Montréal, PQ: McGill University, 2007. <http://www.mcgill.ca/firstyear/workshops> (March 9, 2008).

[7] Concordia Counselling and Development, *Groups & Workshops—Learning and Study Skills Strategies*. Montréal, PQ: Concordia University, 2007. <http://cdev.concordia.ca/workshops/learning.html> (March 9, 2008).

[8] Student Services, *Study Skills Counselling*. Saint John, NB: University of New Brunswick at Saint John, 2007. <http://www.unbsj.ca/studentservices/study> (March 9, 2008).

[9] Student Affairs and Services Counselling Centre, *Study Skill Links*. St. John's, NL: Memorial University of Newfoundland, 2006. <http://www.mun.ca/counselling/academic/studyskill.php> (March 9, 2008).

[10] D. H. O'Day, *How to Succeed at University*. Toronto: Canadian Scholars' Press, 1990.

[11] M. N. Browne and S. M. Keeley, *Striving for Excellence in College: Tips for Active Learning*. Upper Saddle River, NJ: Prentice Hall, 2001.

[12] P. Schiavone, *How to Study Mathematics*. Scarborough, ON: Prentice Hall Canada, 1998.

Section 2
Professional Engineering in Canada

Chapter 4
The Licensed Professional Engineer

Your university engineering program is not just a set of related courses; it is the entry point into a challenging and respected profession with high admission standards, professional regulations, and a code of ethics. The history of the engineering profession in Canada is full of success stories. However, it also contains some tragic disasters, such as the collapse of the Québec Bridge (shown in Figure 4.1), which influenced the legal regulation of the profession. This chapter discusses the engineering profession in Canada, and how university graduates enter the profession. In particular, this chapter describes

- the characteristics of a profession,
- how the engineering profession is regulated by law, and
- the academic and experience requirements for entering the engineering profession.

Figure 4.1   The photo shows the wreckage of the Québec Bridge, which collapsed during construction on August 29, 1907, killing 75 workmen. The cause of the collapse was traced back to errors in the design, and the tragedy spurred discussion of the need for government regulation of the engineering profession. Provincial and territorial laws regulating engineering were passed during the decade following the tragedy.

4.1   ENGINEERING IS A PROFESSION

The following definition of a profession is attributed to S. C. Florman, an engineer and prolific writer:

> A profession is a self-selected, self-disciplined group of individuals who hold themselves out to the public as possessing a special skill derived from training and education and who are prepared to exercise that skill in the interests of others. [1]

Engineering satisfies this definition, as do the older organized professions, such as medicine and law. Engineers possess a high level of skill and knowledge, obtained from lengthy education and experience. Engineering is a creative vocation with a positive purpose. However, the typical working environment differs from that of other professionals. Most engineers are employees of companies and work in project teams; other professionals are often self-employed and work on a personal basis with clients. The difference is illustrated in the following quote, which emphasizes that the engineering profession is highly regarded, in spite of the employee status of most of its members:

> The hard fact of the matter is that people need physicians to save their lives, lawyers to save their property and ministers to save their souls. Individuals

will probably never have an acute, personal need for an engineer. Thus, engineering as a profession will probably never receive the prestige of its sister professions. Although this may be an unhappy comparison, the engineer should take note that physicians and lawyers both feel that the prestige of their professions has never been lower, and they are mightily concerned; yet [. . .] engineers are considered to be sober, competent, dedicated, conservative practitioners, without such devastating problems as embezzlement or absconding members and without the constant references to malpractice and incompetence. [2]

4.2   REGULATION OF THE ENGINEERING PROFESSION

Since all professions involve skill or knowledge that cannot be evaluated easily by the general public, governments usually impose some form of regulation or licensing on them. The purpose of regulation is to prevent unqualified persons from practising, to set standards of practice that protect the public, and to discipline unscrupulous practitioners.

The United States was the first country to regulate the modern practice of engineering. The state of Wyoming enacted a law in 1907 as a result of instances of gross incompetence during a major irrigation project [1]. In Canada, spurred by the Québec Bridge collapses of 1907 and 1916, provinces began to regulate engineering. For example, such a law was passed in New Brunswick in 1920. The Associations in several provinces now also regulate the profession of geoscience, beginning in Alberta in 1955. At present, all provinces and territories of Canada, and all of the United States, have licensing laws to regulate the engineering profession and the title of Professional Engineer.

There are three typical methods of government regulation: by direct control through government departments, by establishing independent agencies, and by permitting the professions themselves to be self-regulating bodies, which determine standards for admission, professional practice, and discipline of their members. In Canada, engineering is self-regulating, as are all of the major professions (such as medicine, law, and accounting). Each provincial and territorial government has passed a law that designates a licensing body, called an Association or (in Québec) an Ordre, that regulates the engineering profession.

In most of Canada, engineering and geoscience are viewed in law as branches of a single profession. Eight jurisdictions regulate engineers and geoscientists, together, in the same legislative acts (Alberta, British Columbia, Manitoba, New Brunswick, Newfoundland, Northwest Territories, Nunavut, and Saskatchewan). Three provinces regulate geoscientists as an independent self-governing profession, equivalent to the engineering profession (Ontario, Nova Scotia, and Québec). Prince Edward Island and Yukon regulate engineering, but do not regulate geoscience as a profession. In this book, discussion of the regulation of engineering typically includes the regulation of geoscience.

In the United States, agencies appointed by the state governments write the regulations and license engineers. In Britain, chartered institutes promote the practice of engineering for the public benefit, but the associated laws do not regulate the term *engineer*. The sign "engineer on duty" is found outside many garages.

4.2.1   Case study of a critical event: The Québec Bridge tragedy

Introduction   The Québec Bridge is the longest cantilevered span in the world, but the structure collapsed during construction, killing 75 workmen in the wreckage (shown in Figure 4.1). The story of the Québec Bridge is marked by grand ambition, regrettable negligence, and a tense drama in the final hours before the disastrous 1907 collapse. The redesigned bridge still stands today. The disaster is particularly relevant to engineers, because it stirred Canadians to demand regulation of the profession.

At the time, the 1907 tragedy was the worst design or construction accident that had ever occurred in North America, and remained so for over 70 years. (The collapse of a hotel walkway in Kansas City in 1981 killed 114 people and injured over 200.) The Québec Bridge collapse is discussed in detail in several recent texts [3, 4], but the inquiry reports and bridge description written shortly after the tragedy are still worth reading [5–7].

Description of the tragedy

The proponents of the Québec Bridge intended to build a cantilevered span of 550 m (1800 ft) between supports. This length was chosen mainly because of the location of the supporting bedrock. The span was a challenge because it exceeded the 521 m (1710 ft) spans on the Forth Bridge in Scotland, which were then the longest cantilevered spans in the world.

The Québec Bridge & Railway Company hired Theodore Cooper of New York as the consulting engineer responsible for designing the bridge and guaranteeing its strength. Cooper was a senior engineer and had supervised many important projects. His assistant, Peter Szlapka, was a design engineer, educated in Germany, with 27 years of experience. Szlapka worked under Cooper's direction, drawing up the details of the bridge design. Cooper and Szlapka worked in New York; the beams, columns, and other bridge parts were fabricated at the Phoenix Company in Pennsylvania, and were shipped to the construction site in Québec, where hundreds of workmen were erecting the bridge, supervised by many site engineers and inspectors.

The construction scheme was to build each half of the bridge out from the opposite shores until the two halves met in mid-stream. The south side was started first, but as it reached out about 200 m, warning signs were observed—some of the compression members were bending. The site engineers notified Cooper by telegram that these members were deforming, and Cooper sought to visualize the problem and recommend a solution. The exchange of messages and attempts to find the reasons for the deformed members continued for about three weeks. By August 27, 1907, the situation was deemed "serious" by a senior site engineer, Norman McLure, who suspended erection of the bridge until Cooper could review the design and authorize work to continue. McLure then left for New York, where he convinced Cooper of the gravity of the problem. Cooper confirmed McLure's decision to suspend the construction and sent a telegram ordering "Add no more load to bridge till after due consideration of facts." Unfortunately, during McLure's absence and unknown to McLure or Cooper, chief site engineer Edward Hoare mistakenly ordered work to resume.

The telegraph message, which might have saved many lives, was relayed to the site at Québec. Testimonies disagree about whether or not the telegram was delivered, and if delivered, whether Hoare read it, but the workers were not recalled from the worksite. Ninety-two men were reportedly working on the structure when it collapsed at the end of the workday on August 29, 1907. A few reached safety in the midst of the falling girders and the ear-splitting fractures of beams and cables that reportedly were as loud as artillery explosions, but within less than a minute, 75 workmen were killed, crushed, or lay trapped and drowning in the cold water of the St. Lawrence River. The sound of the collapse was heard in Québec City, several kilometres away.

Fortunately, the falling wreckage missed the steamer Glenmont, which had passed under the structure only minutes before the collapse. The Glenmont attempted to pick up survivors, but none were found. The falling debris carried many trapped souls to death in the deep water.

The accident investigation

A royal commission was immediately ordered to investigate the collapse and find its cause. The commission conducted a lengthy inquiry and wrote a very thorough summary of the design and the cause of the failure, and made many important recommendations, valuable to bridge designers around the world.

In assessing blame, the commission's most scathing criticism was levelled at design engineer Theodore Cooper and his assistant, Peter Szlapka. Although Cooper had personally sought and obtained ultimate design authority for the project, he visited the Québec site only when the supporting piers were being built and was never on-site during the actual bridge erection. Moreover, he visited the steel fabrication workshop in Pennsylvania only three times during the project. In addition, the commission found the chief site engineer, Edward Hoare (who ordered work to resume on the fateful day), to be "not technically competent" to supervise the work. Communication problems were obviously also key factors in the tragedy, and better efforts should have been made to overcome the obstacles caused by the long distances between the design engineer, the fabricator, and the erection site.

In particular, the commission found serious errors and deficiencies in Cooper's design. Most importantly, Cooper's initial estimates of the dead-loads on the bridge were not recalculated as the design progressed. The design process normally starts with initial estimates of beam and column sizes, and the weights (dead-loads) of these estimated components are then used to calculate the stresses in the structure. If the stresses are too high, then the sizes are changed and the stresses are recalculated. This iterative process must be performed as many times as necessary, but Cooper and Szlapka failed to do so. Cooper's load and size estimates were low, leading to erroneously low dead-load estimates. The actual stresses were well above the limits for safe design. Moreover, Szlapka later criticized Cooper's curved compression chords, which buckled during the collapse, as being introduced for "artistic" reasons.

The new bridge design

Within a year after the tragedy, the federal government recognized that the Québec Bridge was an essential link in the railway routes that were being built across Canada, and authorized a new bridge construction project. The earlier plans were reviewed, together with the report of the royal commission, and a new design was adopted, using the same span distances and support locations. Two years were spent removing the massive twisted steel and debris from the 1907 collapse. New piers were built on the bedrock, and the new bridge was designed, manufactured, and erected by the St. Lawrence Bridge Company.

Unfortunately, a second tragedy occurred in 1916, during the final stages of construction, killing another 13 workmen. The new erection plan was to build both ends of the bridge part-way out from the shore, then to float the assembled centre span into the middle of the river and raise it into position. This plan worked smoothly in its initial stages but as the centre span was being lifted, it slid off its four corner supports into the river, carrying 13 men to their deaths and injuring 14 others. The cause of this failure was traced to material flaws. The centre span was rebuilt and successfully raised into place the following year. The Prince of Wales formally declared the bridge open in a ceremony on August 22, 1919.

Lessons learned

The 1907 Québec Bridge disaster made the public realize that only competent and ethical people should be permitted to practise engineering. In the decade after the opening of the Québec Bridge, the first provincial laws to license professional engineers were passed. A group of dedicated engineers instituted the Ritual of the Calling of an Engineer to encourage the ethical practice of engineering. Engineers who accept this oath are permitted to wear the iron ring discussed in Section 5.7 of Chapter 5. The iron rings used in the early ceremonies were allegedly made from steel scrap salvaged from the 1907 Québec Bridge collapse. Canadian professional geoscientists, following the engineering tradition, have established the Ritual of the Earth Science Ring. Some engineers in other countries, such as the United States, have copied the Canadian ritual, and hold a similar iron ring ceremony.

The scope and responsibilities of the engineering profession have expanded over the past century. Many current branches of engineering were unimaginable in 1907, and in most parts of Canada, engineering and geoscience are licensed as branches of the same profession. Provincial and territorial laws now permit only licensed professional engineers or professional geoscientists to make technical decisions "wherein the safeguarding of life, health, property or the public welfare is concerned."

4.2.2   The laws regulating engineering

To practise engineering in Canada, you must obtain a licence. For example, Figure 4.2 shows an engineering licence issued in Ontario, but licensing laws (or acts) exist in all provinces and territories. Each licensing law establishes an Association (an Ordre in Québec) to regulate the engineering profession and usually geoscience as well, as listed in Table 4.1. In this book, we use the term *Association* (with a capital letter, to distinguish its meaning from that of a generic association) to refer to any of these licensing bodies, including the Ordre.

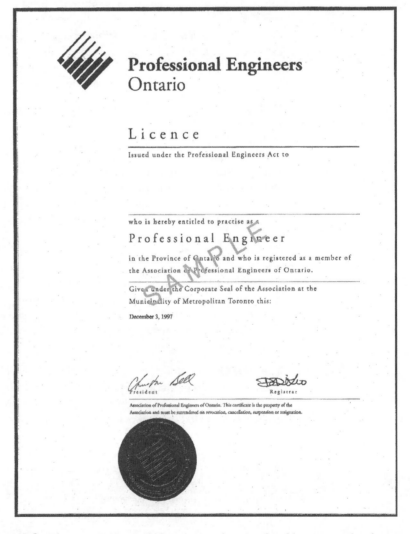

Figure 4.2   The engineering profession in Canada is regulated by provincial and territorial law. A typical engineering licence is shown above. (Courtesy of Professional Engineers Ontario)

TABLE 4.1   The provincial and territorial Associations that regulate the engineering profession in Canada, with their acronyms and web sites.

Association of Professional Engineers, Geologists and Geophysicists of Alberta	(APEGGA)	www.apegga.com
Association of Professional Engineers and Geoscientists of British Columbia	(APEGBC)	www.apeg.bc.ca
Association of Professional Engineers and Geoscientists of the Province of Manitoba	(APEGM)	www.apegm.mb.ca
Association of Professional Engineers and Geoscientists of New Brunswick	(APEGNB)	www.apegnb.com
Professional Engineers and Geoscientists of Newfoundland and Labrador	(PEG-NL)	www.pegnl.ca
Association of Professional Engineers, Geologists and Geophysicists of the Northwest Territories (representing NWT and Nunavut)	(NAPEGG)	www.napegg.nt.ca
Association of Professional Engineers of Nova Scotia	(APENS)	www.apens.ns.ca
Professional Engineers Ontario	(PEO)	www.peo.on.ca
Association of Professional Engineers of Prince Edward Island	(APEPEI)	www.apepei.com
Ordre des ingénieurs du Québec	(OIQ)	www.oiq.qc.ca
Association of Professional Engineers and Geoscientists of Saskatchewan	(APEGS)	www.apegs.sk.ca
Association of Professional Engineers of Yukon	(APEY)	www.apey.yk.ca

The purpose of laws for licensing engineers is to protect the public, and the goal of the Associations established by the laws is to safeguard life, health, property and the public welfare, as discussed at length by Andrews in [3]. As mentioned above, most provinces regulate engineering and geoscience in the same act, but three provinces (Ontario, Québec, and Nova Scotia) regulate geoscientists separately from engineers, and Prince Edward Island and Yukon regulate engineers, but have not yet passed laws to regulate geoscientists.

Under the authority of the licensing acts, the Associations are empowered to monitor the standards of professional practice and to discipline practitioners where necessary. Each Association has independently developed detailed regulations, by-laws, and a code of ethics. In 1936, the Associations created an "umbrella" body called the Canadian Council of Professional Engineers (CCPE), which changed its name in 2007 to Engineers Canada. The role of Engineers Canada is to coordinate the engineering profession on a national scale by promoting consistency in licensing and regulation.

Consistent laws help engineers to move across Canada and to practise in different provinces and territories. Engineers Canada develops detailed policies, guidelines, and position statements at the national level, and the Associations are encouraged to review and adopt the documents, as appropriate. As a result, while each province and territory regulates the engineering profession independently, the laws across Canada are basically similar. The discussions of engineering law in this book therefore apply generally to all of Canada, although many examples are drawn from Ontario, which licenses almost half of Canada's engineers. All of the engineering and geoscience licensing laws are available on the Internet. They can usually be found on the Association or Engineers Canada web sites [8, 9].

The legislative act is the basic document that regulates the profession. In addition, regulations, by-laws, and codes of ethics have the force of law, since they are created under the authority of the act. For clarity, the difference between these documents is described in the following paragraphs.

Regulations   Although *regulations* require government approval, the Association usually prepares the regulations (not the legislature), under the authority of the act. Regulations provide more specific rules, details, or interpretations of clauses of the act. For example, the act typically states that academic and experience requirements for licensing will be set, but the regulations state these requirements in detail.

Code of ethics

By-laws

By-laws are rules for running the Association itself. They concern the meetings of the council, financial statements, committees, and other internal matters. In some provinces, the by-laws are part of the regulations.

A *code of ethics* is a set of rules of personal conduct to guide individual engineers. In some provinces, the code of ethics may be part of the regulations; in other provinces, it is a by-law. The code of ethics is discussed in more detail in Chapter 5.

In each province and territory, the engineering profession is self-regulating; that is, the engineers themselves regulate their profession by electing the majority of members to the Association council, which typically contains members appointed by the lieutenant-governor-in-council (the provincial government). Engineers also confirm, by ballot, the by-laws established by the council. For self-regulation to work effectively, engineers must be willing to participate in Association activities and to serve in the elected positions at the various council levels.

4.2.3   The legal definition of engineering

Engineers Canada has proposed a simple, national definition of the practice of professional engineering as follows. The "practice of professional engineering" means

> . . . any act of planning, designing, composing, evaluating, advising, reporting, directing or supervising, or managing any of the foregoing, that requires the application of engineering principles and that concerns the safeguarding of life, health, property, economic interests, the public welfare or the environment. [10]

This is an extremely broad definition. The term *engineering principles* is generally interpreted to mean those subjects defined in a university-level engineering curriculum: mathematics, basic science, engineering science, and complementary studies.

The purpose of this national definition is to promote uniformity of engineering law throughout Canada, thus assisting engineers to practise engineering in different provinces and territories. However, while every province has adopted a legal definition of engineering, only a few are similar to the Engineers Canada definition, and no two definitions are identical. You will find the legal definition for your province or territory by searching the provincial act on your Association's web site, listed above in Table 4.1. Andrews summarizes all of the provincial and territorial definitions in reference [3].

The provincial legislative acts define engineering practice and place a responsibility on the engineer to ensure that life, health, property, and the public welfare are protected. However, some engineering graduates accept temporary or permanent jobs that do not carry these responsibilities. Must these graduates be licensed as professional engineers? The following advice may be useful.

The key point is that almost every engineering job involves decisions that affect life, health, property, and the public welfare, including the environment, even if only indirectly or remotely. If the terms of a job truly do not meet the above definition, then licensing is not required, of course, but you should ask whether the job is really engineering. Moreover, in certain grey areas of activity where licences are rare, it is far better to have a licence that is not needed, than to break the law by practising illegally.

The lack of a licence may hinder your promotion, or limit future career advances. It is very awkward to apply for a job for which you are not legally qualified. Therefore, even graduates who work outside the mainstream of engineering may profit from being licensed, since the licence opens up many career opportunities.

Finally, your licence illustrates your respect for yourself and your profession, since unlicensed graduates may not legally use the title Professional Engineer or its abbreviation,

P.Eng. Many engineers who leave the profession and are no longer responsible for engineering decisions still maintain their licences, as a matter of honour and pride in their training, experience, and accomplishments.

4.3   ADMISSION TO THE ENGINEERING PROFESSION

The legislative acts in the provinces and territories define the admission requirements for the profession. The requirements are similar, but not identical, across the country. To qualify for a licence, an applicant typically must

- be a citizen of Canada, or have permanent resident status;
- have reached the age of majority (typically 18 years);
- satisfy the academic requirements;
- pass the professional practice examination;
- satisfy experience requirements;
- be of good character, as confirmed by referees.

The admission process is illustrated in Figure 4.3 for students in accredited university engineering programs. Regulations for admission change from time to time. In the past decade, the experience requirements were raised in most provinces from two years to four, with criteria added to define the quality of the experience. At the same time, an internship process was instituted to help prospective engineers through the process. Consult the information provided by your provincial Association for advice about preparing your personal information, academic qualifications, and engineering experience.

Most Associations have a student membership designed to promote communication between engineering students and their profession. A student membership may be

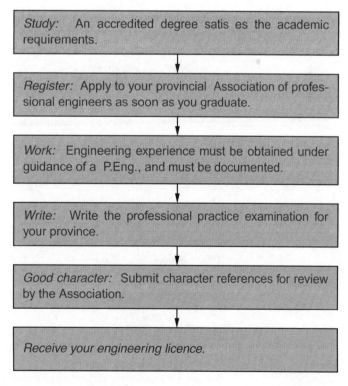

Figure 4.3   The steps to take to become an engineer through an accredited program.

very useful in the early stages of your professional career. Your Association is easily contacted through the Internet. The Engineers Canada web site (www.engineerscanada.ca) links to all Associations.

4.3.1   Academic requirements

The provincial or territorial licensing Association evaluates each applicant's academic record and has final authority on all matters related to academic requirements. The qualifications of each applicant are evaluated according to the requirements given above.

Accredited degree programs

The Associations rely on the Canadian Engineering Accreditation Board (CEAB) for advice on Canadian engineering programs. The CEAB, a standing committee of Engineers Canada since 1965, evaluates engineering degree programs in Canada at the request of the universities. It also evaluates the accreditation process in countries where similar systems exist, and as a result of mutual recognition agreements, graduates of accredited programs in several countries are given reciprocal recognition of their academic degrees. The CEAB grants *accreditation* to Canadian programs but uses the term *substantial equivalency* for programs outside of the country. A mutual recognition agreement has been in effect with the Accreditation Board for Engineering and Technology in the United States since 1980 and, since 1989, an agreement sometimes called the Washington Accord has listed accreditation in the following countries as substantially equivalent: Canada, Australia, Ireland, New Zealand, the United Kingdom, and the United States. Accreditation agencies in other countries have since joined the Washington Accord and are listed in the annual CEAB Accreditation Criteria and Procedures report. The 2007 document [11] lists agencies in South Africa, Hong Kong, Japan, Singapore, Korea, and Taiwan (Chinese Taipei).

Engineers Canada concluded an agreement in 1999 to recommend that programs in France listed by the Commission des titres d'ingénieur be treated as substantially equivalent to Canadian programs. This agreement has been ratified by most Canadian licensing Associations.

The CEAB mandate was extended in 1997 to include the evaluation of programs outside of Canada. A few programs in Austria, Costa Rica, and Russia are listed in reference [11] as substantially equivalent to accredited Canadian programs.

Other engineering degrees

Applicants for an engineering licence without a CEAB-accredited engineering degree or one covered by international agreement must submit the details of their degree programs so they can be evaluated individually by the licensing Association. In recent years the PEO, for example, has received more applications and granted more licences to this category of applicants than to those with degrees from accredited programs. Technical examinations may be required in order to confirm that the degree meets minimum requirements.

Applicants without equivalent degrees

Applicants without a CEAB-accredited engineering degree or equivalent may be admitted to the engineering profession after writing examinations. The Canadian Engineering Qualifications Board (CEQB), another standing committee of Engineers Canada, advises licensing bodies on examinations, maintains a list of foreign engineering educational institutions, and promotes uniformity of treatment of applicants across the country.

The examination program depends on the applicant's previous education, but completing it is not an easy task, for several reasons:

- There are approximately 16 three-hour university-level admission examinations for each branch of engineering. An applicant may be exempt from some subjects, depending on his or her academic record or experience. Applicants who require more than nine examinations are not normally admitted to the examination program.

- The examination system is not an educational system. Persons applying for the examinations must study on their own and present themselves when they are prepared to write and pass the examinations.
- The licensing Associations do not offer classes, laboratories, or correspondence courses to prepare for the examinations, and there are no tutorial services to review examination results.

4.3.2   Experience requirements

To obtain a licence, you must have four years of experience, except in Québec, where three years are required. According to the national guidelines developed by the CEQB [12], the experience must be at the appropriate level, following the conferring of an engineering degree or the completion of equivalent engineering education. An applicant who has not satisfied the experience requirements is typically registered, temporarily, as an engineering internship trainee (EIT), member in training (MIT), or similar designation, depending on the province or territory. Most Associations have mentorship programs to help applicants to obtain advice from an engineer, who might also serve as one of the referees needed to vouch for character. Internship and mentorship programs are especially useful for graduates in work environments where there are few practising engineers.

General requirements   Work experience acceptable for admission must possess the following characteristics, according to the Engineers Canada national guidelines for admission:

- The experience must be in areas generally satisfying the definition of engineering.
- The experience is normally in the same area as the applicant's engineering degree.
- The experience must be up to date.
- The application of theory must be included.
- There should be broad exposure to areas of management and the interaction of engineering with society.
- The experience must demonstrate progressively higher responsibility.
- Normally, experience is obtained under the guidance of a professional engineer. In addition to the above criteria, the factors given below are typically considered for admission; however, provincial requirements may differ slightly, and criteria may change.

Canadian experience   At least 12 months of the experience mentioned above must be obtained in a Canadian jurisdiction under the supervision of a person legally authorized to practise professional engineering.

Equivalent experience   Appropriate credit will be given for equivalent experience, following the conferring of an engineering degree, for any of the following:

- experience obtained outside Canada;
- a post-graduate degree or combination of degrees;
- teaching at or above third-year university engineering level or the graduating year in a college;
- military experience.

Pre-graduation experience   Well-documented work-term or internship experience, up to a limit of one year, is usually also accepted as satisfying a portion of the experience requirements. The experience must be obtained after the midpoint of the undergraduate degree.

Documentation   Check the current requirements for the proper method to record the details of your experience. The following data is generally required:

- dates of employment, by month and year;
- names and locations of employers;
- detailed descriptions of the technical responsibilities and the services or products involved;
- dates of periods of absence from employment.

Experience in a different field   If your experience is not in the field of engineering for which your degree was awarded, the Association will evaluate the appropriateness of the experience.

4.3.3   The professional practice examination

Some provincial Associations create their own professional practice examination; others use the Alberta (APEGGA) exam, which is nationally available. The examination tests knowledge of ethics, professional practice, law, and liability. Every applicant for a licence must successfully complete the examination. Exemption is permitted only for applicants who are applying to be reinstated after an absence or for applicants with at least five years of membership in another Canadian Association.

Time limits   You must submit a licence application before you will be permitted to write the professional practice examination. In some provinces, you may not write the examination until one year after graduation from university, and you must pass the exam not later than two years following the date of submitting the application for membership (or the date of successful completion of all other examination requirements, whichever is later). The best advice is to obtain some experience after graduation, write the examination, and then complete the experience requirements for your application.

Exam schedules   The examinations are generally administered several times each year. The provincial Association should be contacted for precise locations and dates. These dates and other registration information are published on the Internet. The provincial Associations and web sites are listed above in Table 4.1.

4.3.4   Offering engineering services to the public

All provincial and territorial Associations impose licensing requirements on partnerships or corporations that offer engineering services to the general public. The purpose is to identify the licensed engineers in the corporation who are assuming responsibility for the corporation's engineering work. A corporate engineering licence is typically called a *permit to practise* or a *certificate of authorization*, depending on the province or territory.

Some Associations require individual engineers offering services to the public to satisfy additional licensing criteria, such as additional experience and professional liability insurance (also called *errors and omissions insurance*). Some acts exempt individuals (sole proprietorships) from the insurance requirements, providing that clients are informed, in writing, that engineering services are not covered by liability insurance. Typically, the client must acknowledge and accept this condition.

These additional licensing requirements are deemed necessary to achieve the Association's main responsibility, which is protecting the public. However, each province and territory interprets this responsibility differently, and no two acts are identical on all issues. Andrews [3] summarizes these additional licensing requirements. If you are planning to offer engineering services to the public, you must be licensed as an engineer, and you must contact your Association to determine what additional licensing, experience, or insurance requirements apply in your province or territory.

4.4   THE PURPOSE OF PROVINCIAL ASSOCIATIONS

In concluding this chapter, the authors would like to stress that the primary purpose of licensing is to protect the public, not to help engineers. However, a structure that includes acts, Associations, regulations, by-laws, and codes of ethics makes engineering a very well-organized profession. In fact, public confidence in the engineering profession is very high.

Although some Associations, in addition to their licensing function, also provide fringe benefits—such as group insurance, retirement savings plans, employment advice, chapter-level technical meetings, and social events for members—this is not their primary purpose. Occasionally, people who see only these superficial aspects may believe that the licensing bodies are advocacy or service groups for engineers. They are not; they were set up to protect the public by regulating the engineering profession. The provision of member services is quite minor and does not conflict with regulating the profession.

In most self-regulated professions, there is a two-body organizational structure in which one organization regulates the members of the profession, and an independent organization works on behalf of its members by setting professional fees and organizing pension plans and other activities. The legal profession is a good example: in each province, the Law Society regulates members, and the Bar Association works on their behalf. Similarly, in medicine, the College of Physicians and Surgeons regulates medical doctors, and the provincial medical association works on behalf of its members. A similar structure has been proposed in engineering, but at present exists only in Ontario, where regulation is separated from service: the Association (PEO) regulates engineers, and the Ontario Society of Professional Engineers (OSPE) undertakes a role of advocacy, member services, and opportunities for professional development.

For the most current information on recent developments, academic and experience requirements, and admission procedures, consult the web site of your provincial Association, listed in Table 4.1. Additional information can be found through the Engineers Canada web sites [8–12].

4.5   FURTHER STUDY

1.   Choose the best answer for each of the following questions.
   (a) How does your university engineering program differ from most arts and science programs?
      i. The engineering program has more scheduled hours.
      ii. The engineering program is accredited by CEAB.
      iii. The engineering program satisfies the technical requirements leading to a professional designation (P.Eng.).
      iv. All of the above are correct.
   (b) A provincial Association will require an applicant for an engineering licence who is a graduate of an accredited Canadian engineering program to write
      i. only the professional practice examination.
      ii. four confirmatory exams.

       iii. four technical exams from the applicant's branch of engineering.

       iv. all technical exams for the applicant's branch of engineering.

(c) The primary purpose of the provincial and territorial Associations that license engineers is

       i. to benefit engineers in general.

       ii. to exclude technologists and foreign engineers.

       iii. to protect the public.

       iv. to protect the government.

(d) How many years of relevant engineering experience are required by most provinces (except Québec) to qualify for a licence to practise engineering?

       i. one year   ii. two years   iii. three years   iv. four years

(e) The engineering profession is "self-regulating," as are all of the major professions, such as law and medicine. What does "self-regulating" imply?

       i. The laws and regulations are left entirely to the engineers themselves.

       ii. The laws are set by the government, but the engineers elect a council and monitor the profession and administer the laws.

       iii. The government establishes a licensing body and appoints engineers to oversee the profession.

       iv. The "learned" engineering societies assess credentials of applicants and award "chartered" status to engineers when they reach a suitable level in the society.

(f) Geoscientists influence public health, safety, and welfare, particularly in oil, gas, and mineral exploration, environmental studies, mining activities, and construction of major engineering works such as dams and bridges. How are geoscientists regulated in most provinces and territories in Canada?

       i. Geoscientists are regulated in the same acts as engineers.

       ii. Geoscientists are regulated as are engineers, by separate (but equivalent) acts.

       iii. Geoscientists are not regulated.

       iv. Geoscientists are regulated by "learned" geoscience societies, such as the Canadian Geotechnical Society (CGS).

(g) The collapse of the Québec Bridge in 1907, killing 75 workmen, was a critical event that stimulated the drafting of laws to regulate the engineering profession. The main cause of the Québec Bridge collapse was traced to

       i. the steamer Glenmont, which passed beneath the bridge shortly before the collapse.

       ii. an overloaded train passing over the bridge.

       iii. failure to deliver the telegraph message ordering workmen to leave the bridge.

       iv. negligence of the design engineers to calculate the dead-load properly.

(h) The professional practice examination, which all applicants must normally write before obtaining a licence, contains questions on

       i. ethics, professional practice, law, and liability.

       ii. ethics, accounting, law, and liability.

       iii. engineering and technology, ethics, and accounting.

       iv. the environment, ethics, and accounting.

(i)   In order to obtain an engineering licence, an applicant must have suitable experience. At least how much experience must have been obtained in Canada or in a Canadian engineering environment?

   i. six months   ii. one year   iii. two years   iv. four years

(j)   The main purpose of Engineers Canada is

   i.   to represent Canadian engineers in labour negotiations.

   ii. to regulate the engineering profession at the provincial level.

   iii. to coordinate the engineering profession on a national scale.

   iv. to coordinate foreign engineering relief aid.

2.   Inspect the web site of your provincial or territorial Association, in order to answer the following.

(a)   Is there a student membership category? If so, how do you become a student member? What are the benefits of student membership?

(b)   What title does your Association assign to engineering graduates in training for engineering practice?

(c)   Does the Association require practising engineers to show evidence of continuing competence in order to maintain their licensed status?

3.   Is there a provincial engineering advocacy association in your province? If so, do the following.

(a)   Determine and list activities that could, in principle, overlap with the activities of the regulatory Association. Do their terms of reference specify their relationship with the regulatory Association?

(b)   Determine the conditions of membership.

(c)   Is there a student membership category?

4.   Do any provinces or territories impose licensing requirements additional to those listed in Section 4.3? If so, what are the requirements, and where are they in force?

4.6   REFERENCES

[1] H. MacKenzie, "Opening address for the debate on the *Professional Engineers Act 1968–69, Bill 48,*" in *Legislature of Ontario Debates, 28th Session, 1969*, vol. 5, pp. 4791–4800, Toronto: Queen's Printer for Ontario, 1969.

[2] J. B. Carruthers, 1978. Personal communication to G. C. Andrews.

[3] G. C. Andrews, *Canadian Professional Engineering & Geoscience: Practice & Ethics*. Toronto: Nelson-Thomson, third ed., 2008.

[4] H. Petroski, *Engineers of Dreams: Great Bridge Builders and the Spanning of America*. New York: Vintage Books, 1995.

[5] H. Holgate, *Royal Commission: Quebec Bridge Inquiry*. Ottawa: Government of Canada, 1908. 7-8 Edward VII, Sessional Paper No. 154.

[6] G. H. Duggan, ed., *The Québec Bridge*. Montréal: Canadian Society of Civil Engineers, 1918. Bound monograph prepared originally as an illustrated lecture.

[7] Canada Department of Railways and Canals, *The Québec Bridge over the St. Lawrence River near the City of Québec*. Ottawa: Governor-General in Council, 1919. report of the Government Board of Engineers, Department of Railways and Canals Canada.

[8] Canadian Council of Professional Engineers, *P.Eng., The Licence to Engineer*. Ottawa: Canadian Council of Professional Engineers, 2002. <http://www.pneg.ca> (March 9, 2008).

[9] Canadian Council of Professional Engineers, *The Four Steps to Becoming a P.Eng.* Ottawa: Canadian Council of Professional Engineers, 2002. <http://www.peng.ca/english/students/four.html> (March 9, 2008).

[10] Canadian Engineering Qualifications Board, *Guideline on the Definition of the Practice of Professional Engineering.* Ottawa: Canadian Council of Professional Engineers, 2002. <http://www.engineerscanada.ca/e/files/guideline_definition_with.pdf> (March 9, 2008).

[11] Canadian Engineering Accreditation Board, *Accreditation Criteria and Procedures.* Ottawa: Engineers Canada, 2007. <http://www.engineerscanada.ca/e/files/report ceab.pdf> (March 9, 2008). Pre-publication data at <http://www.engineerscanada.ca/e/acc_programs_2.cfm> (September 10, 2008).

[12] Canadian Engineering Qualifications Board, *Guideline on Admission to the Practice of Engineering in Canada.* Ottawa: Canadian Council of Professional Engineers, 2001. <http://www.engineerscanada.ca/e/files/guideline_admission_with.pdf> (March 9, 2008).

Chapter 5
Professional Engineering Ethics

Students entering engineering programs have high ideals, and aspire to be highly skilled, accurate, dependable, ethical professionals. However, every profession attracts a few unscrupulous individuals who want to profit from unprofessional behaviour. Unprofessional behaviour harms the public, reduces public confidence in the profession, and may also end a promising career. Reports of malpractice in other professions, such as medicine, law, and accounting, appear fairly frequently in the news media. Fortunately, the engineering profession has fewer complaints of this type, but they do occur.

For example, a contractor may offer a bribe to the engineer supervising a construction project, if the engineer will allow the contractor to use cheap, substandard materials or methods. Offering a bribe and accepting a bribe are both illegal, but in addition to criminal charges, a professional engineer who accepts a bribe is also subject to disciplinary action by the licensing Association. Upon conviction, the discipline may include a reprimand, a fine, or even the loss of a licence to practise engineering. Ethical behaviour is therefore extremely important in professional activities.

In order to guide professional engineers, each provincial licensing Association publishes a code of ethics. These codes vary slightly from province to province, but they express the same ethical principles. This chapter discusses these principles, as well as

- legal significance of the code of ethics;
- applications of ethics in the workplace;
- definitions of professional misconduct;
- disciplinary powers of the Associations;
- ethical use of engineering computer programs and the engineer's seal; and
- significance of the iron ring, worn proudly by Canadian engineers.

5.1   INTRODUCTION TO PROFESSIONAL ETHICS

As explained in the previous two chapters, each province and territory of Canada has passed a law (act) to regulate the engineering profession. These acts establish engineering as a profession, and they require professional engineers to follow a code of ethics, which requires high standards of professional conduct. The code of ethics for your province or territory is found on your Association's web site. The web sites are listed in Table 4.1 of Chapter 4.

The main purpose of the code of ethics is to protect the public. The code of ethics is not a voluntary guide. To ensure that engineers are aware of the code of ethics, applicants for engineering licences are required to write a professional practice examination, in which the code of ethics must be applied to hypothetical cases in engineering practice. Examples of typical exam questions are given at the end of this chapter. Moreover, to ensure that engineers comply with the code of ethics, each act specifies disciplinary actions to be imposed on engineers who disregard the code.

Codes of ethics impose several duties on the practising engineer, including duties to society in general, to employers, to clients, to colleagues, to the engineering profession, and to oneself. The wording of these codes is typically based on common sense and natural justice. Therefore, it is not necessary for you to memorize the code; most engineers find that they follow it intuitively and never need to worry about charges of professional misconduct. However, a special case may arise if an engineer's employer acts unethically.

For example, consider the case where an engineer learns that the employer is illegally polluting waterways by discharging toxic waste, in violation of Canada's Environmental Protection Act. The engineer might be faced with agreeing to an unethical action (pollution) or confronting the employer and possibly losing his or her job. It should be emphasized that such serious situations are rare, but do occur. The Association is usually available to provide advice and to mediate. If the employer is an engineer, or a corporation licensed to practise engineering by the professional Association, then the code of ethics applies equally to the employer. In this case, toxic pollution is not only unethical but it is illegal, and if the employer will not stop it, both the code of ethics and the Environmental Protection Act require the pollution to be reported to Environment Canada.

An employee engineer should never have to choose between unethical behaviour and a disruption of employment. Such problems arise very infrequently, and the first step is to try to solve the problem by discussing it with the employer. If that attempt fails and internal solutions are clearly impossible, then a confidential contact should be made with the Association.

5.1.1   Codes of ethics: General principles

Codes of ethics [1] usually include statements of general principles, followed by instructions for specific conduct that emphasize the duties of the engineer to society, to employers, to clients, to colleagues, to subordinates, to the profession, and to himself or herself. Although the various codes express these duties differently, their intent and the results are very similar. The following paragraphs summarize what the codes of ethics have in common:

Duty to society — A professional engineer or geoscientist must consider his or her duty to the public—or to society in general—as the most important duty. In other words, professionals have a duty to protect the safety, health, and welfare of society whenever society is affected by their work. In return, the professions receive the privilege of self-regulation. That is, the government delegates its authority to the Associations, which define standards of admission, discipline licensed members, and regulate the profession. This arrangement benefits society, because the Associations ensure that professionals are competent, reliable, up to date, and ethical.

Duty to employers — A professional engineer or geoscientist must act fairly and loyally to the employer, and must keep the employer's business confidential. Furthermore, a professional is obliged to disclose any conflict of interest.

Duty to employers — A professional engineer or geoscientist in private practice has the same obligations to clients as an employee has to the employer.

Duty to colleagues — A professional engineer or geoscientist must act with courtesy and goodwill toward colleagues. This golden rule is supported by all major ethical theories. Professionals should not permit personal conflicts to interfere with professional relationships. Most codes of ethics state specifically that fellow professionals must be informed whenever their work is reviewed.

Duty to employees and subordinates — A professional engineer or geoscientist must recognize the rights of others, especially if they are employees or subordinates.

Duty to the profession — A professional engineer or geoscientist must maintain the dignity and prestige of the profession, and must avoid scandalous, dishonourable, or disgraceful conduct.

Duty to oneself — Finally, a professional engineer or geoscientist must ensure that the duties to others are balanced by the individual's own rights. A professional person must insist on adequate payment, a satisfactory work environment, and the rights awarded to everyone through the Canadian *Charter of Rights and Freedoms*. The professional also has a duty to strive for excellence and to maintain competence in the rapidly changing technical world.

The provincial and territorial codes of ethics [1] contain the seven general duties described above, expressed with minor wording variations. Some codes of ethics impose additional duties. As previously mentioned, you can read the code of ethics for your Association on the Association's web site listed in Table 4.1 of Chapter 4.

5.2 ETHICS IN THE WORKPLACE

Everyone wants to work in a fair, creative, productive, and professional environment, and the applicable code of ethics can help to establish such an environment. Every Association code of ethics states that professionals must show "courtesy and goodwill toward colleagues" or emphasizes the need for fairness, integrity, cooperation, and professional courtesy. These characteristics are essential in any professional organization, and one purpose of the code is to create a productive and professional workplace.

Although engineering students are not legally bound by the provincial code of ethics, it is a general rule in universities that any behaviour that interferes with the academic activity of others may be classified as an academic offence, which may cause the university's discipline code to be invoked. Academic offences include plagiarism, cheating, threatening behaviour, or other behaviour that has no place in the workplace or in a school for professionals. A professional atmosphere is equally important in the engineering student's workplace—the academic environment of classrooms, study rooms, libraries, residences, and the job sites where students work between academic terms. The following examples illustrate the importance of ethical conduct in the student work-place.

Professional behaviour

Engineering students are expected to act professionally toward employers, colleagues, and subordinates, even though they are not legally governed by a code of ethics. In particular, students on work-terms or internships have an obligation to act professionally on job sites and to keep employers fully informed. The required behaviour includes simple matters such as courtesy, punctuality, and appropriate clothing. For example, hard hats and steel-toed shoes are essential on a construction site but may be inappropriate in a design office.

As a second example, consider how unprofessional behaviour can undermine the student job-placement process. University placement staff put a great deal of effort into attracting employers to campus. Employers, in turn, invest time and money interviewing students for job openings. If a student accepts a job offer from one employer, whether verbally or in writing, then fails to honour it when a better offer arrives from a second employer, the student would clearly be behaving unprofessionally. If the commitment cannot be honoured because of circumstances beyond the student's control, then there is an obligation to inform the first employer immediately through the placement department and try to minimize the damage. In most cases, an alternative can be negotiated, but only if the student acts promptly and ethically.

Teamwork

As stated earlier, engineering has become a team activity because of the increasing complexity of projects. Engineering students must work effectively with engineers and other professional staff—and the most important goal is the successful completion of the project.

Engineering teams usually include persons with widely different abilities, interests, and education who cooperate by contributing their particular expertise to advance the project. The best engineering team will use each person according to his or her strengths and willingness to contribute to the whole effort. Professionals should not be judged by extraneous factors, such as race, religion, or sex. In addition to being unprofessional and contrary to codes of ethics, such discrimination is contrary to provincial and federal laws on human rights. Within the engineering profession, we must aim for a higher standard of conduct than the minimum set by law. This is the purpose of the code of ethics and is what we would expect of a rational profession like engineering.

Ethical problems

An engineer or an engineering undergraduate may occasionally be faced with an ethical dilemma. For example, suppose that you have a colleague or co-worker who has developed a serious personal problem such as drinking, drugs, or mental or emotional imbalance. You are faced with an ethical choice: do you help to conceal the problem and let the individual's health deteriorate, or do you try to get medical or other professional intervention, knowing that this may affect your friend's employment or end your friendship? Both choices are unpalatable.

The solution to an ethical dilemma depends on an evaluation of all factors of the case, using the code of ethics as a guide. As the codes of ethics state, an engineer has a duty both to colleagues and to the employer, and this is the root of the dilemma. In view of these conflicting duties, it is usually impossible to give a simple resolution of such a dilemma. The solution requires gathering all of the pertinent information, evaluating the alternative courses of action, and selecting the one that achieves, or comes closest to achieving, the desired goal. When both alternatives are unpleasant, as in the above example, the least undesirable alternative must be chosen.

Resolving disputes   In creative activities such as engineering, differences of opinion are common; in fact, diversity may help to achieve a team's goals. However, disputes must not be allowed to undermine the engineering team, and the best way to settle a dispute is through courteous, direct communication, with the expectation that a full review of the dispute will lead to its solution. In fact, this is the meaning of "good faith" in item 7(i) of the code of ethics. This straightforward technique will usually yield a good solution that will be accepted by everyone affected by it.

If you are involved in a dispute, you should never file a formal complaint until all possibilities for personal, informal resolution are exhausted. Sometimes, but very rarely, external agencies or authorities must be contacted to solve ethical problems in the workplace. This action, sometimes called "whistle-blowing," should be the absolute last resort. The professional Association is available for advice in these matters.

5.2.1   Whistle-blowing

Occasionally, but rarely in a professional career, it may be necessary to "blow the whistle" on unethical activity. Most engineers will likely never need to be concerned about the process. However, if an engineer observes unsafe, unethical, or illegal practices, the code of ethics requires that action be taken. The action always begins by assessing the degree of danger or illegality involved, and then following the chain of management within the organization to remedy the problem. Only after all internal routes have been unsuccessful should an engineer blow the whistle by going outside of the organization.

For example, consider the case mentioned earlier in this chapter, where an engineer discovers that the employer is illegally polluting waterways by discharging toxic waste in violation of Canada's Environmental Protection Act. The following steps might be useful to resolve such a case:

Get the facts and identify the urgency   If the engineer has tested the effluent, and has documented proof of the toxicity, then the degree of danger is fairly high. Such waste disposal is not only unethical; it is illegal, so immediate action is necessary. It is also essential to identify the person in charge of the waste disposal, because that person will be most effective in resolving the problem.

Consider the solution   The engineer must also decide on the simplest remedial action, in advance of any confrontation. That is, the engineer must not merely complain about a problem; the engineer must be prepared to offer a clear, simple, and preferably cost-effective solution to the problem.

Speak to the key person   Usually, an informal, personal conversation with the person involved, describing the problem and proposing a solution, yields the best results. In many cases, the person responsible may not be aware of the problem, and will be eager to solve it.

Going higher   If the key person is not receptive to the engineer's presentation of the problem, and has no valid reason for refusing to remedy it, then the engineer must go over the head of this person and farther up the chain of management. This is not whistle-blowing, because the action is internal, and is the expected remedial action in a properly run organization. The engineer's goal is not to embarrass anyone, but to reduce the organization's liability for an unethical or illegal activity.

Blowing the whistle

When all internal avenues have been closed, and no action is forthcoming, then it may be necessary to go outside the organization. The licensing Association may be able to mediate in most cases, but illegal activities must eventually be reported to the regulatory bodies (such as Environment Canada), if the public health or welfare is involved. In fact, failure to take action may be considered to be professional misconduct or even complicity in the violation [1].

Although whistle-blowing is quite rare, several Associations have defined reporting procedures in publications available on their web sites. For example, PEO publishes a public information guide on the engineer's duty to report [2].

5.3   PROFESSIONAL MISCONDUCT AND DISCIPLINE

The duty of the professional Associations is to protect the public welfare and to act on complaints from the public. When complaints are made, the Associations investigate, try to mediate, and where necessary, take legal action. The action varies, depending whether the complaint concerns a licensed or unlicensed person or corporation.

Enforcement of the act

The purpose of the provincial or territorial licensing act is to protect the public, so only educated, experienced, competent professionals are allowed to practise. People or corporations that practise engineering or geoscience without a licence are breaking the law (the act). Associations are responsible for enforcing the act by prosecuting offenders in court. Each act typically states that it is an offence for an unlicensed person to

- practise professional engineering or professional geoscience, or
- use the title Professional Engineer, Professional Geoscientist, or the like, or
- use a term or title to give the belief that the person is licensed, or
- use a seal that leads to the belief that the person is licensed.

Most of the complaints are easily resolved, because unlicensed practitioners are frequently unaware that they are contravening the act, and, when informed, they promptly stop the offending behaviour, as described in Chapter 2 of reference [1].

Professional discipline

A second way to protect the public is to discipline professionals. The Association is granted a wide range of authority to discipline any licensed member who is shown to be negligent, incompetent, or guilty of professional misconduct. This authority is clearly defined in the provincial engineering act, and typically includes the power to fine the engineer, revoke or suspend the engineering licence, and, if appropriate, to monitor, inspect, or restrict the work done by the engineer. Results of discipline hearings may be published at the discretion of the discipline committee. The provincial and territorial acts are very similar, although not identical. They typically specify six causes for disciplinary action:

- professional misconduct, also called unprofessional conduct,
- incompetence,
- negligence,
- breach of the code of ethics,
- physical or mental incapacity, and
- conviction of a serious offence.

Although the Association staff receive and administer the complaints, discipline decisions are made by a discipline committee, composed mainly of professional engineers.

5.4   COMMON PROFESSIONAL COMPLAINTS

Conflict of interest

A common complaint to the provincial and territorial Associations concerns "conflicts of interest," which are mentioned prominently in every code of ethics. A conflict of interest occurs whenever a professional has a personal preference or financial interest that interferes with a duty to the employer, to the client, or to society. For example, an engineer who receives payments or benefits from two sources for the same service usually has a conflict of interest, because the engineer's duty to the client or employer may be compromised. As another example, if an engineer specifies that a certain product must be used on a project because the supplier paid the engineer a secret commission, then the engineer has a conflict of interest. In fact, accepting a secret commission is not only unethical but illegal.

A professional person must try to avoid conflicts of interest. In some cases, a conflict of interest may be unavoidable or may be very minor. When it cannot be avoided, then the conflict must be disclosed to the people involved, to ensure that everyone is aware of it and to ensure that the conflict does not affect professional decisions. An unavoidable conflict of interest is often acceptable if it has been fully disclosed.

Breach of standards

Another common complaint to the provincial and territorial Associations concerns the clauses in the code of ethics requiring the engineer to be competent. In design work, this requires the engineer to follow commonly accepted design codes and standards. Such standards are easy to obtain, thanks to the Internet. One of the first steps in the design process is gathering information. Therefore, at the start of every design project, the design engineer should routinely search the Internet for appropriate design standards and safety regulations. A simple search for standards might pay immense rewards by contributing to a safe design and helping to avoid potential injury or financial loss.

5.4.1   Case studies in ethics

In each of the following situations, identify a course of action that is consistent with the code of ethics and avoids any appearance of professional misconduct. Try to prepare a response before referring to the authors' suggested answers, which follow the cases themselves.

Case study 5.1: Peak flow dilemma

You work for a consulting engineering company that specializes in the design of sewage treatment plants, and you have been assigned to study the sewage treatment plant in a small town. The plant was constructed about 20 years ago and generally operates very well. However, at least two or three times per year, during severe rainstorms, the plant is overloaded, and operators are forced to discharge untreated sewage into the river that flows by the town. You have measured the peak sewage flows and calculated that the plant capacity would need to be increased by about 40 % to cope with these occasional peak loads. However, during your work, you discovered drawings showing that several buried storm drains are improperly connected to the sewage system, and this extra flow explains why the overloads occur at the sewage plant only during rainstorms: half of the water treated during storms is rainwater. Obviously, if the storm drains were rerouted, the sewage plant would have adequate capacity.

You tell your boss about your discovery. Your boss explains that if you recommend that the town expand its sewage plant, then your employer would bid on the lucrative contract for this work and would likely get the contract. However, if you recommend that the town upgrade and reroute its storm-drain system, the contract cost will be much lower and would likely be won by a competing company that specializes in storm-drain work. Your boss suggests that you conceal the information about the storm drains and recommend that the town increase the sewage plant capacity. Either way, the problem will be solved, so your company might as well share in the profit. What should you recommend in your report?

Case study 5.2: Light bulb commission

You are the chief design engineer in an electrical design company. You have been awarded a contract to manufacture specialized lighting equipment for a nearby major airport extension. You contact several light bulb manufacturers for specifications and prices on the bulbs needed for the runway lighting. Some, but not all, of the information is available over the Internet, but one company representative visits you personally, provides all of the information that you need, and offers you a "confidential" cash commission for every hundred bulbs that you order. You review the sales literature and realize that the company manufactures the best bulbs available for brightness, shock resistance, and longevity, although its prices are a little higher than competitors' prices. You would probably select these bulbs anyway, so should you accept the commission from the sales representative?

Case study 5.3: Expert witness

You are in private practice as a consulting engineer in manufacturing processes. You are contacted by company A to give advice on a computer-controlled milling machine in its machine shop that does not cut metal within the guaranteed tolerances and is constantly malfunctioning. The manager at company A explains that the machine was purchased about a year earlier from the manufacturer, company B, but the machine has never operated properly. Company B is nearby, and its technicians have made many service visits, with no useful results. When you see the machine, you remember that you were involved in the design of the control software, several years earlier, at an early stage of development of the milling machine. You provided advice to company B, and the development was carried out by its engineers, but you know the machine fairly well. However, the engineers from company A tell you that they want to hire you to analyze the machine and to testify as an expert witness when they sue company B. What ethical issues arise here, and what should you do?

Case study 5.4: Surveyor's assistant

Your employer has assigned you the task of hiring an assistant to help the survey crew. The assistant carries equipment and clears sight-lines for the surveyors in rough bush country. You place an advertisement on the company web site. The best-qualified person who answers the advertisement coincidentally happens to be your cousin, whom you met a few times at family gatherings. You do not know the cousin very well, but your last names are the same, so other employees may know that you are related and may think you are favouring your relatives. Should you hire your cousin?

Case study 5.5: Whistle-blowing dilemma

Assume that you are a recently licensed professional engineer, working for a consulting engineering company that is supervising the construction of a major building. You assist your boss in monitoring the delivery of materials (sand, gravel, concrete, and steel) and components (doors, windows, roofing, etc.) to the job site, which is almost the size of a city block. On behalf of the client, you routinely count the material and components delivered, and ensure that they are installed according to the plans. Occasionally, you notice small discrepancies. The invoices do not agree with the materials delivered, and you report the shortages to your boss, who listens, but tells you to ignore each report because, "In a project this large, some shrinkage occurs." However, one day you notice a truck leaving the site with a few doors and windows that should have been unloaded. When you stop the truck, the driver tells you: "This part of the load is going to your boss's new cottage." You refuse to let the truck leave the site, but your boss intervenes and overrules you, on the basis that the components are the wrong size and the paperwork to return them to the manufacturer is in order. You suspect that your boss might be stealing from the job site by redirecting materials for personal use. What should you do?

5.4.2   Suggested solutions to case studies

Ethical courses of action, for each of the cases above, are suggested below.

Suggested solution 5.1: Peak flow dilemma

Under the code of ethics, you have an obligation to put the public interest ahead of narrow personal gain. Moreover, you have an obligation to complete your task honestly, competently, and professionally. To conceal the real problem with the sewage system would be dishonest and unprofessional. If you follow the boss's dishonest suggestion and the true facts concerning the storm drains should later become known, you could be charged with concealing a conflict of interest, unprofessional conduct, or both; and if found guilty, you could be subject to a fine, reprimand, or even loss of your professional engineering licence. Therefore, without hesitation, you would recommend the reconnection of the storm drains as the best choice in this case.

Suggested solution 5.2: Light bulb commission

Accepting a secret commission is both unprofessional and illegal. The code of ethics requires the engineer to act as a faithful agent of the employer. In fact, Ontario specifically defines secret compensation from more than one party, for the same service, to be professional misconduct. You therefore have a conflict of interest; to avoid any appearance of professional misconduct, this conflict must be disclosed to your employer. When the employer knows all the facts, a fair decision can be made. It is possible, but unlikely, that your employer would allow you to accept the commission. Most likely, the employer would insist on purchasing bulbs from a company with more honest salespeople, or, if the bulbs are purchased from the representative anyway, the employer would expect a price reduction equal to the commission.

Suggested solution 5.3: Expert witness

Although your prior knowledge of the defective machine may seem to be an asset, your previous work for company B may conflict with your work for company A as an expert witness. When you worked for company B, you undoubtedly gained knowledge about the company's technical methods, processes, and business affairs, which might become part of the lawsuit planned by company A. Under the code of ethics, you have a continuing obligation to your former client to keep such matters confidential. Moreover, you do not know whether your earlier advice may be part of the problem with the machine. You therefore have a conflict of interest on two levels: your possible personal responsibility for the design problem, and your continuing obligations to company B. An expert witness is expected to provide an impartial assessment of the facts of the case, regardless of which side pays the expert. You are not likely to be impartial when you are investigating your own work, and your previous work for company B creates obligations and gives an appearance of possible bias. Therefore, the offer of employment as an expert witness for company A should be declined.

Suggested solution 5.4: Surveyor's assistant

You have advertised properly and your cousin has received no favouritism in the hiring process, so you have acted as a "faithful agent" for your employer, as required by the code of ethics. However, because the best candidate is your cousin, other employees may perceive that some favouritism was given. In cases such as this, which occur fairly often, the best procedure is to make a list of the applicants, and write a brief summary explaining what is needed for the job, the reasons why you are recommending the person selected, and disclose that this person is your cousin. You would then pass this information and all of the applications on file to your boss for a final decision. If you have made the right choice, your boss will confirm it; if you have unwittingly been biased in favour of your cousin, then your boss will correct the error.

Suggested solution
5.5: Whistle-blowing
dilemma

In this case, whistle-blowing would be unjustified with such flimsy evidence, and might be a career-limiting trap. You have only a verbal allegation, which might have been a joke by the truck driver, and it has been contradicted by your boss. Stealing materials from a job site is a serious offence, particularly for a professional, and action should never be taken on the basis of mere suspicions. You brought the discrepancies to your boss's attention, your boss has taken an apparently valid action, and you should not proceed unless you have more information. You would, of course, be more diligent in watching for evidence that corroborates or disproves the allegation. For example, if you checked the paperwork for the order, and found that the components were, indeed, returned to the manufacturer, then you would likely be glad that you had not rushed to judgment. However, if you learned that the components are missing, that your boss is indeed building a cottage, and that materials were taken from the workplace at the cottage site, then you would have to act. Otherwise, you might be considered to be an accomplice in the theft. Assuming that you obtain clear evidence of theft, even by misdirection, you would follow the process suggested earlier in this chapter, and suggest a simple remedial action, perhaps returning the materials or reimbursing the client. Then you would meet with your boss and lay out your evidence. If your boss should refuse to cooperate, you would go to your boss's boss, or to the client, who would likely turn the matter over to police. Obviously, you would be a key witness, so you must have solid evidence. It is extremely unlikely that involving the news media would benefit the course of justice.

5.5   THE PROFESSIONAL USE OF COMPUTER PROGRAMS

Computer software is essential to all aspects of engineering design, testing, and manufacturing. Several ethical concerns are created by the use of software, and some of these cross the boundary of ethical responsibility to become legal issues. Concerns to be discussed briefly include: liability for computer errors, software piracy, plagiarism from the Internet, and protection against computer viruses.

Liability for
computer errors

The engineer is responsible for decisions resulting from his or her use of computer software. In future, this responsibility may be shared, as software development becomes the responsibility of the software engineering profession, but at present, the engineer, not the software developer, is legally responsible for engineering decisions.

Significant engineering programs are never provably defect-free. However, if an engineering failure results from faulty software, legal liability cannot be transferred to the software developer, any more than it can be transferred to an instrument manufacturer because of faulty readings from a voltmeter. To put it even more clearly: *the engineer cannot blame the software* if the engineer makes decisions based on incorrect or misunderstood software output.

In the event of a disaster, the software developer may be liable for the cost of the software, but the engineer will likely be legally liable for the cost of the disaster. Therefore, when software is used to make engineering decisions, the engineer must:

- be competent in the technical area in which the software is being applied,
- know the type of assistance provided by the software,
- know the theory and assumptions upon which it was prepared,
- know the range and limits of its validity,
- test the software to ensure that it is accurate.

The extent and type of tests will vary, depending on the type of software, but the tests must be thorough. Usually, the engineer must run test examples through the software and compare the output with independent calculations. In some safety-critical applications, computations are performed by two independently written programs and accepted only if the results agree. However, the engineer must never use software blindly without independent validation.

Software piracy

Piracy is the unauthorized copying or use of computer software and is, quite simply, theft. Software piracy occurs more frequently than other types of theft because software can be copied so easily and because the risks of piracy are not very well known.

Software is protected by copyright and trademark laws. Piracy is an infringement of the developer's rights and is clearly unethical. Engineers who commit software piracy are subject to civil litigation and, in some cases, criminal charges, as well as professional discipline if the conduct of the engineer is deemed to be professional misconduct.

In addition, it is short-sighted to use unauthorized software in engineering, because an engineer who uses such software runs a much greater risk of legal or disciplinary action if a project runs into problems. In any legal proceeding, the use of unauthorized software would be convincing evidence of professional misconduct.

Organizations such as the Canadian Alliance Against Software Theft (CAAST) have been formed to combat software piracy. CAAST is an alliance of several software publishers, created with the goal of detecting and prosecuting cases of software copyright infringement in Canada. CAAST acts very aggressively through the Internet to reduce software piracy by educating the public, detecting infringers, and enforcing the copyright laws.

The ethical use of software stimulates software development and increases creativity, productivity, and job opportunities. Don't get involved in software piracy!

Plagiarism from the Internet

Plagiarism is another ethical problem that has been aggravated by the software explosion. Plagiarism is defined as taking intellectual property, such as words, drawings, photos, artwork, or other creative material that was written or created by others, and passing it off as your own. Plagiarism has become more common in recent years, mainly because of the convenience of cutting and pasting information from the Internet. Plagiarism is always unethical and is specifically contrary to several sections in engineering codes of ethics.

Plagiarism could lead to disciplinary action if the actions of the engineer are deemed to be professional misconduct.

Engineering students should be aware that plagiarism can result in severe academic penalties and can delay or abort a promising engineering career. All universities expect students to know what plagiarism means and to avoid it.

When you submit a document with your name on it, such as an engineering report, you take responsibility for everything in the document except for material that is specifically identified as coming from other sources. If material created by others is not clearly and completely cited, then you are liable to be charged with plagiarism.

Computer viruses

Like other professionals, engineers depend on their computer systems to run effectively and efficiently. The proliferation of computer viruses that damage or overload computer systems is an ever-growing threat. Virus vandalism can cause expensive and dangerous failures. Individuals who participate in creating or disseminating computer viruses are subject to criminal prosecution, and every engineer has a duty to expose such conduct.

Figure 5.1 A typical professional engineer's seal. On an actual seal, the name of the licensed engineer appears on the crossbar. (Courtesy of Professional Engineers Ontario)

5.6 PROPER USE OF THE ENGINEER'S SEAL

The provincial law (act) provides for each professional engineer to have a seal, such as that shown in Figure 5.1, denoting that he or she is licensed. All final drawings, specifications, plans, reports, and other documents involving the practice of professional engineering should bear the signature and seal of the professional engineer who prepared and approved them. This is particularly important for services provided to the general public. The seal has legal significance, since it implies that the documents have been competently prepared. In addition, the seal signifies that a licensed professional engineer has approved the documents for use in construction or manufacturing. The seal should not, therefore, be used casually or indiscriminately. In particular, preliminary documents should *not* be sealed. They should be marked "preliminary" or "not for construction."

The seal signifies that the documents have been prepared or approved by the person who sealed them, implying an intimate knowledge and control over the documents or the project to which the documents relate. An engineer who knowingly signs or seals documents that have not been prepared by the engineer or under his or her direct supervision may be guilty of professional misconduct. The engineer may also be liable for fraud or negligence if misrepresentation results in damages.

Engineers are sometimes asked to "check" documents, then to sign and seal them. The extent of work needed to check a document properly is not clearly defined, but such a request is usually not ethical. The engineer who prepared the documents or supervised their preparation should seal them. If an engineer did not prepare them, then perhaps the preparer should have been under the supervision of an engineer. The PEO *Gazette*, for example, reports many disciplinary cases involving engineers who improperly checked and sealed documents that later proved to have serious flaws.

5.7 THE IRON RING

The engineering codes of ethics enjoin each engineer to act in an honest, conscientious manner. However, there is a much older voluntary commitment, written by author and Nobel Prize winner Rudyard Kipling and first used in 1925, called the Obligation of the Engineer, which is the focus of a ceremony known as the Ritual of the Calling of an Engineer.

Those who have participated in the ceremony and made such a commitment can usually be identified by the wearing of an iron ring on the small finger of the working hand.

The ceremony is conducted by the Corporation of the Seven Wardens, which does not seek publicity although it is not a secret society. The corporation is totally independent of the provincial licensing Associations and the universities. Its members are volunteers.

The wardens usually conduct the ceremony in the late winter or early spring of each year, and invite students who are eligible for graduation to participate. The wardens allow attendance by previously ringed engineering graduates, who are often parents, grandparents, or others who wish to present a ring to a graduating student. The ceremony is not open to the public although, at a few institutions, students are allowed to invite a small number of family members.

Following the long-standing success of the uniquely Canadian ritual, ceremonies with similar intent but different obligation and ring have been introduced in the United States, beginning in 1970.

The engineering iron ring does not signify that a degree has been awarded or that the wearer is a Professional Engineer, and it carries no direct financial benefit. However, it is a reminder that the wearer has participated in the ceremony and has voluntarily agreed to abide by the obligation. The obligation is brief, but it is a solemn commitment, in the presence of practising engineers and other graduating students, to maintain high standards of performance and ethics.

5.8   FURTHER STUDY

The questions following the Quick Quiz illustrate ethical dilemmas that are found in engineering practice. Questions 5, 6, and 7 have been adapted from Ontario professional practice examinations. These questions should be answered by citing and explaining the code of ethics sections and the professional misconduct sections that apply.

1.   Choose the best answer for each of the following questions.

(a)   The principal purpose of a code of ethics is to

   i.   raise public esteem of the profession.

   ii.   control admission to the profession.

   iii.   protect the public by enforcing high standards of professional conduct.

   iv.   protect the public by discouraging unlicensed practitioners.

(b)   Almost all provincial codes of ethics state that the engineer must consider the duty to public welfare as paramount. What does *paramount* mean in this context?

   i.   The public safety must be placed ahead of personal gain.

   ii.   The engineer must pay all appropriate income, business, and sales taxes.

   iii.   Public projects (for provincial or federal governments) must be safer than private projects.

   iv.   Public projects must be scheduled for completion before private projects.

(c)   Although provincial codes of ethics state that public welfare is paramount, the codes also impose a duty to keep the employer's business affairs confidential. Therefore, a dilemma may occur. For example, consider the case where an employer has an unsafe work site, or plans to use substandard materials in a bridge support structure, thereby creating a public-safety hazard.

If the engineer cannot convince the employer to follow safe construction practices, then the engineer is encouraged by the code of ethics to

   i. follow the employer's instructions and keep the information confidential.

   ii. report the situation to the news media.

   iii. try to resolve the problem with the employer, and ask the Association to mediate.

   iv. report the situation immediately to the police.

(d) The term *conflict of interest* means (when used in a code of ethics) that the engineer

   i. is working with a person whose personality conflicts with the engineer's personality.

   ii. has a personal or financial interest that conflicts with the employer's interests.

   iii. has committed an unprofessional act.

   iv. has lost interest in a project.

(e) An engineer is assigned, by an employer, to purchase materials for a construction project and to supervise the construction. In collaboration with a partner, the engineer creates a delivery company that purchases the materials, delivers them to the construction site, and charges the costs to the engineer's employer, with an added profit for the engineer and the partner. The engineer's employer is not aware that the engineer is the half-owner of the delivery company. Has the engineer infringed the code of ethics? If so, what should be done?

   i. No infringement has occurred; the engineer is performing the required duties.

   ii. No infringement has occurred if the delivery company is in the partner's name.

   iii. A conflict of interest has occurred, but no action need be taken if the delivery company is in the partner's name.

   iv. A conflict of interest has occurred; the engineer must disclose this conflict to the employer and ask whether the employer will allow the arrangement to continue.

(f) Which of the following is *not* grounds for charging an engineer with professional misconduct?

   i. gross negligence

   ii. incompetence

   iii. conviction of a traffic offence

   iv. conviction of a serious criminal offence

(g) Which of the following is grounds for charging an engineer with professional misconduct?

   i. failing to correct or report a dangerous work site under the engineer's control

   ii. sealing a drawing prepared by a technologist under the engineer's direct supervision

   iii. accepting a secret commission from a supplier for buying the supplier's products

iv. sealing a drawing by an unlicensed person not under the engineer's direct supervision

v. making public statements that are not based on firm knowledge and conviction

(h) Which of the following is grounds for charging an engineer with professional misconduct?

 i. An engineer signs and seals a report as a favour to a friend, even though the report was not prepared or checked by the engineer.

 ii. An engineer undertakes work outside the engineer's area of competence.

 iii. An engineer fails to inform an employer or client of a conflict of interest.

 iv. An engineer fails to correct or to report a situation that may endanger the public.

 v. All of the above.

(i) An engineer designs a machine using software purchased from a commercial software company. The machine later fails, and it is discovered that the engineer relied on the output from the software, which was grossly in error. What is the likely outcome, concerning the liability for the cost of replacing the failed machine?

 i. The software developer is fully liable; the software was faulty, and this is the root cause.

 ii. The liability would be shared equally between the engineer and the software developer.

 iii. The liability would be shared, but the software developer would likely have to pay more.

 iv. The engineer is fully liable; the engineer cannot blame the software developer, who is liable only to reimburse the cost of the software.

(j) An engineer designs a circuit-board layout for a client, using pirated electrical circuit design software, obtained from the Internet. The circuit-board design fails, because spacing is inadequate for installation of the chips. The client has spent much money in purchasing unusable materials and in preparing prototype circuit boards, which must now be scrapped. Obviously, the design software was grossly inadequate for the task. What is the likely outcome?

 i. No one is to blame; the pirated software was faulty, and this is the root cause.

 ii. The engineer is fully liable for the client's direct loss and the costs of any delay.

 iii. The engineer is fully liable for the client's direct loss plus the costs of any delay, and may also be reported to the provincial Association for disciplinary action based on negligence, incompetence, or unprofessional conduct.

2. John Jones is a professional engineer who works in the engineering department for a medium-sized Canadian city. He has been assigned to monitor and approve, on behalf of the city, each stage of the construction of a new sewage treatment plant, since he was involved in preparing the specifications for the plant. The contract for construction has been awarded, after a competitive

bidding process, to the ACME Construction Company. About 10 days before construction is to begin, he finds a gift-wrapped case of rye whiskey on his doorstep, of approximate value $600. The card attached to the box says, "Looking forward to a good professional relationship," and is signed by the president of ACME Construction. Is it ethical for Jones to accept this gift? If not, what action should he take?

3. Alice Smith is a professional engineer with several years of experience. Ima Turkey, who is a graduate of a school of engineering but has never registered as a professional engineer, approaches her. Turkey offers Smith $1000 if she will put her seal and signature on documents that Turkey has prepared to make them acceptable to the city official who issues building permits. Is it ethical for Smith to do this?

4. René Brown is a professional engineer who has recently been appointed president of a medium-sized dredging company. Executives of three competing dredging companies approach him. He is asked to cooperate in competitive bidding on dredging contracts advertised by the federal government. If he submits high bids on the next three contracts, then the other companies will submit high bids on the fourth contract and he will be assured of getting it. This proposal sounds good to Brown, since he will be able to plan more effectively, if he is assured of receiving the fourth contract. Is it ethical for Brown to agree to this suggestion? If not, what action should be taken? If Brown agrees to this suggestion, does he run any greater risk than the other executives, assuming that only Brown is a professional engineer?

5. As chief engineer of the XYZ Company, you interviewed and subsequently hired Mr. A for an engineering position on your staff. During the interview, Mr. A spoke of his engineering experience in Québec, where he worked previously, and stated that he was "a member of the Order of Engineers of Québec." You assumed that he was a licensed professional engineer in your province, also. You had business cards printed for his use describing Mr. A as a professional engineer, and he accepted and used these cards without comment. Some months later you received a call from a client, complaining that Mr. A was calling himself a professional engineer when, in fact, he was not licensed to practise in your province. Upon investigation, you found this to be true. You fired Mr. A immediately. Was your action ethical in this matter? Was Mr. A's action ethical or legal? Refer to the code of ethics, the act, or both in your answer.

6. You are a professional engineer employed by a consulting engineering firm. Your immediate superior, who is also a professional engineer, is the project manager and prepares the invoices for work done on your projects. You accidentally find an invoice for recent work that you performed for a client. You are surprised to see that your time has been reported incorrectly. You decide to check further into this by reviewing your time sheets. The time sheets show that time charged to other work has been deliberately transferred to a different job. You try to raise the subject with your boss but are rebuffed. You are quite sure something is wrong, but are not sure where to turn. You examine the code of ethics for direction. What articles are relevant to this situation? What action must you ethically take?

7. You are an engineer with XYZ Consulting Engineers. You have become aware that your firm subcontracts nearly all of the work associated with the setup, printing, and publishing of reports, including artwork and editing. Your wife has some training along this line and has some free time. You decide to form a com-

pany to enter this line of business together with your neighbour and his wife. Your wife will be the president, using her maiden name, and you and your neighbours will be directors.

Since you see opportunities for subcontract work from your company, you believe that there must be similar opportunities from other consulting firms. You are aware of the existing competition and their rates charged for services and see this as a nice little sideline business. Can you ethically do this? If so, what steps must you take?

5.9   REFERENCES

[1] G. C. Andrews, *Canadian Professional Engineering & Geoscience: Practice & Ethics*. Toronto: Nelson-Thomson, third ed., 2008. Sections 3.1.1 and 3.1.2 have been adapted, with minor changes, from this book, with permission of the publisher.

[2] Professional Engineers Ontario, *A Professional Engineer's Duty to Report: Responsible Disclosure of Conditions Affecting Public Safety*. Toronto: Professional Engineers Ontario, 2001. <http://www.peo.on.ca/complaints/duty_to_report.pdf> (March 9, 2008).

Chapter 6
Project Planning and Scheduling

Every project, whether it involves design, development, or construction, will benefit from systematic planning and scheduling. In fact, almost every aspect of everyday life could be improved by better planning or scheduling. These two basic terms will be employed as follows:

- *Planning* is the determination of all the activities required to complete a project or similar enterprise and their arrangement in a logical order.

- *Scheduling* is the assignment of beginning and end times to the activities.

Planning, then, is determining *how* to do something, and scheduling is deciding *when* to do it. In any project, the purpose of planning and scheduling is to achieve the minimum time, minimum waste of time and material, and minimum total cost. These objectives cannot always be achieved. For example, achieving the minimum time is typically difficult at minimum cost. However, with proper planning and scheduling, the tradeoff between these objectives can be seen in advance, and optimal choices can be made. The material in this chapter is contained in publications such as references [1–4].

6.1   GANTT CHARTS AND THE CRITICAL PATH METHOD

Charts can be used to aid the visualization of planning and scheduling activities. There are several suitable formats, but the most common is probably the bar chart, also called the *Gantt chart*, after its inventor. Many project-management software tools assist with the creation and modification of such charts. A basic example is shown in Figure 6.1. The chart shows activities, in order of starting times, on the vertical scale; the horizontal scale indicates time. The time intervals required by the activities are shown by horizontal bars, and as the project proceeds, notes may be added or the style of the bars modified to show activities, for example, that are critical or exceeding their planned duration. At any time, the activities in progress and those scheduled to start or end soon can be determined. However, if a problem occurs with an activity (if delivery of material is late, for example), the basic Gantt chart does not show whether other activities will be affected or whether the delay will affect the completion date of the whole project.

Critical path method   A technique called the *critical path method* (CPM) gives detailed scheduling information. CPM is a modified form of the "program evaluation and review technique" (PERT), developed by the U.S. Navy in 1958 to speed the design of the Polaris missile. It proved to be an instant success by cutting 18 months from the completion date of the project, and it has been the standard method of planning used in the aerospace and electronics industries and in many construction projects ever since. CPM is particularly suitable for projects composed of easily defined activities of which the durations can be accurately estimated (most construction projects and some software engineering projects, for example, fall into this category).

Many planners require CPM to be employed to monitor and control the timetable of a project, but they still use simple Gantt charts when discussing or reporting progress.

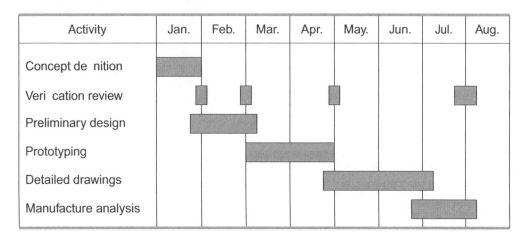

Figure 6.1   A basic Gantt chart for a design project.

6.2   PLANNING WITH CPM

To plan a project using CPM, follow these two steps.

1. List each activity involved in the completion of the project.
2. Construct an arrow diagram that shows the logical order of the activities, one activity per arrow.

When the arrow diagram is complete, it will show all the activities in the project, in the proper order. The planning phase is therefore complete. The two steps above may actually be repeated several times, since the action of constructing the arrow diagram will remind the planner that an activity has been omitted or perhaps that one activity should be divided into two more specific activities. The list of activities and the arrow diagram are then modified until they are complete and correct. However, before discussing details of the arrow diagram, we must define two terms more accurately: *activities* and *events*.

- An *activity* is any defined job or process that is an essential part of the project. Each activity in the project is represented by an arrow in the arrow diagram such as shown in Figure 6.2. Each activity has an associated time duration Δt.
- An *event* is a defined time. All activities begin and end at events, represented by circles or nodes, as shown in Figure 6.2. In some contexts, events are called "milestones," which are defined steps on the way to completion of the project.

An arrow diagram, therefore, is a graph, in which the nodes are events and the branches are arrows representing activities. To construct an arrow diagram, we start by drawing a circle for the *start event*, which is the beginning of the project. The first activity arrow is then drawn from the start event, and the other activity arrows are joined to it in the sequence in which the activities must be performed. The following simple example illustrates the planning procedure.

EXAMPLE 6.1

TIRE CHANGING

For three or four weeks each autumn, when the weather gets cold, tire stores (in some climatic regions) are crowded with people who want to purchase winter tires. If these stores could improve the efficiency of selling and mounting tires, then there would be fewer delays, customers would be more content, and tire sales would increase.

The activities for a typical two-tire purchase are listed in Table 6.1 along with estimated activity times. Consider such a purchase as a project. How would you plan and schedule it for minimum delay? Suppose that there are two cases: a small, one-person tire store, and a large, fully staffed tire store.

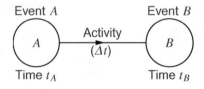

Figure 6.2   Activities and events in an arrow diagram, with time interval $\Delta t = t_B - t_A$.

TABLE 6.1 Activities for the sale and installation of winter tires.

Activity	Time (min)
1. Customer drives car into tire-store garage.	2
2. Customer inspects catalogue and selects tires.	30
3. Sales clerk confirms stock on hand.	5
4. Stockroom clerk takes tires to garage.	10
5. Mechanic raises car and removes wheel 1.	5
6. Mechanic mounts new tire on wheel 1 and balances it.	10
7. Mechanic replaces wheel 1.	5
8. Mechanic removes wheel 2.	3
9. Mechanic mounts new tire on wheel 2 and balances it.	10
10. Mechanic replaces wheel 2.	5
11. Clerk writes bill; client pays for tires and installation.	10
12. Mechanic lowers car and drives it out of garage.	2

The arrow diagram can be created easily, using the list of activities in the table. If the tire store has only one person acting as sales clerk, stockroom clerk, and mechanic, then the simple diagram of Figure 6.3 results. The process cannot be improved if only one person is involved, since the activities must be performed sequentially.

However, if the tire store employs a sales clerk, a stockroom clerk, and at least *two* mechanics (and has two tire-mounting machines), then the arrow diagram can be redrawn as shown in Figure 6.4. Since both tires are installed at the same time, the time for the transaction is reduced, as will be seen.

We now look at the process critically. The list of activities is in a logical order, beginning with the arrival of the customer and ending with the departure. However, it is not necessarily the most efficient order. For example, why must the car be in the garage while the customer inspects the catalogue or pays the bill? The bill could be paid either before or after the tire change, thus freeing the shop and equipment for part of the time. With these changes in mind, the process can be redrawn as in

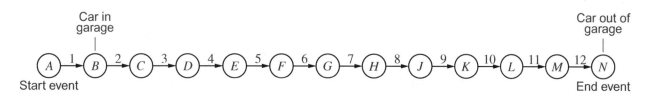

Figure 6.3 A one-operator tire purchase. The label I is often omitted to avoid confusion with the number 1.

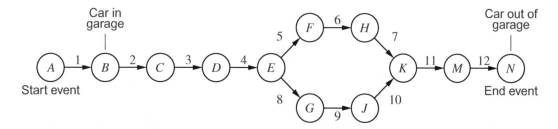

Figure 6.4 A large-store tire purchase, with paths showing independent activities.

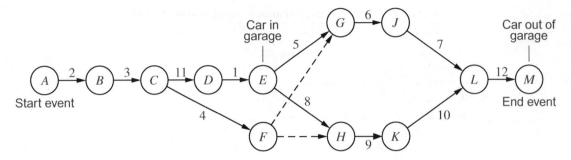

Figure 6.5   The improved procedure, with tires taken from stock simultaneously with payment.

Figure 6.5, showing that the customer inspects the catalogue and selects the tires (activity 2) and pays the bill (activity 11) before the car enters the garage (activity 1). The stock clerk delivers the tires to the garage (activity 4) while the customer pays and then drives the car into the garage. The dashed lines in this figure are called *dummy activities,* which take zero time but are included to show the proper sequence of events. In this case, they are required in order to show that the tires must be in the garage (activity 4) for mounting to take place (activities 6 and 9). In the next section, the concept of scheduling is introduced, and we can calculate the amount of time saved.

6.3   SCHEDULING WITH CPM

When the initial planning is complete, scheduling can begin. We say "initial" planning because we may, as a result of scheduling, decide to change the plan. Two terms associated with scheduling must be defined.

- The *earliest event time (EE)* for an event is the earliest time at which the activities that precede the event can be completed.
- The *latest event time (LE)* for an event is the latest time at which the activities that follow the event can commence without delaying the project.

The EE and LE times are easily calculated, as shown on the following pages. Since the EE and LE times are associated with events, they are usually included in the event circles (the nodes of the graph), as shown in Figure 6.6, to make the arrow diagram more understandable.

Calculating earliest event times   The EE value at the start event is zero. At any other event, the EE value is the sum of the activity times for the arrows from the start event to that event, but if there is more than one path from the start event, the EE value is the largest of these path times.

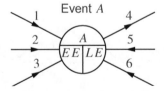

Figure 6.6   The format for writing earliest event time (EE) and latest event time (LE) in an event circle.

The calculation is usually done by working from left to right until the end event is reached. The *EE* value at the end event is the total time *T* required for the project.

Calculating latest event times

The calculation of *LE* times is similar to that of *EE* times, except that the path traversal is carried out in reverse, beginning with the end event. The end event *LE* value is *T*. To calculate the *LE* value for any other event, the activity times for the arrows between that event and the end event are subtracted from the total time *T*, but if there are two or more paths to the end event, the largest of the path times is subtracted from *T*. The *LE* value for the start event must be zero, which serves as a check for arithmetic errors.

The critical path

A path with the longest path time from the start event to the end event is said to be "critical," since additional delay in such a path delays the whole project. Conversely, if the critical path time is reduced, then a reduction of the project time may be possible. All non-critical paths have spare time available for some activities. Events with equal *EE* and *LE* values are on a critical path.

EXAMPLE 6.2

TIRE CHANGING (EXAMPLE 6.1 CONTINUED)

Consider again the tire-changing example discussed previously; the activities and their durations are shown in Table 6.1. We shall find the critical path for both the one-person and fully staffed stores.

The planning graph for the one-person operation, shown in Figure 6.3, has been redrawn in Figure 6.7, showing *EE* and *LE* values in the event circles. The activity time Δt is shown in parentheses below each arrow. As discussed previously for the one-person operation, the CPM arrow diagram is a simple sequence of activities, so the relationships between Δt, *EE*, *LE*, and *T* values are simple. The total project time is the sum of the activity times; that is, $T = 97$ min. In this simple case, $EE = LE$ at every event, so every activity and every event is on the critical path. If there is a change in any activity time, there is a corresponding change in the project completion time.

Consider the fully staffed tire store of Figure 6.8, which is Figure 6.4 with the scheduling information included. The figure shows that simultaneously mounting two

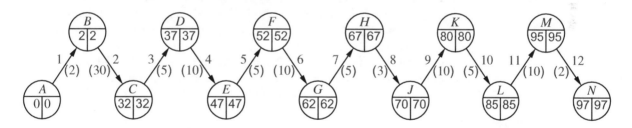

Figure 6.7 The schedule for one operator, from Figure 6.3, showing event times and a total time $T = 97$ min.

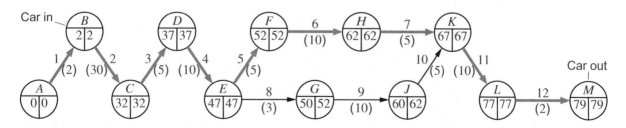

Figure 6.8 The schedule for the large store, from Figure 6.4, showing event times and a total time $T = 79$ min. The critical path is indicated by the thick arrows.

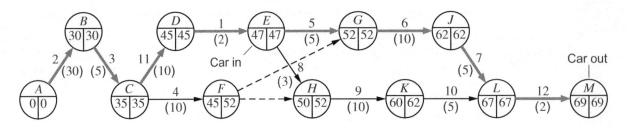

Figure 6.9   The improved procedure, from Figure 6.5, showing event times and a total time T = 69 min.

tires (activities 6 and 9) reduces the total project time to T = 79 min. The critical path is indicated in Figure 6.8 by thick arrows. To reduce the total project time, it is necessary to examine and improve activities on this path.

The improved procedure shown in Figure 6.5 is redrawn in Figure 6.9 with the scheduling information included. The total project time has been further reduced to T = 69 min. In addition, grouping the sales and billing activities and separating them from the shop activities has required the car to be in the garage from EE = 47 to EE = 69, a reduced time of only (69 − 47) min = 22 min. This is clearly an improvement, freeing the garage for other work. The project could probably be further improved, but this single cycle of planning and scheduling has illustrated how a methodical approach leads the planner, almost automatically, to think about methods of improvement.

Float time   A final important definition will be introduced. Activities that are not on the critical path have some spare time, usually called *float time* or *slack time*. We can calculate this time F as follows: if an activity starts at event A and ends at event B, then F equals LE at event B minus EE at event A, minus the activity time Δt. In equation form:

$$F = LE_B - EE_A - \Delta t. \tag{6.1}$$

As an example, consider activity 9 in Figure 6.9, which can start as early as EE = 50 min (event H) and must end before LE = 62 min (event K). The difference is 12 min, although activity 9 requires only 10 min. Therefore, we have (62 − 50 − 10) min = 2 min float time.

The float time is significant for project managers. If a delay occurs during an activity, the completion of the project will not be affected, as long as the delay is less than the float time for that activity. Activities on the critical path have zero float time.

6.4   REFINEMENT OF CPM

The tire-changing example of Section 6.3 is rather simple, but it includes all of the basic CPM concepts. It shows how the CPM method forces the planner to ask questions that may lead to improvements. The improvement of an adequate but inefficient plan is called "optimization." In simple cases, the list of activities shows the planner the optimal course of action and the arrow diagram may not be needed.

It may be thought that the techniques for calculating EE and LE times and the total time T are rather formal and mechanical. However, the calculation of the total project time T can be done in no other way, regardless of the scheduling technique. The reverse process, the calculation of LE values and the identification of the critical path, is unique to CPM and distinguishes it from other methods. The critical path and the LE times provide valuable information when delays occur in the middle of a project. The use of CPM can provide insight that may suggest changes to counteract or eliminate the delays.

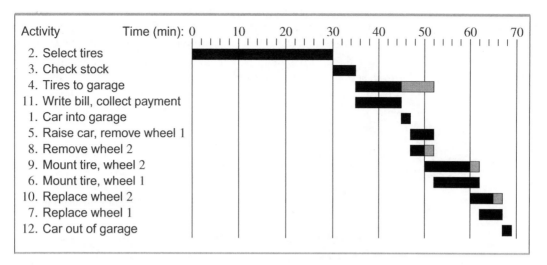

Figure 6.10 Gantt chart for the tire-changing example, illustrating the improved procedure of Figure 6.9 with slack times shown in grey.

The arrow diagrams sometimes appear quite complicated, even for simple problems such as the tire-store example discussed above. However, the diagram is a permanent record of the logical decisions made in the planning process. The diagram becomes more important as the number of activities increases. When the activity count is large (approximately 100), it is necessary to use one of the many CPM computer programs developed to calculate EE, LE, T, and float times. These programs typically list the activities in order by start times; some will produce a Gantt chart, which is usually easy to understand. The Gantt chart for the tire-store example is shown in Figure 6.10, where the solid bars are activity times and the grey bars are float times. The chart corresponds to the arrow diagram in Figure 6.9.

6.5 SUMMARY OF STEPS IN CPM

The following eight steps outline the use of CPM in planning and scheduling a project.

1. List all the activities in the project, and estimate the time required for each activity.
2. Construct the arrow diagram, in which each arrow represents an activity and each event (node) represents a point in time.
3. Calculate the earliest event time (EE) for each event by calculating the maximum of the path times from the start event. The end event EE value is the total project time T.
4. Calculate the latest event times (LE) for each event by subtracting the maximum of the path times to the end event from T. The start event LE should be zero.
5. Calculate the float time for each activity using Equation (6.1).
6. Identify the critical path. Events that have identical EE and LE values have no spare time and are on the critical path. The activities that join these events and have zero float time are the critical path activities.

7. Optimize the project. When the diagram is finished and values of *EE*, *LE*, *T*, and *F* have been calculated, it is possible to survey the project and look for ways to reduce time and cost, eliminate problems, and prevent bottlenecks.

8. Use the information obtained to keep the project under control. Do not use it just for initial planning and file it away. The main strength of CPM is its ability to identify courses of action when crises occur during the project.

6.6   FURTHER STUDY

1. Choose the best answer for each of the following questions.

   (a) The planning component of project planning and scheduling
       i. establishes and organizes the steps to be followed to complete a project.
       ii. optimizes project objectives.
       iii. attempts to minimize time, waste, and cost.
       iv. i and ii.
       v. i, ii, and iii.

   (b) A Gantt chart is
       i. a project-planning tool but not a project-scheduling tool.
       ii. a project-visualization tool.
       iii. a project-scheduling tool but not a project-planning tool.
       iv. useful for revealing how delays in one project activity will affect other project activities.

   (c) The critical path method
       i. is superior to a Gantt chart.
       ii. simultaneously incorporates project planning and scheduling.
       iii. uses slack time to accommodate uncertainties in activity durations.

   (d) The critical path method
       i. yields a project plan that minimizes project time.
       ii. can provide guidance on how to optimize an existing project plan.
       iii. uses either time or cost to identify the critical path of the project.

   (e) The critical path method starts by
       i. identifying project objectives.
       ii. identifying the critical path of the project.
       iii. listing project activities.
       iv. building a Gantt chart.

   (f) Critical path method events
       i. describe the activities essential to the project.
       ii. are also referred to as milestones.
       iii. measure the time required to complete a project activity.
       iv. are also referred to as critical path activities.

   (g) Dashed lines are used in critical path method diagrams to
       i. connect the earliest event time (*EE*) with the latest event time (*LE*).
       ii. represent locations of float time in a project.
       iii. represent activities that take zero time.
       iv. identify an activity that is optional or where a choice between activities to follow exists.

(h) In the tire-changing example (Example 6.1) of the critical path method, the time to complete the project was reduced from 97 min to 69 min by

    i. hiring more people.

    ii. recognizing that certain activities could be run in parallel.

    iii. inserting float times into strategic activities.

    iv. i and ii. v. ii and iii.

(i) In the critical path method, the slack time of an activity

    i. can always be calculated as the difference between the latest event time (LE) of an event and its earliest event time (EE).

    ii. is the time when workers rest.

    iii. can only be calculated once the critical path method diagram is complete.

    iv. provides opportunities for accommodating unexpected project delays.

(j) Identify the statement or statements that are true for the critical path method.

    i. Achieving a desired minimum time to completion is guaranteed.

    ii. It is impossible for a project activity on the critical path to have a non-zero float time.

    iii. A unique critical path in the project is always readily identified by the CPM.

    iv. The critical path of a project must be identified before float times can be calculated.

6.7   REFERENCES

[1] K. G. Lockyer and J. Gordon, *Project Management and Project Network Techniques*. London: Pitman Publishing, sixth ed., 1996.

[2] J. J. O'Brien and F. L. Plotnick, *CPM in Construction Management*. New York: McGraw-Hill, fifth ed., 1999.

[3] A. Harrison, *A Survival Guide to Critical Path Analysis*. Oxford: Butterworth Heinemann, 1997.

[4] S. A. Devaux, *Total Project Control: A Manager's Guide to Integrated Project Planning, Measuring, and Tracking*. New York: John Wiley & Sons, Inc., 1999.

Chapter 7

Safety in Engineering Design

No engineering design or workplace environment can ever be absolutely free of hazards; however, usually with little effort it is possible to reduce the risk of injury or illness to an acceptable level. Although all engineers must be concerned with safety, these matters can also be considered as a technical specialty, and there is a technical society [1] for loss prevention specialists.

To deal with hazardous situations effectively, the engineer needs a methodical procedure for recognizing hazards and introducing remedies. This chapter discusses some basic methods of recognizing hazards and reducing them by introducing

- safety responsibilities of the engineer,
- guidelines and principles for recognizing and controlling hazards,
- applicable safety codes and standards.

7.1   RESPONSIBILITY OF THE DESIGN ENGINEER

Health and safety issues usually receive public attention only after an accident such as a bridge collapse, a railway derailment, a spill of toxic chemicals, or a gas explosion. These disasters are reported in the news from time to time, although the numbers of such incidents have decreased over the years as education, codes, and standards have improved. For example, fatal boiler explosions were common in the late 1800s, when steam was first being used for engines and heating. However, since the development of the ASME boiler and pressure-vessel design code, boiler explosions have disappeared, even though steam at much higher temperatures and pressures is widely used for electrical power generation and for heating large buildings.

Engineers may be responsible for managing situations that contain potential danger for those present or those who will occupy or use the result of the work. Examples of potential danger are the presence of high voltages, high temperatures, high velocities, toxic chemicals, and large amounts of energy of many kinds, such as mechanical, hydraulic, thermal, or electrical energy. In addition, health or safety hazards may be encountered in construction, manufacturing, or maintenance processes in the factory, worksite, or field installation.

An engineer carries a serious responsibility when supervising a design or construction project, because failure to act to correct a potentially dangerous situation or failure to follow codes and standards is, by definition, professional misconduct. The engineer who neglects health and safety aspects of a design runs the double risk of disciplinary action by the engineer's regulatory Association (as discussed in Chapter 5), as well as potential legal liability if damage or injury should occur as a result of design deficiencies or inadequate safety measures.

There are two groups of people whose health and safety must be considered: the eventual users of the device, product, or structure being built and the workers manufacturing it or its components. The safety of any design or construction project must be examined explicitly with respect to both of these groups.

7.2   PRINCIPLES OF HAZARD RECOGNITION AND CONTROL

There is a general procedure, described briefly below and explained in more detail later in this chapter, for dealing with a hazard.

1. Identify and assess the hazard.
2. Try to prevent or eliminate the need for creating the hazard.
3. If the hazard cannot be eliminated, then it should be treated as a form of signal that emanates from a "source" and follows some "path" to a "receiver," the human worker or user of the design, where it may inflict harm. The application

TABLE 7.1   Examples of source-path-receiver analysis and hazard control methods.

Hazard	Control Measures		
	Source	**Path**	**Receiver**
Mechanical	1. Enclosure guards 2. Interlocking guards (mechanical, electrical) 3. Reduction in speed 4. Limitation of movement	1. Guard by location (rope off area, etc.) 2. Remote control	1. Education 2. Rules and regulations for for clothing, etc. 3. Pull-away devices 4. Aids for placing, feeding, ejecting workpieces 5. Two-hand trip switch buttons
Noise	1. Enclosure 2. Surface treatment 3. Reduction of impact forces	1. Building layout 2. Increase distance 3. Acoustic fibres 4. Mufflers	1. Protective equipment: earmuffs, earplugs 2. Limit exposure time
Electrical	1. Low voltage instruments 2. Fuses, circuit breakers 3. Insulation 4. Lock-outs 5. Labelling, test points	1. Grounding 2. Use of ground fault detectors	1. Protective equipment 2. Education
Thermal (heat or cold)	1. Shielding 2. Insulation 3. Painting 4. Ventilation 5. Limiting physical demands of the job	1. General ventilation	1. Select acclimatized personnel 2. Acclimatization program 3. Adequate supply of water 4. Special clothing; ventilated suits 5. Proper work-rest schedules 6. Limiting exposure time
Chemical	1. Isolate or substitute 2. Change of process	1. Ventilation	1. Protective equipment, respirators, etc.

of this analogy is called *source-path-receiver analysis,* and identifies three locations where action can be taken to prevent the damage. Some examples are shown in Table 7.1.

4. If the above steps prove unsuccessful and the resulting design proves to be unsafe, then remedial action is essential: recall the unsafe devices, notify people of danger, assist the injured, and so on, as appropriate.

The following paragraphs outline a basic set of principles for assessing hazards.

Assess the capabilities and limitations of users

Designers must realize that the equipment or products they are creating will ultimately be used by persons whose physical and mental abilities may vary considerably. Designing an item for a general user is more demanding than creating products for highly select user groups such as airline pilots, for example. General users have wide variations in abilities, and their minimum skill level should not be overrated.

Anticipate common errors and modes of failure

Experience has shown that when a design goes into widespread use, there is validity to Murphy's law: "Anything that can go wrong will go wrong." Thus, designers must try to anticipate what can go wrong with their solutions and modify the design to prevent these unwanted events, or if prevention is not possible, at least to minimize the consequences and warn of the hazard.

How can this be done? In general, it means asking a series of questions such as, "Can a given event or sequence take place? If it can, what will be the result? Can this result lead to illness, injury, or death? If so, what can be done to prevent this?" This process is known as "idiot proofing."

Evaluate designs for safety and health

Evaluation of a design for safety and health risks is usually undertaken as part of a design review. While the process is by no means foolproof, it can help considerably in the elimination of most obvious hazards. It may also prove helpful in establishing a defence against a future product liability lawsuit by demonstrating that the hazardous nature of the product was explicitly considered and prudent control steps were taken.

Provide adequate instructions and warnings

Many safety-related incidents can be traced to poorly designed and prepared operating instructions or maintenance manuals, as well as inadequate warning labels. When these items are prepared, designers should carefully consider the people who will be using their products or machines. Warnings should be permanently affixed in bright colours near all danger points in locations where they will readily be seen. If possible, these warnings should be permanently attached to the product in an indestructible form. Pictorial warnings have been found to be more effective than written messages.

Design safe tooling and workstations

One of the most common industrial injuries involves a worker inserting a hand into a machine closure point that is closing. These accidents occur in spite of machine guards when the effect of a guard can be circumvented by a careless operator. It is better to have integral or built-in systems that prevent irregular actuation. If correctly designed, such systems can be almost impossible to disable.

Consider maintenance needs

There are nine basic rules for making certain that a product can be safely maintained and repaired. They are as follows.

1. *Accessibility.* Parts should be arranged so that the most frequently replaced items can be reached with a minimum of effort.
2. *Standardization.* If possible, interchangeable parts, set in common locations, should be used on different models of the product.
3. *Modularization.* It may be possible to replace an entire unit without the need to repair malfunctioning individual components. This technique is particularly useful for field repairs.
4. *Identification.* Marking, coding, or tagging products makes them easier to distinguish. Colour coding of electrical wiring is a good example.
5. *Safety considerations.* When the product is being serviced or repaired, the worker must not be placed in an unsafe situation. For example, sufficient clearance should be provided, particularly in dangerous locations, such as near high-voltage sources.
6. *Safety controls.* Prevent the machine from being turned on remotely (from another switch location) while maintenance is performed.
7. *Storage areas.* Provide separate storage areas for special tools, such as those needed for adjustment.
8. *Grounding.* Ground the machine to minimize electrical hazards.
9. *Surfaces.* Provide proper walking surfaces to prevent accidents due to slipping or tripping.

Provide clear indications of danger

Anticipate incorrect assembly, installation, connection, or operation, and prevent them through design. Prevent a malfunction in any single component or subassembly from spreading and causing other failures. These techniques are part of fail-safe design.

When hazards cannot be eliminated, signs and labels recommended by standards institutes such as the American National Standards Institute (ANSI) or the International

Figure 7.1   Elements of standard hazard signs and product labels. The background is red for the danger panel, orange for the warning panel, and yellow for the caution panel. Standard pictograms include the yellow warning triangle, the blue circle showing a mandatory action (wearing a hard hat), and the barred red circle on a white background prohibiting an action (no thoroughfare).

Organization for Standardization (ISO) should be displayed. The warnings indicate the nature and severity of the hazard and the means of avoiding it. Figure 7.1 shows elements of standard signs and product safety labels. The principal signal words are as follows.

DANGER   The danger sign warns of extreme or imminent risk of death or injury. The lettering is white on a red background.

WARNING   The warning sign denotes a specific potential hazard that could result in injury or death. This panel has black lettering on an orange background.

CAUTION   The caution sign is used to warn of risks or unsafe practices that could result in minor or moderate injury. The panel has black lettering on a yellow background.

A safety sign or warning label includes a panel with one of the above signal words, and may include explanatory text and one or more pictograms such as illustrated in Figure 7.1. The pictograms have three principal formats as illustrated in the figure: the triangle for warning signs, a blue circle showing mandatory action such as wearing protective clothing, and a barred red circle prohibiting an action. Hazard signs and labels intended for international distribution may require symbol-only formats because of the many languages involved, but North American standards do not conform totally with this practice.

Control energy density   High energy densities increase the possibility of accidents and should be avoided if possible. For example, include appropriate pressure-relief valves or sensors with automatic shutoff facilities that operate when out-of-range conditions are detected.

Initiate a recall   The final remedial action is the product recall, as a result of recognizing a real or potential hazard after a device, structure, or system has been put into operation. Action is taken to prevent the potential hazard from becoming a reality. Recalls may be instituted for one or more of five principal reasons.

1. Analysis reveals the presence of a potential hazard that can result in a pattern of serious incidents.
2. Reports are received from users or others of unsafe conditions, unsafe incidents, or unsafe product characteristics.
3. An incident reveals a previously unforeseen product deficiency.
4. A government standard or similar regulation has been violated.
5. The product does not live up to its advertised claims with regard to safety.

7.3   ELIMINATING WORKPLACE HAZARDS

People are often required to work in environments where conditions are less than ideal. Such work may expose them to a variety of job-related stresses that can affect their health over time or increase their chances of becoming involved in an accident. The definitions of *stress* and *strain* in this context are different from conventional engineering terminology. *Stress* refers to any undesirable condition, circumstance, task, or other factor that impinges on the worker. *Strain* refers to the adverse effects of these stress sources (or stressors) on performance, safety, or health. For example, extremely high (or low) values of temperature, relative humidity, and workplace lighting as well as excessive amounts of noise and vibration are typical stresses that workers may encounter.

A common approach practised extensively in areas of product safety involves the use of checklists. Frequently such lists take the form of specific questions addressed to the designer. These are intended to prompt the designer to investigate the most common hazards associated with design, choice of materials, manufacturing processes, and functional and maintenance requirements. Examples of checklists are given in Table 7.2 for machine design and Table 7.3 for checking hazards in the workplace.

Another important area of concern for both workers and product users relates to chemical contaminants that may be present in production environments or released by products. As a minimum, the designer should be fully aware of any hazards that may be associated with the product. The designer should know how to measure them, recognize the symptoms they produce, and understand the basic steps needed to reduce or eliminate any associated risks to health or safety. Such measures can be applied to either the source, the path, or the user, as explained below.

Source control   *Source control* refers to techniques such as capturing, guarding, enclosing, insulating, or isolating a suspected hazard.

Path control   *Path control* means increasing the distance between the source of the hazard and the receiver. Techniques that are useful here are muffling for noise, grounding for electricity, and improved ventilation to remove toxic byproducts from the air.

TABLE 7.2   Hazard checklist for machine design.

1. Is the machine designed so that it is impossible to gain access to hazard points while the power is on?
2. Are the controls located so that the operator will not be off-balance or too close to the point of operation whenever actuation is required?
3. Are the power transmission and fluid drive mechanisms built as integral parts of the machine so that the operator is not exposed to rotating shafts?
4. Is the machine designed for single-point lubrication?
5. Are mechanical rather than manual devices used for holding, feeding, and ejecting parts?
6. Are there automatic overload devices built into the machine? Are fail-safe interlocks provided so that the machine cannot be started while it is being loaded, unloaded, or worked on?
7. Is there a grounding system for all electrical equipment?
8. Are standard access platforms or ladders provided for the inspection and maintenance of equipment? Are walking surfaces made of non-slip materials?
9. Are equipment components designed for easy and safe removal and replacement during maintenance and repair?
10. Are all corners and edges rounded and bevelled?
11. Are all sources of objectionable noise minimized?
12. Are all control knobs and buttons clearly distinguishable and guarded so that they cannot be accidentally activated?

TABLE 7.3 Hazard checklist for workplace layout.

1. Design equipment so that it is physically impossible for the worker to do something that would hurt himself, herself, or others.

   Examples of such protective design include the following:

   (a) A rotary blade that will not start unless a guard is in place.

   (b) The inclusion of interlocks to prevent operation of a machine unless the operator's limbs and body are in a safe position.

   (c) One-way installation: connecting pins that are asymmetrical so that they will fit into a connector in only one way.

2. Cover or guard any moving parts of machinery that could cut a worker or fly off.

3. Make sure that the plant is thoroughly surveyed to detect the presence of noxious gases or other toxic air contaminants.

4. Provide a sufficient number of conveniently located fire extinguishers and an automatic sprinkling system.

5. Use non-slip surfaces on floors and stairways. Eliminate steep ramps used with rolling devices, such as forklifts.

6. Use reliable equipment that will not fail at unscheduled times.

7. Eliminate design features associated with accidents; redesign the workspace to eliminate awkward postures, to reduce fatigue, and to keep workers alert while performing repetitive tasks.

8. Label hazards clearly and conspicuously.

9. Provide warning devices.

User control   *User control* refers to providing personal protective equipment to workers, thus reducing their exposure to hazards. Also, schedules can be modified to reduce stress, and improved training can be obtained. A general scheme showing examples of control techniques is shown in Table 7.1 on page 88.

7.4   COST–BENEFIT JUSTIFICATION OF SAFETY ISSUES

Generally there is a cost justification of safety programs, although the savings from such programs are often difficult to predict precisely. The savings may come from a number of different areas:

- reduced workers' compensation insurance costs,
- improved productivity from reduced error rates,
- a more stable and content workforce,
- more consistent output, resulting in better quality control,
- less government involvement to enforce safety standards,
- confidence in the operating equipment, yielding higher output,
- improved communication and employee morale.

7.5   CODES AND STANDARDS

The word *standards* has a general meaning in everyday use, but in the context of engineering design, the term refers to documents describing rules or methods that serve as models of professional practice. Written standards are published by technical societies, as discussed in Chapter 2, but government agencies and commercial organizations also publish standards. Following a standard in design may be optional but is evidence that the work has been conducted to a professional level of competence.

Codes and *regulations*, on the other hand, are parts of or given authority by statutes, by-laws, or collections of them, by which a national or local government requires specific practices to be followed, including adherence to particular standards.

Internationally, there is a trend toward performance-based codes and away from prescriptive codes. In Canada, performance-based codes start by specifying code objectives and hence are also referred to as objective-based codes. Prescriptive codes specify exact physical characteristics to be satisfied, such as maximum physical dimensions, minimum hardness, or minimum strength, for example. Objective-based codes associate a specified characteristic (such as reduction of risk, endurance, aesthetics, or accessibility) with a performance requirement (such as time tolerance, robustness, capacity, or power). A prescriptive requirement is specified when a performance requirement cannot be established or is inappropriate. Objective-based codes may specify example alternatives for acceptable solutions to the performance requirement. The 2005 edition of the National Building Code of Canada uses an objective-based format.

Objective-based codes admit more flexibility and innovation in design, but they also require more technical sophistication of design engineers.

EXAMPLE 7.1

FIRE ESCAPES

An objective-based code might set as an objective the need to protect people from fire by enabling them to reach a place of safety. The associated performance requirement may specify a minimum time to reach a place of safety once a fire is detected, and perhaps also specify a minimum distance to an exit as a prescriptive requirement. As an alternative acceptable solution the code may then offer the use of sprinklers.

Examples of national standards organizations are the following:

- Standards Council of Canada (SCC),
- American National Standards Institute (ANSI),
- Deutsches Institut für Normung (DIN),
- Association Française de Normalisation (AFNOR),
- British Standards Institute (BSI).

National model codes and many national standards have no force in law unless they are adopted (or adapted) by the province, territory, and, in some cases, municipality, with the authority to establish legal codes or regulations.

The Standards Council of Canada (SCC) is a Crown corporation that promotes and coordinates the development and application of national and international standards. Its publications assist in finding international standards [2] and standards referenced in federal legislation. Students and professors at Canadian universities can obtain access to standards without charge by contacting the SCC.

Two international organizations that create and approve standards are the International Organization for Standardization (ISO) and the International Electrotechnical Commission (IEC). The national standards organizations are members of these bodies.

7.5.1   Finding and Using Safety Codes and Standards

Many codes and standards have been developed over the years to set minimum acceptable health and safety levels. Applying applicable codes and standards for safety and other factors is not only good professional and business practice, but failure to do so may be judged to be professional misconduct, as discussed in Chapter 5. Therefore, you may be faced with determining which codes and standards apply to your work. The following paragraphs may be of assistance.

Prior practice   You may be designing modifications to products for which adherence to standards has been documented or to products in the same area. Checking similar prior work or consulting experienced engineers in the field is a primary means of determining which standards apply. You should check whether standards used previously have been changed.

No better source of advice can be found than consulting with an engineer qualified in the specialty and place involved in the project.

On-line databases

The most convenient search method is to search the vast standards databases provided by the SCC and ANSI, accredited standards developers such as the Canadian Standards Association (CSA), and more area-specific organizations such as the IEEE and the American Society for Testing and Materials (ASTM).

Catalogues

Not surprisingly, given the large number of published standards and applicable codes, there are catalogues listing them, published mainly by the standards organizations such as listed above and by industry-specific bodies such as the Society of Automotive Engineers (SAE) or by commercial testing organizations such as Underwriters Laboratories (UL). On-line catalogues [2, 3] are becoming the standard source for finding standards. Finally, the cataloguing bodies also provide search services for finding standards that may apply to specific situations.

Search assistance

Some of the same agencies that list standards also have listings or links to government regulations and statutes. References [2] and [4] are good starting places.

The statutes and regulations that originate from national, regional, and local governments contain the codes covering engineering and other professional work, particularly as it affects public safety.

The following list is a sampling of codes by government level.

Federal regulations and model codes

Canada Occupational Safety and Health regulations	Canadian Electrical Code
	The National Building Code
The Labour Code	Canadian Environmental Protection Act
Hazardous Product Act	

Provincial regulations

provincial building codes	provincial electrical codes
Construction Safety Act	Drainage Act
Employment Standards Act	Labour Relations Act
Fire regulations	Municipal Act
Planning Act	Surveyors Act
Industrial Safety Act	Operating Engineers Act
Elevators and Lifts Act	Boilers and Pressure Vessels Act
Occupational Health and Safety Act	Environmental Protection Act

Municipal regulations

Each town or city may impose additional regulations or laws or modify codes to suit local conditions.

An engineer beginning work on a new project should ask whether the work may be governed by some code or law. In the case of electrical networks, roads, bridges, buildings, elevators, vehicles, boilers, pressure vessels, and other works affecting the public, the answer will be "yes. " Consult with more experienced engineers, and determine the codes and laws that apply.

7.6　FURTHER STUDY

1.　Choose the best answer for each of the following questions.

(a)　High temperature, high humidity, or high noise levels in a workplace

i.　represent possible strains for workers

ii.　are not allowed by safety codes or standards

        iii. represent possible stresses for workers

        iv. can be eliminated by use of the source-path-receiver hazard-control method

(b) The source-path-receiver hazard-control method

        i. does not require caution, warning, or danger signs if the receiver is protected from the hazard.

        ii. uses checklists to ensure common hazards are not missed.

        iii. requires the engineer to implement three safety measures, one at each of the source, the path, and the receiver.

        iv. may not eliminate a hazard.

(c) Implementing a health and safety program

        i. often saves money.

        ii. is not required if a company has sufficient workers' compensation insurance.

        iii. is concerned only with worker safety and not product quality control.

        iv. may enable a company to substitute its own safety standards for government safety standards.

(d) A design engineer

        i. must meet all codes and standards.

        ii. may legally be expected to meet a higher safety standard than required by codes.

        iii. must meet only those codes and standards required by law.

        iv. can meet a code requirement by implementing a safety design that can be proven to be safer than the existing code requirement.

(e) The safety codes applicable in Canada are

        i. objective based.

        ii. continually changing.

        iii. the legal responsibility of standards organizations such as the CSA.

        iv. the legal responsibility of the engineering societies such as the IEEE.

(f) A design that meets all safety codes and standards

        i. may still represent a potential safety liability for the signing engineer.

        ii. no longer represents a potential safety liability for the design engineer.

        iii. does not require further safety improvements.

        iv. will never be a risk to the public.

(g) Engineers must follow all codes and regulations that apply to their work

        i. because they are legally bound to do so.

        ii. because they may be charged with professional misconduct.

        iii. because they may be charged in civil or criminal court if they fail to do so, and an accident or failure occurs.

        iv. because their work cannot be patented otherwise.

        v. for the first three of the above reasons.

        vi. for all of the above reasons.

(h) The roof of the Hartford Civic Center, designed with extensive use of computer programs, collapsed under the weight of ice and snow in 1978. Who or what was legally responsible for the failure of the roof?

    i. the snow and ice load

    ii the author of the computer programs used to design the roof

    iii. the structural engineer

    iv. the computer programs used to design the roof

(i) It is the legal responsibility of the following to report unsafe construction or manufacturing situations.

    i. Canadian Standards Association personnel

    ii. a construction or manufacturing engineer

    iii. an engineering student

    iv. a construction or manufacturing engineer and Canadian Standards Association personnel

    v. none of these

(j) The safety of any design must be examined from the aspect of safety of the user, but the safety of the workers who produce the design for sale to the public is the sole responsibility of the manufacturing company.

    i. false   ii. true

2. Measurements of the human body generally follow the familiar bell-shaped curve of the Gaussian distribution. There are three basic ways the designer can take into account these differences between people, as follows.

(a) Design for an extreme size, for example, by locating the controls on a machine so that the shortest person can reach them, implying that everyone else can reach them too.

(b) Design for an average, for example, setting the height of a supermarket checkout counter to suit a person of "average" height. Both tall and short cashiers will have to accommodate themselves to the single height available.

(c) Design for an adjustable range. This is the idea behind the adjustable front seat of an automobile. From its closest to its farthest position, it can accommodate over 99 % of the population.

Is any one of the three design options always the safest? For each, can you imagine a design situation where it would be safest? least safe? How would you achieve method (c) so that a design can accommodate over 99 % of the population?

3. Listed below are various methods of reducing hazards. Can you classify each method as a source, path, or receiver control method as in Section 7.3? Do we need additional categories of control?

(a) Prevent the creation of the hazard in the first place. For example, prevent production of dangerous materials, such as nuclear waste.

(b) Reduce the amount of hazard created. For example, reduce the lead content of paint.

(c) Prevent the release of a hazard that already exists. For example, pasteurize milk to prevent the spread of dangerous bacteria.

(d) Modify the rate of spatial distribution of the hazard released at its source, for example, by installing quick-acting shutoff valves to prevent the rapid spread of flammable fluid.

(e) Separate, in space or time, the hazard from that which is to be protected. For example, store flammable materials in an isolated location.

(f) Separate the hazard from that which is to be protected by imposing a material barrier. For example, build containment structures for nuclear reactors.

(g) Modify certain relevant basic qualities of the hazard, for example, using breakaway roadside poles.

(h) Make what is to be protected more resistant to damage from the hazard. For example, make structures more fire- and earthquake-resistant.

(i) Counteract damage done by environmental hazards, for example, by rescuing the shipwrecked.

(j) Stabilize, repair, and rehabilitate the object of the damage, for example, by rebuilding after fires and earthquakes.

4. Find at least one code, regulation, or statute that governs the design of the following products in your community: (i) propane storage tanks, (ii) video recorders, (iii) cell phones, (iv) snowmobiles, (v) highway bridges, (vi) children's rattles, (vii) home plumbing, (viii) automobile gasolines, (ix) ponds, and (x) natural gas pipelines.

5. A software company provides a computer database program that is used to store and transmit medical records. Identify a code, regulation, or statute that applies to this product. Develop one example of an objective-based code requirement that might be applied to such a computer program. Include the following in your model code:

 Overall objective

  Specific objective

   Performance requirements

   Prescriptive requirements (at least one)

  Alternative acceptable solutions (at least one)

Should this medical database program be designed by a professional engineer? Why or why not?

6. Develop a hazard checklist for the design of a telephone. Compare your checklist with another student's list. Did you miss anything important? Revise your checklist as appropriate. How might you ensure that your checklist is as complete as possible without being unwieldy? From your revised telephone hazard checklist generate two checklists, one for the design engineer and one for the manufacturing engineer. Which of these two engineers has a higher level of responsibility for ensuring that a safe product is delivered to the customer?

7.7   REFERENCES

[1] Canadian Centre for Occupational Health and Safety, *Canadian Society of Safety Engineering*. Canadian Society of Safety Engineering, 2001. <http://www.csse.org/> (March 9, 2008).

[2] Standards Council of Canada, "Standards in focus," 2004. <http://www.scc.ca/en/publications/standards/index.shtml> (March 9, 2008).

[3] American National Standards Institute, NSSN: *A National Resource for Global Standards*. Washington, DC: American National Standards Institute, 1998. <http://www.nssn.org/> (March 9, 2008).

[4] Department of Justice Canada, *Justice Laws Web Site: Consolidated Statutes and Regulations*. Ottawa: Legislative Services Branch, 2007. <http://laws.justice.gc.ca/en/index.html> (March 9, 2008).

Chapter 8

Safety, Risk, and the Engineer

Managing and reducing *risk* and increasing its opposite, *safety*, are paramount engineering responsibilities. Several advanced, computer-oriented techniques are available for analyzing hazards and helping to create safe designs. This chapter discusses the following techniques for risk analysis and management:

- checklists,

- operability studies,

- failure mode analysis and its variations,

- fault-tree analysis.

8.1   EVALUATING RISK IN DESIGN

As designs progress in any industry, the specifications tend to require higher performance, lower cost, or both, compared to previous generations of similar designs. Hazards tend to increase because of factors such as greater complexity, greater use of toxic and dangerous substances, higher equipment speeds, temperatures, or pressures, and more complex control systems. In addition, increased consumer awareness of risk results in demands for higher safety standards. The design engineer is caught between the increased hazards and the higher demands for safety.

Risk factors must be considered when evaluating alternatives at every design stage, but particularly during design reviews, which are usually held near the end of the project. The design review is a formal evaluation meeting in which engineers and others examine the proposed design and compare it with the design criteria. The review must include a final check that the design has no serious hazards. Unsafe designs do not occur because questions could not be answered; they usually occur because questions about safety were not asked.

The necessity of answering risk-related questions leads to the study of risk management, which is a structured approach for analyzing, evaluating, and reducing risk. After identifying and ranking the risks, risk-reduction strategies are applied, starting with the most beneficial and continuing until things are "safe enough," the risk has been reduced to an "acceptable level," or available resources are exhausted. This process is examined in the following sections.

8.2   RISK MANAGEMENT

A hazard is anything that has the potential to cause injury, death, property damage, financial waste, or any other undesirable consequence. The purpose of risk management is to reduce or eliminate the danger caused by hazards.

The three-step process

We must be able to identify the hazards that are present, estimate the probability of their occurrence, generate alternative courses of action to reduce the probability of occurrence, and, finally, act to manage the risk. Therefore, risk management can be viewed as a three-step process involving analysis, evaluation or assessment, and decision-making. The analytical methods in this chapter deal mainly with analysis, but all three steps are described briefly below.

Risk analysis

The first step, risk analysis, has two parts: identifying hazards or their undesirable consequences, and estimating the probabilities of their occurrence. Hazard identification and probability estimation require logic, deduction, and mathematical concepts, so risk analysis is objective and mathematical. Once the hazards and their occurrence probabilities have been identified, the consequent damage or injury must be evaluated.

Risk evaluation (assessment)

In the second step, alternative courses of action to reduce hazards are generated, their costs and benefits are calculated, the risk perceptions of the persons affected are assessed, and value judgments are made. Therefore, risk evaluation is less objective than risk analysis. Determining possible options and their acceptability is a tricky and often debatable step in the process. History and experience play a major role. Public perception of a product can change: a previously acceptable level of emissions, for example, may become unacceptable. When all factors are brought together, the evaluation forms the basis for management decisions to control or reduce total risk.

Management decisions
The final stage of risk management involves selecting the risks that will be managed, implementing these decisions, allocating the required resources, and controlling, monitoring, reviewing, and revising these activities.

Good practice
In design, the term *good practice* means following established methods for safe design or construction. Good practice is often embodied in industry standards and government regulations that may be mandatory. However, whether mandatory or not, adherence to good practice does not guarantee that a product will be safe in the hands of the ultimate user or that a production line can be designed, built, operated, and decommissioned with an acceptable level of risk. From the perspective of liability, adherence to good practice is the minimum acceptable level of care expected, and more advanced risk-management methods are usually essential.

8.3　ANALYTICAL METHODS

There are many methods, ranging from informal to highly structured, that can be used to identify hazards and to evaluate risk. Some methods simply identify hazards; others help to determine the consequences or the probabilities of the consequences occurring, or both. Still other techniques extend into risk evaluation by ranking risks according to specified criteria. Many companies modify these standard techniques to suit their own circumstances. The techniques are not mutually exclusive; a combination of methods may be best. Four frequently used methods for risk analysis, which is also called *safety engineering*, will be explained briefly.

8.3.1　Checklists

Checklists are particularly useful when a design has evolved from a previous design for which all hazard sources were carefully listed, so that the consequences of the evolution are easy to identify. Preparing a comprehensive, useful checklist can be onerous, and if the product or process changes, the checklist must be revised. Hazards that are not specifically mentioned in the checklist will be overlooked, and hazard definitions can change with new information or evolving risk perception.

Checklists should be developed as early in the project as possible. In fact, ideally they should be part of the design criteria. The checklists in Table 7.2 and Table 7.3 are examples of a typical format. These examples, as well as the generic headings suggested below, can be modified for developing specific design-review checklists.

Typical headings for **a design-review** safety checklist

1.　General standards and standardization
2.　Human factors: displays and controls
3.　Maintainability in service
4.　Instruction for users and maintenance personnel
5.　Packaging, identification, and marking
6.　Structural materials
7.　Fittings and fasteners
8.　Corrosion prevention
9.　Hazard detection and warning signals
10.　Electrical, hydraulic, pneumatic, and pressure subsystems
11.　Fuel and power sources.

Checklists are built on past experience. For new or radically altered products and processes, checklists should be supplemented by *predictive techniques*, such as in the following subsections.

8.3.2   Hazard and operability studies

The methods in this subsection are used mainly in the process industries to uncover hazards and problems that might arise during plant operation. The hazard and operability (HAZOP) technique could be called *structured brainstorming*. The technique is applied to precisely specified equipment, processes, or systems; therefore, the design must be beyond the concept stage and in a more concrete form before the technique can be used. Variations of the technique can be used at all stages of the life of a plant, such as at preliminary design, final design, startup, operation, and decommissioning.

The study is carried out by a team of experts who, together, have a full understanding of the process to be examined, such as the basic chemistry, process equipment, control systems, and operational and maintenance procedures. To carry out the study, complete information is needed, including flowcharts, process diagrams, equipment drawings, plant layouts, control system descriptions, maintenance and operating manuals, and other information as necessary.

Some definitions and concepts used in HAZOP studies include the following:

- *nodes:* the points in the process that are to be studied
- *parameters:* the characteristics of the process at a node
- *design intent:* how an element in the process is supposed to perform, or the intended values of the parameters at each node
- *deviations:* the manner in which the element or the parameters deviate from the design intent
- *causes:* the reasons why the deviations occur
- *consequences:* what happens as a result of the deviations
- *hazards:* the serious consequences (note the different meaning of *hazard* in this context)
- *guide words:* simple words applied to the elements or parameters to stimulate creative thinking to reveal all of the possible deviations

The prime purpose of HAZOP studies is to identify hazards and operational problems. The hazards and problems must be well documented for subsequent attention, and there must be an effective follow-up to ensure that the HAZOP decisions are implemented. The first step is to identify the nodes in a plant process; each node is then studied, as in the following example.

EXAMPLE 8.1

A HEAT EXCHANGER

Consider a process that includes a heat exchanger in a duct carrying hot gas. Water flows through the coil in order to cool the gas. The water flow into the heat exchanger would be one of the study nodes. The parameters at this node would include flow, temperature, and pressure. The design intent at this node might be to provide water at a specified flow rate, temperature, and pressure. A set of guide words would be applied successively to the parameters. To illustrate, consider the guide words "NO FLOW." The cause of "NO FLOW" could be a closed valve, a broken pipe, a clogged filter, or the failure of the municipal water supply. Each of these causes is realistic, so the deviation could occur and the consequences of the deviation must be examined. The possible consequences could include vaporizing the water in the heat exchanger coil, thus producing dangerously high pressure, or allowing the temperature of the gases to rise, yielding dangerously high rates of reaction elsewhere in the process. Both of these consequences are serious and warrant attention.

The other parameters at the node—temperature and pressure—would also be studied. All other nodes in the process would be studied in a similar manner.

8.3.3   Failure modes and effects analysis

Failure modes and effects analysis (FMEA) is a "bottom-up" process that estimates the reliability of a complex system from the reliability of its components. With the addition of the assessment of the criticality (importance) of failures, a technique called "failure modes, effects, and criticality analysis" (FMECA) results. The technique is inductive, and the analysis is carried out by completing a table, following logical rules [1]. Full details of the component, equipment, process, or complex facility to be analyzed must be available, including drawings, design sketches, standards, product specifications, test results, or other information.

The basic components to investigate first depend on the desired resolution of the analysis. For a chemical plant with several processes, for example, a component might be an individual process in a reactor. If a single process were considered, the components might be the individual pieces of equipment supporting that process. If a specific piece of equipment is be analyzed, say, a pump, the component parts would be the housing, seals, impeller, coupling, motor, and motor control, for example.

FMEA process   The FMEA steps are as follows.

1. List each of the components or subsystems in the unit.
2. Identify each component by part name and number.
3. Describe each component and its function.
4. List all of the ways (modes) in which each component can fail.
5. For each mode of failure, determine the failure effect on other components and on the unit as a whole. Enter the information in the table.
6. Describe how each failure mode can be detected.

FMECA process   In addition to the FMEA analysis, criticality analysis continues with the following:

7. Indicate the action to be taken to eliminate the hazards and identify who is responsible for taking that action.
8. Assess the criticality of each failure mode and its probability of occurrence.

Many forms of tables have been developed for use with FMEA and FMECA techniques. The measure of criticality is the seriousness of the consequence, which may range from a simple requirement for maintenance, through property loss or personal injury, to catastrophe. In the FMECA method, a measure of the consequence is usually combined with the estimated probability of occurrence to weigh the risk associated with each failure.

The potential difficulty in using bottom-up methods for complex products or systems is the large effort required by a large number of components. Another technique, such as the qualitative fault-tree analysis described in Section 8.3.4, may be required to narrow the scope of the analysis. The FMECA method is effective in determining the consequences of single component failures; it is not suitable for determining the effect on the system of the concurrent failure of several system elements.

8.3.4   Fault-tree analysis

In contrast to FMEA, fault-tree analysis is a "top-down" process. First, suppose that a single major event, called the top event, has occurred. Then determine all events that could cause the top event. These contributory events are then analyzed, in the same manner, to determine the events upon which they depend. The process is continued until events are reached that do not depend on other events or need not be further broken down. Independent events are said to be *primary* or *basic*. Events that are not further broken down are called *undeveloped* events. Events can be human errors or failures of equipment.

Fault-tree analysis can be used at any stage in the evolution of a product or process. The events and their relationships are usually represented diagrammatically using standard logic symbols. This results in a tree-like diagram [2], which gives the method its name.

EXAMPLE 8.2   A HAIR DRYER

A hand-held hair dryer can be used to illustrate the fault-tree technique. Assume that the dryer is made from non-conducting plastic, has no metal parts that extend from the inside of the dryer to the outside, and has a two-conductor power cord. Assume also that the dryer is not connected to a power supply protected by a ground-fault-interrupt circuit breaker, as required in bathrooms.

The top event will be assumed to be the electrocution of the user. The purpose of the analysis is to determine how this top event could occur and to find steps to prevent it or, if total prevention is not possible, to reduce its likelihood.

The fault tree is shown in Figure 8.1. The top event will occur only if all of the inputs to the AND gate are present; that is, only if all of the events in the row immediately below the AND gate occur. The shape of the leftmost box identifies an event that is

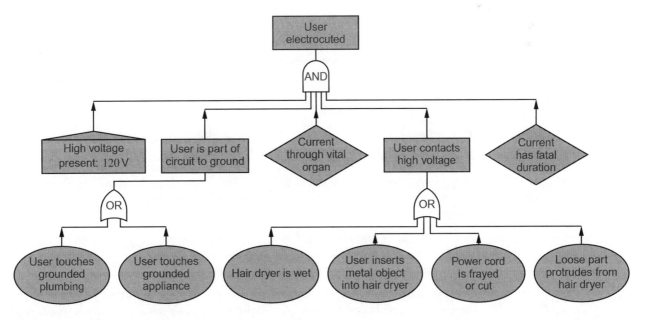

Figure 8.1   Partial fault tree for the hair dryer in Example 8.2. The two diamonds represent undeveloped subtrees, and the leftmost box indicates an expected event.

expected to occur. The dryer uses the normal 120 V house supply, a dangerously high voltage. Two events in the first row are enclosed in diamonds and not developed further. The two remaining events in this row depend on outputs from the OR gates. An OR gate output occurs if any of its input events occur. The inputs to the OR gates are basic fault events and are enclosed in ellipses.

The presence of the second-level AND gate is favourable in preventing the top event, since all of the inputs to an AND gate must be present for a higher event to occur. In a simple tree such as Figure 8.1, the basic or undeveloped events that must occur for the top event to happen can be determined by inspection. Guided by the information in the fault tree, steps can be taken to make the product safer.

Events caused by users Some of the basic fault events depend solely on the actions of the user and cannot be prevented by design changes. However, instructions for the proper use of the hair dryer and conspicuously placed warnings about the hazards of misuse, as discussed in the previous chapter, should decrease the probability of injury and lessen the potential liability of the engineer. In the previous example, inserting fingers or metal objects through the hair dryer openings can bring a person into contact with high-voltage components; this event can be made more difficult by placing the high-voltage components farther away from the openings. The insertion of objects through openings in electrical appliances is a well-recognized hazard, and Underwriters Laboratories [3] and others have standard probes to be used in the certification of products. Of course, this is only one of the requirements for certification.

The analysis described above is qualitative in nature; however, the next step in the analysis is usually quantitative. If failure probabilities for the basic fault events are known, the probability of the top event occurring can be calculated [4]. The failure probabilities for many standard components are available from reliability handbooks and other sources. Tests can be conducted to determine failure probabilities for components or systems for which data is not available. In a more complicated tree, Boolean algebra must be used to determine the sets of basic events that must all occur for the top event to happen. Computer programs exist for the construction and analysis of fault trees.

8.4   SAFETY IN LARGE SYSTEMS

Systems containing many interconnected parts present distinguishing features of a different type than basic products, artifacts, or static structures. Examples for which safety analysis is difficult are space navigation, vehicle control, aircraft control, chemical refining, power generation, and almost any system with a computer embedded in it.

Complexity The first such distinguishing feature is complexity. A system can be thought of as a graph, that is, a set of nodes representing system variables or parameters, joined by branches representing processes or basic subsystems. Then if the number of branches is of the same order as the number of nodes, the system is said to have low complexity, whereas high complexity corresponds to cases where the number of branches is large compared to the number of nodes.

Coupling Another factor of importance is the coupling between parts of the system. In a tightly coupled system, a perturbation in one part may cause changes in many other parts. In a loosely coupled system, perturbations in one part have little effect on other parts.

Response rate From a safety standpoint, the system response rate is very important, particularly as it affects the opportunity for operator intervention. Fast-response runaway processes require very careful safety measures, while a simple alarm may suffice for a process with very slow response time.

Stability   The concepts of feedback and stability are related to response time and complexity. Inter-dependence, through information and control feedback paths, can lead to unstable modes of operation. The avoidance of these modes is a prime consideration in safety design.

Robustness   Finally, a design is considered robust if it brings about fail-safe or fail-soft conditions in the event of trouble. A fail-safe system can suffer complete loss of function without any attending damage. A fail-soft system may suffer loss of functionality in the event of failure but retains a minimum level of performance and safety, such as the possibility of manual control.

In conclusion, a large system may be reasonably safe if it is not too complex and is loosely coupled, slow to respond, stable, and robust with respect to part failures. Safe operation will be difficult to achieve for a complex system that is tightly coupled, with fast response rate, many feedback paths, and sensitivity to part failures.

8.5   SYSTEM RISK

The engineering management of risk requires the quantification of the probability of hazardous events and their cost of occurrence. Because high-cost, high-probability events tend to be designed out of systems, higher probability will typically occur with the lower costs, and lower probability with the higher costs. Intense debates sometimes arise where the probability is very small but the cost is very severe, particularly when the cost applies only to very few beneficiaries of the process. Consider, for example, safety improvements on highways with low traffic flows: accidents may have a low probability but may involve fatalities when they occur.

One definition of risk r is the product of the probability p of an event and the event cost c. Thus,

$$pc = r. \tag{8.1}$$

Now take the logarithm of both sides to obtain

$$\log(p) + \log(c) = \log(r), \tag{8.2}$$

so that the constant-risk loci are straight lines when the above relation is plotted using log-log scales, as illustrated in Figure 8.2. The figure gives a simple interpretation of the tradeoff between event cost and probability; the difficulty in using such definitions is in obtaining precise estimates of these quantities.

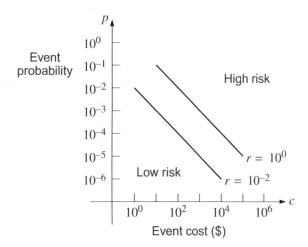

Figure 8.2   Illustrating lines of constant risk. Events in the upper-right part of the chart have high risk; low-risk events are in the lower left.

Defining the exposed population

The probability of a hazardous event must be determined and defined relative to the population exposed to it. Some hazards have very low probabilities when averaged over the total population but may be more probable if only the participating population is considered. For example, the mortality of astronauts and coal miners must be evaluated relative to the number of participants, not the population as a whole. Similarly, when accident rates are compared for different modes of travel, they are often expressed in accidents per passenger-kilometre to give a defensible comparison.

Event cost

The cost of event consequences may be even more difficult to define. Some costs, such as the cost of warranty replacement or repair and the cost of maintenance and service, may be relatively easy to estimate. However, the costs borne by others, including the total cost to society, may be impossible to estimate.

8.6 EXPRESSING THE COSTS OF A HAZARD

In product safety analyses, costs of consequences are normally measured in monetary terms, including legal costs, which can be very high. The costs to society of an event, however, are not as simple to predict, particularly when the public environment is affected.

The risk of a particular hazard to the human population is usually termed *mortality*: the probability of death per year for exposed members of the population, or as loss of life expectancy expressed in days. The latter has the advantage that safety measures such as smoke alarms and air bags can be given a negative loss figure; that is, the gain in life expectancy by their use can be evaluated.

The wealth of an industrialized society depends on the creativity of its engineering sector, and technical advances almost always involve some risk. For example, in the last 160 years, life expectancy at birth in Canada has increased by a factor of 2. This gain results primarily from improvements in safety and sanitation, communication, transportation, water supply, and food processing, and from medical and health improvements. The loss in life expectancy from the hazards of industrialization are small relative to the gains. Nevertheless, it is human nature, and thus engineering nature, to seek improvement. Large-scale projects now must be given a life-cycle cost analysis so that the designers see the full cost of the plant, including decommissioning and disposal of wastes, and not merely the construction and start-up costs.

8.7 FURTHER STUDY

1. Choose the best answer for each of the following questions.

   (a) A design engineer who adheres to good practice
      i. has met the minimum acceptable level of hazard care expected but may still be liable for insufficient risk management.
      ii. may not be meeting the acceptable level of care expected.
      iii. must ensure that all hazards are eliminated.
      iv. guarantees that an acceptable level of risk has been met.

   (b) Hazard checklists
      i. are designed to be used by people who are not knowledgeable about the product or process.
      ii. predict hazards on the basis of past experience.
      iii. encourage innovation.
      iv. are not useful for predictive risk analysis.

(c) A hazard and operability (HAZOP) study
   i. uses a structured procedure to avoid the unreliability of brainstorming a list of hazards.
   ii. may be a reasonable substitute for a hazard checklist.
   iii. generates a hazard checklist.
   iv. surveys the judgment of a team of experts to identify hazards.

(d) Identifying who is responsible for taking action to eliminate a hazard is a standard component of
   i. a fault-tree analysis (FTA).
   ii. a failure modes and effects analysis (FMEA) and a failure modes and effects criticality analysis (FMECA).
   iii. a failure modes and effects criticality analysis (FMECA).
   iv. a hazard and operability (HAZOP) analysis.

(e) Fault-tree analysis (FTA)
   i. can only provide qualitative results.
   ii. is a bottom-up risk analysis tool.
   iii. is a top-down risk analysis tool.
   iv. ensures that all possible failures are considered.

(f) A failure modes and effects analysis (FMEA)
   i. ensures all possible failures are considered.
   ii. is well suited to identifying concurrent system failure hazards.
   iii. only provides qualitative results.

(g) Top-down risk analysis tools include the following (identify all that apply).
   i. failure modes and effects analysis (FMEA)
   ii. hazard and operability studies (HAZOP)
   iii. fault-tree analysis (FTA)
   iv. checklists

(h) When financial risk is measured as the product of hazard event probability and cost, then
   i. risk increases with the cost of hazard event consequences.
   ii. a log-log graph is required to visualize the risk.
   iii. it is expected that the hazard event cost will include all costs.
   iv. risk accuracy may still remain a major difficulty.

(i) Mortality risk
   i. can be measured in more than one way, leading to more than one possible risk-management decision.
   ii. is a better measure of risk than monetary risk.
   iii. is uniquely defined in terms of loss of life expectancy.
   iv. measures the financial risk if someone dies.

(j) A large, complex engineering system is usually reasonably safe when
   i. the system is not too complex to model, responds quickly, is stable, has well established safety procedures, and exhibits robustness.
   ii. the system is not too complex to model, responds slowly, is stable, involves loosely coupled processes, and exhibits robustness.

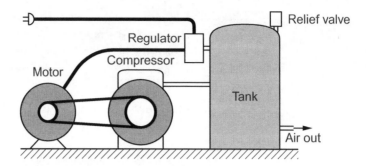

Figure 8.3 Compressed-air supply unit.

iii. the system is not too complex to model, responds quickly, involves loosely coupled processes, and exhibits robustness.

iv. the system is not too complex to model, responds slowly, is stable, has well established safety procedures, and exhibits robustness.

2. Suppose that you have designed a portable compressed-air supply system, as shown in Figure 8.3, for filling scuba tanks and for driving pneumatic tools in garages and factories. The system consists of an electric motor, an air compressor, an air tank, a regulator, and a pressure-relief safety valve. The regulator contains a pressure sensor connected to a power switch. The motor is switched on when the tank pressure drops below a fixed value and off at a slightly higher pressure. The pressure-relief valve is set to open at a higher pressure than the regulator motor off-pressure. Explosion of the air tank is clearly a dangerous hazard. Three events are assumed to possibly lead to a tank explosion:

(a) an internal tank defect such as poor welding,

(b) an external cause, such as a plant vehicle colliding with the tank,

(c) excess pressure in the tank. The excess pressure can occur only if both the control unit and the pressure-relief valve fail:

- The pressure sensor might fail to shut off the motor because of switch failure or human error, such as setting the switch incorrectly or propping it open.
- The pressure-relief valve might fail to open because of mechanical valve failure or human error, such as incorrectly setting the valve or locking it shut.

Construct the fault tree for the system described above. Explosion of the air tank is the top event.

8.8 REFERENCES

[1] B. Dodson and D. Nolan, *Reliability Engineering Handbook*. New York: Marcel Dekker, Inc., 1999.

[2] H. Kumamoto and E. J. Henley, *Probabilistic Risk Assessment and Management for Engineers and Scientists*. New York: IEEE Press, 1996.

[3] Underwriters Laboratories, *Household Electric Personal Grooming Appliances, Safety Standard 1727*. Northbrook, IL: Underwriters Laboratories, 2000.

[4] J. R. Thomson, *Engineering Safety Assessment: An Introduction*. New York: John Wiley & Sons, Inc., 1987.

Chapter 9
Environmental Sustainability

For centuries, human society regarded Earth's resources as inexhaustible. Previous generations concerned themselves only with finding ways to extract resources and discovering out of-the way locations to dump waste. We assumed that the environment would be able to absorb and dissipate all the garbage, sewage, and other wastes we produced. In recent years we have come to realize that these assumptions are false. Our resource consumption and waste disposal are not sustainable. This simple fact has immense consequences for our society and for the next generations of engineers, who will be faced with solving many of the resulting problems. In this chapter we answer the following questions:

- What is sustainable development?

- How is sustainability related to climate change and energy consumption?

- What do the licensing Associations expect professional engineers to know and do about sustainability?

- What can individuals and engineers do to make our future sustainable?

Figure 9.1 Billowing smokestacks were once considered signs of prosperity, but now are recognized as evidence of wasteful operations, health risks, and part of the cause of global warming.

9.1   DEFINING SUSTAINABILITY

Sustainability is an old concept, summarized in the ancient proverb: "We do not inherit the earth from our ancestors; we borrow it from our children." The basic goal of sustainability is to ensure the continuing quality of the environment. In 1987, the Brundtland Commission of the United Nations defined sustainable development in its report, *Our Common Future:*

> Sustainable development is development that meets the needs of the present, without compromising the ability of future generations to meet their own needs [1].

Paul Hawken, in his book *The Ecology of Commerce*, defined sustainability more simply:

> Sustainability [. . .] can also be expressed in the simple terms of an economic golden rule for the restorative economy: leave the world better than you found it, take no more than you need, try not to harm life or the environment, make amends if you do [2].

To achieve sustainability, we must answer two fundamental questions: What kind of planet do we want for our children, and what kind of planet can we get? The first question has ethical implications, but the second question is both technical and societal. Engineers, scientists, and economists can solve the technical problems, but society must be willing to accept major changes in lifestyle. Also, society must act quickly, because decisions by previous generations have already limited what we can get.

Sustainable living and development are essential today, because the welfare of future generations is threatened by two vices of the past and the present: careless disposal of waste, and excessive consumption of resources. These are separate problems,

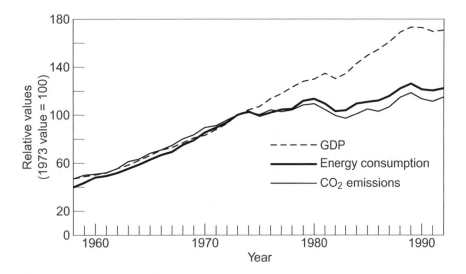

Figure 9.2 Canadian GDP, energy consumption, and CO_2 emissions relative to 1973. A deliberate reduction in oil deliveries known as the OPEC oil embargo occurred in 1973 (data from Chapter 11 of [3]).

but they are linked because emissions from burning fossil fuels contribute to global warming and climate change. Countries with high energy consumption generally have a large gross domestic product (GDP) that, in turn, is linked with large amounts of emissions and waste. For example, a large GDP typically involves manufacture of vehicles, machinery, and appliances that consume much energy when in service.

Figure 9.2 illustrates the links between GDP, energy consumption, and CO_2 emissions. First, GDP, energy consumption, and emissions are generally strongly related, as indicated by the nearly constant slopes before and after 1973. Second, massive societal change is possible with minimal effect on standard of living (GDP), as shown by the reduced slopes for energy consumption and CO_2 emissions, which indicate a massive shift to more efficient energy use following the 1973 Organization of Petroleum Exporting Countries (OPEC) oil embargo (also called the 1973 OPEC energy crisis). Understanding the link between engineering achievements, such as increased efficiencies, and economics is critical as we strive for a sustainable future, and is part of the multidisciplinary engineering described later in this chapter.

9.2   AN OVERVIEW OF SUSTAINABLE THINKING

When the Second World War ended in 1945, Canadians looked forward to an era of peace and prosperity. Industries, geared for war, converted their factories to produce appliances and vehicles. Petrochemical industries provided a selection of magical new materials—plastics—made from petroleum feedstock. Agro-chemical industries promised that new pesticides, herbicides and fertilizers would bring profitability to farms and the end of world hunger. The average person could fuel a car and heat a home effortlessly, using oil or natural gas drawn from massive reservoirs in the Canadian West.

A new era of electrical generation and distribution also started, as newly developed nuclear generating plants were built to augment electric power produced by hydro-electric and fossil-fuel plants. Visions for the future contained utopian predictions about nuclear energy, such as, "It is not too much to expect that our children will enjoy in their homes electrical energy too cheap to meter" [4]. In the 1950s, cheap electric power was made available to almost everyone in Canada. Jet engines, which were at an early experimental stage before the war, provided easy international travel, and vacations abroad became affordable. Air conditioning units and television sets, which were virtually non-existent in pre-war days, became common. At the same time, the world population continued to grow, from less than 1 billion people in 1800 to nearly 7 billion now. Many people aspired to a lifestyle that consumed more resources in a month than our pre-war ancestors consumed in a year. For decades, no one saw problems with such consumption-oriented lifestyles.

Silent Spring, 1962

In 1962, Rachel Carson described the dangers of pesticide use in her book *Silent Spring* [5]. Carson, a trained biologist, was investigating why songbirds did not return in the spring. She discovered that bird populations were dying because pesticides such as dichloro-diphenyl-trichlorothane (DDT) were being applied indiscriminately. Carson's book led to recognition that indiscriminate use of agricultural chemicals can be hazardous to bird, fish, animal, and human life.

The Population Bomb, 1968

Paul Ehrlich's book *The Population Bomb* predicted that population growth may eventually outpace agricultural food supply [6]. In a later book, Ehrlich linked population growth to environmental problems such as global warming, rain forest destruction, and air and water pollution [7]. Population growth is a basic challenge to sustainability, but it is an ethical and societal problem, beyond the control of engineers. However, as members of society, we all have a responsibility to monitor the problem and suggest solutions.

The Limits to Growth, 1972

In 1972, the Club of Rome, an organization concerned with the problems of humankind, published a report entitled *The Limits to Growth*. The report warned that uncontrolled human consumption had the potential to make our planet uninhabitable [8]. The report describes one of the first computer simulations of the behaviour of human populations. A simple "world model" simulated the creation or consumption of five basic elements over time: population, capital, food, non-renewable resources, and pollution. The "standard" run, which simulated behaviour from 1972 into the future, showed industrial output per capita peaking about the year 2000, with the production of non-renewable resources decreasing sharply thereafter. This computer analysis is naïve by current standards, but it is significant because it stimulated further research into global sustainability.

Gaia, 1979

James Lovelock's book, *Gaia, a New Look at Life on Earth*, likened our planet Earth to a self-regulating living being, with abilities to adapt and heal itself, like other organisms [9]. Many challenged the Gaia concept on the basis that the assumed healing phenomena did not exist very clearly. However, Gaia is a good metaphor. It emphasizes that we are the custodians of a living organism—Planet Earth—and we should manage it as we would a cherished family home that we want to pass on to future generations. If we damage the environment, we will regret our negligence.

The Brundtland Report, 1987

The Brundtland Commission, charged by the United Nations with the task of responding to growing concerns about the environment, issued a report: *Our Common Future* [1]. The Brundtland Report defined the concept of sustainable development, and proposed a compromise that accepted continued industrial development provided that it did not impair the ability of future generations to enjoy an equal level of prosperity. The report popularized the term "sustainable development." It is a well-accepted concept, but definitions still vary: to environmentalists who emphasize the word *sustainable,* it means that we must protect the environment from harmful change; whereas to many others who emphasize the word *development,* it means that business can continue as usual.

Montreal Protocol, 1987

The Montreal Protocol on Substances that Deplete the Ozone Layer was signed in 1987 to take effect in 1989 [10]. Certain useful fluorine and bromine-based compounds, called chlorofluorocarbons, have been shown to reduce the amount of ozone in the atmosphere. The purpose of the Montreal Protocol and its subsequent amendments is the eventual total elimination of these compounds. Although ozone is a pollutant at ground level, a layer of ozone in the stratosphere filters out harmful ultraviolet rays and is essential to life on earth. Fortunately, the Montreal Protocol has been very effective in stabilizing the ozone layer, and scientists predict that it will begin to recover in coming decades. Developing countries have, on average, a 10- to 15-year grace period to match Canada's commitments under the protocol. From acceptance and compliance perspectives, the Montreal Protocol is the most successful international environmental treaty.

IPCC, 1988

The World Meteorological Organization (WMO) and the United Nations Environment Programme (UNEP) established the Intergovernmental Panel on Climate Change (IPCC) in 1988. The IPCC members are scientists, experts from all over the world. The panel reports are comprehensive, scientific, and balanced. The IPCC does not conduct research, but monitors research around the world. It provides an objective opinion on climate change, its causes, its consequences, and how to reduce its effects or adapt to them. IPCC reports are essential documents for guiding discussions of global warming and climate change. The IPCC *Fourth Assessment Report* was released in 2007, and is discussed later in this chapter. The IPCC is a co-recipient of the 2007 Nobel Peace Prize.

The Earth Summit in Rio, 1992

An "Earth Summit" conference was held in Rio de Janeiro, where 165 nations, including Canada and the United States, voluntarily agreed to reduce greenhouse gas (GHG) emissions, because these are a known cause of global warming and climate change. This agreement, called the UN Framework Convention on Climate Change (UNFCCC), set a goal of reducing GHG emissions to 1990 levels by 2000. The goal was not achieved.

The Kyoto Protocol, 1997

More than 160 countries met in Kyoto, Japan, to negotiate new GHG emission targets. More than 80 countries agreed to reduce their emissions to an average level of 5.2 % *below* 1990 levels by the year 2010. Each country was allotted a different target. There was disagreement over issues such as credits for carbon dioxide "sinks" such as forests (which absorb carbon dioxide); whether countries could pay credits instead of reducing emissions; and what rules were fair for developing nations. In March 2001, the United States announced that it would no longer participate in the Kyoto Protocol. In December 2002, the Canadian Parliament voted to endorse the Protocol. Canada's target was to reduce its emissions of greenhouse gases to 570 Mt (megatonnes) of carbon dioxide by 2010. This amount is 6 % lower than total greenhouse gas emissions in 1990; however, emissions have increased since 1990. In fact, Canada's predicted emissions for 2010 are about 810 Mt, representing a 42 % increase over our 2010 Kyoto goal. In 2007, Prime Minister Harper announced that Canada could not meet the Kyoto target and would be negotiating a new international agreement, with more realistic "aspirational" goals [11].

Bali roadmap, 2007

In 2007, the United Nations Framework Convention on Climate Change (UNFCCC) adopted the Bali "roadmap," a process for negotiating an international agreement on climate change, to follow the Kyoto agreement when it ends in 2012 [12]. Key agreements were also reached on technology transfer and on reducing emissions from deforestation. Canada's position on future emissions targets in Bali was consistent with Canada's Clean Air Act. Tabled in 2006, this act sets intensity-based emissions targets, in sharp contrast to the total emissions targets of the Kyoto Protocol [13]. Intensity-based emissions targets require that the emissions per joule of energy consumed decrease, but permit total emissions to increase. In the Bali negotiations, Canada pushed for equal responsibility for developed and developing countries alike.

9.3   THE PROCESS OF GLOBAL WARMING AND CLIMATE CHANGE

The Industrial Revolution led to improved living conditions in the 1800s but, at the same time, it led to the beginning of human-induced global warming. Coal-fired steam engines replaced human and animal labour, making life easier. Trains, mills, and factories ran on steam power, and billowing smokestacks were a sign of industrial activity and prosperity. The use of coal grew so rapidly that it blackened many of the buildings in the industrial towns of central England—at the time this seemed to be a negligible effect compared to the benefits of steam power. However, the blackened buildings were omens of *global warming*, a general name for a four-step sequence that begins with burning fossil fuels and ends in climate change, as follows.

Gas emission   1.   The combustion of coal, oil, natural gas, and other hydrocarbon fuels produces waste gas, mainly carbon dioxide, which is released into the atmosphere. Decaying foliage has always emitted carbon dioxide and methane, while living plants absorbed the carbon dioxide through photosynthesis, resulting in approximate equilibrium. However, after the Industrial Revolution, human activities began to produce more carbon dioxide than was absorbed.

Greenhouse effect   2.   Components of the Sun's radiation pass through the atmosphere and warm Earth's surface. The absorbed energy is eventually re-emitted as thermal radiation, which is partially blocked by carbon dioxide (CO_2), methane (CH_4), and other greenhouse gases (GHGs) in the atmosphere. This transparency to some types of radiation and blocking of other types is called the "greenhouse effect." The products of combustion and other human activity contribute to this effect [15] by releasing greenhouse gases into the atmosphere. The average lifetime for carbon dioxide in the upper atmosphere (stratosphere) is many decades. Consequently, the impact of current greenhouse gas emissions will be with us for decades.

Global warming   3.   The greenhouse effect is essential to human life, since it cushions Earth from the stark temperature extremes that exist on planets without an atmosphere. However, small deviations in Earth's solar energy balance can produce large effects leading either to global warming or to global cooling as occurs in ice ages. Over the past two centuries, greenhouse gas concentrations have increased dramatically in the atmosphere. For example, Figure 9.3 shows that atmospheric carbon dioxide

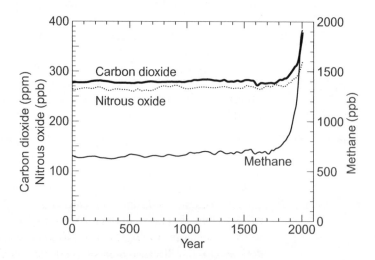

Figure 9.3   Concentrations of important long-lived greenhouse gases from year 0 to 2005. The units are parts per million (ppm) and parts per billion (ppb). (Data from Chapters 2 and 6 of [14])

remained nearly constant at 280 ppm (parts per million) for 2000 years until approximately the year 1800, when it began to rise to current levels in the neighbourhood of 380 ppm. This rise in CO_2 increases the greenhouse effect. It is therefore reasonable to expect Earth's surface temperature to increase. There is now widespread scientific agreement that global warming is occurring [12], although the severity of the consequences are still under debate.

Climate change   4.   Global warming is only a small deviation in Earth's solar energy balance, but it can produce dramatic climate changes such as severe storms, droughts, and floods.

9.4   THE CONSEQUENCES OF CLIMATE CHANGE

The research into global warming and climate change has had detractors and skeptics, of course. In 2001, Bjorn Lomborg's book *The Skeptical Environmentalist* challenged widely held conclusions from environment research, and predicted a rosy life for future generations [16]. The book continues to generate debate about climate change predictions [17].

In 2006, Al Gore, former U.S. vice-president, produced the award-winning documentary film *An Inconvenient Truth: A Global Warning*, based on his book of similar title. The film and book explain environmental research so that it is understandable by the average citizen, and the key message is that global warming is a real and present danger to our way of life [18]. Gore was a co-recipient of the 2007 Nobel Peace Prize.

9.4.1   Ending the Debate About Climate Change

The debate about climate change effectively ended when the Intergovernmental Panel on Climate Change (IPCC) issued its comprehensive *Fourth Assessment Report* (AR4) in 2007. The AR4 took six years to prepare, and its conclusions are based on research by over 800 authors in 130 countries, reviewed by 2500 scientific reviewers. The four-part report is long and technical, but summaries are freely available on the Internet in reference [19] and companion documents.

The IPCC reports show great certainty, based on extensive evidence, that climate change is directly linked to global warming, caused by greenhouse gases that result mainly from human burning of fossil fuels. A few of the many IPCC conclusions are summarized as follows.

Human cause   Worldwide atmospheric concentrations of carbon dioxide, methane, and nitrous oxide have increased markedly as a result of human activities since 1750. Current levels now greatly exceed pre-industrial values.

Temperature rise   Global temperatures will increase by 1.8 °C to 4.0 °C in the next century, depending on future fossil fuel use, technological change, economic development, and population growth in the absence of climate-control initiatives such as the Kyoto Protocol. This expected temperature increase will not be uniform; the greatest temperature increases will be observed in the Arctic and Antarctic. Even if greenhouse gas concentrations are kept constant at year 2000 levels, a warming of about 1°C will occur in the next century as a result of GHGs already emitted. The temperature rise may not appear to be great but the effects are surprising.

Sea level rise   Observations of the decline in ice volume around the world lead to the prediction that sea levels will rise by 18 cm to 59 cm or more, a change that would produce the risk of floods in vulnerable coastal cities. Sea level predictions are less precise than those for temperature rise because of incomplete data on the melting of the Greenland ice sheet. If the entire sheet were to melt the sea level would rise 7 m, but that is not expected, although recent observations suggest faster melting than previously expected.

Present observations   Scientists and meteorologists have observed numerous long-term climate-related changes. These include changes in arctic temperatures and ice, ocean salinity, wind patterns, and extreme weather conditions including drought, floods, heat waves, and intense tropical cyclones. Eleven of the twelve years from 1995 to 2006 rank among the 12 warmest years in the instrumental record of global surface temperature since 1850.

Other consequences   The IPCC lists many possible consequences of climate change, including severe inland flooding and drought, melting of sea ice, insect plagues, extinction of species, bleaching of corals, and possibly even major changes in ocean currents.

Feedback   An important factor in the science of global warming and climate change is the effect of feedback [14, 20]. Feedback is studied in mathematical detail in advanced engineering courses, but it can be described roughly as the two-way interaction between different objects or quantities. The result of the interaction can be stabilizing or destabilizing, desirable or undesirable. Two examples of destabilizing, undesirable environmental feedback are the following. First, forest fires release carbon dioxide and other GHGs into the atmosphere, leading to global warming and drier conditions in which more forest fires occur. As a second example, sea ice is very effective in reflecting sunlight back into space, but as the ice melts, the darker water absorbs more energy from the Sun, thereby causing more ice to melt.

Irreversibility   A book by George Monbiot claims that if average global temperatures increase by 2°C, which the book states to be probable, then vast peat bogs in the sub-arctic, presently under permafrost, will begin to decay and release greenhouse gases, leading to even greater warming that is irreversible [21].

Summary   The emission of greenhouse gases is changing our environment, and unless serious efforts are made to reduce these emissions, climate change will lower the quality of life of future generations. The burning of fossil fuels (coal, oil, gas) is the main source of increasing GHGs.

9.4.2   Ethical Implications of Climate Change

The Brundtland Commission was concerned about environmental degradation because it leads to poverty and economic disparities between societies. The 2007 IPCC report showed that global warming exacerbates disparities, because the economic loss caused by climate change will fall hardest on the poorest nations. This disparity raises some very basic questions of fairness.

- Is it ethical or fair for richer countries to burn fossil fuels indiscriminately, thereby creating GHG emissions and indirectly imposing climate change on poorer countries? Is it ethical or fair to require poor or undeveloped third-world countries to meet the same emissions standards as Western countries, which have emitted about 20 times as much GHG per capita for the past century?
- How will the industrialized nations respond to the millions of "climate" refugees created in Africa when droughts reduce crops, or in the Netherlands, Bangladesh, and the Pacific islands when sea levels rise and flood these low-lying countries?

Ethically, sustainability is simple fairness. It is unfair and unethical to harm others through negligence, inefficiency, greed, or abuse. In this case, the "others" are future generations, including our own children. If the present generation fails to combat global warming, it will cause a serious reduction in the quality of life for future generations, particularly those living in the poorer countries.

9.5   EXCESSIVE CONSUMPTION AND THE DEPLETION OF OIL AND GAS

Climate change is not the only serious problem affecting sustainability. We have finally realized that the planet's resources are large but finite. We are consuming some resources so quickly that, within the lifespan of the present generation, these resources will become scarce and very expensive. If we cannot reduce consumption or find substitutes, our society will face serious disruption. Examples of such resources are fossil fuels (such as oil and gas but excluding coal), fresh water, fish stocks such as the Canadian East Coast cod fishery, and various species of wildlife. How can we maintain our standard of living without depriving future generations of these resources?

Peak oil and gas

Natural gas and oil are the most important resources that are approaching their predicted peak production rate. These resources are fundamental to our lifestyle: they provide energy to refine, manufacture, and distribute the commodities required by developed societies. They are also needed to generate the electric power that lights our homes, cooks our food, and even entertains us via computers and television. However, oil and natural gas production rates are now approaching the critical point at which they will no longer keep pace with demand. When demand exceeds supply, shortages occur and prices rise, as happened in 1973 during the OPEC oil embargo.

In order to predict future oil and gas supply and demand, we must know the current production and consumption rates, make educated guesses on how they may change, and estimate the amount of oil and gas remaining under Earth's surface.

Growth rates

Between 1850 and 2006, world population increased 520 % to 6.555 billion, corresponding to a growth rate of 1.06 % per year [22]. Over the same time interval, world energy consumption increased 850 % at an average growth rate of 1.38 % per year [23, 24]. Multiplying these two factors together (population × annual energy consumption per capita) yields the world's total annual energy consumption. Between 1850 and 2006, the total annual energy consumption increased by a factor of 43; that is, an astounding 4300 %. This total growth corresponds to a constant annual growth rate of about 2.4 %. Figure 9.4 shows this astonishing growth, categorized by energy source.

In 1850, total energy consumption per person was nearly all from wood, water, and wind power, consumed at a rate equal to 12 % of the total rate in 2006. In 2006, *renewable* per capita consumption was 11 % of the total, which means that the renewable energy consumed per person has remained essentially unchanged since 1850, and the substantial increase in standard of living since then has been fuelled entirely by nonrenewable energy sources.

Doubling time

The consumption curves in Figure 9.4 are approximately exponential. Growing exponential functions double in height in a fixed time, and the doubling times for two intervals with slightly different growth rates are noted on the figure. For an exponential curve with a 2.5 % relative annual rate of increase, the doubling time is approximately 27 years. Therefore, if total world energy consumption continues to increase at a constant rate equal to the current 2.5 %, the demand for energy will double in a mere 27 years (in the year 2035 approximately), or about one generation. More importantly, during this 27-year doubling interval, the total amount of fossil fuels we will consume will equal all the fossil fuels consumed by humans since the dawn of history! The global warming caused by the greenhouse gas emissions from this fossil fuel consumption should be obvious from the previous discussions—it will trigger irreversible climate change. Moreover, to double our consumption, we must ask whether fossil fuel production can meet this demand. This question requires us to discuss oil and gas production rates.

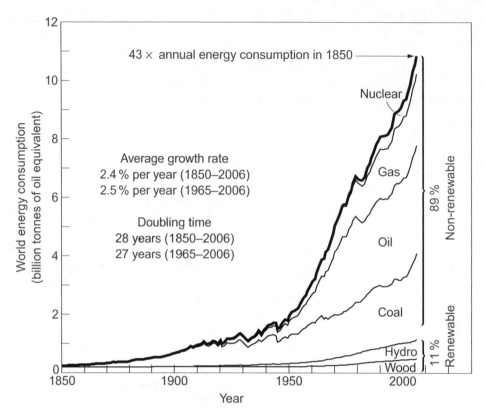

Figure 9.4   Primary annual world energy consumption 1850 to 2006 [22–24]. A tonne of oil equivalent equals 42 gigajoules (GJ) or 12 megawatt-hours (MWh) of thermal energy.

Peak production

Oil and gas production (flow) rates have a known physical limit because, in the life of an oil or gas well, the discovery, exploitation, and depletion follow known patterns. When we add the production rates of all the wells in known reserves, we obtain the total oil and gas production rate. Taking account of well-production patterns, trustee Colin J. Campbell of the U.K. Oil Depletion Analysis Centre produced forecasts of total oil and gas peak production shown in Figure 9.5. The figure shows regional oil and natural gas peaks that have already occurred, as well as those forecast to 2050.

The best-known example of a predicted and verified peak in hydrocarbon production is the oil peak of 1970, known as Hubbert's peak after the author who predicted it in 1956 from a simple model for oil-well production in the 48 contiguous U.S. states [25].

Although some researchers argue that Campbell's forecasts in Figure 9.5 are overly pessimistic, all agree that a peak in oil production is coming soon, perhaps in a few years, but within two decades at most [24]. Natural gas is expected to peak soon afterwards. After the peak, production rates will drop because the oil and gas must come from less-accessible reserves, from stimulating older wells, or from mining oil sands, all of which are slower and more expensive methods of extraction.

Gap between production and discovery

A production peak inherently lags a discovery peak. Figure 9.6 summarizes Campbell's evaluation of oil production and oil discoveries. Since 1984, world oil production has exceeded oil discoveries. This growing deficit between production and discoveries is the most important evidence confirming that a world oil-production peak is approaching.

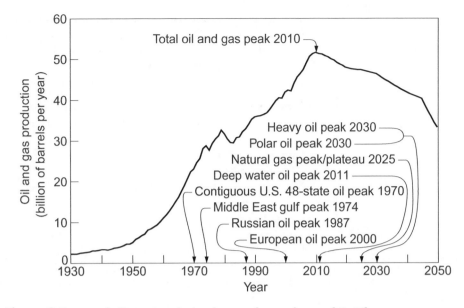

Figure 9.5   Campbell's 2006 total oil and gas production forecast [26, 27].

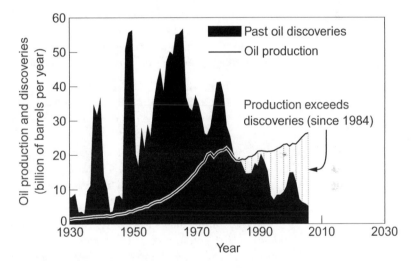

Figure 9.6   The growing gap between world oil production and discoveries [27].

Reducing fossil fuel dependence

We have only two choices if we want to reduce society's dependence on fossil fuels. Both will take a long time. We can

- decrease our energy consumption to a level that can be sustained with renewable sources such as solar, wind, and geothermal energy, or
- exploit another non-renewable energy resource such as nuclear energy which, being non-renewable, will itself eventually peak.

Both of these choices involve great engineering challenges and opportunities, but we must realize a critical truth: *we consume enormous quantities of energy, so there is no quick fix.*

Nuclear energy is the classic example of a rapidly developed energy technology. Political and military interests sped the development of nuclear energy, but it still took about 40 years to develop the technology from scientific feasibility to engineering feasibility, then to commercial feasibility, utility integration, and finally, significant use. This example is evidence that all other major energy sources have needed or will need as much or more development time, perhaps much more. This implies that the full impact of global warming will be upon us before we can implement significant sustainable energy sources.

What next?   Unless there are large, rapid lifestyle changes to reduce energy use, or remarkable advances in renewable energy production, we will see increased dependence on nuclear energy and coal for the next century. For example, Ontario is planning more nuclear plants, and China is building hundreds of coal-fired generating plants to meet growing energy demands.

Coal is a dirty fuel; burning coal emits greenhouse gases and other serious pollutants. However, fossil fuels will be burned extensively for years to come in order to avoid economic collapse while we search for alternative energy sources. In reference [28], Jaccard suggests that carbon capture and sequestration (CCS) methods can allow the burning of fossil fuels without releasing greenhouse gases or other pollutants to the atmosphere. He further suggests that fossil fuels represent the cheapest source of clean energy for at least the next century. However, developing and applying the required techniques will take many years.

9.5.1   The Ethical Implications of a Peak in Oil and Gas Production

Developing countries are striving to reach the standard of living enjoyed by developed countries, and world population is increasing, so world energy consumption levels are almost certain to increase. If we cannot move away from fossil fuels or restrain the rising consumption, some very basic questions of fairness and personal sacrifice arise.

- Is it ethical or fair for the current generation to consume non-renewable resources inefficiently and thoughtlessly, thus depriving future generations, who may need these resources for survival in the midst of climate change and sharply rising prices?
- Is it ethical or fair for a government to restrict population growth? China, for example, introduced a "one child" policy many decades ago. Is it fairer to restrict population in an orderly way or to let wars, disease, and famine sort out the winners and losers?

The ethical issues raised by reaching the peak of oil and gas production are virtually identical to the ethics of climate change. As mentioned previously, sustainability is simple fairness. It is unfair and unethical to harm others through negligence, inefficiency, greed, or abuse. Obviously, we cannot accept the extreme options of wars, disease, and famine, so we must seek orderly methods to reduce our dependence on fossil fuels, to adopt a less energy-intensive lifestyle, and to increase the availability of renewable energy.

9.6   GUIDELINES FOR ENVIRONMENTAL PRACTICE

The most important guide for engineers is the same as the Hippocratic oath for medical doctors: "First, do no harm." Engineers must be able to say "no" when environmental degradation is proposed. In particular, engineers have a specific obligation to follow environmental regulations and guidelines, so that engineering projects do not make the sustainability problem worse. Environmental guidelines are published by many organizations, but those published by the engineering licensing Associations are among the most relevant, since the codes of ethics of the Associations require engineers to follow them.

In Alberta, for example, the first clause in the APEGGA code of ethics is that "Professional engineers, geologists, and geophysicists shall, in their areas of practice, hold paramount the health, safety and welfare of the public, and have regard for the environment." The APEGGA *Guideline for Environmental Practice* further explains this duty. The *Guideline* encourages licensed professionals to be involved actively with environmental issues, and to anticipate and prevent rather than react to environmental problems. Professionals are urged to seek a golden mean between "the two extremes of absolute preservation and unfettered development." One interpretation of this golden mean is sustainable development. Professionals should help to formulate environmental laws, to enforce them, and to be true stewards of the environment [29]. Briefly, the *Guideline* states that professional engineers, geologists, and geophysicists should:

1. Understand and monitor environmental and sustainability issues;
2. Use specialists in environmental and sustainability when needed;
3. Apply professional and responsible judgment;
4. Ensure that environmental planning and management is integrated into all activities that are likely to have any adverse effects;
5. Include the costs of environmental protection when evaluating the economic viability of projects;
6. Recognize the value of environmental efficiency and sustainability; consider full life-cycle assessment to determine the benefits and costs of environmental stewardship, and endeavour to implement efficient, sustainable solutions;
7. Solicit input from stakeholders in an open manner, and strive to respond to environmental concerns in a timely fashion;
8. Comply with regulatory requirements and endeavour to exceed or better them; disclose information necessary to protect public safety to appropriate authorities;
9. Work actively to improve environmental understanding and sustainability practices.

The Alberta *Guideline for Environmental Practice* was adapted by Engineers Canada, and is now proposed as a national standard [30]. Newfoundland and Labrador, Nova Scotia, Ontario, Saskatchewan, and British Columbia have adopted the Engineers Canada guideline, or have developed similar environmental guides [31, 32].

A British engineer, long involved in the oil and gas industry, made the following comment on sustainability:

> It is important to distinguish sustainability from environmental compliance. Compliance with environmental regulations is an essential, daily, operational requirement, but sustainability is a long-range strategy to combat a slow-moving, planet-wide terminal condition. Sustainability requires innovative thinking, persistence and possibly some sacrifice. Decades may pass before the social acceptance, legislation and treaties are devised to deal effectively with sustainability. Engineers must, of course, ensure that regulations are followed, but in planning projects and activities, engineers must aim their conceptual thinking at the higher hurdle of sustainability [33].

In summary, engineers have a duty to strive for efficiency, to gather information before making environmental decisions, and to get the best possible advice in order to assess projects and activities for their sustainability. Although the guidelines do not clearly say so, if we are to achieve a sustainable society, engineers must also decline to participate in projects or activities that are clearly unsustainable.

9.7   WHAT WE CAN DO: PERSONAL LIFESTYLES

Pursuing sustainability is important because anything less is equal to treating other species and future generations unfairly. It is unfair and unethical to harm others through negligence, inefficiency, greed, or abuse. In addition, every code of engineering ethics requires us to make the health, safety and welfare of the public our first concern (or "paramount" duty). This duty should not fall solely on engineers although they are normally part of the solution.

Examples of unsustainable inefficiencies abound. Our consumer society, even with recycling regulations in place, permits the following.

- Aluminum ore (bauxite) is extracted from Earth's crust, refined using large amounts of electrical energy, sold as aluminum foil, and discarded after a single use in thousands of dispersed landfill sites from which it cannot be recovered economically.

- Computers, television sets, radios, and other electronic products, manufactured using exotic minerals and materials, are discarded to landfill, even though they are still functional, as newer models come onto the market.

- Jet aircraft are a serious obstacle to sustainability. No technical substitutes exist for the jet engines that propel airplanes. The carbon dioxide emitted per passenger in a transatlantic flight is approximately equal to the annual use of gasoline in an automobile. Jet engines also emit water vapour, which has an effect similar to GHGs when emitted at high altitude. Travel of otherwise well-meaning people, for purposes as benign as visiting relatives or tourism, is a threat to sustainability [21].

- Plastic bags are used to carry groceries, plastic blister packs encase retail products from electronics to toys, and even chewing gum comes doubly wrapped. Excessive packaging for convenience or advertising, rather than protection, is the norm.

- Automobiles consume large quantities of fossil fuels, are a major source of greenhouse gases, and emit other unhealthy chemicals that pollute the air. Massive suburbs have grown outside cities, situating adults far from work and children far from schools. Coffee shops build drive-through lanes that accustom people to wasting energy while waiting. Automobiles are built and advertised for speeds that are illegal, for accelerations that are unnecessary, and for capacities that are never filled.

Reduce, reuse, recycle   The above examples of wasteful consumption are the exact opposite of the sustainability strategy in the slogan "reduce, reuse, recycle." This practice, if followed conscientiously, is the first step to a sustainable future. For example, if we reduce our driving, heating, or use of electricity, we immediately reduce the need for fossil fuels.

To begin envisioning the next sustainability step beyond "reduce, reuse, recycle," consider the thinking of McDonough and Braungart in their book, *Cradle to Cradle: Remaking the Way We Make Things* [34]. They interpret "reduce, reuse, recycle" as an approach that "perpetuates our current one-way, 'cradle to grave' manufacturing model, dating from the Industrial Revolution, that creates such fantastic amounts of waste and pollution in the first place." In contrast, McDonough and Braungart propose a "cradle-to-cradle" principle, in which all materials used to create a product are returned to their original state, recycled to a state of readiness for reuse, or continually recycled. In effect, we discard nothing as waste in our landfills, waterways, or atmosphere. Cradle-to-cradle thinking is a challenge to designers and manufacturers, but it would be a key step toward sustainability.

The efficiency paradox

Consider next the history of the automobile, particularly the evolution of engine fuel economy. Starting with the Model T Ford in 1908, design improvements led to increases in the mass, room, comfort, power, and fuel economy of automobiles. However, by the late 1960s, room, comfort, and power were given higher priority than fuel economy. Manufacturers were responding to customer demand which, in an era of inexpensive gasoline and negligible government regulation, placed a low priority on fuel economy. This all changed with the 1973 OPEC oil embargo. Fuel prices skyrocketed. Smaller, more fuel-efficient foreign vehicles took a noticeable foothold in the North American market, and a rush to design smaller cars ensued. Fuel efficiency sold cars for a while but, by the late 1970s, smog was of greater concern to the public. This resulted in the introduction of catalytic converters. Catalytic converters reduce engine emissions, but they also reduce fuel economy, so for a time, engine designers focused on improving fuel efficiency to regain the losses from catalytic converters. Eventually however, priorities again focused on room, comfort, and power over fuel economy, as highlighted by the 2001 milestone when the sale of light trucks—SUVs, minivans, and pickups—surpassed car sales in North America for the first time. In 2001, the Union of Concerned Scientists observed, "With light trucks now accounting for more than half of all vehicles sold, the average new vehicle travels less [distance] on a gallon of gas than it did in 1980" [35].

Contrary to popular belief, efficiency improvements do not necessarily lead to a more sustainable future, a fact sometimes called the *efficiency paradox*. Although technology improvements allow for better energy efficiency, those savings are often lost to greater consumption. For example, the efficiency of air conditioning units has risen 17 % since 1990, but the number of units in use increased by 36 % over that time. Similarly, sales of light trucks, SUVs, and vans rose by 45 % between 1995 and 2005—nine times faster than passenger cars—but on average, they have 25 % lower fuel efficiency than cars [36]. Efficiency improvements are an important part of sustainability, so the work of engineers is critical, but without major societal changes in consumer thinking and expectations, achieving sustainability is unlikely in our lifetimes. Fortunately, there is a ray of hope. New U.S. government efficiency standards have begun to be applied to light trucks, the first "made in Canada" fuel economy standards for cars and light trucks were announced in 2008, and recent drastic fluctuations of fuel prices are having an effect on both travel volume and the types of vehicles purchased.

Rethink

The above examples should make it clear that the key to bringing sustainability changes to our consumer-oriented society is a re-assessment of our priorities and consumption. In short, we must rethink expectations and lifestyles. The sustainability mantra of "reduce, reuse, recycle" should be updated to read

Reduce, Reuse, Recycle, **RETHINK**

with emphasis on *rethink*. As a society, we must develop new ways to avoid inefficient or excessive consumption of energy.

9.8   WHAT WE CAN DO: ENGINEERING FOR SUSTAINABILITY

Every code of ethics requires engineers to make the health, safety and welfare of the public our first concern: our "paramount" duty. However, this duty should not fall solely on engineers, because they are not the problem: they are part of the solution. Wasteful practices, accepted by society for centuries, must change. Fortunately, engineers can assist society to make these changes by promoting energy efficiency, encouraging research into alternative energy sources, modelling alternatives, and showing the environmental consequences of design decisions.

Recall the two fundamental questions of sustainability: What type of planet do we want? What type of planet can we get? Engineers have a key role to play in sustainability, because engineers have the knowledge and skills to determine what is technically possible. However, society must decide what it wants. Sustainability requires that our huge consumption-driven society must change its attitudes, laws, and way of life. This is a major disruption, and it will require debate, discussion, and courage. Engineers must provide feedback from our knowledge of the question "What type of planet can we get?" to help society answer "What type of planet do we want?"

Engineers rarely speak out in political and ethical debates—even in the debates about sustainability—but society needs engineers in these debates. The discussion below suggests how engineers can help society move toward sustainability.

Modelling

Global climate and general circulation models (GCMs) have steadily increased in sophistication as new knowledge and detail have been included. A 40-year review of climate modelling is found in reference [37].

GCMs are sophisticated tools for modelling the atmosphere and the possible effects of climate change. These models are applicable for the sustainable design of land use, coastal structures, erosion control, buildings, and towns. All models have some uncertainty, of course, but uncertain predictions of temperature and climate are more useful than complete ignorance. The design engineer must know the capabilities and limitations of any model and its result. From the pyramids to the space shuttle, engineers have used models with varying degrees of uncertainty to yield great designs. It is now time to use GCMs and other models to design for sustainability.

Life-cycle analysis

Life-cycle analysis (LCA) evaluates the total environmental impact of a product from cradle to grave or, in other words, from source material to disposal. The effects considered by some LCAs, for example, are those associated with emissions such as CO_2, SO_x, NO_x, phosphates, or other chemicals, or with the amount of water and energy consumed. Specific toxic emissions such as arsenic and lead are also sometimes considered, and efforts have been made to include mass and economic considerations [38].

One application of LCA is for sustainability decision-making. Consider, for example, the choice between buying either cotton-cloth diapers or biodegradable disposable diapers for a child. Environmental impact should be a factor in the decision. An LCA for the two alternatives may estimate the CO_2 emissions and effects on water and landfills as follows.

- Cloth: The LCA would likely start with the CO_2 emissions from the fertilizer and the tractor fuel needed to grow the cotton for the cloth diapers. The analysis would also include the water and energy consumed to wash and dry the diapers repeatedly, and the small mass eventually discarded to a landfill.

- Disposable: Correspondingly for the disposable diapers, the LCA would include the CO_2 emissions from manufacturing a much larger mass of absorbent material, the water and energy used in their manufacture and distribution, and the larger mass of diapers sent to a landfill over the length of the child's infancy.

Before an LCA comparison can be used to decide on the best environmental alternative, a case-specific analysis is generally required, along with an understanding of the effects of alternatives. For example, consider the diaper choice, above. If the cloth diapers are washed in cold water and dried in the open air, they will emit less CO_2, consume less energy, and contribute less mass to landfills, but will consume more water than the disposable diapers. The decision maker must then weigh the environmental-impact factors; for example, water consumption may be more critical than CO_2 emissions in a drought-stricken country.

The movement to create an international LCA standard by the International Organization for Standardization (ISO) [39] is presently hampered by serious restrictions on data and uncertainties about the correct theoretical scope. For confidentiality, cost, and image reasons, manufacturers are not willing to make the necessary LCA data publicly available. In addition, defining the scope is often difficult. For example, in the cotton diaper analysis above, does one include the energy needed to produce the farmer's food, or does one simply stop at the tractor and fertilizer energy consumed? In spite of these limitations, LCA is evolving into a vital tool for sustainability decision-making.

Multidisciplinary engineering and systems thinking

Economic concerns and outdated customs are the basic reasons why society is resisting the attack on global warming, climate change, and the depletion of our non-renewable resources. Engineers must bridge the gap between science and economics to arrive at good solutions. Scientists attempt to understand the technical issues and economists develop economic models, but it is the engineer who works in the world between the two, seeking technical solutions that are economically feasible. The technical–economic link is but one example of the types of multidisciplinary links that must be exploited in order to realize a sustainable future.

Multidisciplinary engineering requires multidisciplinary knowledge, for which experts in different fields collaborate. It also requires *systems thinking*, in which it is recognized that apparently unrelated activities often interact significantly.

The need for multidisciplinary collaboration arises because no individual can be an expert in all fields.

The need for systems thinking is evident in engineering design optimization: optimizing individual subcomponents of a system generally will not optimize the larger system. For example, typical automotive design methods minimize fuel consumption and emissions for standard highway and city driving, for typical cycles of acceleration, idling, and cruising. However, standard conditions exist only for a portion of real drivers. The larger system is not optimized. More importantly, optimizing the efficiency of an automobile that will likely spend its working life transporting only one or two people does not optimize the efficiency of our transportation system as a whole. We need to work toward optimizing the larger system. In brief, we need systems thinking.

The Gaia hypothesis (discussed previously) describes the world as a living organism, and is a good metaphor for systems thinking [9]. However, we also need numerical evaluations to bring systems thinking into practice. Life-cycle analysis is an example of a systems-thinking tool that helps us to understand the environment and the effect of humanity on it.

Multidisciplinary engineering helps us to understand how apparently independent systems affect one another. For example, although manufacturing, town planning, and earth science may be independent disciplines, no industry can build a factory without considering the proximity to employees, the distance and the quality of roadways linking the factory to raw materials and markets, the availability of water for manufacturing, and many similar factors. Engineers must seek expert advice from non-engineering disciplines such as environmental studies, political studies, economics, cultural studies, and psychology. New "linked" disciplines, such as industrial ecology, are beginning to meet the need for multidisciplinary engineering knowledge and for approaches better suited to tackling the problem of sustainability. These linked disciplines will continue to grow.

Next steps

As mentioned earlier, Jaccard [28] proposed that we use fossil fuels for many decades to come in order to avoid economic collapse while we search for alternative energy sources. If the required processes can be made to work as well as Jaccard suggests, then we can reduce greenhouse gases and other pollutants, but there is still an urgent need to develop alternative energy sources. Jaccard's book won the prestigious 2006 Donner

Prize for the top Canadian book in public policy, and represents a Canadian voice describing how humankind can reach a sustainable future. The announcement by the Canadian federal government in 2008 that carbon capture and sequestration (CCS) will be compulsory by 2012 for new oilsands plants is encouraging [40]. Unfortunately, many other relatively modest and timely proposals provided by Jaccard and others continue to be ignored by governments [41].

There is an old saying: "Where there is a will, there is a way." Engineers can lead the way to a sustainable future, but at the same time, society must have the will and resolve to seek a sustainable future.

9.9   CONCLUSION

Ethics and justice require humanity to share equally the burdens of climate change and the decline of oil production. Although they are different problems, their main cause is the same: excessive consumption of fossil fuels. To maintain our standard of living, we must drastically reduce our dependence on fossil fuels and rapidly move to other energy sources. Unfortunately, few people are prepared to deny themselves what they see as their entitled standard of living. Society must develop the strength to change these outdated customs and habits, and to pass the legislation needed to achieve sustainability.

As engineers, we have a key role in the move toward sustainability. We must ensure that our projects and activities achieve maximum efficiency in terms of the energy, materials, and labour consumed. However, efficiency improvements alone will not be enough to avoid the crises of climate change and the peak of oil production. We must apply sustainability concepts to our everyday work, and we must try to lead within our spheres of influence. We need not be martyrs in the fight for sustainability, but for ethical reasons, we should avoid projects or activities that clearly lead to an unsustainable future.

Research, innovation, and new ideas are essential. We must work together to imagine, innovate, invent, and create a sustainable future. Fortunately, today's engineering students live in a world of unparalleled opportunity. The information revolution is still in its early stages, and it will continue to multiply our strength and intelligence.

Sustainability is the greatest challenge ever presented to engineers. If engineers can help society evolve to a high but sustainable standard of living without the predicted problems of unrest, deprivation, and suffering, it will be our greatest accomplishment.

9.10   FURTHER STUDY

1. Choose the best answer for each of the following questions.
    (a) In 1987, the Brundtland Commission wrote a report that
        i.   was made into a very popular motion picture.
        ii. defined sustainable development in a meaningful way.
        iii. was skeptic al about the need for sustainable development.
        iv. defined sustainability as an economic golden rule.
    (b) Sustainable development is defined as development that
        i.   is achieved by voluntary effort.
        ii. maximizes progress, growth, expansion, and consumption.
        iii. does not reduce the ability of future generations to meet their needs.
        iv. makes a continuously increasing profit.

(c) Global warming is caused by greenhouse gases (GHGs), which trap heat radiated away from the earth's surface. The GHGs are emitted by the

   i. release of chlorofluorocarbon refrigeration gases.

   ii. burning of coal, oil, and wood for heating homes.

   iii. combustion of gasoline in automobiles.

   iv. all of the above.

(d) Global warming is important because it will

   i. lead to climate change, causing storms and floods.

   ii. raise global temperatures and cause the extinction of many species.

   iii. lead to climate change, causing droughts, agricultural losses and starvation.

   iv. all of the above

(e) The debate over global warming effectively ended

   i. in 2001, when Bjorn Lomborg wrote a book about global warming.

   ii. in 2006, when Al Gore made a movie film about global warming.

   iii. in 2007, when the IPCC linked global warming to wasteful energy use.

   iv. in 2007, when Canada set intensity-based emission standards.

(f) The efficiency paradox refers to the observation, in the last few decades, that

   i. improved efficiency always reduces total energy consumption.

   ii. increased consumer demand always exceeds efficiency improvements.

   iii. bigger vehicles are always more efficient.

   iv. designers will not improve engine efficiency without government regulation.

(g) A constant, positive, energy-consumption growth rate

   i. is necessary for sustainability.

   ii. increases energy consumption linearly.

   iii. increases energy consumption exponentially.

   iv. is necessary to maintain a healthy economy.

(h) To become fully developed, a new renewable-energy technology will require at least

   i. 20 years.

   ii. 40 years.

   iii. 50 years.

   iv. 60 years.

(i) The best way for an engineer to work towards a sustainable future is to

   i. refuse to work for an oil company.

   ii. assist clients and employers to achieve whatever they want.

   iii. satisfy environmental guidelines and government regulations.

   iv. assist clients, employers, and society to understand the full impact of their engineering projects on the environment.

(j) Life cycle analysis (LCA)

   i. extends a product's useful life.

   ii. calculates a product's life expectancy using fatigue analysis.

   iii. evaluates the total environmental impact of a product from cradle to grave.

   iv. evaluates the total impact of the environment on the product.

2. Develop a life-cycle analysis (LCA) for a car. First, decide on the metrics you will consider, such as CO_2 emissions and energy consumption. Second, consider the LCA boundary. For example, will you or will you not consider the CO_2 emissions from the mine that extracted the iron ore used to produce the steel in the car? Third, draw a diagram showing the connections among all the elements that go into producing a car and contributing to your LCA metrics calculations. Next, attempt to quantify an LCA-determined environmental impact from a car by using the *Greenhouse Gases, Regulated Emissions, and Energy Use in Transportation* (GREET) software available from Argonne National Laboratories at <http://www.transportation.anl.gov/modeling_simulation/GREET/>. Finally, discuss the environment impacts associated with a car.

3. Translate the energy consumption of Canadians into practical terms that would be better appreciated by the public. Today, Canadians consume energy at a rate of 13.5 kW per person. Convert this rate into units of 60 W light bulbs per person or 4.5-horsepower lawnmowers per person. Document how an average Canadian consumes at this rate. What can be done to reduce Canadian energy consumption?

9.11   REFERENCES

[1] World Commission On Environment and Development, *Our Common Future*. New York: Oxford, 1987. Brundtland Report, <http://www.un-documents.net/wced-ocf.htm> (Match 9, 2008).

[2] P. Hawken, *The Ecology of Commerce: A Declaration of Sustainability*. New York: HarperBusiness, 1993.

[3] Ministry of the Environment, *The State of Canada's Environment*. Ottawa: Environment Canada, 1996. <http://www.ec.gc.ca/soer-ree/English/SOER/1996report/Doc/1-1.cfm> (March 9, 2008).

[4] L. L. Strauss, "Speech to the National Association of Science Writers, New York City," *New York Times, September 17*, 1954.

[5] R. Carson, *Silent Spring*. Boston: Houghton Mifflin, 1962.

[6] P. R. Ehrlich, *The Population Bomb*. New York: Ballantine Books, 1968.

[7] P. R. Ehrlich and A. Ehrlich, *The Population Explosion*. Toronto: Simon and Schuster, 1990.

[8] D. H. Meadows, D. E. Meadows, J. Randers, and W. W. Behrens, *Limits to Growth: A Report for the Club of Rome's Project on the Predicament of Mankind*. New York: Universe Books, 1972.

[9] J. Lovelock, *Gaia: A New Look at Life on Earth*. New York: Oxford, 1987.

[10] United Nations Environment Programme (UNEP), *Handbook for the Montreal Protocol on Substances that Deplete the Ozone Layer*. Nairobi, Kenya: UNEP, seventh ed., 2006.

[11] A. Freeman, "Canada gets its way on climate change," *The Globe and Mail, November 24*, 2007.

[12] *United Nations Framework Convention on Climate Change (UNFCCC)*. Bonn, Germany, 2008. <http://unfccc.int> (March 9, 2008).

[13] Environment Canada, *Clean Air Act*. Ottawa, ON: Government of Canada, 2006. <http://www.ec.gc.ca/cleanair-airpur/Clean_Air_Act-WS1CA709C8-1_En.htm> (March 9, 2008).

[14] International Panel for Climate Change, "Summary for policymakers," in *Climate Change 2007: The Physical Science Basis. Contribution of Working Group I to the Fourth Assessment Report of the Intergovernmental Panel on Climate Change*

(S. Solomon, D. Qin, M. Manning, Z. Chen, M. Marquis, K. B. Averyt, M. Tignor, and H. L. Miller, eds.), (New York), Cambridge University Press, 2007. <http://www.ipcc.ch/ipccreports/ar4-wg1.htm> (March 9, 2008)

[15] R. W. Jackson and J. M. Jackson, *Environmental Science: The Natural Environment and Human Impact*. Harlow, U.K.: Longman, 1996. page 317.

[16] B. Lomborg, *The Skeptical Environmentalist: Measuring the Real State of the World*. New York: Cambridge University Press, 2001.

[17] S. Schneider, J. Holdren, J. Bongaarts, and T. Lovejoy, *Misleading Math about the Earth*. New York: Scientific American, 2002.

[18] A. Gore, *Inconvenient Truth: The Planetary Emergency of Global Warming and What We Can Do About It*. Emmaus, Pa.: Rodale Press, 2006.

[19] International Panel for Climate Change, "Summary for policymakers," in *Climate Change 2007: Synthesis Report* (B. P. Jallow, L. Kajfež-Bogataj, R. Bojariu, D. Hawkins, S. Diaz, H. Lee, A. Allali, I. Elgizouli, D. Wratt, O. Hohmeyer, D. Griggs, and N. Leary, eds.), New York: Cambridge University Press, 2007. <http://www.ipcc.ch/ipccreports/ar4-syr.htm> (March 9, 2008).

[20] K. Knauer, ed., *Global Warming*. New York: Time Books, 2007.

[21] G. Monbiot, *Heat: How to Stop the Planet from Burning*. Toronto: Random House Anchor Canada, 2007.

[22] International Programs Center (IPC), Peter Johnson, *Historical Estimates of World Population*. Washington, D.C.: United States Census Bureau (USCB), 2008. <http://www.census.gov/ipc/www/worldhis.html> (March 9, 2008).

[23] BP International, *Statistical Review of World Energy 2007*. London: BP p.l.c., 2007. <http://www.bp.com/productlanding.do?categoryId=6848&contentId=7033471> (March 9, 2008).

[24] J. D. Hughes, "The energy sustainability dilemma: Powering the future in a finite world," in *Proceedings of Plug-in Hybrid Electric Vehicle (PHEV) Conference: Where the Grid Meets the Road*, (Winnipeg, Man), 2007. Keynote address, <http://www.pluginhighway.ca/proceedings.php> (March 9, 2008).

[25] M. K. Hubbert, *Nuclear Energy and Fossil Fuels*. San Antonio, TX: American Petroleum Institute Spring Meeting, 1956.

[26] C. Campbell, "Oil depletion–update through 2001," 2001. <http://www.hubbertpeak.com/campbell/update2002.htm>, (March 9, 2008).

[27] C. Campbell, 2006. Personal communication reported in reference [24].

[28] M. Jaccard, *Sustainable Fossil Fuels: The Unusual Suspect in the Quest for Clean and Enduring Energy*. New York: Cambridge University Press, 2006.

[29] The Association of Professional Engineers, Geologists and Geophysicists of Alberta, Edmonton, AB, *Guideline for Environmental Practice*, 2004. <http://www.apegga.org/pdf/Guidelines/18.pdf> (March 2008).

[30] Canadian Engineering Qualifications Board, *National Guideline on Environment and Sustainability*. Ottawa: Canadian Council of Professional Engineers, 2006. <http://engineerscanada.ca/e/files/guideline enviro_with.pdf> (March 9, 2008).

[31] L. Thorstad, C. Gale, H. Harris, J. Haythorne, and P. Jones, *Guidelines for Sustainablility*. Vancouver B.C.: The Associaton of Professional Engineers and Geoscientists of British Columbia, 1995. <http://www.apeg.bc.ca/ppractice/documents/ppguidelines/sustainabilityguidelines.pdf> (March 9, 2008).

[32] Professional Engineers Ontario, "Environmental guidelines for the practice of professional engineering in Ontario," in *Guideline of Professional Practice*, Toronto: Professional Engineers Ontario, 1988. Revised 1998, <http://www.peo.on.ca/Guidelines/Professional_practice_rev.pdf> (March 9, 2008).

[33] D. Burningham, 2007. Personal communication to G. C. Andrews.

[34] W. McDonough and M. Braungart, *Cradle to Cradle: Remaking the Way We Make Things*. New York: North Point Press, 2002.

[35] Union of Concerned Scientists, "Sales of SUVs, minivans, and pickups surpass cars for first time," 2008. <http://www.ucsusa.org/news/press_release/sales-of-suvs-minivans-and-pickups-surpass-cars-for-first-time.html> (March 9, 2008).

[36] S. McCarthy, "Dim prospects that 'energy efficient' will pay off: CIBC," *The Globe and Mail*, November 27, 2007.

[37] K. McGuffie and A. Henderson-Sellers, "Forty years of numerical climate modelling," *International Journal of Climatology*, vol. 21, pp. 1067–1109, 2001.

[38] M. Raynolds, M. D. Checkel, and R. A. Fraser, "The relative mass-energy-economic (RMEE) method for system boundary selection—a means to systematically and quantitatively select LCA boundaries," *Int. J. of Life Cycle Assessment*, vol. 5, no. 1, pp. 37–46, 2000.

[39] S. L. Jackson, *The ISO 14001 Implementation Guide: Creating an Integrated Management System*. Toronto, ON: John Wiley & Sons, Inc., 1997.

[40] D. Ebner and N. Scott, "Awash in cash, oil patch braces for changes," *The Globe and Mail*, March 11, 2008.

[41] J. Simpson, "Who will rid us of this troublesome GST cut?," *The Globe and Mail*, December 27, 2007.

Section 3
Engineering Measurements

Chapter 10
Measurements and Units

Prior to the systematic definition of the unit systems that are taken for granted today, many regions and towns had their own distinct standards for measuring commodities (see Figure 10.1). This chaos has been simplified gradually by international agreement, starting almost two centuries ago, although the need for uniform measurement standards was recognized much earlier.

Figure 10.1   Before the introduction of SI units, measurements were specific to particular purposes, trade goods, or locations. The iron reference standards in this digitally enhanced photograph are attached to the gateway wall of the pre-revolutionary Hôtel de Ville in Laon, France. The T shape provides reference lengths for measuring barrels, the rectangles for bricks and roof tiles, and the rightmost bar is for measuring cloth.

This chapter describes the engineering unit systems in current use, explains the difference between fundamental and derived units, and outlines a useful method for converting units. You will learn

- the definition, components, and uncertainty of measurements;
- the elements of the unit systems used by engineers in this and other countries;
- rules for correctly writing quantities with units;
- elementary descriptions of the most commonly used unit quantities in the SI and FPS unit systems;
- the usefulness of unit algebra.

The analysis of existing measurement methods and the invention of new techniques is an active technical art, with a community of specialists and regular journal publications and conferences [1], but the fundamentals are firmly fixed, except for occasional slight redefinition of the basic units.

10.1   MEASUREMENTS

Engineers frequently conduct or supervise tests and experiments that require physical measurements, such as tests of material qualities, soil and rock properties, manufacturing quality control, and experimental verification of design prototypes. A measurement that is adequate for the job at hand must be sufficiently accurate and repeatable, two properties that will be discussed in Chapter 11. This chapter concentrates on unit systems.

Measurements and units

A *measurement* is a physical quantity that has been observed and compared to a standard quantity, called a *unit*. The written representation of the measurement consists of two parts: a numerical value and a name, symbol, or combination of symbols that define the reference standard. For example, a distance may be measured in metres, millimetres, inches, feet, or other units, and the numerical value will depend on the unit chosen. The unit is a physical quantity that has been accepted according to experience and often international agreement as the standard by which certain measurements will be made. For example, the kilogram is defined to be the mass of a metallic object that is kept in Paris, France.

Base and derived units
Some units of measurement are defined in terms of others; for example, pressure may be measured in pascals. One pascal is defined as one newton per square metre, and since its definition depends on other units, the pascal is called a *derived unit*. The units from which all others are derived are called fundamental units or *base* units. How many fundamental units are required? For all normally measured physical quantities, the answer is seven. The several unit systems in common use provide definitions for fundamental units and a list of other units derived from them.

Dimensions
The words *units* and *dimensions* are sometimes used as synonyms; however, in the context of measurements, it is better to say that the dimensions of speed, say, are "distance divided by time," whereas the units of speed may be "kilometres per second" or "millimetres per year." Thus the fundamental dimensions include mass, distance, time, and other quantities corresponding to the fundamental quantities in a unit system.

10.2   UNIT SYSTEMS FOR ENGINEERING

The set of definitions and rules called the International System of Units, the Système International d'Unités, or simply SI [2], has been adopted by almost all countries, with the notable exception of the United States where, nevertheless, the system is used in specific industries.

Introduction of the metric system
The story of the engineering project to define the standard metre has been the subject of a best-selling historical account [3] and at least one historical novel. In the late 1700s, when new scientific thought was flourishing and Europe was in political ferment, a measurement system "for all people, for all time" was proposed, to be derived from nature rather than from a fabricated object. The reference metre was chosen to be one ten-millionth of the distance at sea level from the north pole to the equator. Determining this length required a survey of a significant distance along a meridian of longitude and extrapolation to the quarter meridian of Earth.

The French Académie des Sciences chose the meridian from Dunkerque through Paris, France, to Barcelona in Spain, and charged two groups led by savants of the highest reputation with the survey mission. A major engineering project, the survey lasted seven years and required specially designed instruments, perseverance in the face of accident, revolution, and war, and written reports. However, the nature and inevitability of measurement error (see Chapter 11) were not yet fully understood. An unexplained systematic discrepancy led the leader of one of the two survey parties to delay his report and to alter data by hand. Then the extrapolation of the survey to the quarter meridian was hindered by new knowledge of the irregularity of the shape of Earth. The delay caused by surveying difficulties and the withheld data had, in the meantime, forced a provisional length of the metre to be chosen. Although its precision has been refined several times since the original definition, this unintended length is still in use. Modern measurements show the quarter meridian to be approximately 10 002 000 m.

The survey project was conducted primarily in France, but the results were of international interest. The new system was introduced in France and ignored by most people, then rejected by Napoleon in 1812, and finally reintroduced in 1837 after several changes of government. The British were little inclined to adopt a system from a country with which they had been at or near war for decades, and which had produced the anti-monarchist excesses of the French Revolution. The need for uniform standards was acknowledged in the United States, but relations with France were strained at times and, in some quarters, the adoption question was reduced to a simplified choice: "Shall we mold our citizens to the law, or the law to our citizens?" The latter was preferred. Acceptance was often associated with political upheaval. The system was adopted as a symbol of nationhood in Germany and Italy during political unification, in the Spanish and French colonies by decree, in Russia and Eastern Europe after the revolution of 1917, in Japan in 1945 at the end of war, in India at independence from Britain in 1947, and in China after the Communist accession in 1949. Britain, Australia, and Canada finally began a systematic switch to SI in the 1970s. The United States also began adoption at that time under President Ford, but the initiative was cancelled by President Reagan.

There are several conclusions that can be drawn from this early engineering project. One is that a technical decision may have to be taken under conflicting arguments about its validity. Indeed, although almost all scientific measurements use SI units, the system is still the subject of emotional debate. A second conclusion is that decisions affecting broad society may be accepted only very slowly and can easily become political issues.

One might ask why other measurements, such as time, are not based on a decimal system. Such units were proposed and a scheme in which there were three 10-day intervals (called decades) in a month, 10 hours of 100 minutes in a day, and 400 degrees in a circle was used for a while, but soundly rejected by most people. It appears that the base-60 scale used now for time and angle originated in Sumeria about 4000 years ago.

Absolute and gravitational systems

The SI base units and some derived units are listed in Table 10.1. The SI unit system is called an *absolute* system because mass is a fundamental unit and Newton's second law (force = mass × acceleration) is invoked to derive the force due to gravity. *Gravitational* systems adopt force as a fundamental unit and determine mass from Newton's second law. Unit systems are classified according to whether they are gravitational or absolute and whether they use metric or English units.

In Canada and the United States, the traditional unit system is an English gravitational system, called the FPS gravitational system, in which distance, force, and time are fundamental quantities, measured in units of feet, pounds, and seconds. Both FPS and SI systems are in use in Canada, and students must be familiar with both.

The SI and the FPS systems, as well as other unit systems sometimes found in references, are compared in Table 10.2 and discussed briefly below.

Absolute systems

- The SI system is preferred in Canada, although quantities such as land survey measurements performed using other systems can be expected to be encountered indefinitely. Where exports, particularly to the United States, are significant, many industries continue to use versions of English or U.S. unit systems.

- The CGS system uses centimetres, grams, and seconds and was previously used extensively in science.

Gravitational systems

- The FPS absolute system is very rarely used and is not listed in the table.

- The FPS gravitational system is the traditional system used in North America. Students must be familiar with it for a few more decades.

- The metric MKS gravitational system is rarely used. This system is not listed in Table 10.2.

Hybrid systems

The American engineering system and the European engineering system are occasionally still encountered. These are called hybrid systems, since both mass and force are fundamental units; the European hybrid units are not shown in the table.

TABLE 10.1   Base and derived SI units

Symbol	Unit Name	Quantity	Definition
M	metre, meter	length	base unit
kg	kilogram	mass	base unit
s	second	time	base unit
K	kelvin	temperature	base unit
°C	degree Celsius	temperature	(kelvin temperature) $- 273.15$
N	Newton	force	$m \cdot kg \cdot s^{-2}$
J	joule	energy	$N \cdot m = m^2 \cdot kg \cdot s^{-2}$
W	watt	power	$J/s = m^2 \cdot kg \cdot s^{-3}$
Pa	pascal	pressure	$N/m^2 = m^{-1} \cdot kg \cdot s^{-2}$
Hz	hertz	frequency	s^{-1}
Electrical and Electromagnetic Units			
A	ampere	current	base unit
C	coulomb	charge	$A \cdot s$
V	volt	potential	$J/C = m^2 \cdot kg \cdot s^{-3} \cdot A^{-1}$
Ω	ohm	resistance	$V/A = m^2 \cdot kg \cdot s^{-3} \cdot A^{-2}$
S	siemens	conductance	$1/\Omega = m^{-2} \cdot kg^{-1} \cdot s^3 \cdot A^2$
F	farad	capacitance	$C/V = m^{-2} \cdot kg^{-1} \cdot s^4 \cdot A^2$
Wb	weber	magnetic flux	$V \cdot s = m^2 \cdot kg \cdot s^{-2} \cdot A^{-1}$
T	tesla	flux density	$Wb/m^2 = kg \cdot s^{-2} \cdot A^{-1}$
H	henry	inductance	$Wb/A = m^2 \cdot kg \cdot s^{-2} \cdot A^{-2}$
Dimensionless Quantities			
rad	radian	plane angle	$m/m = 1$; $1/(2\pi)$ of a circle
sr	steradian	solid angle	$m^2/m^2 = 1$; $1/(4\pi)$ of a sphere
mol	mole	particle count	base unit ($\simeq 6.02 \times 10^{23}$)
Light			
cd	candela	intensity	base unit
lm	lumen	flux	$cd \cdot sr$
lx	lux	illuminance	lm/m^2

TABLE 10.2   Comparison of unit systems

	Dimensions	Absolute		Gravitational	Hybrid
		SI	CGS	FPS	American
Fundamental	Force [F]	–	–	lb	lbf
	Length [L]	m	cm	ft	ft
	Time [T]	s	sec	sec	sec
	Mass [M]	kg	g	–	lbm
Derived	Force [F]	newton $(kg \cdot m/s^2)$	dyn $(g \cdot cm/sec^2)$	–	–
	Mass [M]	–	–	slug $(lb \cdot sec^2/ft)$	–
	Energy [LF]	joule $(N \cdot m)$	erg $(cm \cdot dyn)$	ft $\cdot$ lb	ft $\cdot$ lbf
	Power [LF/T]	watt $(N \cdot m/s)$	erg/sec	ft $\cdot$ lb/sec	ft $\cdot$ lbf/sec
	Pressure [F/L^2]	pascal (N/m^2)	dyne/cm^2	lb/ft^2	lbf/ft^2

Hybrid systems were popular for a time because units on both sides of Newton's second law equation could be arbitrarily defined; that is, the weight of an object (which is a force) could also be used as its mass. However, the use of both units, such as pound mass (lbm) and pound force (lbf), leads to confusion. To use hybrid systems, Newton's second law must be rewritten as

$$F = k_g ma, \tag{10.1}$$

where the constant k_g equals $1/g$, and where g is the acceleration of a falling object (32.2 ft/sec^2 or 9.80 m/s^2). This system should be avoided, as should the European metric hybrid system mentioned above.

10.3   WRITING QUANTITIES WITH UNITS

Standardized rules for correctly and unambiguously representing quantities with units should be followed whenever possible. There are sometimes very slight differences between published standards, usually because of the time required for approval of modifications. This book follows reference [4]. Figure 10.2 shows an example of a quantity with units to illustrate the following items.

1. The symbols denoting a physical quantity consist of a number or formula that represents a number, which may be negative, followed directly by its unit symbol or symbols. The number is separated from the unit symbols by a narrow space or, if unavailable, by a normal space, except that no space is used with the symbols °, ′, ″ when they designate plane angle as degrees, minutes, and seconds, respectively:

10.25 km	not	10.25km
15 °C	not	15°C
37.5°	not	37.5 °

2. The unit symbols must be in roman (upright) type regardless of the surrounding text. The number is normally in roman type and may be in decimal, scientific, or other notation as discussed in the next chapter. If the number is represented by a formula, then the symbols in the formula are normally in italic or "math italic" type with superscripts and subscripts in italic or roman type as appropriate:

10.25 km	not	10.25 km
ab^2c N	not	ab^2c N

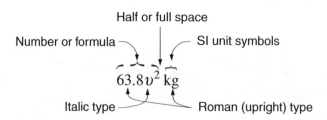

Figure 10.2   A physical quantity is written as a number or a formula representing a number, followed by unit symbols.

3. SI unit symbols are lowercase in general, except when they are derived from the proper name of a person, in which event they normally begin with a capital letter, regardless of whether there is a prefix:

$$15 \text{ kN} \qquad \text{not} \qquad 15 \text{ kn}$$

However, when the full name of a unit, such as a newton, is used in a sentence but is not the first word, the name is not capitalized. The name "degree Celsius" is a special case.

4. The unit may be preceded by a magnitude prefix listed in Table 10.3. The prefix is regarded as an inseparable part of the symbol; thus $3 \text{ km}^2 = 3 \times (\text{km})^2 = 3 \times 10^6 \text{ m}^2$, not $3 \times 1000 \times (\text{m})^2 = 3000 \text{ m}^2$. An international standard for computer-related magnitude prefixes that are powers of 2 has been proposed but is not in widespread use. Other computer-related magnitude prefixes are typically not separated by a space: the M in 128MB stands for 1024×1024, so $128\text{MB} = 134\,217\,728\text{B}$.

5. Unit symbols, together with prefixes if any, are treated like algebraic factors that can be multiplied or divided with numbers or other unit symbols. Multiplication between units is indicated by a half-height (centred) dot or a half-space, division by a slash (solidus) or a negative superscript:

$$27 \text{ kg} \cdot \text{m/s}^2 \quad \text{or} \quad 27 \text{ kg m/s}^2 \quad \text{or} \quad 27 \text{ kg} \cdot \text{m} \cdot \text{s}^{-2}$$

6. Unit symbols are not modified with subscripts:

$$V_{max} = 200 \text{ V} \quad \text{not} \quad V = 200 \text{ V}_{max}$$

7. It must be clear which numerical quantity and unit symbols are related:

$$3.7 \text{ km} \times 2.8 \text{ km} \qquad \text{not} \quad 3.7 \times 2.8 \text{ km}$$
$$87.2 \text{ g} \pm 0.4 \text{ g or } (87.2 \pm 0.4)\text{g} \quad \text{not} \quad 87.2 \pm 0.4 \text{ g}$$

8. Unit symbols are not mixed with unit names in expressions, and mathematical symbols are not applied to unit names. Thus, in a sentence, use kg/m^2 or kilogram per square metre, but not kilogram/m^2.

9. When long numbers are written in groups of three, the groups should be separated by a non-breaking half space rather than the comma often used in North America or the period used in some European countries:

$$93\,000\,000 \text{ miles} \quad \text{not} \quad 93,000,000 \text{ miles}$$
$$21\,298.046\,83 \text{ m} \quad \text{not} \quad 21298.04683 \text{ m}$$

Grouping is strongly preferred for numbers containing five or more adjacent digits. Four-digit numbers are not split except for uniformity when they are in a table with

TABLE 10.3 Magnitude prefixes in the SI unit system by symbol, name, and numerical value.

Y	yotta	10^{24}	M	mega	10^6	f	femto	10^{-15}
Z	zeta	10^{21}	k	kilo	10^3	a	atto	10^{-18}
E	exa	10^{18}	m	milli	10^{-3}	z	zepto	10^{-21}
P	peta	10^{15}	μ	micro	10^{-6}	y	yocto	10^{-24}
T	tera	10^{12}	n	nano	10^{-9}			
G	giga	10^9	p	pico	10^{-12}			

longer numbers or compared with longer numbers, as on the left-hand axis of Figure 18.5 on page 383, for example. If a number is split on one side of the decimal point, it is usually split on the other side as well.

10.4   BASIC AND COMMON UNITS

Unit definitions in both SI and FPS systems are described below and compared in Table 10.2. Handbooks [5, 6] and textbooks [7] list others. When working with different unit systems, you must be aware of the fundamental difference between absolute and gravitational systems of units and the importance of Newton's second law in defining these systems.

Force
Force is a push or a pull; it causes acceleration of objects that have mass. In the FPS gravitational system, force is a fundamental unit, expressed in pounds (lb). In SI, the unit of force is the newton (N), which is the force required to give a mass of one kilogram an acceleration of one metre per second squared, derived using Newton's second law. A newton is about one-fifth of a pound or, more accurately, 1 lb = 4.448 222 N.

Length
Length or distance is a fundamental unit in all systems. The FPS unit is the foot (ft) and the SI unit is the metre (m). To convert from one system to the other, by definition, 1 ft = 0.3048 m. The metre is defined to be the distance travelled by light in a vacuum in 1/299 792 458 of a second. The United States disagrees with most other countries on the spelling, but either *meter* or *metre* is accepted when used consistently. In Canada, it is generally accepted that a *metre* is a unit of measurement, and a *meter* is a measuring instrument.

Mass
Mass is a measure of quantity of matter. Mass should not be confused with weight, which is the force of gravitational acceleration acting on the object; thus a change in gravitational acceleration causes a change of weight but not of mass. The kilogram is the fundamental unit of mass in SI and is defined to equal the mass of a specific object kept in Paris. In the FPS gravitational system, the unit of mass is the slug, derived using Newton's second law. One slug is the mass that accelerates at one foot per second squared under a force of one pound: 1 slug = 14.593 90 kg.

Time
Time is a fundamental unit in all systems and is measured in seconds, abbreviated "sec" in the FPS gravitational system, but simply "s" in SI. The second is defined as 9 192 631 770 periods of the radiation corresponding to the transition between the two hyperfine levels of the ground state of the cesium 133 atom.

Pressure
Pressure has the derived units of force per unit area. In the FPS gravitational system, pressure is measured in pounds per square inch (psi) or pounds per square foot (lb/ft^2). In SI units, the unit of pressure is the pascal (Pa): 1 Pa = 1 N/m^2, and 1 psi = 6.894 757 kPa.

Work and energy
Work is defined as the product of a force and the distance through which the force acts in the direction of motion. *Energy* has the same units and is the capacity to do work. Both are derived units in the SI and FPS systems. In the FPS gravitational system, work is measured in foot pounds (ft lb), inch pounds (in lb), horsepower hours (HP hr), British Thermal Units (BTU), and other units; the SI unit is the joule (J), and 1 ft $\cdot$ lb = 1.355 818 J.

Power
Power is the rate of doing work. In the FPS gravitational system, power is measured in foot pounds per second (ft lb/sec) or horsepower (HP) (1 HP = 550 ft $\cdot$ lb/sec). In SI units, power is measured in watts (W): 1 W = 1 J/s = 1 N $\cdot$ m/s, and 1 ft $\cdot$ lb/sec = 1.355 818 W.

Temperature

Temperature is an indirect measure of the amount of heat energy in an object. There are four common temperature scales: Fahrenheit, Rankine, Celsius, and kelvin.

On the Fahrenheit scale used in the FPS system, water freezes at 32 °F and boils at 212 °F. Fahrenheit temperatures can be converted to Rankine by adding a constant, since the degree size is equal; t °F corresponds to $(459.67 + t)$ °R. The Rankine scale measures temperature from absolute zero and is still in common use in engineering thermodynamics in North America.

On the Celsius scale (which is a slight modification of the older centigrade scale), water freezes at 0 °C and boils at 100 °C. In fundamental SI units, water freezes at 273.15 K. The two scales have identical unit difference, so that t °C corresponds to $(273.15 + t)$ K. Absolute zero, where molecular motion stops, is the same in both Rankine and SI units (0 °R = 0 K). Note that the degree symbol (°) is not used with the kelvin symbol in SI notation.

Dimensionless quantities

Some measured quantities are defined as ratios of two quantities of the same kind, and thus the SI units cancel, leaving a derived unit, which is the number 1. Such measured quantities are described as being dimensionless, or of dimension 1. Many coefficients used in physical modelling and design are dimensionless; for example, the coefficient of friction is the ratio of two forces. Another example is the measurement of angle, but in this context the names "radians" and "degrees" are used for the dimensionless units. Recall that an angle in radians is the ratio of arc length over radius, and in degrees, it is the ratio of arc length divided by circumference, multiplied by the number 360, a scale factor.

The litre

The litre, a special name for one cubic decimetre, is not included in the SI units but is accepted for use with them and is often given the symbol L to avoid confusion with the number 1.

U.S. and imperial units

There are differences between the U.S. and imperial units of identical name that deserve attention, particularly the units for volume. One Canadian or imperial gallon equals $4.546\,09 \times 10^{-3}\,\mathrm{m}^3$, whereas the U.S. gallon equals $3.785\,412 \times 10^{-3}\,\mathrm{m}^3$, or about 83.3 % of the imperial gallon. There are 160 imperial fluid ounces per imperial gallon but 128 U.S. fluid ounces per U.S. gallon. A summary such as reference [6], Appendix B of [4], or Chapter 5 of [7] should be consulted for lists of conversion factors.

10.5 UNIT ALGEBRA

As seen in Section 10.3, a measured quantity is written as a number, or more generally as a formula for a number, together with the associated unit symbol or symbols. Ordinary algebra can be performed using such quantities, with the restriction that only quantities with the same units can be equated, added, or subtracted.

Consider the conversion of quantities between unit systems. Suppose, for example, that a measured power has been found to be 20 000 ft · lb/min, and this is to be converted to horsepower, which is defined as 550 ft · lb/sec. Then the written measured quantity is modified as shown:

$$20\,000\,\frac{\mathrm{ft} \cdot \mathrm{lb}}{\mathrm{min}} \times \frac{1\,\mathrm{min}}{60\,\mathrm{sec}} \times \frac{1\,\mathrm{HP}}{550\,\mathrm{ft} \cdot \mathrm{lb/sec}} = \frac{20\,000}{60 \times 550}\,\mathrm{HP} = 0.606\,\mathrm{HP}, \qquad (10.2)$$

where the original quantity has been multiplied by the number $1 = \frac{1\,\mathrm{min}}{60\,\mathrm{sec}}$ and again by $1 = \frac{1\,\mathrm{HP}}{550\,\mathrm{ft}\,\cdot\,\mathrm{lb/sec}}$ in order to cancel the unwanted unit symbols. Sometimes, particularly when the numerical values are given by formulas rather than by pure numbers, the unit symbols are enclosed in square brackets, [ ], to avoid confusion.

Unit algebra may also be performed without specifying the unit system, as in the dimensional analysis [8] of models. Let [T] represent an arbitrary unit of time, and similarly let mass be represented by [M] and length by [L]. Consider the equation from dynamics for distance s travelled by an object in time t, as the result of constant acceleration a, with initial velocity v:

$$s = vt + \frac{1}{2}at^2. \tag{10.3}$$

To derive the dimension of s, rewrite Equation (10.3) using only the dimension symbols for each of the quantities:

$$\text{dimension of } s = \frac{[L]}{[T]} \times [T] + \frac{[L]}{[T]^2} \times [T]^2, \tag{10.4}$$

and then perform cancellations to reduce the right-hand side to $[L] + [L]$. These two terms can be added since they have the same dimension. Therefore the dimension of s is $[L]$, or length, as required.

The simple concept that units obey the rules of algebra as if they were numbers is a powerful check on calculations. Checking by unit conversion and cancellation that all terms of an equation have the same units, or that the dimensions are equal as in the above example, gives confidence that a blunder has not been committed in developing the equation.

10.6   FURTHER STUDY

1.   Choose the best answer for each of the following questions.

(a)   The written representation of a measurement contains

   i. a numerical value and symbols indicating the unit or units of the measurement.

   ii. a numerical value.

   iii. an exact count of the number of units of a quantity that are present.

(b)   The unit of energy in the SI system is the

   i. pascal.   ii. newton.   iii. watt.   iv. metre/second.   v. joule.

(c)   In an absolute system of units, force is

   i. a fundamental or base unit.   ii. a derived unit.

(d)   An inductor is an electrical component that transfers energy to and from a magnetic field. The inductance L of a linear inductor is given by $L = \lambda/i$, where λ is the magnetic flux and i is the current passing through the element. The unit of flux is the weber (Wb), which in base SI units is $m^2 \cdot kg \cdot s^{-2} \cdot A^{-1}$, and the unit of current is the ampere (A). Therefore, the base SI units of inductance are

   i. $m^2 \cdot kg \cdot s^{-2} \cdot A^{-1}$ ii. $m^2 \cdot kg \cdot s^{-2}$ iii. $V \cdot s \cdot A^{-1}$

(e)   The correctly written quantity in the following list is

   i. (2 to 18) MHz   ii. 2 to 18 MHz   iii. 2 MHz $-$ 18 MHz

(f)   What must the units of α be if the following equation is correct?

$$\left(\alpha \frac{km}{m^3}\right)^{-1} = \frac{8.83 \text{ L}}{100 \text{ km}}$$

$$\text{i. m} \quad \text{ii. } \frac{\text{ft}^3}{\text{L}} \quad \text{iii. } \frac{\text{mi}}{\text{gal}} \quad \text{iv. } \frac{\text{m}^3}{\text{L}} \quad \text{v. } \frac{\text{km}}{\text{m}^3}$$

(g) The incorrectly written quantity in the following list is

   i. $60 \text{ kg} \pm 5 \text{ kg}$ ii. $(60 \pm 5) \text{ kg}$ iii. $60 \pm 5 \text{ kg}$ iv. 60 ± 3.5

(h) In the FPS gravitational system, the unit of mass is the slug.

   i. true   ii. false

(i) The incorrectly written quantity with SI units in the following list is

   i. $78.3 \times 10^{-7} \text{ Cm}^{-2}$ ii. $78.3 \times 10^{-7} \text{ C/m}^{-2}$

   iii. $78.3 \times 10^{-7} \text{ C} \cdot \text{m}^{-2}$ iv. $78.3 \times 10^{-7} \text{ C/m}^{-2}$

(j) Inspect the following quantities carefully. The correctly written measurement is

   i. $28.45\pi r^3 \rho \text{ kg}$ ii. $28.45\pi r^3 \rho \text{ kg}$ iii. $28.45\pi r^3 \rho \text{kg}$

   iv. $28.45\pi r^3 \rho \text{ kg}$ v. $28.45\pi r^3 \rho \text{kg}$

2. The equation $\sigma = My/I$ gives the stress σ at a distance y from the neutral axis of a beam subject to bending moment M. The dimensions are $[F]/[L]^2$ for stress, $[F][L]$ for moment, and $[L]$ for distance. Determine the dimensions of variable I. Can you guess what I represents, from its dimensions?

3. An object weighs 100 lb on Earth. What would it weigh on the Moon, where the acceleration of gravity is 1.62 m/s^2? What is its mass on the Moon?

4. The fuel consumption of vehicles is given as miles ($1 \text{ mile} = 1.609\,344 \text{ km}$) per gallon in the United States, but in litres ($1 \text{ L} = 10^{-3} \text{ m}^3$) consumed per 100 km in Canada. Find the formula for converting the first quantity to the second. What is 32 miles per gallon expressed in litres consumed per 100 km?

5. A direct current $i = 10 \text{ A}$ passes through a wire of resistance $R = 200 \; \Omega$, producing heat energy at the rate $i^2 R$. How much heat is generated in three minutes? Convert the result to FPS units.

6. This is a question that uses dimensional algebra. A pendulum can be constructed from a string with length ℓ and an object with mass m. Suppose that we suspect by observation that the period T of the pendulum swing depends on length ,, acceleration of gravity g, and mass m. Because such relationships are generally algebraic, we suppose that

$$(\text{dimensions of } T) = (\text{dimensions of } \ell)^a \times (\text{dimensions of } g)^b \\ \times (\text{dimensions of } m)^c,$$

for some unknown constants a, b, and c. Rewrite this equation using only generalized dimension symbols as in Equation (10.4). By examining this result, determine these constants and, hence, the general relationship between the period of a pendulum and the parameters ℓ, g, and m.

7. A railway locomotive with a mass of approximately 100 tonnes is travelling at 100 kilometres per hour. In order to stop the locomotive, the kinetic energy must be dissipated as heat. Approximately how many litres of water at 100 °C would this energy convert to steam? You may need to search to find the heat of vaporization of water.

10.7   REFERENCES

[1] Institute of Physics, *Measurement Science and Technology*. IOP Publishing Limited, 2008. <http://www.iop.org/EJ/journal/MST> (March 9, 2008)

[2] International Bureau of Weights and Measures, *The International System of Units (SI)*. Sèvres, France: Bureau International des Poids et Mesures (BIPM), eighth ed., 2006. <http://www.bipm.org/utils/common/pdf/si_brochure_8_en.pdf> (June 23, 2008).

[3] K. Alder, *The Measure of All Things, the Seven-Year Odyssey and Hidden Error That Transformed the World*. New York: The Free Press, Simon & Schuster, Inc., 2002.

[4] B. N. Taylor, *Guide for the Use of the International System of Units (SI)*. Gaithersburg, MD: National Institute of Standards and Technology, 1995. <http://physics.nist.gov/cuu/pdf/sp811.pdf> (March 9, 2008).

[5] F. Cardarelli, *Encyclopaedia of Scientific Units, Weights and Measures*. New York: Springer-Verlag, 2003.

[6] T. Wildi, *Units and Conversion Charts*. New York: IEEE Press, 1991.

[7] B. S. Massey, *Measures in Science and Engineering: Their Expression, Relation and Interpretation*. Chichester: Ellis Horwood Limited, 1986.

[8] E. S. Taylor, *Dimensional Analysis for Engineers*. Oxford: Clarendon Press, 1974.

Chapter 11

Measurement Error

A special vocabulary and special techniques have been developed for describing the inevitable deviations of physical measurements from true values. Computations containing inexact quantities are also possible. In this chapter, you will learn

- the definition of a traceable measurement;

- a classification of uncertainties into systematic and random effects;

- correct use of the words *accuracy, precision,* and *bias;*

- how to write inexact quantities using engineering and other notation;

- the correct use of significant digits.

11.1   MEASUREMENTS, UNCERTAINTY, AND CALIBRATION

What is a measurement? One possible answer might be "A property of a physical object that can be represented using a real number." However, we have to distinguish between counting and measuring using an instrument such as in Figure 11.1. Counting is exact if the set of objects to be counted can be defined and it does not contain too many members. Thus we can count the people in an aircraft, the welds in a pipeline, and with difficulty the number of ants in a colony. However, the grains of sand on a beach are probably too many to count. Therefore, let us distinguish between counting, which is exact, and measuring, which is not. The quantities that are measured are those for which base and derived units described in Chapter 10 exist.

Measured physical quantities may be inexact because the property being measured is not precisely defined. For example, to speak of the thickness of an object, such as the asphalt of a highway, is to assume two parallel plane boundaries, which cease to exist when the object is looked at closely enough.

Range of uncertainty   Even when it is possible to define a "true" value of a physical quantity, the instrument used to obtain this value cannot be constructed perfectly. The true value is conceptually a point on the line representing the real numbers as illustrated in Figure 11.2, but because of imperfect measurement, generally only an estimated true value can be obtained, together with an interval in which the true value lies. The difference between the true value and the measured value is called *measurement error* or *observation error*. In this context, a measurement error does not mean a mistake or blunder. The interval determines the unknown error range, which is synonymously called the *range of uncertainty*, or simply *uncertainty*.

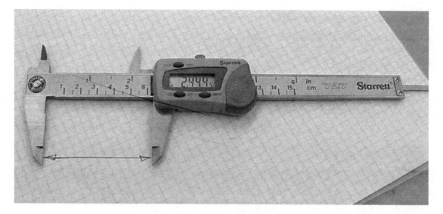

Figure 11.1   A modern digital-readout vernier caliper, with a resolution of 0.0005 inch, or 0.01 mm.

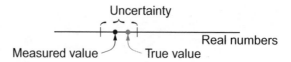

Figure 11.2   Illustrating a true (exact) value, which is a point on the line of real numbers, and its measured estimate, together with an interval of uncertainty.

Traceable measurements A measurement is fundamentally a comparison of a physical object to a standard physical object. Let us suppose that the vernier caliper of Figure 11.1 has been employed to measure the thickness of an object. If the instrument has been calibrated using a set of gauge blocks manufactured for the purpose, and the gauge block manufacturer certifies their accuracy by comparison with a national standard that has been calibrated to the SI standard, then the measurement is said to be *traceable* to the international standard. In Canada, the Institute for National Measurement Standards [1] of the National Research Council provides calibration standards for factories and laboratories.

11.2   SYSTEMATIC AND RANDOM ERRORS

Measurement errors are classified into two categories, systematic errors and random errors, although it is not always easy to identify the extent to which each is present in specific cases. The categories are defined and illustrated below.

11.2.1   Systematic Errors

A systematic error is a consistent deviation, also called a *bias* or an *offset,* from the true value. The error has the same magnitude and sign when repeated measurements are made under the same conditions. Systematic errors can sometimes be detected by careful analysis of the method of measurement, although usually they are found by calibration or by comparing measurements with results obtained independently. Three types of systematic errors are usually encountered: natural, instrument, and personal error, as follows.

Natural error *Natural error* arises from environmental effects. For example, temperature changes affect electronic components and measuring instruments. It may be possible to identify the effects of these phenomena and to apply a correction factor to the measurements. For example, the air buoyancy of a mass weighed by a high-precision equal-arm balance must be calculated, in order to remove its effect from the reading.

Instrument error The second type of systematic error is *instrument error,* or *offset,* and is caused by imperfections in the adjustment or construction of the instrument. Some examples are misaligned optics, meter zero-offset, and worn bearings. In precise work, instruments are usually calibrated (checked) at several points within their range of use, and a calibration curve is included with the instrument. The calibration data permits the engineer to correct the readings for instrument errors. For example, steel surveying tapes are occasionally stretched a few millimetres during use. A stretched tape gives distance measurements that are slightly low. However, if the tape is calibrated, distance measurements can be corrected for the stretch.

Personal error The third type of systematic error is *personal error.* Such error results from habits of the observer; for example, one person may have a tendency to estimate scale values that are slightly high; another may read scale values that are low. Personal error can be reduced by proper training.

11.2.2   Random Errors

Random errors are the result of small variations in measurements that inevitably occur even when careful readings are taken. For example, in repeated measurements, an observer may exert slightly different pressures on a micrometer or connect voltmeter leads in slightly different locations. Random errors from the true value do not bias the measurement, but produce both positive and negative errors with zero mean value. If several measurements are made, there is no reason to favour one observation over any other, but their arithmetic mean is normally a better estimate of the true value than is any single measurement. The estimate improves as the number of observations increases. This technique yields an effective countermeasure against random errors: take repeated measurements and compute the mean of the results.

11.3   PRECISION, ACCURACY, AND BIAS

The terms *accuracy* and *precision* are often misused when measurements are being described. These two words are not synonyms.

The precision of a measurement refers to its repeatability. A *precise* measurement has small random error and, hence, the discrepancies between repeated measurements taken under the same conditions are small.

A measurement that is close to the true or correct value is said to be *accurate*. However, *accuracy* has more than one meaning; some authors use this word to mean low total error, but others use it to mean low systematic error. When this term is used, its meaning should be made clear; otherwise use the word *bias*. To say that a measurement is unbiased is to mean unambiguously that there is no discernible systematic error. The target analogy shown in Figure 11.3 illustrates these words and their relationship to systematic and random errors. The spread (also called scatter or dispersion) of the hits is an example of random error caused by the random motion of the shooter. The average displacement between the hits and the target centre (bull's-eye) is an example of systematic error, such as might be caused by misalignment of the gun sights. Therefore, a small spread of hits located far from the centre is precise but inaccurate shooting, while a large spread around the centre is imprecise but unbiased shooting.

If unbiased measurements are repeated, their mean value approaches the true value as the number of observations increases. That is, if there is no systematic error, the effect of random error can be reduced by averaging.

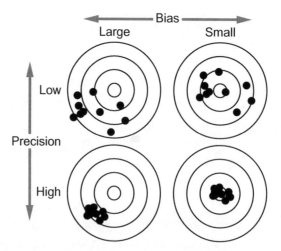

Figure 11.3 Precision, bias, and accuracy: The two right patterns have small bias (small systematic error); the two bottom patterns have high precision (small random error). The lower right pattern is accurate; less commonly the two right patterns would be said to be accurate.

11.4   ESTIMATING MEASUREMENT ERROR

When systematic errors are known and quantified, the numerical observations can be corrected to remove bias. The offset is subtracted from the readings, or the instrument is recalibrated to eliminate the offset. However, the random error remains and must be estimated and quoted with the measurement. In all cases, the technical specifications of an instrument are the first source of error estimates, but reading errors must also be considered, as follows.

Estimating the position of the needle of a gauge or meter requires interpolation between scale markings, and the precision of the result is limited by the ability of the human eye to resolve small distances. Then the precision of the readings will be a fraction of the amount between scale markings, typically one-tenth, and often this will be an adequate estimate of the measurement precision.

Readings taken from instruments with digital display must also be interpreted carefully, since the specifications might indicate less precision than the number of digits displayed. For example, a typical uncertainty for moderately priced multipurpose instruments is 0.1 % of the reading plus one digit.

The precision of a measurement may become evident when the observation is repeated; any digit that changes is suspect. Include only one suspect digit, and record it as the least significant digit in the numerical value of the measurement.

11.5   HOW TO WRITE INEXACT QUANTITIES

A recorded measurement is complete only when a statement about its uncertainty is included. The uncertainty is normally an estimated range and may be stated explicitly, which is always correct but sometimes inconvenient and repetitive, or implicitly, in which case care must be used both in writing and in interpreting the numbers. Showing the uncertainty requires a clear and unambiguous notation.

A quantity written using an ordinary decimal number, for example, 30 140.0, is said to be in *fixed notation*. If it is written as a decimal number with one non-zero digit to the left of the decimal and a power of 10 is appended as a scale factor, for example, $3.014\,00 \times 10^4$, it is in *scientific* notation. If the exponent of 10 is a multiple of 3 to correspond to the SI prefixes, for example, 30.1400×10^3, the number is in *engineering* notation.

11.5.1   Explicit Uncertainty Notation

Sets of measured values are often listed together in tables. When the values have the same uncertainty, it may be specified in a caption or table heading. Otherwise, the uncertainty must be given with each measurement. The measurement may be expressed in fixed, scientific, or engineering notation, and the uncertainty may be given in either absolute or relative form, as will be described.

In fixed notation, the numerical value of the measurement is written together with an estimate of the half-range, when the range is symmetric about the measured value as is often true. For example, a certain measurement of the speed of sound v_s in air at 293 K gives

$$v_s = 343.5 \text{ m/s} \pm 0.9 \text{ m/s} = (343.5 \pm 0.9) \text{ m/s} \tag{11.1}$$

where the estimated maximum error is 0.9 m/s. The unit symbol "m/s" is treated as an algebraic factor multiplying the contents of the parentheses. Rather than indicating the *absolute uncertainty* as above, the *relative uncertainty* may be written as a percentage of the magnitude. In this case,

$$\frac{0.9 \text{ m/s}}{343.5 \text{ m/s}} = 0.26 \times 10^{-2} = 0.26 \text{ \%}, \tag{11.2}$$

so that the measured speed can be written as

$$v_s = 343.5\,(1 \pm 0.26\,\%)\text{ m/s}. \tag{11.3}$$

The unit symbol "%" simply means the number 0.01 when used strictly (see Chapter 11 of [2]), but the ambiguous notation 343.5 m/s ± 0.26 % is sometimes accepted.

Using scientific notation, the above measurement is

$$v_s = (3.435 \pm 0.009) \times 10^2 \text{ m/s} \tag{11.4}$$

which means that v_s lies between 3.426×10^2 m/s and 3.444×10^2 m/s. The uncertainty is written with the same scale multiplier as the value of the measurement. In engineering notation, the above speed is

$$v_s = (343.5 \pm 0.9) \times 10^0 \text{ m/s}. \tag{11.5}$$

11.5.2 Implicit Uncertainty Notation

If a quantity is written without an explicit uncertainty, the uncertainty is taken to be ±5 in the digit immediately to the right of the least significant digit. For example, the statement $t = 302.8$ K is equivalent to $t = (302.8 \pm 0.05)$ K. This convention establishes the uncertainty only to within a factor of 10. Moreover, in fixed notation, ambiguity may result, as shown in the next section.

11.6   SIGNIFICANT DIGITS

The significant digits of a written quantity are those that determine the precision of the number. It is generally a serious mistake to record a quantity to more significant digits than justified by the measurement, with the exception that one or more suspect digits is sometimes retained when the effect of random errors will be reduced by averaging as discussed in Section 11.6.2.

Relative precision is unaffected by the power-of-10 scale factors in scientific or engineering notation. Significant digits are identified as follows:

- All non-zeros are significant, and all zeros between significant digits are significant.
- Leading zeros are not significant.
- Trailing zeros are significant in the fractional part of a number.

In fixed notation, trailing (right-hand) zeros in a number without a fractional part may cause ambiguity. Therefore, if right-hand zeros should be considered to be significant, explicit mention of the fact must be made, or the uncertainty must be included. The following are some examples of numbers in fixed notation:

0.0350 oz	3 significant digits
90 000 000 miles	1 significant digit, ambiguous
92 900 000 miles	3 significant digits, ambiguous
(92 900 000 ± 500) miles	5 significant digits

In scientific notation, the integer part is normally one non-zero digit, and the number of significant digits is one more than the number of digits after the decimal point. To illustrate, the distance from Earth to the Sun is written as shown:

9×10^7 miles	1 significant digit
9.3×10^7 miles	2 significant digits
9.290×10^7 miles	4 significant digits

In engineering notation, all of the digits except leading zeros are considered to be significant, and the exponent of 10 in the scale factor is a multiple of 3. In engineering notation, the above distances would be written:

0.09×10^9 miles	1 significant digit
93×10^6 miles	2 significant digits
92.90×10^6 miles	4 significant digits

11.6.1 Rounding Numbers

When a number contains digits that are not significant, rounding is used to reduce the number to the appropriate number of significant digits. Rounding should not be confused with truncation, which means simply dropping the digits to the right of a certain point. Rounding drops digits but may increase the rightmost retained digit by 1, typically according to the following rules.

When the leftmost discarded digit is less than 5, then the retained digits are unchanged; for example, rounding to three or two digits,

$$3.234 \;\rightarrow\; 3.23 \quad \text{or} \quad 3.2$$
$$9.842 \;\rightarrow\; 9.84 \quad \text{or} \quad 9.8. \tag{11.6}$$

When the leftmost discarded digit is greater than 5, or is a 5 with at least one nonzero digit to its right, then the rightmost retained digit is increased by 1; for example, rounding to three or two digits,

$$3.256 \;\rightarrow\; 3.26 \quad \text{or} \quad 3.3$$
$$9.747 \;\rightarrow\; 9.75 \quad \text{or} \quad 9.7 \text{ but } not \text{ 9.8.} \tag{11.7}$$

When the leftmost discarded digit is a 5 and all following digits are 0, then the rightmost retained digit is unchanged if it is even; otherwise it is increased by 1. Compared to rounding to the next higher digit, this rule avoids introducing a bias in the mean by rounding a set of numbers. The resulting final digit is always even; for example, rounding to two digits,

$$3.25 \;\rightarrow\; 3.2$$
$$3.250 \;\rightarrow\; 3.2$$
$$3.350 \;\rightarrow\; 3.4. \tag{11.8}$$

11.6.2 The Effect of Algebraic Operations

When computations are performed using inexact measured quantities, the results are also inexact. The quantities are entered to the number of digits justified by experimental error, and computations are performed to the full precision of the computer. However, the final computed value must not be written using more significant digits than are justified; it must be rounded to imply the correct interval of uncertainty. Basic rules will be given for writing the result of simple operations.

Addition   Let x and y be two measured values, with (unknown) measurement errors Δ_x, Δ_y, respectively, in the ranges given by implicit notation. Then the sum of the true values is

$$(x + \Delta x) + (y + \Delta y) = (x + y) + (\Delta x + \Delta y) \tag{11.9}$$

where $x + y$ is the calculated sum and $\Delta x + \Delta y$ the resulting error. The magnitude of the error in the sum is $|\Delta x + \Delta y|$, corresponding to an absolute uncertainty that is at most twice the uncertainty of the least precise operand. Therefore, for a small number of additions or subtractions, the result is often rounded to the absolute uncertainty of the least precise operand.

Subtraction   The analysis for addition shows that the absolute uncertainty can at most double with each addition. This conclusion is similarly true for subtraction, but the *relative* uncertainty, and hence the number of significant digits, may change drastically. For example, $5.75 - 5.73 = 0.02$ with an implied error of ± 0.01, so the result can only be written to one significant digit at most, rather than the three digits of the operands. The following examples illustrate addition and subtraction:

4.16	0.123	6.162	25.4
-12.3214	-178	-12.3214	3.1416
91.2	0.002164	6.150	0.3183
83.0	-178	-0.009	28.9

Multiplication and division   The relative uncertainty in a product or ratio is typically at most the sum of the relative uncertainty of the factors. This result is shown for the product as follows; a similar analysis holds for division. Given two quantities $x + \Delta x = x(1 + \Delta x/x)$ and $y + \Delta y = y(1 + \Delta y/y)$ as before, the relative errors are $\Delta x/x$ and $\Delta y/y$, often expressed in percent. Then the computed product of the two measured values x and y is simply xy, but including the errors in the computation gives

$$(x + \Delta x)(y + \Delta y) = xy + y\,\Delta x + x\,\Delta y + \Delta x \Delta y$$

$$= xy\left(1 + \frac{\Delta x}{x} + \frac{\Delta y}{y} + \frac{\Delta x}{x}\frac{\Delta y}{y}\right). \tag{11.10}$$

Typically, the relative errors $\Delta x/x$ and $\Delta y/y$ are small, so the rightmost term in the parentheses can be ignored, and the relative error of the product is at most approximately twice the largest relative uncertainty of the factors. Consequently, the result of a multiplication is often rounded to the number of significant digits of the factor with the fewest significant digits. The following examples illustrate this rule:

$$2.6857 \times 3.1 = 8.3$$
$$(489.5)^2 = 239\,600$$
$$236.52/1.57 = 151 \tag{11.11}$$
$$25.4 \times 0.866\,025 = 22.0$$

Caution   These simple rules must be used with care, since implicit notation specifies precision only to within a factor of 10. Furthermore, the rules for single operations are not always applicable to complex calculations. Consider the product of four measured values, each given to two significant digits, implying an uncertainty of ± 0.05:

$$p = 1.1 \times 1.2 \times 1.3 \times 2.4 = 4.1184. \tag{11.12}$$

Rounded to two digits according to the precision of the individual factors, the result would be written as $p = 4.1$, which implies that $4.05 \le p \le 4.15$. However, in the worst case, when the errors have the same sign and maximum magnitude, the actual range minimum and maximum are given by the calculations

$$1.05 \times 1.15 \times 1.25 \times 2.35 = 3.5470,$$
$$1.15 \times 1.25 \times 1.35 \times 2.45 = 4.7545; \tag{11.13}$$

that is, $3.5470 \le p \le 4.7545$. If the worst case is required, the result should be written as $p = 4$, implying that $3.5 \le p \le 4.5$, which approximates the calculated

TABLE 11.1 Significant digits appended to the mean of n measurements to indicate increased precision compared to a single measurement.

Measurements n	Appended Digits m
1 to 9	0
10 to 999	1
1000 to 99 999	2
$\vdots$	$\vdots$
10^k (k odd) to $10^{k+2} - 1$	$(k + 1)/2$

range. However, judgment may be needed about whether a worst-case analysis is appropriate.

This example illustrates a key method for performing complex calculations: specify the precision of the arguments; perform intermediate calculations to the full precision available; determine the precision of the result; and round the result to show the correct precision.

Arithmetic mean
The arithmetic mean of a set of unbiased measurements of a single quantity is more precise than individual measurements in the set and so may be written with additional significant digits. The uncertainty in the mean of n observations is $1/\sqrt{n}$ of the uncertainty in one observation. Each reduction of uncertainty by a factor of 10 allows an additional significant digit, so appending m digits to the mean implies that

$$\frac{1}{\sqrt{n}} = \left(\frac{1}{10}\right)^m. \tag{11.14}$$

Inverting and squaring both sides gives

$$n = 10^{2m}, \tag{11.15}$$

from which

$$m = 0.5 \log_{10} n. \tag{11.16}$$

Converting m to integer values produces Table 11.1, which shows that no digits should be added for a mean of fewer than 10 measurements, one for 10 to 999, and so on, or perhaps more conservatively, depending on the uncertainty and independence of individual measurements.

11.7 FURTHER STUDY

1. Choose the best answer for each of the following questions.
    (a) A measurement of a constant pressure is repeated 15 times using a meter that has a precision of 0.5 %. The arithmetic mean of these readings is calculated to be 40.405 kPa. In a report, this value should be written as
        i. 40.40 kPa   ii. 40 kPa   iii. 40.405 kPa   iv. 40.4 kPa
    (b) A set of measurements having insignificant systematic error but significant random error is
        i. imprecise and biased.   ii. imprecise and unbiased.
        iii. precise and unbiased.   iv. precise and biased.

(c) The number 0.745×10^4 is in scientific notation.

    i. false   ii. true

(d) Four measured values have been written with their precision expressed implicitly and combined in the formula $(1.32 \times 40.31) - (0.09738 \times 501.80)$. Expressed to the correct number of significant digits, the result is

    i. 4.3×10^0 ii. 4.344   iii. 4.3   iv. 4.340

(e) Identify the incorrect statement.

    i. A set of precise measurements may contain significant error.

    ii. Systematic and random errors can simultaneously affect a measurement.

    iii. Left-hand zeros are significant in fixed notation.

    iv. All digits to the right of the decimal point are significant in scientific notation.

    v. The significant digits of a number give a measure of the precision of the number.

(f) The following measurements have been made: 84.52, 3.0, 41.081. Their correctly written sum is

    i. 128.6010   ii. 129   iii. 128.   iv. 128.6   v. 128.60

(g) Compared to the precision of individual measurements, the arithmetic mean of 40 measurements subject to random error can be written using

    i. two additional significant digits.

    ii. one fewer significant digit.

    iii. one additional significant digit.

    iv. as many significant digits as for the individual measurements.

(h) The arithmetic mean of a set of unbiased measurements of the same quantity

    i. has unknown precision compared to individual measurements.

    ii. is more precise than a single measurement in the set.

    iii. is as precise as a single measurement in the set.

    iv. is less precise than a single measurement in the set.

(i) Several numbers have been rounded to three significant digits as shown. The incorrectly computed operation is

    i. $27.550 \rightarrow 27.6$ ii. $27.500 \rightarrow 27.5$ iii. $27.450 \rightarrow 27.5$

    iv. $27.350 \rightarrow 27.4$ v. $27.455 \rightarrow 27.5$

(j) Written in engineering notation, the quantity 13 824 s is

    i. 13.824×10^3 s   ii. 139.32×10^3 s   iii. 1.3824×10^4 s

    iv. 1.3824 ks   v. 13 824 s

2.   A dinosaur skeleton discovered in 1990 was estimated to be 90 000 000 years old. Does this mean that the skeleton was 90 000 010 years old in the year 2000? (Adapted from reference [3])

3.   The original observations by Dr. Wunderlich of the temperature of the human body were averaged and rounded off to 37 °C, which was the nearest Celsius degree. Therefore, the precision of the measurement was presumably ±0.5 °C. When this measurement was converted to the Fahrenheit scale, it became 98.6 °F. What is the correct interpretation of the tolerance on the Fahrenheit figure?

Recently, extensive measurements of body temperature gave a mean of only 98.2 °F. Convert this to an equivalent kelvin temperature with the proper tolerance. (Adapted from reference [3])

4. The notation 343.5 m/s $\pm$ 0.26 % was described as ambiguous on page 149. What rule about units does it break?

5. Write the answers to the following exercises according to the discussion in this chapter.

(a) $xy/z =$?, where $x = 405$ V, $y = 53.92$ V, and $z = 16.02$

(b) $a + b + c =$?, where $a = 28.1$, $b = 97$, and $c = 43.567$

(c) $\alpha t =$?, where $\alpha = 0.0143$ s^{-1} and $t = 30$ s

(d) $p - q - r =$?, where $p = 33.6$, $q = 18.1$, and $r = 3.53$

6. Perform the calculation shown, and express the result to the correct number of significant digits. Which of the three operands is the most precise? How much does the most precise operand contribute to the final answer?

$$28\ 402 + 1.30 \times 10^4 - 3100 + 32.897\ 34$$

11.8 REFERENCES

[1] National Research Council Canada, "Institute for national measurement standards," 2002. <http://inms-ienm.nrc-cnrc.gc.ca/main_e.html> (March 9, 2008).

[2] B. N. Taylor, *Guide for the Use of the International System of Units (SI)*. Gaithersburg, MD: National Institute of Standards and Technology, 1995. <http://physics.nist.gov/cuu/pdf/sp811.pdf> (March 9, 2008).

[3] J. A. Paulos, *A Mathematician Reads the Newspaper*. New York: Harper Collins, 1995.

Section 4
Engineering Graphics

Chapter 12
Engineering Graphics

12.1 INTRODUCTION

It has been estimated that 92% of all engineering information is disseminated as graphics of some form; the remaining 8% comprises written and verbal communication [1]. Therefore it is no overstatement to say that *graphical communication skills* are among the most important that an engineer can possess, at least as far as pure design synthesis and analysis are concerned. Establishing healthy and productive working relationships, negotiating contracts, promoting and defending ideas, developing a capacity for unbiased listening, knowing how to prioritize among multiple tasks and supervisors, learning how to communicate effectively in a large multidisciplinary team, are all critical to a successful and satisfying career as an engineer. But, it is impossible to function as an engineer without a thorough understanding of the geometric principles that form the foundation for engineering graphics.

Engineering graphics is significantly more than the drawing of components so they can be manufactured. Graphics are applied Euclidean geometry. Algebra is an abstraction of geometry. In fact, there is an inverse relationship between the level of difficulty of a problem expressed algebraically, and its geometric expression. Moreover, before an engineering problem can be solved, the problem must be somehow visualized. Albert Einstein is on record as saying that he thought in terms of images, not words. He would transcribe his problem formulations from pictures into equations and words. The ability to *think visually* is a cornerstone of engineering skill.

For a concrete example consider the expression, '*a picture is worth a thousand words*'. Compare the required written instructions to describe unambiguously how to get from the Mackenzie Engineering Building at Carleton University in Ottawa, Ontario, to the MacDonald Engineering Building at McGill university in Montréal, Québec, to a road map that graphically illustrates the exact route for the journey.

The task of unambiguous written or verbal description of the physical dimensions and characteristics required for the manufacture of an object, exactly as specified, verges on impossible, even when the receiver of the instructions speaks the same language as the giver of the instructions. Imagine having to make a tool based on the following description.

The tool has a handle and a heavy, irregularly shaped head, both cast as one metal piece. The handle has a rubber grip. The handle runs lengthwise, perpendicular to the head. One end of the head has a blunt face, while the opposite end has two flattened stems formed by a tapered groove. The length of the handle is 30 cm and the head measures 10 cm, end-to-end. The tool weighs 1 kg.

From the written description, it is difficult to get an exact mental image of the object. The conceptual features of the tool, on the other hand, are described unambiguously by Figure 12.1.

The term '*engineering graphics*' covers a broad spectrum of different applications ranging from the conceptual design sketches made on any convenient supply of paper, typically paper napkins, computer solid models of every component of a device, such as an automobile, aircraft, power plant, computer, etc.. Thus engineering graphics has evolved into six major categories:

1. descriptive geometry;
2. orthographic multi-view working drawings;
3. technical illustration;
4. nomography;

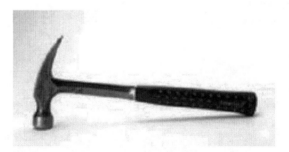

Figure 12.1   This picture is worth at least 75 words.

5. graphical approximations;

6. empirical equations.

Each of the above will be cursorily introduced in the following pages, but detailed discussion is beyond the scope of this book. The interested reader should refer to [2], or any of the many other textbooks on the subject.

12.2 WHY BOTHER WITH GEOMETRY?

Before taking a closer look at geometry, it will be helpful to discuss why it is needed. In the late 1800's geometry was quickly falling into disfavour among mathematicians. It was considered *'old fashioned'* and completely *'known'*. It was generally accepted that nothing new was left to be discovered. The fashion was to work in the emerging fields of algebra, despite the protestations of Albert Einstein (1879–1955) and Hermann Minkowski (1864–1909). The trend was towards *rationalization* of all areas of applied mathematics, including engineering, building on things such as the *Lagrangian* energy balance approach to dynamics developed by Joseph-Louis Lagrange (1736–1813). This rationalization involved the formulation of governing mathematical relations without resorting to the drawing of figures. The concept worked for the mathematicians of the 18th century because they could visualize the geometry associated with the algebraic abstraction they were developing. The problem is that it is easy to verbally describe a hammer if you have seen one before and have a mental picture of it in your head. If you had never seen one, would it be possible to identify errors in the description?

Consider the curve of intersection between the cylinder, described by the parametric equation in t and s as

$$\begin{bmatrix} x \\ y \\ z \end{bmatrix} = \begin{bmatrix} t \\ 7 - 3s \\ s \end{bmatrix}, \tag{12.1}$$

and the hyperboloid, described by the parametric equation in t and s as

$$\begin{bmatrix} x \\ y \\ z \end{bmatrix} = \begin{bmatrix} 83\sqrt{t^2 + 1}\cos(s) - 54 + 60t \\ 83\sqrt{t^2 + 1}\sin(s) + 66 + 54t \\ t \end{bmatrix}. \tag{12.2}$$

Can you visualize the curve of intersection? Could you tell, just by looking at Equations (12.1) and (12.2), that they represent a cylinder and a hyperboloid? Did you notice that Equation (12.1) is actually a plane, not a cylinder? What if you had based an important engineering decision based on a misinterpretation of Equation (12.1)? Wouldn't it be better to verify an algebraic interpretation with a plot of the equations of the surfaces? The surfaces corresponding to Equations (12.1) and (12.2) are shown in Figure 12.2.

A more insidious problem is that the geometry of the world we live in (at least macroscopically) is fundamentally different from the world that we can see. Consider Figure 12.3. We know that when we look at a set of train tracks, the rails seem to gradually get closer as they recede until they appear to intersect at a point on the horizon. Moreover, all lines parallel to the rails seem to meet at the same point. If such were the

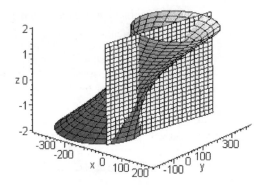

Figure 12.2   Intersection between a plane and an hyperboloid.

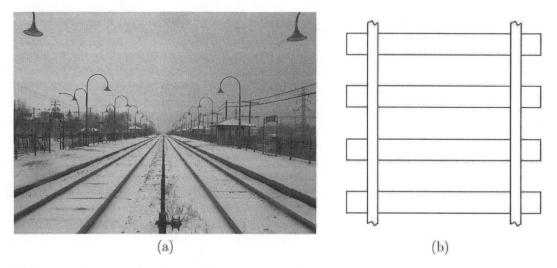

(a)   (b)

Figure 12.3   (a) What we see. (b) What is *really* there.

case, then train axles would require a feature permitting the distance between the
wheels to vary with the distance moved along the rails. Clearly, wheel axles on a train
have a fixed length, hence the distance between the rails must be constant.

The contradiction between physical reality and the reality we perceive visually
can only be explained by means of geometry. In fact, geometry was saved from scientific extinction by the work of geometers such as Felix Klein (1849-1925), David
Hilbert (1862–1943), and Donald Coxeter (1907–2003). See [3, 4, 5], respectively.
Among Klein's greatest contributions is an algebraic means to classify different
geometries.

In 1872 Felix Klein gave his famous inaugural address at the Friedrich-Alexander
University in Erlangen, Germany, the text of which is now known as the *Erlangen Programme* [6]. Relying on the earlier work of Arthur Cayley [7], it was intended to show
how Euclidean and non-Euclidean geometry could be established from projective
geometry. However, Klein's contributions turned out to be more general, leading to a
whole series of new geometries. Today, they are known as *Cayley-Klein geometries* and
the spaces in which they are valid are *Cayley-Klein spaces* [8].

The Erlangen Programme concerns the invariants of transformations, but we consider here only linear transformations of the form:

$$\begin{bmatrix} x_1' \\ x_2' \\ \vdots \\ x_n' \end{bmatrix} = \begin{bmatrix} t_{11} & t_{12} & \cdots & t_{1n} \\ t_{21} & t_{22} & \cdots & t_{2n} \\ \vdots & \vdots & \ddots & \vdots \\ t_{n1} & t_{n2} & \cdots & t_{nn} \end{bmatrix} \begin{bmatrix} x_1 \\ x_2 \\ \vdots \\ x_n \end{bmatrix}, \tag{12.3}$$

or in vector-matrix notation:

$$\mathbf{x}' = \mathbf{T}\mathbf{x}$$

The term *'linear transformation'* refers to any non-singular one-to-one transformation that maps the points on a line onto the points of a different line, in any dimensional space. In terms of Equation (12.3), the coordinates of n-dimensional points, represented by the n-dimensional vector on the right, are transformed by the $n \times n$ matrix into the n-dimensional vector on the left (the *image* of the original point). Given an $n \times 1$ vector $[x_1, x_2, \ldots, x_n]^T$, and an $n \times n$ matrix $\mathbf{T}$, Equation (12.3) is essentially a set of n linear equations in n unknowns.

According to Felix Klein's Erlangen Programme, the following propositions are always valid:

1. A geometry on a space defines a group of linear transformations in that space.
2. A group of linear transformations in a space defines a geometry on that space.

What this means is that the character of a geometry is determined by the relations which remain invariant under the associated group of linear transformations. Based on the Erlangen Programme, the most general geometry is the one with the fewest invariants, which translates to constraints on the elements of the matrix in Equation (12.3). The generality comes at the expense of the ability of the geometry to describe features of elements in the space. The most general geometry is *projective geometry* (the elements of the matrix in Equation (12.3) can take on any real value), while one of the most restrictive is *Euclidean geometry* (the matrix in Equation (12.3) must contain a proper orthogonal sub-matrix).

The exact nature of the problem is that we live (at least locally) in Euclidean space, while our vision is essentially restricted to the projective plane. In Euclidean geometry metric quantities (i.e. measurements such as the distance between points, the angle between lines, etc.) must be preserved by linear transformations. Whereas in projective geometry metric properties, as such, do not even exist! In projective geometry, the relative distance between points depends on how the set of points is viewed.

Figure 12.4 illustrates how a cube is essentially projected onto the plane of vision of an observer. Clearly, the shape and size of the cube depends on the relative location of the focal point of the observer's eyes. While the *camera obscura* model of the mechanics of human vision is overly simplified, the effect of projecting 3D Euclidean space onto a 2D plane through a single point is exact. Thus, two people viewing the same object at the same time, necessarily from different locations in space, will never see exactly the same thing. To reconcile this, a reliable way to describe physical objects is needed if they are to be designed and manufactured. This is essentially the tool supplied to us by Gaspard Monge. Instead of the rays emanating from the cube (called *projectors*), all converging at a finite focal point, and intersecting the plane of vision (called the *projection plane*), the projectors are all parallel to each other and perpendicular to the projection plane. The result is *orthographic projection* and *descriptive geometry*.

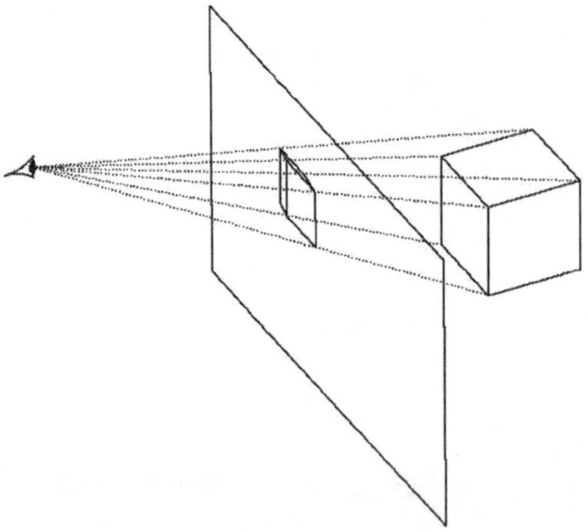

Figure 12.4   One-point perspective model of the mechanics of human vision.

12.3   DESCRIPTIVE GEOMETRY

Descriptive geometry is a collection of geometric tools used to describe physical geometric elements (points, lines, curves, planes, surfaces, etc.) of objects as they exist in the three-dimensional (3D) physical space described by 3D Euclidean geometry and Cartesian coordinates, so that they can be exactly represented on a piece of two-dimensional (2D) paper, or projected on to the 2D surface of a computer screen.

Gaspard Monge (1747–1818), an engineer and officer in Napoleon's army, is credited with discovering descriptive geometry. Its first applications were for precisely aiming artillery. It was a very fast way to graphically determine the angle at which the barrel of a canon had to be set, in order to hit a target at a known distance, using a known charge and gauge of canon ball. The opponents of Napoleon's army had to use trigonometric tables and numerical triangulation, requiring cumbersome, relatively slow, and error-prone manual calculations. The end result was that Napoleon's artillery would always be able to quickly destroy the enemy's artillery. Because of this, descriptive geometry was a military secret. After the ultimate defeat of Napoleon, the knowledge of descriptive geometry was made generally available. It was quickly adapted and applied to most design problems, particularly in the areas of mechanism and machine design, structures, and railroad construction.

12.3.1   Orthographic Projection

The fundamental tool of descriptive geometry is *orthographic projection*. This is where geometric elements of an object are projected onto a plane with mutually parallel rays, all orthogonal to the plane. See Figure 12.5. The plane is called a *projection plane*, while the parallel rays are called *projectors*. When geometric features of a three-dimensional object are projected onto a plane, some of the information describing the object is lost. That is, in the plane there are two linearly independent coordinates, while in 3D space there are three. To fully describe the object in terms of orthographic projection more than one projection is necessary. Manipulating the projections reveals true lengths, angles, shapes, and other metric quantities. Many detailed examples can be found in [2].

To use descriptive geometry for design, it is convenient to use geometric tools provided by Euclid (~300 BC), Gaspard Monge, and algebraic tools provided by the French

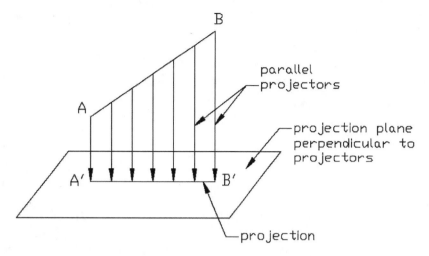

Figure 12.5   Points of a line in 3D space projected orthographically onto a 2D plane.

philosopher and mathematician, René Descartes (1596–1650). In Euclidean, and, by extension, descriptive geometry, the fundamental element is the *point*. That is, objects are described as continuous sets of points. A line segment in 3D Euclidean space extending from point A to point B may be finite, but it contains an infinite number of points. The point set is continuous, but this is difficult to implement algebraically. For instance, there is no *implicit equation* (a single equation in terms of the (x, y, z) coordinates of points on the line) for a line in 3D Euclidean space. The equation must be specified *parmetrically*, in terms of a point on the line, a vector parallel to the line, and a real-valued parameter to scale the vector. If the parameter, t, is allowed to vary as $-\infty \le t \le \infty$, then the points contained on the line are given *explicitly* in terms of t. This is meaningless in the absence of a way to discretize space. This is what Cartesian coordinates provide: a means to discretize continuous geometric elements into a finite set of points bounded by a beginning and an end point.

Let 3D space be partitioned by three arbitrary, but mutually orthogonal, planes. Being mutually orthogonal means that each plane is perpendicular to the other two (see Figure 12.6). These three planes partition space into 8 regions. Place the origin of a right-handed Cartesian coordinate system at the point of intersection of the three planes. Assign the coordinate axes as shown in Figure 12.6. Traditionally, the region of space having $-x$ coordinates is ignored, leaving four quadrants numbered as in Figure 12.6.

12.3.2 Third and First Angle Projection

The three mutually orthogonal planes are called principal planes. To project the geometric elements of an object onto the principal planes the object must be placed somewhere relative to the coordinate origin. Two conventions have developed. These are called *first* and *third angle projection*. In both conventions the *observer* is understood to be in the first quadrant. In third angle projection, the object is placed in the third quadrant. The principal planes separate the object and observer. In first angel projection, the object is placed in the first quadrant. Third angle projection is the convention in North America, Great Britain, and Australia, whereas first angle projection is used almost everywhere else in the world.

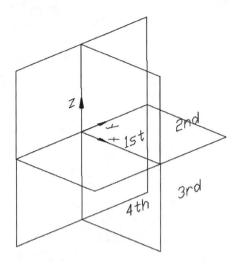

Figure 12.6   Three mutually orthogonal planes.

12.3.3 Third Angle Projection

In *third angle projection* the object is traditionally thought of as being placed, conceptually, inside a glass box, three of whose walls are the principal projection planes. In order for an object to be contained entirely in the third quadrant the (x, y, z) Cartesian coordinates of the points that define the object must have the following signs: $(+, +, -)$. For example, the orthographic projections of a point with the Cartesian coordinates $(3, 3, -4)$ onto the three principal planes is illustrated in Figure 12.7.

The three principal planes are traditionally named the *frontal (F) plane*, the *horizontal (H) plane*, and the *profile (P) plane*. In third angle three view working drawings, the views are called the *front, top* and *right side views*, respectively. Points in the H plane are described by (x, y) coordinates. Points in the F plane are described by $(x, -z)$ coordinates. Points in the P plane are described by $(y, -z)$ coordinates. However, the convention is to place the P plane (which is parallel to the Y-Z plane) at a convenient positive value of x, keeping projections in the principal views from overlapping.

Notation.   It is important to adopt a notation convention to keep track of, and specify, the different projections of points. This is because auxiliary projection planes frequently must be used to solve problems, in addition to the principal projection planes. Points are described with uppercase letters, while the projection is identified with a superscript on the right-hand side of the letter. Thus Q^H indicates the horizontal projection of point Q, while Q^F and Q^P indicate the frontal and profile projections of point Q.

Folding Lines (Reference Lines).   The projection planes seen in the space model in Figure 12.7 (a) must be *unfolded* to allow the representation of 3D space in the plane of a sheet of paper. Figure 12.7 (b) shows the manner in which the H plane is unfolded about the x axis, and the P plane is unfolded about a line parallel to the z axis, into the F plane. The unfolded glass box is shown in Figure 12.7 (c).

The *folding line*, or *reference line*, as it is also called, is the line of intersection of two adjacent projection planes. Folding lines should always be shown in descriptive geometry drawings, as this is a zero-reference line for measuring distances. The folding line is identified by the two intersecting planes that define it. For example, the H-F folding line is the line of intersection between the H and F planes. In the drawing, the folding lines are identified as in Figure 12.7 (c). The relative locations of the principal views are shown in Figure 12.8 (a).

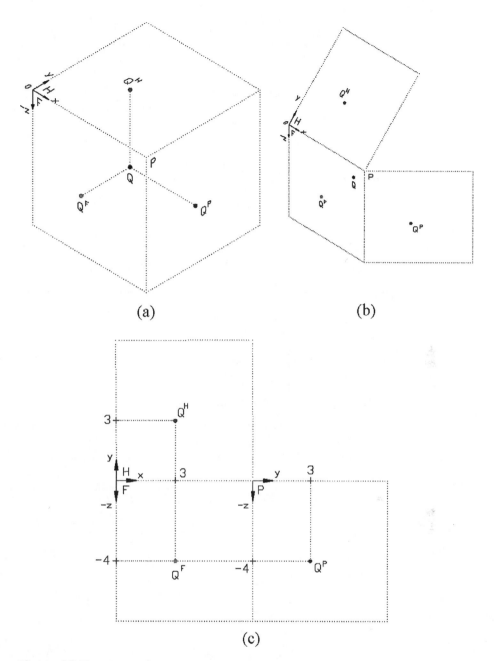

Figure 12.7   Three orthographic projections of a point in 3D space.

Superimposing the Cartesian Coordinate System.   The most convenient location for the origin of the Cartesian coordinate system is the point of intersection between the three principal planes. The x axis is then directed along the H-F folding line The $-z$ axis is parallel to the F-P folding line.

12.3.4 First Angle Projection.

The object is placed entirely in the first quadrant. In order for an object to be contained entirely in the first quadrant the (x, y, z) coordinates of the points that define the object must have the following signs: $(+, -, +)$. Now the object is between the observer and the projection planes. It is traditional in first angle projection to unfold the glass box into the H plane. The end result is similar to that of third angle projection, except that the relative positions of the principal planes are different. This is demonstrated in Figure 12.8.

In Figure 12.8 (a) point $Q(3, 3, -4)$ is shown in third angle, while in Figure 12.8 (b) point $R(3, -4, 3)$ is shown in first angle projection. Note the differences in the coordinate axis directions, and the relative locations of the views. Figure 12.9 helps to show how the quadrant and the unfolding affect the relative positioning of the views.

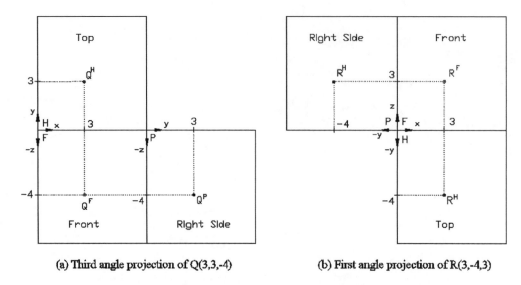

(a) Third angle projection of Q(3,3,-4)   (b) First angle projection of R(3,-4,3)

Figure 12.8   Three relative positions of the principal planes in third and first angle projection.

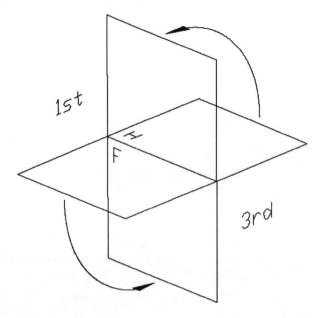

Figure 12.9   Three relative positions of the principal planes in third and first angle projection.

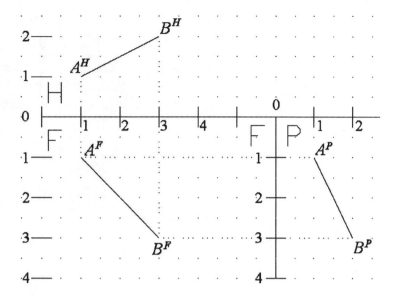

Figure 12.10   Three principal positions of line segment AB in third angle projection.

EXAMPLE 12.1

Consider the line segment defined by points A(1, 1, −1) and B(3, 2, −3). Construct the F, H, and P views of line segment AB in third angle projection.

SOLUTION

In the H plane there are only x and y coordinates, so the horizontal projections are $A^H(1, 1)$ and $B^H(3, 2)$. In the F plane there are only x and $-z$ coordinates, so the frontal projections are $A^F(1, -1)$ and $B^F(3, -3)$. In the P plane there are only y and $-z$ coordinates, so the profile projections are $A^P(1, -1)$ and $B^P(2, -3)$. The projections are shown in Figure 12.10 (note that scales have been drawn on the figure; normally this is not done).

12.4 TECHNICAL ILLUSTRATION

Technical illustration is used as a graphical description. Graphics is one of the engineer's most effective tools for developing concepts, solving problems, and analysis, but is can also be the best means of communication. This idea is supported by history. The earliest examples of written communication are the well known cave drawings, found through-out the world, which document early human experience. Examples of this *prehistoric* form of written expression can be found on every continent on the planet.

Good graphical descriptions are efficient, and are not affected by language barri-ers. We all know the meaning of certain graphical symbols in an intrinsic way. For ex-ample, anyone who has spent a long layover in an airport anywhere in the world knows what the sign in Figure 12.11 means. There is little room for misunderstanding. Howev-er, the graphical illustration is stylized, and technically inaccurate. The goal of technical illustration is to communicate an idea, not necessarily technical exactness.

Technical illustration takes many different forms, ranging from crude hand drawn sketches to illustrations found in catalogues and instruction manuals. Inevitably, howev-er, the illustration involves some form of projection of 3D object onto 2D paper. We will focus on a subclass called *pictorial drawing*. Of these we shall look at *perspective*,

Figure 12.11   An important example of effective graphical communication.

oblique, isometric, and *axonometric projection*. While multi-view orthographic projection is frequently employed, we will save the discussion for Section 12.5.

12.4.1 Perspective Projection

Perspective projection is used primarily by architects and commercial artists to describe the external appearance of an object. It is the most realistic form of pictorial because it closely resembles the view seen by the human eye, or a camera. In perspective projection the projectors intersect at finite points, called vanishing points (VP). The representation on the projection plane may be considered the view that would be seen by a single eye at a known point in space (the station point). The picture is formed on the projection plane by the intersections of the projecting lines from the object to the focal point of the eye. This is illustrated in Figure 12.4. The three basic kinds are *one-point, two-point*, and *three-point perspectives* depending on the number of vanishing points used in their construction. Figure 12.13 compares and contrasts the three types. Methods for constructing perspective projections are beyond the scope of this book, but the interested reader can find detailed descriptions in [2].

One-Point Perspective.   The projection plane is parallel to two principal axes. Thus, features parallel to the projection plane appear in true shape, see Figure 12.12. Receding lines along one of the principal axis converge to a vanishing point. A one-point perspective is used almost exclusively for interior-room views. It gives the observer the illusion of looking into the room. One of the most famous paintings ever created is *The Last Supper* by Leonardo da Vinci. In it, da Vinci employed one-point perspective to draw the attention of the viewer to Christ.

Two-Point Perspective.   In this type of perspective projection the object being drawn is positioned such that two sides are at an angle to the projection plane, requiring two vanishing points on the horizon. However, the vertical axis is parallel to the projection plane so that vertical lines remain vertical, and true length. However, because only the vertical lines remain undistorted, planes containing vertical lines are distorted. Figure 12.13 (b) illustrates two-point perspective projection.

Three-Point Perspective.   If the projection plane is not parallel to any principal axis of the object, a three-point projection occurs with the visual rays converging to

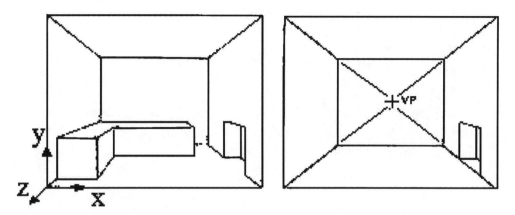

Figure 12.12   One-point perspective.

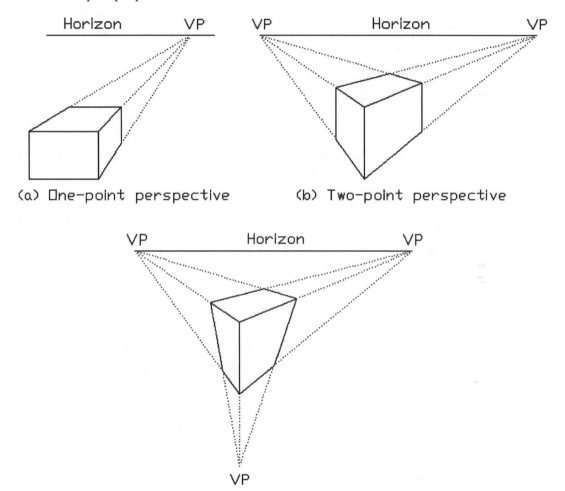

Figure 12.13   Comparison of one-, two-, and three-point perspectives.

three vanishing points. See Figure 12.13 (c). This is the most general perspective projection. Three-point perspectives are typically used to draw large objects, such as high-rise buildings, aircraft carriers, rockets, etc.. They are the most realistic projections, but also the most complex to construct.

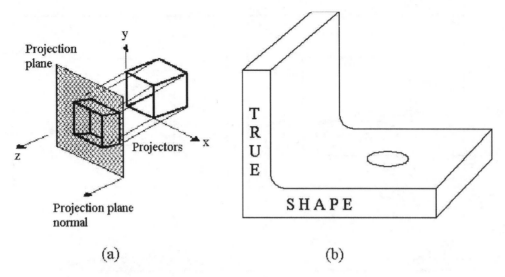

Figure 12.14   (a) Oblique projection plane; (b) Front face is true shape.

12.4.2 Oblique Projection

An orthographic view can be a 3D pictorial view if the object being projected reveals a 3D effect. An oblique projection is an orthographic projection whose parallel projectors are at an oblique angle to the projection plane. See Figure 12.14 (a). In other words, it is an orthographic projection with a single receding axis. One face of the object is parallel to the projection plane, and thus appears in true shape, illustrated in Figure 12.14 (b). That is, the front face of the object is parallel to the viewer, therefore that face is true size. Circular features appearing on the front face remain circular. The remaining visible faces are drawn using an arbitrary, convenient scale along the receding axis.

Oblique projections are easy to construct and are often used to give an indication of depth. Lack of perspective foreshortening makes comparison of sizes easier. While they are a large departure from realistic representation, oblique projections are frequently used precisely because they are the easiest 3D drawings to construct.

12.4.3 Isometric and Axonometric Projection

An *axonometric projection* is the most general orthographic projection. It is best understood by first considering a special case, called *isometric projection*. Imagine a cube placed inside the conceptual third quadrant glass cube as shown in Figure 12.15. The cube is oriented such that the projections of its edges in the H-plane intersect at equal angles: 120°. The corner of the cube closest to the H-plane can be considered as the origin of a right-handed coordinate system whose orthogonal axes are directed along the edges. Lines parallel to these axes are *isometric* lines.

The H-plane projection of the symmetric cube in Figure 12.15 is an *isometric* projection of the cube. The term *iso* refers to the fact that the x', y', and z' all possess the same *metric*. That is, a millimetre along the x'-axis is the same length as a millimetre along the y'- and z'-axes. Thus the projected cube is also symmetric. All sides are rhombuses (a rhombus is a parallelogram with sides that are equal in length).

To simplify construction of isometric views, foreshortening along the isometric axes is not considered. That is, it can be shown that the cube edges are foreshortened by $\sqrt{2}/\sqrt{3}$ times their actual length. Due to this engineering convenience of representation, a cube with 100mm length edges would be drawn with 100mm length edges in the

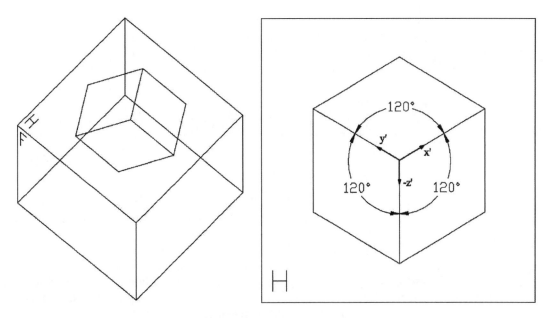

Figure 12.15   Cube in the 3rd quadrant appearing in the H-plane such that all edges are equally distorted.

isometric view. Features that are not parallel to the isometric axes become distorted in the isometric view because the projected angles between edges are not orthogonal. Thus, a circle on one of the cube faces would project as an ellipse. See Figure 12.16.

CAD packages, such as AutoCAD, or IntelliCAD, provide an *ISOMETRIC* grid for quick, and easy construction of isometric views. The *STYLE* option of the *SNAP* command allows changing between the standard rectangular grid, called *STANDARD* (S), and the *ISOMETRIC* grid (I). In this mode, you can make the cross hairs of the cursor *snap* to the grid points that align with the isometric axes. However, isometric views constructed in this way are 2D, and cannot be rotated to show hidden features.

12.5   ORTHOGRAPHIC MULTI-VIEW WORKING AND ASSEMBLY DRAWINGS

Working and assembly drawings are the drawings that are used to transform a design from existence in the imagination to physical existence. They are used to implement the design by manufacturing and assembling all of its components. Principles of de-

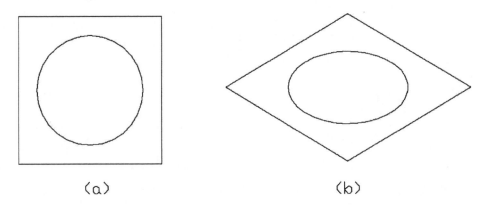

(a)   (b)

Figure 12.16   (a) Circle centred on cube face; (b) Isometric view of the circle is an ellipse.

scriptive geometry and the various graphical techniques are used to communicate all the details required for manufacturing components. The set of all drawings required for producing all the components of the design are the *working drawings*. An *assembly drawing* illustrates how the components of a design fit together. Assembly drawings also give details in a *parts list*, or *bill of materials* regarding material, quantities, names, drawing and part numbers of all components in the assembled parts. Any special assembly instructions are also specified. The following material is based on the American National Standards Institute (ANSI) engineering drawing standards ANSI-Y14.2 through ANSI-Y14.6.

12.5.1   Working and Detail Drawings

As mentioned above, the set of all drawings required for producing all the components of the design are the *working drawings*. A *detail drawing* is a working drawing of a single part within a set of working drawings. The detail drawing in Figure 12.17 is a working drawing because all information required to construct the part is given in the drawing: all relevant dimensions, units, material, and finish are specified. The drawing consists of three orthographic projections, plus an isometric view. The purpose of the isometric view is to enhance clarity. It has become accepted practice to include an isometric view in a multi-view detail drawing.

Working drawings are major components of legal contracts between the designer and client. They document the design details and specifications that have been specified and ap-

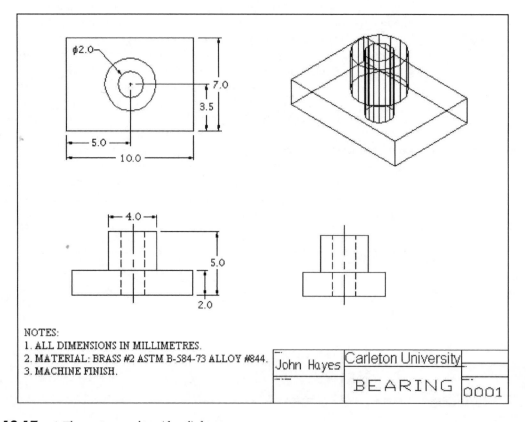

Figure 12.17   A Three-view working (detail) drawing.

proved by the engineering team. For this reason, drawings must be precise, unambiguous, and thorough. Drawings must be as error-free as possible in order to be economically competitive. The quality of the working drawings is usually what stands between success and failure of a design to meet specifications during implementation.

12.5.2 Types of Lines

Drafting conventions and communication requirements have led, over the centuries, to standard line type representations for certain purposes. In North America, the line convention standards are set by the American National Standards Institute in the *Line Conventions and Lettering* document ANSI-Y14.2M. The corresponding ISO standard is ISO-128. These standards specify the exact appearance, pattern and thickness, of the various line types. The standards related to line thickness do not, in general, apply to computer generated drawings, but rather to *pencil and ink drawings* produced manually. The three main types of line are *object, hidden,* and *centre lines*, as shown in Figure 12.18. According to ANSI-Y14.2M-1992 visible and cutting plane lines should be 0.7 mm thick, while hidden and centre lines should be 0.3 mm thick. As Figure 12.18 was produced by computer, the patterns adhere to ANSI-Y14.2M-1992, but the thickness does not. For computer generated drawings it has become acceptable to allow all line types to be of uniform thickness.

Visible features are drawn using object lines which are continuous. But, it is not possible to see every line element, or feature in a 3D object, because some feature will always occlude, or hide, others. These *hidden lines* are represented by dashed lines. Figure 12.17 shows occluded features represented by hidden lines. The use of the word line is just convention. Hidden circles and features of any shape are all represented by hidden lines. Centre lines are composed of long and short dashes. They are used to locate the centres of circular features, or the axis of symmetry of symmetrical features. Centre lines are illustrated as well in Figure 12.17.

12.5.3 Line Type Precedence

When two, or more lines coincide in a particular view only one can be shown. Otherwise, the result would surely end in misinterpretation. ANSI-Y14.2 has been adopted to deal with this. This standard establishes which line types take precedence. Figure 12.19 shows line priority. The order of priority is: visible (object); hidden lines; cutting plane lines; centre lines.

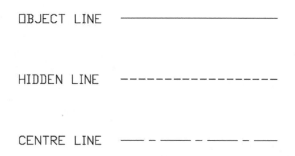

Figure 12.18   Three different types of line.

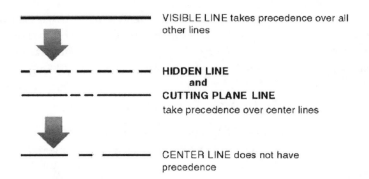

VISIBLE LINE takes precedence over all other lines

HIDDEN LINE
and
CUTTING PLANE LINE

take precedence over center lines

CENTER LINE does not have precedence

Figure 12.19   Line type precedence.

12.5.4 Laying Out a Working (Detail) Drawing

All working and assembly drawings must *always* include a *boarder* and *title block*. The boarder frames the drawing and should be sized to the paper the drawing will be printed on. It is standard practice (ANSI-Y14.3) to allow a margin of at least 0.25 in (7 mm). The title block (discussed in greater detail in Section 12.5.5) is usually placed in the lower right-hand corner of the drawing, as in Figure 12.17. Notes, and any other required written information are placed as needed such that they do not interfere with the drawing, but are clearly visible and legible.

It is good practice to first make a freehand sketch of a component to select the best, most appropriate, and necessary views. While three-view drawings are common, there is no law stating that three views are always required. As the glass box unfolds into six planes, up to six principal views can be selected. This is illustrated in Figure 12.20. Regardless of the number of views used, it is vitally important to remember that descriptive geometry forms the backbone of the detail drawing. Hence, the projected views **must always be aligned.**

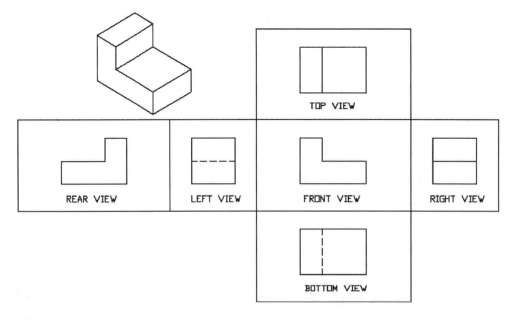

Figure 12.20   Six principal views.

Selection of Views.   An orthographic detail drawing almost always begins with the front view, the remaining views being projected from it. The object is oriented such that *the most descriptive view is selected to be the front view*. Some objects, such as an aircraft, have views that are generally accepted to be front, top and side. Others, such as the block in Figure 12.20, do not, and engineering judgement must be used. This is usually a subjective decision, but can usually be justified. It is also worthwhile to note that it is not required to label the views, as they should be obvious from context, as long as third or first angle projection has been indicated.

It is extremely unusual to have a single view drawing, so at least one view in addition to the front view is required. The top view might be used, if the front view is oriented appropriately. If a side view is required, the one possessing the fewest number of hidden lines should be used. This may mean the left side view should be used instead of the right. If both the left and right side views contain the same number of hidden lines, it is conventional practice to use the right side view.

As mentioned above, aside from the front view, there is usually a decision to be made regarding how many, and which views to use. Figure 12.21 shows the detail drawing for a bearing bracket. It is clear that three views are not needed to describe the bracket. A top view could have been selected, but then two circles, those corresponding to the bearing hole and the countersunk hole immediately beneath it would be indistinguishable in both the top and bottom views. Clearly, the right side view is preferable.

The offset double dashed line connecting the two arrows labelled A is a *cutting plane line*. The cutting plane is labelled according to the letters; in this case it indicates cutting plane A-A. This line shows where an imaginary cut has been made in the front view. The cutting plane is seen in edge view in the front view, and hence appears as a line.

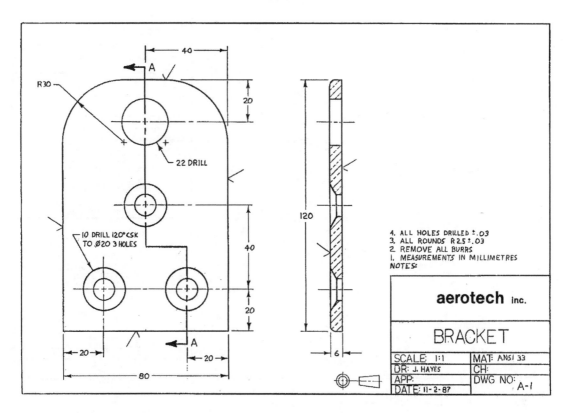

Figure 12.21   Working drawing for a bearing bracket.

The direction of the arrows are always perpendicular to the edge view of the cutting plane and indicate the direction an observer should view the section. If the arrows point to the left, the section appears in the right side view. If the arrows point to the right, then the left side view contains the section. The same rule applies in general: the view containing the section is adjacent to the view showing the edge view of the cutting plane, and is opposite to the direction of the arrows.

The view in Figure 12.21 containing the section is represented in a different way. Material that has been cut by the cutting plane is *hatched*. Different materials are represented by different hatch patterns. The bearing bracket is brass, meaning the brass hatch pattern is used. This is the pattern used in the right side view.

Cutting planes and sectioning are another convention used to enhance the clarity of a drawing. In this case, the right side view is drawn without having to use any hidden lines. Note that the *check-mark* type symbol is a basic surface texture symbol. It indicates that a certain surface finish can be obtained by any method.

12.5.5 Title Blocks, Notes, and Other Information

In addition to the graphical information on a working drawing, some written communication is always necessary. The bare minimum includes the name of the part (or, the title of the drawing), the name of the drafter, the date the drawing was created, and the company name. This information is typically recorded in a *title block*. Figures 12.17, 12.21, and 12.22 show various styles of title block, containing a variety of information and detail. Other information they may include are tolerances, the names of co-workers, or superiors who have *checked* the work for errors, material, finishing instructions, etc..

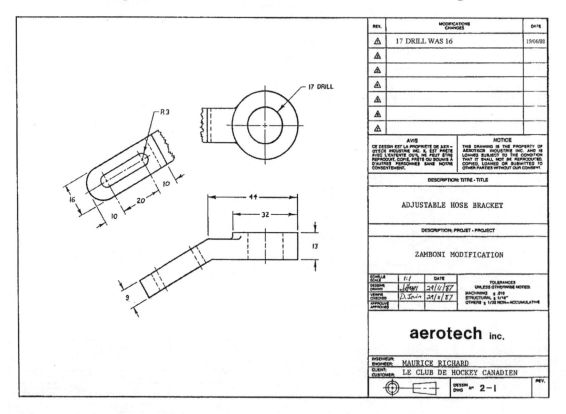

Figure 12.22   Working drawing with an auxiliary view and a revision block.

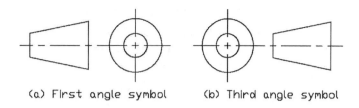

(a) First angle symbol   (b) Third angle symbol

Figure 12.23   (a) First angle projection symbol; (b) Third angle projection symbol.

Depending on the complexity of the project, a set of working drawings may contain anywhere from one, to thousands of drawings! Hence, indicating the number of each drawing in sequence, and the total number of drawings in the set is necessary. For example, this could be indicated by *sheet 6 of 22*, *sheet 35 of 61*, and so on. See the title block in Figure 12.24.

It is expected that the workings drawings will be revised. That is, as the design evolves, changes to dimensions, tolerances, surface finishes, locations, etc., may be required. It is important to log the history of these changes for archival, as well as legal reasons. Thus, in addition to the title block, there is usually either a separate, or integrated block to record the revisions. A revision block, logging changes, can be seen in Figure 12.22.

Third Angle, First Angle Symbols. In North America, Great Britain, and Australia third angle projection is the norm, whereas first angle projection is used almost everywhere else in the world. Hence, if drawings for one subassembly of an automobile design are prepared by an office in Oshawa, Ontario, Canada, while drawings for other components are prepared by an office of the same company in Salzburg, Austria, for a production facility in Mexico, there is great potential for misunderstanding.

To avoid costly production errors caused by confusing first angle with third angle projections, the ISO projection symbols, see Figure 12.23, are used. The symbol depicts a truncated cone in the corresponding projection. The cone is positioned such that the front view shows two concentric circles. In first angle projection, the right-side view appears to the *left* of the front view, hence the first angle symbol. In third angle projection the right-side view appears on the *right* of the front view, as depicted in the symbol. Note, the third angle symbol is used in both Figures 12.21 and 12.22.

12.5.6 Assembly Drawings and Parts Lists

After all the parts have been made, or purchased according to the specifications of the working drawings, they must be assembled according to the instructions contained in an *assembly drawing*. Generally, assembly drawings are either orthographic, or a form of pictorial called *exploded*. The one thing that is common to all assembly drawings, regardless of representation, is the *parts list*, also called a *bill of materials*.

Orthographic Assemblies. The hand vise shown in Figure 12.24 is an orthographic assembly drawing, in which the parts are depicted in their assembled positions. Two views are used to show the axial symmetry of the wing nut location, and presumably the position required for packaging. Each part is numbered with a balloon and leader to connect the balloon to the corresponding part, cross-referencing them with the *parts list*, where more information about each part is given. Each part in the assembly has its own detail drawing in the set of working drawings, containing detailed information and specifications for the part. The parts list identifies the associated drawing numbers, the

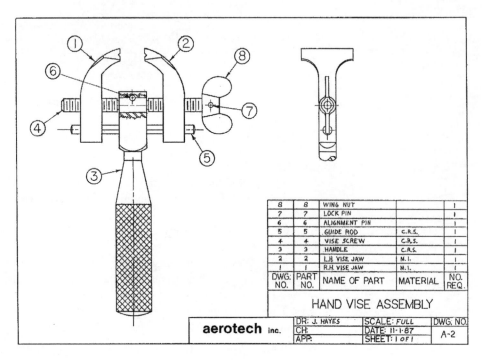

DWG. NO.	PART NO.	NAME OF PART	MATERIAL	NO. REQ.
8	8	WING NUT		1
7	7	LOCK PIN		1
6	6	ALIGNMENT PIN		1
5	5	GUIDE ROD	C.R.S.	1
4	4	VISE SCREW	C.R.S.	1
3	3	HANDLE	C.R.S.	1
2	2	L.H. VISE JAW	M.I.	1
1	1	R.H. VISE JAW	M.I.	1

HAND VISE ASSEMBLY

aerotech inc.

DR: J. HAYES	SCALE: FULL	DWG. NO.
CH:	DATE: 11-1-87	A-2
APP:	SHEET: 1 OF 1	

Figure 12.24   Orthographic *assembly drawing* and *parts list*.

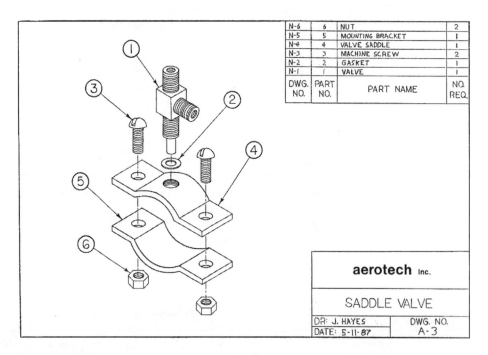

DWG. NO.	PART NO.	PART NAME	NO. REQ.
N-6	6	NUT	2
N-5	5	MOUNTING BRACKET	1
N-4	4	VALVE SADDLE	1
N-3	3	MACHINE SCREW	2
N-2	2	GASKET	1
N-1	1	VALVE	1

aerotech inc.

SADDLE VALVE

DR: J. HAYES	DWG. NO.
DATE: 5-11-87	A-3

Figure 12.25   Exploded *assembly drawing* and *parts list*.

part name, catalogue numbers, quantities required for one assembly, and usually some indication of the material the part is made of.

Exploded Assemblies.   The saddle valve shown in Figure 12.25 is an *exploded pictorial assembly* drawing. The parts have been exploded along their centre lines in an effort to make it easier to understand how the parts should be assembled. Exploded assembly drawings leave little doubt as to how the individual components are related to each other spatially. In fact, the exploded assembly in Figure 12.25 actually reveals an error. Can you spot it?

Balloons containing the part numbers, cross-referencing them to the parts list, are also included. The parts list completes the assembly drawing.

12.6   NOMOGRAPHY

A *nomograph*, or *alignment chart*, is a graphical computer consisting of arrangements of calibrated scales and lines. These are often used in situations where calculations must be performed repetitively and where tight numerical tolerances are not absolutely required (although nomographs can be used to a high degree of numerical accuracy). They are powerful and extremely useful because they can be used to solve non-linear multivariate functions for a single unknown over a specific range. Nomographs are widely used in engineering, and in the natural and physical sciences. Typical examples include: computing drug dosages for prescriptions; selecting resistor, or capacitor values in discrete component circuits; selecting spring constants in suspension systems.

Nomographs are typically constructed to graphically solve for one or more unknowns in an algebraic, or empirical, equation. For example, simple charts can be constructed to convert: kilometers to miles; kilometers per litre to miles per gallon; degrees Farenheit to degrees Celsius; cross-sectional area of a structural member required to support axial or torsional loads. A nomograph is read by *aligning* different scales in a specific way. This involves placing a straight edge to establish a straight line, called an *isopleth*, across the scales and reading the corresponding value on the scale representing the unknown.

EXAMPLE 12.2

In circuit analysis it is often necessary to determine the equivalent resistance of two or more resistors connected in parallel, as in Figure 12.26. It can be shown that the equivalent, or total resistance R_T of two parallel connected resistors, is

$$R_T = \frac{1}{\frac{1}{R_1} + \frac{1}{R_2}}. \tag{12.4}$$

It can be shown that series-connected capacitors, series-connected linear springs, and many other systems, obey the relation in Equation (12.4).

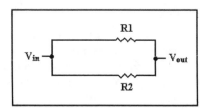

Figure 12.26   A parallel resistor network.

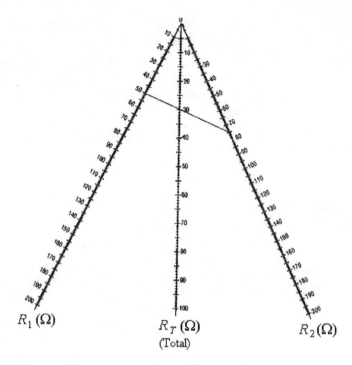

$R_1 (\Omega)$

$R_T (\Omega)$
(Total)

$R_2 (\Omega)$

Figure 12.27   Equivalent resistance nomograph.

Figure 12.27 can be used to graphically compute R_T. The value for R_1 is located on the left-hand scale and the value for R_2 is located on the right-hand scale. The total, or equivalent resistance, is found at the intersection of the isopleth connecting R_1 and R_2 and the middle scale. If $R_1 = 50\Omega$ and $R_2 = 75\Omega$ the isopleth crosses the middle scale at the corresponding value of total parallel network resistance, $R_T = 30\Omega$.

EXAMPLE 12.3

The nomograph in Figure 12.28 is used to predict the conditions that could lead to a river overflowing its banks, causing a flood. It relates the average rainfall intensity and duration to the flow rate through a control volume in the river. Flow rates between 15,000 and 20,000 ft^3/hr are lightly shaded, indicating that the residents in communities on the river banks be warned that flooding danger is low, but of concern. Flow rates between 20,000 and 24,000 ft^3/hr are in a medium shaded region, indicating an increased level of flood alert. Flow rates in excess of 24,000 ft^3/hr are in a dark shaded region, indicating the highest level of alert because flooding is imminent.

Case 1. If it rains 5 inches in 6 hours, should the communities in the vicinity of the river be warned?. The average rainfall intensity (in/hr) is 0.83 in/hr. Construct an isopleth to run horizontally through 0.83 in/hr on the left-hand vertical scale to the vertical line representing 6 hours. Figure 12.28 predicts that the flow rate through a control point in the river will be close to 20,000 ft^3/hr. The point of intersection of the two isopleths falls in the light shaded region, close to the medium shaded region. Residents should be warned that flooding is possible, but not imminent.

Case 2. It rains at an intensity of 1.5 in/hr for a total of 5 hours. The point of intersection of the two isopleths is close to 24,000 ft^3/hr, indicating the danger of flooding is severe, but still not imminent.

Case 3. If it continues to rain for an additional hour at the same rainfall intensity, the flow rate will be close to 28,000 ft^3/hr, indicating that flooding is imminent, and that appropriate action should be taken.

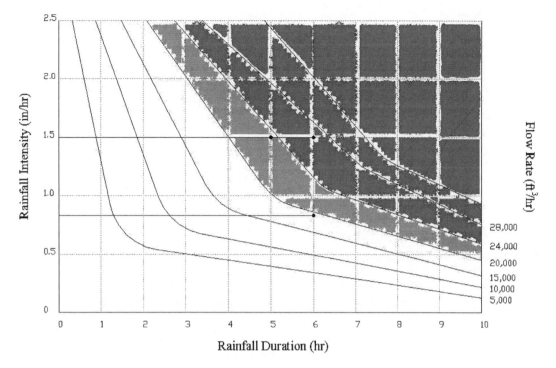

Figure 12.28   A nomograph for predicting flood conditions.

12.7   GRAPHICAL APPROXIMATIONS

Nomographs are excellent, often-used graphical computation tools. They are limited because they can only be used in a certain range of values. Their largest drawback is that in order to use one, you must possess one. There are many graphical techniques for solving certain classes of mathematical relations, the reciprocal of the sum of reciprocals being one of these classes. The advantage of a graphical approximation is that it can be constructed on any scrap of paper; the back of an envelope, for instance.

While there are many examples, it is not the intention of this text to give a comprehensive summary. Rather, the intention is to inform the reader of their existence and importance. This will be done by discussing the graphical method for computing the reciprocal of the sum of reciprocals. As discussed in Section 12.6, nomographs can be constructed for this computation, but we will look at a more straightforward method that can be implemented on 12.2:

EXAMPLE 12.4

Determine the equivalent linear spring constant, k, for two series connected springs having linear spring constants $k_1 = 50 \text{ kg/s}^2$ and $k_2 = 75 \text{ kg/s}^2$.

SOLUTION

Begin by constructing an evenly spaced vertical scale of spring constant values starting at 0 kg/s^2 and terminating with the larger of k_1 and k_2; see Figure 12.29. Construct a perpendicular to the scale through 0 kg/s^2. On this 0 kg/s^2 baseline draw vectors (arrows), parallel to and in agreement with the scale, of lengths k_1 and k_2 at any convenient location. Be sure that the vectors both start on the 0 kg/s^2 baseline. Draw lines connecting the tip of one to the tail of the other. The point of intersection is the equivalent linear spring constant. Due to a geometric theorem concerning the invariance of certain properties of the diagonals of quadrilaterals possessing two parallel sides, the relative location of the lines representing k_1 and k_2 with respect to the scale has no effect on the numerical value

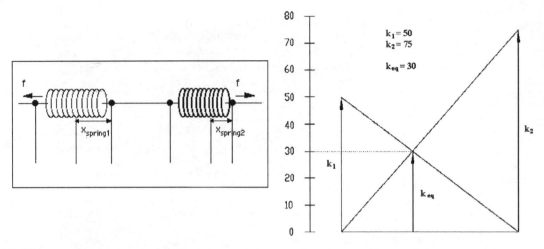

Figure 12.29   Equivalent spring constant for linear springs mounted in séries.

of the solution. The height above the baseline of the intersection of the diagonals does not depend on the distance between the opposite parallel sides.

Comparing this result to Example 12.2, it is seen that both examples are numerically equivalent, differing only in units. Thus the nomograph in Figure 12.27 could also be used for series-connected linear springs.

12.8   EMPIRICAL EQUATIONS

Empirical equations are derived from measurement data acquired from experiments in the laboratory, or from field tests. The data are fitted, typically in a least squares sense, to known classes of curves. It is usually hoped that the data will be *linear*, i.e., that it can be fit to a straight line. Then, the slope of the line represents the constant of proportionality between the variables. To interpret the data and quantitatively compare results, statistical techniques are usually employed. The data itself can be *filtered* to attenuate the effects of *measurement noise*, or uncertainty.

12.8.1   Linear Equations

When experimental data plotted on a square grid lies on a straight line, characterized by the equation $y = mx + b$, it is classified as being *linear*.

EXAMPLE 12.5

An experiment was devised using a linear spring, weights, and a device for measuring the change in spring length under various loads. For linear springs it is known that $F = kx$, the applied force is proportional to the change in spring length from its neutral, or unloaded, length. The constant of proportionality is called the *linear spring constant*, k. When the dimensions of F and x are Newtons (N), and metres (m), the dimensions of the spring constant are kg/s^2. The results of the experiment are given in Table 12.1.

TABLE 12.1   Data for linear spring experiment.

Applied load (mN)	Spring extension (mm)
3.2	0.9
6.3	2.1
8.7	3.1
12.3	3.9
14.7	5.1

When the data are plotted, see Figure 12.30, it is evident they are very nearly linear. We can use them to derive the linear empirical equation, $y = mx + b$ relating the load and deflection. The slope of the best fit line is found to be approximately 3. Moreover, the spring deflection is 0 for the no load condition. Thus we obtain $k = 3 \text{ kg/s}^2$, and $F = 3x$.

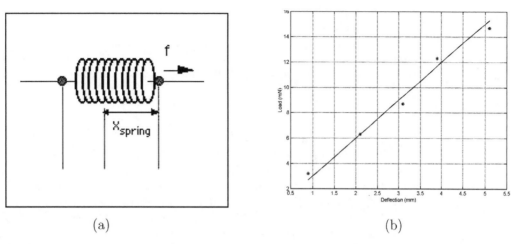

(a)   (b)

Figure 12.30   (a) Deflected spring; (b) load versus deflection graph for the spring data.

12.8.2 Linear Logarithmic Plots: Power Equations

When experimental data plotted on a square grid lies on a curve, characterized by the *power equation* $y = bx^m$, it is governed by the form where y is a function of the product of a constant, b, and the variable x raised to a power, m. However, equations of this class are indeed linear when expressed in logarithmic form. In the example that follows, base 10 logarithms are used, though any base may be used.

EXAMPLE 12.6

The voltage drop across a resistance causes electrical power to be absorbed by the resistance. This is the principle upon which electric heating elements are based. Power dissipated by a simple DC circuit element can be measured indirectly by measuring the voltage drop across the load resistor and the current in the circuit. The power (P) in watts (W) dissipated by the load is then equal to the product of the voltage drop across the load in volts (V) and the current in the circuit measured in amperes (A):

$$P = VI. \tag{12.5}$$

If the load resistance and current in the circuit are measured, we can use Ohm's law, $V = IR$ to rewrite Equation (12.5) as

$$P = RI^2. \tag{12.6}$$

Suppose the following experiment was performed to measure the power dissipated by a load. The circuit consists of a 12V battery connected in series with a 100 kΩ variable resistor and a load. The resistance of the load was measured to be 1.016 kΩ. The variable resistor was set to a minimum value, then increased in approximately equal increments up to the maximum value. At each step the voltage drop across the load was measured. The current in the circuit can be inferred from the voltage drop measurements using Ohm's law:

$$I = V_{\text{load}}/R_{\text{load}}.$$

The voltage drop across the load, in volts, was measured to be 3.170, 2.410, 1.715, 0.848, 0.680, 0.422, 0.324, 0.280, 0.214, 0.176, 0.160, 0.138, and 0.125, respectively. Power can then be computed. The plot of power versus voltage drop across the load, produced in MATLAB, on a square grid is shown in Figure 12.31 (a). The shape of the plotted data suggests that the relationship between power, voltage, and hence current, is a power equation. If the relationship, $P = I^2R$ were not known apriori, and had to be determined empirically, it is not immediately obvious how to proceed to determine the power.

However, the logarithm of the power equation yields $y = bx^m$ some surprising results. Comparing the general power equation to Equation (12.6), we immediately see that we have $P = RI^m$, where m is the unknown power. Taking the logarithm of this yields:

$$\log P = \log R + m \log I, \tag{12.7}$$

Which is a linear relationship!

The data is then plotted on a logarithmic grid (obtained using the *loglog* plot command in MATLAB). The slope of the line in Figure 12.31 (b) is the power that satisfies the relationship $P = RI^m$. Caution must be used, because the scales are *not* linear. The slope is still computed as $\Delta y/\Delta x$. Recall that on a grid the increments are logarithmically spaced within evenly spaced *decades*, integer powers of 10. Moreover, recall that $\log x = y$ if, and only if, $10^y = x$. Thus $\log 10 = 1$ because $10^1 = 10$. Referring to Figure 12.31 (b), the slope is computed to be:

$$m = \frac{\Delta y}{\Delta x} = \frac{\log 4 - \log 1}{\log 2 - \log 1} = \frac{0.6020}{0.3010} = 2. \tag{12.8}$$

What remains is to determine the y *intercept*, b. This occurs where the line crosses the y axis, i.e., where $x = 0$. Again, caution is in order, as $1 = 0$. It is to be seen that the line in Figure 12.31 (b) crosses the y axis with the y coordinate $10 = 1$. As the axes are scaled to be mW and mA, the constant 1 refers to $m\Omega$. Thus in the relation $P = RI^m$, the y intercept must be multiplied by 1000 to be dimensionally consistent.

We can conclude that the empirical equation relating the data is $P = I^2R$. While this equation was already known, this example serves to demonstrate the utility of linearizing appropriate functions by using logarithms.

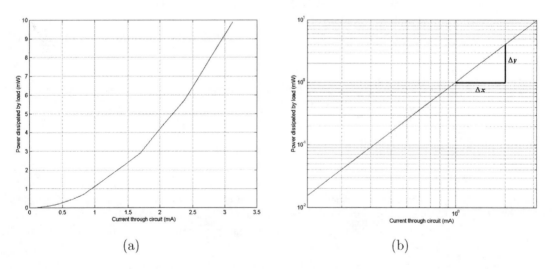

Figure 12.31   Current versus power dissipated by load: (a) square grid plot; (b) logarithmic (loglog) plot.

12.8.3 Semi-Logarithmic Plots: Exponential Equations

Certain physical relationships are governed by equations in *exponential form*,

$$y = bm^x. \tag{12.9}$$

When the data governed by the exponential form is plotted on a grid where the y axis is logarithmic and the x axis is linear a straight line will result. Taking the base 10 logarithm of Equation (12.9) gives:

$$\log y = \log b + x \log m. \tag{12.10}$$

Equation (12.10) is linear, but the slope, m, is given as a logarithm, whereas in Equation (12.7) it is linearly defined. In an exponential equation the slope is

$$\log m = \frac{\Delta \log y}{\Delta x}. \tag{12.11}$$

Hence, the slope is given by taking the antilog of Equation (12.11):

$$m = 10^{\frac{\Delta \log y}{\Delta x}}. \tag{12.12}$$

The y intercept, b, is located for the value of the graph corresponding to $x = 10^0$.

EXAMPLE 12.7

This example illustrates how to extract the constants b and m from a semi-logarithmic plot of data gathered to determine the half-life decay of radioactivity modelled by the exponential relationship $y = bm^x$. The data are plotted on a linear grid in Figure 12.32 (a), revealing an exponential form. The data are replotted on a semi-log grid in Figure 12.32 (b), giving a line that can be used to determine the constants b and m in the half-life exponential equation $R = C^t$, where R is the radioactivity in Roentgens, C is a proportionality constant (the product of the logarithmic y intercept, b, and the slope, m), and t is the time, measured in years.

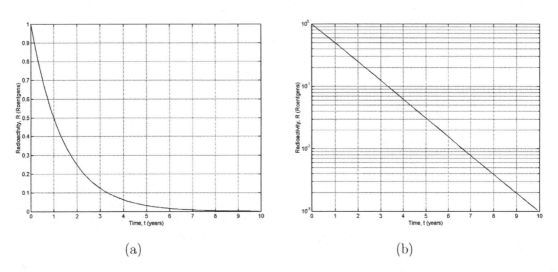

(a)   (b)

Figure 12.32   Half-life decay of radioactivity: (a) square grid plot; (b) semi-logarithmic (semilogy) plot.

Examining Figure 12.32 (b) the y intercept is seen to be $b = 10^0 = 1$. The slope is determined as:

$$\log m = \frac{\log \frac{1}{2} - \log 1}{1 - 0} = \log \frac{1}{2}. \tag{12.13}$$

The slope is thus

$$m = 10^{\log \frac{1}{2}}. \tag{12.14}$$

Substituting m back into Equation (12.9) gives

$$y = 10^{\log \frac{1}{2} x}. \tag{12.15}$$

Using the following identities

$$a^{rs} = (a^r)^s, \quad \log_b\left(\tfrac{1}{x}\right) = -\log_b x, \quad 10^{\log x} = x, \tag{12.16}$$

Equation (12.15) can be simplified to the desired exponential form of the empirical equation:

$$y = \left(10^{\log \frac{1}{2}}\right)^x = \left(10^{-\log 2}\right)^x = \left(10^{\log 2}\right)^{-x} = 2^{-x}. \tag{12.17}$$

12.8.4 Exponential Growth and Decay: Non-Linear Equations

An extremely important class of equations describes growth and decay characteristics of time-varying single variable systems. These equations are not linear on logarithmic or semi-logarithmic grids. But, they govern a broad range of heat transfer, charging, vibration, and many non-engineering type problems. These equations take the following form:

$$y = s + ae^{-(t/\tau)}, \tag{12.18}$$

where s is the *steady state* constant value (the asymptote of the flat portion of the curve in the upper right-hand side of Figure 12.35, a is a scaling constant, e is the irrational real number whose natural logarithm is 1 ($\ln e = 1$)[†], t is time, and τ is the time constant. For this class of empirical equation τ is defined to be the time it takes to reach $(e - 1)/e \approx 63\%$ of the steady state value, s. Note, t and τ must have the same units.

EXAMPLE 12.8

As a piece of metal heats up and cools down, its size changes proportionally. It is very important to know the *warm-up* characteristics of an industrial robot over the course of a continuous cyclic task. This is because the positioning capability of the robot changes as the motor gear boxes heat up and change the physical dimensions of the metal components.

Consider the KUKA KR-15/2 robot shown in Figure 12.33. The robot controller can move the six individual links that are serially connected by six independent *revolute joints*, i.e., joints that permit rotation about a single axis. It can be programmed to give the coordinate reference frame {E} any position and orientation within its workspace

---

[†]The numerical value for e may be approximated by evaluating the limit: $e = \lim_{h \to 0} (1 + h)^{1/h}$.

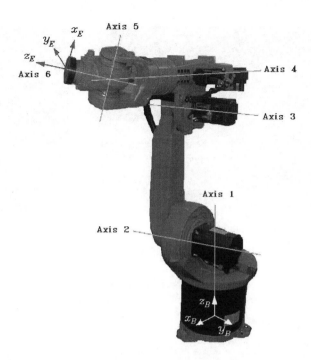

Figure 12.33   A KUKA KR-15/2 industrial robot.

relative to the non-moving base reference frame $\{B\}$. To compute the joint angles required to position and orient $\{E\}$ as desired, the controller uses a geometric model of the robot based on the *nominal* distances between the joint axes. There are relatively constant differences between the nominal distances and the actual values that are due to manufacturing tolerances and can be calibrated. However, dimensional expansion and contraction of the joints and links due to thermal effects is much more difficult to compensate for. It turns out that this type of behaviour is governed by Equation (12.18), and the constants can be determined empirically.

An experiment was devised to determine the thermal expansion behaviour of the KUKA robot shown in Figure 12.33 for a sequence of cyclically repeated motions starting with the robot components at room temperature [9]. Figure 12.34 are images of the robot taken with an infra-red camera. The small square areas in the figure are regions where average temperature measurements were extracted from the infra-red images. In an infrared thermal image the colours are calibrated to represent temperature. The robot was programmed to repeat a sequence of motions, and then present itself to the infra-red camera for temperature measurement. This was repeated for 15 hours (900 minutes).

Figure 12.34 (a) is the infra-red image at the beginning of the experiment, and Figure 12.34 (b) is the image at the end of the 15 hours of continuous motion. In (a) the robot has the same colour as the background, indicating no discernable difference in temperature between the robot and the environment. In (b) there is a noticeable difference between the robot and the background colour. This is an indication that the energy lost in the motors and gearboxes through friction has been transferred to the joints and links through the motor flanges as heat.

After the average temperature was extracted from the square regions in the thermal images, the time history of temperature change was plotted. The time history from the six areas on the upper arm of the robot are plotted in Figure 12.35 (a). The relatively flat curve on the bottom is room temperature, taken from the leftmost square area seen

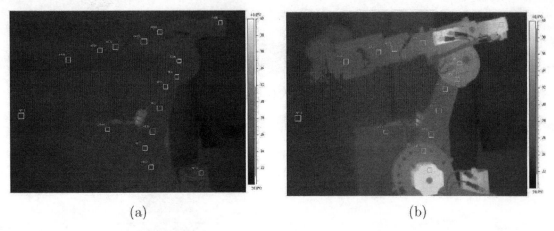

(a)   (b)

Figure 12.34   Infrared camera thermographs of robot: (a) cold start; (b) after 15 hours continuous operation.

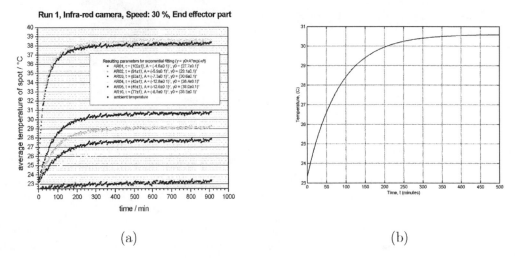

(a)   (b)

Figure 12.35   Empirical data plots: (a) heat-up curves of areas on the end effector; (b) heat-up curve of a single area.

in both Figures 12.34 (a) and (b). The heat-up empirical equations for each square region were then determined and a statistical mean was used to approximate the thermally induced dimensional distortion for the entire robot.

12.8.5 Implicit Empirical Equations

Empirical equations are not limited to explicit algebraic description of physical phenomena. They can be implicitly embedded in geometric models. Solid models created by CAD software packages are examples of implicit empirical equations.

EXAMPLE 12.9

Consider a typical cable connector, like the ones shown in Figure 12.36. An integrated optical-robotic system was developed to measure the external profile of arbitrarily shaped cable connectors for subsequent manufacture of a jig to hold the connectors accurately in place during an automated cable-tree assembly and wiring process [10]. The geometric model, a large array of the coordinates of discrete points, is essentially the empirical equation of the cable connector. That is, any desired point on the cable connector can be interpolated from the array.

Figure 12.36   A cable connector.

The required measurement information for creating a geometric model of the exterior features of a cable connector between the planes perpendicular to the pin ends and the wire input portal was obtained by stacking a series of horizontal cross sections of the connector. The sections were obtained by projecting a laser light plane onto the connector. A laser diode light source can be considered as a point, P. The projected laser line, created with special line optics, is a line that does not contain P. The laser plane is thus determined by the line and point P, as shown in Figure 12.37 (a).

A cable connector was mounted in a fixture such that its longitudinal axis was perpendicular to the plane of the laser line, illustrated in Figure 12.37 (b). The trace of the plane on the connector was viewed by a CCD camera. Both the laser and camera were mounted on a KUKA KR-15/2 robot. Since there are always some invisible features when seen from any particular vantage point, more than one view is necessary. For the experiment it was decided that eight views in the plane of the section were sufficient. The images were rectified using some elementary projective geometry [11] and the result is a

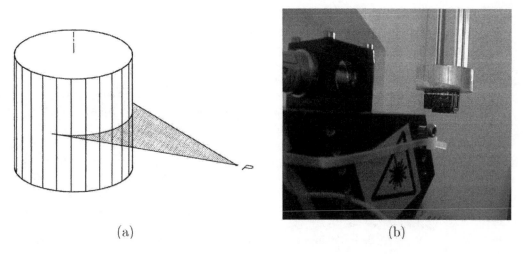

(a)   (b)

Figure 12.37   Laser light planes: (a) laser diode point light source conceptual model; (b) light plane trace on a cable connector.

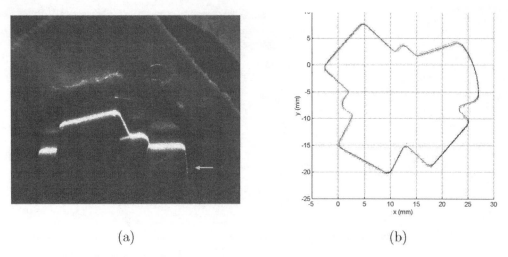

(a)   (b)

Figure 12.38   Planar cross section of cable connector: (a) CCD camera view; (b) reconstructed planar cross-section.

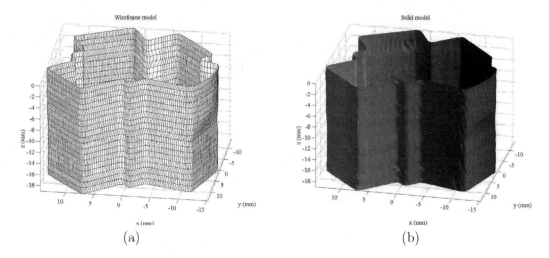

(a)   (b)

Figure 12.39   Implicit empirical equation: (a) wireframe; (b) solid model.

planar section of the connector yielding all of its external features. Figure 12.38 (a) is the CCD camera view of the connector from one vantage point, while Figure 12.38 (b) shows the rectified image of all eight views in one of the sections.

The measurements all took place about the axis of rotation of joint 1, axis 1 (see Figure 12.33), but this is not a necessary requirement. Once an initial robot assembly configuration had been attained, the measurements for an entire section (i.e., the trace of the object being measured in the plane of the laser line) was obtained. The plane of the laser line was chosen to be parallel to the xy-plane in the robot base frame, i.e. the floor.

Once the planar cross-sections were stacked and arranged on a axis, a wireframe solid was constructed in MATLAB. This is shown in Figure 12.39 (a). The solid model is shown in Figure 12.39 (b). This solid model is the implicit empirical equation of the cable connector shown in Figure 12.36.

12.9   REFERENCES

[1] R.M. Lueptow. *Graphics Concepts*. Prentice-Hall, Englewood Cliffs, N.J., 2000.

[2] J. Earle. *Engineering Design Graphics*, 10*th* edition,. Prentice-Hall, Englewood Cliffs, N.J., 2000.

[3] F. Klein. *Elementary Mathematics from an Advanced Standpoint: Geometry*. Dover Publications, Inc., New York, N.Y., U.S.A., 1939.

[4] D. Hilbert and S. Cohn-Vossen. *Geometry and The Imagination*, English translation by Nemenyi, P., of *Anschauliche Geometrie*, 1932. Chelsea Publishing Company, New York, N.Y., U.S.A., 1952.

[5] H.S.M. Coxeter. *Introduction to Geometry*, second edition. University of Toronto Press, Toronto, On., Canada, 1969.

[6] F. Klein. "Vergleichende Betrachtungen über neuere geometrische Forschungen, Erlangen", reprinted in 1893; *Mathematische Annalen*, vol. 43: pages 63–100, 1872.

[7] A. Cayley. "A Sixth Memoir Upon Quantics". *Philosophical Transactions of the Royal Society of London*, vol. 155: pages 725–791, 1859.

[8] I.M. Yaglom. *Felix Klein and Sophus Lie, Evolution of the Idea of Symmetry in the Nineteenth Century (translated by Sergei Sossinsky)*. Birkhäuser, Boston, Mass., U.S.A., 1988.

[9] M. Leitner, M.J.D. Hayes, R. Ofner, C. Sallinger, and P. O'Leary. "Thermal Effects and Consequences for Repeatability of an Industrial Robot". *Proc. 18th Canadian Congress of Applied Mechanics (CANCAM)*, St. John's NF. Canada, pages 299–300, 2001.

[10] M.J.D. Hayes, M. Leitner, R. Ofner, C. Sallinger, and P. O'Leary. "An Integrated Optical-Robotic Measurement System". *Proc. 18th Canadian Congress of Applied Mechanics (CANCAM)*, St. John's NF. Canada, pages 287–288, 2001.

[11] M.J.D. Hayes, P.J. Zsombor-Murray, and A. Gfrerrer. "Largest Ellipse Inscribing an Arbitrary Polygon". *Proceedings of the 19th Canadian, Congress of Applied Mechanics (CANCAM 2003)*, University of Calgary, Calgary, AB., Canada, pages 164–165, June 1–5, 2003.

Chapter 13

Freehand Sketching

OBJECTIVES

After reading this chapter, you should be able to

- Explain why freehand sketching is important in design
- Freehand sketch lines and circles
- Sketch an oblique 3-D projection
- Sketch an isometric 3-D projection
- Sketch an orthographic multiview projection
- Sketch an auxiliary view

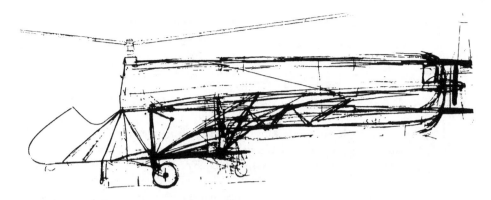

Figure 13.1   Helicopter inventor Igor Sikorsky's sketch of an early helicopter prototype demonstrates the visual impact of freehand sketching. (Used with permission of the Sikorsky Aircraft Corporation, Stratford, CT. © Sikorsky Aircraft Corporation, 2007. ["Straight Up," by Curt Wohleber, *American Heritage of Invention and Technology*, Winter, 1993, pp. 26–39.])

13.1   WHY FREEHAND SKETCHES?

An integral part of the creative design process is *ideation*, the generation of concepts or ideas to solve a design problem. Often freehand sketching can be used to explore and communicate mental concepts that come about in the mind's eye. The process of sketching can solidify and fill out rough concepts. Furthermore, sketching captures the ideas in a permanent form that can be used to communicate the concept to others. In this way, sketches often act as stepping stones to refine and detail the original concept or generate new ideas. Many great design ideas are first sketched on the back of an envelope or in a lab notebook, such as the freehand sketch of an early design of a helicopter by inventor Igor Sikorsky, shown in Figure 13.1.

While computers are the workhorses for engineering graphics, initially generating ideas on a computer display is rare. A more common scenario is sketching an idea on paper and subsequently refining the concept on paper using more rough sketches. This often occurs simply because all that is needed for a freehand sketch is a pencil and a paper. Freehand sketching *quickly* translates the conceptual image from the mind's eye to paper. Engineers often communicate via rough freehand sketches to refine and improve the design. Sketches are much more useful than detailed CAD drawings early in the design process, because they are informal, quickly and easily changed, and less restrictive. It is only after clarifying the design concept by iterating through several freehand sketches that it is possible to draw the object using computer graphics. In fact, often an engineer will sit down to create a CAD drawing of an object using a freehand sketch as a guide.

This chapter focuses on the rudimentary elements of freehand technical sketching, because in many ways freehand sketching is the first step in CAD.

13.2   FREEHAND SKETCHING FUNDAMENTALS

Freehand sketching requires few tools: just a pencil and paper. Sometimes it is helpful to use translucent paper, vellum, or tracing paper, to allow overlaying successive versions of a sketch, but this is not necessary. It may be tempting to use straight-edged triangles or rulers for drawing straight lines and a compass to draw circles. But these instruments often slow down the process and distract from the purpose of sketching, which is to create a

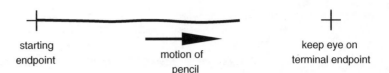

starting
endpoint

motion of
pencil

keep eye on
terminal endpoint

Figure 13.2   Sketching a line.

quick, rough graphical representation of the image in the mind's eye. Generally, sketching has three steps, although the steps are usually subconscious. First, the sketch is planned by visualizing it, including the size of the sketch on the paper, the orientation of the object, and the amount of detail to be included in the sketch. Second, the sketch is outlined using very light lines to establish the orientation, proportion, and major features of the sketch. Finally, sharpening and darkening object lines and adding details develops the sketch.

All sketches are made up of a series of arcs and lines, so the ability to draw circles and straight lines is necessary. A straight line is sketched in the following way. First, sketch the endpoints of the line as dots or small crosses. Then place your pencil on the starting endpoint. Keeping your eyes on the terminal point, use a smooth continuous stroke to draw the line between the points, as shown in Figure 13.2. Nearly horizontal or vertical lines are frequently easier to draw than inclined lines, so it may be helpful to shift the paper to draw the line horizontally or vertically. For long lines, it may be helpful to mark two or three points along the line and use the procedure between consecutive points or to make two or three shorter passes lightly with the pencil before a final darker line.

A circle can be sketched by using the steps illustrated on the left side of Figure 13.3. First, draw light horizontal and vertical lines crossing at the center of the circle. Second, lightly mark the radius of the circle on each line. Finally, connect the radius marks with a curved line to form a circle. Another technique is to lightly draw a square box the same size as the circle diameter, as shown on the right in Figure 13.3. Then lightly draw the diagonals of the box as well as the horizontal and vertical centerlines between the midpoints of the sides of the box. The diagonals and centerlines should intersect at the center of the circle. Mark the radius on the diagonals, and sketch the circle within the box. It is sometimes helpful to mark the radius on the edge of some scrap paper and mark the radius at as many points as desired, in addition to the marks on the centerlines and diagonals. Arcs are sketched in much the same way as circles, except that only a portion of the circle is sketched. It is generally easier to sketch an arc with your hand and pencil on the concave side of the arc.

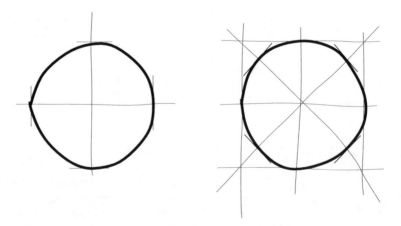

Figure 13.3   Sketching a circle.

13.3   BASIC FREEHAND SKETCHING

Many times, particularly during the conceptual stage of design, it is necessary to immediately communicate a graphical image to others. It has been said that some of the best design engineers are the ones who can sketch an idea clearly in a minute or so. The goal of the sketch in this case is not to show the details of the part, but to provide another person with a clear idea of the concept. For example, a design engineer may need to show a sketch to a manufacturing engineer to get input on the manufacturability of a part. If the concept is at an early phase, CAD drawings would not have been created yet. So the design engineer needs to use a freehand sketch of the part.

The sketch of Sikorsky's helicopter in Figure 13.1 exemplifies the power of freehand sketching. A brief glance at this sketch provides immediate insight into the concept that is being shown. One does not need to study the sketch to know what is being sketched, even if the viewer has never seen the concept before. These quick ideation sketches are not difficult to draw and require no artistic talent, just some practice.

Two types of pictorial sketches are used frequently in freehand sketching: oblique and isometric. The ***oblique projection*** places the principal face of the object parallel to the plane of the paper. The ***isometric projection*** tilts the part so that no surface of the part is in the plane of the paper. The advantage of the oblique projection is that details on the front face of the object retain their true shape. This often makes oblique freehand sketching easier than isometric sketching, where no plane is parallel to the paper. The disadvantage of the oblique projection is that it does not appear as "photorealistic" as an isometric projection. In other words, an isometric projection is similar to what a photograph of the object would look like.

13.3.1   Oblique Sketching

Often freehand sketching begins with light thin lines called ***construction lines*** that define enclosing boxes for the shape that is being sketched. Construction lines are used in several ways. First, the construction lines become the path for the final straight lines of the sketch. Second, the intersections of construction lines specify the length of the final lines. Third, points marked by the intersection of construction lines guide the sketching of circles and arcs. And finally, construction lines guide the proportions of the sketch. This last item is of crucial importance if the sketch is to clearly represent the object. For example, if an object is twice as wide as it is high, the proportions in the sketch must reflect this. Proper proportions of the boxes defined by the construction lines will result in proper proportions of the sketch.

An oblique freehand sketch is easy, since it begins with a two-dimensional representation of the front face of the object. Figure 13.4 shows the steps involved in quickly sketching a part with a circular hole.

Step 1: Horizontal and vertical construction lines are lightly drawn to outline the basic shape of the main face of the part. This is known as ***blocking in*** the sketch. If you are using a pencil or felt-tip marker, press lightly when drawing the construction lines to produce a thin or light line. If you are using a ball-point pen, draw a single light line.

Step 2: Sketch in the face of the part using the construction lines as a guide. How you sketch the outline of the part depends on the type of pen or pencil that you are using. The idea is to thicken the lines of the part, compared with the construction lines. If you are using a pencil or a felt-tip marker, pressing hard for the outline of the part will result in heavy or dark lines. If you are using a ball-point pen, the line width does not depend much on how hard you press. In this case, the outline of the

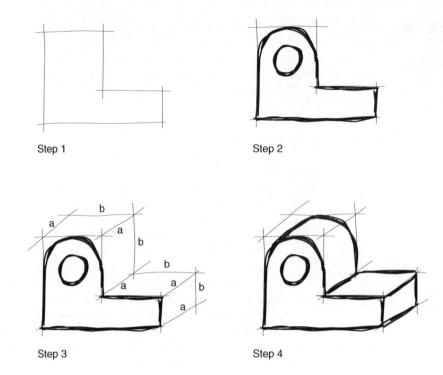

Step 1

Step 2

Step 3

Step 4

Figure 13.4　Creating a simple oblique freehand sketch.

part is sketched with a back-and-forth motion of the pen to thicken the lines of the part, compared with the construction lines as shown in Figure 13.4. The straight lines are usually sketched first, followed by the arcs. The circle for the hole in the part is added last to complete the face of the part.

Step 3: Sketch ***receding construction lines*** (lines labeled *a* extending into the plane of the paper, as shown in Figure 13.4) at a convenient angle. All of the receding lines must be parallel to each other and are usually at an angle of 30° to 45° with respect to the horizontal. The receding lines end at the appropriate depth for the object. Then add the vertical and horizontal lines (lines labeled *b* in the figure) at the back plane of the part. This blocks in the three-dimensional box enclosing the object.

Step 4: Sketch in and darken the lines outlining the part. Again, it is usually easiest to sketch in the straight lines first, then the arcs, and finally any details. Because the construction lines are light compared with the outline of the part, they are not erased.

The final sketch, while rough and lacking detail, clearly shows the design intent for the part.

13.3.2 Isometric Sketching

Isometric freehand sketches are somewhat more difficult to master than oblique sketches because no face is in the plane of the paper for an isometric projection. The steps to construct a simple freehand isometric sketch are shown in Figure 13.5.

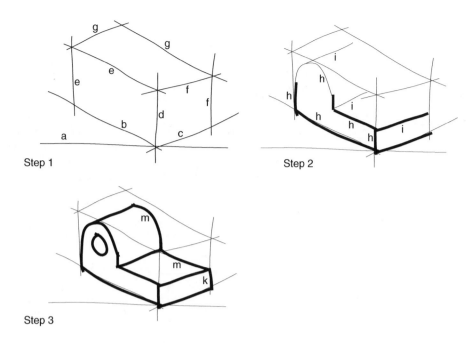

Figure 13.5   Creating a simple isometric freehand sketch.

Step 1: Sketch a light horizontal line (*a*). From this line, draw two intersecting lines at an angle of approximately 30° to the horizontal (*b* and *c*). Then draw a vertical line (*d*) through the intersection of the previous three lines. The three lines labeled *b*, *c*, and *d* form the isometric axes of the sketch. Next sketch the box to block in the front face of the part (*e*). These lines should be parallel to axes *b* and *d*. Similarly, sketch the lines to block in the right face (*f*), making sure that the lines are parallel to axes *c* and *d*. Finish this step by sketching lines parallel to the axes to complete the box that encloses the part (*g*).

Step 2: The outline for the front face is added by sketching in lines and curves (*h*). Then outline the front face using heavy lines. In this case, a single heavy line that can be produced from pressing hard on a pencil or felt-tip marker is used. Next, lines are sketched to indicate the depth of the features of the front view (*i*). These lines should be parallel to axis *c*. They can be darkened after they are drawn lightly.

Step 3: Finally, a line is added to complete the back corner of the part (*k*). Lines and arcs are added to complete the back face of the part (*m*). Then the hole detail is added. Circular holes appear as ellipses in isometric projections, as discussed in the next section.

The choice of whether to use an oblique projection or an isometric projection is often arbitrary. Because the oblique projection is easier to sketch, it is sometimes preferred. On the other hand, an isometric projection provides a more photorealistic image of the object.

13.4   ADVANCED FREEHAND SKETCHING

The sketching methods described in the previous section were focused on sketches in which the face of the object is in a single plane. Freehand sketching is somewhat more difficult when the face of the object is not in a single plane. The difficulty here is accurately depicting the depth of the object. Oblique and isometric projections are still useful, though somewhat more complicated than those in the previous section. In addition, orthographic projections are also valuable.

13.4.1 Oblique Sketching

The steps leading to an oblique freehand sketch of a more complicated object are shown in Figure 13.6. Because the face of the base of the object and the face of the upper portion of the object are in different planes, it is necessary to begin with a box that encloses the entire object before sketching either face. Some of the construction lines are removed after they are used in this example. This was done here to make the sketch clearer. However, it is not necessary in practice if the construction lines are initially drawn as light lines.

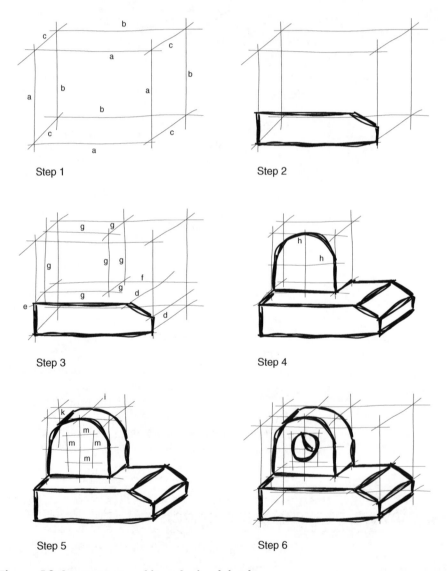

Figure 13.6   Creating an oblique freehand sketch.

Step 1: To begin, construction lines to form a box that encloses the object are drawn to block in the sketch. Notice that the front and back faces of the box are rectangular with horizontal and vertical sides. The receding construction lines are parallel and set at an angle of 30° to 45° to the horizontal. The easiest way to draw this box is to first draw the front rectangle (*a*). Then draw an identical second rectangle above and to the right of the first rectangle (*b*). Finally connect the corners with the receding construction lines (*c*).

Step 2: Now the front face of the base of the object can be sketched in the front rectangle. The lines are appropriately darkened.

Step 3: Certain features of the front face of the base extend backward along or parallel to the receding construction lines. For example, the lines (*d*) forming the chamfer (the angled cut on the right side of the base) can be sketched parallel to receding lines (*c*). Likewise, the receding line for the upper left corner of the base can be sketched (*e*). Then the base can be finished with a horizontal line on the back face (*f*). Now it is possible to block in the upper rounded portion of the object to create a box (*g*) that encloses the upper protrusion within the larger box that encloses the entire object.

Step 4: The front face of the upper portion of the object can be sketched in this box. Then receding lines corresponding to the chamfer and the left edge of the base can be darkened. In addition, the lines forming the back face can be sketched. Note that the line forming the back edge of the chamfer is parallel to the line forming the front edge of the chamfer. Construction lines (*h*) on the front face of the upper portion are drawn to the center of the circle for the hole.

Step 5: A receding construction line (*i*) extending from the peak of the front face to the plane of the back face is sketched to aid in aligning the curved outline of the back of the upper portion. The back face is identical to the front face except that it is shifted upward and to the right. This results in the left side of the back face being hidden. A darkened receding line (*k*) finishes the left side of the upper portion of the object. Finally, four construction lines (*m*) are sketched to block in the circle for the hole.

Step 6: Now the circular hole can be sketched in and darkened. It may help to draw diagonals to aide in sketching the hole. The back edge of the hole is also added to complete the sketch. The construction lines may be erased, but usually the construction lines are retained if they are made properly as light lines.

Oblique sketching is often aided by the use of graph paper with a light, square grid. The process is identical to that shown in Figure 13.6, but it is easier to keep the proportions correct by counting the number of boxes in the grid to correspond to the approximate dimensions of the part. Graph paper further improves the sketch by helping keep lines straight, as well as more accurately horizontal or vertical.

13.4.2 Isometric Sketching

Isometric freehand sketches of more complex objects start with an isometric box to block in the sketch. Then faces are sketched and additional features are blocked in. Finally details are added. The steps used to construct an isometric sketch are shown in Figure 13.7. Some of the construction lines are removed as the sketch proceeds, to make the sketch clearer for the purpose of this figure. Normally, removing construction lines is not necessary.

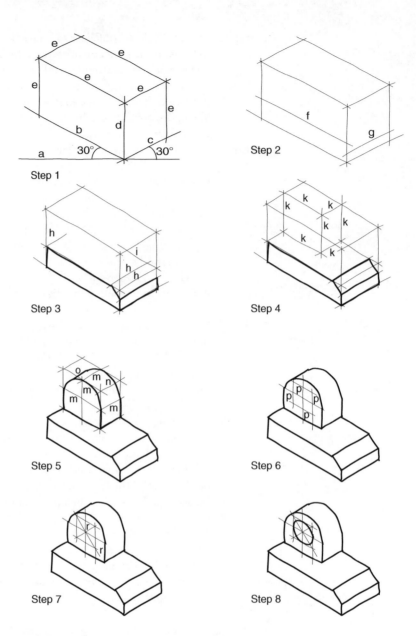

Figure 13.7   Creating an isometric freehand sketch.

Step 1: To begin, sketch a light horizontal line (*a*). From this line, draw two intersecting lines at an angle of approximately 30° to the horizontal (*b* and *c*) and a vertical line (*d*) through the intersection of the previous three lines to form the isometric axes of the sketch. Finish blocking in by sketching lines (*e*) to complete the box so that it will completely enclose the object. Unlike the oblique sketch, it is often better not to sketch hidden construction lines on the back side of the box when blocking in.

Step 2: Block in the front face of the part (*f*) so that the construction line is parallel to the isometric axis. Similarly, sketch the line to block in the right face (g). Note that the line on the right face (g) intersects the vertical line (d) at a lower point than the line on the front face (f), because of the chamfer on the right edge.

Step 3: Sketch the left face and the right face, and darken the lines. This completes the faces that are in the front planes of the box. Now sketch in three lines (h) parallel to the isometric axis (c). The left line (h) is the top edge of the base. The middle line (h) finishes the chamfer. The right line (h) is used to aid in sketching a construction line for the back edge of the base. Finish this step by sketching the construction line (i) along the back edge of the base.

Step 4: Now the face of the chamfer can be darkened and the angled line at the back edge of the chamfer can be added. This completes the angled face of the chamfer. Next the protrusion above the base can be blocked in with seven lines (k). It may help to sketch in the lines on the top face of the protrusion first, followed by the lines on the front face, and finishing with the lines on the right face.

Step 5: The front face of the upper protrusion is sketched first, using light lines. Construction lines (m) are added to help identify the locations of the endpoints of the arc for the front and back faces of the protrusion. The rounded rear face (n) is sketched lightly so that it is identical to the front face, except that part of it is not visible. The line at the top left edge of protrusion (o) is added. Then all lines forming the upper portion of the object are darkened. In addition, the line forming the top edge of the base on the back side is darkened along the construction line (i), up to where it meets the protrusion.

Step 6: The details related to the hole are added next. Circles in isometric projections are difficult to draw because they are seen at an angle and appear as ellipses with their major axes at an angle to the horizontal. The center of the hole is where two lines (m) intersect on the front face of the upper portion of the object. The lines (p) forming the parallelogram to enclose the ellipse for the hole are added. Each side of the parallelogram should be parallel to one of the isometric axes. The sides of the parallelogram should be equal to one another in length.

Step 7: To help in sketching the ellipse, construction lines forming the diagonals of the parallelogram (r) are added to the front face of the protrusion. These diagonals, which should be perpendicular to each other, will be along the major and minor axes of the ellipse.

Step 8: Now the ellipse that represents the circular hole can be sketched. A few simple points help in sketching ellipses more easily. The ellipse touches the parallelogram at the midpoints of the sides of the parallelogram. These midpoints are located where the lines (m) on the front face intersect with the lines (p) of the parallelogram. Start drawing the hole by sketching the gently curved arc between the midpoint at the top of the parallelogram and the midpoint on the right side of the parallelogram. Repeat for the gentle arc between the midpoints on the left side and the bottom side of the parallelogram. Continue by sketching a sharply curved elliptical arc between the midpoints of the parallelogram on the left side and the top side. Finish the hole by sketching the sharply curved arc between the midpoints on the bottom side and the right side. Finally, darken and make heavy the lines outlining the hole and any remaining edges of the part.

Isometric sketching is made substantially easier by the use of isometric grid paper. This paper has a grid of lines corresponding to lines *b*, *c*, and *d* in Figure 13.7. The procedure for using isometric grid paper is the same as that described above, but using the isometric grid paper keeps the proportions of the part consistent. One simply counts grid boxes to approximate the dimensions of the object. The grid paper also aids in sketching straight lines parallel to the isometric axes.

13.4.3 Orthographic Sketching

In some cases it is necessary to sketch orthographic projection views rather than oblique or isometric projections. Because orthographic views are two-dimensional representations, they are not as difficult to sketch as pictorial projections. But there are several techniques that make freehand sketching of orthographic views easier and more efficient. The process for sketching three orthographic views of the object in the previous two figures is shown in Figure 13.8.

Step 1: Begin by blocking in the front, top, and side views of the object using the overall width, height, and depth of the object. It is usually easiest to start with a ***bounding box*** of the front view that represents the outer dimensional limits of the front face of the object. Then extend the construction lines between views to properly align the views and maintain the same dimension in different views. For instance, line (*a*) represents the bottom edge and line (*b*) represents the top edge in both the front view and the right-side view. The distance between lines (*a*) and (*b*) is the height dimension in both views. The top view and right view can be thought of in terms of the projection of that side of the object onto the walls of a glass box and then unfolding the glass box to show the projections in the plane

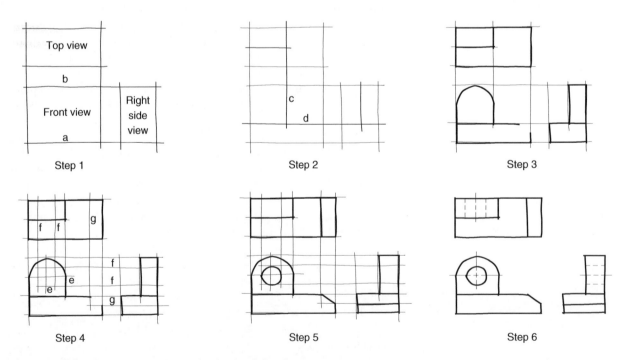

Figure 13.8 Creating an orthographic freehand sketch.

of the paper. The space between the views should be large enough so that the drawing does not look crowded and should be about the same for all views. Be sure that the left and right sides of the top view remain aligned with the left and right sides of the front view. Likewise, the top and bottom of the front and right views should be aligned.

Step 2: Block in the upper protrusion in all three views. Note that line (c) extends across the top and front views to ensure that the width of the protrusion is consistent in both views. It may help to think again in terms of the glass box. For instance, the top view should represent what the object looks like when viewed through the top wall of the glass box. Line (c), which blocks in the upper protrusion, extends to the front view to show the protrusion from that view. Likewise, line (d) extends across the front and right-side views to show the upper front edge in both views.

Step 3: The outline of the object is darkened to clearly show the shape of the object in all three views. Care must be taken in darkening lines. For instance, the right corner of the front view should not be darkened, because the detail of the chamfer has not yet been added.

Step 4: Construction lines for the holes and other details are added next. The center of the hole is positioned with construction lines (e). Then construction lines (f) that block in the hole are drawn. These construction lines extend between views to project the hole to the top view and to the right-side view. Construction lines extending between views (g) are also added for the chamfer.

Step 5: Now the hole and chamfer are sketched and darkened to show the completed object.

Step 6: Finally, centerlines (long-dash, short-dash) that indicate the center of the hole are added to all three views. For the top and right views, the centerlines extend along the axis of the hole. In the front view, the centerlines cross at the center of the hole. Hidden lines (dashed lines) that indicate lines hidden behind a surface are also added to the top and right views. Construction lines may be erased as was done in this figure, but that is not usually necessary.

The quality of the sketch can often be improved by using square grid graph paper to keep proportions and act as a guide for horizontal and vertical lines. Some engineers prefer to use a straight-edge to produce a nicer sketch, but this is usually not necessary with practice and sufficient care in sketching.

13.4.4 Sketching Auxiliary Views

When one of the faces of the part is at an angle to the orthographic planes, it may be necessary to sketch an *auxiliary view* so that the features on the angled face are not distorted. The view is based on the observer looking at the object along a ***line of sight*** that is perpendicular to the angled face. Sketching an auxiliary view seems quite challenging at first, but following a step-by-step approach makes it nearly as easy as sketching a standard orthographic view. Consider the object shown in Figure 13.9, having an angled face with a circular hole and keyway (rectangular cutout). Only the auxiliary view shows the circle without any distortion.

Details of sketching an auxiliary view vary, depending on the nature of the object to be sketched. However, Figure 13.10 shows the steps that would usually be used for the object shown in Figure 13.9, as an example.

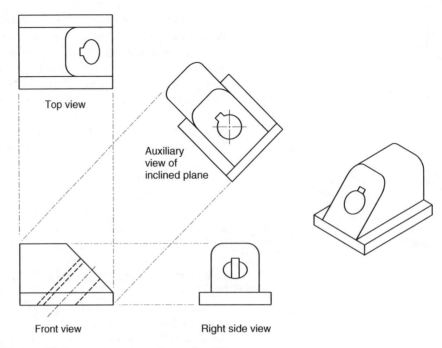

Figure 13.9 Auxiliary view of an inclined face.

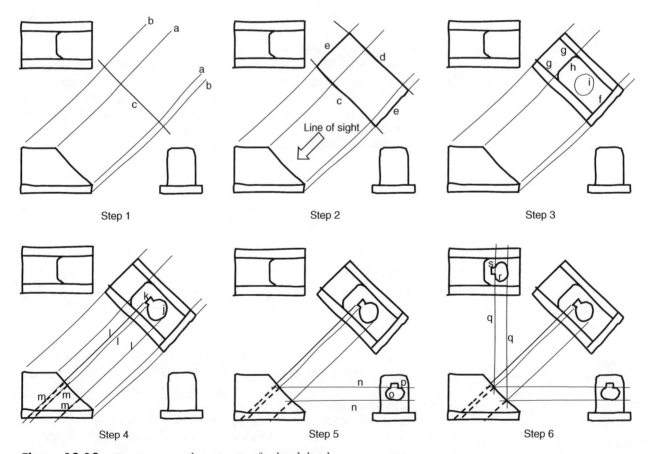

Figure 13.10 Creating an auxiliary view in a freehand sketch.

Step 1: The sketch begins with the three standard orthographic views with a few differences from the way they would normally be done. First, details on the inclined face are omitted from the views until later in the sketching process. In this case, the hole and keyway on the inclined face are not sketched. Second, the three views are separated by a substantial distance. The side view is spaced about twice its width from the front view. Likewise, the top view is spaced about two times its vertical dimension above the front view. This is done to provide space for the auxiliary view. Once these views are sketched, the sketch of the auxiliary view can be done. This begins by sketching two construction lines (*a*) that are perpendicular to the inclined face in the front view and are located at the upper and lower edges of the inclined face. Next, two additional construction lines (*b*) are added. These lines are parallel to the first construction lines and are located at the extreme upper left and lower right edges of the object. These lines will be used to block in the view in the auxiliary plane. The first edge of the object (*c*) is sketched perpendicular to the construction lines (*a*) and (*b*). This line can be drawn any convenient distance from the front view, but usually it is drawn to approximately line up with the lower edge of the top and the left edge of the side view, as shown.

Step 2: Now the outline of the object, as viewed along the line of sight perpendicular to the inclined face, can be blocked in by adding a construction line (*d*). Then the boundaries of the object are added by darkening lines (*c*), (*d*), and (*e*). These are sometimes called *silhouette lines* because they define the outer edges, or silhouette, of the part in the image plane as viewed looking toward the inclined surface in the direction of the arrow indicating the line of sight.

Step 3: The details of other edges evident in the auxiliary view can be added beginning with line (*f*) for the lower edge of the inclined face, followed by lines (*g*) that indicate the inside edges of the flanges, which protrude from either side of the main body of the part (most easily seen as the widest portions of the part in the side view). The curved upper edge (*h*) of the inclined surface can be sketched next. Finally, the circle for the hole (*i*) can be sketched. The hole appears circular in the auxiliary view, which, of course, is the reason for sketching the view in the first place—to show the inclined face and its features without distortion.

Step 4: The hole can be darkened (*j*) and the rectangular keyway (*k*) can be sketched next. Now that the features of the inclined plane have been sketched in the auxiliary view, they can be projected back to the other views. Lines (*l*) that bound the upper and lower portions of the hole and the upper extent of the keyway are drawn parallel to the other construction lines from the auxiliary view so that they extend across the front view. In the front view, these lines correspond to the hidden lines of the hole, which can be darkened as dashed lines (*m*).

Step 5: The upper and lower extent of the hole in the front view can be projected to the side view with construction lines (*n*). Once this is done, it is relatively easy to position and sketch the hole (*o*), which is elliptical in this view, and the keyway (*p*).

Step 6: In a similar way, construction lines (*q*) represent the leftmost and rightmost extents of the hole in the front view that can be projected to the top view. With these lines drawn, the elliptical hole (*r*) and keyway (*s*) are sketched to complete the drawing.

PROFESSIONAL SUCCESS: WILL FREEHAND SKETCHING EVER BECOME OBSOLETE?

CAD has almost totally eliminated pencil-and-paper drawings. But what about pencil and paper freehand sketching? Although many computers offer "paint" or "draw" programs, it is unlikely that freehand sketching will disappear soon. Just as it is easier to do a calculation in your head or on a piece of scratch paper rather than finding a calculator and punching in the numbers, it is easier to sketch an image on a piece of paper (or a napkin!) than to find a computer, log in, and start the appropriate program. Pencil-and-paper freehand sketches are quick, efficient, easily modified, and easily conveyed to others. And all that is needed is a pencil and a scrap of paper.

Even if the pencil and paper are totally replaced by laptop or handheld computers someday, freehand sketching skills will still be useful. Instead of using a pencil on a piece of paper, a stylus can be used on a touch screen. The only difference is the medium. The freehand sketching techniques themselves are unlikely to change much, although sketching software that automatically assists in generating oblique or isometric sketches as they are drawn is a logical enhancement to freehand sketching.

Notice how the auxiliary view is used to more accurately sketch the features (hole and keyway) that are on the inclined surface when they are projected to the front, side, and top views after the auxiliary sketch has been created. Of course, the technique for sketching auxiliary views depends on the nature of the object that is being sketched. For instance, if the inclined surface were on the left edge of the front view instead of the right edge, the auxiliary view would be sketched to the left and above the front view instead of to the right. Likewise, the examples shown in this chapter for oblique, isometric, and orthographic sketches only demonstrate the typical steps that can be used to generate freehand sketches. The exact steps that are used will vary with the details of the object that is being sketched. The steps in freehand sketching become more obvious with practice and experience.

KEY TERMS

Auxiliary view	Ideation	Receding construction
Blocking in	Isometric sketch	lines
Bounding box	Line of sight	Silhouette lines
Construction lines	Oblique sketch	

Problems

For Problems 1–9, the items shown in Figures 13.11, 13.12, and 13.13 are 2 inches wide, 1.5 inches high, and 1 inch deep. The holes in Figures 13.11b, 13.11c, 13.11d, 13.12c, and 13.12d are through holes. The hole in Figure 13.12b is through the front face only.

1.   Create freehand oblique sketches of the objects in Figure 13.11. (The objects are shown as oblique projections, so you must simply recreate the drawing by freehand sketching.)

2.   Create freehand oblique sketches of the objects in Figure 13.12. (The objects are shown as isometric projections.)

3.   Create freehand oblique sketches of the objects in Figure 13.13. (The objects are shown as orthographic projections.)

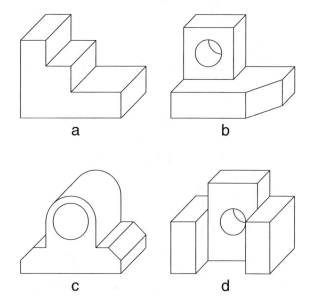

a   b

c   d

Figure 13.11

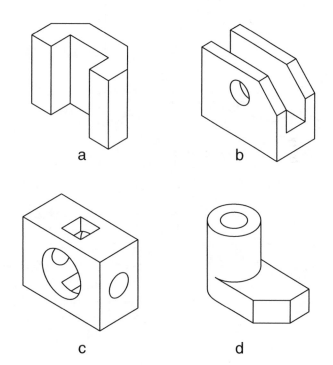

a   b

c   d

Figure 13.12

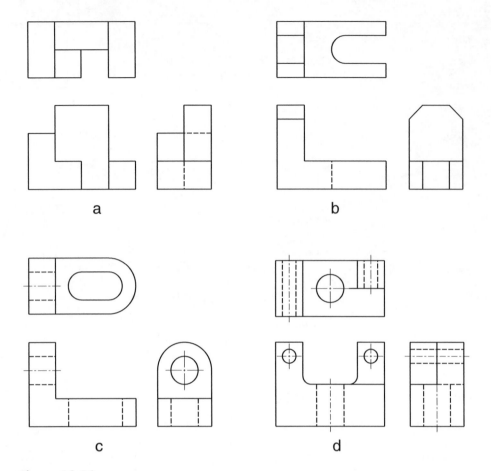

Figure 13.13

4. Create freehand isometric sketches of the objects in Figure 13.12. (The objects are shown as isometric projections, so you must simply recreate the drawing by freehand sketching.)

5. Create freehand isometric sketches of the objects in Figure 13.11. (The objects are shown as oblique projections.)

6. Create freehand isometric sketches of the objects in Figure 13.13. (The objects are shown as orthographic projections.)

7. Create freehand orthographic sketches of the objects in Figure 13.13. (The objects are shown as orthographic projections, so you must simply recreate the drawing by freehand sketching.)

8. Create freehand orthographic sketches of the objects in Figure 13.11. (The objects are shown as oblique projections.)

9. Create freehand orthographic sketches of the objects in Figure 13.12. (The objects are shown as isometric projections.)

10. Consider the pizza cutter shown in Figure 13.14. **(a)** Create a free-hand orthographic sketch of the guard (item 3) in the figure. **(b)** Create a free-hand orthographic sketch of the blade (item 6) in the figure.

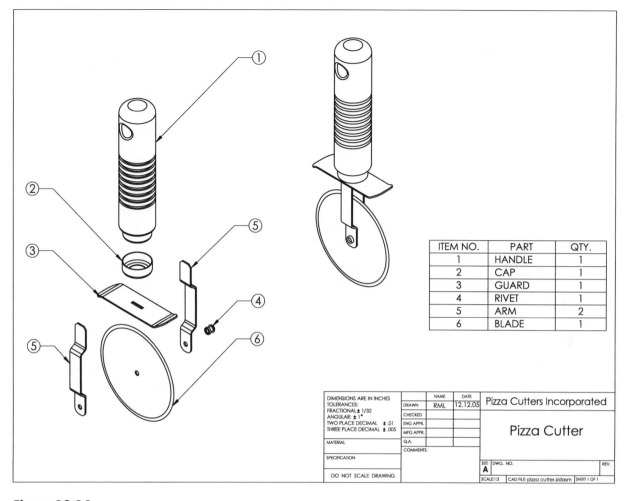

ITEM NO.	PART	QTY.
1	HANDLE	1
2	CAP	1
3	GUARD	1
4	RIVET	1
5	ARM	2
6	BLADE	1

DIMENSIONS ARE IN INCHES		NAME	DATE	Pizza Cutters Incorporated	
TOLERANCES: FRACTIONAL± 1/32 ANGULAR: ± 1° TWO PLACE DECIMAL ±.01 THREE PLACE DECIMAL ±.005	DRAWN	RML	12.12.05		
	CHECKED				
	ENG APPR.			Pizza Cutter	
	MFG APPR.				
MATERIAL	Q.A.				
	COMMENTS:				
SPECIFICATION				SIZE A DWG. NO.	REV.
DO NOT SCALE DRAWING				SCALE:1:3 CAD FILE: pizza cutter.sldasm SHEET 1 OF 1	

Figure 13.14

11.   (a) Create a freehand isometric sketch of a cube with a vertical circular hole centered in the top surface and extending through the cube. The diameter of the hole should be about one-half the length of the sides of the cube. (b) Create a free-hand isometric sketch of a cube with a vertical square hole centered in the top surface and extending through the cube. The sides of the hole should be one-half the length of the sides of the cube and should be oriented so they are parallel to the sides of the cube.

12.   Create a freehand orthographic sketch of a coffee mug. Only two views are necessary to fully represent the mug.

13.   Figure 13.15 shows several views of an object. Create a freehand sketch of the auxiliary view of the surface that is indicated.

14.   Figure 13.16 shows the dimensioned front view and several different corresponding right-side views, each with a horizontal width of 1 inch. Create a freehand sketch of the orthographic views (front, top, and right side) as well as an auxiliary view of the inclined surface for the corresponding right-side view.

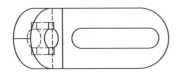

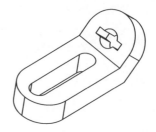

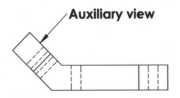

Auxiliary view

Figure 13.15

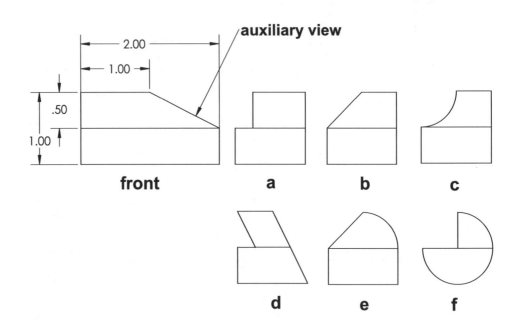

Figure 13.16

Chapter 14

Standard Practice for CAD Drawings

OVERVIEW

Drawing standards and conventions are used to clarify engineering drawings and simplify their creation. For example, standard sizes for drawings are used, and standard types and weights of lines designate different items on a drawing. Although CAD software automates most aspects of a drawing, many decisions are still up to the user. For example, the proper placement of dimensions on drawings is helpful in making the drawing more readable. In addition, internal or small details of the part can be displayed using special views. Screw threads are too detailed to be clear on most drawings, so standard representations are used for screw threads.

OBJECTIVES

After reading this chapter, you should be able to

- Explain why drawing standards are used
- Choose the proper sheet layout
- Read and understand the scale of a drawing
- Differentiate different linetypes used in engineering drawings
- Properly place dimensions on a drawing
- Read and understand section, auxiliary, and detail views on a drawing
- Read and understand screw thread designations on a drawing
- Read an assembly drawing

213

14.1   INTRODUCTION TO DRAWING STANDARDS

Not only is the accurate and clear depiction of details of a part necessary in an engineering drawing, but it is also necessary that the drawing conform to commonly accepted standards or conventions. There are two reasons for the existence of standards and conventions. First, using standard symbols and projections ensures a clear interpretation of the drawing by the viewer. An example of the problem of differing presentations is the use of the third-angle orthographic projection in North America and the first-angle orthographic projection elsewhere in the world. (The top and bottom views and the right and left views are reversed in third-angle and first-angle projections.) This can bring about confusion if, for example, a U. S. engineer tries to interpret a German drawing. A second reason for using conventions is to simplify the task of creating engineering drawings. For example, the symbol Ø associated with a dimension indicates that the dimension is a diameter of a circular feature. Without this convention, it would be more difficult to unambiguously represent diameter dimensions on a drawing.

Most CAD programs automatically use a standardized presentation of drawings, usually based on standards from the American National Standards Institute (ANSI; see **www.ansi.org**) in the United States and the International Standards Organization (ISO; see **www.iso.org**) in the rest of the world. Other standards that are often included as options in CAD software include BSI (British Standards Institution), DIN (Deutsches Institut für Normung, or German Institute for Standardization), GB (Guojia Biaozhun, Chinese standards), GOST (standards for the Commonwealth of Independent States of the former Soviet Union), and JIS (Japanese Industrial Standards). The differences between the commonly used standards are relatively minor, and are typically related to symbols that are used and the details of how dimensions or other items appear on a drawing. For example, Figure 14.1 shows the dimensions of a part in one view using both the ANSI and ISO standards. Notice that the numbers for the dimensions in the ANSI standard are ***unidirectional***, having the same orientation, whereas the values for the dimensions in the ISO drawing are ***aligned*** with the dimension line. Although the ISO standard may seem a bit harder to read, particularly for someone who usually uses the ANSI standard, both standards convey the same information. The BSI, DIN, GB, GOST, and JIS drawings look identical to the ISO drawing shown in Figure 14.1, although other minor details not shown in this drawing may differ.

Even with the use of CAD software to ensure standard presentation in drawings, it is up to the engineer to implement drawing standards in some cases. An example is in

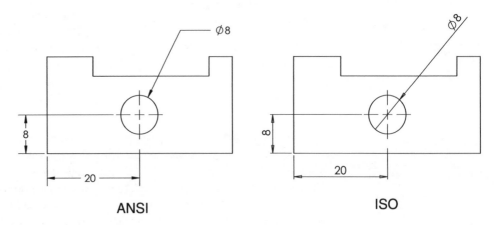

Figure 14.1   Drawings of the same object using the ANSI and ISO standards.

the placement of dimensions in a drawing. The user controls where dimensions appear on the drawing. Furthermore, even in cases where the CAD software automatically implements drawing standards, it is still necessary to understand what the conventions mean so that they are properly interpreted.

There is some variability among different CAD software packages in how various details are shown. For instance, the length of centerlines, the type of line used for hidden lines, and the shape of arrowheads may differ from one CAD software package to another. An example is the gray color sometimes used for hidden lines. Although hidden lines are generally shown as dashed lines in final drawings, they may be shown as gray or other colors while the part is being modeled. Another example is the length of the lines forming the cross at the center of the circle in Figure 14.1. These lines should normally be quite short to form a small cross, as shown in the figure. However, the length of these lines depends on settings in the software. If the user does not adjust the settings properly, the lines can be much longer or shorter. In most cases these variations are not significant. However, in this book, examples are shown that were created using different standard CAD packages, so they may differ slightly from one another in terms of these details.

14.2   SHEET LAYOUTS

Engineering drawings are created on standard-size sheets that are designated by the code indicated in Table 14.1. The ISO drawing sizes are just slightly smaller than ANSI sizes. Engineering drawings are almost always done in "landscape" orientation so that the long side of the drawing is horizontal. The choice of drawing size depends upon the complexity of the object depicted in the drawing. The drawing should be sized so that the projections of the part, dimensions, and notes all fall within the borders of the drawing with adequate spacing, so that the drawing is not cluttered. The drawing should be large enough so that all details are readily evident and readable. As a result, regardless of the physical size of the part, simple parts are usually drawn on smaller sheets because it is not necessary to show much detail. Complex parts are usually drawn on larger sheets so that there is room to show adequate detail. When using CAD software, it is necessary to consider the printed drawing size in addition to the drawing size on the computer screen. On the computer screen, it is possible to zoom in to read detailed items, but this cannot be done for a printed drawing. Consequently, the sheet size should be chosen carefully.

TABLE 14.1   Standard Sheet Sizes.

ANSI	ISO
A—8.50″ × 11.00″	A4—210 mm × 297 mm
B—11.00″ × 17.00″	A3—297 mm × 420 mm
C—17.00″ × 22.00″	A2—420 mm × 594 mm
D—22.00″ × 34.00″	A1—594 mm × 841 mm
E—34.00″ × 44.00″	A0—841 mm × 1189 mm

The *title block* on a drawing records important information about the drawing. Normally the title block of a drawing is in the lower right corner of the drawing. ANSI standard title blocks can be used, but often individual companies use their own standard title block. The title block, such as the one shown in Figure 14.2, is used primarily for drawing control within a company. The title block includes information regarding the part depicted in the drawing, such as its name and part number; the person who created the drawing; persons who checked or approved the drawing; dates the drawing was created,

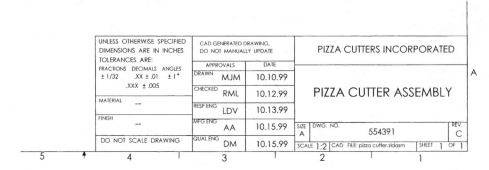

Figure 14.2   A typical title block.

revised, checked, and approved; the drawing number; and the name of the company. This information allows the company to track the drawing within the company if questions arise about the design.

Other information can appear in the title block to provide details about the manufacture of the part, such as the material for the part, the general tolerances, the surface finish specifications, and general instructions about manufacturing the part (such as "remove all burrs"). Many times, though, this information is shown as notes on the drawing rather than in the title block.

Finally the title block provides information about the drawing itself, such as the units used in dimensioning (typically inches or millimeters) and the scale of the drawing. The **scale** of the drawing indicates the ratio of the size on the drawing to the size of the actual object. It can be thought of as the degree to which the object is enlarged or shrunk in the drawing. Scales on drawings are denoted in several ways. For instance, consider an object that is represented in the drawing as half of its actual size. Then the drawing is created such that 1 inch on the drawing represents 2 inches on the physical object. This can be reported in the Scale box in the title block as HALF SCALE, HALF SIZE, 1 = 2, 1:2, or $1/2'' = 1''$. In the numerical representations, the left number is the length on the drawing and the right number is the length of the actual object. A part that is drawn twice as large as its physical size would be denoted as DOUBLE, 2× (denoting "2 times"), 2 = 1, or 2:1. In some cases, such as architectural drawings, the scale can be quite large. For instance, $1/4'' = 1'-0''$ corresponds to a scale of 1:48, where " denotes inches and ' denotes feet. Common scales used in engineering drawing are 1 = 1, 1 = 2, 1 = 4, 1 = 8, and 1 = 10 for English units and 1:1, 1:2, 1:5, 1:10, 1:20, 1:50, and 1:100 for metric units. A 1:1 scale is often specified as FULL SCALE or FULL SIZE.

14.3   LINES

The types of lines used in engineering drawing are standardized. Different linetypes have different meanings, and understanding these different types of lines makes interpreting drawings easier. The linetypes vary in thickness and in the length and number of dashes in dashed lines. Most CAD software automatically produces linetypes that correspond to the way the line is used in the drawing. Figure 14.3 shows some of the more commonly used linetypes:

- **Visible lines** (thick, solid lines) represent the outline of the object that can be seen in the current view.
- **Hidden lines** (thin, dashed lines) represent features that are hidden behind surfaces in the current view.

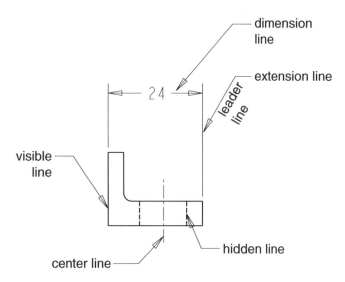

Figure 14.3   Types of lines used in drawings.

- *Centerlines* or *symmetry lines* (thin, long-dash/short-dash lines) mark axes of rotationally symmetric parts or features.
- *Dimension lines* (thin lines with arrowheads at each end) indicate sizes in the drawing.
- *Extension lines* or *witness lines* (thin lines) extend from the object to the dimension line to indicate which feature is associated with the dimension.
- *Leader lines* (thin, solid lines terminated with arrowheads) are used to indicate a feature with which a dimension or note is associated.

Other linetypes are used for break lines (lines with zigzags) that show where an object is "broken" in the drawing to save drawing space or reveal interior features and cutting plane lines (thick lines with double short dashes and perpendicular arrows at each end) that show the location of cutting planes for section views. The arrowheads for dimension lines, leader lines, and other types of lines may be filled or not filled, depending on the CAD software. Many engineering graphics textbooks prefer filled arrowheads.

It is common in technical drawings that two lines in a particular view coincide. When this occurs, a convention known as the *precedence of lines* dictates which line is shown: visible lines have precedence over hidden lines, which have precedence over centerlines. An example is shown in Figure 14.4. In the top view, line A is shown as a solid visible line, since the visible line that forms the top left edge has precedence over the dashed hidden line for the side of the hole. Line B of the top view is shown as a dashed hidden line, since it has precedence over the centerline of the hole. Likewise, line C in the side view is shown as a visible line, since the edge on the right side has precedence over the centerline of the hole. Visible lines, hidden lines, and centerlines all have precedence over extension lines.

Conventions also exist for the intersection of lines in a drawing. For instance, an extension line is always drawn so that there is a slight, visible gap between its end and the outline of the object, as shown in Figure 14.3. Similarly, *center marks* appearing at the center of a circle are drawn so that the short dashes of each line intersect to form a small cross, as shown in Figure 14.5. Fortunately, CAD software automatically takes care of most of the details related to lines, as well as their length and position. The engineer or designer need only know how to properly interpret the various linetypes.

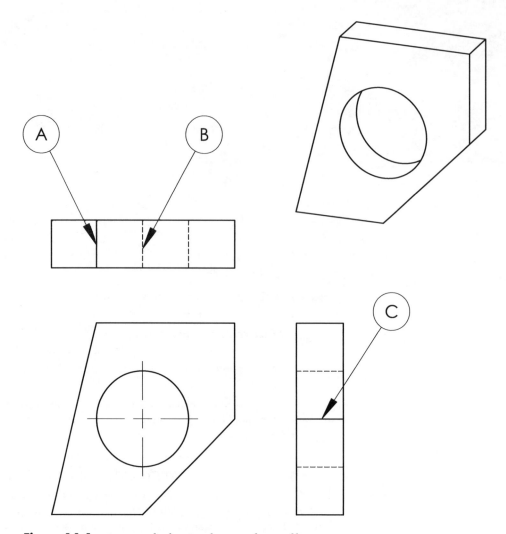

Figure 14.4   An example showing the precedence of lines.

14.4   DIMENSION PLACEMENT AND CONVENTIONS

Engineering drawings are usually drawn to scale, but it is still necessary to specify numerical dimensions for convenience and to ensure accuracy. In general, sufficient dimensions must be provided to define the geometry of the part precisely, but redundant dimensions should be avoided. Furthermore, dimensions on the drawing should reflect the way the part is made or the critical dimensions of the part. For example, Figure 14.5 shows three drawings of a plate with two holes. Figure 14.5a is ***overdimensioned***, having one redundant dimension. It is clear that, given the distances from the left edge to the left hole, the distance from the right edge to the right hole, and the overall width of the plate, the distance between the holes has to be 6 mm. Thus, the 6-mm dimension could be omitted. However, the dimensions that are shown in the drawing often suggest which dimensions are most important. If the 6-mm dimension in Figure 14.5a were omitted, it would suggest that the distance between each hole and the nearest edge of the plate is more important than the distance between the holes. But suppose, instead, that the distance between the holes is critical. This might be necessary if the holes in the plate are supposed to align with another part. Then the dimensions shown in Figure 14.5b

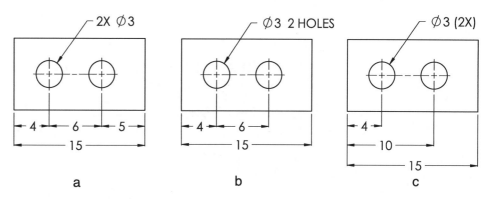

Figure 14.5   (a) An overdimensioned drawing; (b) A dimensioning scheme that emphasizes the 6-mm distance between the holes; (c) A dimensioning scheme that emphasizes the distance from the left edge to each hole.

would clearly indicate that the distance between the holes is the most important dimension by omitting the dimension from the right hole to the right edge. Figure 14.5c indicates that the distance from the left edge to each hole, not the distance between the holes, is critical. The engineer or designer must consider the optimal way to display dimensions to clearly convey which dimensions are most important.

The position of the dimensions is also important. Figure 14.6 shows several examples of incorrect ways of dimensioning a drawing. It is best to avoid having dimensions inside the boundary of the object, as is the case in Figure 14.6a. Dimensions should be kept outside the boundaries of the object whenever possible, unless clarity is improved in some way by having them inside the boundary. Dimension lines should not be too close to the boundaries of the object, as is the case with the 40-mm dimension in Figure 14.6b. A typical spacing is 10 mm ($\frac{3}{8}$ inch) for the distance of the first dimension from the object and 6 mm ($\frac{1}{4}$ inch) for the spacin.ween subsequent dimensions. It is also difficult to interpret the drawing when the dimension line coincides with a visible line of the object, as is the case in Figure 14.6b for the 20-mm dimension (the dimension line coincides with the center mark line) and the 25-mm dimension (the dimension line looks like a continuation of the upper boundary of the part). In Figure 14.6c, the dimensions are in a random order with some smaller dimensions farther from the boundary of the object (such as the 10-mm dimension) than larger dimensions (such as the 40-mm dimension). This results in dimension lines crossing extension lines, which should be avoided. It is often helpful to stack the dimensions in order of increasing length as shown in Figure 14.6d. However, there are three problems in this case. First, placing the dimension numbers right above one another is somewhat difficult to read. Second, there is a redundant dimension—the 5-mm dimension is unnecessary. Third, the 10-mm dimension is so small that there is no dimension line, and only the arrowheads appear. This is readily corrected by placing the arrowheads outside of the extension lines instead of inside, as shown in Figure 14.6e. In addition, in this case the dimension numbers are staggered, or offset, by a small amount to make them more easily readable. All the dimensioning conventions are aimed at making the drawing as easily readable as possible so that the information on the drawing is conveyed clearly to the reader.

It is natural for a person reading the drawings to look for the dimensions of a feature in the view where the feature occurs in its most characteristic shape and where it is visible (as opposed to hidden). This is known as ***contour dimensioning***. For example, the location and size of a hole should be dimensioned in the view where the hole appears as a circle. Likewise, it is best to show the overall dimensions of the object in a view that

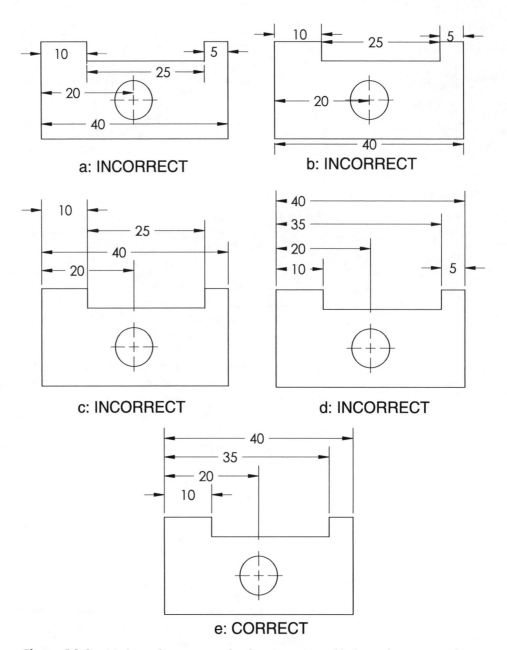

Figure 14.6 (a) Placing dimensions on the object is incorrect; (b) Placing dimensions so that dimension lines align with visible lines of the object or are very close to the object is incorrect; (c) Placing dimensions in random order is incorrect; (d) Overdimensioning is incorrect; (e) A properly dimensioned drawing.

is most descriptive of the object. If possible, both the horizontal and vertical location of a feature should be dimensioned in the same view. The upper part of Figure 14.7 shows an object properly dimensioned in millimeters to show the relation of the dimensions to the features in the most obvious manner. In the lower part of Figure 14.7, the dimensioning has several problems. The overall vertical dimensions of the L-shaped profile, the 8- and 35-mm dimensions, are shown on the right view where it is not clear that the object is L-shaped. The diameter of the hole is shown in a view where the hole is shown

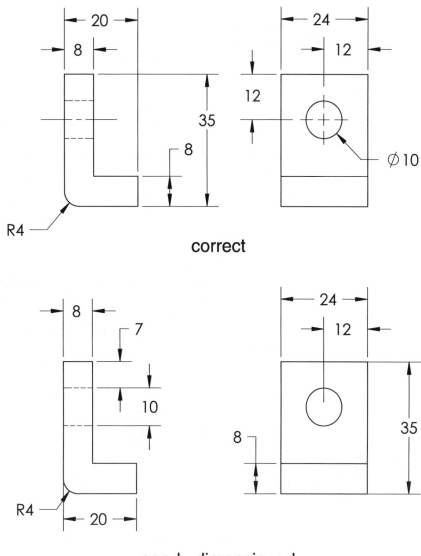

correct

poorly dimensioned

Figure 14.7 Properly and improperly dimensioned drawings.

only as a pair of parallel hidden lines, not as a circle. And the vertical location of the hole is shown in one view, while the horizontal location is shown in another view. Finally, the vertical location of the hole is shown as a distance to its edge (the 7-mm dimension). Generally, the locations of holes should be dimensioned to the center of the hole.

The conventions for millimeter and inch dimensioning are different. For millimeter dimensioning, dimensions less than 1 mm have a zero preceding the decimal point, and integer dimensions may or may not include a decimal point and following zeros. Thus, legitimate millimeter dimensions are 0.8, 6, 8.00, and 1.5. Inch dimensions do not include a zero before the decimal point for values less than 1 inch. Zeros to the right of the decimal point are usually included. Legitimate inch dimensions are .800, 6.00, 8.00, and 1.500. For both millimeter and inch dimensions, the number of digits to the right of the decimal point may be used to indicate the tolerance (acceptable variation). It is standard practice to omit the units for dimensions. However, it is wise to note the units in the title block or as a note on the drawing.

Circles and arcs are dimensioned using special symbols and rules. A radius is denoted using a leader line with an arrow pointing at the arc, as shown in the upper portion of Figure 14.7. Sometimes a small cross is placed at the center of the radius. The position of the center should be dimensioned unless the radius is for a rounded edge, in which case the arc is positioned by virtue of being tangent at its ends to the sides forming the corner that is rounded, as shown in Figure 14.7. The dimension for a radius begins with a capital letter R to indicate radius. Full circles are dimensioned using the diameter with a leader line having an arrow pointing at the circle, as shown in Figures 14.1 and 14.7. If space permits, the leader line can extend across a diameter of the circle with arrows at each end of the diameter. The dimension for a diameter begins with the Greek letter phi (Ø) to indicate diameter. The location of the center of the circle must also be dimensioned.

Sometimes maintaining clarity makes it preferable to dimension several concentric circles from a side view, where the circle does not appear as a circle, thus violating the rule to dimension a feature in its most characteristic shape. This also permits the depth of the feature to be indicated along with the diameter in the same view of the object. Figure 14.8 shows how concentric circles can be dimensioned from a side view. The diameter dimensions to the left use Ø to indicate diameter. The dimensions above the object indicate the length of the features corresponding to particular diameters along the axis.

Angles are dimensioned as decimals or in degrees and minutes (60 minutes is one degree), so that 32.5 and 32°30′ are equivalent, where ′ indicates minutes. The dimension line for an angle is drawn as an arc with its center at the apex of the angle, as shown in Figure 14.9a. Here a combination of angles and length dimensions are used to fully dimension the object. Note that the arrows are "inside" for the 76° dimension and "outside" for the 45° dimension. Either type can be used, depending on the space available

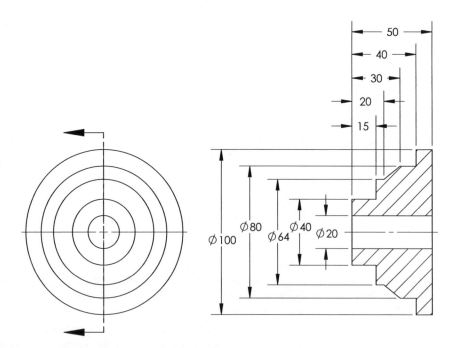

Figure 14.8 Proper dimensioning of concentric circles.

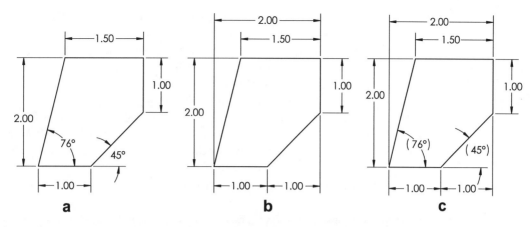

Figure 14.9   (a) Properly dimensioned object using angles; (b) Properly dimensioned object without using angles; (c) Angles are in parentheses to indicate that they are reference dimensions.

and readability. Figure 14.9b shows how the same shape can be dimensioned without using any angles. In some ways, this figure is less clear than Figure 14.9a, because some extension lines cross and there are more dimension lines. At first glance, it may appear that Figure 14.9b is overdimensioned, since the 2-inch dimension on the top is simply the sum of the two 1-inch dimensions on the bottom. However, strictly speaking, all of these dimensions are necessary. If the lower right 1-inch dimension were omitted, the upper-right corner of the object would not necessarily be constrained to be 90°. In practice, when lines are drawn at right angles, a 90° angle is usually implied, so the lower right 1-inch dimension could be omitted without creating any ambiguity. Figure 14.9c shows the length dimensions in addition to the angles. While this drawing is **overdimensioned**, the display of the angles may aid in clarifying the dimensions for the reader of the drawing. Whether to include extra dimensions depends on what critical aspects of the dimensions need to be indicated on the drawing. If it is necessary that the angle in Figure 14.9c be exactly 45°, then this angle should be specified on the drawing and the 1-inch horizontal dimension should be in parentheses to indicate it is a ***reference dimension*** provided for convenience to the reader. On the other hand, if the 1-inch dimension is critical, it should be indicated on the drawing and the angle could be provided as a reference dimension for convenience, as shown in Figure 14.9c. Reference dimensions are provided only for information to help in interpreting the drawing. They are not intended to be measured or to be used to govern the manufacture of the part. Generally, it is preferable to show the dimensions in the clearest form possible. For this object, Figure 14.9a is superior to the other dimensioning schemes by using the fewest dimensions that overlap the least.

Multiple features that are identical need not be individually dimensioned. For example, the diameter of the two 3-mm holes in Figure 14.5a are dimensioned with a leader line to one hole with the dimension 2 × Ø3. The 2× indicates "two times." Alternative dimensions are Ø3 (2×), Ø3 2 PLACES, or Ø3 2 HOLES.

There are several other "rules" for dimensioning:

- Dimension lines should be outside of the outline of a part whenever possible.
- Dimension lines should not cross one another.
- Dimensions should be indicated on a view that shows the true length of the feature. This is particularly important when dimensioning features that are on a surface that is at an angle to the plane of the orthographic view.

- Each feature should be dimensioned only once. Do not duplicate the same dimension in different views.
- Dimension lines should be aligned and grouped when possible to promote clarity and uniform appearance. See, for example, the placement of the horizontal dimensions in Figure 14.6e.
- The numerical dimension and arrows should be placed between the extension lines where space permits. If there is space only for the dimension, but not the arrows, place the arrows outside of the extension lines. When the space is too small for either the arrows or the numerical value, place both outside of the extension lines. See Figure 14.7 for examples.
- Place the dimension no closer than about 10 mm ($\frac{3}{8}$ inch) from the object's outline.
- Dimensions should be placed in clear spaces, as close as possible to the feature they describe.
- When dimensions are nested (such as the horizontal dimensions in Figure 14.6e), the smallest dimensions should be closest to the object.
- Avoid crowding dimensions. Leave at least 6 mm ($\frac{1}{4}$ inch) between parallel dimension lines.
- Extension lines may cross visible lines of the object.
- Dimensions that apply to two adjacent views should be placed between the views, unless clarity is enhanced by placing them elsewhere. The dimension should be attached to only one view. Extension lines should not connect two views.
- Dimension lines and extension lines should not cross, if possible. Extension lines may cross other extension lines.
- A centerline may be extended to serve as an extension line, in which case it is still drawn as a centerline.
- Centerlines should not extend from one view to another view.
- Leader lines are usually sloped at about 30°, 45°, or 60° and are never horizontal or vertical.
- Numerical values for dimensions should be approximately centered between arrowheads unless several dimensions are nested, as in Figure 14.6e. In this case, dimensions should be staggered.
- When a rough, noncritical dimension (such as a round) is indicated on a drawing, add the note TYP to the dimension to indicate that the dimension is "typical" or approximate.
- Sometimes it is helpful to include a ***reference dimension*** that is redundant or otherwise unnecessary, but is included for the convenience of the person reading the drawing. Such dimensions are usually in parentheses.

14.5   SECTION VIEWS

The cutaway view of a device appeared first in various forms in the 15th and 16th centuries to show details of parts hidden by other elements. These cutaway views have evolved to ***section views*** in which interior features that cannot be effectively displayed by hidden lines are exposed by slicing through a section of the object. To create a section view, a cutting plane is passed through the part and the portion of the part on one side of the cutting plane is imagined to be removed. In a section view, all visible edges and contours behind the cutting plane are shown. Hidden lines are usually omitted. The portion of the object that is sliced through is designated with angled crosshatch lines known as section lining.

Section views are easily demonstrated by considering a block with a hole that has a large diameter part way into it and a smaller diameter through the remainder of it, as shown in Figure 14.10a. In this case, the object is sectioned along a cutting plane parallel to the right and left sides of the block and through the center of the hole, as indicated in Figure 14.10b. If the right half is cut away, the remaining portion of the object looks like Figure 14.10c, revealing the cross section at the cut that clearly shows the two diameters of the hole. In a drawing, the cross section is defined and shown schematically by using two views, as shown in Figure 14.10d. Key to the interpretation of a section view is the clear representation of where the cutting plane is and from which direction it is viewed. This is accomplished using a ***cutting plane line*** (long dash, short dash, short dash, long dash, with perpendicular arrows at each end). The cutting plane line, A-A, shows where the cutting plane passes through the object in the front orthographic view. The arrows on either end of the cutting plane line show the direction of the ***line of sight*** for the section view. Thus, the section view shown to the right of the front view is what the viewer would see if the portion of the object that is "behind" the

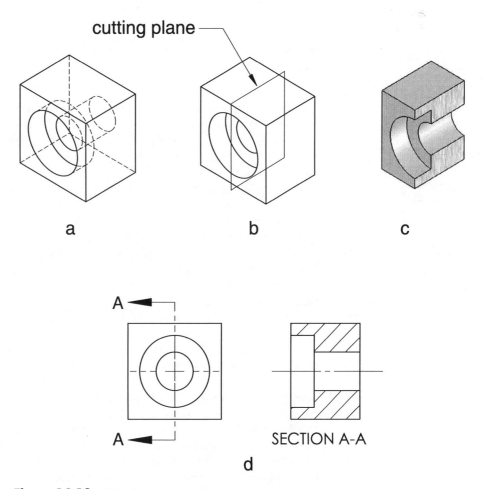

Figure 14.10   Creating a section view.

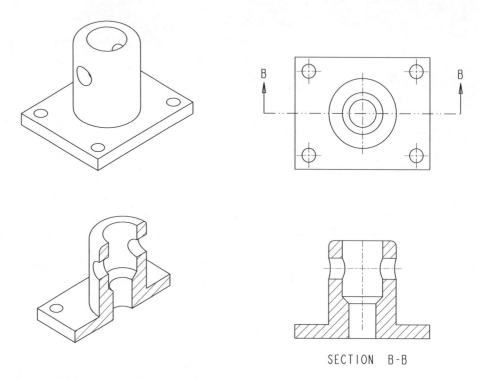

SECTION B-B

Figure 14.11   The full section is the orthographic view at the lower right.

direction that the arrows are pointing is removed. The section view is placed to the right of the front view to be consistent with the convention of the third-angle projection (as if unfolding the glass box after the portion of the object is removed). The two diameters of the hole are evident, with the surface where the material has been "cut" away shown as ***crosshatched*** having angled, parallel lines drawn on the surface that was cut. This view is designated SECTION A-A to correspond to the cutting plane line A-A. This type of section in which a single plane goes completely through an object is known as a ***full section***.

A slightly more complicated example of a full section is shown in Figure 14.11. The whole object is shown in the upper-left portion of the figure, and the sectioned object is shown with a portion removed just below it. The right side of the figure shows a top view of the object with the cutting plane displayed. Imagine that the material on the side of the cutting plane in the direction the arrows are pointing is retained, and the material behind the arrows is removed. Then the projection of the retained portion appears as SECTION B-B when viewed in the direction of the arrows.

Much more sophisticated section views can be created for complicated parts. In all cases, though, clear definition of the cutting plane line and the direction of the line of sight for the view are critical. For example, Figure 14.12 shows a ***half section*** of the same part. The cutting plane extends halfway through the object to show the interior of one half of the object and the exterior of the other half. This type of section is ideal for symmetrical parts in which it is desired to show internal and external features in a single view. When only a portion of the object needs to be sectioned to show a particular internal detail, a ***broken-out section*** like that shown in Figure 14.13 can be used. A break line separates the sectioned portion from the unsectioned portion, but no cutting plane line is drawn.

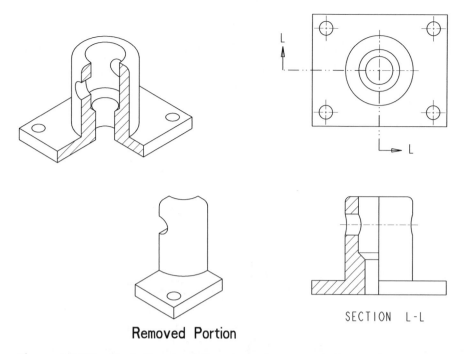

Removed Portion

SECTION L-L

Figure 14.12   The half section is the orthographic view at the lower right.

An ***offset section*** like that shown in Figure 14.14 is used to show internal details that are not in the same plane. The cutting plane for offset sections is bent at 90° angles to pass through important features. Only the segments of the cross section that would be visible when projected along the line of sight are shown in section H-H; the changes of

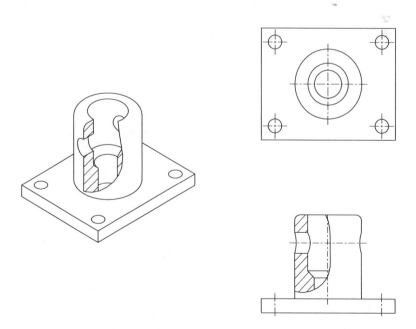

Figure 14.13   The broken-out section is the orthographic view at the lower right.

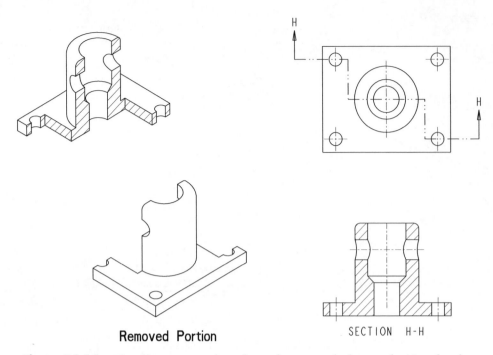

Removed Portion

SECTION   H-H

Figure 14.14   The offset section is the orthographic view at the lower right. Note that the horizontal holes in the cylindrical upper portion of the part have curved edges in the section view due to the shape of the part, whereas the vertical holes in the flat flange at the bottom of the part have straight edges.

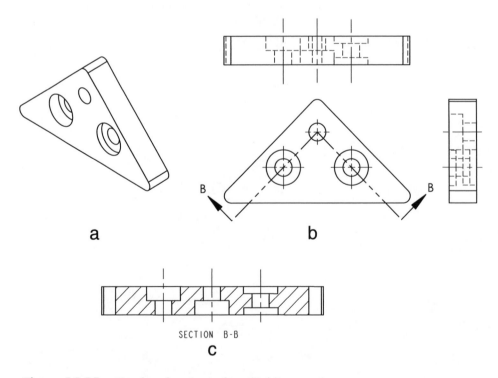

a

b

SECTION   B-B

c

Figure 14.15   The aligned section is shown in (c).

plane that occur at the 90° offsets are not represented with lines on the section view. A variation of the offset section is the ***aligned section***. The holes in the triangular object shown in Figure 14.15a are different from one another. However, the orthographic projections in Figure 14.15b cannot show the holes clearly, because the hidden lines overlap in the standard views. The aligned section shown in Figure 14.15c clearly distinguishes the three different hole styles. Unlike the offset section, which shows only the segments of the cross section that are projected and visible along the line of sight, the aligned section stretches out the offset segments of the cross section side by side into a single plane and projects them as if they were a full section. This makes the overall length of the aligned section in Figure 14.15c longer than the length of the bottom side of the front view in Figure 14.15b. As a result, an aligned view cannot be projected directly from the front view. Again, the 90° offsets are not shown on the section view.

Sometimes it is helpful to show the cross section at a certain point along the length of an object. One way to do this is with a ***removed section***, shown in Figure 5.16. In this case the cross section of the contoured handle at the point indicated by the section line is displayed. Often, removed sections are used to show a slice at a point along the length of an object that indicates the contour of a complicated shape. Although only one removed section is shown in Figure 14.16, several other removed sections could be displayed to show how the cross section of the handle changes from point to point along its

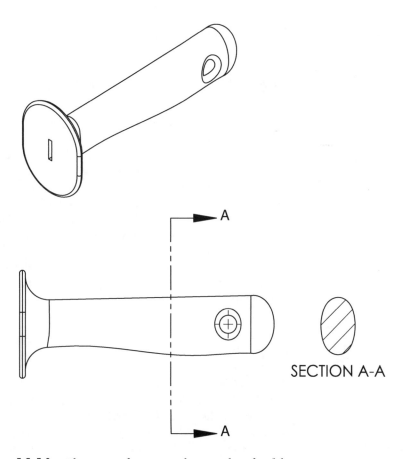

Figure 14.16   The removed section is shown to the side of the part.

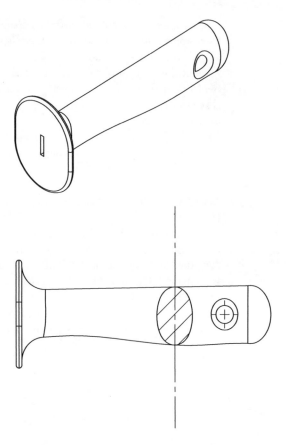

Figure 14.17　The revolved section is superimposed on the part.

length. Removed sections are a bit different from a full section in that they need not be positioned according to the usual alignment of views. In addition, removed sections are often *partial views* in which only the section itself is shown without displaying features that are not part of the section, but would normally be visible when viewing in the direction of the line of sight as defined by the arrows of the section line. An alternative to the removed section is the ***revolved section***, shown in Figure 14.17. In this case, the cross section is revolved 90° and then superimposed on the part at the position where the part is sliced. This can be quite helpful to show the shape of the cross section of an elongated feature such as a spoke, web, or aircraft wing that might not be apparent from the standard orthographic views.

14.6　AUXILIARY AND DETAIL VIEWS

An ***auxiliary view*** is often convenient to display the details of a part that are not readily visible or are distorted when viewed in one of the principal orthographic views. An example is shown in Figure 14.18. The sloped surface A has a large circular hole that is perpendicular to the plane, which is shown as a pair of parallel hidden lines in the front view. However, from the top view or the right view, the hole does not appear circular.

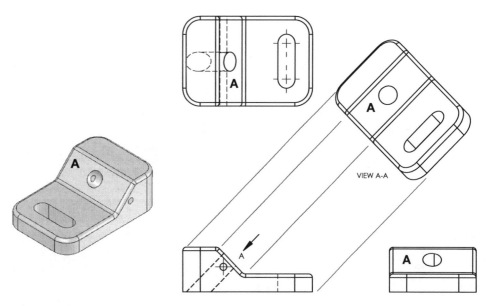

Figure 14.18   Auxiliary view of plane A. The labels A on the isometric projection and on the auxiliary and right views are not included on standard drawings.

Likewise, surface A is not displayed at its true size in these views, because it is not parallel to the plane of the paper. The only time that surface A will have true size and shape is when it is viewed along a line of sight that is perpendicular to the plane. To show the true size and shape of surface A and the large hole, an auxiliary view is created. The line of sight, indicated by the arrow with A next to it in the front view, is perpendicular to the inclined surface A. The fine construction lines parallel to the line of sight define the alignment of the edges between the front view and the auxiliary view A. In this auxiliary view, surface A is parallel to the paper. Notice that the surface and the hole are not distorted: surface A is its true size and shape, and the hole in the surface appears circular. Creating an auxiliary view manually is challenging, but CAD software makes the process quite simple. Often all that is necessary is to identify an edge, in this case the edge of surface A in the front view, and indicate that an auxiliary view is desired. The software automatically creates the view and positions it properly.

Note that some details, such as center marks for the holes and rounded edges, as well as some hidden lines, have been omitted in Figure 14.18. This was done to aid in clarity of the drawing. This is a common practice in engineering drawings. The key is to provide the maximum clarity in the drawing while retaining all of the information that is necessary to create the object. Sometimes this requires omitting confusing lines, marks, or symbols.

In some cases, it is necessary to make clear details of the part that are not readily evident in the views normally shown in the drawing. For instance, a particular detail may be so small that it cannot be shown clearly on the same scale as the remainder of the part. This is done using an auxiliary ***detail view*** consisting of a small portion of the object magnified to make the small feature clear. An example is shown in Figure 14.19. In this case the small rivet holding the blade onto the arms of the pizza cutter is too small to see in the orthographic views. The region of interest near the rivet is circled in the leftmost projection of the pizza cutter, which is a full-section view. The letter B on

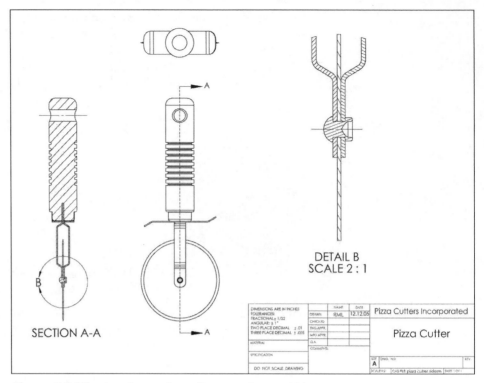

Figure 14.19   Detail view of a small section of an assembly.

the circle directs the reader to a magnified detail view B in the upper-right part of the drawing. The cross section of the rivet is clearly visible in this detail view. Since several parts are shown in cross section, a variety of ***crosshatch lines***, also known as ***section lines***, with different angles and spacing between the lines are used to distinguish one part from another. Generally, the crosshatch lines are drawn at a 45° angle and spaced about $\frac{1}{16}$ inch, or 1.5 mm, apart. However, to avoid confusion with visible lines, it is important that

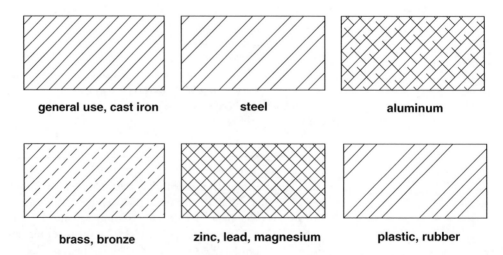

Figure 14.20   ANSI standard section lines for several materials.

the crosshatch lines be drawn so that they are not parallel to any visible lines of the bounding area that is crosshatched. In the detail view in Figure 14.19, the orientations of the crosshatch lines have been carefully adjusted so that none are parallel to visible lines. Furthermore, crosshatch lines perpendicular to visible lines of the bounding area should be avoided. It is also important that the crosshatch lines for separate portions of a single part be the same. For example, the section lines for individual parts are the same above and below the rivet in Figure 14.19. Usually standard parts such as fasteners, washers, springs, bearings, and gears are not crosshatched. But in the case of Figure 14.19, the rivet detail is integral to the assembly, so it is helpful to show its cross section with crosshatching to indicate how it fits with the other parts. Crosshatching can be used to designate the type of material, although this is not frequently done. ANSI standard section lines for a variety of materials are shown in Figure 14.20. In most CAD software, the selection of the type of crosshatching is quite easy.

14.7   FASTENERS AND SCREW THREADS

Fasteners include a broad range of items such as bolts, nuts, screws, and rivets used to "fasten" parts together. In most cases, fasteners are standard parts purchased from an outside vendor, so detail drawings of fasteners are rarely necessary. Nevertheless, threaded holes and threaded shafts are sometimes represented on a drawing.

The geometry of screw threads is too complicated to draw exactly in an engineering drawing and screw threads are standard, so either of two simple conventions is used to indicate screw threads, as shown in Figure 14.21. The **schematic representation** is used when a realistic representation of the side view of a screw thread is desired.

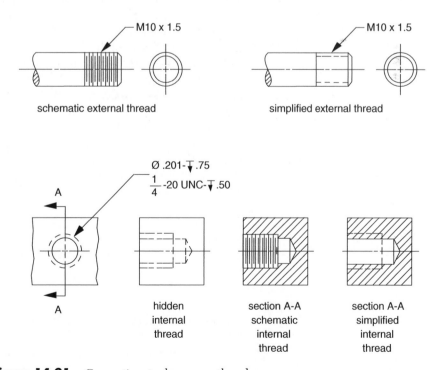

Figure 14.21   Conventions to show screw threads.

For an external thread, the lines that extend across the entire diameter represent the ***crest***, or peak, of the thread, while the shorter lines in between represent the ***root***, or valley, of the thread. The distance between crests or between roots is called the ***pitch***. On a drawing, the crests and roots are shown perpendicular to the axis of the threaded section rather than helical as they actually appear on the physical thread. In the end view, threads are depicted with concentric circles. The outer circle is the largest diameter of the screw thread, known as the ***major diameter***, and the inner circle is the smallest diameter of the screw thread, or ***minor diameter***. In the end view of the external thread, both diameters are shown as solid circles. In the ***simplified representation*** of external screw threads, the threads are omitted altogether. The major diameter is represented as a solid line in the side view, and the minor diameter is represented with a dashed line.

The end view of an internal thread is shown as two concentric circles representing the major and minor diameter, but the major diameter is a hidden line. For a side view of a hidden internal screw thread, the major and minor diameters are both shown as hidden lines for both schematic and simplified screw thread representations. In a cross section, internal threads can be shown in either the schematic or the simplified representation, as shown. For a hole that does not go completely through the part, called a ***blind hole***, the lines in the side view representing the minor diameter continue deeper than the thread and come to a point. This represents the hole that is drilled prior to tapping, or cutting threads in the hole. The hole needs to be longer than the threaded section to permit the tool that is used to cut the threads, or tap, to penetrate deeply enough to fully cut the threads in the portion of the hole to be tapped.

Screw threads are specified in terms of the nominal (major) diameter, the pitch, and the thread series. For instance, the designations $\frac{1}{4}$-20 UNC, .25-20 UNC, or $\frac{1}{4}$-20 NC all indicate a major diameter of .25 inch, a pitch of 20 threads per inch, and the Unified Coarse (UNC) series. The diameter of the hole drilled before tapping an internal thread is specified in a wide variety of machinist and engineering handbooks. In this case, the proper hole to be drilled has a diameter of .2010 inch, which corresponds to a number 7 drill. To make an internal thread of this size, a machinist would first drill a hole using a number 7 drill bit and then cut the threads using a $\frac{1}{4}$-20 tap. For screw threads with a nominal diameter less than .25 inch, a number designation is used to specify the nominal diameter. For example, the designation 10-32 UNF indicates a nominal diameter of .1900 inch, 32 threads per inch, and the Unified Fine (UNF) series. The pitch is equal to 1 divided by the number of threads per inch.

Metric threads are specified in a slightly different way. A designation M10 × 1.5 indicates a metric thread with a 10-mm major diameter and a pitch of 1.5 mm between crests of the thread. The number of threads per mm is 1 divided by the pitch. Other letters and numbers may follow the thread specification to denote tolerances and deviations of the thread, but for many cases these are not necessary. In addition, for a blind hole, the depth of the thread can be specified in several ways. Following the thread designation, the notation X .50 DEEP, THD .50 DP, or a downward arrow with a horizontal bar at its tail followed by .50 all indicate that the thread should extend .50 inch below the surface of the piece, as shown in Figure 14.21. (THD indicates "thread," and DP indicates "deep.") The threaded depth is usually 1.5 to 2 times the nominal diameter of the screw thread.

The dimensions for a threaded hole are indicated on a drawing using a leader line with the arrow pointing at the major diameter, as shown in Figure 14.21. Threaded holes are usually dimensioned in the view where they appear as circles, rather than in a side

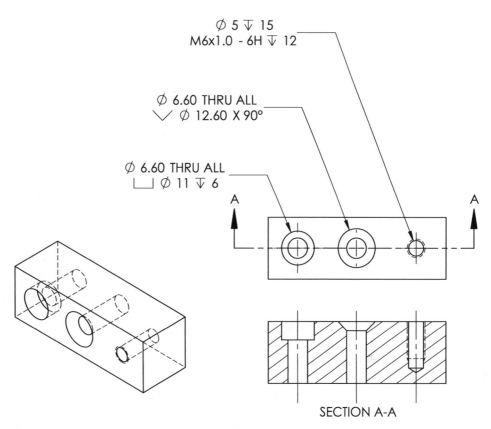

Ø 5 ⌄ 15
M6x1.0 - 6H ⌄ 12

Ø 6.60 THRU ALL
⌵ Ø 12.60 X 90°

Ø 6.60 THRU ALL
⌴ Ø 11 ⌄ 6

SECTION A-A

Figure 14.22   Showing counterbore holes, countersink holes, and threaded holes on a drawing.

view of the threaded hole. Multiple threaded holes of the same specification are typically denoted in the same way as other multiple features using the notation (2X) or 2 TIMES at the end of the thread designation.

Bolts, which are often called machine screws, and nuts are usually shown only in a parts list and are not included on any drawings, except perhaps an assembly drawing. Nuts and bolts are specified in the same way as threaded holes, plus a bolt length and the type of head. For instance .25-28 UNF X 1.50 HEXAGON CAP SCREW or .25-28 NF X 1.50 HEX CAP SCR indicates a .25-28 Unified Fine series bolt that is 1.5 inches long with hexagonal head. Nuts are specified in terms of their thread and shape, such as M8 X 1.25 HEX NUT.

Frequently the top of a threaded hole is designed so that the head of the bolt is flush with or slightly below the surface. This is called a ***counterbore hole*** or a ***countersink hole***, depending on the shape of the head of the bolt. A counterbore hole has an enlarged cylindrical portion at the top of the hole, to accept the head of a bolt, as shown in the leftmost hole in Section A-A of Figure 14.22. A countersink hole has a conical taper at the top of the hole, shown as the middle hole in Figure 14.22, to accept the conical head of a countersink, flat-head screw. These two holes are dimensioned for a metric M6 bolt. In both cases, the through hole has a diameter of 6.60 mm, designated on the drawing as Ø 6.60 THRU ALL. This diameter is large enough that the bolt slides

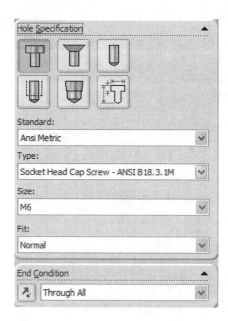

Figure 14.23   Example of using a dialog box to specify a counterbore.

easily into the hole, but is not loose in the hole. The second line of the dimension of the hole indicates the size of the counterbore or countersink. For the counterbore, the U-shaped symbol indicates a U-shaped counterbore at the top of the hole. The diameter of the counterbore is 11 mm and the depth, indicated by the downward arrow, is 6 mm. The countersink is designated with a V-shaped symbol. The diameter of 12.60 mm is the diameter at the top of the conical taper, and the 90 angle is the angle formed at the point of the conical taper.

While this all seems quite complicated, CAD software makes it quite easy to specify a counterbore or countersink by using a menu such as the example shown in Figure 14.23. All that is needed is to specify the shape of the hole (the upper-left button showing a counterbore), the engineering standard for the bolt (ANSI Metric), the type of bolt (Socket Head Cap Screw), the bolt size (M6), the tightness of the through hole (Close, Normal, Loose), and the depth of the hole (Through All). Given this information, the CAD software automatically determines the appropriate diameter, depth, and other specifications for the hole based on standard engineering practice. When the hole is dimensioned in a drawing, this information automatically appears, as shown in Figure 14.22. Threaded holes can be specified in a similar way. All that is needed is the engineering standard for the thread (ANSI Metric), the thread designation (M6 $\times$ 1.0), and the depth into the hole that the thread should extend (12 mm). From this, the CAD software automatically determines the size of the hole to be drilled prior to tapping and the depth that the hole needs to be drilled so that the hole can be tapped to the specified depth. The depth of the hole is the depth of the cylindrical section of the hole, not the depth to the point of the conical portion of the hole. Once specified, this information appears automatically on the drawing, with the first line of the dimension indicating the drill diameter (5 mm) and depth (15 mm) and the second line indicating the thread specification (M6 $\times$ 1.0) and the depth for the threads (12 mm), as shown for the rightmost hole in Figure 14.22. The 6H in the second line indicates a standard thread tolerance grade specifying how much the dimensions of the thread can deviate from the standard dimensions for this thread size.

14.8   ASSEMBLY DRAWINGS

An assembly drawing shows all of the components of a design either assembled or in an exploded view. Many times assembly drawings include sections. Most dimensions are omitted in assembly drawings. Individual parts are not dimensioned, but some dimensions of the assembled mechanism may be included. Hidden lines are seldom necessary in assembly drawings, although they can be used where they clarify the design. Leader lines attached to a ballooned letter or detail number, as shown in Figure 14.24, reference the parts of the assembly. The leader lines should not cross and nearby leader lines should be approximately parallel. Sometimes parts are labeled by name rather than number. The parts list may be on the assembly drawing (usually on the right side or at the bottom) or it may be a separate sheet. The assembly drawing may also include

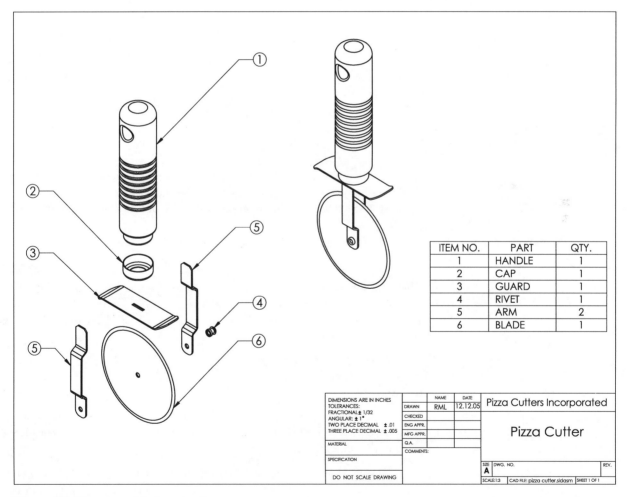

ITEM NO.	PART	QTY.
1	HANDLE	1
2	CAP	1
3	GUARD	1
4	RIVET	1
5	ARM	2
6	BLADE	1

DIMENSIONS ARE IN INCHES		NAME	DATE	Pizza Cutters Incorporated		
TOLERANCES: FRACTIONAL± 1/32 ANGULAR: ± 1° TWO PLACE DECIMAL ± .01 THREE PLACE DECIMAL ± .005	DRAWN	RML	12.12.05			
	CHECKED					
	ENG APPR.			Pizza Cutter		
	MFG APPR.					
MATERIAL	Q.A.					
	COMMENTS:					
SPECIFICATION				SIZE	DWG. NO.	REV.
				A		
DO NOT SCALE DRAWING				SCALE:1:3	CAD FILE: pizza cutter.sidasm	SHEET 1 OF 1

Figure 14.24   Assembly drawing of a pizza cutter.

machining or assembly information in the form of notes on the drawing. Often assembly drawings include assembly sections. These are typically orthographic or pictorial section views of parts as put together in an assembly. The assembly cross section on the left side of Figure 14.19 shows the interior structure of the parts of a pizza cutter and how they fit together. The detail view in the upper right of Figure 14.19 shows the cross section through the rivet to indicate how the parts are assembled.

KEY TERMS

Aligned section	Dimension lines	Precedence of lines
ANSI	Extension lines	Reference dimension
Auxiliary view	Full section	Removed section
Blind hole	Half section	Revolved section
Broken-out section	Hidden lines	Root
Center mark	ISO	Scale
Centerlines	Leader lines	Section lines
Contour dimensioning	Line of sight	Section views
Counterbore hole	Major diameter	Sheet layout
Countersink hole	Minor diameter	Title block
Crest	Offset section	Visible lines
Crosshatch lines	Overdimensioned	Witness lines
Cutting plane lines	Partial view	
Detail view	Pitch	

Problems

1. Three orthographic views and an isometric projection of an object that has over-all dimensions of $4 \times 4 \times 4$ inches are to be shown in a drawing. Determine the best ANSI sheet size for an object of this size at the scales indicated below:
    a. Half size.
    b. 2:1.
    c. 1 = 1.

2. Three orthographic views and an isometric projection of an object that has overall dimensions of $200 \times 200 \times 200$ mm are to be shown in a drawing. Determine the optimal standard metric scale to be used for the ISO sheet sizes indicated below:
    a. A1.
    b. A3.
    c. A4.

3. The drawing shown in Figure 14.25 has many errors in the dimensioning. Sketch or draw with CAD the orthographic views and show the proper placement of the dimensions.

4. The drawing shown in Figure 14.26 has many errors in the dimensioning. Sketch or draw with CAD the orthographic views and show the proper placement of the dimensions. The M10 $\times$ 1.5 threaded hole requires a tap drill of 8.5 mm. Only two views are needed for this part.

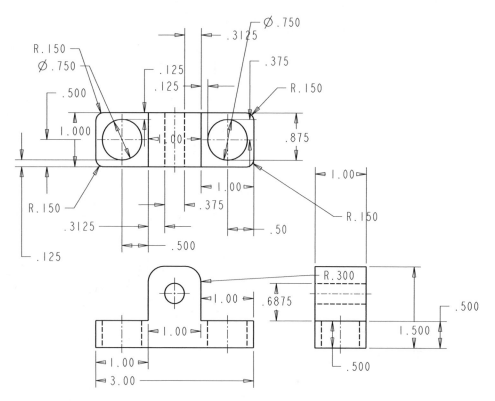

Figure 14.25

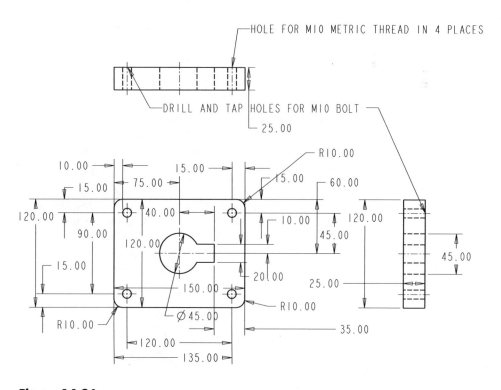

Figure 14.26

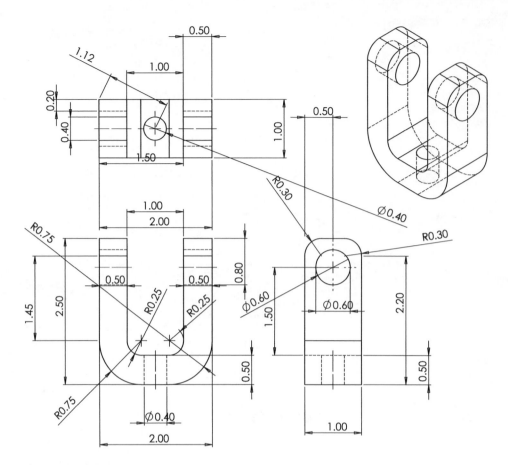

Figure 14.27

5.   The drawing shown in Figure 14.27 is dimensioned using the ISO standard, which has a slightly different look than most dimensions used in this chapter, which use the ANSI standard. However, there are many errors in the dimensioning. Sketch or draw with CAD the orthographic views and show the proper placement of the dimensions, using the ISO standard in which the values for the dimensions are aligned with the dimension line and set above the dimension line.

6.   The drawing shown in Figure14.28 is dimensioned using the ISO standard, which has a slightly different look than most dimensions used in this chapter, which use the ANSI standard. However, there are many errors in the dimensioning. Sketch or draw with CAD the orthographic views and show the proper placement of the dimensions, using the ISO standard in which the values for the dimensions are aligned with the dimension line and set above the dimension line.

7.   Sketch the following section views for the object shown in Figure 14.29. The threaded holes extend from the top surface approximately halfway through the thickness of the part. The other holes extend through the part.

a.   A-A.

b.   B-B.

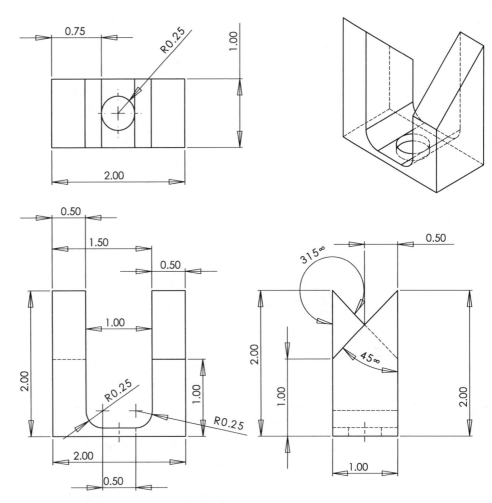

Figure 14.28

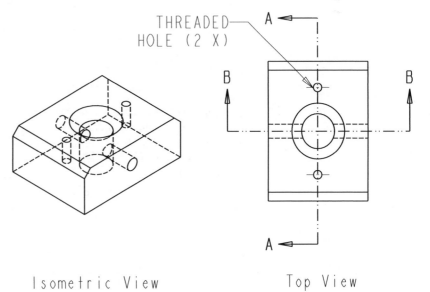

Isometric View

Top View

Figure 14.29

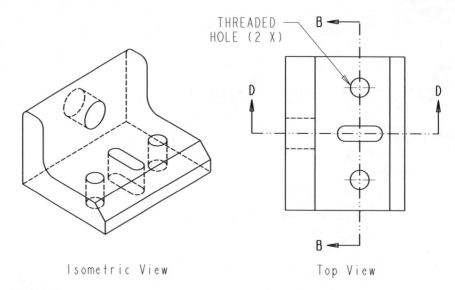

THREADED
HOLE (2 X)

D   D

B

B

Isometric View   Top View

Figure 14.30

8. Sketch the following section views for the object shown in Figure 14.30. All holes extend through the part.
    a. B-B.
    b. D-D.

9. Sketch or draw with CAD section A-A for the object shown in Figure 14.31 using the dimensions in Figure 14.28.

10. Sketch the following section views for the object shown in Figure 14.32. All holes extend through the part.
    a. A-A.
    b. C-C.

11. Figure 14.33, a–f, shows the dimensioned front view and several different corresponding right-side views, each with a horizontal width of 1 inch. Using CAD, draw three orthographic views (front, top, and right side) as well as the auxiliary view of the inclined surface for the corresponding right-side view.

12. Look up the following machine screw threads in an engineering graphics book (such as *Engineering Graphics* by Giesecke, et al.), a machinist's or engineering handbook (such as *Marks' Standard Handbook for Mechanical Engineers*), an industrial supply catalog (such as McMaster-Carr), or on the Internet (search on "tap drill size"). Specify the series (UNC or UNF), tap drill size or number, number of threads per inch, pitch, and nominal diameter.
    a. 4-40.
    b. 6-32.
    c. 8-32.
    d. $\frac{3}{8}$-24.
    e. 6-40.
    f. $\frac{1}{4}$-28.

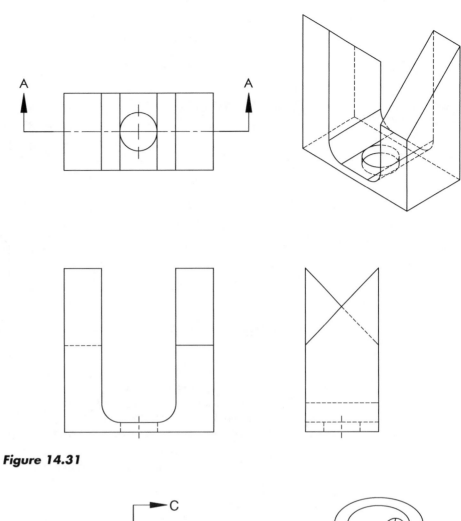

Figure 14.31

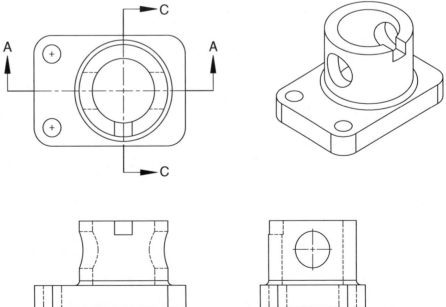

Figure 14.32

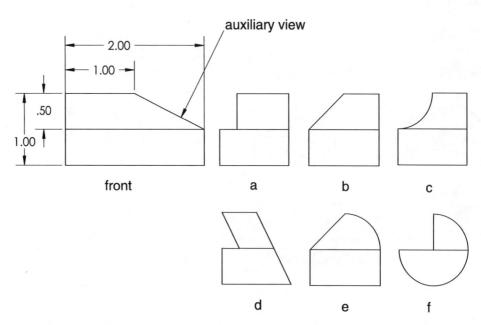

Figure 14.33

13.   Look up the following machine screw threads in an engineering graphics book (such as *Engineering Graphics* by Giesecke, et al.), a machinist's or engineering handbook (such as *Marks' Standard Handbook for Mechanical Engineers*), an industrial supply catalog (such as McMaster-Carr), or on the Internet (search on "tap drill size metric"). Specify the series (course or fine), tap drill size, number of threads per mm, and nominal size.

a.   M2 × 0.4.

b.   M12 × 1.75.

c.   M30 × 3.5.

d.   M30 × 2.

e.   M10 × 1.25.

Chapter 15

Two Dimensional CAD: IntelliCAD

15.1 TWO DIMENSIONAL DRAWING AND THE DESIGN PROCESS

Possibly the most crucial step in the process of design is the communication of the details of the design to the people who will be building it. Fundamentally, this is no different than ordering breakfast. If you are clear, concise, and follow the conventions, you will get the breakfast you are hungry for. If you mumble, change your mind erratically, and repeat yourself, not only will you not get your hoped-for breakfast, what finally comes may be liberally garnished with ingredients not meant for human consumption.

In the design process, the fundamental tool of communication is the *technical drawing*. In design for all flavours of engineering, we are referring to a technical drawing that is a scale image of the eventual item, created using a process called *drafting*. Someone once said a picture is worth a thousand words. In the context of design, this is untrue. A drawing is immeasurably more valuable than any number of words. It is impossible to convey design intent without a drawing. Without the production people understanding the design intent, they cannot produce the part.

Here is a great example: Here is a description of a radial rolling element bearing, and a tapered roller bearing.

> *In a radial rolling element bearing, such as a ball bearing, the purpose is to keep the axis of the inner "race", the tube or shaft, collinear with the axis of the outer "race", while letting the races rotate with respect to one another, while minimizing resistance and wear. In a tapered roller bearing, the rolling elements are of a special type to allow the bearing to reduce friction when the shaft experiences a force in the axial direction, as well as in the usual radial direction, like a wheel. All the while, the inner race is constrained to remain co-linear with the outer race, while the shape of the rolling elements keeps the two planar faces of the bearing a fixed distance apart, so long as the thrust is in the direction of the apex of the cone represented by the inner race. Thus, during axial force and radial force, the bearing reduces rotational friction, while constraining translational motion.*

Pretty horrible, eh? If you are already familiar with the various types of bearings, you probably followed it, but try to imagine reading that, and trying to envision what the heck it's talking about. Now let's look at a two dimensional picture of a radial rolling element bearing, and a tapered roller bearing, see Figure 15.1.

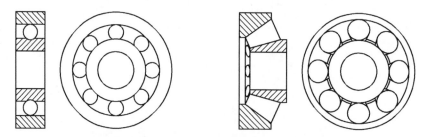

Figure 15.1   A radial *ball* bearing and a tapered roller bearing.

15.1.1 The 2D Drawing

The simplest form of engineering drawing is the 2D drawing. Since about 1992 all 2D technical drawing is done using Computer Aided Design (CAD) software. It is important to understand what 2D implies, here: imagine you are waiting for your breakfast, and want to tell your buddy about this nifty new idea you've got for a DVD organizer. What do you do? You grab a pen and a napkin, and you draw a sketch. What you are doing is simple, but fundamental to the concept of 2D CAD. You are representing a three dimensional object (a DVD organizer) that exists *only in your head* as a two dimensional object on a piece of paper.

Taking this concept a step further, imagine you get out your drawing tools, i.e. pencil, compass, ruler, etc., and draw your idea for a new DVD organizer very, very accurately, such that someone could build a DVD organizer from the drawing you create. Every time they build part of the organizer, they never have to ask themselves "How long should this part be?", or "How thick is this bit?", or even "What type of screws should I use here?", because all of that information is on your very, very accurate drawing. What you've done there using pencil and paper is exactly what you will do much more easily using 2D CAD.

The difference is, the 2D CAD drawing is much easier to make "perfect" than is the drawing done by hand, and being electronic, it is much more easily stored and modified. Other than that, they are the same. A hand drawing is a number of lines and curves which together represent a three dimensional object on a two dimensional surface, a piece of paper. A 2D CAD drawing is a number of lines and curves which together represent a three dimensional object on a two dimensional surface, a computer monitor. Eventually, it will be printed on paper, so the destination is the same, but the 2D CAD journey is a lot more convenient.

Ah, yes. The keen kids in the front row are waving their hands frantically. They want to know why we don't use 3D solid modeling for everything, because it is the cutting edge! (If you don't know what 3D solid modeling is, don't worry. It's the next chapter). There are two reasons to use 2D CAD instead of 3D. Time and Money. We don't always use 3D solid modelers for the same reason you don't drive to the end of the driveway to take out the garbage. It's just not necessary. Also, a first rate 2D CAD package costs about $2000.00. A barely adequate 3D parametric solid modeler costs upwards of $10,000.00.

So, back to the problem of communication.

15.1.2 Flange Mount Bearing

This chapter is not a chapter on bearing selection, but rather on engineering drawings in 2 dimensions. Ignoring the vast majority of the criteria for bearing selection, let's imagine that you've finally found just the right bearing to mount the spinning saw blades to your Super Heavyweight Battlebot. The spinning saw blade, when bashing around in the heat of battle against the armored hide of a robot adversary, experiences a substantial thrust load, so you've decided to use a tapered roller bearing. You've very carefully estimated the loads your bearings will experience, and you've very carefully selected just the right particular model from a manufacturer that you have had good experiences with in the past. On the internet it is possible to find the catalogs for a great many companies, one such is Timken Bearings, who publish their catalogs in Adobe's PDF format. The specific catalog section being used here can be viewed on the web at http://www.timken.com/products/bearings/pdf/BrgDimenIndex-Chap4.pdf. The trouble is, the appropriate bearings aren't mounted bearings, so you must design a mount of some kind to fasten

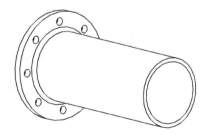

Figure 15.2   A flanged pipe.

the bearing to the Battlebot chassis. The design of your battlebot's spinning drill auger further mandates the use of a flange mount. A *flange* is simply a raised lip sticking out from the edge of something. A *flange mount* indicates that you've drilled some holes in that flange, so now you can bolt something to it.

The bearing you've selected is a Timken tapered roller bearing, part number NA366, whose dimensions are shown below, in Figure 15.3:

| CONE | | | | | CUP | | | | | BEAR-ING | Remarks |
Number	BORE d	WIDTH B	Max Shaft Fillet Radii R"	Weight	Number	OUTSIDE DIA D	WIDTH C	Max Hs'ng Fillet Radii r"	Weight	WIDTH T	
365 Series (cont) *370DEE	50.000 1.9685	88.900 3.5000	.8 .03	1.12 kg 2.47 lb							
NA366	50.000 1.9685	25.006 .9845	3.5 .14	.72 kg 1.59 lb	362XD	89.985 3.5427	49.949 1.9665	.5 .02	.56 kg 1.24 lb	50.013 1.9690	
					*363D	90.000 3.5433	42.070 1.6563	.8 .03	.46 kg 1.01 lb	50.013 1.9690	
					*363DC	90.000 3.5433	42.070 1.6563	.8 .03	.50 kg 1.10 lb	50.013 1.9690	
					364XD	90.000 3.5433	42.862 1.6875	.8 .03	.51 kg 1.12 lb	50.013 1.9690	

Figure 15.3   Timken tapered roller bearing with dimensions. From http://www.timken.com/products/bearings/pdf/BrgDimenIndex-Chap4.pdf, p 12.

So, you're using this tapered roller bearing because there is a significant axial load. You need to make sure that there are features on both the shaft and the flange mount which will transfer that load from the shaft, though the bearing, and into the frame. You think, scratch your head, and come up with the following concept sketch:

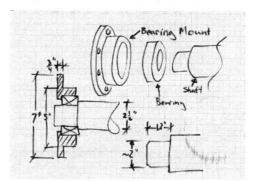

Figure 15.4   Flange mount and bearing conceptual sketch.

Notice in particular the coffee ring, and the general messiness of the drawing. A sketch is just that. It's a tool for you and others to help understand the general idea of the drawing, rather than the specifics of its construction. When the time comes to manufacture, a whole new level of sketch is required, unless you plan to build everything you design yourself. You don't have a machine shop, so you need to send the parts out to be fabricated. If you send a napkin, a couple of catalogs, and a four minute audio tape of you explaining what the heck your "drawing" is supposed to mean to a machinist, that machinist will call you names, and you will deserve it.

You want to communicate with the machinist efficiently and completely, such that you need only send one set of drawings, he has no questions, and in a usefully short time you have the parts. "Efficiently" means that the machinist has to work as little as possible to figure out what you mean. "Completely" means that that drawing states, beyond any question, *exactly* what it is you want. That drawing is a part of a legal contract between you and the machinist, so you must not foul it up, or you are out time and money, potentially a great deal of both.

The drawing standards used in technical drawings have been relatively unchanged for a long time. They represent a method of producing simple, understandable drawings, including a set of drawing conventions, nomenclature, and symbols that collectively *are* what is meant by the terms "drafting" or "technical drawing".

There are a number of interesting features on these drawings which might be unfamiliar to you. The first is shown below, in Figure 15.7, which is a detail taken from Figure 15.6. What this detail shows is called a *Dimensional Tolerance*.

15.1.3 Dimensional Tolerances.

The bearing description is provided with some really important information, from a drawing perspective: the dimensions of the bearing. But it takes more than the basic dimensions of the bearing to be able to design a housing and shaft for the bearing which will <u>definitely</u> fit the bearing. We require the *tolerance* of the shaft size.

Tolerances are exactly what they sound like. How much error can you tolerate, before the machine doesn't work? The fact is, it is impossible to build anything to a specified dimension. There is *always* a certain amount of error. If I ask you to draw a line exactly 6 cm long, then I measure your line with a micrometer, will it turn out to have been exactly 6 cm? Certainly not. No matter how accurate a measuring device you use to build something, there is the possibility of a measuring device that is so much better that it would reveal error undetectable by the original instrument.

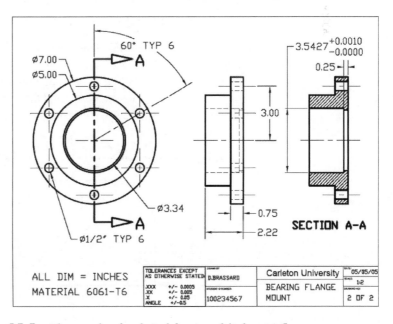

Figure 15.5   The completed technical drawing of the bearing flange mount.

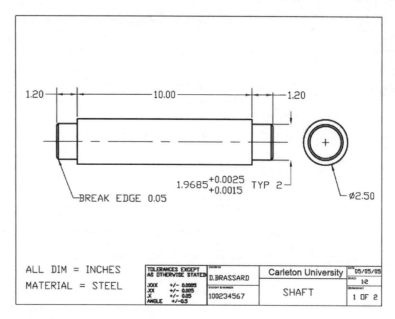

Figure 15.6   The completed technical drawing of the stepped shaft.

$$1.9685^{+0.0025}_{+0.0015}$$

Figure 15.7   Detail of shaft diameter dimension, from Figure 15.6.

Another issue is cost. If you are being paid $30.00 per hour, and you are asked to draw a line 6 cm, give or take a centimeter, it will take maybe a few seconds to take out the ruler, line up the end of the pencil with zero, carefully draw the line so that you are definitely past 5 cm, but not out to 7 cm. If you are asked to draw a line 6 cm long, give or take one half millimeter, it will take some measure of time longer, in all likelihood, you will have to bring a another instrument besides the pencil and ruler into play, perhaps an eraser and erasing shield, or a compass/divider. Thus, the 6-plus-or-minus-1-cm line is the *less expensive line*!. So, if our application isn't harmed by a fairly coarse line, we should save money using a 6 ± 1cm line. In general, it is always worth the time to determine the actual tolerance required for a measurement. . . except when it isn't. . . this is an area where experience will come to your aid.

INCH SYSTEM BEARINGS
CONE FITTING PRACTICE (inches)   **CLASS: 4 AND 2 CONES**

CONE BORE		DEVIATION FROM MINIMUM CONE BORE AND RESULTANT FIT												
		ROTATING CONE		ROTATING OR STATIONARY CONE		STATIONARY CONE								
Range	Tolerance	Ground Seat		Unground or Ground Seat		Unground Seat		Ground Seat		Unground Seat		Hardened and Ground Seat	
	Does not apply to TNASW and TNASWE. type bearings.	Constant Loads With Moderate Shock		Heavy Loads, or High Speed or Shock		Moderate Loads, No Shock		Moderate Loads, No Shock		Sheaves, Wheels, Idlers		Wheel Spindles	
Over	Inclusive	Cone Seat Deviation	Resultant Fit	Cone Seat Deviation	Resultant Fit	Cone Seat Deviation	Resultant Fit	Cone Seat Deviation	Resultant Fit	Cone Seat Deviation	Resultant Fit	Cone Seat Deviation	Resultant Fit
0	3.0000	0.0000 +0.0005	+0.0015 +0.0010	0.0015T 0.0005T	+0.0025 +0.0015	0.0025T 0.0010T	+0.0005 0.0000	0.0005T 0.0005L	0.0000 -0.0005	0.0000 0.0010L	0.0000 -0.0005	0.0000 0.0010L	-0.0002 -0.0007	0.0002L 0.0012L
3.0000	12.0000	0.0000 +0.0010	+0.0025 +0.0015	0.0025T 0.0005T	Use Average Tight Cone Fit of 0.0005 in./in. of Cone Bore		+0.0010 0.0000	0.0010T 0.0010L	0.0000 -0.0010	0.0000 0.0020L	0.0000 -0.0010	0.0000 0.0020L	-0.0002 -0.0012	0.0002L 0.0022L
12.0000	24.0000	0.0000 +0.0020	+0.0050 +0.0030	0.0050T 0.0010T			+0.0020 0.0000	0.0020T 0.0020L	0.0000 -0.0020	0.0000 0.0040L	0.0000 -0.0020	0.0000 0.0040L	---	---
24.0000	36.0000	0.0000 +0.0030	+0.0075 +0.0045	0.0075T 0.0015T			+0.0030 0.0000	0.0030T 0.0030L	0.0000 -0.0030	0.0000 0.0060L	0.0000 -0.0030	0.0000 0.0060L	---	---

EXAMPLE: If the minimum cone bore = 3.0000 inches, the suggested shaft size = 3.0015 in. to 3.0010 in for a cone fit of 0.0015 in tight to 0.0005 in tight.

Figure 15.8   Timken tapered roller bearing shaft tolerances.

INCH SYSTEM BEARINGS
CUP FITTING PRACTICE (inches)   **CLASS: 4 AND 2 CUPS**

CUP OD			DEVIATION FROM MINIMUM CUP OD AND RESULTANT FIT							
			STATIONARY CUP				STATIONARY OR ROTATING CUP		ROTATING CUP	
Range		Tolerance	Floating or Clamped		Adjustable		Non Adjustable or in Carriers, Sheaves - Clamped		Sheaves - Unclamped ‡	
Over	Inclusive		Cup Seat Deviation	Resultant Fit	Cup Seat Deviation	Resultant Fit	Cup Seat Deviation	Resultant Fit	Cup Seat Deviation	Resultant Fit
0	3.0000	+0.0010 / 0.0000	+0.0020 / +0.0030	0.0010L / 0.0030L	0.0000 / +0.0010	0.0010T / 0.0010L	-0.0015 / -0.0005	0.0025T / 0.0005T	-0.0030 / -0.0020	0.0040T / 0.0020T
3.0000	5.0000	+0.0010 / 0.0000	+0.0020 / +0.0030	0.0010L / 0.0030L	0.0000 / +0.0010	0.0010T / 0.0010L	-0.0020 / -0.0010	0.0030T / 0.0010T	-0.0030 / -0.0020	0.0040T / 0.0020T
5.0000	12.0000	+0.0010 / 0.0000	+0.0020 / +0.0030	0.0010L / 0.0030L	0.0000 / +0.0020	0.0010T / 0.0020L	-0.0020 / -0.0010	0.0030T / 0.0010T	-0.0030 / -0.0020	0.0040T / 0.0020T
12.0000	24.0000	+0.0020 / 0.0000	+0.0040 / +0.0060	0.0020L / 0.0060L	+0.0010 / +0.0030	0.0010T / 0.0030L	-0.0030 / -0.0010	0.0050T / 0.0010T	-0.0040 / -0.0020	0.0060T / 0.0020T
24.0000	36.0000	+0.0030 / 0.0000	+0.0060 / +0.0090	0.0030L / 0.0090L	+0.0020 / +0.0050	0.0010T / 0.0050L	-0.0040 / -0.0010	0.0070T / 0.0010T	--	--

Figure 15.9   Timken tapered roller bearing housing tolernaces.

In order to choose exactly the right tolerances for this bearing, you must refer to the table of tolerances for the shaft and bearing housing, shown in Figures 15.8 & 15.9.

Bearing part number NA366 has a 1.9685" bore, and an outside diameter of 3.5427". Assuming that we are going to specify a ground finish for the shaft (grinding is a machining operation which results in a marvelously smooth finish), and since we plan to commit violence on other robots with this assembly, i.e. Heavy Shock Loads, referring to Figure 15.4, our *tolerance* is that the shaft diameter, as built must lie between the basic dimension +0.0015, and the basic dimension +0.0025, or:

$$1.9685\genfrac{}{}{0pt}{}{+\ 0.0025}{+\ 0.0015}.$$

This way of writing a tolerance is called a *deviation tolerance*. We could write the same information as:

$$\frac{1.9710}{1.9700}$$

In this form it is called a *limit tolerance*. Which type of tolerance you employ is up to you, generally, if you are provided with a deviation tolerance from your selection resource (the bearing catalog, here), it is good practice to simply copy that directly. You are less likely to make a mistake copying than converting. That said, the limit tolerance is easier for the machinist to use directly, and it annoys machinists to no end to see more than one type of tolerance on a single drawing.

Pay attention here: It is not mandatory to use tolerances! Apply a tolerance to only those dimensions which <u>must</u> have them! Most dimensional tolerances can be taken care of with a general tolerance note, a sample of which is shown in Figure 15.10, as well as in both Figures 15.5 & 15.6.

```
TOLERANCES EXCEPT
AS OTHERWISE STATED:

.XXX        +/- 0.0005
.XX         +/- 0.005
.X          +/- 0.05
ANGLE       +/-0.5
```

Figure 15.10   A sample general tolerance note.

A general tolerance note allows you to tolerance by just using your common sense, as you design and draw. An example is the stepped portion of the shaft in Figure 15.6. Its length is dimensioned with only two decimal places. So long as the shaft goes completely though the bearing bore, who cares how long it sticks out beyond, within reason? Why spend money hiring a machinist to care?

The next drawing symbol you might be unfamiliar with is a *section line*, as illustrated in Figure 15.11. What section lines, and more important, section views do is allow us to see details of the part which would otherwise be obscured by a jumble of hidden lines, object lines, and dimensions.

15.1.4 Section Views.

In the flange bearing mount we're designing, there is a ridge on the inside designed to limit the axial movement of the bearing itself. Without this, the bearing can simply slide through the housing. Unfortunately, because of the radial array of mounting holes in the bearing mount, it is hard to see the details of the ridge. Just look at the middle (hidden line) view shown in Figure 15.12 and the left hand view in Figure 15.13.

Figure 15.11   A section line.

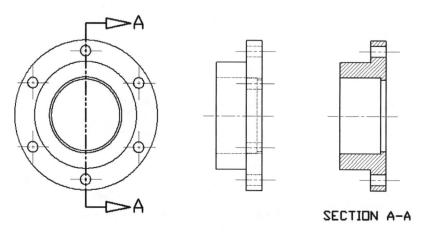

Figure 15.12   The flange mount bearing drawing, less title block and dimensions.

Of the two views shown in Figure 15.13, which one shows the actual geometry of the flange mount more clearly? Plainly it is the section view.

Simply put, the dashed line in the front view identifies a plane on which the part has been cut in half. You can think of it just like that: Someone cut the part in two, blotted the cut in ink, and stamped it on the page, leaving the hatch marks. The hatched areas tell us which areas of the part intersect the section plane, and which lie behind the section plane, as though we were actually looking at half a part. The arrows attached to the section line point in the direction that will be "up", or away from the paper in the section view.

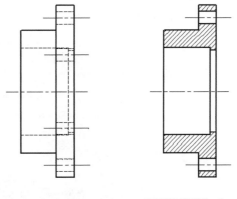

SECTION A-A

Figure 15.13   The hidden line drawing (left) and section view (right) of the flange mount bearing.

As with tolerances, section views are not mandatory, they should be used <u>only</u> when they are the best way to represent the geometry of the part understandably. For example, look at the shaft we are designing, in Figure 15.14. There is no section view in the shaft drawing, yet its geometry is obvious. Keep your drawings as simple as will convey all that you need, <u>and nothing more</u>.

Figure 15.14   The shaft drawing, less title block and dimensions.

15.2   DRAFTING WITH INTELLICAD

IntelliCAD is *computer aided drafting* (CAD) software that can be used to create engineering drawings. Start IntelliCAD by clicking on the Windows Start button (bottom left), and click on **Programs > IntelliCAD 2000.** A dialog asking for a template will be displayed - click OK.

Once IntelliCAD has loaded, move the mouse around until you see a crosshair cursor. The IntelliCAD window has a number of important features, see Figure 15.15:

1.   The standard Windows drop-down menus.
2.   The standard Windows toolbar below the menus, it includes: File-New, File-Open, File-Save, and Print.
3.   The graphics area - that's the area where you draw.
4.   The command area - this small window (by default) has space for three lines of text - this is where you type commands. Typing commands in IntelliCAD is like having a conversation and IntelliCAD's half of the conversation comes from the text in the command area.
5.   Commands may also be used via the toolbars. The toolbars may be customized.
6.   The status area, at the bottom of the IntelliCAD window, this includes the current cursor position.

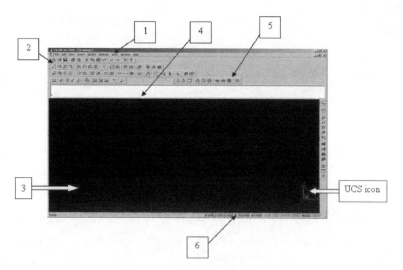

Figure 15.15   The IntelliCAD graphical user interface.

15.2.1 Command Entry

Typically there are three ways of giving the same command!

1.   Type the command using the keyboard - the command is displayed in the command area.
2.   Select the command from a menu.
3.   Select the command's icon from a toolbar. However, to type the command in the command area, you need to know its name!

Next, we'll look at some elementary *survival* commands.

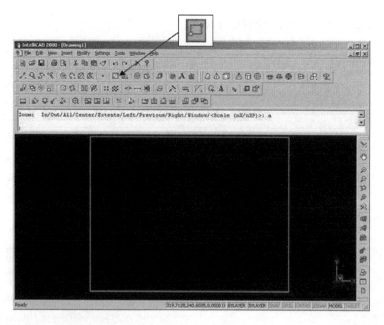

Figure 15.16   The rectangle.

Draw a Rectangle. Select **Insert > Rectangle** (or type **rectange,** the **enter**) from the menu, or click the 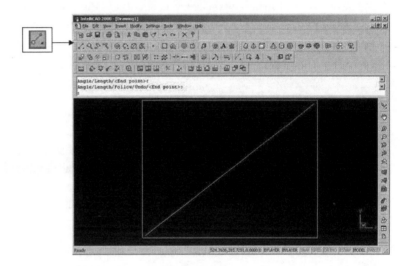 icon, then type: 15, 15, enter; then at the next prompt, 415, 315, enter; these are absolute Cartesian coordinates. Hopefully IntelliCAD drew a rectangle, which fits comfortably in the IntelliCAD graphics area. If you can't see the rectangle, type **z** [**space**] **a** [**space**] (zoom all) - this instructs IntelliCAD to redraw the view, "zooming out" to show all the graphics on the drawing. You should now see the image in Figure 15.16.

Saving a Drawing.   Select the Save icon from the standard toolbar. The drawing has not been saved before, so IntelliCAD will display the SAVE AS dialog box, select the appropriate Drive and Directory (for example: **S:$arch$u1234567**), type the drawing name (for example **TUT1**), and then select "**OK**".

Figure 15.17   The line.

Drawing Lines.   Type **LINE**. Instead of **LINE,** you can also type: **l,** which is an

"alias" - in other words, a short-cut. You can also click the toolbar icon . The exact positions of these lines is not important. Move the crosshair to near the bottom-left of the rectangle and click the left mouse button, then move the crosshair to the top-right of the rectangle and again click the left mouse button. Press **enter** to terminate the command, and then press **enter** again to re-start the command! You should now have something similar to Figure 15.17.

Remember this! If you press **enter** after you finish a command, the command is reissued. Now type: **QUIT, enter**. You will be prompted to save the changes you've made -click OK.

15.2.2 Editing an Existing IntelliCAD Drawing

To load a drawing, start Windows Explorer and select the appropriate Drive and Directory. Once Explorer is showing the correct directory then double-click on your drawing.

If you can't find your drawing (in Windows Explorer) then press F5 (function key 5), this tells Explorer to update the directory display; if you still can't find your drawing then perhaps you saved the drawing in some other directory - load IntelliCAD and then select the File menu, at the bottom of the File menu is a list of recently opened drawings, select your drawing from the list.

Coordinate Systems.   When specifying positions you can use Cartesian or Polar Coordinates. Cartesian coordinates are simply a X value, a comma, and a Y value, for example: **100,100.** Polar coordinates are a Distance followed by a < symbol and an angle, for example: **10 < 25**. Angles are measured in degrees, with 0 = East and 90 = North. Any of these numbers can have decimal values.

The positions specified above are "**absolute coordinates**", because they specify a particular position. IntelliCAD can also use "**relative coordinates**" to specify a position relative to the current position, for example: **5.6,-3.4** and **16.32 < 62.**

So far, we have been using only the fixed World Coordinate System (WCS). The user cannot change the WCS. Its basis directions are the same as the User Coordinate System (UCS) icon, however the UCS is user defined. It is beyond the scope of this tutorial, but you can read about it in the IntelliCAD help pages. Use the F1 function key, or select **Help** > **IntelliCAD** Help, and type UCS as the keyword.

Snap Modes.   It is often useful to be able to draw something from (for example) the end of another shape. IntelliCAD has a large selection of "snap modes" for this purpose. The most commonly used snap modes are "Endpoint" (which snaps to the end of the selected graphics entity) and "Intersection" (which snaps to the intersection of two graphics entities).

The entity snap modes can either be typed or they can be selected from the snap toolbar:

To get IntelliCAD to display the Entity Snap Modes toolbar, select "Toolbars" from the "View" menu and then select "Toolbars" and then "Entity Snap". Or, right-click the mouse anywhere in the free gray area containing the toolbar icons, see Figure 15.18. Left-click on "Entity Snaps" in the selection window. Note, you can move the toolbars by left-clicking and holding on the double stripe at the left end of a toolbar and dragging it to the location you want. A simple way to turn Entity Snap ON or OFF, is to double-click on "ESNAP" in the status Area. If no snap settings have been set, the "Esnap Settings" dialog box will be displayed.

Drawing using ESNAP.   Let's draw a line that is positioned accurately with respect to the line we drew earlier. The ⬛ icon causes the cursor to snap to the end point of a line. Type l and press enter. At the default prompt <Start of line> click the icon. You should see what appears in Figure 15.19.

Move the cursor box so that it covers the end of the line near the lower left corner of the rectangle and right-click. Place the end point of the line in the upper left area of the rectangle so you get something like that shown in Figure 15.20.

Drawing a Circle Tangent to Two Lines.   Click and hold the ⬛ toolbar icon. Then select the Circle Radius-Tangents icon, second from the bottom, shown in Figure 15.21. Type "50" when prompted for the **Radius of circle** in the command area, and press enter. Select one of the lines as the **first tangent point** by moving the small cursor box to any location on the chosen line and left-clicking. Move the cursor box to any location on the other line and left-click. A circle with a radius of 50 units will be drawn tangent to the two lines, see Figure 15.22.

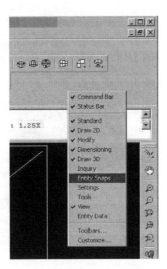

Figure 15.18   Entity Snaps.

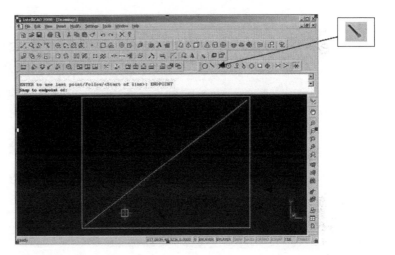

Figure 15.19   Start of line.

Erasing Objects.   When the need arises to erase objects from the drawing, select **erase** from the modify menu (or type: **E, enter**). Let's erase the upper tangent line to the circle. Click anywhere on the line and press **enter.** You will see something like Figure 15.23. Now press **enter**. IntelliCAD 2000 should automatically redraw the area around the erased line. If any image residue remains, press F7 twice to redraw.

An alternate way to delete is to click on the object to be deleted and then press the keyboard's "Delete" key. Click on the line in the same place and press "Delete".

15.2.3 Dimensioning

For this tutorial drawing, as for most drawings, we will have to set some dimensioning parameters. Sections 15.3 and 15.4 go into greater detail, consider this as a light introduction. Select from the menu **Settings > Dimension Settings.** The **Dimension Settings** window will appear, looking something like what is illustrated in Figure 15.24. Now, execute the following steps:

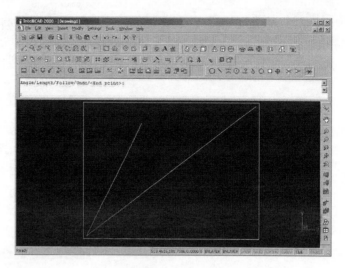

Figure 15.20   Two lines.

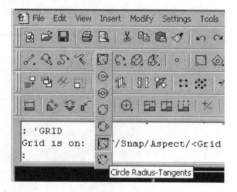

Figure 15.21   Circle Radius-Tangents icon.

1.   Click on the **Arrows** tab, select User-defined arrowheads, and set the **Arrow size** to 12.0000.
2.   Click the **Format** tab and set the **Distance around dimension text** to 6.0000.
3.   Click the **Lines** tab and set the **Origin from offset** to 5.0000; set the Extend past dimension to 4.0000.
4.   Click the **Text** tab and set the **Text height** to 10.0000.
5.   Click the **Units** tab and set the **Decimal places** to 1.

Now dimension the left hand edge of the rectangle. Click the button (linear dimension) in the Dimensioning toolbar. Press ENTER to select entity, and select the left edge of the rectangle. Drag the dimension to a reasonable location. The dimension text should read 300.0.

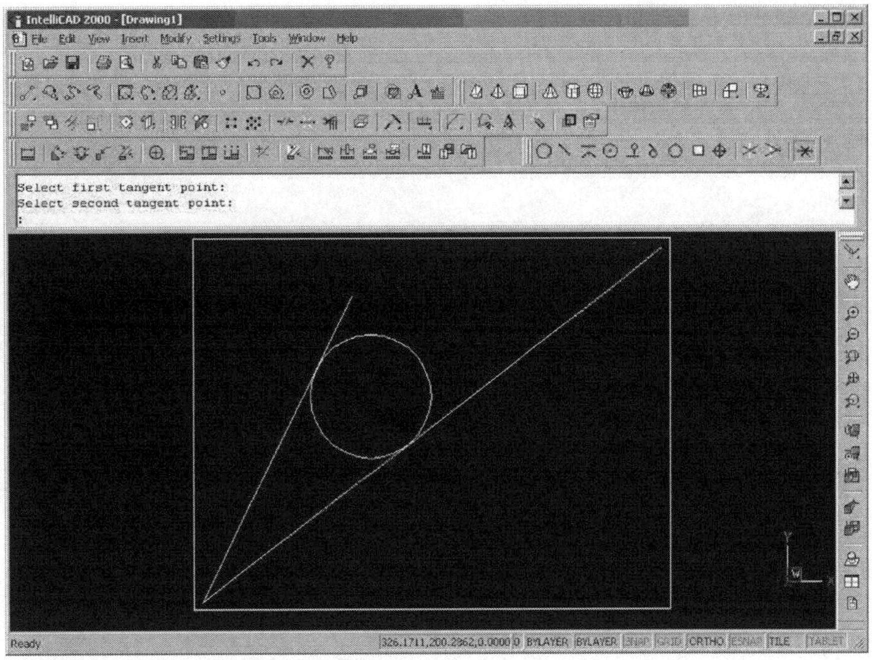

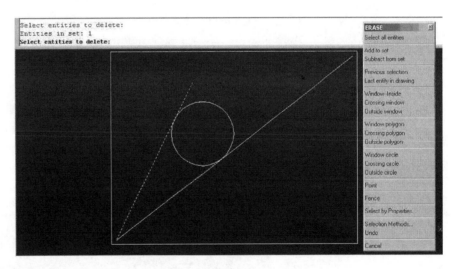

Figure 15.22   Circle tangent to two lines.

Figure 15.23   Line selected to be erased.

Now let's draw arrows on the ends of the line that is tangent to the circle. There are many ways to do this; we shall use the dimensioning leader. Click the  button (leader) in the Dimensioning toolbar. At the prompt **Start of leader** type **end** and press **enter**, or click the  **ESNAP** button. Select one of the ends of the line. For the prompt **Next**

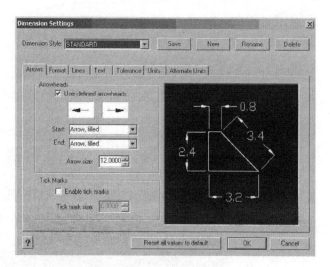

Figure 15.24   The **Dimensions Settings** window.

point, type **mid** and press **enter**, or click the 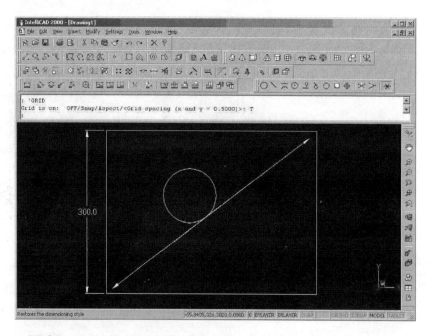 **ESNAP** button. Since we just want the arrow and no dimension text, after pressing **enter**, press the escape button on the keyboard. This will release you from the leader command having drawn an arrow without leader text. This is quite a useful trick. To finish, do the same for the opposite end of the line. Your drawing should now look like the one in Figure 15.25.

15.2.4 Other Useful Commands

To redraw the screen type **r** and press **enter.** This will clean up any items left on the screen after constructing objects.

Figure 15.25   The finished tutorial drawing.

A fast way to redraw is to turn the **grid** on and off. Do this by pressing the function key F7 twice. The **grid** can be used to help draw, especially using **grid snap.**

Zooming and panning are indispensable commands.

Zoom in Real Time.

1. Simultaneously press Ctrl+Shift and click and hold the left mouse button.
2. To zoom in, move the cursor up the screen. To zoom out, move the cursor down the screen.
3. To stop zooming, release the mouse button.

Pan in Real Time.

1. Simultaneously press Ctrl+Shift and click and hold the right mouse button.
2. Move the cursor in the direction you want to pan.
3. To stop panning, release the mouse button.

Hatch **Command.**   The term *hatch* applied to engineering drawing means a pattern used to give the effect of shading. You can view the hatch patterns available for use with IntelliCAD by typing *hatch patterns* in the help index window (see Figure 15.26).

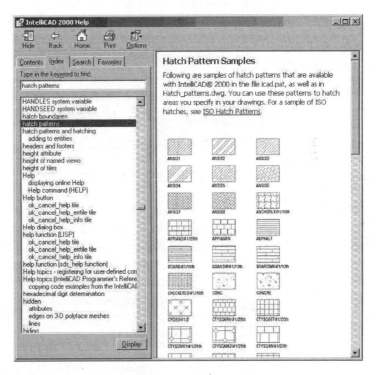

Figure 15.26   Hatch patterns.

The hatch command will be illustrated with a descriptive geometry exercise illustrating the visibility of the pair of intersecting planes. Suppose you had successfully determined the line of intersection (LoX) of the two planes ABC and DEF as shown in Figure 15.27, and established the visibility. Note the LoX and plane boundaries have been used to trim the invisible portions of the occluded planes.

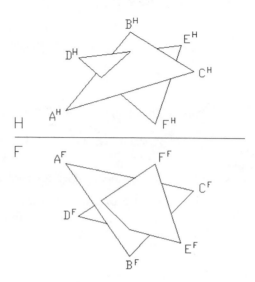

Figure 15.27   Planes ABC and DEF.

There are many ways to go about using the hatch command. The easiest way is to *select an area for hatching*. But, first, you must select a hatch pattern. This can be done using the following steps.

To Specify a Predefined Hatch Pattern.

1. Do one of the following:
    (a) Choose Insert > Hatch.

    (b) On the Draw 2D toolbar, click the Boundary Hatch tool,
    (c) Type *bhatch* and then press Enter.
2. From the Boundary Hatch dialog box, click the Pattern Properties tab.
3. In the Pattern Type list, click Predefined. With Predefined, you can apply a scale factor to make the pattern larger or smaller than the default size.
4. For Scale, enter the scale factor as a percentage of the default.
5. For Angle, enter the angle of the pattern in degrees (1-360). The default angle is clockwise; you can change the angle of any hatch pattern by entering a numerical value.
6. For ISO Pen Width, enter the pen width. If you choose a predefined, ISO standard pattern, you can scale the pattern based on the ISO pen width.
7. To copy the pattern properties from an existing hatch, choose Copy Hatch Properties and select the hatch.
8. To associate the hatch pattern to its boundary entities, under Hatch Attributes, select the Associative check box.
9. To continue, go to the next section and begin with step 2.

To Select an Area for Hatching.

1. Do one of the following:
    (a) Choose Insert > Hatch.

    (b) On the Draw 2D toolbar, click the Boundary Hatch tool,
    (c) Type *bhatch* and then press Enter.
2. From the Boundary Hatch dialog box, click the Boundary tab.
3. Choose one of the following Island Detection Options:
    (a) **Nested Islands** The outer entity and all its islands are considered for hatching.
    (b) **Outer Only** Only the outer entity and its outer island are considered for hatching.
    (c) **Ignore Islands** Only the outer entity is considered for hatching.
4. To keep the boundary, select the Retain Boundaries check box.
5. Click Select Boundary Set and select the entities either individually or by choosing a selection method from the prompt box.
6. To complete entity selection, press Enter.
7. Click Select Area, specify the area to be hatched, and then press Enter.
8. Click OK.

NOTE: When you specify an area to be hatched, you must click within the closed perimeter of the boundary, not on the boundary polyline itself.

For this example, the ANSI37-METRIC pattern was selected and the scale was 0.1. In general, you will have to experiment with various scales until you are happy with the result. Figure 15.28 illustrates one possibility.

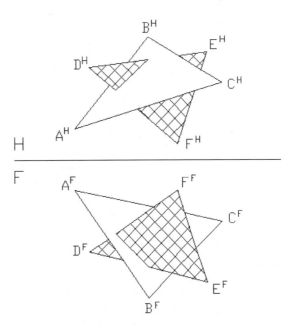

Figure 15.28   The ANSI37-METRIC hatch pattern.

15.2.5 Printing a Drawing.

1. From the menu, select *File > Print* . . .
2. The *Print* dialogue box will pop-up. Click the *Print Setup* . . . button. In the *Print Setup* window that pops-up select either *Portrait*, or *Landscape*, whichever best suits the orientation of your drawing and click on OK
3. Back in the *Print* window, click on *Window* in the *Print Area* options. Additionally, select the *Print only area* within specified window option. Next, click on the *Select Print Area* button.
4. Enclose the entire drawing, including the title block, in the window (move the magnifying-glass cursor to the lower left corner of the drawing and left click. Drag the window to the upper right corner and left click again.
5. Click the *Print Preview* . . . button. If you like what you see, click the *Print* button in the previewer window, otherwise click *Print Settings* and reset the print window.

15.3 INTELLICAD 2000 SHAFT DRAWING TUTORIAL

Intellicad 2000 is an inexpensive yet functional 2D CAD program which re-creates many of the functions of the market dominating 2D CAD programs. Everything we'll do here using Intellicad can be done using the other software, in an only slightly different fashion. We're going to become familiar with this program by using it to re-create Figures 15.5 and 15.6 from the introduction. Remember them?

15.3.1 Starting IntelliCAD

First, let's open Intellicad 2000. If you didn't read Section 15.2, the setup is repeated here. If it is a brand new installation of IntelliCAD 2000, what you should is illustrated in Figure 15.29.

Note that the background colour in Figure 15.29 is different from the figures in Section 15.2. By default, drawings are displayed on a black background. You can change this colour and specify the background screen colour that you want. To change the background colour choose **Tools** > **Options**, and click the **Display** tab. In the following examples, the background colour is white. The colours of geometric entities, text, dimensions, etc. will be automatically adjusted when the background colour changes.

15.3.2 Setting Up IntelliCAD

We need to do a number of things before we should really start drawing. Most importantly, we need to set up our layers, and customize our toolbars so we can move as speedily as possible.

First, let's activate some more toolbars. Right click in the toolbar area, and a menu will pop up, like the one illustrated in Figure 15.30. Click on "Dimensioning" and "Entity Snaps", so that the menu and toolbars looks like those shown in Figure 15.31.

We won't use these toolbars right away, but this is still in general a good time to do this step. It will make you more efficient at this sort of thing in the future if you spend a few minutes setting up the program so it is maximally familiar to you.

Next we should set up some layers. Remember layers are exactly what they sound like. It is as though you are drawing on several transparent sheets, one on top of the other, this gives you the ability to take one sheet away at a time. This is a powerful tool, as we will see. In the meantime, go to the command window, and type:

la<enter>

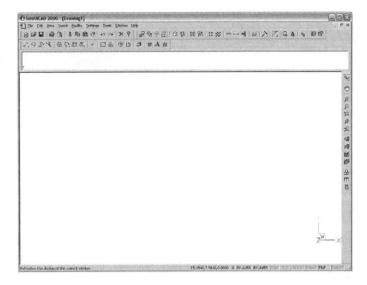

Figure 15.29   The IntelliCAD graphical user interface.

Figure 15.30   The toolbar menu.

The dialog box shown in Figure 15.32 will appear:

We need to add several layers. In order that we can clearly see which layer is which, we should give each layer a different line colour. You can choose whichever colors you want, as the plot must be in black and white, but for the purpose of this exercise, use the color scheme used here.

We also need to change the linetype of certain layers, in order to conform with drawing standards. To create a new layer, we should click the "New Item" icon ( ) not once, but a few times, so that our dialog box looks like Figure 15.33.

Notice " **NewLayer6**" is highlighted. This can be done by clicking any of the layer names, waiting a moment, and clicking again. In this fashion, we can change the names of the layers. Do this slow-double-click thing, and change the name of " **NewLayer6**" to

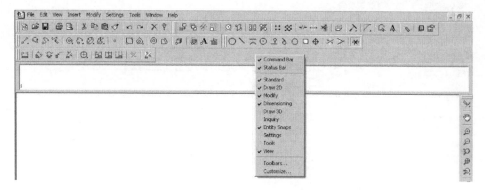

Figure 15.31   Toolbars.

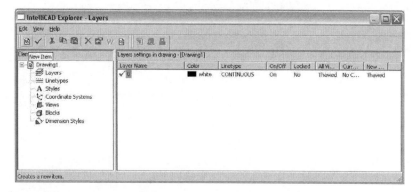

Figure 15.32   Layers in IntelliCAD Explorer.

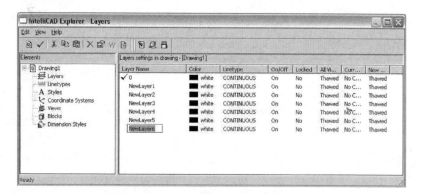

Figure 15.33   Six new layers.

"**OBJ**" By single-clicking in the appropriate box to the right of a given layer's name, we cha change the other attributes, like the layer's screen colour, or linetype. For example, to the right of "**OBJ**", click on the black rectangle that is paradoxically labeled "white". The dialog box illustrated in Figure 15.34 will appear.

This is the colour palette dialog box, shown here in 16 shades of gray. Marvellous. Click on the yellow rectangle.

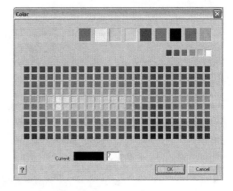

Figure 15.34   Colour palette dialogue box.

Performing the same steps, change the name of "**NewLayer5**" to "**CTR**", and change the colour to red. Now click on the word "**CONTINUOUS**" to the right of "**OBJ**". The dialog box illustrated in Figure 15.35 will appear.

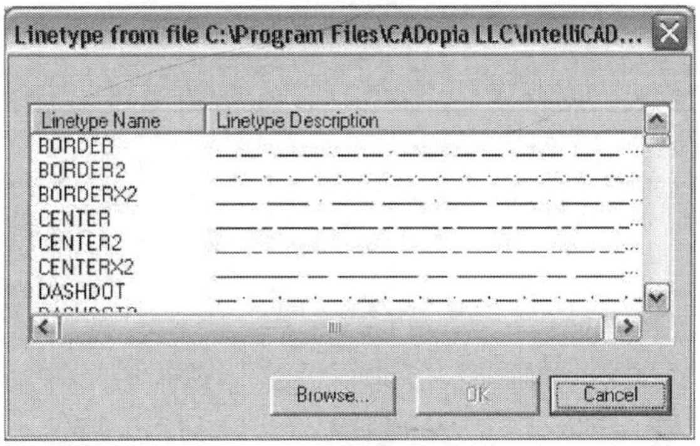

Figure 15.35   Linetype dialogue box.

This dialog shows virtually all of the linetypes used in engineering drawing. We are going to use the **CTR** layer to identify the center points of circles (hence the name), so we use the drawing-standard linetype for this purpose **CENTER**. Choose **CENTER**, and click OK. The resulting layer dialog should now look like that in Figure 15.36

Repeat these steps, creating new layers as needed to wind up with the following layers:

DIM, cyan, CONTINUOUS
HID, light gray (9), HIDDEN (just scroll down)
TEXT, green, CONTINUOUS
TITLE, white, CONTINUOUS
HAT, dark grey (8), CONTINUOUS

We may need other layers later, but we can use the **la** command anytime. Your layers dialog should look like Figure 15.37, now.

Notice the checkmark next to layer 0. The checkmark denotes which layer is "active" that is, which layer we are currently able to draw using. We don't in general want to ever use the 0 layer, so let's instead fast-double-click the **CTR** layer. You should be seeing Figure 15.38.

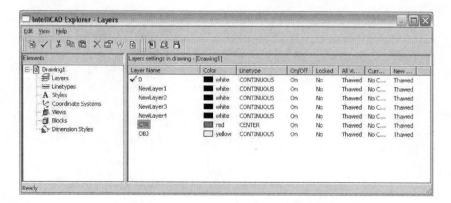

Figure 15.36   Layers.

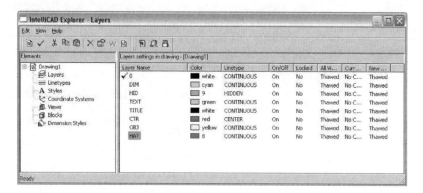

Figure 15.37   Layers.

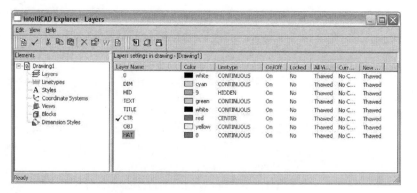

Figure 15.38   Layers.

You might have figured out that **OBJ** stands for object, and we intend to draw the actual geometry of our part using this layer, so I bet you're a little surprised to be asked to use the **CTR** layer. You're going to be shown a really neat trick for quickly drawing geometry. Go ahead and close the layer dialog.

Now, the usual way, save your work so far as **"shaft.dwg"**.

We're going to start with drawing 1 of 2, the shaft, as it has the easiest geometry.

15.3.3 Drawing the Geometry of the Shaft

Recall this sketch shown in Figure 15.39, presented in the introduction to this chapter, Section 15.1.

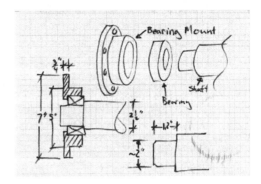

Figure 15.39   Flange mount and bearing conceptual sketch.

Turn on the **"ORTHO"** function in the status area, at the bottom right of the IntelliCAD window, by double clicking on the word **"ORTHO"**, there.

Remember, the **ORTHO** feature means that you can only create features which are directly up and down, or directly side to side from where you start the feature. Let's show this by drawing a line which goes horizontally across the drawing window.

Lets get this right out in the open: Writing these tutorials takes a bearishly long time. We've established that you can execute a command from any of 1) The drop down menus, 2) the toolbar icon, or 3) typing the command in the command window. From here on out, the command will be executed in the way that makes this tutorial the least amount of work to assemble.

We want to draw a line. So do one of the following:

1. Click the **"line"** icon:
2. Use the drop down menus: **Insert>line**
3. Type **"line"** in the command window.

Well, typing line in the command window is far the easiest. There are two reasons for this. One is that so long as the IntelliCAD 2000 window is in the foreground, anything you type will appear in the command window. The other is that you don't have to actually type **"line"**, you can just type **"l"**, and hit enter, and this will still launch the **line** command. Many of IntelliCAD's functions have these contractions. If you suspect there might be one, feel free to use the help menu, accessible by hitting **F1**.

Assuming you're right handed, this command window thing should strike you as being very efficient. One hand is on the mouse, the other is on the keyboard, typing in the commands, economizing on movement. It works really well, and trust me, you will get good at it. So launch the line command by typing:

L <enter>

Click someplace towards the left edge of the graphics area to start the line, and move the mouse towards the right hand side of the graphics area. Notice how the line is perfectly horizontal, however the crosshairs wiggle up and down as you move the mouse. This is the effect of the **ORTHO** command we activated earlier. DO NOT CLICK TO END THE LINE.

Your screen should look like the one shown in Figure 15.40

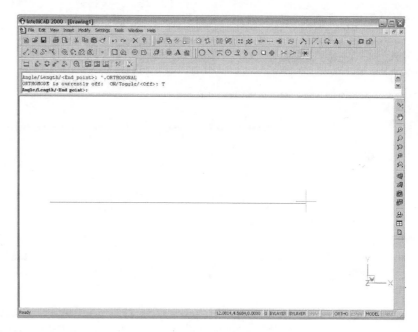

Figure 15.40   Continuous line.

Look in the command window:

```
Angle/Length/<End point>: '.ORTHOGONAL
ORTHOMODE is currently off:  ON/Toggle/<Off>: T
Angle/Length/<End point>:
```

What does that mean? What it means is, you don't have to click to end the line. You can type in coordinates, such as **5,3<enter>** to end the line five units to the left, and three units up from where we started the line. Alternatively, you could type **5<25<enter>**, which will draw a 5 unit long line at 25 degrees from the start click. The really cool one is the one we'll actually use. Type:

14<enter><enter>

in the command window. What has happened is that the computer has drawn a line from the start point, 14 units in the direction of the cursor, which, because of the **ORTHO** command, was horizontally to the right of the start point. The first **<enter>** told the program we were done typing after the "4", the second **<enter>** told the program we were done with the line command. Now, you should have something like the one shown in Figure 15.41.

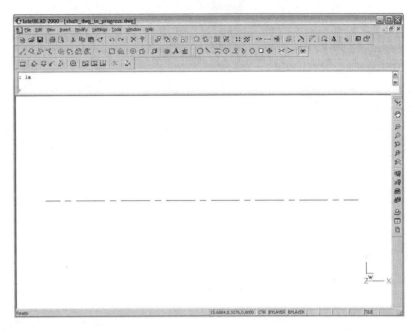

Figure 15.41   Centre line.

Now, draw a vertical line, 4 inches long, that makes a reasonably symmetrical cross with the horizontal line we just drew. Don't worry, it only has to be *reasonably* symmetric. You should wind up with something like Figure 15.42.

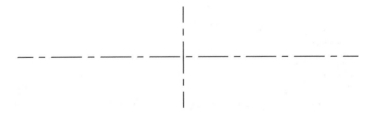

Figure 15.42   Centre lines.

Save your work.

We're taking advantage of the symmetry of the shaft to make our lives easier. We do this using the **"OFFSET"** command, which we can launch by typing in the command window: **O<enter>**

Recall that the **OFFSET** command is an easy way to copy lines and arcs a set distance from the original, along a line perpendicular to that line or arc. What is a line perpendicular to an arc? Well, think of it this way. Offsetting a circle results in concentric circles. Offsetting a line results in parallel, equal length lines.

Let's make some parallel lines. In the command window, type:

O<enter>

IntelliCAD immediately wants an option from you. How far apart should the lines be? Type:

1.25<enter>

Now it wants you to "select an entity". By entity, they mean a line or arc. Choose the horizontal line, move the cursor above it, and click once. You should see something like Figure 15.43.

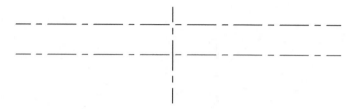

Figure 15.43   Centre lines.

The **"OFFSET"** command should still be active. Click the original horizontal line again, and offset it down this time. You should see something like Figure 15.44.

Figure 15.44   Centre lines.

Hit **<enter>,** or right click to exit the offset command. Now, launch the offset command again. When it asks you for the offset distance, you can either hit enter to use 1.25 again, or you can type in a new number. We want a new number. Type:

0.98425<enter>

No, that number is not just arbitrary. Look at the full technical drawing of the shaft, and see if you can see where this number comes from. You might start getting the idea of where we're going with this.

Offset the original horizontal line both up and down, until you see something like Figure 15.45.

Now, use the offset command to offset the **vertical** line 5 units, and 6.2 units, both left and right, until it looks like Figure 15.46.

Are you starting to see where this is going?

We're going to start using the **TRIM** command to make things clearer. Launch the trim command by typing in the command window:

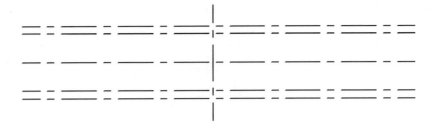

Figure 15.45   Centere lines.

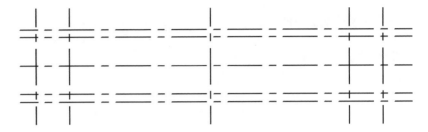

Figure 15.46   Centre lines.

TR<enter>

There is a very important option displayed:

```
: tr

Select cutting entities for trim <ENTER to select all>:
```

If you want to cut one particular line, with one other particular line, you would click one line to act as the scissors, and hit **<enter>,** and another line to be cut, on the side you want to have disappear, then hit **<enter>.**

For our purposes we want to hit **<enter>** to select all. This means that when we click a line, it will vanish to the next line it crosses. You selected all, and now you are ready to trim. Click on one of the lines in the upper right corner, so that your drawing looks like Figure 15.47.

Now that you have mastered the trim command, keep trimming until your drawing looks like Figure 15.48.

Now, delete the vertical centerline, and select (by simply left clicking on them) all the lines that are not the original horizontal centerline we started with. You should see something like Figure 15.49.

Now that all those lines are selected, while the pointer is over any of the selected lines, hold down the **right mouse button** until a menu appears. From that menu, choose **PROPERTIES**. A dialog box will appear like Figure 15.50.

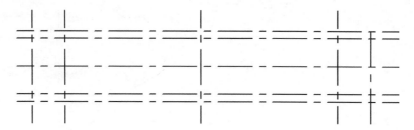

Figure 15.47   Trimmed centre line.

Figure 15.48   Something looking more like the shaft.

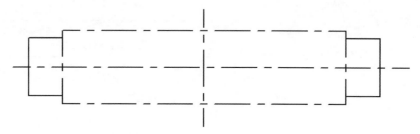

Figure 15.49   Selected centre lines.

In the upper left corner there is a drop down menu called "**Layer**" which is highlighted in the above figure. Click the arrow at the right, and a menu will drop down, listing all the available layers. Select "**OBJ**", and click **OK**. Your drawing should now look like Figure 15.51.

And, just like that, we are nearly done the side view of the shaft!

Remember, the ends of the stepped shaft have to be pressed into the bore of the bearings we selected. He sharp edges of the shaft will make it really hard to get the shaft started into the hole. We need to put a chamfer on the shaft ends. This is really easy. In the command window, type:

Chamfer<enter>

or

Cha<enter>

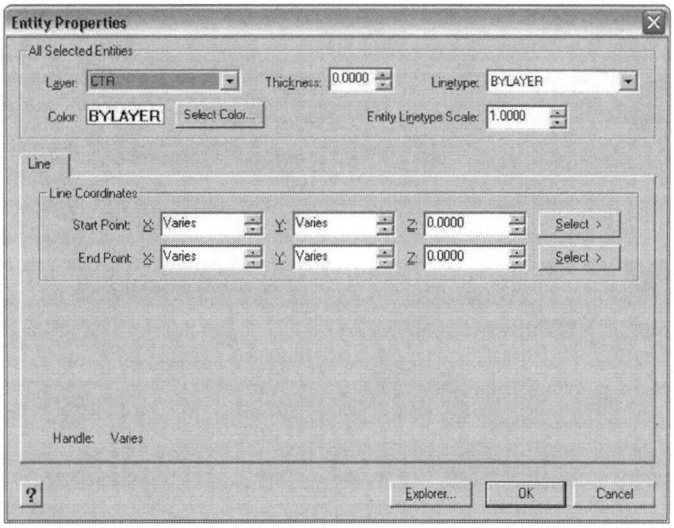

Figure 15.50   Entity properties.

Figure 15.51   Starting to look more like the shaft.

You may not use the **CHAMFER** command very often so it might be useful to recognize and use its icon: 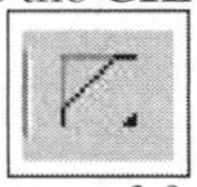 . It might not be worth your while remembering the contractions (ie cha) for lesser used functions.

As with nearly every other command there are options for the **CHAMFER** command which are shown in the command window.

```
: cha

Chamfer (dist1=0.5000, dist2=0.5000):  Settings/Polyline/<Select first entity>:
```

Obviously, chamfer distances of 1/2 unit and 1/2 unit are way too large, so we need to type:

S<enter>

This brings up another dialog box! See Figure 15.52.

Change the distances in the lower left hand corner from 0.5 and 0.5 to 0.05 and 0.05, and click **OK**.

Now click, one after the other, on the two lines indicated in the left side of Figure 15.53.

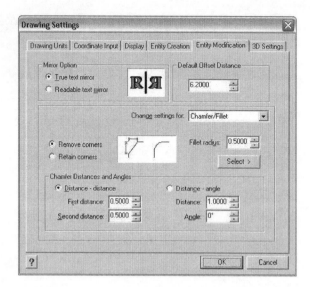

Figure 15.52   Drawing settings.

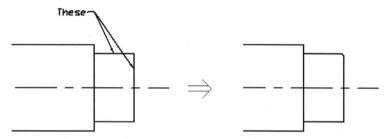

Figure 15.53   Selected lines for the chamfer.

Recall that you can repeat the last command by right clicking anywhere in the drawing area. Right click to repeat the CHAMFER command, and chamfer the other 3 corners, so that you drawing looks like Figure 15.54.

Figure 15.54   Almost the shaft.

Last but not least, we need to draw lines connecting the edges of the chamfers, so that this two dimensional representation of the side view of the shaft will resemble the view from the side of an actual 3D shaft.

We need to set an entity snap, and draw some lines. Entity snaps which are selected BEFORE the IntelliCAD command stay activated over many operations, and must be manually turned off. Entity snaps which are activated AFTER the IntelliCAD command are automatically disabled after one use. We wish to emply an "**INTERSECTION**" snap

several times, so we will click the icon for the intersection snap: .

Notice that this toolbar button "depresses" and remains "depressed". No, I am not referring to a general sense of malaise cause by using IntelliCAD, I am saying that the button looks as if it has been pushed, and stayed in afterwards.

Another neat trick is that an entity snap menu can be activated by holding down **<shift>**, and right clicking anywhere. Handy.

Now, we need to change the active layer. Activate the layer dialog by typing LA, and change the active layer to OBJ.

Now activate the "**LINE**" command, by typing **LINE** or **L** in the command window (note it does not have to be uppercase), or clicking the toolbar icon, as before.

The **INTERSECTION** entity snap means that the line we start drawing by left clicking will start on the closest intersection of two pre-existing lines, so long as that intersection is inside the "box" of the cursor. Very handy. Similarly, the line will terminate at the closest intersection inside the box, when we left click again.

Draw two lines to make your drawing look like Figure 15.55.

Figure 15.55   Completed side view of the shaft.

And that's it! We are finished drawing the side view of the stepped shaft!
Save your work!

Now, we need to do an end view. You saved your work, right? OK, move the view over

a bit, using the pan icon ( ) bar at the bottom of the IntelliCAD window. It should look Figure 15.56.

Now, switch the active layer back to **CTR**. Remember, the layer dialog can be accesses using the command **LA**, and the active layer is the one with the checkmark next to it.

Leave the **ORTHO** command active, as well as the entity snap **INTERSECTION**.

Also activate the entity snaps **ENDPOINT** ( ) and **PERPENDICULAR** ( ).

Using these active commands, draw a number of lines, so your drawing looks similar to Figure 15.57.

These are going to be used as construction lines. The most important thing to assure is that the line extending from the center line of the shaft is **shorter** than the others.

Change the active layer to **OBJ**. Ensure that the entity snaps **ENDPOINT, PER-PENDICULAR** and **INTERSECTION** are still active. Also activate the **CENTER**

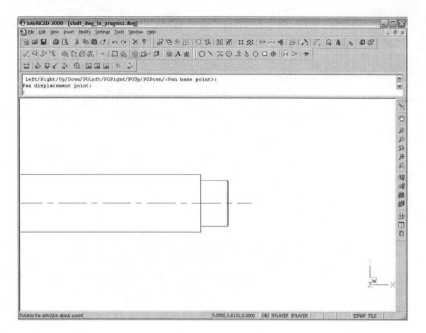

Figure 15.56   Panned shaft view.

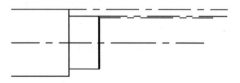

Figure 15.57   Construction lines.

( ) entity snap. Remember, the entity snaps are continuously active, if they look as if they were real buttons that have stayed "pushed", like this:

Also remember that any snap you activate before activating a drawing command (like **LINE**) will remain active until you manually de-activate it.

If you activate **ENDPOINT** then **LINE**, the **ENDPOINT** snap will remain active after you're finished your next "click". If you activate **LINE**, then **ENDPOINT**, the **ENDPOINT** snap will de-activate after your next click. OK, back to the drawing:

Activate the circle command, by locating it in the menu (Insert > circle), clicking the icon ( ), or typing in the command window:

C<enter>

Click on the extension of the centerline we drew to locate the center of the circle, and click as close as possible to the next line directly upward. The entity snaps we activated earlier make this very easy. Your drawing should look like Figure 15.58.

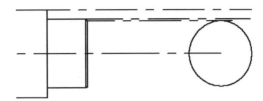

Figure 15.58   Construction lines.

What we've done is created what are called "construction lines", so named because we use them to construct our geometry, then we delete them! The circle we have just drawn has precisely the diameter of the outer chamfered part of the stepped shaft. I think you see where this is going.

Draw two more circles, the same way the first was done, touching the two construction lines we haven't used already, so that your drawing looks like Figure 15.59.

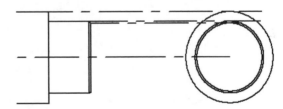

Figure 15.59   Construction lines.

Now, delete the construction lines, and your drawing should resemble Figure 15.60. We're done the geometry of the shaft!

Save your work! Now, all we need to do is add the border and dimensions.

15.3.4 Inserting and Formatting the Title Block in Paper Space

In the lower right hand corner, you will see, once again, the status area:

15.4540,7.9810,0.0000   0   BYLAYER   BYLAYER   SNAP   GRID   ORTHO   ESNAP   TILE   TABLET

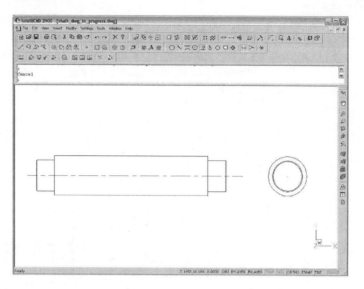

Figure 15.60   Two views of the shaft.

Notice, second from the right, is the word "**TILE**". What tile refers to is the orientation of the drawing window(s). We are looking through one, but if there were more than one, they would be tiled.

Double click the word **TILE**. Are the usual two other ways to do this, but for this, they are a pain in the neck. Stick with double clicking the word in the status area.

When you double click **TILE**, the following dialog shown in Figure 15.61 appears.

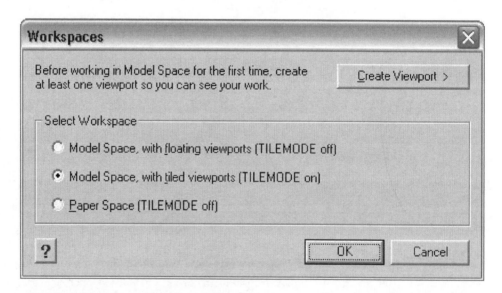

Figure 15.61   Workspaces dialogue box.

Click the radio button to the left of "Paper Space (**TILEMODE off**)", and **OK**. Don't Panic, the shaft is supposed to disappear right then.

What this has done is moved us from the design process to the drawing process. We aren't thinking about the geometry of the part, now, we're thinking about how we'll turn this into a good engineering drawing. Hence, we aren't concerned with the <u>model</u>, but with the <u>paper</u>.

From the drop down menus, select:

Insert > Insert Block

Which launches the shown in Figure 15.62.

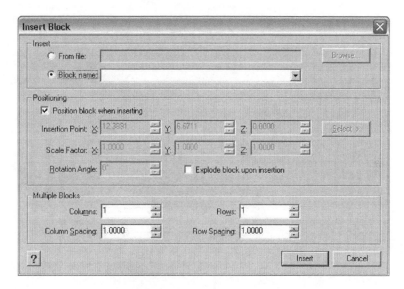

Figure 15.62   Insert Block dialogue box.

Select the radio button next to "From file:". The "Browse" button will become available. Click "Browse", and find the file "TitleBlock.dwg". Highlight it, and click OK.

The "Insert Block" dialog above will appear, again. Un-check the box next to "Position block when inserting", and modify the values in the window until the dialog appears like Figure 15.63.

What we've told IntelliCAD is that we'd like to insert the drawing file "Title-Block.dwg" as a block, at the origin, using a scale factor of 1. A block is simply a group of entities that have been associated with one another, and are treated as one entity.

Your IntelliCAD window should now look like Figure 15.64.

Save your work.

There are a number of other options which must be setup, to tell IntelliCAD what size of paper we intend to print on, and what parts of the virtual "paper" that is our drawing window in paperspace we intend to print on that paper.

From the drop down menus, select:

File > Print Setup

You will see the dialog illustrated in Figure 15.65, with the possible exception of which system printer you have active:

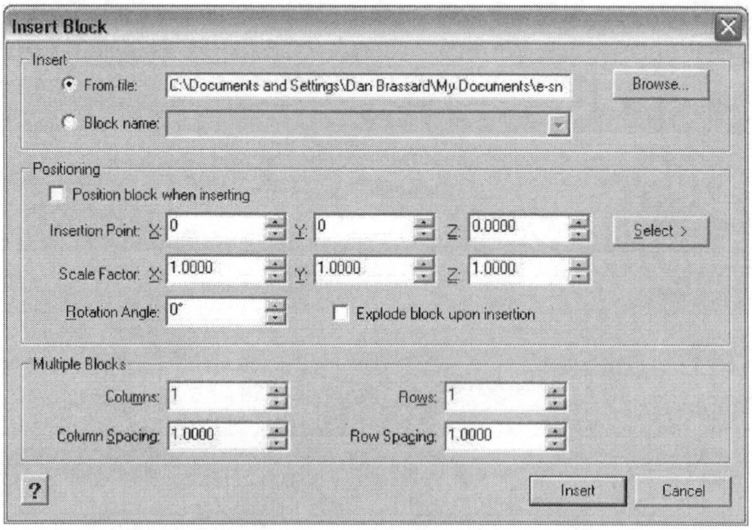

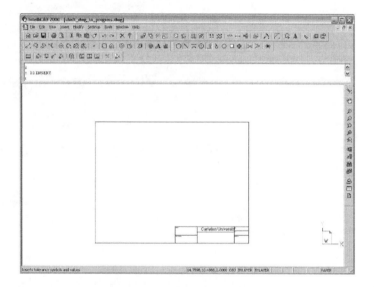

Figure 15.63   Insert Block dialogue box.

Figure 15.64   Inserted title block.

Change Orientation to "Landscape", and make sure the size is set to "Letter", the default. Ensure that next to "Name" is the designation of the printer you actually intend to use. Once all the above are set up, click **OK**.

You will have to perform this "Print Setup" step every time you open IntelliCAD. Sorry.

Next, we must define the limits of the "domain" of paperspace that we actually want to use as a drawing. We do this using the "**LIMITS**" command. Before we actually set the drawing limits, it is important to remember 3 things here:

1.   We inserted the Title Block at 0,0

2.   Letter size paper, in the landscape orientation is 11" × 8.5".

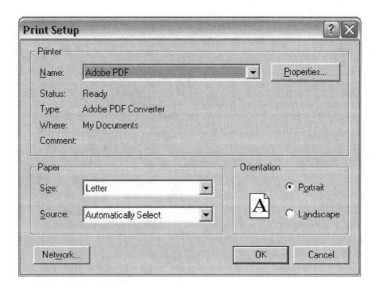

Figure 15.65   Print Setup dialogue box.

3.   The title block is 10.5" × 8".

Activate the **LIMITS** command by typing in the command window:

LIMITS<enter>

The following text appears in the command window:

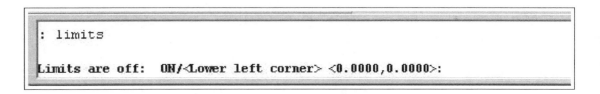

This is asking for the coordinate in paperspace that will be the lower left hand corner of the actual piece of paper. In order to center our Title Block on the piece of paper, we should type in the command window:

−0.25,−0.25 <enter>

Now, IntelliCAD wants us to locate th upper right hand corner of the piece of paper. Type in the command window:

@11,8.5 <enter>

There. Now we've set up our drawing. To see the effect of all this, from the drop down menu, select

File > print

The dialog illustrated in Figure 15.66 will appear.

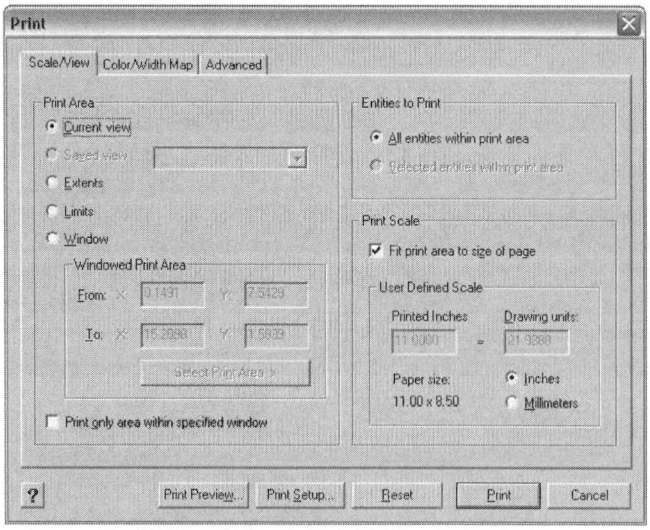

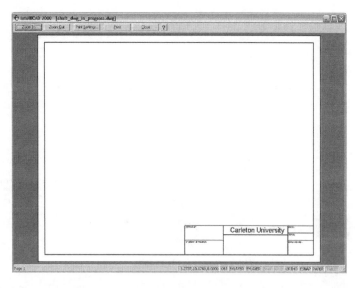

Figure 15.66   Print dialogue box.

Under "Print Area", click the radio button next to "Limits". Now, our printout will include everything within the "limits" we defined a minute ago. Under "Print Scale", uncheck "Fit print area to size of page", and change the scale to 1 Printed inch = 1 Drawing Unit. **DO NOT CLICK OK!**

Just for fun, click the "Print Preview" button at bottom, just left of center. Your window should then look like Figure 15.67. Exactly what we're looking for, minus a stepped shaft,

Figure 15.67   Print preview.

give or take.

Save your Work!

15.3.5 Creating a Viewport

You should have your entity snaps still activated, as previous. Using the LA command, create a new layer, called **VPORTS**, and give it the color **WHITE**. Make sure **VPORTS** is the active layer.

What we need to do now is open a window inside our title block which will allow us to see the drawing geometry, while setting some scale factor. To do this, we use the MVIEW command. In the command window, type:

MVIEW

The **MVIEW** command will ask you to choose two corners, choose the locations shown below. Remember, the object snaps are still active, and will help you. See Figure 15.68.

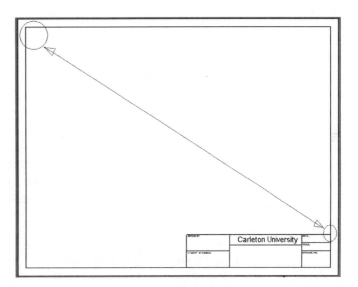

Figure 15.68   Choose two corners.

Your IntelliCAD window should look like Figure 15.69.

You have created a viewport, through which we can see the geometry of the shaft, fitted into the title block! Remember, that centerline we drew first that is still in the middle shaft was 14 units long. The long dimension of the title block is just 10.5 units, so we must be seeing things which exist in paperspace at one scale, while viewing things that exist in model space at another scale. This is very, very powerful.

You will notice that so long as you are in paperspace, you cannot alter your model geometry. This is OK, as you can't accidentally foul it up. Now, here is the really cool part: Activate the **LAYERS** dialog, by typing LA in the command window.

Make the DIM layer active. Now, by single clicking on the word "**THAWED**" to the right of the word "**VPORTS**", freeze the **VPORTS** layer. The word **THAWED** will be replaced by the word **FROZEN**.

Close the LAYERS dialog. You will see that the viewport border has disappeared, but the shaft is still visible. One step closer to a clear and legible engineering drawing.

Now, we know that the Title Block is at one scale, but the Shaft is at another. We need to know just exactly which is which, and more importantly, we need to specify which is which.

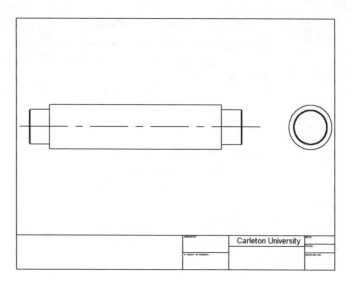

Figure 15.69   Viewport.

In the status area, double click the word **PAPER** (remember, it was double click-ing **TILE** that let us switch to paperspace), then, from the dialog which comes up, select "**Model Space with floating viewports (TILEMODE off)**", and click OK.

Now, we are working directly in modelspace, while looking thorough our viewport in paperspace. This lets us place our dimensions properly. We need to make sure we are looking at the shaft at some scale which is sensible. 4:1 or 1:4 are examples of sensible scales. 321.6:5 is not a sensible scale. It has to be a handy multiplication.

We need to use the ZOOM command to look at the shaft, through it's viewport, at some appropriate scale factor. In the command window, type:

ZOOM <enter>

You will see a window as follows:

Now, type:

0.5XP <enter>

The Title block will stay the same, but the shaft will shrink a small amount. What has happened is the shaft model has been zoomed to appear at 1/2(0.5) scale, as compared with paperspace (XP). Get it? XP, by paperspace.

Return to paperspace by double clicking on the word **MODEL** in the status area, and selecting the appropriate radio button, then OK.

Use the pan and zoom functions to arrange your border so that you drawing looks like Figure 15.70. Then, return to modelspace.

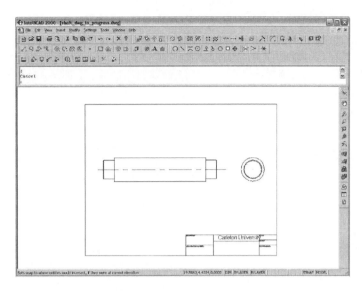

Figure 15.70   Paperspace.

IMPORTANT NOTE: Do not PAN or ZOOM while you are looking at modelspace through a viewport in paperspace. Switch back to paperspace before using these commands!

Save your Work.

15.3.6 Dimensioning the Drawing

In other CAD packages, it is possible to dimension in Paperspace, and have the dimensions reference the geometry of the model. IntelliCAD is not one of those packages. Because we cannot dimension in paperspace, we must do so in modelspace. Remember, however, modelspace is at 1/2 scale with respect to paperspace, so we will have to scale our dimensions to match. No problem.

IntelliCAD is a little funny, though. It is important to get the dimensions right the first time, as they are very difficult to individually modify. If a given dimension has the wrong number of decimal places, the wrong tolerance, etc., it must be deleted, and redone from scratch. A pain.

From the dropdown menu, select:

Settings > Dimension Settings

The very fist dimension we want to place is the dimension of the diameter of the narrow portions of the shaft, with the appropriate dimensions. The appropriate dimensions can be read directly from the Timken Bearing catalog tables in the Introduction.

You should be looking at the Dimension setting dialog, as in Figure 15.71. Notice in the upper left corner, there is a grayed drop down menu with the word **STANDARD** in it. This is good news for us, as it means that the programmers of IntelliCAD have set the default dimension style to one of the many industry standards. In the name of efficiency, we'll stick with that standard.

The two tabs in the dimension dialog we will be most concerned with are the **TOLERANCE** tab, and the **UNITS** tab. Click on the **TOLERANCE** tab. You should see the window shown in Figure 15.72.

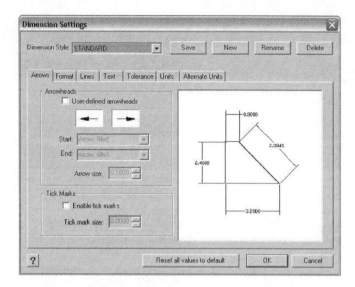

Figure 15.71   Dimension setting dialog.

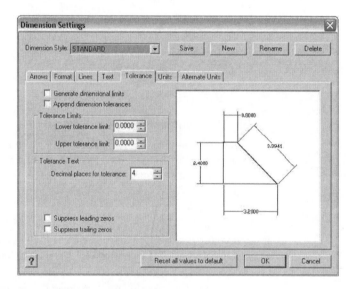

Figure 15.72   Tolerance setting dialog.

Check the box next to "Append dimension tolerances". Recall that the tolerance we wish to show on the diameter of the reduced portions of the shaft is as follows:

$$1.9685\genfrac{}{}{0pt}{}{+\ 0.0025}{+\ 0.0015}$$

If, in the dialog above, we put in the numbers 0.0015 as the tolerance lower limit, and 0.0025 as the tolerance upper limit, we would get a tolerance display like this:

$$1.9685\genfrac{}{}{0pt}{}{+\ 0.0025}{-\ 0.0015}$$

This is obviously not right, so we need to enter −0.0015 as the lower tolerance limit. Just like in math, a negative times a negative equals a positive! The software enters a negative for the lower limit, so to have it display a positive, we have to fiddle. No problem, right?

Your Dimension settings dialog should look like Figure 15.73.

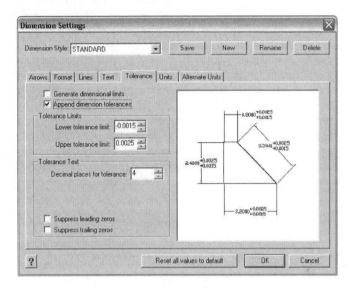

Figure 15.73   Dimension settings with tolerances.

Notice in particular the preview window, with our lovely dimensions, all set up. Now click on the **UNITS** tab. You should see Figure 15.74.

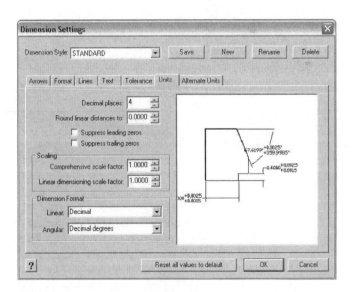

Figure 15.74   Units dimension settings dialogue box.

First, we need to ensure that we will see 4 decimal places. The number of decimal places is displayed in the little window next to "**Decimal places:**". By default it is four decimal places. Great. We also need to set a **comprehensive scale factor**, under **Scaling**.

Recall that we are looking at the modelspace objects at a scale factor of 1/2. We want the dimensions to appear at 1:1 scale, so we must set a comprehensive scale factor of 2. Thus, the dimensions will be twice as large, so when viewed at 1/2 scale, will be the right size. No problem.

Now, we're going to place our first dimension. Make sure that you haven't turned off any of those entity snaps! Those will be very useful in placing dimensions. Also ensure that the word appears in the status area.

From the toolbars, locate the linear dimension icon (   ), and click it. Now, on the drawing select the corners of the step, as shown in Figure 15.75.

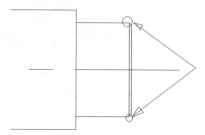

Figure 15.75   Select the intersections shown.

Now, you can place your dimension. Wherever you click will be the position that the numerical value of the distance will be placed. Place the dimension as in Figure 15.76.

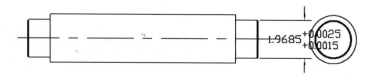

Figure 15.76   Dimensions.

Now, you might have noticed that this looks awful. No problem. Left click anywhere on the dimension to select it, and use the "grips" (green squares) to drag and drop the dimension value where you want it. Place it as shown in Figure 15.77.

Save your work.

Now, we don't need any more toleranced dimensions, right? So we need to make some changes in the dimension setting dialog box. Essentially, we need to turn off the tolerances, and reduce the number of decimal places to two. Recall that to access the dialog, use the pull down menus:

Settings > Dimension Settings

Click the **UNITS** tab, and change the values until you see the following Figure 15.78.

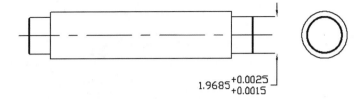

Figure 15.77   Dimension placement.

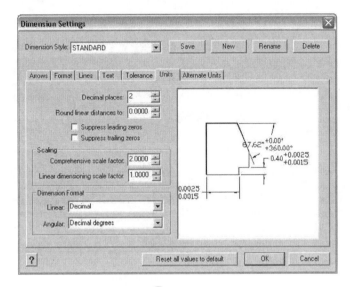

Figure 15.78   Dimension settings: units.

The click the Tolerance tab, and un-check the "Append dimension tolerances" option, until the dialog looks like Figure 15.79.

No problem. Go back to your drawing, and place some more linear dimensions, until your drawing looks like Figure 15.80.

IntelliCAD has one great virtue. It is free. This, in turn, means the university can afford to purchase the licence. That being the case, it has certain limitations, and one of those limitations is that you will never get the dimensions to behave properly. Leaders will be the wrong length, as will extension lines. Extension lines will meet the drawing at the wrong place, and there is no way to fix it. In any other major package, these issues would be fixable, but we will have to live with them.

Now, we want to place a diametral dimension. In the dimension toolbar, locate this

icon: ()

Read the next line completely, before doing what it says:

left click on the above icon, and HOLD DOWN THE MOUSE BUTTON.

The icon will drop down, like this: (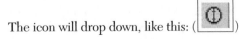)

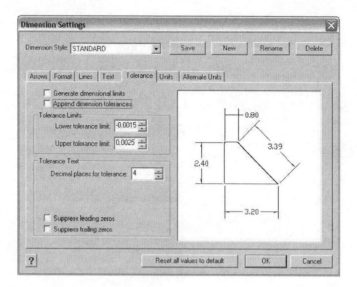

Figure 15.79   Dimension settings: tolerances.

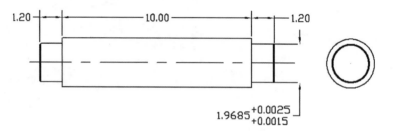

Figure 15.80   Linear Dimensions.

You want to click the icon in that drop down that looks like a diameter:

Now, that icon is a "**DIAMETER**" dimension until you do all that again. Which you won't, right?

So, click the **DIAMETER** icon, and, just by clicking on the circle once, then placing the dimension, dimension the outermost circle of the end view, like Figure 15.81.

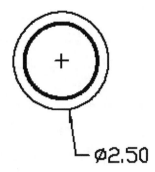

Figure 15.81   Diameter Dimension.

Pretty easy, eh? The only thing we have left to do, is dimension the chamfer, which we

do using a leader. Locate and click on the LEADER icon (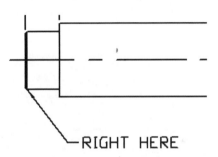), in the dimension toolbar.
Click on the bottom left part of the chamfer, as illustrated in Figure 15.82.

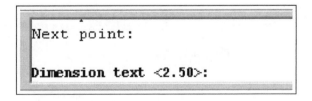

Figure 15.82   Diameter Dimension.

left click again where you wish the "elbow" in the leader to be, then right click, or
hit enter to finish drawing the leader line itself. You will see a prompt in the command
window, something like this:

```
Next point:

Dimension text <2.50>:
```

Type in the command window the text you want to appear:

    BREAK EDGE 0.05 <enter>

You should have a drawing like Figure 15.83.
And, we are done dimensioning the shaft! Not too bad, eh?

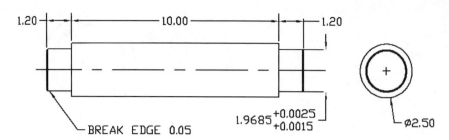

Figure 15.83   Dimension shaft.

All we need to do now is insert the text in the title block, and insert that general tolerance note. We leave the title block text until last, as the information in it may change as the drawing progresses, and there is no point in doing work twice.

Save your work.

15.3.7 Inserting Text.

Change the active view to **PAPERSPACE** by double clicking the word **MODEL** in the status area, and selecting the **PAPERSACE** radio button in the resulting dialog.

Use the dynamic pan and zoom functions to move in on the lower left corner of the title block, as in Figure 15.84.

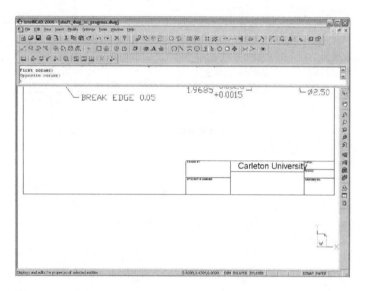

Figure 15.84   Panned drawing.

We need to learn how to insert text, now. Guess what, it's dead easy. First, turn off all the entity snaps. Set the active layer to **TEXT**. In the draw toolbar, where we activated

the **LINE** command, a long time ago, find the **TEXT** icon (![A icon]), and click it. You will see the following prompt in the command window:

```
:
: DTEXT
Text: Style/Align/Fit/Center/Middle/Right/Justify/<Start point>:
```

Click in the box marked DRAWN BY: as shown in Figure 15.85.

DRAWN BY

STUDENT ID NUMBER:

Figure 15.85   DRAWN BY box.

Once you click there (don't worry about the precise location; this is just about looking pretty), you will see the following prompt in the command window:

```
: DTEXT
Text: Style/Align/Fit/Center/Middle/Right/Justify/<Start point>:
Height of text <0.1250>:
```

You may have any number between the <>'s. We want to change it to 0.125. It's not really important, as the height will have to change based on the length of your name! Type in:

0.125<enter>

It will now prompt you for a rotation angle. 0 is fine, so just hit <enter>. Then it will prompt you to enter your name. Do so, and type <enter>. You should now see something like Figure 15.86.

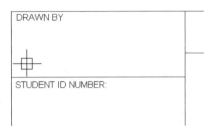

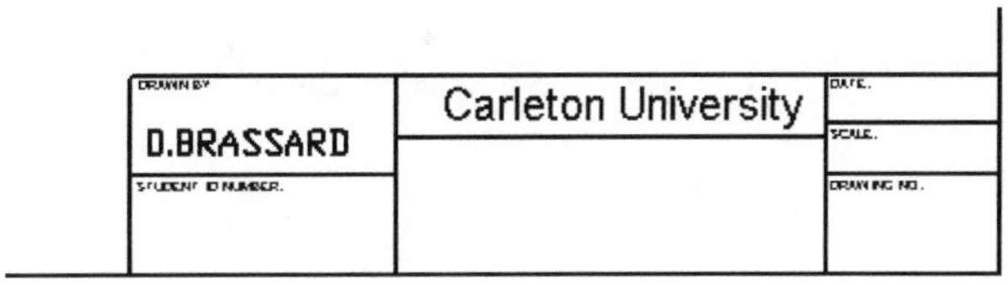

DRAWN BY

D.BRASSARD   Carleton University   DATE.

SCALE.

STUDENT ID NUMBER.   DRAWING NO.

Figure 15.86   Inserted text.

Now, you're simply going to do the same thing a few more times, until your text box looks like this, except with your name and student number, see Figure 15.87. Using the sizes, as illustrated in Figure 15.88. We are within sniffing distance of being done, here. Let's insert the general tolerance note. From the drop down menus, select:

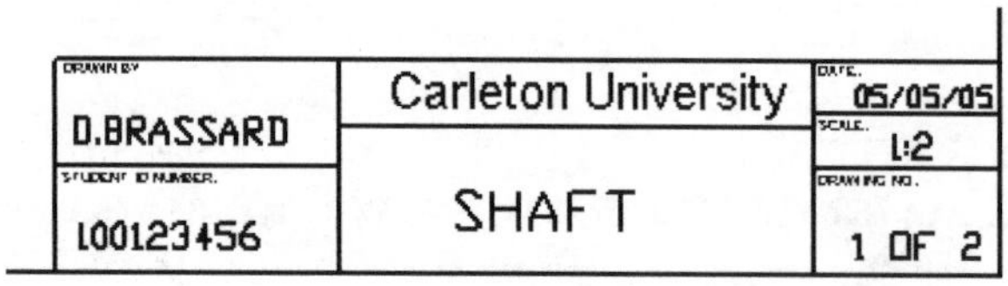

DRAWN BY	Carleton University	DATE. 05/05/05
D.BRASSARD		SCALE. 1:2
STUDENT ID NUMBER. L00123456	SHAFT	DRAWING NO. 1 OF 2

Figure 15.87   Filled in title block.

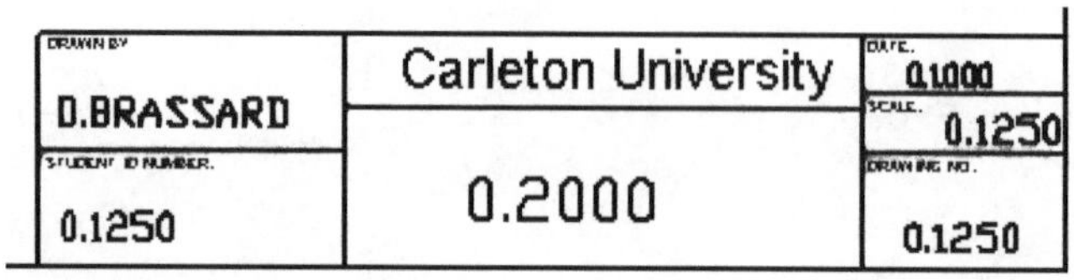

DRAWN BY	Carleton University	DATE. 0.1000
D.BRASSARD		SCALE. 0.1250
STUDENT ID NUMBER. 0.1250	0.2000	DRAWING NO. 0.1250

Figure 15.88   Filled in title block.

Insert > Insert Block

And, just as we did to insert the Title Block itself, click on the radio button next to "**From file:**", and click **BROWSE**. Navigate to the **file tolerance_note.dwg**, and click **OK**, then **INSERT**.

Now, we will be prompted to select the location to insert the block. First, activate the

ENDPOINT entity snap (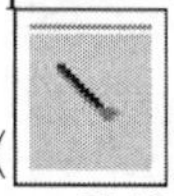). Since we are activating ENDPOINT after activating the command (in this case INSERT), it will only remain active for one click.

Select the location shown in Figure 15.89.

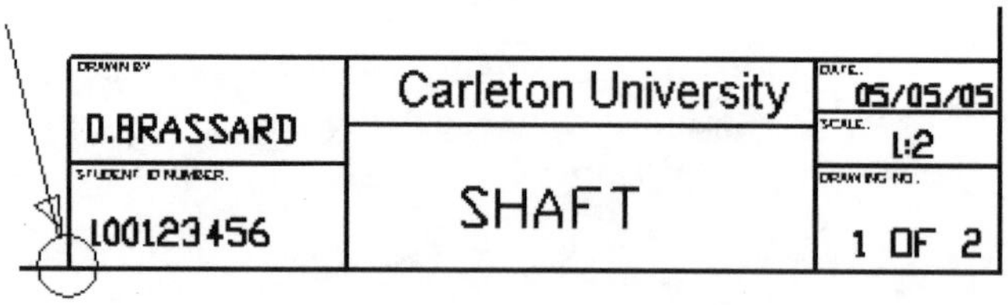

DRAWN BY	Carleton University	DATE. 05/05/05
D.BRASSARD		SCALE. 1:2
STUDENT ID NUMBER. L00123456	SHAFT	DRAWING NO. 1 OF 2

Figure 15.89   Select this end-point.

IntelliCAD will now prompt you to specify scale factors and rotation angles. Click **<enter>** through them until they stop showing up. You should now have something similar to Figure 15.90.

Two more bits of text, and the drawing is done. We need to tell the machinist what units we've used for this drawing, and we need to tell the machinist what to make the part out of. Using the **TEXT** command, as before, inset text at a height of **0.1800** as in Figure 15.91.

There is just one more bit of bookkeeping left. It is customary, in engineering drawings, for the lines defining the geometry of the part be thicker than the lines which

TOLERANCES EXCEPT AS OTHERWISE STATED	DRAWN BY D.BRASSARD	Carleton University	DATE. 05/05/05
.XXX +/- 0.0005 .XX +/- 0.005 .X +/- 0.05 ANGLE +/-0.5	STUDENT ID NUMBER. 100123456	SHAFT	SCALE. 1:2 DRAWING NO. 1 OF 2

Figure 15.90   Tolerance note.

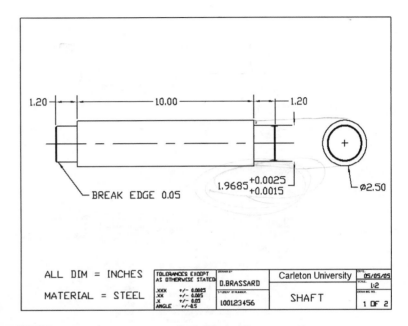

Figure 15.91   Dimensions, notes, and title block information.

represent centers, dimensions, etc. In order to do this, we use the print dialog, which can be accessed from the drop down menus:

File > Print

The second tab of the resulting dialog box is "Color/Width Map". Click on it, and you will see something like Figure 15.92.

The first thing we need to do, is change the output color of every single color we used in out layers to, paradoxically, **WHITE**. Do this by clicking the colored rectangle under "Output Color", and picking **WHITE** from the palette. Your dialog should now look like Figure 15.93.

Now, we've done all of our object lines in the OBJ layer, which is the only one colored yellow. So, under "**Line Width**", next to "**yellow**", click the number 0.010, and change it to 0.035.

This changes our drawing from the left side of Figure 15.94 to the right. Isn't that nicer? Save your work!

Congratulations, you've completely finished the drawing of the shaft! Next, we need to start on the bearing housing.

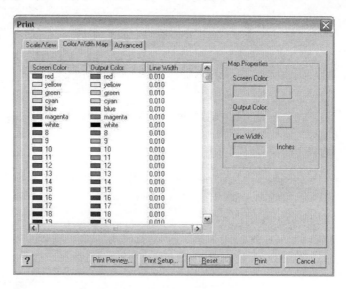

Figure 15.92   Color/Width Map.

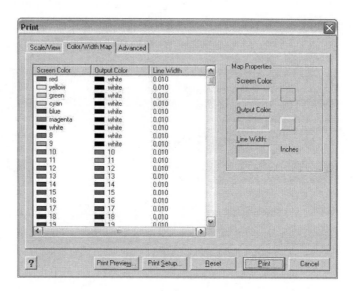

Figure 15.93   Options in Color/Width Map.

15.4   INTELLICAD 2000 "BEARING FLANGE MOUNT" DRAWING TUTORIAL

In this section, we are going to draw the bearing flange mount shown previously in Figure 15.5. We will only cover those steps which are significantly different from the shaft drawing done in Section 15.3. You are on your own setting up the title block, etc., since this was all covered in Section 15.3.

First, set up your layers as shown in Figure 15.95. Set the **OBJ** layer as the active layer.

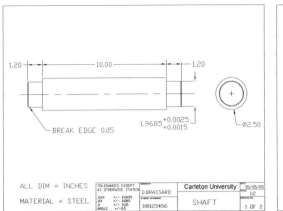

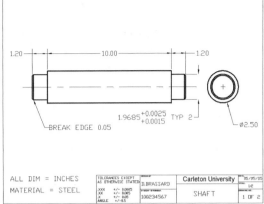

Figure 15.94   Drawing with different line weights.

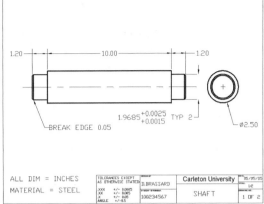

Figure 15.95   Layres for the bearing flange mount drawing.

First, we will draw the front view of the bearing flange. To do this, we need to draw some concentric circles. Activate the circle command, by clicking the toolbar icon, using the drop down menu, or typing in the command window:

C <enter>

Then left click anywhere in the drawing window. There is an important option in the command window:

```
: CIRCLE
2Point/3Point/RadTanTan/Arc/Multiple/<Center of circle>:
Diameter/<Radius>:
```

The program wants to know whether the length you are about to input, whether by clicking elsewhere in the command window, or typing a value, is the diameter or radius. By default, it is set to radius. In the command window, type:

D <enter>

Now, the program wants you to input a diameter. In the command window, type:

3.34 <enter>

A circle now appears on your drawing window that is exactly 3.34 drawing units in diameter. It should appear as in Figure 15.96.

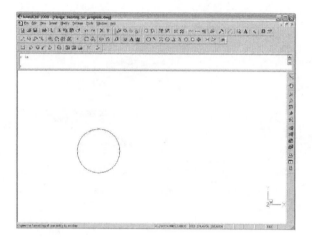

Figure 15.96   The 3.34 unit diameter circle.

Now in the entity snap toolbar, locate the **CENTER** entity snap. It has an icon like this: [icon] This can be accessed in a variety of other ways, as usual. Remember, since we are activating this entity snap while no other commands are active, it will remain in force until we manually de-activate it.

Use that entity snap, and the **CIRCLE** command (C) to draw 3 more circles, concentric to the first, with diameters of:

1.   3.5427
2.   5.00
3.   7.00

You should now see what appears in Figure 15.97.

Ensure no command is active, by hitting <**ESC**> a few times. Now activate the

END-POINT ([icon]) and **MIDPOINT** ([icon]) entity snap. Remember, these will stay on! Now, activate the **LINE** command, and start a line form the center of the circles.

To finish the line, activate the **QUADRANT** ([icon]) entity snap, and select the top of the outermost circle. The **QUADRANT** command will turn right off.

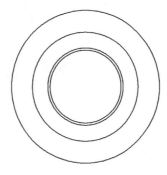

Figure 15.97   The four concentric circles.

You should now see something like the left side of Figure 15.98. Use the trim command to make it look like the right side of Figure 15.98.

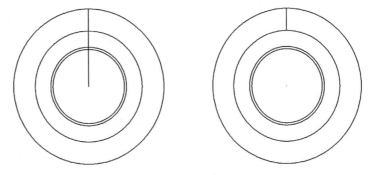

Figure 15.98   Preparing to add the first bolt hole.

Now, use the **CIRCLE** command and the **MIDPOINT** object snap that was activated previously to draw a 0.5 diameter circle right on the midpoint of that short line, like Figure 15.99. Highlight that short line by left clicking on it. Activate the **ORTHO** command

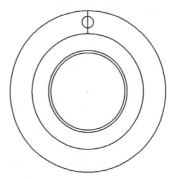

Figure 15.99   Preparing to add the first bolt hole.

in the status area by double clicking it, and use grip editing to extend the ends of the line a bit beyond the circles it touches, st that it looks like Figure 15.100. Highlight that same

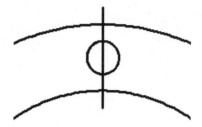

Figure 15.100   Preparing to add the first bolt hole.

line once again, and activate the **COPY** command, by typing in the command window:

COPY <enter>

The command window will ask you for a base point. Click at the top of the line. The command window will now want a second point, which represents the place where the object will be copied. This is very important: Select exactly the same place you just picked. That's right, make another copy of that line directly over the first!

Now activate the **ROTATE** command, by typing in the command window:

RO <enter>

You will see the following in the command window:

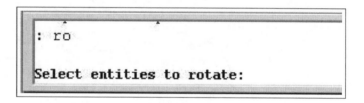

We want to select one of the two overlapped lines, but not both. This is easy. If we click on the lines, only one will be selected. If we select the lines using a window, both will be selected. Easy.

Left click directly on the overlapped lines, just one click, and hit enter to finish "**select(ing) entities to rotate**". There is a new prompt in the command window:

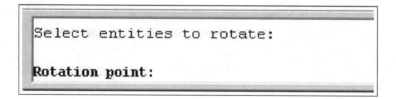

Use the entity snap **CENTER** that you already activated to select the center of the 0.5 unit circle.

Recall that the **ORTHO** option is on, still, and use it to specify a rotation of 90 degrees. In this usage, "specify a rotation" means "wiggle the mouse, until you see a cross". Click to complete the **ROTATE** command. Select the two lines, and using the **PROPER-TIES** dialog, change their layer to CTR. You should now see something like Figure 15.101.

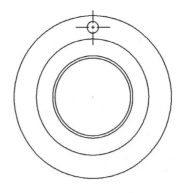

Figure 15.101   Preparing to add the remaining bolt holes.

Now, we want there to be an array of evenly spaced holes around the flange. We do this using the **ARRAY** command, which is most easily launched by typing in the command window:

AR <enter>

This will create the usual bunch of nag screens. The fist indicates that we must select the entities to array.

"Select entities to array:"

Select the 0.5 unit circle, but NOT the two lines, and hit enter. The next option is:

"Type of array: Polar/<Rectangular>:"

As we want a polar array, and a rectangular array is the default, we must type in the command window:

P<enter>

Which brings up the option:

"Base/Center of polar array:"

With the aid of the CENTER entity snap you activated earlier, select the center of the concentric circles. The nest option is:

"Enter to specify angle between items/!number of items to array¿:"

In the command window, type:

6<enter>

The next option is:

"Angle to array (+ for ccw, -for cw) <360:"

Just hit **<enter>,** as 360 is exactly what we want. The nest option is:

"Rotate entities around the array? No/<Yes>:"

It is OK if the circles are rotated, so we just type:

<enter>

You should now see something like Figure 15.102.

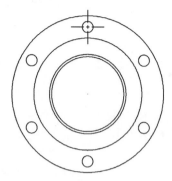

Figure 15.102   Adding the remaining bolt holes.

You may realize that if we had used the option "**No**", when faced with the option **"Rotate entities around the array? No/<Yes>:"**, the crossed centerlines would have rotated properly also. Yes, that is what is supposed to happen, but a bug in IntelliCAD prevents it from executing non-rotated polar arrays. We're going to have to use the **COPY** command.

Recall that the **CENTER** entity snap is still active. Highlight the two crossed center-lines, then launch the copy command, by typing in the command window:

C<enter>

You will see the option:

Multiple/Vector/<Base point>:"

We want to feed the program a base point by selecting the center of the circle through which the centerlines cross. Use the **CENTER** entity snap to make this easier for you, by clicking as something like that shown in Figure 15.103.

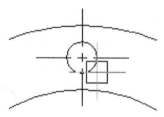

Figure 15.103   Base point selection.

Now click as shown in Figure 15.104. Notice the **ORTHO** command makes the objects you are copying appear to move directly sideways. Don't worry, It'll work properly.
Now, you should see Figure 15.105.
Now, repeat those steps until your drawing looks like Figure 15.106.

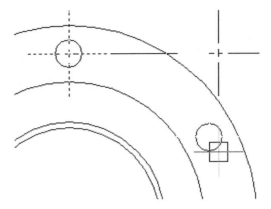

Figure 15.104   Base point selection.

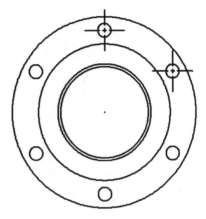

Figure 15.105   Manipulating the copied lines.

And just like that, we're done the front view of the bearing. The center of the concentric circles does not need crossed centerlines, as they will appear automatically as we dimension, later.

Now, we can go about constructing the side view, using construction lines, just as we did for the shaft. The difference is, we used the side view of the shaft, a bunch of rectangles to define a series of concentric circles. This time, we will use a bunch of concentric circles to define a bunch of lines and rectangles.

15.4.1 Drawing the Side View

Before activating any other command, activate the **QUADRANT** snap. Also change the active layer to **CTR.** Let the **QUADRANT** snap help you draw construction lines like Figure 15.107.

Now, approximately 3 drawing units from the right hand edge of the front view, draw a vertical line like the one in Figure 15.108.

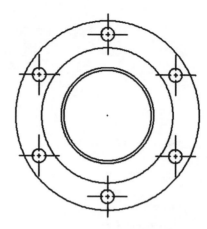

Figure 15.106   Bolt holes and centre lines.

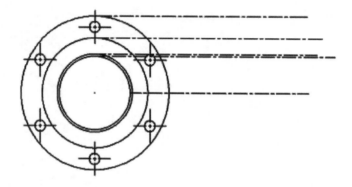

Figure 15.107   Construction lines.

Use the **OFFSET** command to offset that vertical line to the right 1.4665 units. Offset that new line a further 0.500 units to the right, and that newest line, a further 0.2500 units to the right, until you see something like Figure 15.109.

Save your work.

Now, activate the **ENDPOINT** and **INTERSECTION** entity snaps, and change the active layer to **OBJ.** We're going to do some tracing! Remember, since we don't have an active command, those entity snaps will remain on until we manually turn them off. Using those snaps to help you, draw **LINES** until your drawing looks like Figure 15.110.

Note that the new lines are darker, for illustration purposes, here. Yours will be the same thickness as the construction lines, but solid. Now, set the **HID** layer active, and draw **LINES** until your drawing looks like Figure 15.111.

Here's the really cool part. Set the **CTR** layer active. While you are in the **LAYERS** dialog, change both **OBJ** and **HID** to **FROZEN.** Your drawing will look like Figure 15.112. Now, delete lines, until your drawing looks like Figure 15.113.

Now, using the **LAYERS** dialog, thaw the **OBJ** and **HID** layers, and you will see Figure 15.114. What we just did really demonstrates the power of CAD. Imagine what

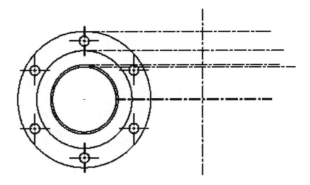

Figure 15.108   Vertical line.

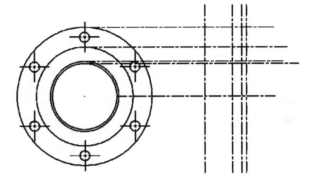

Figure 15.109   Vertical construction lines.

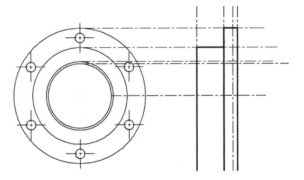

Figure 15.110   Object line in the right-side view.

a pain it would be to create that side view by doing ordinate input? It makes no sense, so why do it?

OK, we need to have some symmetry, so we need to **MIRROR** only the horizontal lines in the side view. Select them all by windowing from left to right, through them. Now, activate the **MIRROR** command, by typing in the command window:

Mi<enter>

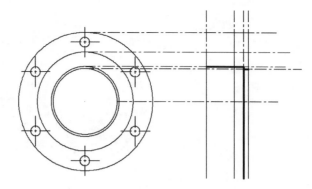

Figure 15.111   Drawing the hidden lines.

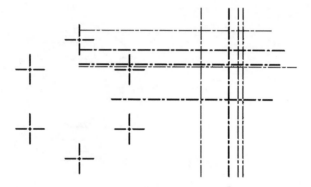

Figure 15.112   Frozen object and hidden line layers.

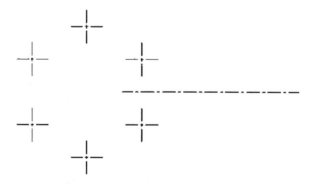

Figure 15.113   Erased lines.

In the command window, you will be given the option to select:

"Start of the mirror line:"

Select the left hand side of the one construction/centerline we didn't delete. The next option is

"End of mirror line:"

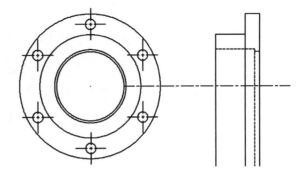

Figure 15.114   Erased lines.

Select the right hand end of that same construction/center line. We now see the option:

"Delete the original entities? <N>:"

Since NO is the default, and No is the answer to the question, just hit **<enter>**. You should now see Figure 15.115.

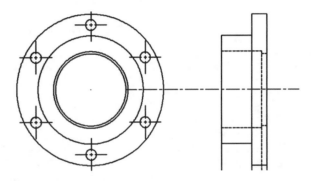

Figure 15.115   Constructing the right-side view.

Now, use the **TRIM** command to clean up the drawing, so that you are left with Figure 15.116.

Now, it's plain that the dashed lines (on the **HID** layer) must represent geometry that would be hidden within the part if we were looking at an actual part, at the same orientation, as the drawing view. So, you can see that we're left out a whole bunch of hidden geometry: The bolt holes. We have to put those in.

Using construction lines, **LAYERS**, **TRIM** and the **MIRROR** command exactly as we did before, create a side projection of the bolt holes, so that your drawing looks like Figure 15.117.

Now, use grip editing to clean up those centerlines. Remember that the **ORTHO** command is still active, so you can just highlight the centerlines, and click-and-drag their endpoints, until the drawing looks neat, like Figure 15.118. And just like that, our side view is done.

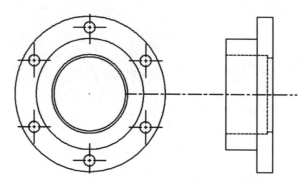

Figure 15.116   Trimmed lines.

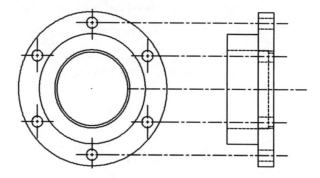

Figure 15.117   Constructing orthogonally projected bolt holes.

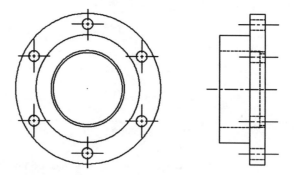

Figure 15.118   Orthogonally projected bolt holes.

Unfortunately, our drawing is not. At some point you are going to have to dimension that ridge on the inner bore of the part, and those bolt holes are going to make it virtually impossible to do so legibly. When our internal geometry is too messy to allow understandable dimensions, that is the signal it is time to use a section view.

Save your work.

15.4.2 Drawing the Section View

First, let's draw some triangles. Set the **SEC** layer active. We are going to use the **LINE** command, and ordinate input to create what will become arrowheads on our section line. Start a line, floating in space, anywhere on the drawing sheet. For the next points, type in the command window:

> **@0,0.5<enter>**

> **@1.2,-0.25<enter>**

> **c<enter>**

"**C**" in this usage tells IntelliCAD to close the "loop" you're creating. There, our arrowhead is done, and you should see something like Figure 15.119.

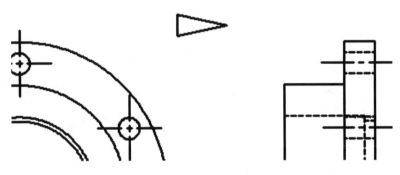

Figure 15.119   Arrowhead.

There is no rule regarding how big the arrowhead should be, but this geometry looks roughly how arrowheads should look, don't you think? Recall that a section line in one view represents a cutting plane which will create the section represented by the section view. The arrows point in the direction that will be oriented "up" in the section view.

To make our lives simpler, we want to be able to simply copy and modify our existing side view, rather than re-inventing the wheel, so obviously the section line should pass vertically though the front view.

Use the **LINE** command, **QUADRANT** entity snap, and grip editing to create a line vertically through the line of symmetry of the front view, and about one drawing unit beyond, at both top and bottom, as in Figure 15.120.

For the sake of clarity, delete the vertical centerlines for both the top and bottom bolt hole. This has already been done in the previous image. Draw a 1 unit horizontal extension using the **LINE** and **ENDPOINT** entity snaps at the top of the section line, as in Figure 15.121.

Now, we will move the arrowhead to the appropriate place. Select the arrowhead. Activate the **MOVE** command by typing at the command line:

> **M<enter>**

You will see the option:

> **"Vector/<Base point>:"**

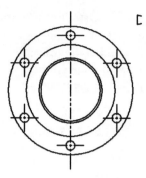

Figure 15.120   Section line.

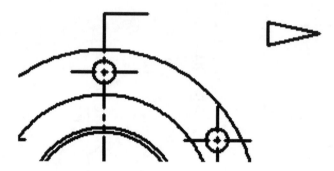

Figure 15.121   Moving the arrowhead.

Click on the **MIDPOINT** entity snap (remember, it's only going to be active for one selection!), and select the middle of the vertical line in the triangle.

The next option is:

"Displacement point:"

Click on the end of the section line you created (remember **ENDPOINT** is active), to create the image in Figure 15.122.

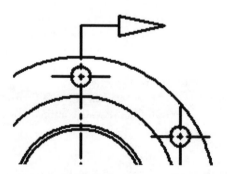

Figure 15.122   Moved arrowhead.

Now, COPY that line and triangle to the bottom ENDPOINT of the vertical section line, creating what you see in Figure 15.123. Now, without changing layers, use the TEXT

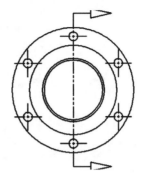

Figure 15.123   Both arrowheads on the section line.

command to insert a big capital "A" at the tip of the arrowhead, with a text height of 6.0000. Your drawing should now look like Figure 15.124. And, just like that, the section line is done.

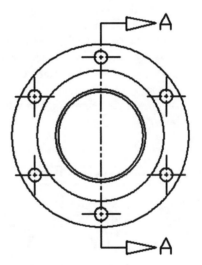

Figure 15.124   Section A-A.

Now, we need to make the section view. The easiest way to do that for this drawing, is to **COPY** the side view 6 drawing units to the right. Select the entire side view, and activate the copy command by typing in the command window:

Co<enter>

It will ask for a base point, just like usual, this time. Click anywhere in the drawing window, anywhere at all, and when it asks you for a displacement point, type in the command window:

@6.0<enter>

And you should see Figure 15.125.

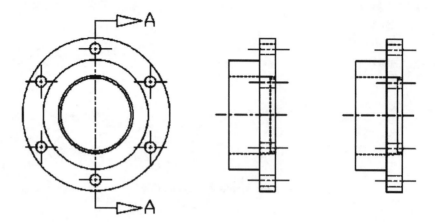

Figure 15.125   Copied right-side view.

First things first: We placed the tow A's on the section line, so that we could label our section view. It's important to label the section view, as some drawings will be so complicated, they will need more than one section view. The fist is labeled "SECTION A-A", the second would be labeled "SECTION B-B"

Underneath the copied side view (the one on the right), still on the SEC layer, insert text saying "SECTION A-A" with a text height of 0.400. Now, in your section view, of the four visible bolt holes, remove the middle two entirely. Your drawing should look like Figure 15.126. Now, convert ALL the hidden lines (those on the HID layer) in the section

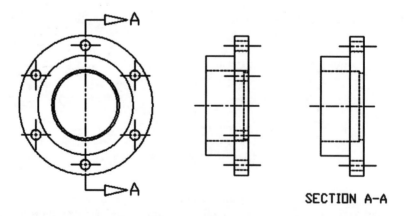

SECTION A-A

Figure 15.126   Section A-A text for right-side view.

view only to object lines (use the PROPERTIES dialog to place them on the **OBJ** layer). Your section view now looks like the left side of Figure 15.127. Use the TRIM command to cut down that middle line, to obtain something like the right side of Figure 15.127.

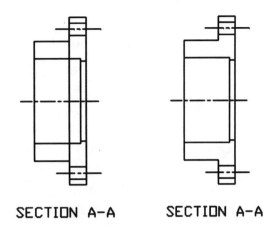

SECTION A-A   SECTION A-A

Figure 15.127   Deleting the correct part of the middle construction line.

Save your work.

All that's left is to insert the hatchmarks. Use **PAN** and **ZOOM** until we're looking closely at the top of the section view, as in Figure 15.128.

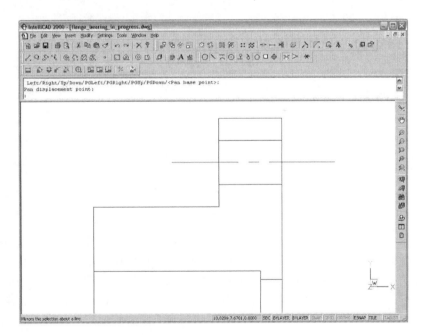

Figure 15.128   Zoomed in on the upper part of Section A-A.

Now, it's time to learn to use the **HATCH** command. Set the **HAT** layer active. Activate the **BOUNDARY HATCH** command by using the dropdown menu:

Insert > Hatch

Clicking the toolbar icon (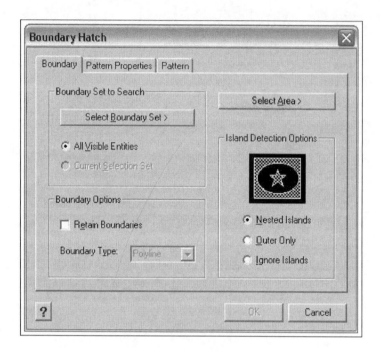) , or typing in the command window:

Bhatch\<enter>

Any of these will launch the **BOUNDARY HATCH** dialog:

Click on the second tab, **"Pattern Properties"**:

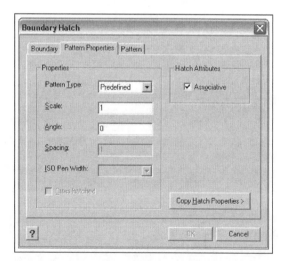

While these values are correct for our drawing, had we wanted a different density of hatch lines, we would alter the Scale option. Should we want one area to be hatched diagonally up and to the right, but another are hatched diagonally up and to the left, we would change the Angle to 90 degrees. Click on the **"Pattern"** tab:

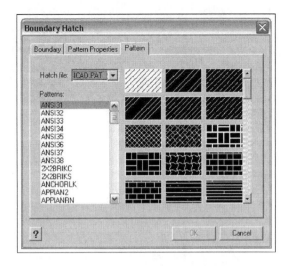

Once again, ANSI31 is fine as a hatch pattern for us, but there are lots of other patterns that can in some cases represent different material, like wood, brick, or dirt. Also, if we are doing a section view of many parts assembled, it is nice to have different patterns and angles, so the part can be differentiated. Go back to the first tab **"Boundary"**.

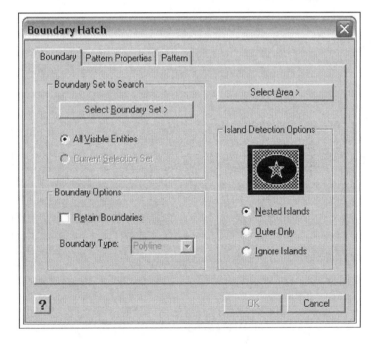

In the upper right hand corner is a button **"Select Area"**. Click it. You will be returned to your drawing. So, any closed space you click inside will be automatically hatched. Remember, you have entity snaps on, so you must make sure that no lines are within your selection square. That's why we zoomed in on this. Click inside the appropriate area to make your widow look like Figure 15.129.

Type **<enter>** to return to the **BHATCH** dialog, and click **OK** to accept the changes. Repeat these steps, including the **PAN** and **ZOOM** to hatch the same areas on the bottom of the section view.

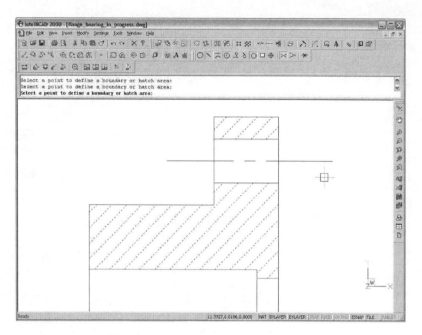

Figure 15.129   Hatched Section A-A top half.

Type in the command window:

Z<enter>a<enter>

to zoom to all. You should see something like Figure 15.130.

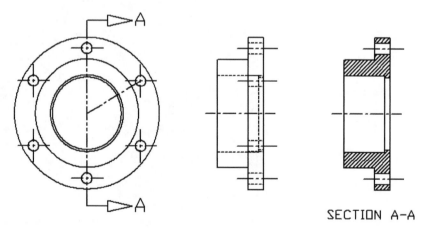

SECTION A-A

Figure 15.130   Finished geometry with additional centre line.

There is only one thing left to do: We need to draw a single centerline from the center of the front view, to the center of the upper right hand bolt hole, like in the front view of Figure 15.130. The purpose of that line will become obvious, very soon.

15.4.3 Formatting the Title Block

This part is exactly the same as it was with the shaft drawing, so you're on your own Insert the block in paperspace, set up the drawing limits, set up all the text, and insert the tolerance note, exactly as last time. You see Figure 15.131.

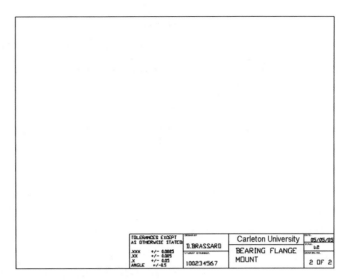

Figure 15.131   Formatted title block.

Insert a viewport (using the **MVIEW**) command, exactly as before, and freeze the viewport layer. The appropriate zoom factor for this drawing is once again:

0.5XP

So our scale is obviously 1:2. Your drawing should look like Figure 15.132. Notice

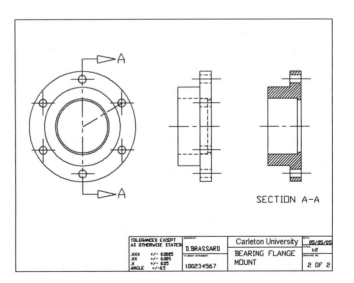

Figure 15.132   . . . still needs work.

that the centerlines aren't always showing as centerlines. We need to set the linetype scale, here. In the command window, type:

Ltscale<enter>

The command window wants an input, it is asking you:

New current value for Itscale (greater than zero) <1.000>:

IntelliCAD is a bit buggy, here. In order to get this to work properly for me, I had to input a scale factor of 0.25. In order to fine tune this so that centerlines are obviously centerlines, etc, you may actually have to physically print, then change this value. You should see something like Figure 15.133.

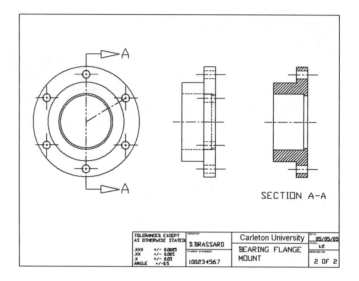

Figure 15.133   Effects of changing LT scale.

Notice all the centerlines are now obviously centerlines, the hidden lines are now obviously dashed, and everything seems to be in roughly the right place.

Save your work.

Change the active layer to **DIM.** Now, using the **DIMENSION STYLES** dialog (from the drop down menu **(Settings > Dimension Styles),** set up the tolerance (+0.0010/−0.0000), and select 4 decimal places. Dimension the inside of the section view, see Figure 15.134. Hint: If you're having trouble dimensioning, it might help to freeze the **HAT** layer.

Save your work.

Now use the **DIMENSION STYLES** dialog to set 2 decimal places, with no tolerances, and place the 7 new dimensions as in Figure 15.135.

Save your work.

Now use **DIMENSION STYLES** to set for zero decimal places. Find the

ANGULAR DIMENSION icon ( ), and click it. Select the section line, and the center line connecting the center of the front view to the upper right bolt hole, and place the dimension as shown in Figure 15.136.

Highlight the angular dimension you just placed, and right-click-and-hold to access the **PROPERTIES** dialog:

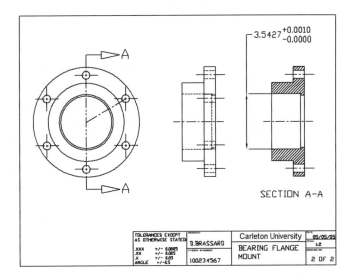

Figure 15.134   Adding linear dimensions.

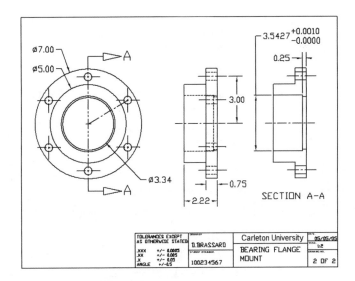

Figure 15.135   Adding more dimensions.

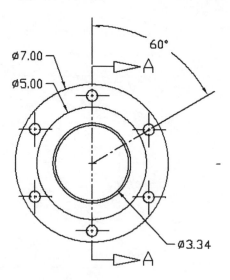

Figure 15.136   Adding angular dimensions.

In the window next to **"Dimension Text:"** are the symbols <>. These symbols refer to the actual value of the dimension, in this case 60 degrees. After the <>, enter the following:

　　TYP 6

and click **OK**. Your drawing should look like Figure 15.137.

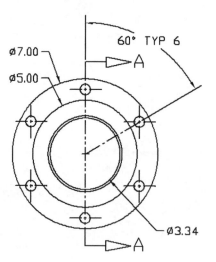

Figure 15.137   Adding notes to dimensions.

　　What the "TYP 6" means is that we are telling the machinist that all 6 of the measurements that resemble this one are in fact exactly the same as this one. This can be a fantastic shortcut, and can keep your drawings a lot neater.
　　Save your work.

Open the dimension settings dialog, and click on the tab "Units":

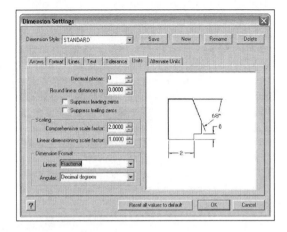

Notice at the bottom, under **"Dimension Format"**, the format has been changed to **"Fractional".** Make this change, and click **OK**.

Now add a diametral dimension to the lower right bolt hole, resulting in something like Figure 15.138.

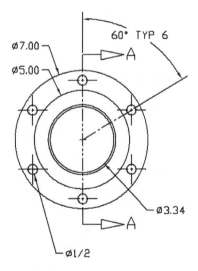

Figure 15.138   Adding diametral dimensions.

We used a fraction, because we are trying to tell the machinist which drill size to use, not the size of the hole. A drill size says "I just want a hole here", whereas a decimal dimension implies that the bore of the hole must have soma characteristic, such as surface finish, that you forgot to put in your drawing.

Now, use the properties dialog to add the following to that fractional dimension:

"TYP 6

Note, that open quote," is deliberate. It is also an inch symbol. So, if you would be so kind as to set the **TEXT** layer active, and (in paperspace) add the material and dimension notes in the bottom left (just like for the shaft drawing). We're nearly done!

Now, set up your Color/Width map (a tab under the **PRINT** dialog) like this:

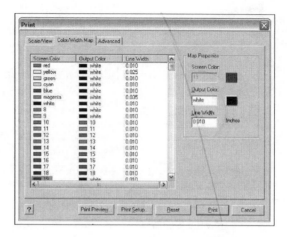

Don't forget to thaw the **HAT** layer! Now, you can print out a lovely drawing, like Figure 15.139.

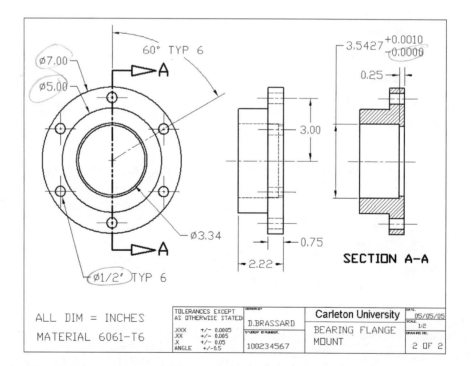

Figure 15.139 The finished drawing.

And now we're done!

Chapter 16

3D Solid Modeling: Pro/ENGINEER Wildfire

16.0 INTRODUCTION TO PRO/ENGINEER

Pro/ENGINEER®, developed by Parametric Technologies Corporation (PTC), is a set of programs that are used in the design, analysis, and manufacturing of mechanical systems. Pro/ENGINEER is often referred to as Pro/E. The technological advancement and productivity advantages have made Pro/ENGINEER a robust and versatile parametric solid modeling solution for product development. An assortment of supplementary modules exists for managing tasks ranging from sheet metal operations, piping layout, mold design, wiring harness design, NC machining and other functions. Pro/E is becoming an industry standard for Computer-Aided Design.

IntelliCAD involves geometric modeling where as Pro/E involves feature-based, parametric, solid-modeling. To help understand the difference consider the following definitions.

Feature-based: The feature-based functionality of Pro/E enables designers to create parts and assemblies by defining physically meaningful features like extrusions, slots, sweeps, cuts, holes, slots, fillets, rounds, etc.. The designer works with actual parts on the computer screen, not just low-level geometrical elements like lines, circles and arcs. Features are defined by setting values and characteristics of elements like reference planes and axes, surfaces, direction of creation, shape, dimension, etc. Pro/E handles all the geometric details.

Parametric: The values assigned to the different attributes (mainly dimensions) of the model features define the physical shape of the part. Important changes can be easily incorporated at any point during the design process and the changes circulate through the model automatically.

Solid Modeling: Wireframe models (as done with 2D CAD systems) are inadequate for many design, manufacturing and visualization tasks. Hence solid modeling evolved. Solid modeling means that the computer model will contain all the information that a real solid object would have. The model has a volume and thus if provided with a value for the density of the material it has mass and inertia.

Pro/ENGINEER vs. Conventional CAD Systems:

Pro/ENGINEER vs. Conventional CAD Systems	
Pro/ENGINEER	**Conventional CAD Systems**
Solid model and wireframe model	Wireframe model
Parametric model	Fixed-dimension model
Feature-based modeling	Geometry-based modeling
A single data structure and full associativity	Function-oriented data structures with format interpreters
Subject-oriented sub-modeling systems	A single geometry-based system
Manufacturing information associated with features	Texts attached to geometry entities
Generation of an assembly by assembling components	Generation of an assembly by positioning

16.1   GETTING STARTED WITH PRO/E

This Primer is designed to teach new users some of the basic functions in Pro/E Wildfire. You can probably go through the assignment without reading much of the material presented in this Primer. But all this material will prove to be useful when you work on your project and going through the Primer will certainly save you time and headache while working with Pro/E.

You are about to discover the world of sophisticated solid modeling software, and it might be the most complicated software you have learnt so far. However Pro/E is extremely user friendly and you will be comfortable using the basic functions with only a little bit of practice. Mastering the tremendously large command set of Pro/E would require a considerably long time. But you can be assured that it won't take you long to fall in love with Pro/E once you get started. So here the joyride begins.

16.1.1 Opening Pro/E

After logging onto a workstation click on the **Start** button at the bottom left of the screen on the Windows taskbar. Then depending on the operating system of your workstation click on:

All Programs > PTC > Pro ENGINEER > Pro ENGINEER

-or-

Programs > PTC > Pro ENGINEER > Pro ENGINEER.

Figure 16.1 Default Pro/E screen after loading.

Pro/E launches like a typical Windows application and usually it takes sometime for the program to load. Once Pro/ E has loaded the screen will look approximately like Figure 16.1 which is the default Pro/E screen.

16.1.2 Setting the Working Directory

Pro/E will save all your files and also look for related files in the working directory chosen. Therefore make sure that you have your personal folder (or some other folder in it) in the H:/ drive selected as the working directory. To do this click **File> Set Working Directory** and choose your personal directory in H:/ from the pull-down menu of the *Select Working Directory* dialogue box. You can also do this by using the pop-up menu in the Folder Navigator (see Section 16.1.3).

16.1.3 User Interface

Navigator:
The left portion of the screen is called the **Navigator.** It is used for various purposes and has some related buttons at the top such as **Model Tree, Folder Browser, Favorites, Connections, Working Directory, Create a new Folder** and **Delete Selected Folders.** If you move your mouse cursor over these you will see their names appear on a pop-up tool-tip and also at the bottom of the screen.

Browser:
The browser is the portion on the right side of the screen. It operates as any general web-browser and includes many internet communications tools. The main objective of the browser is to provide instant connectivity among users. The initial content of the Browser is the **Pro/ENGINEER Wildfire Web Guide.** The Guide is part of the **PTC** Website offering tools for learning Pro/E Wildfire quickly and efficiently.

Figure 16.2   Vertical Slashes on Navigator and Browser Frames.

Resizing the Navigator and Browser Areas:

Dragging left/right on the vertical slashes (Figure 16.2) resizes the **Navigator** and **Browser** areas. You can temporarily hide the Browser or Navigator by placing the mouse cursor over the thin-textured **arrows along the right side of the browser/ navigator frame** and clicking the left mouse button.

Main Graphics Area:

If you hide the **Navigator** and **Browser** areas you will see the Graphics Area which is the largest area in the Pro/ENGINEER Wildfire window. Parts are displayed and manipulated in this main Graphics Area. You have control over the scale and viewing angle of your part. When you start the system the Graphics Area is empty as shown in Figure 16.3.

Some shortcut buttons will not appear or will not be activated until a part is loaded. When you are actually working on a part, the Pro/E Wildfire window generally looks more like the one shown in Figure 16.4.

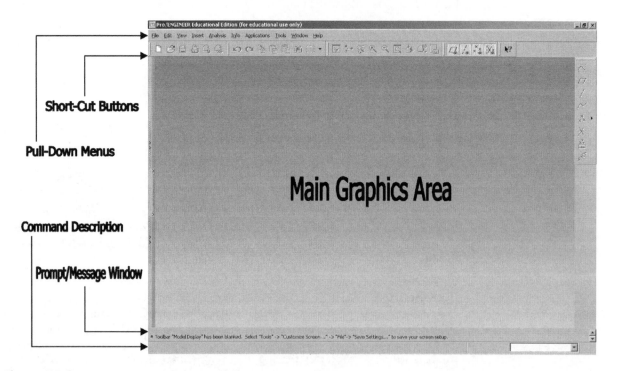

Figure 16.3   Empty Graphics Area after loading Pro/E.

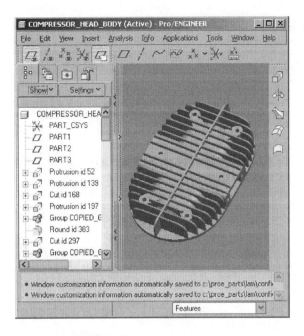

Figure 16.4   Pro/E Window while working on an active part.

16.1.2 Model Tree

At the beginning the **Model Tree** button is disabled. But if you load a part it becomes activated and by clicking on it a list of the features found in the current part will be displayed (Figure 16.5). Objects in a model can also be selected using a model tree. More about the model tree is discussed later on.

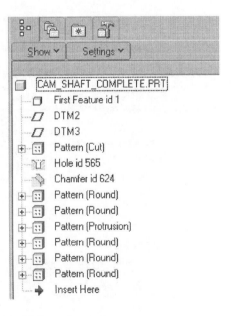

Figure 16.5   Pro/E Model Tree of an active part.

16.2   GENERAL INTERACTIONS

Interactions with Pro/E are done in a number of different ways. Some of the very basic ways of entering commands are discussed below.

- **The Menu Bar:** The main pull-down menu of Pro/E Wildfire is a direct analog of that of any standard Windows program and it is located across the top of the Pro/E window. Many of these options have the same functions as common Windows commands. All the main options in the system are contained in the **Menu Bar.** If one of these buttons is chosen a pull-down menu is displayed revealing further options (Figure 16.6). Many of the menu commands will open up a second level menu and have a ➤ symbol beside them.

The Toolbars: Most of the useful tools employed to create and manipulate geometry are located on the toolbar (Figure 16.7 shows the Toolbar). They are positioned as a set of buttons on the right side of the graphics window. The system provides many different Toolbars, each containing a series of icons which activate different functions i.e. **Tools.** For example, to create a solid **Feature** called a **Protrusion,** you choose the icon for the

Extrude Tool . More about these will be discussed later.

- **Dashboard:** The Dashboard is displayed when any of the model creation buttons are selected from the Toolbars. The Dashboard consists of the defining attributes of a feature, which gives the designer the ability to control how the

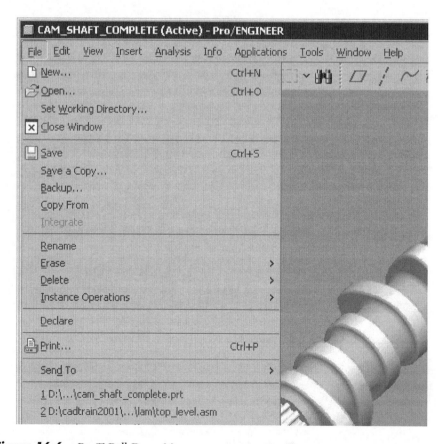

Figure 16.6   Pro/E Pull-Down Menus.

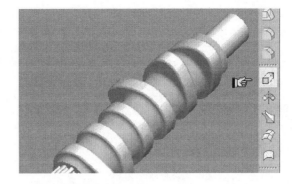

Figure 16.7   The main toolbar of Pro/E and the Extrude tool.

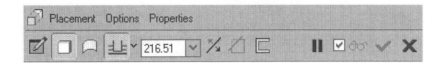

Figure 16.8   The main Dashboard for the Extrude tool.

feature is created. For example when the extrude tool is chosen the following Dashboard is displayed (Figure 16.8) at the bottom of the screen.

- **Short-cut Buttons:** These buttons are located right below the menu bar and are indicated in Figure 16.9 below. If the cursor is slowly moved across these buttons a pop up box will show the names of these buttons and a brief command description will appear at the bottom of the Pro/E window.

- **Command/Message Window:** During command execution brief messages including errors and warnings will be displayed on the prompt/message window below the area. Sometimes command input will be needed from the user

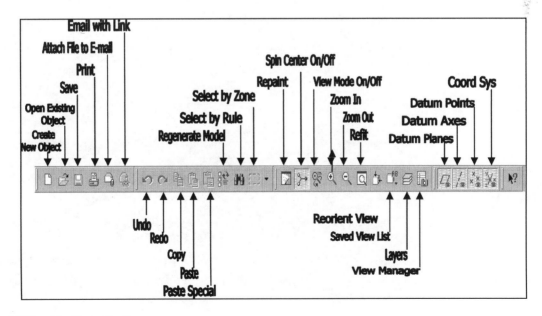

Figure 16.9   The Short-Cut Buttons.

in response to prompts in the command/message window. Usually the keyboard is only used to enter alpha-numeric data, such as numerical values, object and file names etc. None of the other commands in the system will be activated while Pro/E is expecting a response from the user in the command window.

- **Mouse Functions:** Pro/E is designed to use with a 3-button mouse. The system makes use of a 3-button mouse to perform many functions. Generally, clicking, selecting, dragging, drawing etc are done with the Left Mouse Button. The Right Mouse Button is basically used in pop-up menus. The most common functions of the Middle Mouse Button deal with manipulating the display.

16.3   CREATING A SIMPLE OBJECT

This part of the Primer describes how to create a new part and how to add the first few features for creating a solid model. An assortment of discrete features generates a solid model. Many different means are used to create features but primarily features are defined by extruding a 2D profile in 3D space. This sweep may be linear over a specific distance, or even revolved about an axis.

The purpose of this exercise is to generate a solid model using Pro ENGINEER Wildfire. After completion of the exercise the solid model of the bearing should look like Figure 16.10. Please go through all the steps in order to get a good grasp of the very basics of Pro/E. It is the minimum you should know for doing the final project.

1. **Starting Pro/E:** After opening the Pro/E close the Navigator and Browser panes.
2. **Setting Working Directory:** Set the working directory as your personal directory in the H:/ drive.

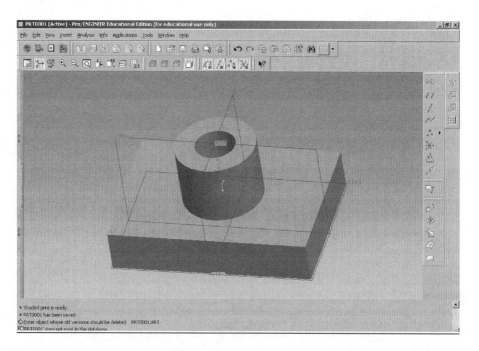

Figure 16.10   The Completed Bearing.

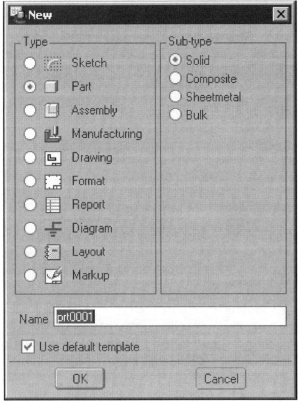

Figure 16.11   New Dialogue Box.

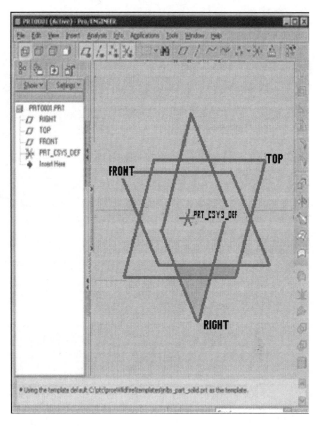

Figure 16.12   Pro/E Window for new part with default datum planes.

3.   **Starting a New Part:** Choose the Create a new object ![icon] icon or click **File > New.** The window shown in Figure 16.11 will open. Keep the default radio button settings i.e. **Part** as type and **Solid** as sub-type. Type 'Bearing' as the part name instead of the default part name, check the **Use Default Template** option at the bottom and click **OK.** The Pro/E window will now display the model tree and 3 standard datum planes (x, y, z coordinate system) (Figure 16.12) and **BEARING** will appear in the title area of the graphics window. It is possible to create a part without using any kind of default template, but at this very basic level we are going to stick to the default options. The Template defines standard data that you want all parts to contain.

![icon] **Datum Planes:** When you create a new part using a Template, several of the features already in the part are the Default Datum Planes and the Default Coordinate System. The Default Datum Planes are three datum planes which are perpendicular to each other (Figure 16.13). These planes intersect at the default origin of the default co-ordinate system of your part.

Each Datum Plane has two sides. Yellow denotes the front of a plane and red indicates the back. The Default Datum Planes are automatically named FRONT, TOP, and RIGHT. Since these datum are part features, you can use them as references when you begin your model.

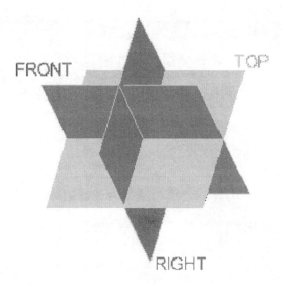

Figure 16.13   Datum Planes Perpendicular to Each Other.

Further datum planes can be created, as well as datum axes, points and curves for highly specific reference requirements. Although the Datum Planes are not required to be able to model a part, using them is considered the best practice.

4.   **Using Protrusion:** For creating a protrusion for the base of the bearing click

the **Extrude** icon ⬚ on the right toolbar or from the Menu bar click **Insert> Extrude** (Figure 16.14). The system will now open up the extrude Dashboard (Figure 16.15), which displays the options for creating the protrusion.

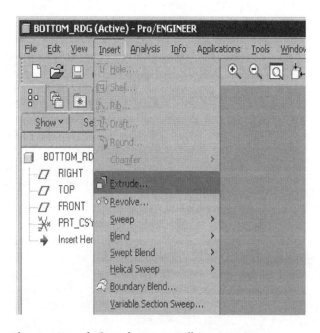

Figure 16.14   Choosing Extrude from the Insert Pull-Down Menu.

Figure 16.15   The Extrude Dashboard.

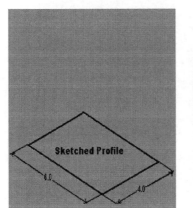
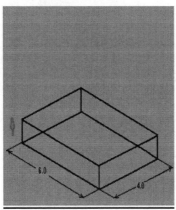
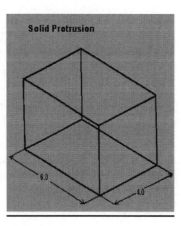

Figure 16.16   From Sketched Curve to Solid Model.

Protrusion: The most basic type of feature to create is a protrusion. You draw a 2-D shape and Pro/E protrudes it through the 3rd dimension in a defined direction for a specified distance (Figure 16.16). A solid feature is created when the profile is extruded.

5. **Defining the Sketch Orientation:** From the Extrude Dashboard click the **Placement** button and then click **Define** from the popup box. The system shows the Sketch Dialogue Box (Figure 16.17), which displays options which control how you specify the orientation of the Sketch relative to the part. The system indicates what it expects you to define by highlighting the text box next to **Plane.**

Figure 16.17   Pro/E Window while working on an active part.

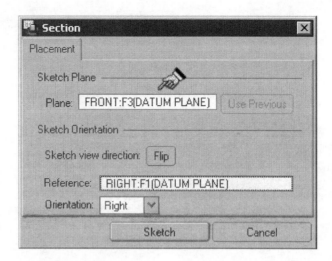

Figure 16.18   Completed Sketch Dialogue Box

As you click the **Define** button the Sketch window should show up containing the following information by default (Figure 16.18). If it doesn't you have to supply the information by clicking and selecting the planes from the graphics area or in the Model Tree. When you select a sketch plane, its name is displayed in the text field.

In the **Plane** textbox the system expects the name of a datum plane or surface on the part to act as the sketching plane, i.e. this is the plane on which you will draw the sketch. The Sketch plane can also be a planar surface of an existing solid.

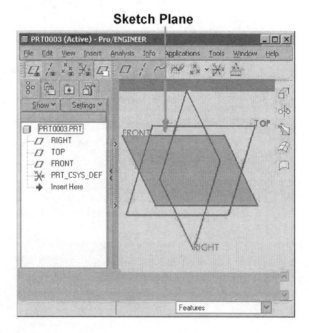

Figure 16.19   Sketch Plane.

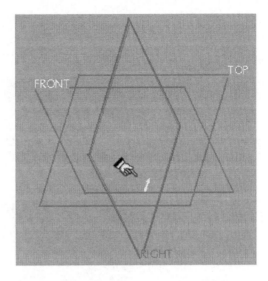

Figure 16.20   Positive and Negative Direction Indicator Arrow.

When you specify the plane a yellow arrow appears at the edge of the FRONT plane pointing in the direction the system assumes it should create the Protrusion (Figure 16.20). You can either accept this direction or flip it to the opposite direction by choosing the **Flip** button Flip in the Sketch dialog box. For now leave it pointing towards the back which is the positive direction.

In addition, you must specify another plane called the ***Orientation Plane.*** This plane can either be a Datum Plane or a flat surface on an existing solid. As soon as you choose a Sketch Plane, the system will attempt to find a plane or surface which is perpendicular to it and label this plane/surface the **Orientation Plane.** Now you can see in the graphics area the RIGHT plane is highlighted in red and in the Sketch dialog box RIGHT is chosen as the Sketch Orientation ***Reference,*** with the ***Orientation*** set to be ***Right.*** You can override this selection by choosing your own Orientation Plane. But for now this will be ok.

What is happening here is when you get into the Sketcher you will be directly looking at the positive side of the FRONT plane. So that the sketch is right way up, you could have chosen either the TOP plane to face the TOP of the screen or the RIGHT plane to face the right of the screen, which is automatically chosen for you.

Once you are satisfied with the Sketch Plane, Direction and Orientation Plane, you can choose the ***Sketch*** button in the Section dialog.

6.   **Setting the References:** After clicking the ***Sketch*** button several things happen—the graphics area color turns to black, an orange square shows up to indicate your sketching plane, two dashed orange lines appear that cross at the center of the screen (Figure 16.21) and at the top right of the screen the ***References*** dialog window opens up. This is because before you begin drawing geometry, you need to locate the sketch in relation to the existing features of the part. These features may be the Default Datum Planes or other solid features. You locate the sketch by defining a **Horizontal** and a **Vertical Reference.**

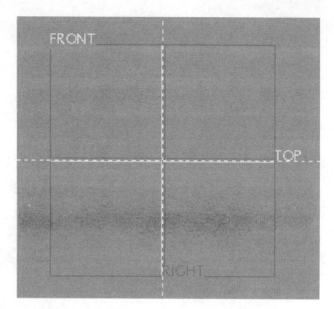

Figure 16.21   The Drawing Window.

These **References** are often assumed by the system and are listed in the **References** dialog (Figure 16.22).

In most cases, especially when you are creating the first few features of a part, the Intent Manager will find the References on its own. If you do not like the References the system finds, you can simply select new ones. Also the number of references you select is not limited, you can have several references to make yourself more comfortable during the drawing.

The **References Status** at the bottom of the dialog window indicates if you have enough references for Sketcher to locate your sketch on the model. **Partially Placed**

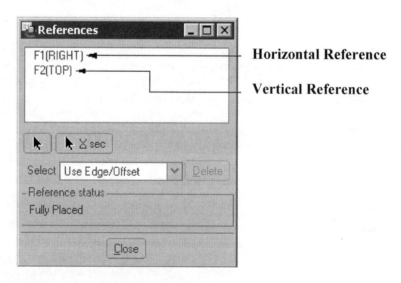

Figure 16.22   *References* Dialog Window.

means there are not enough references. Unless you have **Fully Placed** status, don't proceed beyond this window. For now we will accept the pre-selected options (Figure 16.22). Click **OK** to close this window and begin your drawing. Now you are in the Sketcher mode.

Introduction to Sketcher: A 2D sketch is the basic foundation for creating most features and solid models. The Sketcher is used to make 2D sketches in Pro/E. Thus, it is the crucial and indispensable tool for feature creation in Pro/E. The Sketcher is identical to 2D drafting in IntelliCAD where you draw two-dimensional figures which are controlled in size by specifying dimensions. The shape and location of these features must be specifically defined. In addition to dimensions, the Sketcher also utilizes Constraints. Constraints control the geometric relationship between curves. Examples are making two lines parallel to each other or two arcs concentric.

The Sketcher Toolbar: After entering Sketcher mode the major addition to the screen will be the Sketcher toolbar on the right of the screen, consisting of convenient access to most of the Sketcher options (Figure 16.23). In Sketcher the usual 2D drawing elements are present, such as lines, arcs, circles, rectangles etc. These options are also available through the **Sketch** Menu in the Menu bar.

The Intent Manager: The **Intent Manager** can be thought of as the 'brain' of the sketcher. The **Intent Manager** will anticipate what you are about to do in your drawing and will do many things automatically. If a drawing conations just enough geometric information to be exclusively defined then it can be termed a *Complete* drawing. The Intent Manager ascertains that your drawing has just the right amount of information and is not under or over specified. For example, as you sketch a line from its start point, if the line is nearly horizontal, the Intent Manager snaps it to be horizontal and automatically applies a **Horizontal Constraint** to it. A **Constraint** is a geometric property applied to a curve beyond its dimensional size. Some examples are:

Constraint	Symbol
Equal Length	$L_{1,2,3..}$
Equal Radius	$R_{1,2,3...}$
Symmetry	⟶ ⟵
Horizontal	H
Vertical	V
Parallel	$//_{1,2,3...}$
Perpendicular	$\perp_{1,2,3...}$
Equal Coordinates	--
Tangent Curves	T

Option   Flyout Menus

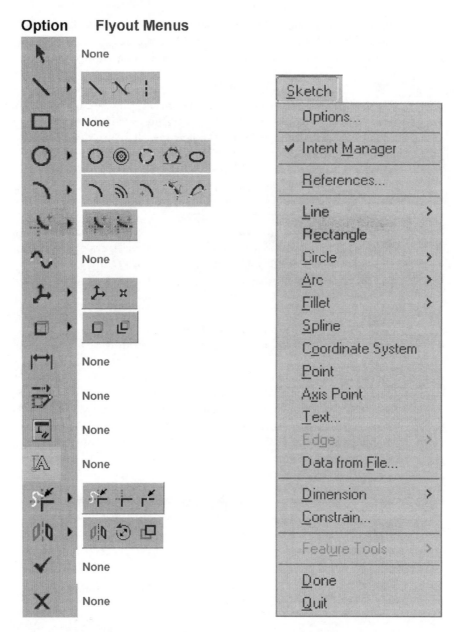

Figure 16.23(a)   The Sketcher Toolbar.

Figure 16.23(b)   The Sketcher options in the Menu bar.

Whenever Intent Manager applies one of the constraints you are notified with the symbols mentioned above. If you don't want to accept the constraint simply exaggerate the geometry.

7. **Sketching the Bearing Base:** You can quickly sketch the basic shape of the profile without specific dimension values. You then alter the sketch by modifying dimensions to fit your design.

You can draw the base of the bearing in the following two ways:

Method 1:

- Click on the Line flyout arrow 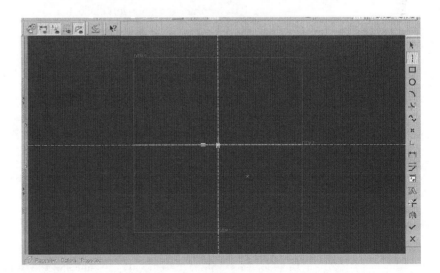 and click on the Centerline tool .

  -or- from the pull-down menus select **Sketch>Line>Centerline.**
  -or- hold down the right mouse button and from the pop-up menu select **Centerline.**

- Place the cursor on the left end of the Horizontal Reference (the dashed orange horizontal line on the screen) and click the left mouse button.

- Move the cursor to the right end of the Horizontal Reference and click the left mouse button.

- Place the cursor on the upper end of the Vertical Reference (the dashed orange vertical line on the screen) and click the left mouse button.

- Move the cursor to the lower end of the Vertical Reference and click the left mouse button.

- Two Centerlines will be created and the screen will look like Figure 16.24 below.

- Click on the Middle Mouse Button. Whenever you are in the sketcher a single mouse middle click will abort the current command and return you to the toolbar with the select command already chosen.

- Click on the Rectangle button .

  -or- from the pull-down menus select **Sketch>Rectangle.**

Figure 16.24   The Sketch Area with Two Centerlines.

- Now you have to specify the two opposite vertices of the rectangle. Click anywhere on the upper left portion of the orange box.
- Now move your cursor to the right of the orange box. When you see two small red arrows on the two sides of the upper side of the rectangle, indicating symmetry, stop moving your cursor to the right anymore. Next move your cursor down. When you again see two small red arrows on the two sides of the left side of the rectangle, left click again. The rectangle has to be symmetric with respect to both the horizontal and vertical centerlines.
- Middle click to abort the rectangle command. The sketched entities are displayed in yellow.

Method 2:

- Click on the Line toolbar button .
  -or- from the pull-down menus select **Sketch>Line>Line.**
  -or- hold down the right mouse button and from the pop-up menu select **Line.**
- Click anywhere on the upper left corner of the orange box and move you cursor down. Look for the V symbol indicating a vertical line.
- When you come to the Horizontal Reference (the dashed orange horizontal line on the screen) left click.
- Then move your cursor down and look for the V symbol. When you see two L_1 symbols beside each of the vertical lines indicating they are of equal length left click.
- Now move your cursor to the right and look for the H symbol indicating a horizontal line. If the L_1 symbol shows up again ignore it.
- When you come to the Vertical Reference (the dashed orange horizontal line on the screen) left click.
- Move your cursor to the right again and look for the H symbol. When you see two L_2 symbols beside each of the horizontal lines indicating they are of equal length left click.
- Now move your cursor up and look for the V symbol. When you reach the Horizontal Reference left click.
- Move your cursor up again, looking for the V symbol and when you see the third L_1 symbol left click.
- Then move the cursor towards the left and look for the H symbol. When you reach the starting point left click.
- Middle click to exit the line command.

8. **Dimensioning the Sketch:** After the sketch of the rectangular shape is completed the Intent Manger will put two dimensions on the sketch. These may be for the length and width of the rectangle or any of these dimensions may be the distance from horizontal or vertical reference to the vertex of the rectangle. These dimensions will appear in grey and will be similar to the ones shown in Figure 16.25.

These dimensions set by the sketcher are called 'Weak Dimensions'. The dimensions that the user specifies for the feature are known as 'Strong Dimensions' and they appear in yellow. You will have to modify the values of the dimensions set by the intent manager and change them to 'Strong Dimensions'. You are going to specify the height and width of the rectangle.

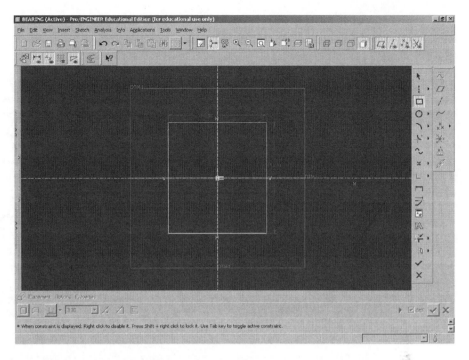

Figure 16.25   Preliminary Sketch with Weak Dimensions.

- If the weak dimensions are for the length and width then simply double click on the numerical value of the length and it will become highlighted. In the text box type in 10 and press ***Enter.*** The length will change to 10. Click anywhere on the screen to remove the red highlights. In the same way, change the width to 7. Now you can select the dimension text and drag it to a better location.

- If one of the weak dimensions is not the length or the width then you will have to create a new dimension. To do this click on the ***Dimension*** button form the

    right toolbar ![dimension icon]. Left click on the two vertexes of the rectangle that share the dimension and then middle click on the screen where you want the dimension to appear. Once this dimension shows up modify it the same way mentioned before.

Now the sketch should look like Figure 16.26.

Strong and Weak Dimensions: If there is not enough information to define the drawing sketcher will assign sufficient missing dimensions as weak dimensions. The values of these dimensions are chosen at random for the first features in a part and must be reset to reflect the actual geometry of the part. The weak dimensions are deleted by the Intent Manager when they are no longer necessary for defining the geometry, but the strong dimensions are not deleted without your permission. However, if a dimension is redundant the Intent Manager will let you know which dimensions are making the drawing over-constrained.

9.   **Accepting the Sketch:** When all the dimensions are filled up and you are

    satisfied with the sketch click on the blue **Check Mark** option ![check mark] at the

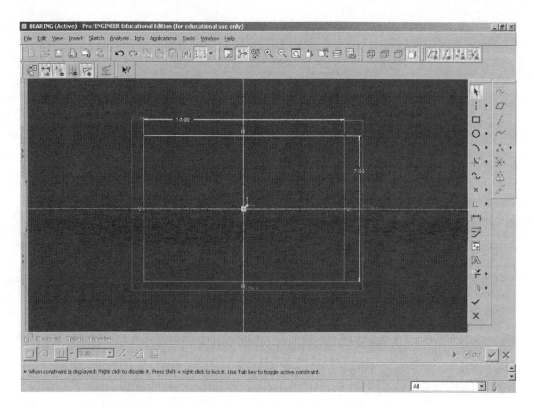

Figure 16.26   Final sketch of the base with appropriate dimensions.

bottom of the sketcher toolbar to continue with the protrusion. Now the system exits the Sketcher and returns to the model view in the regular graphics window. The finished outline of the profile, i.e. your sketched 2D shape and the depth dimension are shown (Figure 16.27).

10. **Setting the Protrusion Depth:** You can specify the depth of the protrusion in two ways. The depth is defined by a default number (probably 216.51) which appears on the yellow shaded image of the feature and also on a textbox in the **Extrude Dashboard.** You can double click on any of these and the default number becomes highlighted. Type in 2 for the depth of the bearing base and press **Enter.** You can now turn this model around with the middle-mouse button and see it from different viewpoints.

11. **Verifying the Feature Geometry:** By clicking on the **View Geometry** button on the right end of the dashboard you can see how your newly created feature will look when it is fully integrated into the part. If there is any mistake, or something else you would like to change then you can click on the button again and carry out the necessary modifications. There won't be much to check for in this very first and really simple feature of the bearing.

12. **Completing the Feature Creation:** Choose the green **Check Mark** button in the dashboard to finish the creation of the base. The rectangular

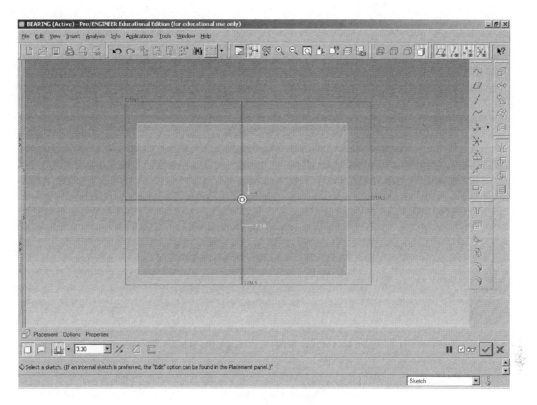

Figure 16.27   Sketch of the Base after returning to the Graphics Window.

block will now appear with its edges highlighted in red, as it is the last feature created.

13. **Saving the Part:** While working with Pro/E it is always a good idea to practice *safe saving*. In general, it is better for the designer (i.e. you) to save the part at a certain point where losing any of the work would be troublesome. Usually it is after a several features have been created with desirable accuracy. However, it is better to make it a habit to save your model frequently, just in case something goes wrong. When things go wrong you can exit from the program and resume your work with the most recently saved version of the part.

You can save your part in several ways.

- Select the save button 🖫 in the top toolbar

  -or- select **File >Save** from the pull-down menus
  -or- pres **CTRL** + **S** as the keyboard shortcut.

The **Save Object** dialogue window will appear with "Bearing" as the model name. Click **OK** and the part will be saved.

Saving while in Sketcher: You can save your work while you are in Sketcher. You don't need this option now, but it might come in handy while working in your project. This will not save the part, but the current sketch will be saved with the file extension *sec*. For complicated sketches this option is really helpful.

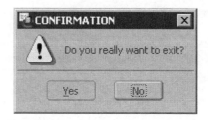

Figure 16.28   The Exit Confirmation Dialogue Box.

12.   **Exiting Pro/E Wildfire:** In the **active** window, click *File >Exit* from the pull-down menus or click the X at the top right corner. The system displays the *CONFIRMATION* Dialog box (Figure 16.28).

If you want to simply exit the system, without saving anything else, click **Yes.** This will remove all files from computer memory and stop the execution of the Pro/ENGINEER Wildfire program. If you click on the X button by accident you can cancel the command. Pro/E will not automatically save anything for you, neither will it prompt you to save your work when you exit. If you exit Pro/E without saving, your new work is **lost.**

13.   **Retrieving an Existing Part File:** Login to the computer, load Pro/E and set your personal directory in H:/ as the working directory. You can access the saved files in two ways: using the **Folder Navigator,** or the standard Windows **File Open** dialog box by clicking the *Open* shortcut button from the top toolbar, or clicking *File >Open* from the pull-down menus. The Folder Navigator is more flexible and gives you more control over file access. Therefore it is discussed in detail here. With the **Folder Navigator Browser** you can **Preview** files before you **Open** them. This allows you to avoid opening the wrong file, which may waste time. When you select a file from the list, the Preview window display the file (part or assembly). Preview is not available for some files. To open a file with **Folder Navigator:**

• Choose the **Folder Browser** icon located just above the **Model Tree** (Figure 16.29)

• Select your personal directory in H:/ from the list.

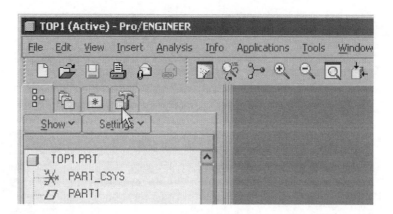

Figure 16.29   The Folder browser Icon in the Folder Navigator.

- Click **bearing.prt** from the list of files displayed.
- If you want to **Open** the file you see in the Preview display, you simply choose

  the **Open File in Pro/E** icon 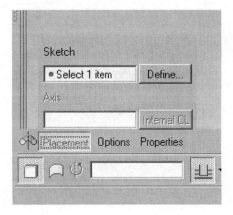.

The part **bearing** now appears in the **Graphics** window—check the Title area of the new Window. It will read:

BEARING (Active) Pro/ENGINEER

14. **Modifying an Existing Part:** We will now add the vertical cylindrical shape on top of the base of the bearing. We can do this in two ways: by using the **Revolved Protrusion** option or by using the **Extrude Protrusion** option. Both are now going to be discussed.

Method 1: Using the Revolved Protrusion

The **Revolved** feature is one of several which are available (you have already used Extrude). By revolving a profile about a centerline, complex cylindrical features can be created. You sketch the axis of revolution as a centerline and a closed profile lying entirely on one side of the axis. To create a feature you can revolve a sketch any number of degrees between **1°** and **360°** about the centerline. You specify the rotation value in the **Dashboard** by selecting angle from the option menu or typing in a number of degrees. For our cylindrical feature we will use a 360° revolve.

- Select the Revolve tool from the right toolbar. The **Revolve** dashboard appears, which is similar to the **Extrude** dashboard and contains similar options.
- Click **Placement > Define** from the Dashboard.
- The Sketch Placement Dialogue Window appears. Select **TOP** as the **Sketch Plane.**
- Select **RIGHT** as the **Orientation Reference Plane.**
- Select **Right** from the **Orientation** option menu.
- Select **Sketch.**
- The system displays the **Sketch** view and the references dialogue window. The system assumes that the **References** should be the **Right** and **Front Datum Planes.** Although the References are *fully placed* we will have some additional references for ease of sketching. Click on the upper horizontal edge and the two vertical edges of the base feature displayed. These will be added

Figure 16.30 Selecting Placement > Define from Dashboard.

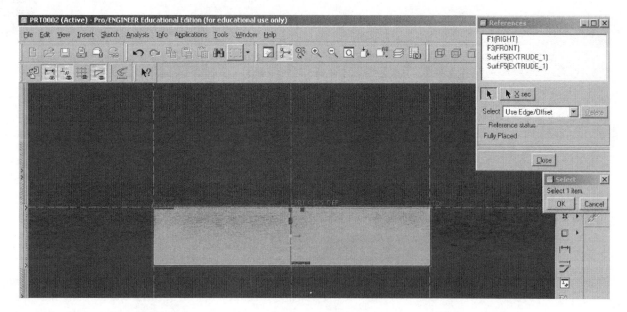

Figure 16.31   Added References.

as references (Figure 16.31). This is not going to be of much help now. But added references are really helpful while working on complex parts.

- Click **Close** to begin sketching.

- Draw a vertical centerline along the vertical reference—this defines the axis of revolution. Click on the **Line** flyout arrow and click on the **Centerline** tool . Click on the vertical reference twice in two different points and the centerline will automatically snap to the vertical.

- Using the Line tool draw the sketch outline as shown below (Figure 16.32).

- Click on the middle mouse button to exit the line mode.

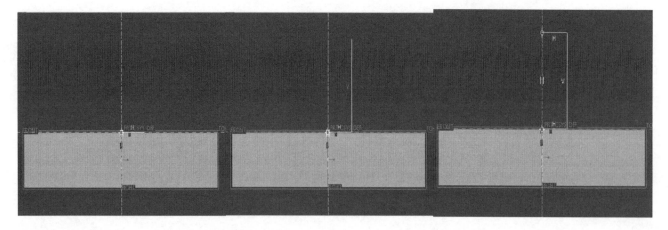

Figure 16.32   Sketching the Revolved Protrusion.

- Click on the dimension text of the vertical line and type in 3.
- Usually revolved features are specified using diameter rather than radius. This process is described below.

Dimensioning a Revolved Feature with Diameter: The curves on the other side of the centerline do not exist, as only half the object is sketched. A special type of dimension representing the diameter can be created.

- Click on the **Dimension** button from the right toolbar .
- Click on the centerline.
- Click on the curve associated with the radius of the feature i.e. the vertical line on the revolved feature.
- Click on the centerline again.
- With the middle mouse button click on the position on the screen where you want the dimension text to appear
- Double click on the dimension text and type in 4. Your sketch should look similar to Figure 16.33.

- Click on the button to accept the sketch.

- In the depth-spec option on the Dashboard **Blind** is selected as the default extrusion and we will leave it as it is.

- Click on the **View Geometry** button to preview the part and select **Accept** .

- Save your part.

Method 2: Using the Extrude Protrusion

- Click on the **Extrude** icon on the right toolbar.

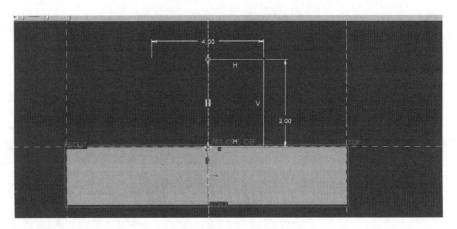

Figure 16.33 Completed Sketch of the Revolved Protrusion.

- Type in 3 for the depth of the protrusion in the specific textbox on the **Extrude Dashboard** (notice that this can be done even before drawing the sketch).
- Leave the default ***Blind*** depth spec option.
- Click on ***Placement>Define***—the *Plane* textbox in the **Sketch Reference** window will be highlighted.
- Click on the top surface of the base feature - this will be our sketching plane. Something similar to "Surf:F4 EXTRUDE_1" will appear on the *Plane* textbox.
- Accept the default *Orientation Reference Plane* and *Orientation* and click on ***Sketch.***
- Accept the default *References* and start sketching.
- Click on the ***Circle*** tool from the right toolbar to draw a circle.
- Click on the intersection of the Horizontal and Vertical References on the screen.
- Move the mouse cursor in any direction on the screen and a circle will appear.
- Middle click to exit the draw circle mode.
- Double click on the dimension text of the diameter and type in 4.
- Click on the [✓] button.
- If for any reason your cylinder appears to be inside the base then just flip the yellow arrow on the cylinder or click on the *Change Depth Direction* [⤢] from the Dashboard.
- Click on the ***View Geometry*** [☑ 👓] button to preview the part and select ***Accept*** [✓] .
- Save your part.

Manipulating the Object Display: Now it is a good time to introduce you to the various ways you can control how Pro/E displays your model on the screen. By altering the scale and/or viewing angle you can control the view display of the part in the active Graphics Area. The **CTRL** key and **SHIFT** key and the middle button on your mouse allow you to quickly Zoom, Spin, and Pan the part while you are using other functions. There are several methods for controlling the display, which are briefly described below.

15. **Zooming the Model:** You can use several methods for zooming. They are:

   a. <u>CTRL + Middle Mouse Button</u>: Press the **CTRL** key and the middle mouse button at the same time and drag vertically. If you have a mouse scroll wheel instead of the Middle mouse button press the scroll wheel. The view zooms in when you move the cursor downwards and zooms out when you move the cursor upwards (Figure 16.34). The initial cursor location is the center of the zoom and the view gets bigger or smaller about that point.

   b. <u>Mouse scroll Wheel</u>: If you have a mouse with a scroll wheel you can zoom in and out the object just by rolling the wheel. Here too the zoom center is the initial position of the mouse cursor.

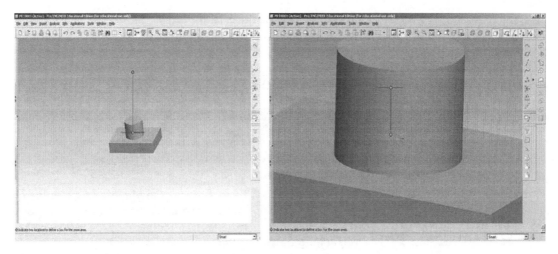

Figure 16.34   Zooming by CTRL+MMB and dragging vertically.

    c.   <u>The View Toolbar</u>: You can also **Zoom** your model by utilizing the short-cut

        buttons **Zoom In** and **Zoom Out** on the **View** toolbar. When you click the **Zoom In** button the cursor changes to a small magnifying glass

        and you have to select (by clicking with the left mouse button) two diagonal corners of a rectangular area, where you want the zoom to occur. After that this area is scaled up so that it occupies the entire graphics area. When you press the zoom out button the scale of the view is decreased about the center of the graphics area. By pressing the zoom out button again and again you can make the image smaller and smaller. To make the model view fit the

        screen simply press the ***Refit*** button.

15.   **Panning the Model:** Press the **SHIFT** key and the middle mouse button at the same time and drag in any direction. Again if you have a mouse scroll wheel instead of the Middle mouse button press the scroll wheel. Then on the screen the model is translated to the direction of dragging about the center of the screen.

16.   **Spinning the Model:** Toggle the spin centre ON and OFF by clicking on the

    spin centre button on the top toolbar. Then the spin centre, a small red-green-blue triad, will appear at the approximate centre of the part. Press the middle mouse button (or the mouse scroll wheel) and the model will spin with the spin center staying fixed on the screen. When the spin centre is turned off the spin occurs around the initial position of the mouse cursor rather than the spin centre.

17.   **Rotating the Model:** Press the **CTRL** key and the middle mouse button (or the mouse scroll wheel) at the same time and drag horizontally. The model will rotate around an axis perpendicular to the screen, which passes through the spin center. This is helpful when you want to reorient the model and by using ***Spin*** alone you are unable to display the exact desired orientation.

18. **Displaying the Default Orientation View:** To display the model you can also use the predefined orientations. To view the object in its default orientation:

- Click the **Saved View List** shortcut button  on the top toolbar and select **Default**

    -or- From the Menu bar select **View > Orientation > Default**

    -or- Press **CTRL+ D.**

19. **Reorienting the View:** For the ease of making the engineering documentation of the model you might like to have your own saved views that you can recall when necessary. To do this from the Menubar click on **View > Orientation > Reorient** or from the top toolbar click on **Reorient View** shortcut button. The dialogue window shown in Figure 35 will appear which allows you to change the display or by rotating the part about a **Spin Center (Dynamic Orient)** or by selecting planes or faces on the part **(Orient by reference).** This way you can create standard orthogonal views. Click on the blue "**Saved Views**" part of the window and the lower half of the window will be expanded. At this very basic level we are not going to deal with the **Dynamic Orient.**

20. **Creating Standard Engineering Drawing Views:** By using the Orient by Reference Dialogue Window you can create customized views of your model. Here we are going to create the standard orthographic views, i.e. FRONT, TOP and RIGHT views and a better isometric view for the engineering drawing. The common method for this is to choose two datum planes or orthogonal surfaces on the model and indicate which way they are going to face in the view that you want. These are called View References and they can

Figure 16.35   Reorient View Dialogue Window.

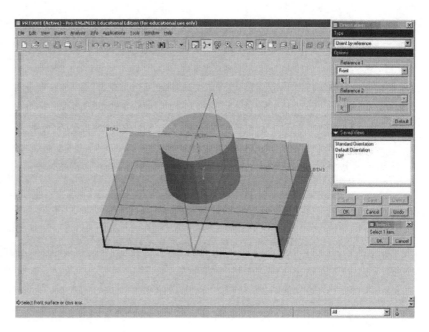

Figure 16.36   Selecting the front surface of the Front View.

face the top, front, right, left, bottom or back of the screen. You have to specify the References in the *Options* area of the dialogue window.

a.   Creating the FRONT View:

- In the *Orientation* dialog box the default *Type* should be set to ***Orient by reference,*** if not change the Type to ***Orient by reference.***

- You are now going to select a plane that defines the Front orientation reference (Reference 1). To select a plane, you need to pick the outline (rectangular edge) of the plane. Click on the Reference 1 pull-down textbox and as shown in Figure 16.36 select the plane that would appear on front in the Front View.

- Now click on the Reference 2 Dialogue Box, it has been set to *Top*, i.e. this reference will face the top of the screen in the FRONT view. Click the upper surface of the base feature as illustrated in Figure 16.37.

- Click on the ***Saved Views*** arrow.

- Click on the **Name** text field and type **FRONT.**

- Click on the ***Save*** button.

- Choose ***OK.*** You can recall this view by selecting its name from the list of **Saved Views.**

- Change to the **Default** view by clicking the ***Saved Views*** button on the top toolbar and choosing it from the **Saved view list.**

- Change back to the **FRONT** view by choosing it from the **Saved view list** (Figure 16.38).

b)   Creating the TOP View:

- Spin the model to a suitable view where it will be easier for you choose different planes and surfaces.

- From the top toolbar click on the *Reorient View* shortcut button.

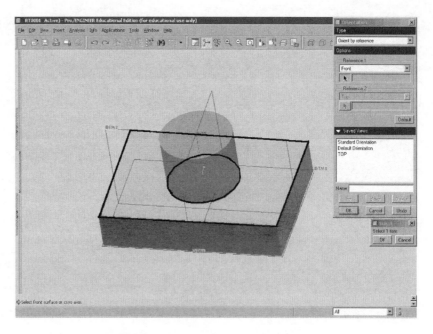

Figure 16.37   Selecting the top surface of the Front View.

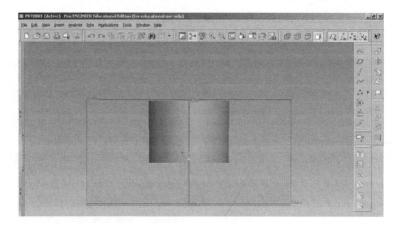

Figure 16.38   Front View of the Bearing.

- For Reference 1 select the top surface of the cylinder or the top surface of the base as in the TOP View this will face the front of the screen (Figure 16.39).
    - Change the *Reference 2* option to *Bottom* by selecting it from the pull-down list.
    - Select the surface that will face the bottom of the screen in the TOP View (Figure 16.39).
    - In the **Name** text field and type **TOP.**
    - Click on the *Save* button.
    - Choose **OK.** The Top View of the bearing should look like Figure 16.40.
- c)   Creating the RIGHT View:

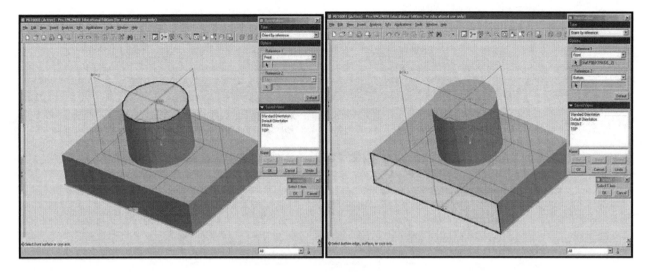

Figure 16.39   Selecting the Bottom and Top surfaces of the Bearing.

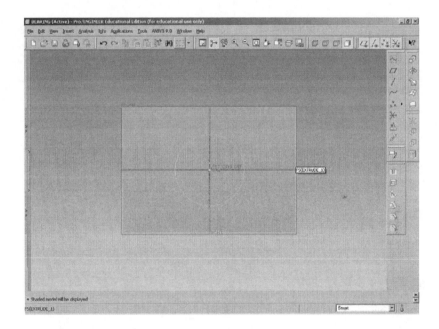

Figure 16.40   TOP View of the Bearing.

You can create the RIGHT View by following similar steps as you did for the FRONT and TOP Views. The RIGHT View should appear as in Figure 16.41 below.

21. **Using the Model Display Commands:** By using the tools on the Model Display toolbar (Figure 16.42) you can change the Display Mode of the view.

These options are:

Wireframe: all object edges are displayed in white.

Hidden Line: visible object edges displayed in white and hidden object lines displayed in grey.

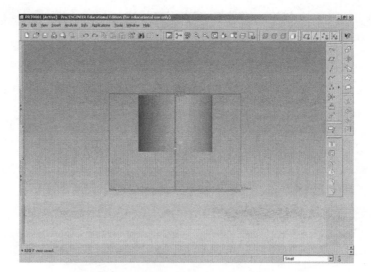

Figure 16.41   RIGHT View of the Bearing.

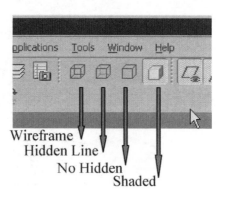

Figure 16.42   The Model Display Toolbar.

No Hidden: Hidden lines are not displayed, visible edges are displayed in white.
Shaded: Solid shaded model is displayed.

Click on each of these buttons and notice the changes in the appearance of your model.

22. **Inserting the Hole Feature:** The last feature you are going to add to the part is a hole. Again to learn different options we are going to describe two ways of adding this hole—by using a hole feature and by using a cut feature. The cut feature can be used to remove any shape of material from the existing part. There are various different types, but we are going to stick to the simple cylindrical hole.

Method 1: Using Hole Feature

- From the Menubar click *Insert > Hole,* the Hole Dashboard show up which is pretty similar to Extrude Dashboard.
- Click on *Placement.*
- For the *Primary Reference* click on the top surface of the cylinder.
- From the pull-down menu select *coaxial* as the hole type.

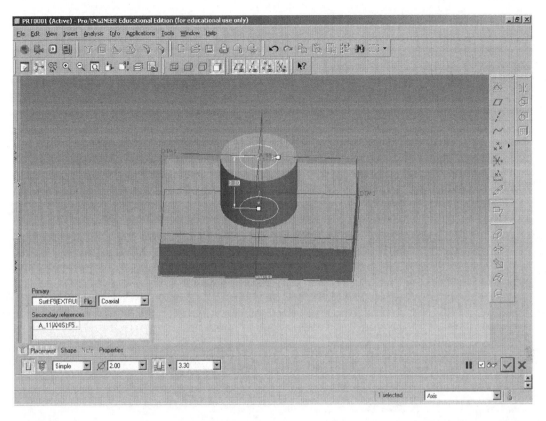

Figure 16.43 The Centerline of the cylinder highlighted as the secondary reference. Also the top surface of the cylinder is highlighted as the primary reference.

- Click on the *Secondary References* box.
- As the secondary reference click on the centerline of the cylinder (see Figure 16.43).
- Click on the *Placement* button again to complete the placement.
- Type in 2 for the diameter of the hole.
- Leave the default simple, straight hole options (Figure 16.44).
- Set the *Depth Spec* as *Through All* (Figure 16.44).
- Verify the hole integrated in the part and click accept ✔.
- Save your part.

Method 2: Using the Cut Feature

- Click on the **Extrude** icon on the right toolbar.
- Click on *Placement>Define*—the *Plane* textbox in the **Sketch Reference** window will be highlighted.
- Click on the top surface of the cylinder – this will be our sketching plane. Something similar to "Surf:F5 EXTRUDE_2" will appear in the *Plane* textbox.
- Accept the default *Orientation Reference Plane* and *Orientation* and click on **Sketch.**
- Accept the default *References* and start sketching.

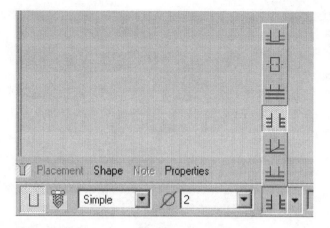

Figure 16.44   Defining the Parameters of the Hole feature.

- Click on the **Circle** tool 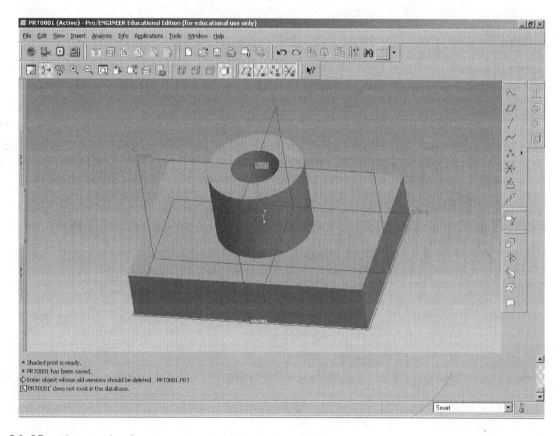 from the right toolbar to draw a circle.
- Click on the intersection of the Horizontal and Vertical References on the screen.
- Move the mouse cursor in any direction on the screen and a circle will appear.
- Middle click to exit the draw circle mode.

Figure 16.45   The Completed Bearing.

- Double click on the dimension text of the diameter and type in 2.
- Click on the button.
- If for any reason your hole appears to go out of the cylinder then flip the

  yellow arrow on the cylinder, or click on the *Change Depth Direction* from the Dashboard.
- Select the **Through All** option for the *Depth Spec* (refer to Figure 16.44).
- Select to make the **Extrude** remove material
- Click on the **View Geometry** button to preview the part and select

  Accept .
- Save your part. It should now appear as in Figure 16.45.

Various Depth Spec options: There are several Depth options available which are applicable according to the specific design requirement of different parts. As you click the pull-down arrow of the depth-spec option on the Extrude Dashboard you can see these options. The meaning of these icons are listed below:

Enter Depth

Enter Depth, Both Sides

Up to Next Surface

Intersect with All Surfaces

Intersect with Selected Surface or Plane

Up to Selected Point, Curve, Surface or Plane

23. **Dealine Trail Files:** Pro/E creates a new file with an incremented numeric sub-extension for each time you save an object. If you open your personal drive H:/ using the operating systems tools you will see that you have numerous files with the same name and different numeric extensions. For example,

bearing.prt.1
bearing.prt.2
bearing.prt.3
bearing.prt.4

The latest version of the file is the one with the highest numeric extension number. The **File Open** dialog box displays only the latest version. You may remove the old versions, as long as they are no longer needed.

You can remove old versions of objects by clicking *File > Delete > Old Versions.*

Make sure that you do not choose All Versions which is also located on this menu. This will delete all your work completely.

Chapter 17

3D Printing

As part of the ECOR 1010 Project requirements, you will be using the ZCorp Z400 or Stratasys Dimension-BST 3D printers to generate a static 3D model of your rendered solid parts, created in Pro/E. This chapter gives you the basic theory of Rapid Prototyping, 3D Printing and the guidelines to practice it.

17.1   RAPID PROTOTYPING

The term *rapid prototyping* (RP) refers to a set of techniques used to automatically construct a scaled model of a part or assembly using three-dimensional computer aided design (CAD) data. Rapid Prototyping allows designers to quickly create tangible prototypes of their designs, rather than just two-dimensional pictures. Often compared to the fictitious "Replicator" from the Star Trek TV series, a 3D printer can create a functional model of an engineer's design, complete with moving parts.

17.2   BASIC OVERVIEW OF RAPID PROTOTYPING

The models created by rapid prototyping have numerous uses. They make excellent visual aids for communicating ideas with co-workers or customers. Prototypes can also be used for design testing. For example, an aerospace engineer might mount a model airfoil in a wind tunnel for measuring lift and drag forces. Prototypes have always been used by designers; RP has provided the means to create them faster and less expensively.

In addition to prototypes, RP techniques can also be used to make tooling (referred to as *rapid tooling*) and even production-quality parts (*rapid manufacturing*). Rapid prototyping is often the best manufacturing process available for small production runs and complicated objects. Of course, "rapid" is a relative term. The process typically takes from 3 to 72 hours depending on the size and complexity of the part, which is much faster than the weeks or months required to make a prototype by traditional means such as machining. These dramatic time savings allow manufacturers to bring products to market faster and more cheaply.

RP technologies are often collectively referred to as *solid free-form fabrication, computer automated manufacturing,* or *layered manufacturing.* It is because the techniques are being increasingly used in non-prototyping applications. The term *layered manufacturing* is particularly descriptive of the manufacturing process used by most commercial RP machines. A software package "slices" the CAD model into a number of thin (~0. 1 mm) layers, which are then built up one atop another.

Prototypes are also useful for testing a design, to see if it performs as desired or needs improvement. It is now easy to perform iterative testing: build a prototype, test it, redesign, build and test, etc. Such an approach would be far too time-consuming using traditional prototyping techniques, but it is easy using RP.

In addition to being fast, RP models can do a few things metal prototypes cannot. For example, Porsche used a transparent stereolithography model of the 911 GTI transmission housing to visually study oil flow. Snecma, a French turbo machinery producer, performed photoelastic stress analysis on an SLA model of a fan wheel to determine stresses in the blades.

As any other technology RP has its limitations. Part volume is restricted to a certain amount depending on the RP machine. Metal prototypes are difficult to make, though this should change in the near future. Apart from these limitations, rapid prototyping is a remarkable technology that is revolutionizing the manufacturing process.

17.3   3D PRINTING

3D Printing is a variation of rapid prototyping. A 3D Printer is less expensive, easier to use and usually faster than a rapid prototyping system. Most importantly a 3D printer can fit in an office environment. Unlike a big rapid prototyping system a 3D printer can be located next to the design engineers so they can turn around jobs promptly and efficiently.

17.4   STL FILES

The .stl file format is an industry standard data transmission format that is necessary for Rapid Prototyping and 3D Printing. This format approximates the surfaces of a solid model with triangles. The file contains the coordinates of the vertices and the direction of the outward normal of each triangle. This is the standard input for most rapid prototyping machines.

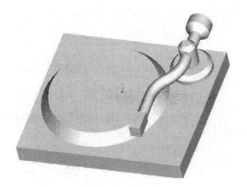 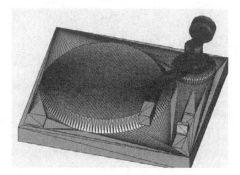

Figure 17.1   Conversion from Pro/E .prt file to .stl file.

3D Systems of Valencia, CA introduced stereolithography (STL), as a simple method of storing information about 3D objects. 3D Systems was one of the first companies to produce physical 3D models from computer 3D data.

STL files reproduce an object's 3D geometry by storing a set number of facets or 3D triangles in a complex digital model. After storing the outer and/or inner surface of a 3D object as facets in an STL file, the digital model can be manipulated, and a physical representation or replica of a 3D model can be made.

The more complex the model, the more triangles produced, and the larger the .stl file size. The 3D model has a higher resolution when the size of the individual facets in a model is small. By decimating the computer model the number of facets can be reduced and the size of the facets increased. But this may decrease the accuracy or resolution of the model as well.

17.5   THE BASIC PROCESS

Although several rapid prototyping techniques exist, all employ the same basic five-step process. The steps are:

1. Creation of a CAD model of the design
2. Conversion of the CAD model to STL format
3. Slice the STL file into thin cross-sectional layers
4. Construction of the model one layer atop another
5. Clean and finish the model

1) CAD Model Creation: First, using a Computer-Aided Design (CAD) software package the object to be built is modeled. Solid modelers, such as Pro/ENGINEER, yield better results in this process. Because solid modelers represent 3D objects more accurately than wire-frame modelers such as AutoCAD. The designer can use a pre-existing CAD file or create a new scaled one solely for prototyping purposes. This process is identical regardless of what kind of machine is being used.

2) Conversion to STL Format: The second step is to convert the CAD file into STL format. Large, complicated files require more time to pre-process and build, so the designer must balance accuracy with manageability to produce a useful STL file. Since the STL format is universal, this process is identical for all of the RP and 3D Print build techniques.

3) Slice the STL File: In the third step, a pre-processing program prepares the STL file to be built. Each rapid prototyping machine usually has its own software for this purpose, such as *ZPrint* for ZCorp Z400 and *Catalyst* for Dimension-BST. Most of these types of software allow the user to adjust the size, location and orientation of the model. Build orientation is important for several reasons. First, properties of rapid prototypes vary from one coordinate direction to another. For example, prototypes are usually weaker and less accurate in the z (vertical) direction than in the x-y plane. In addition, part orientation partially determines the amount of time required to build the model and the amount of support material needed. Placing the shortest dimension in the z direction reduces the number of layers, thereby shortening build time. The model can also be oriented in such a way that the least amount of support material is needed. Built orientation also determines the time required to produce the model. The pre-processing software slices the STL model into a number of layers from 0.01 mm to 0.7 mm thick, depending on the build technique. In some types of software the user can also select the thickness of the layers. The program generates an auxiliary structure to support the model during the build.

4) Layer by Layer Construction: The fourth step is the actual construction of the part. Most RP machines build one layer at a time from polymers, paper, or powdered metal. Most machines are fairly autonomous, needing little human intervention.

5) Clean and Finish: The final step is post-processing. This involves removing the prototype from the machine and detaching any supports. Some photosensitive materials need to be fully cured before use. Minor cleaning and surface treatment may also be required. The appearance and durability of the model can be improved by sanding, sealing, and/or painting.

17.6   3D PRINTING GUIDELINES

The following is a guideline that should be adhered to in order to produce a part that does not crumble and/or break. You may want to create a new, simplified Pro/E solid model that follows them. You may need to make changes to your design so it can be successfully printed.

- **Your assembly *must* fit within** a 1 in^3 cube (1 in $\times$ 1 in $\times$ 1 in) for the Dimension machine or a 3 in^3 cube ($\sqrt[3]{3}$ in $\times$ $\sqrt[3]{3}$ in $\times$ $\sqrt[3]{3}$ in) for the ZCorp machine. You can scale your model to fit within this constraint. You will want to save a new copy of your model (by clicking ***File > Save a Copy***) and then scale it so that you don't get confused with the original dimensions. The steps for doing this are described after this list.

- **The minimum wall thickness is 0.125" (1/8") for the ZCorp machine; the minimum wall thickness is 0.0625" (1/16") for the Dimension machine.** No guarantees can be made as to the structural integrity of the wall.

- Detailed features (0.02"-0.125") are possible, and appear extremely well, so long as they do not protrude very far from a given surface.

- The printed solid models by ZCorp are extremely porous, and as a result, very sensitive to moisture. They may crumble and disintegrate when exposed to water or sweat. Therefore, they should be treated by spraying a coat of enamel, or paint on any exposed surface.

- You are being asked to include your **group number** as a text protrusion on your model, to assist with model identification. The guidelines for this have been included below.
- The inclusion of colour in your assemblies does not make a difference for printing purposes. The models will appear in white only, regardless of what colours and textures that you have specified.
- Your STL filename *must* include your group number, the type of units that you have used (millimeters → mm or inches → in), and the 3D printer that you would like your part printed on (D → Dimension machine or Z → ZCorp machine).

    - A2-2mmD.stl → group 2 in lab section A2, part designed in millimetres (mm), printed on Dimension machine
    - B3-7inZ.stl → group 7 in lab section B3, part designed in inches (in), printed on the ZCorp machine

17.7   SCALING THE MODEL

- From the Menu bar click *Edit > Scale Model* (Figure 17.2).
- In the command/message window you will be prompted for the scale. Type in the desired scale.
- Click the green checkmark button.
- A message window will appear informing you that the model has to be regenerated. Click *Yes.*

You might have to repeat the process to get a suitable model.

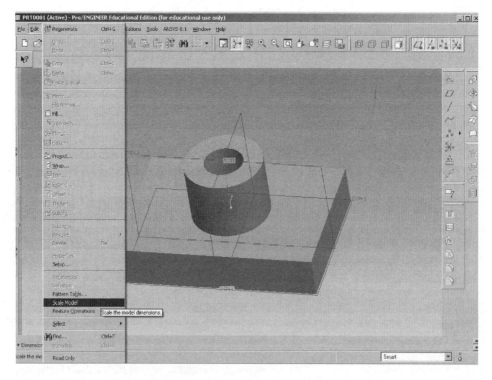

Figure 17.2   Scaling Your Model.

17.8   CREATING TEXT PROTRUSIONS IN PRO/E

Text protrusions can act as labels to help identify parts. To help with file identification, you are being asked to include your group number on your 3D solid model. The protrusion can be placed on any **flat** surface of your model. While many depths and heights are possible for text protrusions, their visibility is limited by the precision of the particular 3D printer.

Text height should be at least 0.25", and text depth should be in between 0.03" and 0.05". These dimensions are extremely important, as anything larger or smaller will not appear properly. Please include only your group number (i.e.A2-2) as a text protrusion.

To create text protrusions in Pro/E:

- Click on click the **Extrude** icon 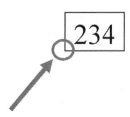 on the right toolbar. The extrude dashboard will appear at the bottom of the screen.
- Click on *Placement > Define.* The **Sketch** dialog window will show up with the plane textbox highlighted.
- Click on the flat surface of your model on which you want your student number to appear.
- Accept all the other default settings and click *Sketch.*
- The **References** dialog window will appear. Select the appropriate references (if needed) and click *Close.*

- In sketcher, click on the text button [A].
- Select the origin of the text. This will be the lower left corner of the text.

234

- Specify the height and orientation of the text by controlling the size and direction of the line that now appears from the text origin point, using the mouse. You can easily change the size of the text height to obtain an exact value after an approximate height has been selected, as you would change a dimension.
- Left click when you are finished drawing the line, the **Text** dialog window will appear (Figure 17.3).
- Type your group number into the "Text Line" textbox.
- Make sure that the current font is font3d (the default font). Also make sure that the Aspect Ratio = 1, and that the Slant Angle = 0.
- Click *Ok.*
- You can change the size and position of the text by left clicking on the text dragging. Dragging horizontally changes the position and dragging vertically changes the size of the text.

- When you are satisfied with text sketch accept it by clicking the [✓] button.

Figure 17.3   The Text Dialogue Window.

- In the depth-spec option on the Dashboard select ***Blind*** .
- Type the depth of the protrusion in the specific textbox on the **Extrude Dashboard.** The text has to appear towards you.
- Either preview or accept the text protrusion.

Exporting a Pro/E File to a .stl File:

- Either click on ***File > Save a Copy,*** or the save a copy button: . This will open up a new dialogue window.
- Save the file in your H:\ directory. For **Type** select STL from the pull down list.

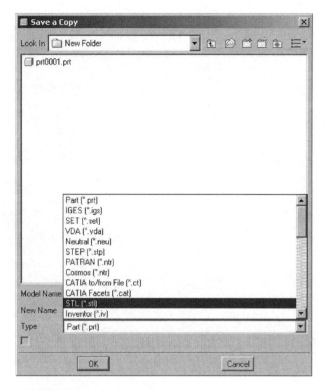

Figure 17.4   Save a Copy Dialog Window.

- Type the desired filename for your .stl file
- Cick **OK.** The **Export STL** dialog window appears.
- In the **Export STL** window:
  - ✓ Select *Default Coordinate System*
  - ✓ Select *Binary* Format
  - ✓ Check *Allow Negative Numbers*
  - ✓ Set the *Chord Height* to 0. It will then default to a value 0.0001-0.0009.
  - ✓ Set the *Angle Control* to 1.

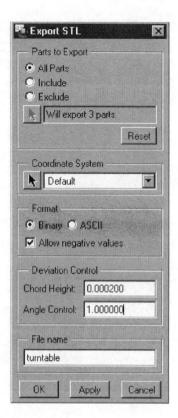

Figure 17.5 Export STL Dialog Window.

✓ The default filename is youfilename. Rename your file as follows: The file name should consist of your group number (i.e. A2-2), the type of units that were used in your part (inches → in or millimetres → mm), and the 3D printer to be used to print your part. This will help with your file identification for 3D printing.

     Ex: A2-2mmD.stl
                B3-7inZ.stl

• Pro/E will then approximate your assembly using the necessary number of triangles, and will write your .stl file to your home directory. Your model will remain active after your STL file has been created (Figure 17.6).

Only Your .stl File is Required for 3D Printing.

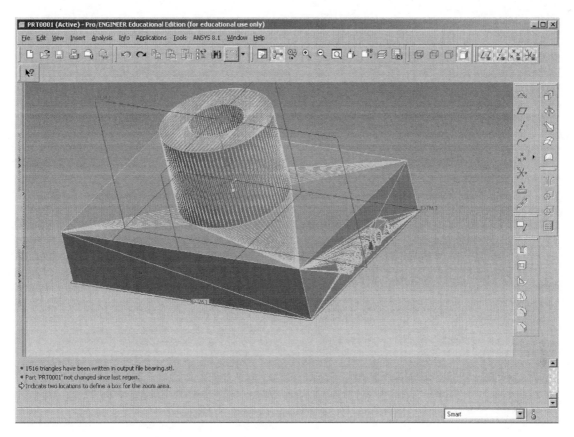

Figure 17.6 STL file for 3D- Printing.

Section 5

Measurement Statistics and Uncertainty

Chapter 18

Describing Engineering Measurement Data

18.1 INTRODUCTION

Measurement is fundamental to engineering. For example, when a component is designed it exists only on paper, or a computer screen. When the component is manufactured it will deviate to some extent from the design. The deviations take many forms and affect virtually every design feature of the component. For mechanical components the dimensions will deviate from the design values because of errors induced by the manufacturing process: holes will vary in size, location, and roundness; plates will vary in length and surface finish. Moreover, the dimensions and overall shape of metallic components will also be affected by temperature changes.

Consider AISI-SAE 1008 carbon steel. In the temperature range 20.00 − 100.00°C this steel has a coefficient of thermal expansion of $\alpha = 12.6 \times 10^{-6}$ m/mK [1]. This coefficient means that the dimensions of any piece of AISI-SAE 1008 carbon steel will grow 12.6 μm for an increase in temperature of 1.00 K. Because of the linear relationship between the Kelvin and Celsius temperature scales we can calculate dimension changes using Δ°C instead of ΔK. Suppose we had a rod of AISI-SAE 1008 that was exactly 1.00 m in length at 20.00°C. What would its length be at 100.00°C? The temperature difference is:

$$\Delta°C = 100.00 − 20.00 = 80.00°C,$$
$$\Delta K = 373.15 − 293.15 = 80.00 K.$$

This temperature induced change in dimension is easy to compute:

$$\Delta l = l\alpha\Delta K,$$
$$= l\alpha\Delta°C,$$
$$= (1.00 \text{ m})(12.6 \times 10^{-6} \text{ m/mK})(80.00 K),$$
$$= 0.001008 \text{ m},$$
$$= 0.00101 \text{ m}.$$

The steel rod becomes 1.01 mm longer when $\Delta°C = 80.00$. This 0.1% difference in length may be unimportant for some applications, but if the AISI-SAE 1008 steel rod were used in a device that was intended to have a positioning accuracy of ±0.1 mm, then temperature changes would have a large impact on performance.

The above example illustrates an important problem associated with direct measurement of simple physical characteristics, like length: changes in ambient conditions cause changes in the physical characteristic. We can call these dimensional deviations **errors.** The trouble is that we can account for, and predict some, like temperature induced dimension changes (assuming we know the temperature difference), but the vast majority cannot be predicted. This means that we need some way to characterize errors in such a way so that we can judge if manufactured components can do the job they were designed for. If we allow a length dimension to vary by ±0.1 mm, then we have a tolerance limit that we can apply to all measured lengths. If the measured length is within the tolerance limit the component can be accepted, otherwise it may have to be rejected.

The preceding discussion is intended to point out the need for engineering measurements, and that we must somehow account for observed error. Unfortunately, most engineering measurements are not as straightforward as measuring the length of a steel rod. More challenging measurement requirements present themselves when measuring velocity gradients in a wind tunnel, or vibrations along a helicopter rotor blade, or stresses in a structural member, or transmission rates in a communications network, etc.. Not only must we account for variations in the characteristics being measured, but also for variations in the measurement system. Even the act of making the measurement will change the characteristic being measured, and not necessarily only in a relativistic way. The remainder of this chapter is devoted to standard ways for describing engineering measurement data.

18.2   STATISTICS

Statistics gives us tools that we can use to make intelligent judgements and informed decisions in the presence of uncertainty, variation, and error. If there were no error, variation, or uncertainty we could dispense with statistics, and many engineers would be incalculably happier. If every aircraft structural component had the same stress corrosion resistance, if the nominal capacitance of every capacitor was exactly equal to the nominal value, if every 1m length steel rod was exactly 1m in length, then a single measurement would be all that was required to completely, and forever, characterize the measured parameter. But, the world is not perfect: uncertainty, variation, and error exist. As a consequence, engineers must deal with large collections of data. Statistics provides methods for organizing the data and for extracting information from it that is needed for decision making.

18.2.1 Descriptive and Inferential Statistics

Data comprises a set of observations of either a single variable, or simultaneous observations of two, or more variables. Statistics is the science of collecting, simplifying, and describing data, as well as making *inferences*, or drawing conclusions from analysis of the data [2]. There are two main branches of statistics. **Descriptive statistics** deals with collecting and simplifying data so that it can be summarized in an organized and comprehensible way. For example, a production facility may produce 1,000,000 lengths of 1m AISI-SAE 1008 steel rod annually. The variation in length among the set of rods may be ±0.0001 mm. The list of the individual lengths of all 1,000,000 rods would be incomprehensible. However, the average length of the entire set, or even the average of the averages of several random subsets, would provide insight on the overall variation of rod lengths.

The other branch of statistics has a definition that is somewhat more abstract. We require the definition of two terms before we can give an exact definition of this second branch. Suppose we have a railroad container filled with millions of washers. The entire collection of all the washers is a **population.** A handful of washers is a **sample** of the population. Now we can define the second branch, which is called **inferential statistics.** It concerns making judgments, or inferences, about a population based on the properties of the data obtained when measuring a characteristic of a sample of the population [2].

18.2.2 Discrete and Continuous Data

A **variable** is any measurable characteristic whose value may change from one element to another in a population. Measurement data consists of observations of one, or more variables. **Univariate** data comprises a set of measurements of a single variable. The following sample of voltages of ten 9-volt batteries is a univariate data set:

$$9.2 \quad 8.7 \quad 8.7 \quad 9.3 \quad 9.2 \quad 8.9 \quad 9.1 \quad 8.8 \quad 8.9 \quad 9.1$$

Bivariate data results when simultaneous observations are made on two variables. Consider a sample of five students from the population of students at Carleton University. The variables in the bivariate data set are weight (kg) and gender (M/F). Note that the weight is a **numerical** quantity, while gender is a **categorical** quantity, either male (M), or female (F). The bivariate data of the sample of the population is:

$$(72.21, M) \quad (49.01, F) \quad (53.57, F) \quad (92.42, M) \quad (44.89, F)$$

When observations are made on more than two variables the result is **multivariate** data. We can expand the bivariate data of the above five students to additionally include age reported in *whole* years, giving:

$$(72.21, M, 19) \quad (49.01, F, 18) \quad (53.57, F, 18) \quad (92.42, M, 20) \quad (44.89, F, 19)$$

The univariate, bivariate, and multivariate data set examples above reveal that there are two distinct types of variable in a mathematical sense. A variable is **continuous** if its possible values are *real numbers*, i.e. consisting of an entire interval on the number line. Clearly, a student's weight measured in kilograms is a real number, and can be reported to any number of decimal places up to the resolution of the measurement device. However, age reported in years, and gender are not continuous variables. These are examples of **discrete** variables. Discrete variables usually result from counting, in which case the values are some subset of the integers. Arguably, age could be represented as a real number, but in the sample data it is rounded to an integer. As such a sample student from the population is either one age, or another, but not in between. Categorical data, such as the gender of a student, is also discrete. The students in the population can be categorized as either male (M), or female (F). There is no possibility for a value to be anything in between.

18.2.3 Data Quality: Variability

Examining the examples of data extracted from population samples from Section 18.2.2 it is clear that variables are exactly that: variable. This brings up the issue of data quality. Some data will be affected by relatively large *random* variations, such as the height of students, fuel consumption rates for private vehicles, or responses to a poll. But, there is an additional component to the variation: measurement error and noise.

The greatest contribution to measurement error and noise comes from the measurement system itself. If the precision, or numerical resolution of the measurement system is of the same order of magnitude as the expected error, the data set will be very corrupted by noise and may not give a useful picture of the sample. This in turn could lead to drawing conclusions about the population, and making decisions that are not based in fact.

A standard *rule of thumb* for selecting an appropriate measurement system, or technique, is that its output be 10 times less variable than the inherent variability in the characteristic being measured. For example, if the error tolerance, the maximum allowable error, on the diameter of a 5 cm diameter shaft was 0.1 mm, then the measurement system used to measure the diameter of sample shafts would need to have a maximum error of 0.01 mm in order for the measurement data to be trustworthy. If the measurement required counting of samples, for example the number of cars entering and leaving a parking lot through one particular access, then the technique for counting would have to account for the possibility of *false* counts. If this source of error was a factor of 10 less than the precision required by the data, then the measurement technique could be employed, and the resulting data treated as *reliable*.

Additional care must be given to the sample itself. Different objects may possess similar characteristics. If the goal of obtaining measurement data from a sample is to make decisions affecting the entire population, then care must be taken to ensure all elements in the sample are indeed members of the population. For example, if you want information on the fuel consumption of gas burning cars, then the sample should not include trucks. The data obtained would likely *skew* the statistical results leading to possibly poor judgements. This aspect of data quality should never be overlooked!

18.3   SUMMARIZING DATA

Crucial conceptual tools in statistical analysis are **measures of central tendency.** As we have seen, data in a sample will have some variation. Information that can help characterize the distribution of the variation among the sample gives extremely useful insight into system components being studied. We can use the information to draw conclusions about production processes, system configurations, communication networks, etc.. Before entering into a discussion on measures of central tendency, it will be helpful to introduce graphical representation of the data in **histograms,** and then to classify various shapes of typical data distributions that frequently arise in the context of engineering data measurement.

18.3.1 Histograms

By far the most common type of graphical representation of engineering measurement data is the **histogram.** Other graphical representations, such as **stem-and-leaf plots, dotplots, pictograms, bar graphs,** and **line graphs** are frequently used as well, but are beyond the scope of this book. The interested reader will find comprehensive introduction to these in [2, 3, 4], and many other textbooks.

In a histogram, the abscissa (the horizontal x-axis) represents values of the random variable x. It is called random, because no matter how carefully the data are measured, random scatter in the values will routinely occur. The frequency (number of occurrences), n, that a measured value occurs is plotted on the ordinate (the vertical axis). But, before we can proceed to generating histograms that will reveal information contained in the data, we must first discuss **frequency distributions,** and the importance of grouping distributed frequencies into **classes,** or **bins.**

Consider the data listed in Table 18.1. It represents the number of breakdowns over the course of one winter (period between October-April) for each snowplow in a fleet of 20. This is discrete data (a snowplow breakdown must be represented by an integer, a truck can't breakdown 0.63 times).

Rather than assigning a value to the number of breakdowns for each truck, it may be more revealing, at least for identifying trends in the data, to group all the distinct values and count the number of times each distinct value occurs instead. It is to be seen examining Table 1 that while there are twenty numbers, one for each snowplow, there are only seven distinct values for x, the random variable. They are 1, 4, 5, 6, 7, 9, and 11, which occur 2, 2, 4, 6, 3, 2, and 1 times, respectively. The number of times a distinct value occurs is called its **frequency.** The frequency of the occurrences of the breakdowns are grouped and listed in Table 18.2. When plotted in a frequency histogram, Figure 18.1, the frequency of the breakdowns is revealed. There seems to be a dominant central value, while the remaining lesser frequencies are more-or-less evenly distributed on either side of this central frequency. This information is not readily evident when looking at the data in Table 18.1.

TABLE 18.1   Breakdowns per truck in a fleet of 20 snowplows.

Truck Number	Number of Breakdowns	Truck Number	Number of Breakdowns
1	5	11	6
2	1	12	5
3	9	13	6
4	5	14	11
5	7	15	7
6	6	16	6
7	6	17	4
8	5	18	6
9	1	19	9
10	7	20	6

TABLE 18.2   Measurements of random variable x (breakdown in a fleet of 20 snowplows).

x_i (Number of Breakdowns)	n_i (Number of Occurrences)
1	2
4	2
5	4
6	6
7	3
9	2
11	1

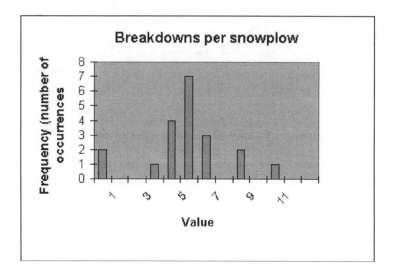

Figure 18.1   Frequency histogram for data set in Table 18.2.

18.3.2 Bins and Classes

As the number of values in the data set becomes larger, the frequency distribution by itself, as in Table 18.2, becomes less comprehensible. This is especially true when the range of the random variable values is large. Suppose it varied between 0 and 10,000. In this case the x-axis must be segmented somehow.

Suppose you were the manager of a very large engineering project involving the design of a large passenger transport aircraft. The design team may consist of thousands of employees. As project manager, you must keep track of the hours spent on all the various design activities that range from selecting the tires for the landing gear, to designing the control surface actuation, to designing the various control subsystems in the cockpit, to designing the subsystems for the engines, and everything else in between. In this type of large project, some components must be completed before others can begin. To ensure that the project will finish on schedule the manager must monitor the time spent on the various interrelated sub-projects. If some problems are encountered by a sub-design team, the manager can reallocate resources. That is, by tracking the hours, the manager can see which sub-projects are ahead of schedule, and those that are behind. Workers and equipment can be reallocated from teams that are ahead to those that are behind the schedule. The actual data in Table 18.3 has been divided into intervals of equal width of $\delta x = 100$. That is, one design team recorded a number of hours somewhere between 0 and 100 hours, two teams recorded a number of hours that fits in the interval between

100 and 200 hours, and so on. These intervals are called **classes,** or **bins.** Clearly, the size of the bin relative to the range of the values of the data has an effect on the graphical representation in the histogram. The histogram in Figure 18.2 (b) represents exactly the same data as in Figure 18.2 (a), however the bins are one tenth the size. That is, in Figure 18.2 (b) $\delta x = 10$, while in Figure 18.2 (a) it is $\delta x = 100$. In Figure 18.2 (b) with $\delta x = 10$, it appears that the most frequent number of recorded hours is 4 at between 790–800 hours. Whereas, in Figure 18.2 (a) with $\delta x = 100$, we see 11 teams recorded hours in the interval 400–500.

The upper and lower bounds on the bin size are known as **class limits.** The lower bounds of 0, 100, 200, etc. for the data in Table 18.3 are called the **lower class limits.** The values 99, 199, 299, etc. are the **upper class limits.** The distance from one lower class limit to the next is the **class width,** or **bin size.** Note that this definition is not the distance from the lower class limit to the upper class limit.

Another associated number is the **class mark.** It is defined to be the midpoint of a class. In other words, the number half way between the lower class limit and the upper class limit. For the data in Table 18.3 the class mark of the 0–100 class is 49.5. This is because that class is bounded by the integers 0 and 99, not 100. Recall, the class width is 100, the distance between two adjacent lower bounds. When the class width is

TABLE 18.3   Aircraft design team hours.

x_i (Time in Hours)	n_i (Number of Sub-Projects)
100	1
200	2
300	4
400	6
500	11
600	10
700	7
800	5
900	3
1000	2
1100	1

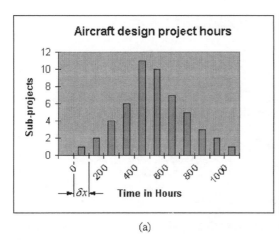

(a)

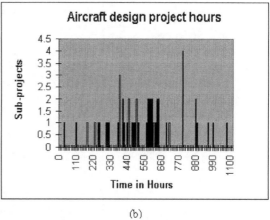

(b)

Figure 18.2   (a) Frequency histogram of hours for various design teams on a large air transport project; (b) Effect of changing the bin size for the same data.

an odd integer, the class mark will be a whole number. When the class width is an even integer, as in the example above, the class mark will be a fraction. Class marks can be used to simplify computations involving the data. For example, the class mark can be used to approximate the value of all the data in a class. This is especially useful when, for instance, original data is lost and all that remains is the histogram.

18.3.3 Appropriate Bin Size (Class Width)

Figures 18.2 (a) and (b) illustrate the importance of selecting an appropriate bin size. Consider the data listed in Table 18.4. It represents the resistance of twenty 1 Ω ($\pm5\%$) resistors. There are a total of $N = 20$ individual measurements, x_i, where $i = 1$, 2, . . . , 20. Suppose each resistance measurement was taken at random, but under identical conditions.

The data from Table 18.4 is plotted in Figure 18.3. Note that the abscissa (x-axis) has been divided into $K = 9$ intervals of 0.1 Ω. The frequency, or number of occurances, n_i, of measured values that fall in the interval defined by $x - \delta x \leq x \leq x + \delta x$ is plotted on the ordinate (the vertical axis). For a small number of N, K should be conveniently

TABLE 18.4   20 Measurements of random variable x (resistance of 1Ω ($\pm5\%$) resistors).

i	x_i (Ω)	i	x_i (Ω)
1	0.98	11	1.02
2	1.07	12	1.26
3	0.86	13	1.08
4	1.16	14	1.02
5	0.96	15	0.94
6	0.68	16	1.11
7	1.34	17	0.99
8	1.04	18	0.78
9	1.21	19	1.06
10	0.86	20	0.96

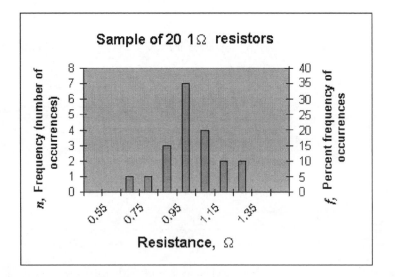

Figure 18.3   Histogram and frequency distribution for data set in Table 18.4.

selected; however it should be that $n_i \geq 5$ for at least one interval. If $N > 40$ the number of K intervals required for meaningful statistical analysis is given by the relationship [5]

$$K = 1.87(N - 1)^{0.40} + 1. \tag{18.1}$$

18.3.4 Frequency Distribution

The *frequency distribution* is found by dividing each particular value n_i by the total number of occurrences, N:

$$f_i = \frac{n_i}{N}.$$

The *percent frequency distribution* is simply the frequency distribution multiplied by 100 (the right-hand vertical scale in Figure 18.3). The sum total of the number of occurrences must equal the total number of measurements,

$$\sum_{i=1}^{K} n_i = N,$$

see Section 18.4 for a review of **summation notation.** Similarly, the area under the percent frequency distribution must equal 100%:

$$100 \times \sum_{i=1}^{K} f_i = 100\%.$$

18.4   SUMMATION NOTATION

In our development of statistics and probability, we shall employ sums of many numbers. An extremely convenient way to express such sums compactly is the **summation notation** [6]. To illustrate, consider a collection of numbers $\{y_1, y_2, \ldots, y_n\}$. The sum of the collection of numbers can be represented by

$$\sum_{i=1}^{K} y_i = y_1 + y_2 + \cdots + y_n, \tag{18.2}$$

where the Greek capital letter Σ (*Sigma*) denotes a sum, while y_i represents the ith number in the collection. The letter i is the **index of summation,** and assumes successive integer values, in this case ranging from $i = 1$ to $i = n$. The range of the index of summation is indicated by the expressions below and above Σ. It does not have to range from 1 to n, however. Consider the following example.

EXAMPLE 18.1

Compute $\sum_{i=1}^{5} i(i - 3)$.

SOLUTION

In this case $y_i = i(i - 3)$. To compute the sum we substitute 2, 3, 4, and 5 for i and add the resulting terms. Thus,

$$\sum_{i=2}^{5} i(i - 3) = 2(2 - 3) + 3(3 - 3) + 4(4 - 3) + 5(5 - 3)$$

$$= -2 + 0 + 4 + 10$$

$$= 12.$$

18.5   THE SHAPE OF A FREQUENCY DISTRIBUTION

The histogram is routinely used to enable engineers to make intelligent use of the data it represents. It is a powerful engineering tool. When appropriate bin sizes are employed, the resulting shape of the frequency distribution can yield tremendous insights on the physical processes that generate the characteristics being measured. The trends that are so clearly portrayed in a histogram can also reveal information about the data set that is unknown, a priori.

18.5.1   Normal Distribution

This bell shaped distribution of data is also known as *Gaussian* distribution after the 18th century mathematician, Carl Friedrich Gauss, despite the fact that DiMoivre and Laplace independently suggested it slightly earlier. Most physical characteristics that are continuous, or regular in time or space fit a normal distribution. For these variables, the measured data is **unimodal** (rises to a single peak value then declines), and symmetrically distributed about some central tendency; see Figure 18.4 (a).

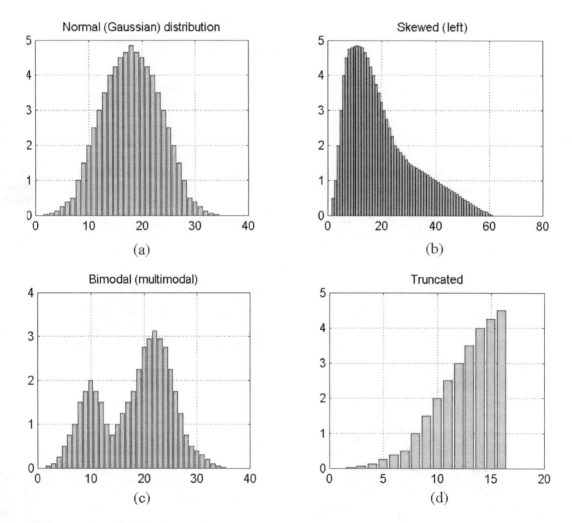

Figure 18.4   Some standard distribution shapes.

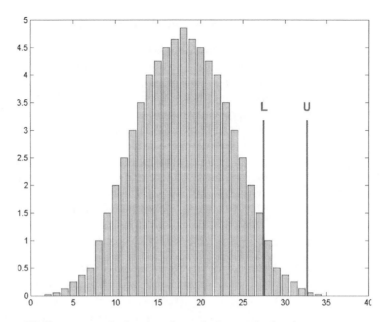

Figure 18.5   A normally distributed sample that is outside tolerances.

After specifying requirements for a characteristic of a component, the data acquired from a sample of measurements can reveal if the components satisfy the requirements. Suppose you were recycling a specific gage of steel wire used to reinforce concrete and had a specialized cutter that was adjusted to cut the wire to a specific length. Suppose the machine is very fast and cuts at the rate of 1000 cuts per minute. The requirement on the length is specified by lower and upper bounds on the length, and indicated in Figure 18.5 by **L** and **U**, respectively. Suppose the bounds were 27.5 cm and 32.5 cm. If the histogram in Figure 18.5 represents length measurements of a sample of lengths cut by the machine, it is obvious that the machine needs further adjustment in order to increase the *typical* bar length. But, it is additionally clear that the process variation is so large that making machine adjustments that will simply shift the next set of data to the left will fail to bring a very large proportion of cut bar lengths to within specifications. Armed with this information, an engineer can make intelligent decisions, backed up by data, and weigh alternative courses of action to address the problem.

18.5.2 Skewed Distribution

A **skewed** distribution is a departure from normal distribution that is still unimodal, see Figure 18.4 (b). The data can be skewed either to the right, or left, each indicating something different about the data set.

In data that is **skewed right** the data to the left of the highest frequency, or number of occurrences, drops off sharply. Data to the right drops off much more slowly. Data distributions that are skewed right are frequently encountered when the variable corresponds to the useful life of machines, or the sales over time of a specific version of a product.

Data can also be **skewed left.** In this case data to the right of the highest frequency, or number of occurrences, drops off sharply. Data to the left drops off much more slowly. One may expect a data distribution that is skewed left when the variable represents the height of a sample of the human population when the sample includes individuals of all ages, including children.

18.5.3 Bimodal (Multimodal) Distribution

Bimodal, or **multimodal** distributions, see Figure 18.4 (c), would appear to represent a great departure from normal distribution, however this is not necessarily so. It can represent an important piece of information about the population: the sample may contain elements from two, or more, essentially different populations.

Suppose that a sample from a large shipment of cylindrical shafts, with machining operations all performed by lathe, had their major diameters measured. Further suppose that the resulting histogram was the bimodal distribution in Figure 18.4 (c). If the units on the horizontal axis are mm's, we immediately observe that there are two different peak diameters. If the manufacturer's guaranteed *nominal* maximum diameter was 10.000 mm, what could you conclude from the measurements presented in the histogram? As an engineer, what action, if any, would you recommend be taken?

The bimodal nature of the data may have several explanations. The following may be possible explanations stemming from the machining process.

1. The shafts were machined on two different lathes.
2. They were all produced on the same lathe, but by two different machinists.
3. The shafts were all produced by the same machinist on the same machine, but the job was interrupted for some other, necessitating two different machine setups.

Still, it may be that there are no anomalies associated with the machining at all. The cause may instead reside in the measurement process.

1. The shafts were measured using two different instruments.
2. They were all measured with the same instrument, but by two different technicians.
3. The shafts were all measured by the same technician using the same instrument, but the instrument acquired an offset through some damage.

All of the above reasons seem plausible. It appears there is not sufficient information to formulate a complete answer. There are two possible courses of action. One would be to request that the sample be remeasured. If the second set of measurements yield the same bimodal distribution, then the source is very likely due to the manufacturing. The other course of action would be to contact the manufacturer, and give them the results of the measurements. If you are a valued customer, and there is indeed a manufacturing problem, then your value as a customer will likely increase.

18.5.4 Truncated Distribution

Similar to multimodal distributions, a **truncated** data distribution, illustrated in Figure 18.4 (d), is usually the result of some cause outside of the process that generated the characteristic reported by the measurements. For example, if the data in Figure 18.4 (d) represented some other characteristic of another set of cylindrical shafts, it may be that the sample had been 100% inspected and sorted, removing all shafts whose measured characteristic exceeded the peak value, prior to the sample being measured.

18.6 MEASURES OF CENTRAL TENDENCY

To add some mathematical power to our ability to analyze the data represented in a histogram we will develop more precise summaries of data distributions. All of the histograms presented in Section 18.5 indicate that the data all tend towards at least one maximum value represented by the peaks in the data. We will develop tools to characterize the tendency in the data towards that value.

18.6.1 The Central Limit Theorem

A very interesting result in mathematical statistics is the **central limit theorem.** It states that the sample data distribution can always be approximated by a normal distribution, when the sample size N is sufficiently large. In other words, the distribution will approach normal as N increases, regardless of the shape of the distribution of the original data.

This has very important implications for the mathematical formulation of measures such as the **standard deviation,** which are based on normal distribution, but also introduces an important measure by itself. The accuracy of an estimate of the behavior of an entire population based on a sample relies on the size of the sample. When we discuss probability distributions in the next chapter we will use **z-estimators** for relatively large samples, and **t-estimators** for relatively small. The question is, when is N large enough?

It has been generally accepted to take $N \geq 30$ as a *large enough* sample size to invoke the central limit theorem and assume the sample data distribution is sufficiently normal. In general, this causes little in the way of problems. However, there are cases, as when the data is already symmetric about a single central value, when substantially smaller values of N are sufficient. There are also many cases where substantially greater than $N = 30$ samples are required, this is especially true for highly skewed sample data.

The infatuation with the central limit theorem is understandable because a very large number of small random deviations almost always converges to a normal distribution. However it ignores the fact that *real* data often poorly approximates the normal distribution, if at all. The standard deviation, denoted σ, is a measure of the likelihood that the next measurement will be within a specific tolerance of the true value. It will be discussed in greater detail later, and the claim will be made, based on the normal distribution, that on average measurements will be within $\pm\sigma$ of the true value 68.26% of the time, $\pm2\sigma$ 95.45% of the time and $\pm3\sigma$ 99.73% of the time. Taking this to the extreme range of the distribution, it can be computed that a value will be out by $\pm20\sigma$ only one time out of 2×10^{88} [7]. However, experience has shown that experimental data are occasionally just way off. A data point like this is called an **outlier.** The occurrence of outliers in the data is significantly more frequent than one time out of 2×10^{88}.

Moreover, the vast array of statistical tools generally employed deal only with **statistical errors,** which *average out* if the data set is large enough. However, measurements can also be affected by **systematic errors,** that will not disappear regardless of how large the sample size is. For example, the calibration of a metal gage typically depends on temperature. Making measurements all at the same wrong temperature will introduce systematic error into the data that is usually not easy to cope with. **Robust statistics** deals with instances involving poor approximations of normal distribution, cases where outliers are important, and systematic error [7].

18.6.2 The Arithmetic Mean

Given a collection of N values, the **arithmetic mean** of these data is the mathematical average. That is, the sum of all the values divided by the number of values, N:

$$\text{mean} = \frac{\text{sum of all the values}}{N}.$$

As we have discussed, a collection of data may represent an entire population, or a sample of the population. There are distinct symbols for each. The **arithmetic mean of a population** is expressed as:

$$\mu = \frac{1}{N}\sum_{i=1}^{N}x_i, \tag{18.3}$$

where μ is the population of the mean, and N is the total number of elements in the population.

The **arithmetic mean of a sample** is expressed as:

$$\bar{x} = \frac{1}{N}\sum_{i=1}^{N}x_i, \tag{18.4}$$

where $\bar{x}$ is the sample of the mean, and N is the total number of elements in the sample of the population.

It is worthwhile to make the remark that in a normal distribution, the mean should be the central value.

EXAMPLE 18.2

Compute the arithmetic mean of the following sample:

$$[4 \quad 3 \quad 7 \quad 4 \quad 5 \quad 4]$$

SOLUTION

Because this is a sample, use Equation (18.4) with $N = 6$ to obtain

$$\bar{x} = \frac{1}{N}\sum_{i=1}^{N}x_i = \frac{4 + 3 + 7 + 4 + 5 + 4}{6} = \frac{27}{6} = 4.5.$$

Caution must be exercised when using the arithmetic mean because it is very sensitive to extreme observations. The presence of outliers can excessively enlarge, or reduce, the numerator in Equation (18.4), resulting in a value for $\bar{x}$ that does not seem to fit the trend. For example, suppose the police use radar equipment to measure the speed of vehicles on a residential street where the speed limit is 50 km/hr, and record the following sample of speeds:

$$47 \quad 48 \quad 51 \quad 48 \quad 49 \quad 46 \quad 120 \quad 50 \quad 49 \quad 48$$

Applying Equation (18.4) we obtain $\bar{x} = 55.6$ km/hr, which seems unreasonable, as most of the speeds are less than 50 km/hr. The anomaly is caused by the one speed that is vastly different, 120 km/hr. Clearly, the driver of the car going 120 in a 50 km/hr residential zone should be put in jail and lose their driver's licence. If we remove this value from the data and recalculate the mean, we obtain $\bar{x} = 48.8$ km/hr, which seems more reasonable.

18.6.3 The Class Mean

There is an alternate procedure for computing the mean of a sample employing the **class method.** This formulation uses the data classes established for a histogram. It is defined as:

$$\text{class mean} = \frac{\sum_{i=1}^{N}n_i CM_i}{\sum_{i=1}^{N}n_i}, \tag{18.5}$$

where n_i is the frequency (the value on the vertical axis of the histogram) of the ith class, or bin, and CM_i is the ith class mark. The class mean can provide a useful approximation of the arithmetic mean.

EXAMPLE 18.3

Reconsider a subset of the data presented in Table 18.3. The individual design team hours recorded for the duration of the project are listed in Table 18.5. Bins of appropriate size are established, and the data is collected into the corresponding bin and listed in Table 18.6, and plotted in the histogram shown in Figure 18.6.

TABLE 18.5   Aircraft design team hours.

335	211	555	560	427	560	821	330	550	172
431	875	684	75	499	221	407	356	950	762
126	784	542	698	472	638	531	610	330	410
477	551	321	402	899	688	431	692	505	372
700	236	610	708	552	721	242	490	431	525

TABLE 18.6   Aircraft design team hours collected in their bins.

Bin	Bounds	CM	n	nCM
100	0–99	49.5	1	49.5
200	100–199	149.5	2	299
300	200–299	249.5	4	998
400	300–399	349.5	6	2097
500	400–499	449.5	11	4944.5
600	500–599	549.5	10	5495
700	600–699	649.5	7	4546.5
800	700–799	749.5	5	3747.5
900	800–899	849.5	3	2548.5
1000	900–1000	949.5	1	949.5
Σn			50	
ΣnCM				25675

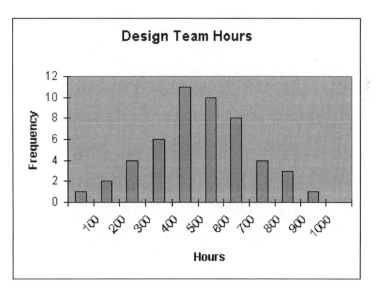

Figure 18.6   Project hour distribution.

Applying Equation (18.5) to the data in Table 18.6 yields the class mean:

$$\text{class mean} = \frac{\sum_{i=1}^{N} n_i CM_i}{\sum_{i=1}^{N} n_i} = \frac{25675}{50} = 513.5.$$

If we use Equation (18.4) to compute the arithmetic mean using the full data in Table 18.5 we obtain $\bar{x} = 509.5$. The class mean approximation of 513.5 differs from the arithmetic mean of the sample by only 0.785%. If the original data in Table 18.5 were lost, but the data in Table 18.6 were available, the class mean could provide a useful estimate of the mean of the original data.

18.6.4 The Median

Recall from Section 18.6.2 that the arithmetic mean is sensitive to the presence of outliers. This statement also applies to the class mean, and is due to dependence of the mean on a ratio. A measure of central tendency that is insensitive to outliers is the **median.** The median for a set of data is the number that is exactly in the middle between the least and greatest values after the data have been ranked from low to high. In other words, for any collection of numbers half have values that are greater than the median, and half have values that are less. It is denoted $\tilde{x}$ (in words "x tilde"). If the data set has an odd number of members, the median will be exactly one of them. Using a database *sort* function to arrange the data from low to high, the median will be exactly the middle value. If the set has an even number of members, the median will be the arithmetic average of the two values at the centre of the sorted list.

When the 50 members of the data in Table 18.5 are sorted in ascending order with the **sort ascending** command in Microsoft Excel™, it is easy to see that the median is between the 25th and 26th values in the sorted list. In this case the median is:

$$\tilde{x} = \frac{505 + 525}{2} = 515.$$

EXAMPLE 18.4

Reconsidering the data in Example 18.2, it is sorted from low to high:

$$46 \quad 47 \quad 48 \quad 48 \quad 48 \quad 49 \quad 49 \quad 50 \quad 51 \quad 120$$

SOLUTION

Because there are an even number of elements, the median will be the average of the two in the middle: elements 5 and 6. For these data we obtain

$$\tilde{x} = \frac{48 + 49}{2} = 48.5.$$

Recall that the arithmetic mean for this sample is $\bar{x} = 55.6$. This data contains a single outlier, and it is to be seen that the median value of $\tilde{x} = 48.5$ seems to be a better measure of central tendency, because it is independent of the outlier.

However, the mean should never be needlessly abandoned. There is a formula for the mean. There is none for the median, only for its location in the sorted data set.

18.6.5 The Mode

Another measure of central tendency that is insensitive to outliers is the **mode.** It is much less frequently used as a measure of central tendency. In a set of values, the mode is the one that most frequently occurs. Clearly, one immediate problem with the mode is that its existence is not guaranteed. For example, the mode of the integers from 1 to 1,000,000, no integer repeated, does not exist. No two numbers are repeated. For the data in Example 18.4, the mode is 48.

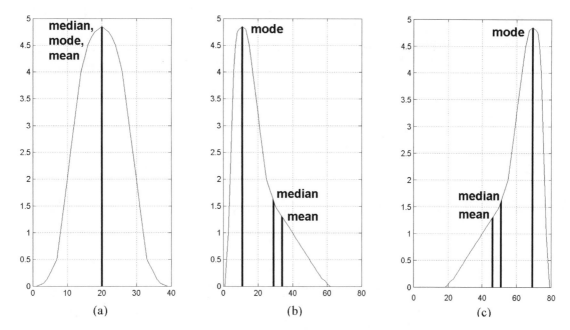

Figure 18.7   Comparison of mean, median, mode.

18.6.6 Comparison of Mean, Median, and Mode

Figure 18.7 illustrates the relationship between the mean, median, and mode as measures of central tendency. When the data is normally distributed, as in Figure 18.7 (a), there is no significant difference between them: for this sample data the mean, median and mode are all equal to the same value, 20. Figures 18.7 (b) and (c) represent data that are skewed to the right and left, respectively. For skewed, or multimodal distributions the value of the mean is pushed away from the value of the mode in the skew direction. The median tends to be less affected, but is additionally skewed correspondingly, such that its value is in between the mode and mean values.

18.7   MEASURES OF DISPERSION

Measures of central tendency allow for determination of the mean, median, and/or mode values for a data sample. In a sense, these values are a measure of the average value among all elements in the data set. However, the central tendency yields no information about how the data in the set is dispersed, or distributed, around the mean, median, or mode. Consider the following different sets of data: [100, 99, 100, 101] and [100, 1, 100, 199]. In both cases the mean, median, and mode are all 100, but the first set of data is significantly less varied than the second.

Measures of dispersion allow for a quantitative description of how the data varies. It is often critically important to know what the distribution is in order to make predictions about the population. For example, the yield strength of structural members in an air frame must not vary outside of specific tolerances. This means that a supplier of such components must be able to provide a description of the variability of components to allow engineers to implement a design that satisfies requirements.

18.7.1 Range

The simplest measure of dispersion is the **range.** The range, r, for a data sample is the difference between the upper, u, and lower, l, extreme numerical values in the set:

$$r = u - l. \tag{18.6}$$

EXAMPLE 18.5

Ten engineering students, selected at random, are asked *how many keys do you have with you?* The following list represents their responses:

$$[5 \quad 2 \quad 6 \quad 5 \quad 4 \quad 1 \quad 5 \quad 7 \quad 4 \quad 6].$$

SOLUTION

For these data the lowest numerical value is $l = 1$, while the uppermost numerical value is $u = 7$. Hence the range is

$$r = u - l = 7 - 1 = 6.$$

18.7.2 Population and Sample Variance

While the range can be a useful measure, it yields little information about precisely how the data is distributed. Consider the following example.

EXAMPLE 18.6

The same sample of ten students in Example 18.5 are additionally asked *how many coins do you have with you?* and their responses were:

$$[7 \quad 2 \quad 2 \quad 6 \quad 1 \quad 7 \quad 4 \quad 7 \quad 7 \quad 2].$$

Comparing the results, both samples have identical ranges of $r = 6$, and identical means of $\bar{x} = 4.5$, however, plotting the histograms reveals vastly different distributions, see Figures 18.8 (a) and (b). The disturbing thing about the second data set in Figure 18.8 (b) is that the most frequently occurring values are at the very extremes of the sample range,

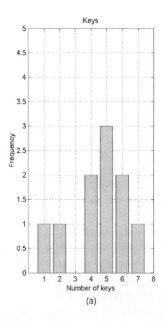
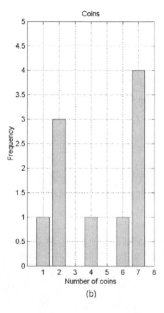

Figure 18.8   Ten engineering students (a) keys, and (b) coins.

relatively far from the mean value. The reassuring thing about the data in Figure 18.8 (a) is that it is clustered near the middle of the range, very close to the mean value. It seems an intuitive requirement for a measure of dispersion is that it be sensitive to how the data is distributed with respect to the mean value.

The difference of a data value from the mean is called its **deviation,** and is expressed as $x - \overline{x}$. This could be a candidate for quantifying dispersion, except that in a normal distribution about half the data is below the mean while the other half is above. If the deviation is averaged over all the data, it will always either cancel out exactly, or be trivially small. Consider the deviation from the mean for the data in Example 18.6. Having calculated the mean to be $\overline{x} = 4.5$, we can compute the individual deviations:

$$4(7 - 4.5) = 10.0$$
$$6 - 4.5 = 1.5$$
$$4 - 4.5 = -0.5$$
$$3(2 - 4.5) = -7.5$$
$$1 - 4.5 = -3.5$$

The average value of these deviations from the mean are

$$\frac{10.0 + 1.5 - 0.5 - 7.5 - 3.5}{10} = 0.$$

To eliminate the cancelling out of the deviations from the mean there are several options. The one that has come to be accepted is to simply square the deviations from the mean. For the data in Example 18.6 the squares of the deviations are:

$$4(7 - 4.5)^2 = 25.00$$
$$(6 - 4.5)^2 = 2.25$$
$$(4 - 4.5)^2 = 0.25$$
$$3(2 - 4.5)^2 = 18.75$$
$$(1 - 4.5)^2 = 12.25$$

The average value of the squares of the deviations from the mean are

$$\frac{25.00 + 2.25 + 0.25 - 18.75 + 12.25}{10} = 5.85.$$

Now, compare this value to that obtained from the data in Example 18.5:

$$(7 - 4.5)^2 = 6.25$$
$$2(6 - 4.5)^2 = 4.50$$
$$3(5 - 4.5)^2 = 0.75$$
$$2(4 - 4.5)^2 = 0.50$$
$$(2 - 4.5)^2 = 6.25$$
$$(1 - 4.5)^2 = 12.25$$

The average value of the squares of the deviations from the mean are

$$\frac{6.25 + 4.50 + 0.75 + 0.50 + 6.25 + 12.25}{10} = 3.05.$$

The data illustrated in Figure 18.8 (a) from Example 18.5 has a variance of 3.05, while that from Example 18.6, illustrated in Figure 18.8 (b) has a variance of 5.85. We can rightly conclude that the more variation from the mean in the data then the greater the variance. This is very useful for comparing two sets of data.

18.7.3 Population Variance

If we possess data for an entire population, we can compute the **population variance.** Given a population containing N elements, the population variance is denoted by σ^2 (where σ is the Greek lower-case *sigma*), and defined by:

$$\sigma^2 = \frac{1}{N}\sum_{i=1}^{N}(x_i - \mu)^2, \tag{18.7}$$

where μ is the population mean as defined by Equation 18.3.

18.7.4 Sample Variance

In practice, it is rare to work with data for an entire population, because the number of elements involved are too great to manage in a reasonable way. We normally have a relatively smaller sample of the population from which we infer characteristics of the population based on the statistics of the sample. The number of independent measurements in a sample data set that are available to estimate a statistical quantity is usually referred to as the *degree of freedom*, ν, of the data in the set. Still, the data will be scattered about a mean value for measurements having a central tendency. If this is so, the freedom of a measurement to assume a particular value is always relative to the mean value. Thus, the degree of freedom, ν, is reduced by one value to $N - 1$. Thus, the **sample variance** of a set of N data values in a sample is defined as:

$$s^2 = \frac{1}{N-1}\sum_{i=1}^{N}(x_i - \bar{x})^2, \tag{18.8}$$

where $\bar{x}$ is the sample mean as defined by Equation 18.4.

EXAMPLE 18.7

Compute the sample variance, s^2, for the data listed in Example 18.5.

SOLUTION

First, we compute the sample mean using Equation 18.4, yielding $\bar{x} = 4.5$. For hand calculations, it is convenient to construct a table listing the individual x_i, the deviations, and the variances, as in Table 18.7.

TABLE 18.7 Variance in number of keys among 10 engineering students.

Value x_i	Deviation $x_i - \bar{x}$	Variance $(x_i - \bar{x})^2$
5	0.5	0.25
2	−2.5	6.25
6	1.5	2.25
5	0.5	0.25
4	−0.5	0.25
1	−3.5	12.25
5	0.5	0.25
7	2.5	6.25
4	−0.5	0.25
6	1.5	2.25
$\Sigma(x_i - \bar{x})^2 =$		30.5

The cardinality of the data set is 10 (i.e. $N = 10$). Apply Equation 18.8, with $N - 1 = 9$, to obtain:

$$s^2 = \frac{1}{N-1}\sum_{i=1}^{N}(x_i - \bar{x})^2 = \frac{30.5}{9} = 3.39.$$

18.7.5 Population Standard Deviation

The **standard deviation** is defined to be the positive square root of the variance. Hence, the **population standard deviation** is denoted σ, and defined:

$$\sigma = \sqrt{\frac{1}{N}\sum_{i=1}^{N}(x_i - \mu)^2}, \tag{18.9}$$

where μ is the population mean as defined by Equation 18.3, and N is the number of elements in the population.

18.7.6 Sample Standard Deviation

The **sample standard deviation** is denoted s, and defined:

$$s = \sqrt{\frac{1}{N-1}\sum_{i=1}^{N}(x_i - \bar{x})^2}, \tag{18.10}$$

where $\bar{x}$ is the sample mean as defined by Equation 18.4, and N is the number of elements in the sample.

18.8 SIGNIFICANCE OF THE STANDARD DEVIATION

The great Russian mathematician Pavnutii Lvovich Tchebysheff (1821–1894) proved a theorem that has been applied to statistical distributions enabling accurate estimations of values of unobserved members of the population to be made, or to predict the outcome of events that have not yet occurred. The theorem permits quantification of how likely it is that the prediction will be correct. Proof of what we shall call **Tchebysheff's Theorem** is beyond the scope of this book, but we can still examine how to use it.

Tchebysheff's Theorem.   Given a number $k \geq 1$, and a set of N measurements, then *at least*

$$1 - \frac{1}{k^2}$$

of the measurements will lie within k standard deviations ($k\sigma$, or ks) of their mean [4].

Tchebysheff's Theorem means the following for any population of data, following any type of distribution (the same statements apply to data samples, but the symbols must be changed accordingly):

- For $k = 1$ then *at least* $1 - 1 = 0$ of the data values will be in the interval $\mu = \sigma$ to $\mu + \sigma$. In other words, in the range $\mu \pm \sigma$.

- For $k = 2$ then *at least* $1 - \frac{1}{4} = \frac{3}{4}$, or 75% of the data values will be in the interval $\mu \pm 2\sigma$.

- For $k = 3$ then *at least* $1 - \frac{1}{9} = \frac{8}{9}$, or 88.9% of the data values will be in the interval $\mu \pm 3\sigma$.

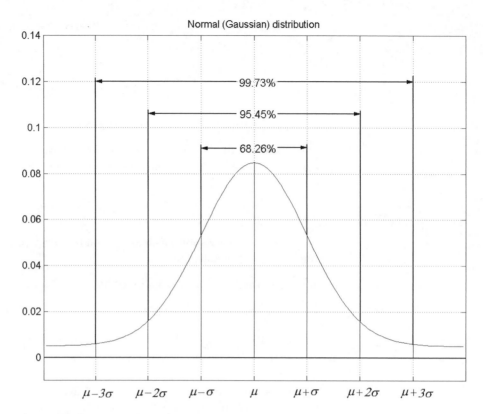

Figure 18.9   Standard deviation boundaries.

Applying Tchebysheff's Theorem results in very conservative estimates because it is valid for any distribution: multimodal, skewed, truncated, normal, etc..Hence the emphasis on *at least*. It turns out that significantly better estimates can be had when the data is a *reasonably* normal distribution. If the distribution is normal, we can then use results developed in Chapter 10 to state the following rule, known as the **empirical rule** because, according to the central limit theorem, it applies to virtually all empirical data (data obtained in an experiment). Given a reasonably normally distributed sample we can expect the following:

- For $k = 1$ then 68.26% of the data values will be in the interval $\mu \pm \sigma$.
- For $k = 2$ then 95.45% of the data values will be in the interval $\mu \pm 2\sigma$.
- For $k = 3$ then 99.73% of the data values will be in the interval $\mu \pm 3\sigma$.

If the data is sampled from a population, the above statements become:

- For $k = 1$ then 68.26% of the data values will be in the interval $\bar{x} \pm s$.
- For $k = 2$ then 95.45% of the data values will be in the interval $\bar{x} \pm 2s$.
- For $k = 3$ then 99.73% of the data values will be in the interval $\bar{x} \pm 3s$.

See Figure 18.9 for an illustration of the relationship between the standard deviation and a perfectly normal distribution.

EXAMPLE 18.8

Determine the standard deviation for the sample data whose variance was determined in Example 18.7. Use the data and the computed value for s to verify the empirical rule, and explain any observed deviations.

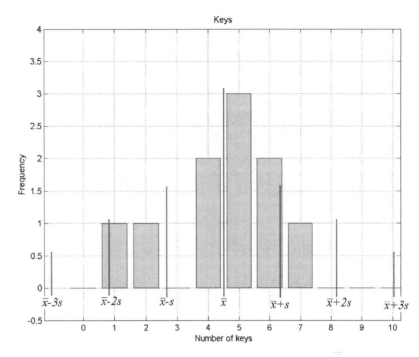

Figure 18.10 Standard deviation boundaries for Example 18.8.

SOLUTION

In Example 18.7 the variance was computed to be $s^2 = 3.39$. Applying Equation 18.10 simply requires determining the positive square root of s^2. We obtain $s = 1.84$.

To verify the empirical rule, plot the data and establish what percentage of the data falls between the s, $2s$, and $3s$ intervals, see Figure 18.10. But the data set is small enough to assess this directly from the data. We see that 60% is in the range $\bar{x} \pm s$, which amounts to $2.66 \le x_i \le 6.34$. However, 100% of the data are in the range $\bar{x} \pm 2s$, or $0.82 \le x_i \le 8.18$. Why does this not agree with the statistical expectations implied by the empirical rule? For an answer, we must consider the size of the sample, and the probability that it is representative of the population. These issues will be considered in Chapter 10.

18.9 REFERENCES

[1] H.E. Boyer and T.L. Gall. *Metals Handbook, Desk Edition*. American Society for Metals, Metals Park, OH., U.S.A., 1985.

[2] W. Chase and F. Brown. *General Statistics, 4th ed.* John Wiley & Sons, Inc., New York, N.Y., U.S.A., 2000.

[3] J. Devore and N. Farnum. *Applied Statistics for Engineers and Scientists*. Duxbury Press, Brooks/Cole Publishing Co., Pacific Grove, CA., U.S.A., 1999.

[4] W. Mendenhall, R.J. Beaver, and B.M. Beaver. *Introduction to Probability and Statistics*, tenth edition. Duxbury Press, Brooks/Cole Publishing Co., Pacific Grove, CA., U.S.A., 1999.

[5] R.S. Figliola and D.E. Beasley. *Theory and Design for Mechanical Measurements, 3rd ed.* John Wiley & Sons, Inc., New York, N.Y., U.S.A., 2000.

[6] D.C. Kay. *Tensor Calculus*. Schaum's Outline Series in Mathematics, McGraw-Hill Book Company, New York, N.Y., U.S.A., 1988.

[7] W.H. Press, S.A. Teukolsky, W.T. Vetterling, and B.P. Flannery. *Numerical Recipes in C, 2nd Edition*. Cambridge University Press, Cambridge, England, 1992.

Chapter 19

Probability: Managing Engineering Measurement Error

19.1. INTRODUCTION

Measurement is fundamental to engineering. Suppose we had a railroad container filled with millions of washers, all having the same *nominal* inside diameter. To get an idea of that nominal value, we might reach in, grab a hand-full of washers and measure the inside diameter. The resulting values comprise a *sample data set,* which we can use to estimate something about the washers in the container as a whole (the *population),* such as the average inside diameter. The obvious question is how close is the average value of the sample data set to the *actual* average of all the population of washers in the container?

Engineering measurements that are repeated under seemingly identical conditions using the same instrument will usually show variations among the measured values. The measurement variations that will be dealt with in this chapter include *bias, repeatability, reproducibility, stability* (or *drift*), and *linearity* [1]. But before we define these, some more elementary issues need be discussed.

19.2.   PROBABILITY DENSITY FUNCTIONS

We begin by estimating the *true mean value* of the population, μ, based on repeated sample measurements of x_i (like the inside diameter of the washers in the container). From a statistical analysis of the data set and the sources of error that influence them the estimate of μ can be expressed as

$$\mu = \bar{x} \pm ks, \tag{19.1}$$

where $\bar{x}$ represents the most probable estimate of the true mean of the population, μ, based on the data, and ks is the *confidence interval* (some number times the sample standard deviation), or *uncertainty* based on some level of probability, $P\%$. When survey results are reported "accurate" to some number "19 times out of 20", what is meant is that the probability level that the results are actually within the range stated by the "accuracy" is $(19/20) \times 100 = 95\%$. However, the term "accuracy" should be used with care; see Section 19.7.

No matter how carefully the data are measured, random scatter in the values will routinely occur. For this reason, the quantity being measured is called a *random variable*. There are *discrete* and *continuous* random variables. The number of washers in a handful is discrete, while the variation among the measured inside diameters is continuous. During repeated measurements of a random variable using the same measurement instrument with conditions in a steady state, the data will generally tend towards one particular value, according to the central limit theorem. Probability deals with the concept that a particular interval of values for a random variable will contain a predictable frequency of measurements relative to all other intervals.

The central, or mean value of the measured quantity, as well as the values scattered about it, can be determined from the probability density of the measured value. The frequency that the variable assumes a particular value, or interval of values, is described by its probability density. Consider the data listed in Table 19.1. It represents the

TABLE 19.1   20 Measurements of random variable x (resistance of 1Ω ($\pm5\%$) resistors).

i	$x_i(\Omega)$	i	$x_i(\Omega)$
1	0.98	11	1.02
2	1.07	12	1.26
3	0.86	13	1.08
4	1.16	14	1.02
5	0.96	15	0.94
6	0.68	16	1.11
7	1.34	17	0.99
8	1.04	18	0.78
9	1.21	19	1.06
10	0.86	20	0.96

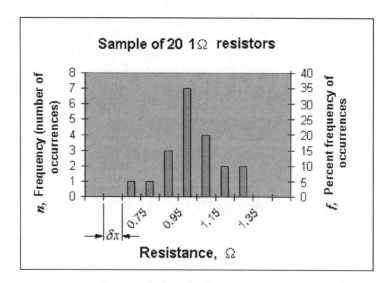

Figure 19.1   Histogram and frequency distribution for data set in Table 19.1.

measured resistance of twenty 1Ω ($\pm 5\%$) resistors. There are a total of $N = 20$ individual measurements, x_i, where $i = 1, 2, \ldots, 20$. Suppose each measurement is taken at random, but under identical conditions. The data is plotted in Figure 19.1.

In Figure 19.1 the abscissa (the x-axis) indicates the value of the random variable between minimum and maximum measured values. Note that the abscissa has been divided into $K = 9$ intervals of 0.1 units (recall Equation (18.1) in Chapter 18). The frequency, n_i, of measured values that fall in the interval defined by $x - \delta x \leq x \leq x + \delta x$ is plotted on the ordinate (the vertical axis).

The graph of the random variable, x, versus the number of occurrences, n (the left-hand vertical scale in Figure 19.1) is called a **frequency histogram.** Recall from Chapter 18 that the **frequency distribution** is found by dividing each particular value n_i by the total number of occurrences, N:

$$f_i = \frac{n_i}{N}.$$

The *percent frequency distribution* is simply the frequency distribution multiplied by 100 (the right-hand vertical scale in Figure 19.1). The sum total of the number of occurrences must equal the total number of measurements over all K intervals,

$$\sum_{i=1}^{K} n_i = N.$$

Similarly, the area under the percent frequency distribution must equal 100%:

$$100 \times \sum_{i=1}^{K} f_i = 100\%.$$

The **probability density function** of the random variable, $p(x)$, is the frequency distribution in the limit as $N \rightarrow \infty$ and $\delta x \rightarrow 0$:

$$p(x) = \lim_{N \rightarrow \infty, \, \delta x \rightarrow 0} \frac{n_i}{N(2\delta x)}. \tag{19.2}$$

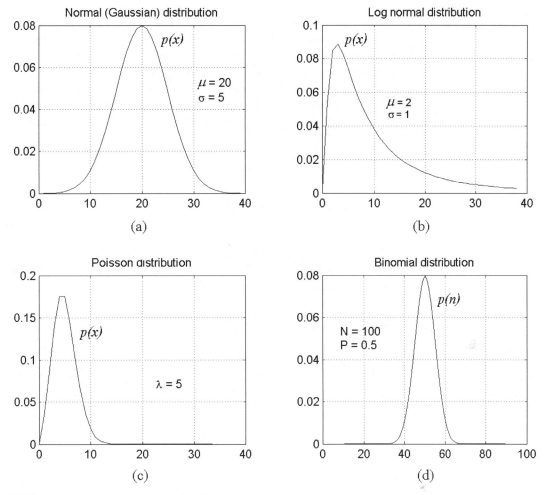

Figure 19.2 Some standard probability distributions.

The probability density function gives the likelihood that a measured variable will assume a particular value on any individual measurement. Additionally, it yields the central tendency of the variable. The best estimate of the true mean value of the measured variable is indicated by the central tendency.

The shape of the curve that the probability density function describes depends on the type of variable it represents and the circumstances affecting the way it is measured. There are many standard probability density functions that describe how the values of a variable will be distributed. The specific values and the width of the distribution depend on the actual characteristic being measured and on the measurement process, but the overall shape of the plot of the data (either a histogram, or a frequency distribution) will most likely fit one of the standard distributions. In practice, histograms of experimental data are used to determine which standard distribution the measured variable tends to follow. The standard distribution is then used to interpret the data. Some commonly used distributions are shown in Figure 19.2, but the interested reader should see [2] and [3] for more complete treatments of this topic.

19.3.   STATISTICAL DISTRIBUTIONS

(a) **Normal Distribution.** This is also commonly known as the *Gaussian* distribution after the 18th century mathematician, Carl Friedrich Gauss, despite the fact that DiMoivre and Laplace independently suggested it slightly earlier. Most physical characteristics that are continuous, or regular in time or space fit a normal distribution. For these variables, the measured data is symmetrically distributed about some central tendency. The probability density function for a random variable x having a normal distribution is *defined* to be

$$p(x) = \frac{1}{\sigma(2\pi)^{1/2}} \exp\left[-\frac{1}{2}\frac{(x-\mu)^2}{\sigma^2}\right], \tag{19.3}$$

where σ is the population standard deviation, and μ is the population arithmetic mean, both defined in Chapter 19. The normal distribution is illustrated in Figure 19.2 (a), where $\mu = 20$ and $\sigma = 5$.

(b) **Log Normal Distribution.** This usually pertains to failure, or durability projections. The outcomes tend to be skeed to the extremities of the distribution. Its mathematical representation is defined to be

$$p(x) = \frac{1}{x\sigma(2\pi)^{1/2}} \exp\left[-\frac{1}{2}\frac{(\text{In}(x)-\mu)^2}{\sigma^2}\right]. \tag{19.4}$$

For an example, see Figure 19.2 (b), where $\mu = 2$ and $\sigma = 1$.

(c) **Poisson Distribution.** This usually fits random counts of the number of occurrences of a relatively rare phenomenon or event across a specific interval of time, or space. Here $p(x)$ refers to the probability of observing x events in time t. In a Poisson distribution, the true mean value is indicated by λ instead of μ. The shape of the Poison distribution is shown in Figure 19.2 (c), and it is defined to be

$$p(x) = \frac{e^{-\lambda}\lambda^x}{x!}. \tag{19.5}$$

Figure 19.2 (c) shows a Poisson distribution where $\lambda = 5$.

(d) **inomial Distribution.**   This distribution fits data describing the number of occurrences, n, of a particular outcome during N independent tests where the probability of any outcome, P, is the same. Many engineering measurements involve repetitions of the same *go, no go* determination. A typical example involves the testing of successively manufactured items, where each will be classified as either conforming or nonconforming to a measurement criterion. It is illustrated in Figure 19.2 (d) where $N = 100$ and $P = 50\% \ (0.50)$, and defined to be

$$p(n) = \left[\frac{N!}{(N-n)!n!}\right]P^n(1-P)^{N-n}. \tag{19.6}$$

19.4.   TRUE MEAN VALUE, VARIANCE, AND STANDARD DEVIATION

Regardless of the distribution, any variable that shows a central tendency can be quantified by its true mean value and variance. The *true mean value*, μ, or *central tendency* of a *continuous* random variable x having a probability density function $p(x)$ can be defined in terms of the probability density:

$$\mu = \int_{-\infty}^{\infty} xp(x)\delta x. \tag{19.7}$$

The width of the density function is a physical measure of the data variation. For a *continuous* random variable the *variance* is defined in terms of the probability as

$$\sigma^2 = \int_{-\infty}^{\infty} (x - \mu)^2 p(x) \delta x. \tag{19.8}$$

The *standard deviation*, σ, is defined to be the positive square root of the variance:

$$\sigma = \sqrt{\int_{-\infty}^{\infty} (x - \mu)^2 p(x) \delta x}. \tag{19.9}$$

Note that a fundamental problem arises because of the definitions of the above integrals. Namely, they assume an infinite number of measurements. Clearly, obtaining an infinite set of measurements is not possible. Real data sets are *finite*, that is, they are composed of less than an infinite amount of data. Note, that a data set is considered large if $N > 30$ [4]. So, what happens if the quantity of data in the set is large? Very large? To make the connection between probability and statistics we shall continue with the infinite statistics mathematical model in Section 19.5. Practical treatment of finite data sets will be addressed in Section 19.6, which makes use of the equations found in Chapter 18.

19.5.   INFINITE STATISTICS

Recall the definition of normal distribution in Equation (19.3). The quantities μ and σ^2 are the *true mean value* and *true variance* of the measured characteristic value x. The exact shape of $p(x)$ depends on the particular values of μ and σ. The largest value of $p(x)$ occurs when $x = \mu$. This implies that, in the absence of *bias* (discussed in Section 19.7), the central tendency of a variable having a normal distribution is towards its true mean value.

Thus, we can predict that the *most probable* value of any single measurement will be the true mean value. But, by itself, that is not really useful information. Of more use would be if we could predict the probability that any *future* measurement would fall within a specific interval. The probability, $P(x)$, that x will assume a value within the range is the integral of $p(x)$ over that particular interval, see Figure 19.3. In other words, the area under $p(x)$ in the interval. This probability is

$$P(\mu - \delta x \leq \mu + \delta x) = \int_{\mu-\delta x}^{\mu+\delta x} p(x) \delta x. \tag{19.10}$$

The standard way to integrate Equation (19.10) is by making the following substitutions. The term $\beta = (x - \mu)/\sigma$ is defined to be the *normal variate* for any value x, and $z = (\Delta x - \mu)/\sigma$ is defined to be the variable that specifies the interval on $p(x)$. We can then write

$$dx = \sigma d\beta, \tag{19.11}$$

and use the definition of $p(x)$ in Equation 19.3 so that Equation (19.10) becomes

$$P(-z \leq \beta \leq z) = \frac{1}{(2\pi)^{1/2}} \int_{-z}^{z} e^{-\beta^{1/2}} d\beta. \tag{19.12}$$

We can use the fact that for a normal distribution $p(x)$ is symmetric about μ to write

$$P(-z \leq \beta \leq z) = 2 \left[\frac{1}{(2\pi)^{1/2}} \int_{0}^{x} e^{-\beta^{1/2}} d\beta \right]. \tag{19.13}$$

The bracketed term in Equation (19.13) is called the **normal error function.** It provides one-half of the probability that a random variable x will assume a value within the interval

$$\mu \pm z\sigma, \tag{19.14}$$

or,

$$\mu - z\sigma \le x \le \mu + 2\sigma. \tag{19.15}$$

The error function is rarely evaluated, rather tables of z values are used, see Table 19.2 for example. More extensive tables can be found in any introductory statistics text book, such as [4], or [5]. It is important to note that some tables of z values do not make use of the symmetry of the normal distribution when evaluating the normal error function. In those tables multiplication by 2 is not necessary. Before using a table of z values, care should be taken to establish if the integration provides the *half area*, as is the case in Table 19.2, or *full area* under the probability density function.

TABLE 19.2   Probability for the Normal Error Function $p(z) = \dfrac{1}{(2\pi)^{1/2}} \int_0^z d^{-\beta^2/2} d\beta$.

$z \dfrac{x-\mu}{\sigma}$	0.00	0.01	0.02	0.03	0.04	0.05	0.06	0.07	0.08	0.09
0.0	0.0000	0.0040	0.0080	0.0120	0.0160	0.0199	0.0239	0.0279	0.0319	0.0359
0.1	0.0398	0.0438	0.0478	0.0517	0.0557	0.0596	0.0636	0.0675	0.0714	0.0753
0.2	0.0793	0.0832	0.0871	0.0910	0.0948	0.0987	0.1026	0.1064	0.1103	0.1141
0.3	0.1179	0.1217	0.1255	0.1293	0.1331	0.1368	0.1406	0.1443	0.1480	0.1517
0.4	0.1554	0.1591	0.1628	0.1664	0.1700	0.1736	0.1772	0.1808	0.1844	0.1879
0.5	0.1915	0.1950	0.1985	0.2019	0.2054	0.2088	0.2123	0.2157	0.2190	0.2224
0.6	0.2257	0.2291	0.2324	0.2357	0.2389	0.2422	0.2454	0.2486	0.2517	0.2549
0.7	0.2580	0.2611	0.2642	0.2673	0.2704	0.2734	0.2764	0.2794	0.2823	0.2852
0.8	0.2881	0.2910	0.2939	0.2967	0.2995	0.3023	0.3051	0.3078	0.3106	0.3133
0.9	0.3159	0.3186	0.3212	0.3238	0.3264	0.3289	0.3315	0.3340	0.3365	0.3389
1.0	0.3413	0.3438	0.3461	0.3485	0.3508	0.3531	0.3554	0.3577	0.3599	0.3621
1.1	0.3643	0.3665	0.3686	0.3708	0.3729	0.3749	0.3770	0.3790	0.3810	0.3830
1.2	0.3849	0.3869	0.3888	0.3907	0.3925	0.3944	0.3962	0.3980	0.3997	0.4015
1.3	0.4032	0.4049	0.4066	0.4082	0.4099	0.4115	0.4131	0.4147	0.4162	0.4177
1.4	0.4192	0.4207	0.4222	0.4236	0.4251	0.4265	0.4279	0.4292	0.4306	0.4319
1.5	0.4332	0.4345	0.4357	0.4370	0.4382	0.4394	0.4406	0.4418	0.4429	0.4441
1.6	0.4452	0.4463	0.4474	0.4484	0.4495	0.4505	0.4515	0.4525	0.4535	0.4545
1.7	0.4554	0.4564	0.4573	0.4582	0.4591	0.4599	0.4608	0.4616	0.4625	0.4633
1.8	0.4641	0.4649	0.4656	0.4664	0.4671	0.4678	0.4686	0.4693	0.4699	0.4706
1.9	0.4713	0.4719	0.4726	0.4732	0.4738	0.4744	0.4750	0.4758	0.4761	0.4767
2.0	0.4772	0.4778	0.4783	0.4788	0.4793	0.4799	0.4803	0.4808	0.4812	0.4817
2.1	0.4821	0.4826	0.4830	0.4834	0.4838	0.4842	0.4846	0.4850	0.4854	0.4857
2.2	0.4861	0.4864	0.4868	0.4871	0.4875	0.4878	0.4881	0.4884	0.4887	0.4890
2.3	0.4893	0.4896	0.4898	0.4901	0.4904	0.4906	0.4909	0.4911	0.4913	0.4916
2.4	0.4948	0.4920	0.4922	0.4925	0.4927	0.4929	0.4931	0.4932	0.4934	0.4936
2.5	0.4938	0.4940	0.4941	0.4943	0.4945	0.4946	0.4948	0.4949	0.4951	0.4952
2.6	0.4953	0.4955	0.4956	0.4957	0.4959	0.4960	0.4961	0.4962	0.4963	0.4964
2.7	0.4965	0.4966	0.4967	0.4968	0.4969	0.4970	0.4971	0.4972	0.4973	0.4974
2.8	0.4974	0.4975	0.4976	0.4977	0.4977	0.4978	0.4979	0.4979	0.4980	0.4981
2.9	0.4981	0.4982	0.4982	0.4983	0.4984	0.4984	0.4985	0.4985	0.4986	0.4986
3.0	0.49865	0.4987	0.4987	0.4988	0.4988	0.4988	0.4989	0.4989	0.4989	0.4990

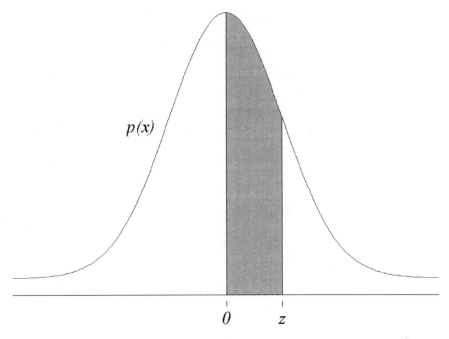

Figure 19.3   Area under the probability density function $p(x)$ for a normal distribution in the interval $0 - z$.

It should now be evident that the statistical terms defined by Equations (19.7)-(19.9) are really a quantification of probability. The area under the probability density function $p(x)$ in the interval $\mu - z\sigma \leq x \leq \mu + z\sigma$ yields the probability that a measured value will be within that interval. For a normal distribution when $z = 1$, 68.26% of the area under the curve of $p(x)$ lies within $\pm 1\sigma$ of μ. This means that there is a probability of 68.26% that a measurement of x will have a value within the interval of $\mu \pm 1\sigma$, i.e., the true mean value plus or minus one standard deviation. As the value of z increases, the area under $p(x)$ increases, hence the probability of occurrence also increases. For instance, when:

$z = 1 \rightarrow 68.26\%$ of the area under $p(x)$ lies within $\pm 1\sigma$ of μ.
$z = 2 \rightarrow 95.45\%$ of the area under $p(x)$ lies within $\pm 2\sigma$ of μ.
$z = 3 \rightarrow 99.73\%$ of the area under $p(x)$ lies within $\pm 3\sigma$ of μ.

The relationship between the area under $p(x)$ and the statistical parameters μ and σ for a normal distribution are illustrated in Figure 19.3.

For historical reasons, infinite statistics based on the normal error function are known as z-statistics, or z-distribution. Table 19.2 contains tabulated values for the normal error function (the term in brackets in Equation (19.13)) on the interval defined by z, as shown in Figure 19.4. Note, to obtain the probability for the full interval (plus and minus) one must multiply the tabulated value by 2.

EXAMPLE 19.1

Using the probability values listed in Table 19.2, show that the probability that an arbitrary measurement will yield a value within the range $\mu \pm 1.96\sigma$ is 0.9500, or 95.00%.

SOLUTION

To estimate the probability that a single measurement will have a value in some interval, we must evaluate the integral

$$\frac{1}{(2\pi)^{1/2}} \int_0^{1.96} e^{-\beta'/2} d\beta.$$

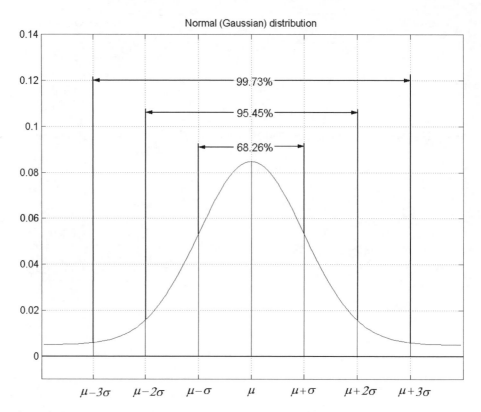

Figure 19.4 Normal error function limits.

Table 19.2 lists solutions to this integral. In Table 19.2 find the row corresponding to $z = 1.9$. Each of the columns in that row add the value in the column heading to the value $z = 1.9$. The eighth column heading is 0.06, and $1.9 + 0.06 = 1.96$, the value we are interested in. The value at the intersection of the $z = 1.9$ row and the eighth column is $P(z) = 0.4750$. This states that the probability that any measurement will produce a value within the interval $0 \leq x \leq \mu + 1.96\sigma$ is 47.50%. However, the normal distribution is symmetric about μ, so the probability that the value indicated by the measurement system would lie within the interval $\mu - 1.96\sigma \leq x \leq \mu + 1.96\sigma = 2(0.4750)$ is $0.9500 \rightarrow 95.00\%$.

We can infer from the above example that a useful way to characterize the variation of a data set of measured values is the standard deviation. The probability that the ith measurement of x will have a value between $\mu \pm z\sigma$ is $2P(z) \times 100 = P\%$, which can be written in the way suggested in Section 19.2:

$$x_i = \mu \pm z\sigma \quad (P\%). \tag{19.16}$$

19.6.   FINITE STATISTICS

Recall the railroad container car containing millions of washers. The main statistical issues regarding finite data sets concern the following question. Can we use the statistics resulting from measuring a sample, say of 50, to characterize the mean size and variance of all the washers in the container? The answer is, within the constraints imposed by probability, it is indeed possible. However, while the true behavior of a variable is described by its *infinite statistics,* the *finite statistics* describe only the behavior of the finite data of a sample, yielding only an estimate of the infinite statistics of the entire population.

Recall from Chapter 9 that finite data sets provide statistical estimates defined as

$$\bar{x} = \frac{1}{N}\sum_{i=1}^{N} x_i, \tag{19.17}$$

$$s^2 = \frac{1}{N-1}\sum_{i=1}^{N}(x_i - \bar{x})^2, \tag{19.18}$$

$$s = \sqrt{s^2}, \tag{19.19}$$

where N is the number of measurements, or repetitions. These quantities are the *sample mean value,* $\bar{x}$; the *sample variance,* s^2; and the *sample standard deviation, s.* The sample mean, $\bar{x}$, provides the most probable estimate of the true mean value, μ, based upon the finite sample of the full data set. The sample variance, s^2, is a measure of the precision of a measurement relative to the sample mean.

The number of independent measurements in a data set that are available to estimate a statistical quantity is usually referred to as the *degree of freedom,* ν, of the data in the set. Still, the data will be scattered about a mean value for measurements having a central tendency. If this is so, the freedom of a measurement to assume a particular value is always relative to the mean value. Thus, the degree of freedom, ν, is reduced by one value to $N-1$. This explains the denominator in Equation (19.18).

19.6.1.   Student-t Distribution

When sample sizes are finite and small, the z-statistics variable described in Section 19.5 does not provide a reliable estimate of the true probability with s used in place of σ. But, the sample variance can be weighted so that it is compensated for the difference between the finite and infinite statistical estimates of a measured variable. The details of how the weight is calculated are beyond the scope of this text, but the interested student can find these details in [4], among many other standard references.

This weighting came from William Sealey Gosset, a chemist and mathematician employed by the Guiness Brewery in Dublin, Ireland. Due to the variability in the ingredients of beer, samples that can be reasonably considered as coming from the same population are usually small. Gosset described his weighting in a paper published in 1908. The distribution is known as *Student-t distribution,* and the associated statistics are known as *t-statistics.* The history behind this curious name comes from the fact that the Irish brewery did not allow publication of research results. Thus Gosset published under the pseudonym of *Student.* The engineering student possessing a fondness for beer may well reflect upon Gosset's contribution to the art and science of engineering!

We know that large samples approach a normal distribution. What Gosset showed was that small samples taken from an essentially normal population have a distribution characterized by the sample size. The population does not have to be exactly normal, only unimodal and basically symmetric. For a normal distribution of x about some sample mean value, $\bar{x}$, one can predict x_i as

$$x_i = \bar{x} \pm t_{\nu,p}s \quad (P\%). \tag{19.20}$$

TABLE 19.3   Student-t distribution t-estimator values.

ν	$t_{\nu,50}$	$t_{\nu,90}$	$t_{\nu,95}$	$t_{\nu,99}$
1	1.000	6.314	12.706	63.657
2	0.816	2.920	4.303	9.925
3	0.765	2.353	3.182	5.841
4	0.741	2.132	2.770	4.604
5	0.727	2.015	2.571	4.032
6	0.718	1.943	2.447	3.707
7	0.711	1.895	2.365	3.499
8	0.706	1.860	2.306	3.355
9	0.703	1.833	2.262	3.250
10	0.700	1.812	2.228	3.169
11	0.697	1.796	2.201	3.106
12	0.695	1.782	2.179	3.055
13	0.694	1.771	2.160	3.012
14	0.692	1.761	2.145	2.977
15	0.691	1.753	2.131	2.947
16	0.690	1.746	2.120	2.921
17	0.689	1.740	2.110	2.898
18	0.688	1.734	2.101	2.878
19	0.688	1.720	2.093	2.861
20	0.687	1.725	2.086	2.845
21	0.686	1.721	2.080	2.831
30	0.683	1.697	2.042	2.750
40	0.681	1.684	2.021	2.704
50	0.680	1.679	2.010	2.679
60	0.679	1.671	2.000	2.660
∞	0.674	1.645	1.960	2.576

where the variable $t_{\nu,P}$ is obtained from Student's weighting function used for finite data sets replacing the z variable. It is called the *t-estimator*. The interval $\pm t_{\nu,P}s$ represents a confidence interval having probability of $P\%$, within which any measured value may be expected.

In essence, the value of the t-estimator is a function of the degrees of freedom, ν, and the probability, P. The t-estimator values are listed in Table 19.3, which are evaluated from the Student-t distribution.

Careful inspection of Table 19.3 reveals that the t-estimator value enlarges the interval size required for a percent probability, $P\%$, to adequately describe x. That is, the magnitude of $t_{\nu,P}s$ increases relative to $z\sigma$ at the same level of probability when N (and by extension ν) is finite. As N increases the t-estimator approaches the corresponding value of the z variable, as s approaches σ. A good rule of thumb is to use the t-statistics when $N \leq 30$. For very small samples ($N \leq 10$), sample statistics can be misleading, and additional information may be required.

19.6.2. Standard Deviation of the Means

Let us return to the railroad container filled with millions of washers. If we were to measure the inside diameter of a sample of N washers and repeat this procedure M times, it would be reasonable to expect that the resulting sample means and sample variances would be different. It turns out that after M replications of N measurements a set of normally distributed mean values would typically be obtained. In fact, this is always the case regardless of the probability density function. The amount of variation in the sample means depends on two values: the sample variance, s^2, and the sample size, N. The variation tends to increase with s^2, and decrease with $\sqrt{N}$.

The variation in the sample statistics is characterized by a normal distribution of the sample mean values about the true mean. This variance is described by the standard deviations of the mean, $S_{\bar{x}}$. This is defined by the relationship

$$s_{\bar{x}} = \frac{S}{\sqrt{N}}. \tag{19.21}$$

The arithmetic mean of the sample means approaches μ as the the sample size increases, according to the Central Limit Theorem. The range over which the true mean value, μ, might lie at some level of probability, P, based on a single sample mean is:

$$\bar{x} \pm t_{v,P} S_{\bar{x}} \quad (P\%). \tag{19.22}$$

Therefore, the estimate of the true mean value based on multiple finite data sets can be expressed as

$$\mu = \bar{x} \pm t_{v,P} s_{\bar{x}} \quad (P\%). \tag{19.23}$$

EXAMPLE 19.2

Compute the following sample statistics for the data set in Table 19.1: (a) determine the sample mean value, $\bar{x}$; (b) estimate the interval over which 90% of the measurements should be expected, $\bar{x} \pm ts$ (90%); (c) estimate the true mean value at 90% based on the finite data set, $\bar{x} \pm ts_{\bar{v}}$ (90%).

SOLUTION

(a) The sample mean is computed for $N = 20$ using Equation (19.17):

$$\bar{x} = \frac{1}{20} \sum_{i=1}^{20} x_i = 1.02.$$

(b) he solution to (a) is used to compute the sample standard deviation using Equations (19.18) and (19.19):

$$\sqrt{\frac{1}{19} \sum_{i=1}^{20} (x_i - 1.02)^2} = 0.16.$$

The degree of freedom in the standard deviation is $v = N - 1 = 19$. Then, using Table 19.3 with $P = 90\%$, we have that $t_{19,90} = 1.729$. Now, the interval in which 90% of the measurements of x should lie is given by Equation (19.20):

$$x_i = \bar{x} \pm (1.729 \times 0.16) = 1.02 \pm 0.28 \quad (90\%).$$

Now, if a 21st measurement were made, there is a 90% probability that its value would be between 0.74 and 1.30.

(c) The true mean value is estimated from the sample mean value using Equation (19.23). But first, we must calculate the standard deviation of the means using Equation (19.21):

$$S_{\bar{x}} = \frac{0.16}{\sqrt{20}} = 0.04.$$

Finally, we can write

$$\mu = \bar{x} \pm t_{19,90}S_{\bar{x}} = 1.02 \pm (1.729 \times 0.04) = 1.02 \pm 0.07.$$

19.7.   MEASUREMENT SYSTEM ERROR

Scientists and engineers sometimes mistakenly assume that measurements are exact, and frequently base analysis and conclusions with this misconception as foundation. It is important to realize that there is variation in any measurement system that affects individual measurements, and subsequently the decisions based upon the acquired data. Measurement system error can be classified into five categories: bias; repeatability; reproducibility; stability; and linearity [1].

One of the objectives of a measurement system study is to obtain information relative to the amount and types of variation associated with a measurement system when it interacts with its environment. For instance, when a temperature probe at room temperature (20°C) is inserted into a beaker of boiling water (100°C), the water temperature is changed by the transfer of heat energy from the water to the probe, thus lowering the water temperature. This information is valuable, since for the average production process it is far more practical, and economically efficient, to recognize repeatability and calibration bias, and establish reasonable limits for these, than it is to provide extremely accurate gages with very high repeatability. Applications of such a measurement system study provide the following:

1.   A criterion to accept new measurement equipment.
2.   A comparison of one measuring device against another.
3.   A basis for evaluating a measuring device suspected of being deficient.
4.   A comparison for measuring equipment before *and* after repair.
5.   A required component for calculating process variation, and the acceptability level for a production process.

The following definitions describe the types of error or variation associated with measurement systems in general.

19.7.1.   Bias

Bias is the difference between the observed mean value of the measurements and the true mean value. The true mean value is also known as a *reference* value, or *master* value. The reference value serves as an agreed-upon reference for the measured values taken from standards (see ASTM D 3980-88, for instance). A reference value can be determined by taking the mean of several measurements with a higher level of measuring equipment (e.g. as provided by a metrology lab). Figure 19.5 illustrates the notion of bias.

Bias is often referred to as *accuracy.* However, since *accuracy* has more than one meaning in the literature, its use as an alternate for *bias* is not recommended.

19.7.2   Repeatability

Repeatability is the variation in measurements obtainedwith one measurement instrument when used several times by one appraiser while measuringthe identical characteristic on the same part. Figure 19.6 indicates the repeatability of a measurement instrument is typically governed by a normal distribution, and can be expressed in terms of the standard deviation.

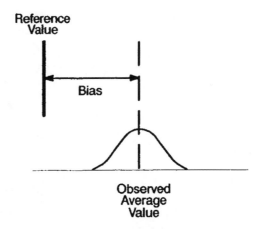

Figure 19.5 Bias.

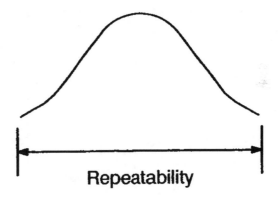

Figure 19.6 Repeatability

19.7.3. Reproducibility

Reproducibility is the variation in the mean value of measurements made by different appraisers using the same measuring instrument when measuring identical characteristics on the same part. Figure 19.7 illustrates the concept, and illustrates that reproducibility can be expressed in term of the standard deviation of the means.

19.7.4 Stability (or, Drift)

Stability, or drift, as it is often called, is the total variation in the measurements obtained with a measurement system on the same master, or parts when measuring a single characteristic over an extended period of time. This is an important characteristic of the measurement system that can only be determined with periodic calibration. See Figure 19.8 for an illustration.

19.7.5 Linearity

Linearity is the difference in the bias values through the operating range of the measurement equipment. Linearity can be expressed as the slope of a line describing the change in observed mean values between opposite extremes of the operating range of the measurement device. Figures 19.9 and 19.10 illustrate linearity.

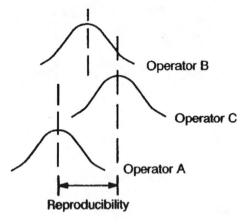

Figure 19.7 Reproducibility.

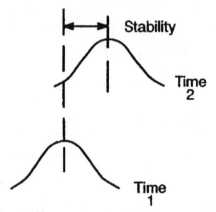

Figure 19.8 Stability (or, Drift).

19.7.6. Accuracy, Precision, and Bias Error

After all the allusions to accuracy in preceding sections, we would be remiss if we did not define it, at least for a measurement system. The measurement system accuracy can be estimated during calibration. If an input value describing the magnitude of a dimension is known *exactly*, then it can be called the *true value* of the input. The *accuracy* of a measurement instrument or system refers to its ability to indicate a true value [6]. If the system is perfectly accurate, it will indicate the true value exactly.

Accuracy can be quantified in terms of a precisely defined number: *absolute error*, ϵ. Absolute error is defined as the difference between the true value of the calibration input applied to the measurement system and the indicated value output of the system:

$$\epsilon = \text{true value} - \text{indicated value} \tag{19.24}$$

The percent accuracy, A, can then be defined in terms of the absolute error by:

$$A = \left(1 - \frac{|\epsilon|}{\text{true value}}\right) \times 100. \tag{19.25}$$

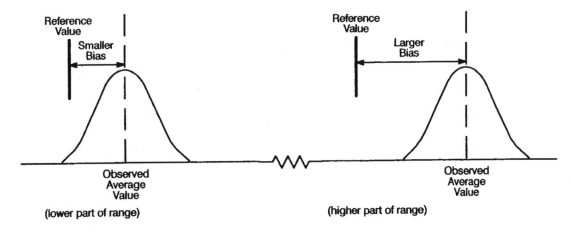

Figure 19.9 Linearity.

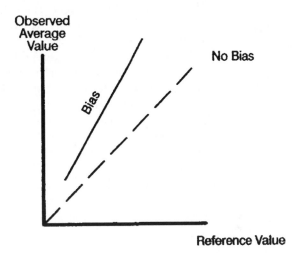

Figure 19.10 Varying linear bias.

IMPORTANT: By definition, accuracy can only be established during a calibration using a known true value.

As mentioned in Section 19.7.2, the repeatability (or precision) of a measurement system is its ability to indicate a particular value upon repeated, but independent, applications of a specific input value. In this case, the true value of the input need not be known exactly. The *precision error* is a measure of the random variation of the indicated value during repeated measurements. Hence, precision error is also called random error.

Precision and accuracy are, in a sense, independent. That is, an estimate of measurement system precision does not require calibration. A system that repeatedly indicates the same wrong value upon repeated application of the same input is precise regardless of its accuracy. In other words, a measurement system may be precise but not accurate.

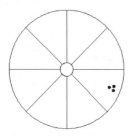

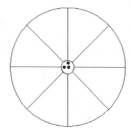

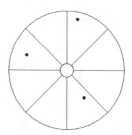

(a) Low accuracy due to bias
   error, but precise.

(b) High accuracy due to low bias
   and precision errors.

(c) Low accuracy due to bias
   and precision errors.

Figure 19.11   Accuracy, precision and bias errors.

If the average value of the measured value differs from the true value, the measured value contains a *bias error*. The bias error is defined in Section 19.7.1 as the difference between the average value and the true value. Both precision and bias affect the accuracy of the system.

The standard way to illustrate the relationship between accuracy, precision, and bias errors is the *dart board* analogy. Consider the dart board in Figure 19.11. In this analogy, the bull's-eye (centre of the dart board) represents the true value. The average value of the measurement deviation gives the bias error. The scatter of the values about the average represents the precision error. In Figure 19.11 (a) the darts were thrown very precisely, but with a bias to the lower right. In Figure 19.11 (b) the darts were thrown accurately, as there is little bias and only a small amount of scatter about the bull's-eye. In Figure 19.11 (c), the darts were thrown with a relatively large amount of scatter. In this particular case it is difficult to quantify the bias error.

19.8   REFERENCES

[1]   *Measurement Systems Analysis Reference Manual,* Chrysler Corporation, Ford Motor Company, General Motors Corporation, 1995.

[2]   C. Lipson and N.J. Sheth. *Statistical Design and Analysis of Engineering Experiments.* McGraw-Hill, New York, 1983.

[3]   I. Miller and J. Freund. *Probability and Statistics for Engineers, 3rd ed.* Prentice-Hall, Englewood Cliffs, N.J, 1985.

[4]   W. Chase and F. Brown. *General Statistics, 4th ed* John Wiley & Sons, Inc., New York, N.Y., U.S.A., 2000.

[5]   W. Mendenhall, R.J. Beaver, and B.M. Beaver. *Introduction to Probability and Statistics,* tenth edition. Duxbury Press, Brooks/Cole Publishing Co., Pacific Grove, CA., U.S.A., 1999.

[6]   R.S. Figliola and D.E. Beasley. *Theory and Design for Mechanical Measurements, 3rd ed.* John Wiley & Sons, Inc., New York, N.Y., U.S.A., 2000.

Chapter 20
Linear Regression and Correlation

20.1 INTRODUCTION

In the previous two chapters we have studied elementary statistics and probability, respectively. Using the techniques described therein, we can analyze a set of experimental data to determine confidence intervals for quantifying the probability that subsequent measurements will be within desired tolerance limits. The next tools to be developed will allow us to determine the relationship, if any, between two variables in a data set. **Regression analysis** is used to establish a mathematical model of an existing trend in the data so that predictions can be made about future values that follow the trend [1]. **Correlation analysis** is used to establish the degree to which two variables are related in a specific sense [1].

Given the variation in the data, the relationship, or trend, is rarely exact. It must be approximated in such a way as to minimize errors in some sense. This can be done geometrically. That is, the data are plotted as points in the Cartesian plane. The orthogonal basis vectors represent the pair of variables being analyzed. So the points in the plane have (x, y) coordinates that are the data. For example, we could plot the the results of an experiment using a linear spring, weights, and a device for measuring the change in spring length of the spring under various loads. The coordinates in the plot would be applied load in units of force, or mass, versus deflection in units of length. It is known that this relationship is linear. Accepting that there will be errors in the measurements, the plotted data will be only approximately linear. **Linear least squares regression** permits calculation of the coefficients of the line that fits the data such that the **sum of the squares of the error** is the least. We can then use the resulting linear equation to predict how the spring will deflect given loading conditions that have not been measured. This type of modelling is essential for simulation the dynamics of a system: automobile suspension, particle accelerator, communications network, building structures under wind loads, etc.

Linear correlation analysis is a descriptive measure of the degree to which two things change relative to each other *linearly*. A correlation analysis must always be performed to establish the validity of a regression analysis. This is a critical point because linear regression *assumes* that the data is linear. For example, we could perform linear least squares regression on data that fits to a circle. We would have the best fit line, though it would be useless for predicting values of one variable given the other, as we would end up with points on a line rather than points on a circle.

It is important to emphasize that the following discussion of linear regression and correlation applies only to bivariate data. Recall that this involves only two variables. However, the following techniques may be applied to multivariate data, but it must be done such that all but two of the variables are held constant.

20.2   LINEAR REGRESSION

Many systems involve elements possessing a linear, or near linear relationship between two variables of interest. For example: the force required to accelerate a particular mass; the voltage drop across a resistor for a given direct current; the strain in a structural element given a load induced stress; the change in length of a piece of metal given a change in temperature. All these relationships, within a certain range, are linear. The slope of the line relating the variables is the constant of proportionality. Familiar equations illustrate the above linear relations:

$$F = ma; \tag{20.1}$$
$$V = IR; \tag{20.2}$$
$$\epsilon = E\sigma; \tag{20.3}$$
$$\Delta l = \alpha \Delta T. \tag{20.4}$$

Equation (20.1) states that force, F, is linearly proportional to the product of mass, m, and acceleration, a. Equation (20.2) states that voltage, V, is linearly proportional to the product of current, I, and resistance, R. Equation (20.3) states that strain, ϵ, is linearly proportional to the product of *Young's modulus*, E, and stress, σ. Equation (20.4) states that the change in length of a piece of metal, Δl, is linearly proportional to the product of the metal's *coefficient of thermal expansion*, α, and change in temperature, T.

In any of these linear relationships the slope of the line is the constant of proportionality relating two of the variables. This implies that given a mass, we could predict its acceleration given an applied force, or predict the force required to attain an acceleration. In this case mass is the constant of proportionality. In other words, the slope of the line is mass. Alternately, we could consider acceleration to be constant, and establish a line relating force and mass. In this case acceleration is the constant of proportionality. Hence, the slope of this line is acceleration. An example, assuming no measurement error, is illustrated in Figure 20.1. In the plot on the left we examine how acceleration varies with force for a constant mass of 50kg. The slope of the line is given as the ratio of the change in the vertical direction to the change in the horizontal direction, giving:

$$\text{slope} = F/a.$$

Dimensional analysis reveals the units of slope:

$$\frac{F}{a} = \frac{[\text{kg} * \text{m/s}^2]}{[\text{m/s}^2]} = [\text{kg}].$$

The slope of the line reveals the mass constant of proportionality is 50kg.

The plot on the right side of Figure 20.1 is that of the relationship between mass and force with acceleration held constant at 2m/s^2. It is to be seen that the slope of this line has different units, in fact, units of acceleration:

$$\text{slope} = F/m.$$

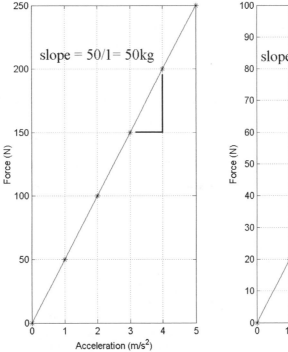
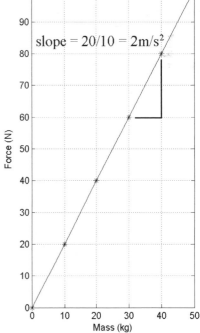

Figure 20.1   Two different plots of $F = ma$.

Dimensional analysis reveals the units of slope:

$$\frac{F}{m} = \frac{[\text{kg} * \text{m/s}^2]}{[\text{kg}]} = [\text{m/s}^2].$$

The slope of the line reveals the acceleration constant of proportionality is 2m/s^2.

The preceding example assumes perfect linear relationships among the variables of interest, and perfect, variation free measurements. Usually, when analyzing designed components relationships among variables of interest are not known, and must be determined empirically, i.e. in an experiment. In this regard linear regression is an extremely powerful tool.

In its current form, linear regression was developed by Sir Francis Galton (1822–1911), a cousin of Charles Darwin. In addition, Galton made significant contributions in the areas of weather forecasting as well as fingerprinting. Linear regression resulted from a study of sweet peas. Galton observed that the average weights of different biological groups of sweet pea seedlings *regressed* towards the average weight of the entire population of seedlings, and not towards the averages of the parental groups.

20.3   SCATTER PLOTS

A very effective way to organize a bivariate data set containing numerical data is a **scatter plot**. Each observation (a single pair of simultaneously measured characteristics) is represented as a point in an orthogonal Cartesian coordinate system. These pairs of coordinates can be described abstractly in terms of their position relative to the x- and y-axes. For historical reasons, the variable assigned to the x-axis is the **independent** variable, and the variable assigned to the y-axis is the **dependent** variable. Creating a scatter plot is illustrated in the following example.

EXAMPLE 20.1

It desired to determine the relationship, if any, between private automobile weight and fuel consumption. Create a scatter plot of the data listed in Table 20.1.

SOLUTION

In this example vehicle weight has been selected to be the independent variable, and hence is plotted on the x-axis. The dependent variable was selected to be the fuel consumption, plotted on the y-axis. Results are shown in Figure 20.2.

TABLE 20.1 Data for vehicle weight versus fuel consumption.

Model	Weight (kg)	City mileage (km/l)
Ford Festiva	810	13
Honda Civic	900	15
Toyota Matrix	1215	13
Acurs RSX	1215	11
Mazda Protégé	1215	12
Subaru Impreza WRX	1395	10
Pontiac Firebird	1440	9
BMW 330 CI	1485	9
Lincolon Continental	1755	6
Chevrolet Suburban	2295	5

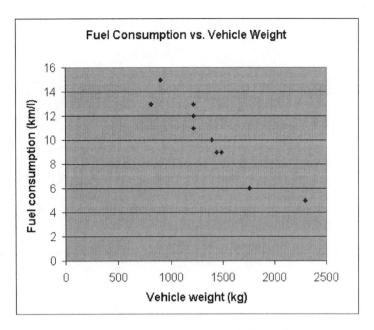

Figure 20.2   Scatter plot of fuel consumption versus vehicle weight.

20.4   THE LEAST SQUARES REGRESSION LINE

In Example 20.1 the plotted points of vehicle weight versus fuel consumption in Figure 20.2 appear to be scattered, although very approximately, about a line. Note that the slope of this line is not 0. If the line were horizontal it would be safe to conclude that there was no relationship between vehicle weight and fuel consumption. Imagine if the graphs in Figure 20.1 were horizontal. This would imply that the product of a constant mass with a varying acceleration would require a constant force. While this contradicts Newtonian physics, it illustrates the point.

If the relationship between dependent and independent variable appears to be linear, it would be useful to have an equation for the *best* line that fits the data in some sense. The line could then be used for interpolation. The next question to ask is how can the equation for the line be determined? The desired constraint on the line is that the the errors, as a whole, be minimized. Since data on the y-axis is *dependent* on the data plotted on the x-axis, we could try to find the line that minimizes the difference between actual value, y, and the corresponding value on the line, $\hat{y}$, with the same x-coordinate. This difference is called the **error** of the estimate, and is also known as the **residual**. It is denoted by e, and illustrated in Figure 20.3:

$$e = y - \hat{y}. \tag{20.5}$$

It is required that the error, e, be minimum for every point along the line. How can this be done? If the sum of the errors is used, cancellation becomes problematic: negative errors will cancel the positive errors, and the line may not yield a minimum error along its entire length for the given data. This problem is easily eliminated by squaring the errors, so that the error values are homogeneously positive. Thus, the line that best fits the data is the one for which the sum of the squares of the error is smallest. The least squares error criterion is known as an **objective function** that is to be minimized over

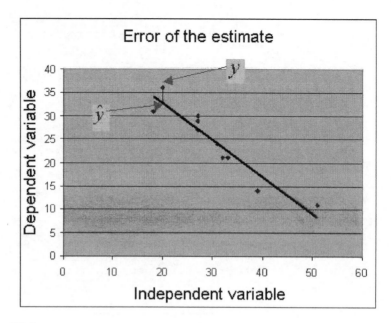

Figure 20.3 Error of the estimate, or residual.

the existing data. This objective function is called the **sum of squares for error**, SSE, and is defined:

$$\text{SSE} = \sum_{i=1}^{N} e_i^2 = \sum_{i=1}^{N} (y_i - \hat{y}_i)^2, \tag{20.6}$$

and is the square of the error summed over all N pairs of data in the set.

The familiar implicit equation of a line in the plane is:

$$y = mx + b,$$

where m is the slope of the line and b is its y-intercept. It can be shown that the line of **best fit**, or **regression line** has the equation:

$$\hat{y} = mx + b, \tag{20.7}$$

where the slope m is given by

$$m = \frac{N\left(\sum_{i=1}^{N} x_i y_i\right) - \left(\sum_{i=1}^{N} x_i\right)\left(\sum_{i=1}^{N} y_i\right)}{N\left(\sum_{i=1}^{N} x_i^2\right) - \left(\sum_{i=1}^{N} x_i\right)^2}, \tag{20.8}$$

and the $\hat{y}$ intercept is given by

$$b = \bar{y} - m\bar{x}, \tag{20.9}$$

where $\bar{x}$ and $\bar{y}$ are the mean values of the measured data values x and y. It is absolutely essential to realize that (Σx^2) and $(\Sigma x)^2$ are entirely different.

TABLE 20.2   Line of best fit sums and averages

Term	Value
Σx	13725
Σy	103
Σxy	130050
Σx^2	20466675
$(\Sigma x)^2$	188375625
Σy^2	1151
$\bar{x}$	1372.5
$\bar{y}$	10.3

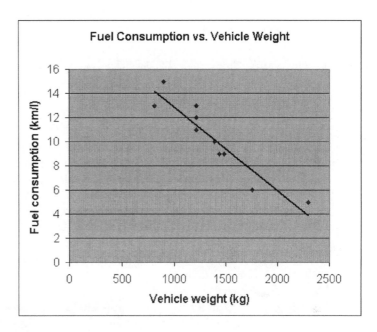

Figure 20.4   Regression line for fuel consumption versus vehicle weight data.

EXAMPLE 20.2

Compute the regression line for the data given in Example 20.1.

SOLUTION

Computing the sums required by Equation (20.8) gives the values listed in Table 20.2. Inserting these into Equations (20.8) and (20.9) reveals the regression line equation, which is plotted in Figure 20.4:

$$\hat{y} = -6.95 \times 10^{-3}x + 19.87. \tag{20.10}$$

20.5   OUTLIERS

Even when most of the data appears to be related linearly, there can be data points which do not follow the trend. They may be affected by anything from measurement error to, and including, sample selection. Since these data points lie outside of the trend, they are called **outliers**. The presence of such a point from the data set typically has a

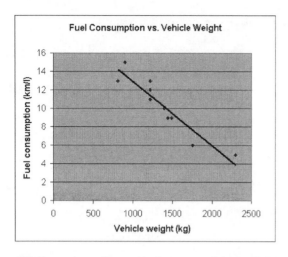
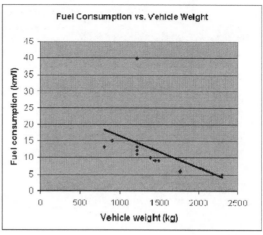

Figure 20.5   Outlier influence on data: original data on left.

significant effect on the computed coefficients of the regression line, possibly leading to inappropriate conclusions.

If, for example, fuel consumption for an eleventh car was added to the data in Table 20.1. Suppose its weight was 1215 kg and fuel consumption was 40 km/*l*. This data point would cause a significant change to the scatter plot, and to the equation of the regression line. For comparison, the original data and the new data are shown in Figure 20.5. Should this data point, which seems to belong to another class of vehicle, be considered as representative of the population? What if it were a new hybrid vehicle whose energy was supplied by a variety of systems in addition to its internal combustion engine. It may be able to go 40 km per liter of gas, but perhaps a large contribution of the power needed to cover that distance was supplied by solar cells. Would it be useful data if the aim was to compare gas powered internal combustion engines? The answer is decidedly *no*.

Data sets should be inspected for the presence of possible outliers. If an outlier has a significant effect on the regression line it is called an **influential observation**. Reasons leading to an explanation of the outlier must be determined. If it is determined that the data does not belong in the sample it can be removed if the reasons for doing so are valid. Regardless, a record should be kept of any data removed from a sample.

20.6   LINEAR CORRELATION

It is very important to realize that applying the linear regression, Equation (20.7), does not create a linear trend in your data. When the regression line is determined, and used to analyze data, it is assumed that the data is linear, or at least reasonably linear. Regression equations exist for fitting data to virtually any type of algebraic trend. The trend could be linear, or nonlinear: exponential, quadratic, logarithmic, etc. In a later chapter different types of data fitting will be discussed for deriving **empirical equations**. An empirical equation is one that describes the exact, or approximate, relationship between a set of variables.

The question that naturally arises is: how good is the fit of the empirical equation, in our case the line of best fit, to the data? The **linear correlation coefficient**, denoted r, quantifies the degree of the linear relationship between the independent and dependent variable (x and y) values. However, it does not indicate how well the data fits a regression line (for that we require the *coefficient of determination*, r^2, discussed in Section 20.7). The linear correlation coefficient can be computed for any two variables regardless of their dimensions. Using the computed value of r, the decision can be made to compute the regression line, or not. That is, it may be that the value of r is such that we must conclude the data is not related linearly, and there is no point in computing the regression line.

20.6.1. Linear Correlation Coefficient, r

The linear correlation coefficient, r, for the sample is computed using three variations on the standard deviation for a sample. Recall that the sample standard deviation for one variable is defined (it is understood that the differences are summed over the index i for all N data in the set):

$$s = \sqrt{\frac{\Sigma(x - \bar{x})^2}{N - 1}}. \tag{20.11}$$

We define the sample standard deviation in variables x and y as s_x and s_y, respectively:

$$s_x = \sqrt{\frac{\Sigma(x - \bar{x})^2}{N - 1}}, \quad s_y = \sqrt{\frac{\Sigma(y - \bar{y})^2}{N - 1}}. \tag{20.12}$$

Using these definitions, one formulation for the correlation coefficient gives:

$$r = \frac{\Sigma(x - \bar{x})(y - \bar{y})}{(N - 1)s_x s_y}. \tag{20.13}$$

In practice, Equation (20.13) is rarely used for manual computations in that form. Rather, the s_x and s_y terms are expanded, and after some algebraic manipulation one obtains [2]:

$$r = \frac{N(\Sigma xy) - (\Sigma x)(\Sigma y)}{\left(\sqrt{N(\Sigma x^2) - (\Sigma x)^2}\right)\left(\sqrt{N(\Sigma y^2) - (\Sigma y)^2}\right)}. \tag{20.14}$$

EXAMPLE 20.3

Determine the linear correlation coefficient, r, for the data in Table 20.1.

SOLUTION

The solution requires determining the appropriate sums and products and inserting them into Equation (20.14). We obtain:

$$r = \frac{10(130050) - (13725)(103)}{\left(\sqrt{10(20466675) - 188375625}\right)\left(\sqrt{10(1151) - 10609}\right)}$$
$$= -0.934141$$
$$= -0.93.$$

Note, we will later require a value of r for an intermediate calculation. For numerical integrity, it is best to *round-off* only the final result, and not intermediate results. While we would report the linear correlation coefficient as $r = -0.93$, the value we should use for subsequent calculations (for example, in determining the **coefficient of determination**, see Section 20.7) is $r = -0.934141$.

20.6.2. Interpreting r

The value of the linear correlation coefficient is normalized such that its value ranges between -1 and 1:

$$-1 \le r \le 1.$$

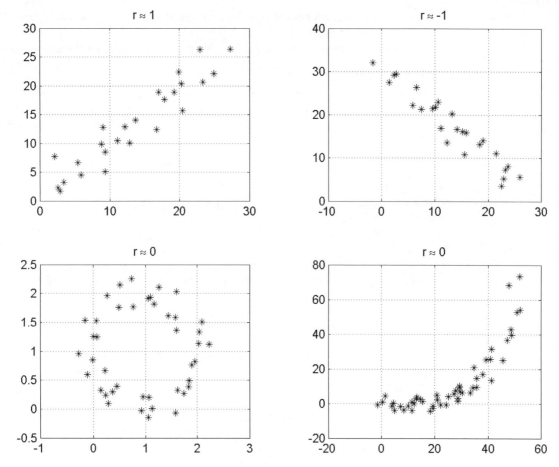

Figure 20.6 Examples of linear and nonlinear relationships.

If $r = 1$ exactly, then all data points are exactly on the regression line and the relationship is, of course, perfectly linear. In this case the regression line has positive slope. The upper-left plot in Figure 20.6 shows data that is highly linear, having $r \approx 1$. On the other hand, if $r = -1$, this indicates the data is perfectly linear, but the slope of the regression line is negative. The upper-right plot in Figure 20.6 illustrates data that is very nearly perfectly linear, having $r \approx -1$.

When $r = 0$, there is no linear relationship between the dependent and independent variables in the data. Highly nonlinear data is illustrated in the bottom two figures in Figure 20.6. In summary, the closer the value of r is to 1, or -1, the stronger the linear relationship. The closer the value is to 0, the weaker the linearity.

20.7 THE COEFFICIENT OF DETERMINATION

As mentioned in Section 20.6, we require some quantified measure of how well the regression line fits the data. The linear correlation coefficient, r, quantifies the degree of the linear relationship between the independent and dependent variable (x and y) values. However, it does not directly indicate how well the data fits a regression line. For instance, what if we had set of data for which $r = 0.70$? How can this information be transformed into something we can easily interpret? One way to proceed is to establish bounds, or cutoff values for r through empirical study. However, it turns out that a very useful improvement of r is obtained by simply squaring it. This yields the **coefficient of determination**, r^2.

The coefficient of determination, r^2, gives the proportion of the variation in the dependent variable, y, that is explained by its linear relationship with the independent variable, x. Because it is *squared*, the negative half of the range of r is annihilated. The value of r^2 is bound between $0 \le r^2 \le 1$. Thus, if $r = -0.70$, then $r^2 = 0.49$. In this case, expressing r^2 as a percentage, only 49% of the variability in y is caused by a linear relationship with x. Clearly, the closer the percentage is to 100%, the closer the relationship between x and y is to linear.

To understand the utility of r^2, we will examine how we are defining *error* in terms of the linear regression line. In this context, every sample contains two sorts of variation: variation that can be explained by linear regression; and variation that cannot. To do this, we require definitions of the sorts of variation we encounter in a single data point in a sample.

Total variation at a single point, $y - \bar{y}$: The deviation between a single value and the mean is defined as the total variation at a single point, and is expressed as:

$$y - \bar{y}.$$

Explained variation at a single point, $\hat{y} - \bar{y}$: When the corresponding value of y is unknown for a known value of x, the value can be estimated from the regression line. This value is denoted $\hat{y}$. We can explain the difference between $\hat{y}$ and $\bar{y}$ because of the linear relationship to the variations in x. To be compatible with the total variation at a single point, we define the explained variation as:

$$\hat{y} - \bar{y}.$$

Unexplained variation at a single point, $y - \hat{y}$: The error, or residual, is defined as the remaining portion of the variation, but its source is unknown. Thus, we define it as the unexplained variation, and define it as the difference between the actual single value, y, and the corresponding linear regression value, $\hat{y}$:

$$y - \hat{y}.$$

Thus, we can characterize the total variation at a single point as the sum of the explained variation plus the unexplained variation:

$$\left(\begin{array}{c}\text{total variation} \\ \text{at a point}\end{array}\right) = \left(\begin{array}{c}\text{explained variation} \\ \text{at a point}\end{array}\right) + \left(\begin{array}{c}\text{unexplained variation} \\ \text{at a point}\end{array}\right), \text{ or}$$

$$y - \bar{y} = (\hat{y} - \bar{y}) + (y - \hat{y}) \tag{20.15}$$

In order to establish the variation for the entire sample, we must sum the squares of the variation over all the values of y in the sample. It can be shown that [3]

$$\sum(y - \bar{y})^2 = \sum(\hat{y} - \bar{y})^2 + \sum(y - \hat{y})^2. \tag{20.16}$$

Similar to Equation (20.15), we can state Equation (20.16) in words as

total variation = explained variation + unexplained variation, or

$$\left(\begin{array}{c}\text{total sum} \\ \text{of squares}\end{array}\right) = \left(\begin{array}{c}\text{sum of squares} \\ \text{for regression}\end{array}\right) + \left(\begin{array}{c}\text{sum of squares} \\ \text{for error}\end{array}\right),$$

which is typically abbreviated as [2, 3]:

$$\text{TSS} = \text{SSR} + \text{SSE}. \tag{20.17}$$

The *total sum of squares* (TSS) is an expression of the variance in all the y-data in the sample. The explained variance, which is the *sum of squares for regresson* (SSR) is the component of the TSS accounted for by the linear dependence of y on x, i.e., the regression line through the sample data. If we now consider the ratio of the SSR to the TSS we obtain an expression for the proportion of the total variation in the sample data explained by the regression line:

$$\frac{\text{explained variation}}{\text{total variation}} = \frac{\text{SSR}}{\text{TSS}}.$$

It can be shown [3] that the above relation is, in fact, the **coefficient of determination**, r^2:

$$r^2 = \frac{\text{explained variation}}{\text{total variation}} = \frac{\text{SSR}}{\text{TSS}}. \tag{20.18}$$

Thus, the coefficient of determination, r^2, reveals the proportion of the variation in y explained by its linear relationship with x, in other words, the regression line. The closer to $r^2 = 1$ (or, expressed as a percentage, 100%), the closer are the y values to the $\hat{y}$ values. This in turn means r^2 can be used to directly evaluate the strength of the linear relationship between y and x. The easiest way to compute it is to compute the linear correlation coefficient, r, and square it.

EXAMPLE 20.4

Compute and interpret the coefficient of determination for the data used in Example 20.1.

SOLUTION

In Example 20.3 we computed the linear correlation coefficient to be $r = -0.93$. Before blindly accepting that simply squaring r will yield the coefficient of determination, let us compute the ratio SSR/TSS. To compute SSR, we obrain the values for $\hat{y}$ from Equation (20.10), and use $\bar{y}$ computed in Example 20.4, and listed in Table 20.2, giving

$$SSR = \sum (\hat{y} - \bar{y})^2 = 78.623058. \tag{20.19}$$

We similarly obtain TSS:

$$TSS = \sum (y - \bar{y})^2 = 90.100000. \tag{20.20}$$

We can now compute the ratio:

$$\frac{\text{SSR}}{\text{TSS}} = \frac{78.623058}{90.100000} = 0.872620. \tag{20.21}$$

Now, we compare the above ratio to r^2, and find:

$$r^2 = (-0.934141)^2 = 0.872620 = \frac{\text{SSR}}{\text{TSS}}. \tag{20.22}$$

It is clear, at least for this example, that $r^2 = \frac{SSR}{TSS}$. In general, this result holds [3]. Rounding the value to two decimal places, we get $r^2 = 0.87$.

A value for the coefficient of determination of $r^2 = 0.87$ means that about 87% of the variation in fuel consumption is explained by the variation in vehicle weight. About 13% of the variance is not explained. This portion may be due to measurement error, observation error, or incompatibility among elements in the sample. For example, one car may have a turbo-charged diesel engine, thereby having greater fuel efficiency than the same model of car, but having a regular gas burning engine.

20.8   REFERENCES

[1]   J. Devore and N. Farnum. *Applied Statistics for Engineers and Scientists*. Duxbury Press, Brooks/Cole Publishing Co., Pacific Grove, CA., U.S.A., 1999.

[2]   W. Chase and F. Brown. *General Statistics, 4th ed*. John Wiley & Sons, Inc., New York, N.Y., U.S.A., 2000.

[3]   W. Mendenhall, R. J. Beaver, and B. M. Beaver. *Introduction to Probability and Statistics*, tenth edition. Duxbury Press, Brooks/Cole Publishing Co., Pacific Grove, CA., U.S.A., 1999.

Section 6

Introduction to Excel

Chapter 21
Microsoft Excel Basics

21.1 INTRODUCTION TO WORKSHEETS

A *spreadsheet* is a rectangular grid composed of addressable units called *cells*. A cell is addressed by referencing its column letter and row number. A cell may contain numerical data, textual data, or formulas (equations).

Spreadsheet application programs were originally intended to be used for financial calculations. The original electronic spreadsheets resembled the paper spreadsheets of an accountant. One characteristic of electronic spreadsheets that gives them an advantage over their paper counterparts is their ability to automatically recalculate all dependent values whenever a parameter is changed.

Over time, more and more functionality has been added to spreadsheet programs like Excel. A variety of mathematical and engineering functions now exists within Excel. Numerous analytical tools are also available, including scientific and engineering tools, statistical tools, data-mapping tools, and financial-analysis tools. Auxiliary functions include a graphing capability, database functions, and the ability to access the Internet.

SECTIONS

OBJECTIVES

After reading this chapter, you should be able to perform the following tasks:

- Describe how spreadsheets are used by engineers.
- Identify the main components on the Excel screen.
- Name at least two ways to access help for Excel.
- Create and save a new worksheet.
- Open and edit an existing worksheet.
- Undo mistakes.
- Perform spelling checks on text items.
- Preview and print a worksheet.

As an engineering student, you may find that an advanced spreadsheet program such as Microsoft Excel will suffice for many of your computational and data presentation needs. You will still need a word processor, such as Microsoft Word, for working with reports and other documents, but tables and charts may be easily exported from Excel into Word.

Excel also has some capability for database management. However, if you wish to manage large or sophisticated databases, a specialized database application such as Microsoft Access or MySQL is preferable.

In addition, Excel has fairly sophisticated mechanisms for performing mathematical and scientific analyses. For example, you can use the Analysis Toolpack in Excel to perform mathematical analysis. If the analysis is large or very sophisticated, however, you may want to use a specialized mathematical or matrix package such as Mathcad® or Matlab®.

The same principles hold for graphing or statistical analysis. Excel is a general tool that performs many functions for small- to medium-sized problems. As the size or sophistication of the function increases, other tools may be more applicable, such as SigmaPlot® or Origin® for graphing and SAS® or SPSS® for statistical analysis.

Microsoft Excel uses the term *worksheet* to denote a spreadsheet. A worksheet can contain more types of items than a traditional paper spreadsheet. These include charts, links to web pages, Visual Basic programs, and macros. We will treat the terms *worksheet* and *spreadsheet* synonymously in this text. Worksheets stored together in a file are called a *workbook*.

21.2   HOW TO USE THIS BOOK

This book is intended to get you, the engineering student, up and running with Excel 2007 as quickly as possible. (References to Excel 2003 are provided as well.) Examples are geared toward engineering and mathematical problems. Try to read the book while sitting in front of a computer. Learn to use Excel by re-creating each example in the text. Perform the instructions in the boxes labeled **PRACTICE**.

The book is not intended to be a complete reference manual for Excel. It is much too short for that purpose. Many books on the market are more appropriate for use as complete reference manuals. However, if you are sitting at the computer, one of the best reference manuals is at your fingertips. The online Excel help tools provide an excellent resource if properly used. These help tools are described later in this text.

21.3   TYPOGRAPHIC CONVENTIONS USED IN THIS BOOK

Throughout the text, the following conventions will be used:

Selection with the Mouse

The book frequently asks you to move the mouse cursor over a particular item and then click and release the left mouse button. This action is repeated so many times in the text that it will be abbreviated as follows:

Choose **Item**.

If the mouse button should not be released, or if the right mouse button should be used, then this will be stated explicitly.

A button, icon, or menu option that you should select with the mouse will be printed in boldface font. A key you should press will also be printed in boldface font. For example, if you are asked to choose an item from the options shown at the top of the screen, then it will be written as follows:

Choose **Paste** from the Ribbon's Home tab.

Multiple Selections

The book frequently refers to selections that require more than one step. For example, to format a group of cells, perform the following steps:

1. Choose **Cell Styles** from the Excel Ribbon.
2. Choose **Normal** style from the drop-down menu.

Multiple selections will be abbreviated by separating choices with a right arrow. For example, the two steps listed will be abbreviated as follows:

Choose **Cell Styles** → **Normal** from the Ribbon.

Multiple Keystrokes

If you are asked to simultaneously press multiple keys, the key names will be printed in bold font and will be separated with a plus sign. For example, to undo a typing change, you can simultaneously press the **Ctrl** key and the **Z** key. This will be abbreviated as follows:

Press **Ctrl + Z**.

Key Terms

The first time a key term is used, it will be italicized. Key terms are summarized at the end of each chapter.

Literal Expressions

A word or phrase that is a literal transcription will be printed in bold. For example, the title bar at the top of the screen should contain the text **Microsoft Excel**. Another example is the literal name of a box or menu item, as in the following instruction:

Check the box labeled **Equal To**.

21.4   UNDERSTANDING THE EXCEL 2007 SCREEN

This section introduces you to the Microsoft Excel screen. To start the Excel program, use the Windows Start menu (illustrated in Figure 21.1):

Start → Microsoft Office Excel 2007

A screen that resembles Figure 21.2 will appear.

We'll now discuss each of the components on the screen. The Excel screen consists of a number of components, including the following:

- Title Bar
- Ribbon (Menu Bar in Excel 2003)
- Quick Access Toolbar
- Office Button
- Formula Bar
- Work Area
- Sheet Tabs
- Status Bar

Try to become familiar with the names of these components as we proceed, as we will use these names throughout the book. Working generally from top to bottom, we will discuss each of the components in turn.

21.4.1   Title Bar

The bar at the top of the screen is called the *Title bar*. The Title bar contains the name of the worksheet currently being edited, Ch01.xlsx in Figure 21.2. If you are working in an unsaved workbook, the default name **Book1** will appear in the Title bar.

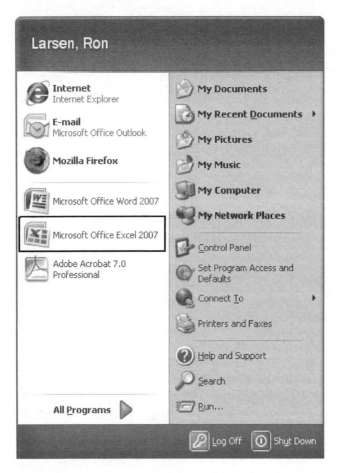

Figure 21.1   Launching Excel from the Start menu.

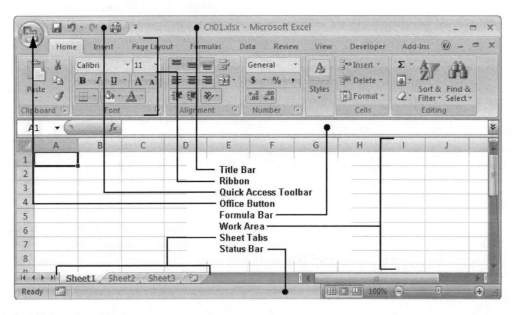

Figure 21.2   The Excel workbook.

Figure 21.3 The Excel Title bar.

Figure 21.3 shows an example of a Title bar. The Title bar contains a number of useful buttons and features (from left to right):

- **Office Button**—The big round button at the left end of the Title bar is the *Office button*. It is present in all Microsoft Office 2007 applications and replaces many of the features that used to be on the File menu in Excel 2003. It is used to

  - Open workbooks
  - Save workbooks
  - Print workbooks
  - Set Excel Options

- **Quick Access Toolbar**—The small collection of buttons just to the right of the Office button is the *Quick Access Toolbar*. This area is designed for your use, to add buttons for the features that you use most often. The small down arrow to the right of the Quick Access Toolbar opens a menu that you can use to customize the toolbar.

- **File Name**—The name of the workbook that is being edited is displayed in the center of the Title bar when the workbook has been maximized to fill the entire work area. If the current workbook is not maximized, then it will be displayed in its own window in the work area, with the file name shown at the left side of the workbook window's Title bar, as illustrated in Figure 21.4.

- **Control Buttons**—The three buttons at the right side of the Title bar are called the *Control buttons*. They are used to control the way the Excel window is displayed.

  - **Minimize Button**—The small flat line is the **Minimize** button. If you click the minimize button the Excel window will disappear from your desktop, except for the Excel icon on the Taskbar, usually at the bottom of the desktop. Click the Taskbar icon to restore the Excel window on your screen.

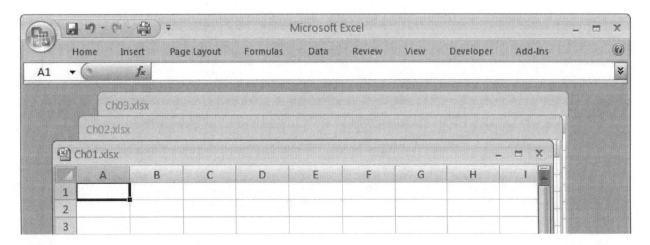

Figure 21.4 Multiple workbooks can be open in the work area.

- **Maximize/Restore Window Toggle Button**—The middle button is a toggle button that changes the display back and forth between two options.

  - If the window is not maximized, then the middle button maximizes the window (causes it to fill the entire desktop).
  - If the window is already maximized, then the middle button restores the window to whatever size it was before it was last maximized.

- **Close button**—The rightmost button on the Excel Title bar is the **Close** button (shaped like an x). Closing the Excel window is equivalent to exiting the Excel program. If you have made changes to the workbook you will be asked if you want to save the workbook before exiting.

21.4.2 Ribbon

The *Ribbon* is a new feature in Office 2007, and it replaces the menu bar, most toolbars, and some dialog boxes. The Ribbon attempts to get everything you need to use Excel right where you can get at it quickly. It is context sensitive, so that when you are editing a chart, the Ribbon tabs related to working with charts are activated. The Ribbon can be minimized, as shown in Figure 21.4, but it is more commonly used in the expanded form shown in Figure 21.5.

The Ribbon is made up of a number of *tabs*:

- **Home tab**—very commonly used commands for formatting and sorting.
- **Insert tab**—used to insert objects such as charts and hyperlinks.
- **Page Layout tab**—used to modify entire sheets (apply themes, set print area, etc.).
- **Formulas tab**—used to insert functions and manage defined names of cells and cell ranges.
- **Data tab**—provides access to sorting and filtering features and to data analysis tools (if activated).
- **Review tab**—used to add comments and track changes to a worksheet.
- **View tab**—used to change the display magnification (zoom), and to show or hide features such as the Formula bar and gridlines.
- **Developer tab**—provides access to the Visual Basic editor and macros; by default, not displayed.
- **Add-Ins tab**—not displayed unless you have installed Excel Add-Ins. Excel Add-Ins are programs written for Excel by other software companies that are intended to extend the capabilities of Excel.

Most of the features you will need for day-to-day problem solving will be on the Home tab. Each tab is divided into *Groups* of related buttons, selection lists, and menus. For example, the Font group on the Home tab (shown in Figure 21.5) contains drop-down lists for font size and style, toggle buttons for font attributes (bold, italic), and

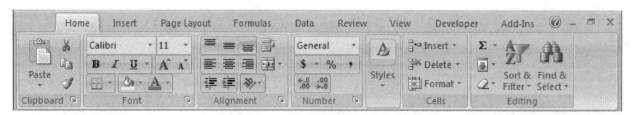

Figure 21.5   The Ribbon's Home tab.

combination buttons (buttons with a small down arrow on the right side) for setting background (fill) and font colors. Clicking the button applies the color shown on the button. Clicking the down arrow opens a color palette so that you can select a color.

When this text instructs you to use a Ribbon option, it will be in the following general form:

Tab → Group → Drop-down Menu → Button

21.4.3 Formula Bar

The *Formula bar*, located just below the Ribbon, displays the formula (or text, or value) in the currently selected cell (called the *active cell*). In Figure 21.6, cell B3 is the active cell, and it contains the formula

$$= 3 + 4$$

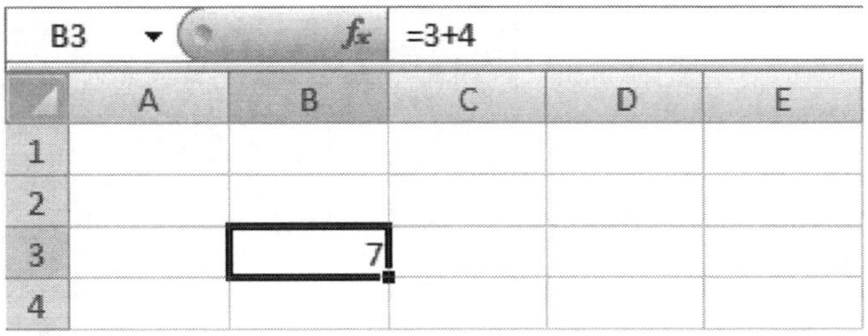

Figure 21.6   The Formula bar displays the contents of the active cell.

When cell B3 is selected, the result of the calculation is displayed in the cell (as shown in Figure 21.6) and the cell contents (the formula) are displayed in the Formula bar.

When you are entering a formula, you can type in the Formula bar or type directly into the cell that will hold the formula. Most people enter formulas directly into the cells, but the Formula bar can be useful when you are entering a formula in a cell near the right edge of the work area.

The left side of the Formula bar is called the Name box. The Name box displays the name of the active cell. In Figure 21.6 the Name box appears in the top-left corner and displays "B3" since that is the active cell.

The **Insert Function** button also resides on the Formula bar. The icon on the **Insert Function** button shows f_x, a common nomenclature for "function."

Click in cell C3 to make it the active cell, then click on the **Insert Function** button. The Insert Function dialog box will appear, as shown in Figure 21.7. From the Insert Function dialog box, you can choose a function category and function name. In Figure 21.7, we have chosen the category **Math & Trig** and the function **SIN**.

Near the bottom of the Insert Function dialog box, a brief description of the function is displayed. The dialog box also has a search feature to help you locate a function. There are over 200 built-in functions available in Excel.

Choose the **SIN** function, then click **OK**. The Function Arguments dialog box will appear, as shown in Figure 21.8. This dialog prompts for the arguments to the named function. Arguments may be a range of cells, numbers, or other functions.

A short explanation about the expected arguments appears in the bottom of the window. In this case, the *SIN* function takes its arguments in radians. The formula for converting radians to degrees is also displayed.

Type

pi()/2

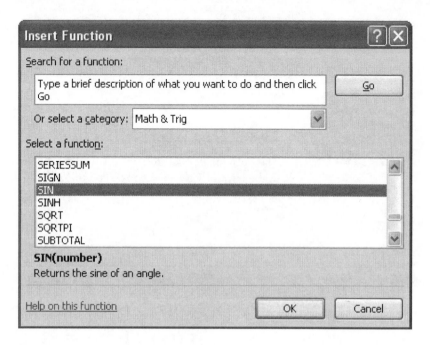

Figure 21.7 The Insert Function dialog box.

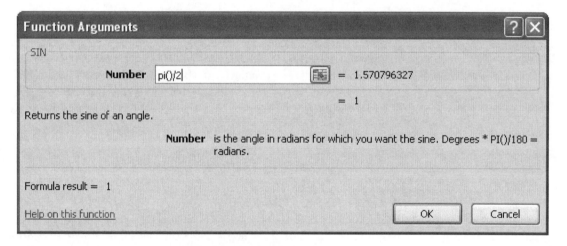

Figure 21.8 The Function Arguments dialog box for the *SIN* function.

as the **Number** argument. The effect of this is to call another built-in function, named *PI* (returns the value of π), and divide the result by 2.

When you click OK the Function Arguments dialog box will disappear and the formula

$$=\text{SIN(PI( )/2)}$$

will be entered into the active cell (cell C3). This is illustrated in Figure 21.9.

21.4.4 Work Area

The *Work area* (also called the *Workbook window*) is the area on the screen where data are entered and displayed. The Work area contains one or more worksheets.

The maximum size for a worksheet is 1,048,576 rows by 16,384 columns (Excel 2003: 65,536 × 256). The columns are labeled A, B, C, . . ., AA, AB, . . ., AAA, AAB, . . ., XFD and the rows are labeled 1, 2, 3, . . ., 1048576.

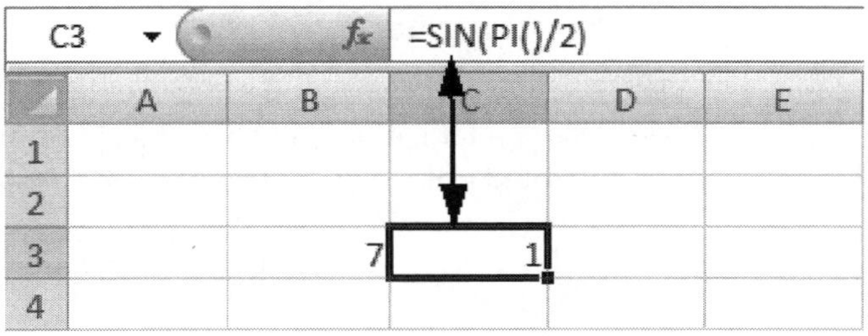

Figure 21.9 The formula = **SIN(PI()/2)** entered in cell C3.

A single cell can be selected by placing the mouse over the cell and clicking the mouse. The selected cell is called the *active cell*. A *range* of cells can be selected by holding the left mouse button down and dragging it over the selected cell range. When a cell range is selected, the first cell selected is the active cell. In Figure 21.10 the cell range B2: C4 is selected, and cell B2 is the active cell.

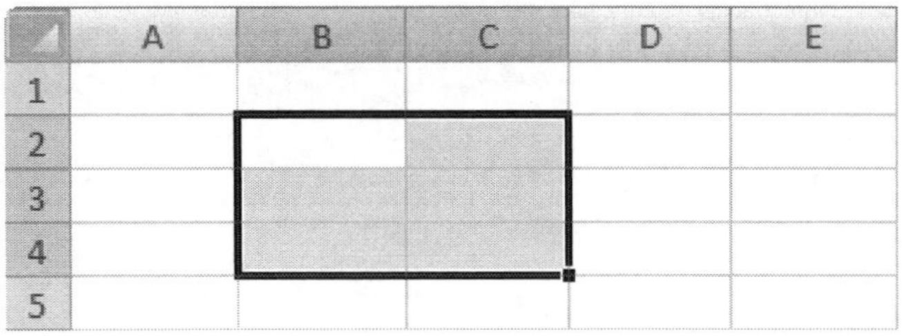

Figure 21.10 Selected cell range B2:C4, with active cell B2.

An entire column can be selected by clicking the left mouse button on the column heading. An entire row can be selected by clicking on the row heading. The entire work-sheet can be selected by clicking on the heading in the top-left corner of the workbook.

21.4.5 Sheet Tabs

The *Sheet tabs* are located at the bottom of the displayed worksheet, as shown in Figure 21.11. You can have more than one worksheet in a workbook. The Sheet tabs identify all of the worksheets in the current workbook.

You can move quickly from worksheet to worksheet by selecting a Sheet tab. You can also use the arrows to the left of the Sheet tabs to move from sheet to sheet, which can be useful when a workbook contains a large number of worksheets. By default, Excel creates three worksheets when you create a new workbook.

The rightmost Sheet tab is actually a button that can be used to add a new work-sheet to the workbook.

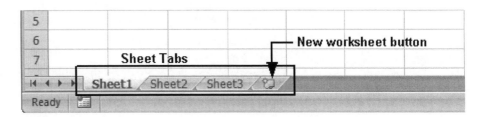

Figure 21.11 The Excel window with the Sheet Tabs indicated.

21.4.6 Status Bar

The *Status bar* is normally positioned at the very bottom of the Excel screen. The Status bar displays information about a command in progress and shows some aggregate values for a selected cell range. In Figure 21.12, the Status bar shows that Excel is in **Ready mode** (ready for data entry). When multiple cells are selected, the average, count, and sum of the selected values are displayed in the Status bar. Right-click on the Status bar to customize the display.

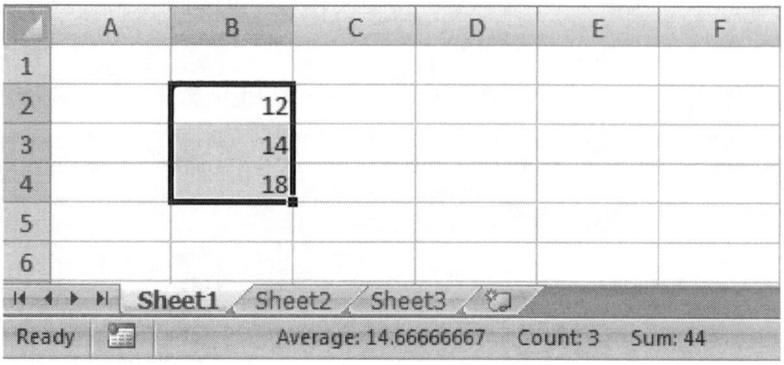

Figure 21.12   The Status bar shows the current data entry mode (Ready), and some aggregate statistics about selected values.

21.5   GETTING HELP

Excel contains a large online help system. To access the help menu, click the Help button on the right side of the Ribbon, as indicated in Figure 21.13. (Excel 2003: choose Help from the menu bar.) The Excel Help window will open, as shown in Figure 21.14.
The Help window provides several ways to obtain help, including:

- Browsing the Help Topic List.
- Searching the Help system.

Each of these methods will be discussed in the next sections.

21.5.1 Browsing the Help Topic List

This method is useful if you have time to read about a general topic. Reading through a topic could serve as a tutorial and may provide related information that can expand your skill base, but it is not the method to use if you have a specific question and you want an immediate answer. To view a Help topic, simply select the title in the Browse Excel Help list.
In Excel 2003, open the Table of Contents using these steps:

1. Choose **Help → Microsoft Excel Help** from the menu bar (or press **F1**.) The Help Task pane will be displayed.
2. Click the Table of Contents link on the Task pane.

NOTE: Excel 2007 users can also open the Table of Contents in the Excel Help window, but the topics in the Table of Contents are exactly the same as the topics in the Browse Excel Help list.

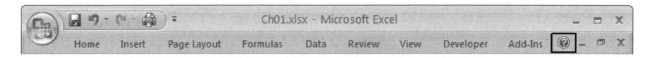

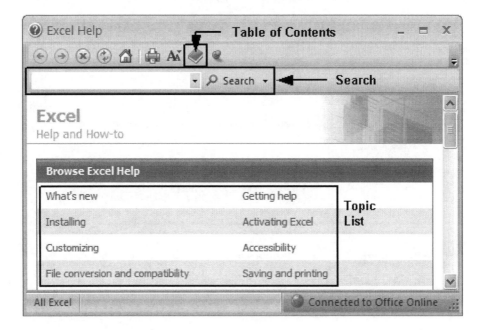

Figure 21.13   The Help button is located on the right side of the Ribbon.

Figure 21.14   The Excel Help window.

21.5.2 Searching the Help System

While the Browse Excel Help list and Table of Contents provide general information about help topics, the quickest way to find answers to specific questions is to search the Excel help system. Simply type a key word or a question into the search box, shown in Figure 21.14. (Excel 2003: There are search fields on the Help Task pane, and on the Menu bar.)

You enter a key word or a question in the search field to search the Help system. Figure 21.15 illustrates the result of searching the help system for the word "sine." Notice that the term "sine" was found in four Help topics. Clicking on any of the Help topic titles will cause the topic to be displayed.

21.6   CREATING AND SAVING WORKSHEETS AND WORKBOOKS

21.6.1 Creating a New Workbook

When the Excel application is started, a blank workbook containing (by default) three worksheets is automatically created. To create another new workbook, follow these steps:

1. Click the **Office** button to open the Office menu shown in Figure 21.16.
2. Click the **New** button. The New Workbook dialog box will open, as shown in Figure 21.17.

Figure 21.15   Results from searching for "sine" in the Help system.

Figure 21.16   The Office menu with New button selected.

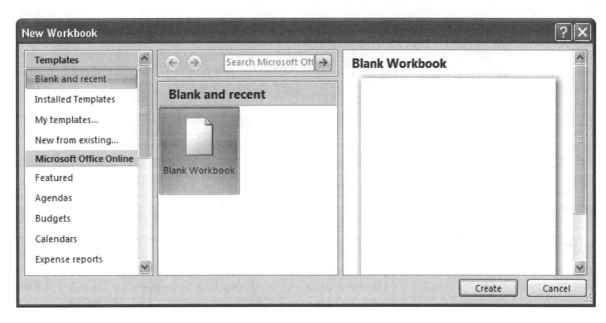

Figure 21.17   The New Workbook dialog.

3. Click the **Blank Workbook** icon to select it, then click the **Create** button to create the new workbook. (Or, double-click the **Blank Workbook** icon.) (Excel 2003: Use File → New, then choose New → Blank Workbook from the Task pane.)

21.6.2 Opening an Existing Workbook

To open an existing workbook, do the following:

1. Click the **Office** button to open the Office menu, shown in Figure 21.18.
2. Click the **Open** button. The Open dialog box will be displayed (Figure 21.19). (Excel 2003: Choose File → Open from the Menu bar.)
3. Browse for the file you want to open. In this example, a workbook named **Ch01.xlsx** has been selected.
4. Click **Open** to open the file in Excel.

From the Open dialog box, you can type in a path and file name in the **File name** field, or you can browse the file system to locate a file. The icons along the left side of the Open dialog box are used to help you find files quickly. By clicking on the icon labeled **My Recent Documents**, you will be shown the locations of your most recently used files. By clicking on the icon labeled **My Documents**, you will be taken to a special folder named **My Documents**. If you are working in a computer lab, be aware that the My Documents folder may be shared by other students. Ask your instructor where you should store your workbooks.

New Excel file extensions

Prior to Excel 2007, the file extension for an Excel file was .xls. With Excel 2007, two new file extensions are being used:

*   .xlsx—the default file name extension, macros disabled.
*   .xlsm—macro-enabled workbook.

Figure 21.18   The Office menu with the Open button selected.

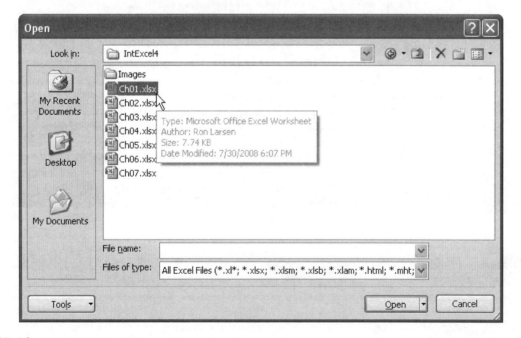

Figure 21.19   The Open dialog box.

The .xlsx file name extension indicates that macros (and Visual Basic programs) have been disabled. This ensures that the workbook cannot transmit a macro virus. If the file you want to open uses the .xlsm file extension, macros and Visual Basic programs are enabled and you should open the file only if you trust the source.

21.6.3 Creating a New Worksheet

Within a workbook, you can have many worksheets. The number of worksheets that you can have in a single workbook is limited only by the available memory on your computer.

To create a new worksheet in an open workbook, click the **Insert Worksheet** button that is the rightmost Sheet tab (See Figure 21.20.) (Excel 2003: Choose Insert → Worksheet from the Menu.)

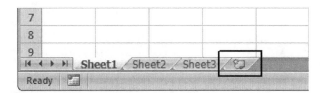

Figure 21.20 The Insert Worksheet button on the Sheet tab row.

You can use multiple worksheets to help keep your work organized. For example, if you are preparing a laboratory report you might use the following worksheets, as shown in Figure 21.21:

- Lab Data
- Report
- Charts

To assign a descriptive name to a worksheet tab,

1. Double-click on the worksheet tab to select the tab and enter text entry mode.
2. Type the new woksheet name.
3. Click anywhere outside the worksheet tab to complete the text entry.

21.6.4 Introduction to Templates

A *template* is a workbook that has some of its cells filled in. If you use similar formatting for many documents, then you will benefit from creating and using a template. You may build your own template or customize preformatted templates and, in time, create a library of your own templates. Excel is installed with a number of sample templates, including one that creates a Loan Amortization Schedule. To open the Loan Amortization template, follow these steps:

Excel 2007

1. Click the Office button to open the Office menu.
2. Click the New button to open the New Workbook dialog box, shown in Figure 21. 22.
3. Choose **Installed Templates** from the **Templates** list.
4. Select **Loan Amortization** from the **Installed Templates** list.
5. Click the **Create** button to open the template.

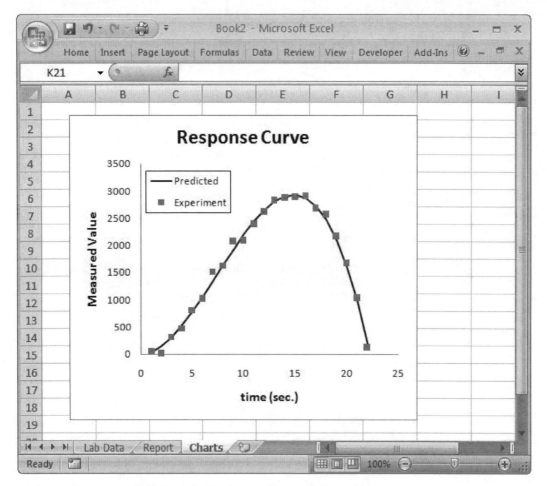

Figure 21.21   Using worksheets to organize your work.

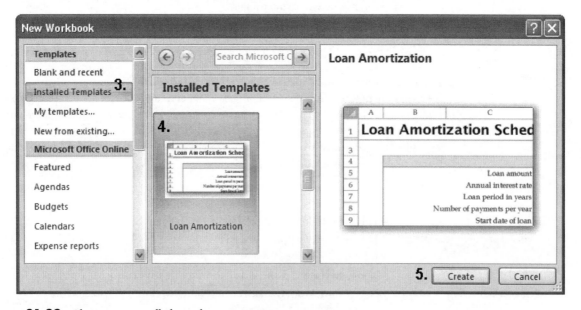

Figure 21.22   Choosing an installed template.

Excel 2003

1. Choose **File → New** from the Menu bar. The New Workbook Task pane will be displayed.
2. Choose **On my Computer ...** from the **Templates** section. The Templates dialog box will open.
3. Choose the **Spreadsheet Solutions** panel.
4. Select the **Loan Amortization** template.

The resulting Loan Amortization workbook is quite large; only a portion is shown in Figure 21.23.

The Loan Amortization template is a preassembled worksheet. Fill in the blank cells labeled

- Loan amount $15,000 in this example
- Annual interest rate   5%
- Loan period in years   4 years
- Number of payments per year   12
- Start data of loan   1/1/2009

The worksheet will build an amortization table for you. An amortization table shows a list of required payments on a loan and the amount remaining to be paid after each payment. When all of the required values are entered, the worksheet is automatically completed to show the required payments.

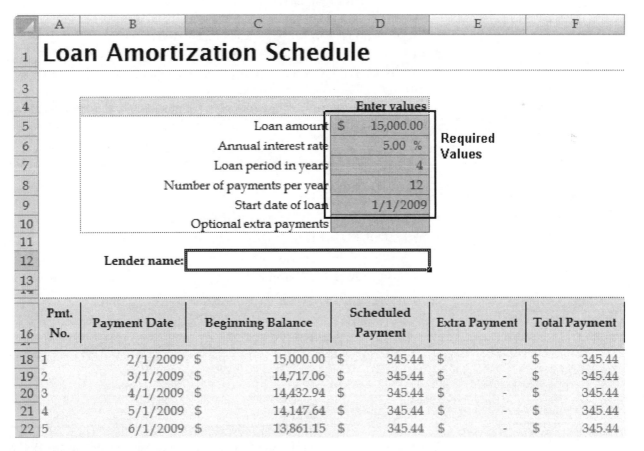

Figure 21.23   A portion of the Loan Amortization Schedule.

21.6.5   Opening Workbooks with Macros

A *macro* is a short computer program that records a group of tasks. Excel stores macros in a Visual Basic (programming language) module. Macros allow a set of frequently repeated commands to be stored and then executed with a single mouse click whenever needed.

Macros are very powerful tools. However, macros can contain a *macro virus* that will infect files on your computer. For this reason, you should only enable macros if you are certain of the origin of the macro. If you are unsure of the source of a macro, you should check the document by using virus-protection software before opening the document. Virus-protection software is not provided with Microsoft Excel and must be purchased separately.

In Excel 2007, there are now two file extensions used with workbooks:

- .xlsx—the default file name extension, macros disabled.
- .xlsm—macro-enabled workbook.

The default .xlsx file name extension tells you that macros (and Visual Basic programs) are disabled. This ensures that the workbook cannot transmit a macro virus. The .xlsm file extension means macros and Visual Basic programs are enabled; you should be careful when opening .xlsm files.

Because of the harm that can be done by macro viruses, Excel comes with Macro Security enabled. To check or change the level of macro security on your installation of Excel, follow these steps:

Excel 2007

1. Click the **Office** button to open the Office menu.
2. Click the **Excel Options** button at the bottom of the Office menu. The Excel Options dialog will open as shown in Figure 21.24.
3. Choose the **Trust Center** panel.
4. Click the **Trust Center Settings ...** button (shown in Figure 21.24). The Trust Center dialog box will open.
5. Click **Macro Settings**. The current level of protection is shown in the Macro Settings option list.

In Figure 21.25, the security is set so that macros are disabled, but you are notified (and have an option to enable it if desired).

Excel 2003

1. Choose **Tools → Options** from the Menu bar.
2. Choose the **Security** tab.
3. Click the **Macro Security** button. The Security dialog box will open.
4. Choose the **Security Level** tab.

The current level of protection is shown in the option list.

21.6.6   Saving Documents

The first time you save an Excel workbook, you need to assign the workbook a name and choose a folder. To save a document for the first time, follow these steps:

Excel 2007

1. Click the **Office** button to open the Office menu.
2. Move the mouse over the **Save As ...** button. The **Save a copy of the document** options are displayed as shown in Figure 21.26.

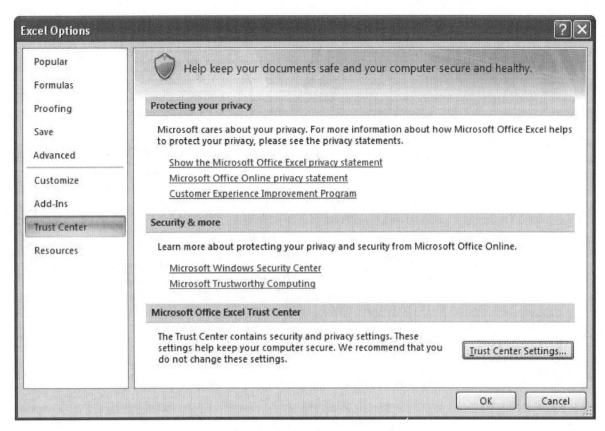

Figure 21.24   The Excel Options dialog box, Trust Center panel.

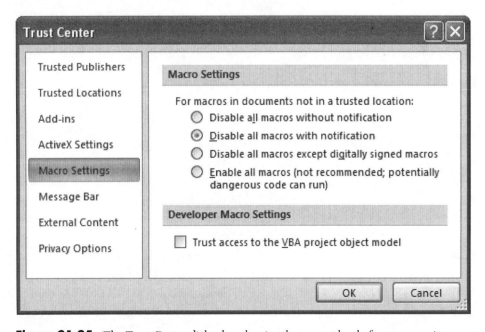

Figure 21.25   The Trust Center dialog box showing the current level of macro security.

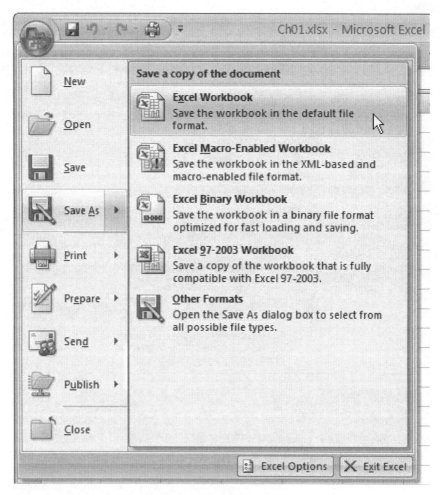

Figure 21.26   The Save As options.

3. Select one of the following **Save** options:
    *   Excel Workbook (.xlsx)—this is the default format in Excel 2007.
    *   Excel Macro-Enabled Workbook (.xlsm)—use only if macros or Visual Basic programs are stored with the workbook.
    *   Excel Binary Workbook (.xlsb)—rarely used except for very large workbooks.
    *   Excel 97-2003 Workbook (.xls)—used if compatibility with older versions of Excel is needed.
    *   Other Formats (e.g., htm)—used to access various less-common formats such as .htm for web pages.
4. The Save As dialog will open as shown in Figure 21.27.
5. Browse for the desired folder to store the workbook.
6. Enter the workbook name in the **File name** field. In this example, "Ch01" was entered as the workbook name. You do not need to enter the file extension; Excel will automatically add the file extension shown in the **Save as type** field (.xlsx in this example).
7. Click **Save** to save the workbook with the entered file name in the selected folder.

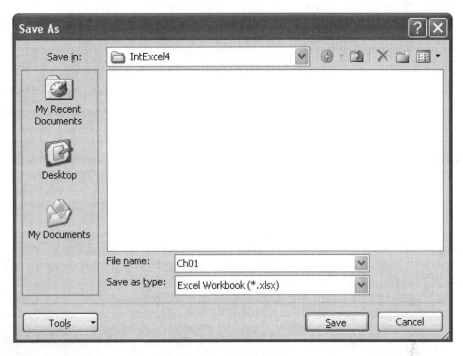

Figure 21.27   The Save As dialog box.

Excel 2003

1.   Choose **File** → **Save** As from the Menu bar. The Save As dialog box will open.
2.   Browse for the desired folder to store the workbook.
3.   Enter the workbook name in the **File name** field.
4.   Click **Save** to save the workbook.

To save an open document that was previously named, follow these steps:

Excel 2007

1.   Click the **Office** button to open the Office menu.
2.   Click the **Save** button to resave the workbook with any changes.

Or, click the **Save** button on the Quick Access Toolbar.

Excel 2003

Choose **File** → **Save** from the Menu bar.

You should save your work frequently. It is also important to make backup copies of your important documents on floppy disks, CDs, or some other physical device. There are many tales of woe from students (and professors) who have lost hours of work after a power failure.

21.6.7 The AutoRecover Feature

Excel has an automatic recovery feature, called *AutoRecover*, that can help protect your work from a power failure. When AutoRecover is on, Excel automatically saves a copy of your workbook periodically. Then, if there is a power failure or Excel crashes for any reason, you can open the most recent copy of your workbook to recover most of your work.

NOTE: AutoRecover files are erased each time you save your workbook, so using AutoRecover is not equivalent to creating backup copies of your important workbooks. The task of making backup copies is something that you must perform manually.

To check or change the AutoRecover features, follow this procedure:

Excel 2007

1. Click the **Office** button to open the Office menu.
2. Click the **Excel Options** button at the bottom of the Office menu. The Excel Options dialog will open as shown in Figure 21.28.
3. Choose the **Save** panel.
4. If the box next to **Save AutoRecover information** is checked, then the AutoRecover feature is active.
5. Use the **every** field to change the time interval.

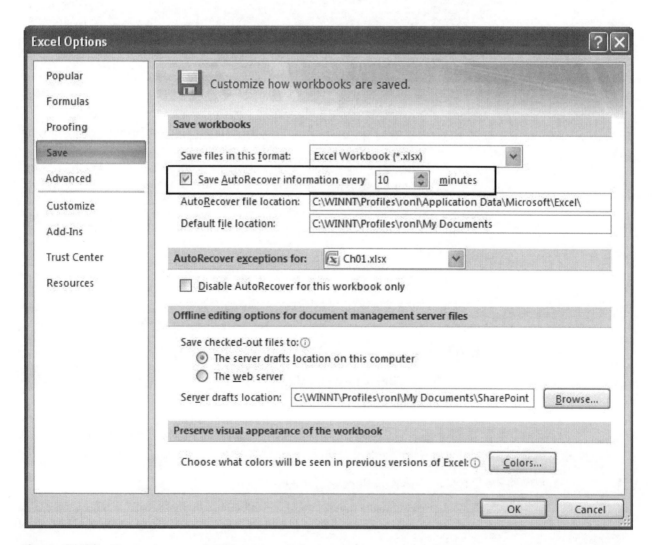

Figure 21.28   The Excel Options dialog box, Save panel.

Excel 2003

1. Choose **Tool → Options** from the Menu bar. The Options dialog box will open.
2. Chose the **Save** tab.
3. If the box next to **Save AutoRecover info** is checked, then the AutoRecover feature is active.
4. Use the **every** field to change the time interval.

While you have the Options dialog box open, take some time to view the other user options that may be customized. Browse through the other tabs on the Options dialog box. Until you become more familiar with Excel, you should probably leave most of the options set to their default values.

21.6.8 Naming Documents

It is important to develop a methodical and consistent method for naming worksheets. Over time, the number of worksheets that you maintain will grow larger, and it will become harder to locate or keep track of them. Documents that are related should be grouped together in a separate folder. Do not use the default workbook names (i.e., Book1, Book2, Book3, etc.), or chaos will soon ensue.

If documents are not given meaningful names, then the documents may be inadvertently overwritten. Documents that have very general names (e.g., Workbook), will be difficult to locate later.

One approach that students might use is to create a folder for each course, and use the assignment number with a brief description as the workbook name. In the example shown in Figure 21.29, ENGR 101 might be a computer course, and ENGR 262 a fluid mechanics course.

File formats and file extensions

Prior to Excel 2007, the file extension for an Excel file was .xls. Excel 2007 has a new file format as well as new file extensions (.xlsx and .xlsm). The new file format is called *Office Open XML* and it is intended to improve file management and data recovery. Excel 2007 users need to be aware that **workbooks saved in the new format cannot be read in older versions of Excel**. However, workbooks saved in Excel 2003 (or older versions) can be opened in Excel 2007.

Figure 21.29 Using folders to organize homework files.

Figure 21.30   Saving a workbook for older versions of Excel.

A common scenario during a transition from one version of a program to another is that you may use a new version at school or work, and still have the older version at home (or vice versa). As long as you continue to use the older version of Excel, you will need to save your workbooks using the old format. The **Save As** option on the Office menu provides an option to **Save As → Excel 97-2003 Workbook** (shown in Figure 21.30). This ensures that older versions of Excel can open the saved workbook.

21.7   MOVING AROUND A WORKSHEET

There are several methods of moving from place to place in an Excel worksheet. If the worksheet is relatively small, all of these methods will work equally well. As a worksheet grows in size, movement becomes more difficult, and you can save a lot of time by learning the various movement methods.

The currently selected cell is called the *active cell*, and the cell name (e.g., D3) is displayed in the *Name box* on the left-hand side of the Formula bar, as shown in Figure 21.31.

The three general methods for moving around a document are as follows:

* Movement by using the keyboard.
* Movement by using the mouse.
* Movement by using the Go To dialog box.

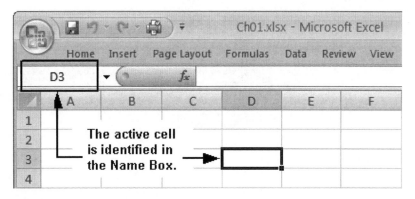

Figure 21.31   The active cell (D3) is identified in the Name Box.

21.7.1 Movement by Using the Keyboard

The keyboard may be used to select a worksheet from a workbook. The keyboard may also be used to navigate around a single worksheet quickly and effectively. You may already use the arrow keys to move up, down, left, and right. Combining the Ctrl key with the arrow keys gives you the means for rapid movement. Table 21.1 lists the most frequently used key combinations for movement.

TABLE 21.1   Movement using the keyboard

Key Combination	Action
←	Move one cell to the left
→	Move one cell to the right
↑	Move up one cell
↓	Move down one cell
Ctrl + →	Move to the far right of the worksheet
Ctrl + ↓	Move to the bottom of the worksheet
Page Down	Move down one screen
Page Up	Move up one screen
Ctrl + Page Down	Select next worksheet
Ctrl + Page Up	Select previous worksheet
Home	Move to far-left column of worksheet
Ctrl + Home	Move to top-left cell of worksheet (A1)
End, →	Move to right end of contiguously filled cell range
End, ↑	Move to top of contiguously filled cell range
End, ←	Move to left end of contiguously filled cell range
End, ↓	Move to bottom of contiguously filled cell range

Practice!

1. Open a new workbook.
2. Create several worksheets in the workbook using the **Insert Worksheet** button on the Sheet tab bar. (Excel 2003: Insert → Worksheet.)
3. Create a block of cells containing values, as shown in Figure 21.32.
4. Practice the keyboard movement commands in Table 21.1.
5. Move to the far right and bottom row of a worksheet. What is the maximum size of a worksheet?

	A	B	C	D	E	F
1						
2						
3		1	3	5	7	
4		2	4	6	8	
5		3	5	7	9	
6		4	6	8	10	
7		5	7	9	11	
8						

Figure 21.32   A 5 × 4 block of contiguously filled cells for experimenting with the End key movements.

Answer: A worksheet is 1,048,576 rows by XFD (16,384) columns in Excel 2007 and in 65,536 rows × 256 columns Excel 2003.

21.7.2 Movement by Using the Mouse

The mouse is the most common way to move within a worksheet, at least, fairly small worksheets. To select a worksheet, choose a tab from the Sheet tab bar as depicted in Figure 21.33.

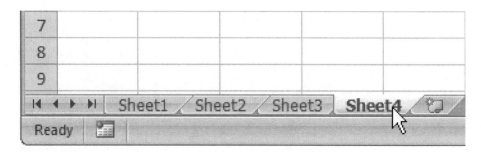

Figure 21.33   Click on a Sheet tab to display that worksheet.

One method of moving around a worksheet with the mouse is to click on a cell. This is most useful if the new insertion point is located on the same screen. If the desired location is on a different page, then the Vertical and Horizontal scrollbars may be used to move quickly to a distant location.

21.7.3 Movement by Using the Go To Dialog Box

If you have a large worksheet that covers many screens, then using the keyboard and mouse can be a cumbersome way of moving through the worksheet. The Go To dialog box offers a method for moving directly to distant locations on the worksheets.

To move to a location using the Go To feature, do the following:

1.   Open the Go To dialog box with Ribbon options: **Home tab → Editing group → Find & Select drop-down menu → Go To . . . button.** (Excel 2003: Edit → Go To.) The Go To dialog box will open, as depicted in Figure 21.34.
     Or, you can press the **F5** key to open the Go To dialog box.
2.   Type in a cell reference. For example, type G36, then click **OK**.

The screen will display cell G36, and it will become the active cell.

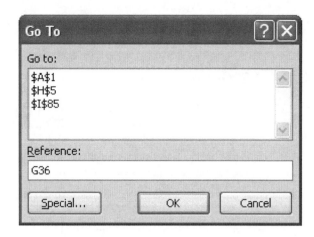

Figure 21.34   The Go To dialog box.

A history of previous references is kept in the **Go To** window, so recently visited cells can be located quickly simply by selecting them with the mouse.

In addition to moving to cells by location, you can move to cells of a particular type. We have not yet shown you how to create cells of different types. However, imagine that you have created a number of cells containing formulas. You can locate formulas with errors in them by using the Go To Special dialog box as follows:

1. Open the Go To Special dialog box with Ribbon options: **Home tab → Editing group → Find & Select drop-down menu → Go To Special . . . button**. The Go To Special dialog box will open, as depicted in Figure 21.35. Or, you can click the **Special . . .** button on the Go To dialog box.
2. Select the type of cell you want to locate (e.g., **Formulas** with **Errors**), then click **OK**.

Figure 21.35   The Go To Special dialog box.

The first formula with an error will become the active cell, and all other formulas with errors will be highlighted.

21.8 SELECTING A REGION

Much of the time spent in worksheet preparation involves moving, copying, and deleting regions of cells or other objects. In this section, we will be selecting regions of cells, but the same principles apply to regions that contain charts, formulas, and other objects. Before an action can be applied to a region, the region must be selected. The selection process can be performed by using either the mouse or the keyboard.

21.8.1 Selection by Using Cell References

In many cases, you will have the option of typing a cell reference. For example, you can type cell references into a formula. A single cell is denoted by its column letter and row number. A rectangular range of cells is denoted by the reference for the top-left and bottom-right cells. For example, the rectangle bordered by B2 on the top left and E5 on the bottom right is denoted as B2: E5 (see Figure 21.36). Note that the first selected cell (cell B2 in Figure 21.36) is shown in a different color, and indicates the active cell.

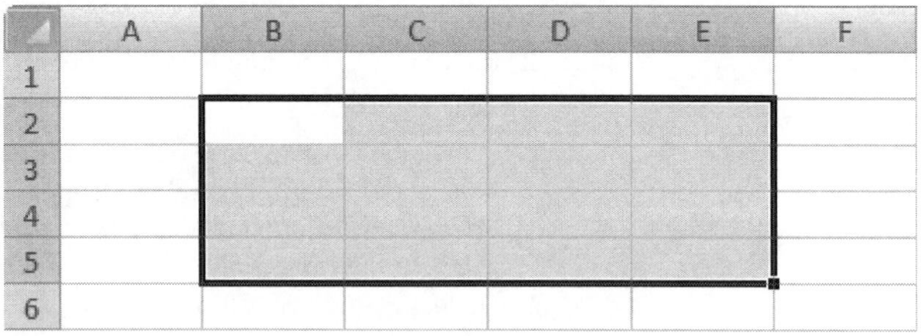

Figure 21.36 The selected cell range B2: E5.

21.8.2 Selection by Using the Mouse

To select a region of cells, called a *cell range*, with the mouse, click the mouse on the first cell in the range, then drag the mouse cursor to the cell at the other end of the range. As you drag the mouse, the selected region will be highlighted.

To select a cell range that is larger than one screen, drag the mouse to the bottom of the screen. If you hold the mouse at the bottom of the screen without releasing the mouse button, the screen will scroll and the selected region will continue to grow. This takes a little practice.

To select a whole column, click on the column header. To select a whole row, click on the row header. This is illustrated in Figure 21.37.

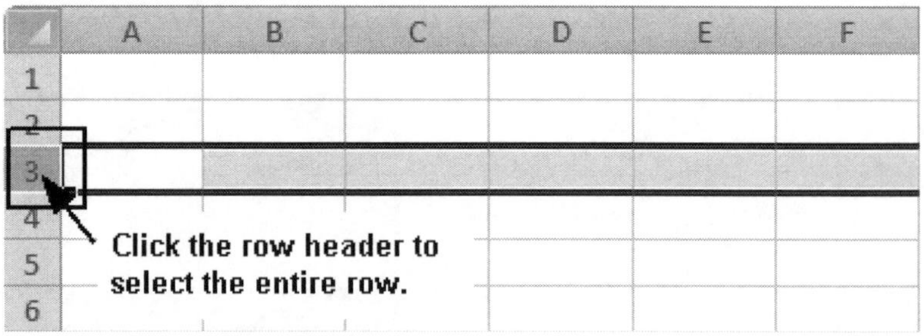

Figure 21.37 Selecting an entire row.

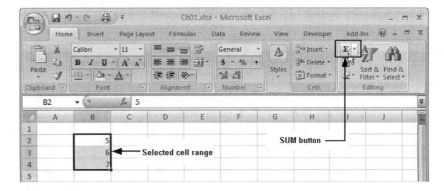

Figure 21.38 The Select All button.

To select the entire worksheet, choose the header at the top-left corner of the worksheet, between A and 1, as illustrated in Figure 21.38. This unlabeled header is called the **Select All** button. This is useful if you are applying a change to every cell in a worksheet.

21.8.3 Selection by Using the Keyboard

An alternative method for selecting regions of a document is to use the keyboard, as follows:

1. Click the mouse on one corner of the region that you wish to select.
2. Hold down the **Shift** key and use the arrow keys to move to the other end of the region.
3. Release the **Shift** key.

The selected region will be highlighted. If you make a mistake and incorrectly select a region, then click the mouse cursor anywhere on the worksheet window before you apply an action (such as delete). If the highlighting disappears, then you have deselected the region.

Practice!

Try the following exercise to practice selecting regions:

1. Click in cell B2 and type the number 5.
2. Press the **down-arrow** key.
3. Type the number 6.
4. Press the **down-arrow** key.
5. Type the number 7.
6. With the mouse, select cell range B2:B4, as shown in Figure 21.39.

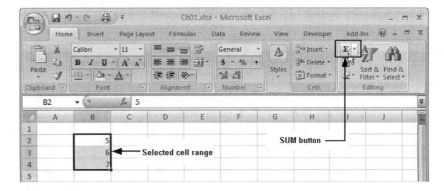

Figure 21.39 Click the SUM button after selecting the cells to be added.

7. Choose the **SUM** button on the Ribbon's Home tab: **Home tab → Editing group → SUM button**. (Excel 2003: **AutoSum** button on the Standard Toolbar.)

A formula for cell B5 will be added that contains the sum of cells B2, B3, and B4. The results should resemble Figure 21.40.

	B5		▼		f_x	=SUM(B2:B4)
	A	B	C	D	E	
1						
2		5				
3		6				
4		7				
5		18				
6						

Figure 21.40   The *SUM* function is entered just below the selected cell range.

21.9   CUTTING, MOVING, COPYING, AND PASTING

Once a region has been selected, you may take several actions, such as delete, move, copy, and paste. As usual, Excel provides several ways to accomplish the same actions. These include using keyboard commands and mouse commands.

The cut, copy, and paste commands make use of a special location called the *Windows clipboard*. The clipboard is a temporary storage location that can be used to hold the contents of a cell, a range of cells, or most other objects such as charts. To view the contents of the clipboard, click the **Clipboard** button at the bottom-right corner of the Clipboard group in the Ribbon's Home tab as shown in Figure 21.41. (You do not need to see the clipboard contents to use the clipboard.)

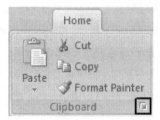

Figure 21.41   The Clipboard group on the Ribbon's Home tab.

21.9.1 Cutting a Region

Cutting a region (e.g., a range of cells) removes the contents of the selected region from the worksheet and leaves them on the clipboard. A region may be cut by using the mouse or the keyboard.

To cut a region using the mouse, follow these steps:

1. Select a region.
2. Click the **Cut** button in the Clipboard group in the Ribbon's Home tab. (Excel 2003: Choose Edit → Cut.)

The region to be cut will be highlighted by a rotating dashed line.

Alternative methods for cutting a selected region include the following:

- Select the region to be cut, then right-click on the selected region. Select Cut from the pop-up menu.
- Select the region to be cut, then press **Ctrl + X**.

No matter which method you use to cut the region, the effect is to place the contents of the region on the clipboard. This will be displayed in the Clipboard Task pane, if the pane is visible. Figure 21.42 illustrates a region of four cells in Column B that have been selected and cut.

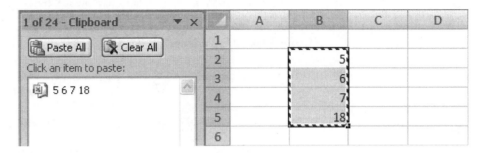

Figure 21.42   Four cells on the clipboard.

Notice that the cut cells have not been removed from the worksheet. The process of cutting the cells marks the cells for removal, but they are not actually removed unless the cut procedure is followed by a paste procedure. This is described in the next section.

21.9.2 Moving a Region (Cut and Paste)

A region may be moved by first cutting the region (to the clipboard) and then pasting it (from the clipboard) to the new location. The cut and paste operation may be performed by using the mouse or the keyboard.

To move a region using the mouse, do the following:

1. Select and cut a region. This places the contents of the region on the clipboard.
2. Select a destination cell or region.
3. Click the **Paste** button in the Clipboard group in the Ribbon's Home tab. (Excel 2003: Choose Edit → Paste from the Menu bar.)

The region of cells should now appear in the new location. If you do not select a destination region of the same size and shape as the cut region, then Excel will create a region with the appropriate size.

Alternative methods for pasting clipboard contents include the following:

- Right-click on the selected destination region, and then select **Paste** from the pop-up menu.
- Select the destination, then press **Ctrl + V**.

21.9.3 Copying a Region

Copying a region is very similar to moving a region, except that the contents of the original region remain intact; they are copied to the clipboard, not cut (moved) to the clipboard.

The copy a region using the mouse, follow these steps:

1. Select a region.
2. Click the **Copy** button in the Clipboard group in the Ribbon's Home tab. (Excel 2003: Choose Edit → Copy.)

The region to be cut will be highlighted by a rotating dashed line.

Alternative methods for cutting a selected region include the following:

- Select the region to be cut, then right-click on the selected region. Select **Copy** from the pop-up menu.
- Select the region to be cut, then press **Ctrl + C**.

NOTE: The keyboard shortcuts for cutting (**Ctrl + X**), copying (**Ctrl + C**), and pasting (**Ctrl + V**) use adjacent keys, shown in Figure 21.43, to make them easier to remember.

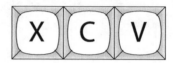

Figure 21.43   Cut (X), Copy (C), and Paste (V) keyboard shortcuts.

21.10 INSERTING AND DELETING CELLS

New cells may be added to a worksheet, and existing cells may be deleted (removed) or cleared (emptied).

21.10.1   Deleting Cells

Deleting a region of cells removes the cells from the worksheet. The vacancies, or holes, that are left behind must be filled in, and Excel will open the Delete dialog box (shown in Figure 21.44) to ask you how you want to fill the vacancies.

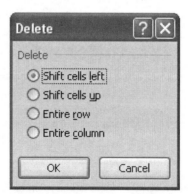

Figure 21.44   The Delete dialog box.

To delete a region of cells, follow these steps:

1. Select the region of cells to be deleted.
2. Right-click the selected region and choose **Delete ...** from the pop-up menu. The Delete dialog box will appear, as shown in Figure 21.44.
3. Choose whether you want Excel to fill the vacancies created by deleting the cells by
    *   shifting the remaining cells up or to the left,
    *   shifting the entire row below the vacancies up, or
    *   shifting the entire column to the right of the vacancies to the left.
4. Click **OK** to close the Delete dialog box and delete the selected cells.

21.10.2 Clearing Cells

To remove the contents of cells without deleting the cells themselves, perform these steps:

1. Select the region of cells to be deleted.
2. Right-click the selected region and choose **Clear Contents** from the pop-up menu. (Or, press the **Delete** key.)

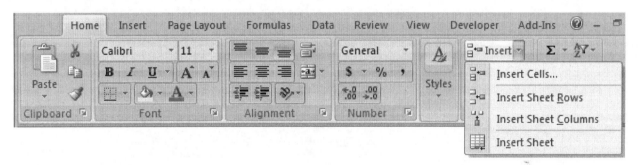

Figure 21.45   The Insert drop-down menu.

21.10.3 Inserting Cells

You can insert new cells, rows, columns, or an entire worksheet using the Insert drop-down menu on the Ribbon's Home tab (see Figure 21.45): **Home tab → Cells group → Insert drop-down menu**. (Excel 2003: Use the Insert menu option.)

21.11 SHORTCUT KEYS

As a novice user, you may have trouble finding commands. The Ribbon in Excel 2007 has been designed to display commonly used commands where you can find them, but it still takes some getting used to. *Shortcut keys* are the quickest way to execute a command and can save time, but they have to be memorized. The good news is that most are commonly used by lots of programs, not just Excel. Table 21.2 lists common shortcut key combinations.

TABLE 21.2   Commonly used shortcut keys

Command	Shortcut
New Workbook	Ctrl + N
Open Workbook	Ctrl + O
Save Workbook	Ctrl + S
Print	Ctrl + P
Undo	Ctrl + Z
Cut	Ctrl + X
Copy	Ctrl + C
Paste	Ctrl + V
Find	Ctrl + F
Replace	Ctrl + H
Go To	Ctrl + G
Format Cells	Ctrl + 1
Help	F1
Spell Check	F7

One method of learning some of the shortcuts is to look at the *Screen Tips* for Ribbon items. Screen Tips are descriptions that are displayed when you let the mouse hover over a Ribbon item. For example, in Figure 21.46, the Screen Tip for the Copy button is shown, and it indicates that the keyboard shortcut for the copy operation is **Ctrl + C**.

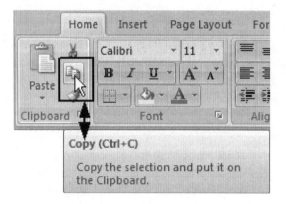

Figure 21.46   The Screen Tips for Ribbon items often indicate the keyboard shortcut.

21.12 FINDING AND CORRECTING MISTAKES

Let's face it, mistakes happen. Finding mistakes in a complex Excel worksheet can be a challenge. A couple of simple fixes are described here:

- Undo (**Ctrl + Z**)
- Spell Check (**F7**)
- AutoCorrect

21.12.1 Undoing Mistakes

Excel allows actions to be undone or reversed. To undo the last action, click the **Undo** button on the Quick Access toolbar (indicated in Figure 21.47) or type **Ctrl + Z**. (Excel 2003: Choose Edit → Undo from the Menu bar.)

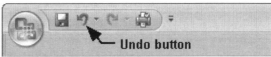

Figure 21.47   The Undo button on the Quick Access Toolbar.

To see the list of recent actions, choose the down-arrow button next to the **Undo** button. From this list, you may select one or more actions to be undone. Note that if you select an action on the list, then all of the actions above it in the list will also be undone! If you accidentally undo an action, then you may redo it by selecting the **Redo** button, which is next to the **Undo** button.

21.12.2 Checking Spelling

Excel can check the spelling of cells containing text. To check the spelling in a region, first select the region, then click the Spelling button on the Ribbon's Review tab: **Review tab → Proofing group → Spelling button**. Or, press the **F7** key. If Excel finds a spelling mistake, then the Spelling dialog box will appear, as shown in Figure 21.48.

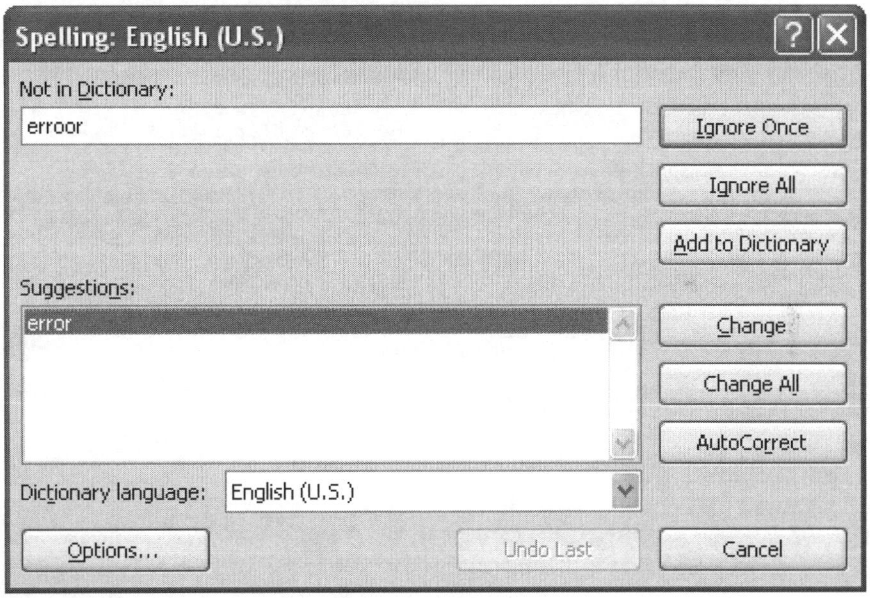

Figure 21.48   The Spelling dialog box.

The text thought to be in error is displayed in the top text box. Suggestions for changes are presented in the bottom text box. At any point in the process, you can choose whether to accept or ignore the suggestions. If you choose a suggested correction, then you may click the Change All button to change all occurrences of the misspelled word in the selected region.

You may add new words to the dictionary by choosing the **Add to Dictionary** button. This will probably be necessary as you proceed through your coursework, since many engineering terms are not in the default dictionary.

21.12.3 The AutoCorrect Feature

The Excel *AutoCorrect* feature recognizes some spelling errors and corrects them automatically. AutoCorrect performs actions such as automatically capitalizing the first letter of a sentence or correcting a word whose first two letters are capitalized.

You can test to see if the AutoCorrect feature is turned on for your installation of Excel. Try typing the letters *yuo*, then press the spacebar. Was the word automatically retyped as *you*? If so, then you have AutoCorrect turned on.

To see your AutoCorrect settings and dictionary, use **Office → Excel Options → Proofing tab → AutoCorrect Options** (Excel 2003: Tools → AutoCorrect Options). The AutoCorrect dialog box will appear, as shown in Figure 21.49.

From the AutoCorrect dialog box, you can select (or deselect) various options. You can also scroll through the AutoCorrect dictionary, add entries to the dictionary, and add exceptions to the dictionary. Creating an exception list will be necessary if you use all of the AutoCorrect features. For example, if you have selected the option that automatically converts the second capital letter to lowercase, you may have an occasional exception. Be careful when adding new entries into the AutoCorrect dictionary. You may inadvertently add an entry for a misspelling that is a legitimate word.

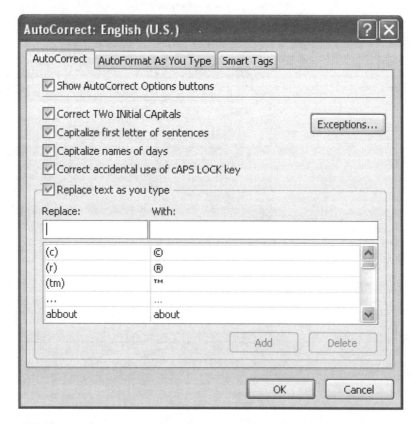

Figure 21.49 The AutoCorrect dialog box.

21.13 PRINTING

Before attempting to print a document, make sure that your printer is correctly configured. See your operating system and printer documentation for assistance.

21.13.1 Setting the Print Area

An Excel 2007 worksheet contains 1,048,576 rows by 16,384 columns. That would be a huge area to print. Excel never prints all cells in a worksheet; it prints a rectangular region that contains all of the cells that have contents. If you want to print a smaller region of a worksheet, you must first set the *print area*. To set the print area, perform the following steps:

1. Select the region that is to be printed.
2. Set the print area using Ribbon options: **Page Layout tab → Page Setup group → Print Area drop-down menu → Set Print Area option**. (Excel 2003: File → Print Area → Set Print Area.)

21.13.2 Previewing a Worksheet

It is advisable to use the *Print Preview* feature to preview a document before printing it. Many formatting problems can be resolved during the preview process. To preview the document as it will be printed, do the following:

1. Set the print area (if you want to print only a portion of your work.)
2. Activate print preview: **Office button → Print submenu → Print Preview**. (Excel 2003: File → Print Preview.)

The Print Preview screen will be displayed, along with the Print Preview Ribbon tab, as shown in Figure 21.50.

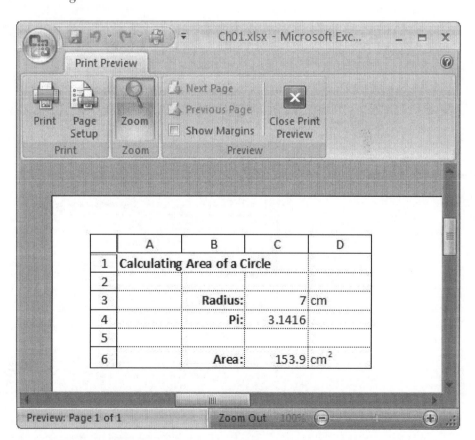

Figure 21.50   The Print Preview screen and Ribbon tab.

There are four very useful commands available on the Print Preview Ribbon tab:

- **Print button**—sends what you are previewing to the printer.
- **Page Setup button**—opens the Page Setup dialog box which allows you to adjust the way your document prints.
- **Show Margins button**—displays margin lines on the preview screen. You can move the margin lines with the mouse to adjust the margins.
- **Close Print Preview button**—gets you back to the Excel worksheet.

To really control the way your worksheet prints, you will want to use the Page Setup dialog box, shown in Figure 21.51. Two of the most useful controls are on the Page panel, shown in this figure.

- Select **Orientation**: Portrait or Landscape.
- **Fit to** 1 page wide by 1 tall.

The Fit to option takes everything that is going to be printed and scales it to fit on the number of pages you indicate. The most common use is to force a worksheet to print on one page.

The **Margins panel** on the Page Setup dialog box provides another way to adjust margins. The **Header/Footer panel** allows you to print a header or footer on each page of the printout. Options include page numbers, author name, file name, or custom text.

Figure 21.51   The Page Setup dialog box, Page panel.

The **Sheet panel** can be used to include

- **Gridlines** (to show the cells)
- **Row and column headings**

on the printout.

21.13.3 Printing a Worksheet

You can print a worksheet in several ways. To print a worksheet, choose one of the following methods:

- Use **Office button → Print sub-menu → Print**. (Excel 2003: File → Print.)
- Click the **Print** button on the Ribbon's Print Preview tab.
- Press **Ctrl + P**.

Whichever method you use, the Print dialog box will open as shown in Figure 21.52. The Print dialog box allows you to select a printer, activate or deactivate collating, indicate the number of copies to print, and select a range of pages. The **Properties** button provides access to a set of options that depends on the type of printer you have connected to your computer or network.

Once you have set the desired printing characteristics, click the **OK** button to send your worksheet to your printer.

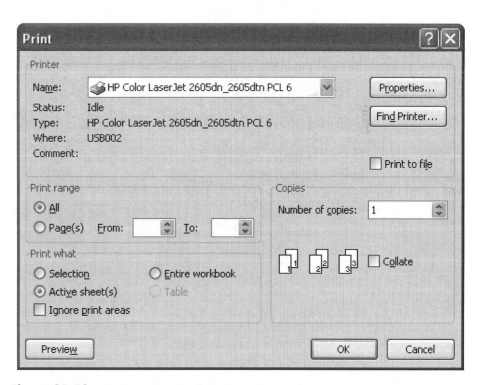

Figure 21.52 The Print dialog box.

KEY TERMS

active cell
AutoCorrect
AutoRecover
backup
cell
cell range
cell reference (e.g., B2)
clipboard (Windows clip-
  board)
close button
column heading
control buttons
copy
cut
dialog box
Excel
file extensions (.xls, .xlsx,
  .xlsm)
formula (equation)

Formula bar
gridlines
group (Ribbon group)
Help System
Home tab
Insert Function button
macro
macro virus
Maximize/Restore button
Minimize button
Name box
Office button
paste
print
print area
print preview
Quick Access Toolbar
range (cell range)
Redo button

Ribbon
Ribbon tabs
row heading
Screen Tip
search
Sheet tab
shortcut keys
spell check
spreadsheet
Status bar
template
Title bar
Undo button
work area
workbook
workbook window
worksheet

Summary

Excel Screen Layout

- Title Bar
- Ribbon
- Quick Access Toolbar
- Office Button
- Formula Bar
- Work Area
- Sheet Tabs
- Status Bar

Office Button

- Open workbooks
- Save workbooks
- Print workbooks
- Set Excel Options

Control Buttons

- Minimize Button
- Maximize/Restore Window Toggle
- Close button

Ribbon

Tab → Group → Drop-down Menu → Button

- **Home tab**—commonly used commands for formatting and sorting.
- **Insert tab**—used to insert objects such as charts and hyperlinks.
- **Page Layout tab**—used to modify entire sheets (apply themes, set print area, etc.).
- **Formulas tab**—used to insert functions and manage defined names of cells and cell ranges.
- **Data tab**—provides access to sorting and filtering features, and data analysis tools (if activated).
- **Review tab**—used to add comments and track changes to a worksheet.
- **View tab**—used to change the display magnification (zoom), and to show or hide features such as the Formula bar and gridlines.

Help System (F1)

- Browsing the Help Topic List
- Searching the Help system

Working with Excel Workbooks

- Create a New Workbook: **Office → New → Blank Workbook → Create**
- Open an Existing Workbook: **Office → Open → (browse to find file) → Open**
- Saving a Workbook:
- First time: **Office → Save As → (browse for folder, assign file name) → Save**
- If already named: **Office → Save** (Or, click **Save** button on Quick Access Toolbar.)

Adding a Worksheet to a Workbook

- Click the **Insert Worksheet** button that is the rightmost Sheet tab.

Excel File Extensions

- .xls—version 2003 or earlier
- .xlsx—the default file name extension in Excel 2007, macros disabled
- .xlsm—Excel 2007 macro-enabled workbook

Moving around worksheet using the keyboard

Key Combination	Action
←	Move one cell to the left
→	Move one cell to the right
↑	Move up one cell
↓	Move down one cell
Ctrl + →	Move to the far right of the worksheet
Ctrl + ↓	Move to the bottom of the worksheet
Page Down	Move down one screen
Page Up	Move up one screen
Ctrl + Page Down	Select next worksheet
Ctrl + Page Up	Select previous worksheet
Home	Move to far-left column of worksheet
Ctrl + Home	Move to top-left cell of worksheet (A1)
End, →	Move to right end of contiguously filled cell range
End, ↑	Move to top of contiguously filled cell range
End, ←	Move to left end of contiguously filled cell range
End, ↓	Move to bottom of contiguously filled cell range

Cut or Copy

1. Select a region.
2. Click the **Cut** or **Copy** button in the Clipboard group in the Ribbon's Home tab.

Paste

1. When there is material on the Clipboard, select a destination cell or region.
2. Click the **Paste** button in the Clipboard group in the Ribbon's Home tab.

Shortcut Keys

Command	Shortcut
New Workbook	Ctrl + N
Open Workbook	Ctrl + O
Save Workbook	Ctrl + S
Print	Ctrl + P
Undo	Ctrl + Z
Cut	Ctrl + X
Copy	Ctrl + C
Paste	Ctrl + P
Find	Ctrl + F
Replace	Ctrl + H
Go To	Ctrl + G
Format Cells	Ctrl + I
Help	F1
Spell Check	F7

Printing

Set Print Area

1. Select the region that is to be printed.
2. Set the print area using Ribbon options: **Page Layout tab** → **Page Setup group** → **Print Area drop-down menu** → **Set Print Area option**.

Print Preview

- Office button → Print submenu → Print Preview.

Print Alternatives

- Use **Office button** → **Print submenu** → **Print**. (Excel 2003: File → Print.)
- Click the **Print** button on the Ribbon's Print Preview tab.
- Press **Ctrl + P**.

Problems

1. Test your understanding by filling in the blanks.

   - The _____ _____ displays the name of the currently open workbook.
   - The Home, Insert, and Page Layout tabs are found on the _____.
   - Clicking on the Save button on the Quick Access Toolbar has the same effect as choosing _____ from the Office menu.

2. What is the maximum number of rows and columns for a single Excel worksheet?

3. Use the Insert Function dialog box to identify the Excel function names for the following mathematical functions:

   _____ sine

   _____ arithmetic mean

   _____ natural logarithm

   _____ convert degrees to radians

   _____ remove or truncate the decimal part of a number

   _____ return e raised to the power of a number

4. Name two ways to undo a mistake.

5. Identify the shortcut keys for the following actions:

   _____ Help

   _____ Copy selected region

   _____ Cut select region

   _____ Move to the beginning of a worksheet

6.   Visit the U.S. National Institute of Standards and Technology (NIST) Physics Laboratory's website about the International System of Units (SI) at http://physics.nist.gov/cuu/units.

Click on the menu item labeled SI units, and locate the table for SI Base Units. Use that table to fill in the missing entries in Table 21.3.

TABLE 21.3 SI base units

Quantity	Name	Symbol
length		m
	kilogram	kg
time	second	
electric current	ampere	
temperature		K
	mole	mol
luminous intensity		cd

7.   The electronic spreadsheet has played an important role in the history of computing. The links presented here discuss the history of electronic spreadsheets. Access these websites with your web browser and then answer the questions that follow:

Power, D.J., A Brief History of Spreadsheets, at http://www.dssresources.com /history/sshistory.html.

Mattessich, Richard. Spreadsheet: Its First Comuterization (1961–1964) at http://www.j-walk.com/ss/history/spreadsh.htm.

- What is the name of the first marketed electronic spreadsheet that was partly responsible for the early success of the Apple computer?
- In what year was Excel originally introduced (for Macintosh computers)?

8.   Excel's trigonometric function *PI* returns an approximation of the mathematical constant π. Read the information about *PI* on the Insert Function dialog box to determine the number of digits of accuracy of the constant returned by this function.

9.   Describe the difference between three of Excel's logarithm functions: LN, LOG, and LOG10. Use the Help system to find the answer to this question.

10.   Explain the difference between Cut-and-Paste and Copy-and-Paste. Which would you use if you needed to

- move a column of values to a new location within a worksheet?
- create a table in a Word document from a table of values in an Excel worksheet (leaving the Excel worksheet unchanged)?

11.   Access Microsoft's website (www.microsoft.com) to find a calendar template for Excel. (Enter *Excel calendar template* in the search box on the Microsoft web page.) How many Excel calendar templates are available for downloading?

12.   Perform a Google® search on the phrase *Excel Tips*. On a scale from 0 (no information) to 10 (massive amounts of information), how much information is available about Excel online?

Chapter 22
Entering and Formatting Data

22.1 INTRODUCTION TO ENTERING AND FORMATTING DATA

Worksheet cells can be filled with numeric values, text, times, dates, logical values, and formulas. In addition, a cell may contain an error value if Excel cannot evaluate its contents. The most common type of data entered into a spreadsheet is numeric data.

You can control the appearance of entered data by modifying the *formatting* applied to the cell containing the data. Formatting of numeric data, for example, allows you to specify the number of displayed decimal places and whether or not to show the value by using scientific notation. Formatting also allows you to set the background and font colors, and to specify the type of border for any cell. Collections of formatting options are called *styles* and Excel 2007 comes with many predefined styles.

Any time you enter data into a cell, Excel automatically assigns a default format (usually *General format*) and a default style, called the *Normal style*. In most situations the default formatting is adequate, so you will not need to make formatting changes in your worksheets very often. However, in this chapter the various formatting options will be presented so that you can control the formatting of your worksheet contents when necessary.

OBJECTIVES

After reading this chapter, you should be able to perform the following tasks:

- Enter numeric, text, and time and date data into a worksheet.
- Quickly enter series of data by using Excel's Fill Handle.
- Format cells, rows, and columns.
- Use passwords to protect your worksheets.
- Format tables.
- Perform sorts on tabulated data.
- Apply conditional formatting to a range of cells.

Here's a list of the most common types of formatting commands you may use to properly represent your data in Excel:

- **General format**—Excel will choose a format on the basis of the contents of the cell. It is the default format for cells containing numbers or text.
- **Currency format**—Excel will display the numeric data with a currency symbol.
- **Accounting format**—Excel will display the numeric data with a currency symbol aligned at the left side of the cell.
- **Date format**—Excel will display the data as a date.
- **Scientific format**—Excel will display the number in scientific notation.
- **Text format**—the contents of the cell will be treated as text.
- **Time format**—Excel will display the data as a time.

22.2   ENTERING DATA

A typical Excel worksheet has some cells that contain data that have been entered from a keyboard. Other cells contain formulas that use the entered data to calculate results, which are then displayed on the worksheet. The usual first step in building a worksheet is entering data.

22.2.1   Entering Numeric Data

Numbers can be typed into cells by using a keyboard, or imported from another source such as another Excel worksheet, a Word table, or a column of values from a website. Numeric values are stored internally with up to 15 digits of precision (including the decimal point).

How Excel determines that a cell contains a number

Each time you enter anything into a cell, Excel checks to see if the new entry appears to be a number, a date, a time, or a formula (an equation). If the new entry cannot be interpreted as any of these specific types, then Excel treats the new entry as text.

Excel will treat a new cell entry as a number if it contains only the following characters:

0 1 2 3 4 5 6 7 8 9
+ − ( ) , . /
$ %
E e

When Excel determines that a cell contains a simple number, it automatically applies the General format. If the $ is included, a Currency format is applied, and if the % symbol is included, a Percentage format is applied. In most cases the default formatting is adequate; however, you can change the applied format when necessary. A list of commonly used cell formats is available as a drop-down list on the Ribbon's Home tab [**Home tab → Number group**], as shown in Figure 22.1.

As you can see in Figure 22.1, Excel 2007 provides two formats for monetary values: Currency and Accounting, and quick access to two date formats, namely, Short Date and Long Date. Both of the monetary value formats include a currency symbol ($ in the US, € in most of Europe), but arrange the values slightly differently, as shown in Figure 22.2.

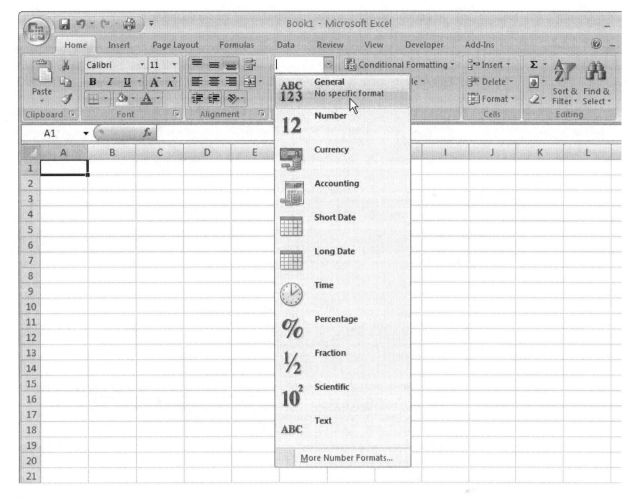

Figure 22.1   Selecting cell number formats from the Ribbon.

	A	B	C	D	E
1					
2		$10.45		**Currency Format**	
3		$100.57			
4		$10,000.63			
5					
6					
7		$ 10.45		**Accounting Format**	
8		$ 100.57			
9		$ 10,000.63			
10					

Figure 22.2   Comparing the Currency and Accounting formats.

Aligning the currency symbols by using the Accounting format makes columns of monetary values easier to read.

The Short Date and Long Date format options shown in Figure 22.1 both apply the Date format to the cells, but display dates with different amounts of information, as shown in Figure 22.3.

	A	B	C	D	E
1					
2		Thursday, February 16, 2012		**Long Date**	
3					
4		2/16/2012		**Short Date**	
5					

Figure 22.3 Comparing date formats.

For additional options, use the [**More Number Formats...**] button at the bottom of the drop-down list (shown in Figure 22.1) to open the Format Cells dialog (Figure 22.4). [Excel 2003: Use menu options **Format → Cells**.]

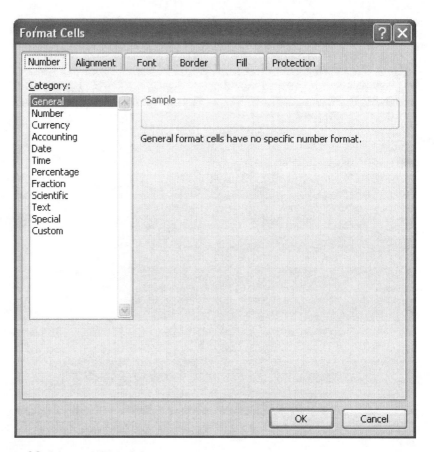

Figure 22.4 Format Cells dialog.

Alternatively, you can open the Format Cells dialog by right-clicking on a cell and choosing Format Cells from the Quick Edit menu, as shown in Figure 22.5.

When you change the format applied to a cell, the internal representation of the number stored in the cell is not changed; only the method for displaying the value is modified.

The General format is Excel's default format. When the General format is used, Excel will apply a format based on the contents of the cell. For example, if you type $3.4 into a cell, Excel will assume that you are entering a monetary value and will automatically convert to Currency format.

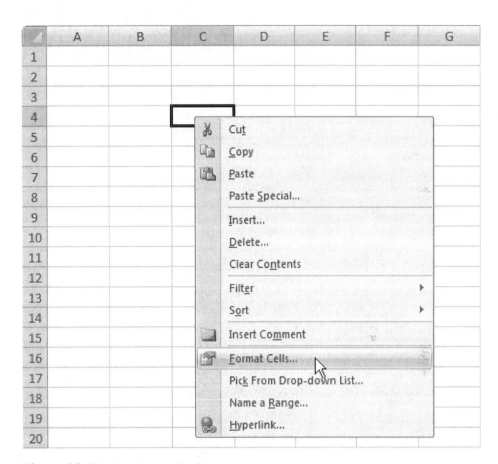

Figure 22.5   Using the Quick Edit menu.

Practice!

Open a blank worksheet, then follow these steps:

1. Enter the values shown in Figure 22.6 into separate cells. Be sure to include the commas, dollar sign, and percentage symbol as shown.

2. Use the format drop-down display (see Figure 22.6) on the Ribbon [**Home tab** → **Number group**] to determine the type of format that Excel automatically applied to each cell.

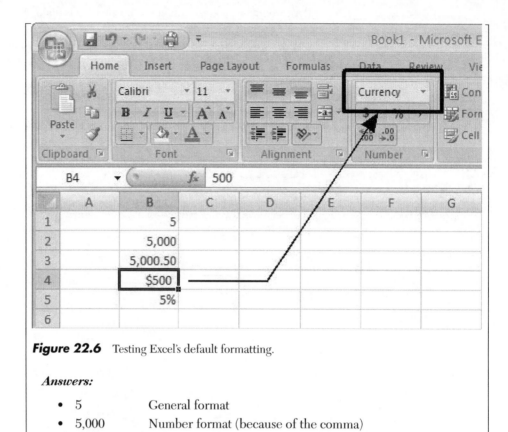

Figure 22.6 Testing Excel's default formatting.

Answers:

- 5   General format
- 5,000   Number format (because of the comma)
- 5,000.50   Number format, two displayed decimal places
- $500   Currency format
- 5%   Percentage format

Practice!

Practice formatting numeric values.

Open a blank worksheet, and then follow these steps:

1. Enter 12023.45 into cells B1 through B4 as shown in Figure 22.7. By default, the cells are formatted in General format. First, format the value in cell B2 using a Number format with no displayed decimal places.

	A	B	C	D
1		12023.45		
2		12023.45		
3		12023.45		
4		12023.45		
5				

Figure 22.7 Values before applying formatting options.

2. Right-click cell B2, and choose **Format Cells** ... from the Quick Edit menu. The Format Cells dialog box will appear (Figure 22.8). Choose the **Number** tab and select "Number" from the list labeled **Category**.

3. Set the scroll box titled **Decimal places** to 0, and check the box labeled **Use 1000 Separator**. Note that this action rounds off the *displayed* value to zero decimal places, but the value *stored* in the cell is not actually changed. If you were to change the number of decimal places to 2, the fractional part of the number would be displayed.

Next, format cell B3 in Currency format.

4. Right-click cell B3, and choose **Format Cells** from the Quick Edit menu. The Format Cells dialog box will appear. Choose the **Number** tab and select **Currency** from the list.

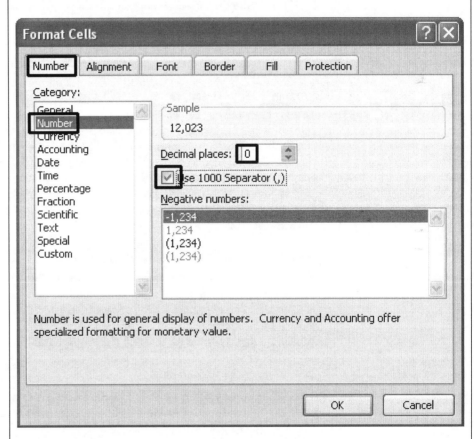

Figure 22.8 Setting the number of displayed decimal places.

5. Select 2 decimal places and select the $ symbol.

Next, format cell B4 in Scientific format. This will display the number in scientific notation, base 10. For example, the number 256 is equal to 2.56×10^2 which is represented in scientific format as $2.56E + 02$.

6. Right-click cell B4, and choose **Format Cells** ... from the Quick Edit menu. The Format Cells dialog box will appear. Choose the **Number** tab and select **Scientific** from the list.

7. Select 6 decimal places.

Your resulting worksheet should resemble Figure 22.9.

	A	B	C	D
1		12023.45		
2		12,023		
3		$12,023.45		
4		1.202345E+04		
5				

Figure 22.9   Values after various formats have been applied.

22.2.2 Entering Text Data

Text is commonly used for titles, headings, and labels. Such text data are entered into cells in the same ways that numeric values are entered. When Excel determines that a cell contains text data, it automatically applies the General format to the cell. (Notice that the General format is Excel's default for both numbers and text.) By default, cells containing text data are left-justified.

If you need to change the contents of a cell, simply double-click on the cell and you will be able to edit the text. Alternatively, select the cell and press the **F2** key to edit the text.

How Excel determines that a cell contains text

Excel determines that a cell contains text data by a process of elimination—a cell entry that is not a number, a date, a time, or a formula is treated as text. A cell that begins with A–Z, a–z, or a single quote ['] will always be treated as text. You can force a cell's contents to be treated as text by entering a single quote before the rest of the cell's contents. When the single quote is used, it will not be displayed but it will cause the cell's contents to be treated as text.

Here are some examples:

- Entering 5.0 in a cell will be interpreted by Excel as numeric data. The General format will be applied, and the value will be displayed right-justified with no displayed decimal places.

- If you include a single quote and enter '5.0 in a cell, Excel will interpret the entry as text data. The General format will be applied and the text value will be displayed left-justified as 5.0. (The single quote will not be displayed.)

Cells containing text data can also be formatted to change font size, color, and other features. Applying formatting to change the appearance of displayed information will be presented later.

Using the Text format

Another way to force a cell's contents to be treated as text data is to apply the *Text format* to the cell. To apply Text format to one or more cells, follow these steps:

1. Right-click on the cell (or selected cell range) to be formatted and choose **Format Cells...** from the Quick Edit menu. The Format Cells dialog box will appear.
2. Choose the **Number** tab on the Format Cells dialog box.
3. Select "Text" from the **Category** list.

NOTE: It is usually preferable to use the General format for text data.

EXAMPLE 22.1

EXAMPLE: HANDLING MISSING DATA

There are times when a complete data set is not available when you are developing your worksheet. By marking missing data as "not available" (or any other nonnumeric text) you can create worksheets that automatically update as the missing data is added.

In this example, exam scores for a group of students have been entered on a worksheet (Figure 22.10). One of the students, Andy, was absent when the exam was given and will take a makeup exam when he gets back. We want the worksheet to automatically recalculate the exam average after his score is added.

	A	B	C	D
1				
2		Name	Score	
3				
4		Ali	85	
5		Andy	not available	
6		Brittnay	82	
7		Eduard	80	
8		Erika	88	
9				
10		Average:	83.75	
11		Count:	4	
12				

Figure 22.10   Example of using text data to handle incomplete data sets.

This example uses an Excel built-in function called *AVERAGE* to calculate the average of the values in a group of cells. One of the features of this function is that it ignores nonnumeric data when calculating the average.

Andy's score is marked as "not available" when the scores are entered. Since "not available" is nonnumeric, his score will be ignored when Excel computes the average score.

The Count result illustrates that only four scores were included when calculating the average.

When Andy's score becomes available it is entered into cell C5, and the average exam score will be automatically recalculated, as shown in Figure 22.11.

	A	B	C	D
1				
2		**Name**	**Score**	
3				
4		Ali	85	
5		Andy	96	
6		Brittnay	82	
7		Eduard	80	
8		Erika	88	
9				
10		Average:	86.2	
11		Count:	5	
12				

Figure 22.11   The worksheet automatically updates when the missing data are added.

Notes:

- The worksheet will not update if the "not available" cells are formatted with the Text format. General format has been used on all cells in this example.
- There is nothing special about the term "not available." Any nonnumeric text can be used.

22.2.3 Entering Date and Time Data

Excel stores dates and times internally as numbers. This allows you to perform arithmetic on dates and times. For example, you can subtract one date from another to determine the number of days between two events.

How Excel determines that a cell contains a date or time

Excel attempts to interpret entered data containing dashes (−) or slashes (/) as dates and entered data containing a colon (:) as a time. Excel also tries to recognize standard abbreviations for months and days. For example, each of the "As entered" cell entries in Table 22.1 will be recognized as a date and/or a time by Excel.

TABLE 22.1   How excel interprets entered dates and times

As Entered . . .	Recognized as . . .	Converted to . . .	Displayed as . . .
December 25, 2005	Date	38711.00000	25-Dec-05
12/25/05	Date	38711.00000	25-Dec-05
Mar 3, 2007	Date	39144.00000	3-Mar-07
8:15	Time (a.m.)	0.34375	8:15
8:15 pm	Time	0.84375	20:15
8:15 am, Mar 3, 2007	Date and Time	39144.34375	3/3/2007 8:15

Automatic conversion to date–time values

When Excel determines that an entered value is a date or a time, it automatically converts the entry to a number, called a *date–time value*, and applies a *Date format* (if you enter a numeric date, such as 12/25/05) or a *Custom format* (if Excel interprets the date from text) to display the date and/or time. In a date–time value, the decimal places are used to indicate time as a fraction of 24 hours. For example, noon has a time value of 0.5, since it is halfway through the 24-hour day.

The digits to the left of the decimal point are used to indicate the number of days since the starting date that was used to compute date–time values. On PCs, the default start date is January 1, 1900. On Macintosh computers, the default start date is January 1, 1904. You can determine which data system is in use on your computer by entering a value of 1 in a cell and then changing the cell's format to Date format. The default start date will be shown in the cell as shown in Figure 22.12 (lower panel).

	A	B	C	D	E
1					
2		1		<< General Format	
3					

	A	B	C	D	E
1					
2		1/1/1900		<< Date Format	
3					

Figure 22.12 Checking the start date.

Excel allows you to choose either start date from the Options menu. Use the **Microsoft Office button**, then click the **Excel Options button** and select the **Advanced group**. Select or clear the **Use 1904 Date System** box in the **When Calculating this Workbook** section. [Excel 2003: Use **Tools → Options**, and then select the **Calculation tab**. Check or uncheck the box labeled **1904 date system**.]

The automatic conversion of dates and times to date–time values is one of the few instances in which Excel actually changes the contents of a cell, not just the way the contents are displayed. This can be frustrating if Excel interprets the value you are entering into a cell as a date or time and automatically changes the value you entered. This would only happen if you were entering a fraction, such as 4/5. The presence of the slash would cause Excel to interpret the entry as a date (April 5), convert the value to a date–time value, and display April 5 of the current year. To enter a fraction, first set the cell's format to the *Fraction format*, then enter the value.

Date and Time display formats

When Excel detects that a date or time has been entered into a cell, it displays the date—time value that is stored in the cell, using the format specified by the **Regional and Language Options** (**Control Panel → Regional and Language Options**) in Microsoft Windows, not Excel. This is implemented in Excel by using a Custom format for each date and time.

If you want to apply a format to a cell containing a date or time, you will probably use the Date format or Time format rather than creating a custom format. A Date format can be applied to a cell or range of cells, as follows:

1. Select the cell or range of cells to be formatted.
2. Right-click the selected cell(s) and select **Format Cells...** from the Quick Edit menu. The Format Cells dialog box will appear.
3. Choose the **Number** tab.

4.   Select **Date** from the Category list.

5.   Choose the display format you would like Excel to use from the **Type** list.

To apply a Time format to a range of cells, follow these steps:

1.   Select the cell or range of cells to be formatted.

2.   Right-click the selected cell(s) and select **Format Cells ...** from the Quick Edit menu. The Format Cells dialog box will appear.

3.   Choose the **Number** tab.

4.   Select **Time** from the Category list.

5.   Choose the display format you would like Excel to use from the **Type** list.

Practice!

Practice entering dates and times in ways that Excel can recognize.

Enter a date in several standard ways to see how many Excel can recognize and convert to date–time values. For example, try December 25, 2005 in the following ways:

- 12/25/2005
- 12/25/05
- 12-25-2005
- Dec-25-05
- December 25, 2005
- 25 December 2005

The results are shown in Figure 22.13.

	A	B	C	D	E	F
1						
2		As Entered	As Displayed		Comment	
3		12/25/2005	12/25/2005		Recognized as a date, displayed with a Date format	
4		12/25/05	12/25/2005		"	
5		12-25-2005	12/25/2005		"	
6		Dec-25-05	Dec-25-05		Not recognized as a date	
7		December 25, 2005	25-Dec-05		Recognized as a date, displayed with a Custom format	
8		25 December 2005	25-Dec-05		"	
9						

Figure 22.13   Testing various ways of entering dates.

22.3   USING THE FILL HANDLE

Data entry can be tedious. The use of the *Fill Handle* allows you to quickly copy a cell into a row or column of cells. Fill Handles can also be used to create a series of numbers in a row or column.

The Fill Handle appears as a small black square in the bottom-right corner of a selected region. An example of a Fill Handle is shown in Figure 22.14.

22.3.1   Using the Fill Handle with the Left Mouse Button to Copy Cells

When the cursor is placed over a Fill Handle, its shape will change to a black cross. Click and hold the left mouse button while dragging the fill handle to the right four or five cells. When the mouse button is released, the value in the original cell will be copied into the new cells, as shown in Figure 22.15.

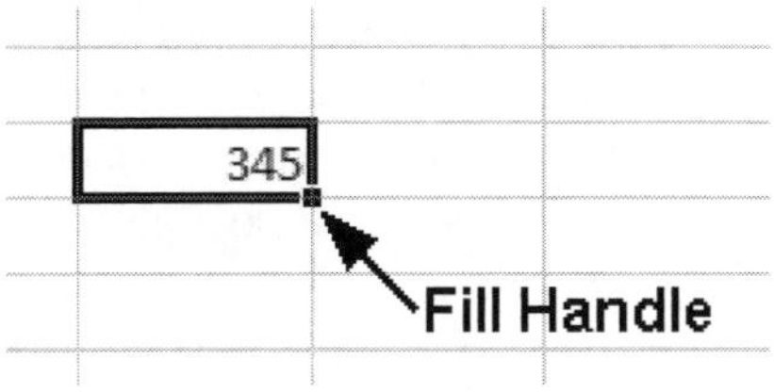

Figure 22.14 The Fill Handle is located at the bottom-right corner of a selected region.

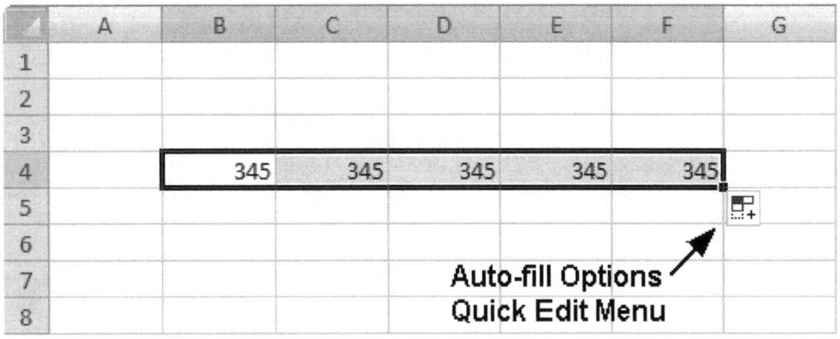

Figure 22.15 Copying cells using the Fill Handle.

22.3.2   Using the Fill Handle with the Left Mouse Button—More Copy Options

After you have copied the cells, a small button will appear near the Fill Handle; this is called the *Auto-Fill Options Quick Edit Menu* (Figure 22.15). If you click on the Quick Edit Menu button, some options for filling the new cells will be displayed. This is illustrated in Figure 22.16.

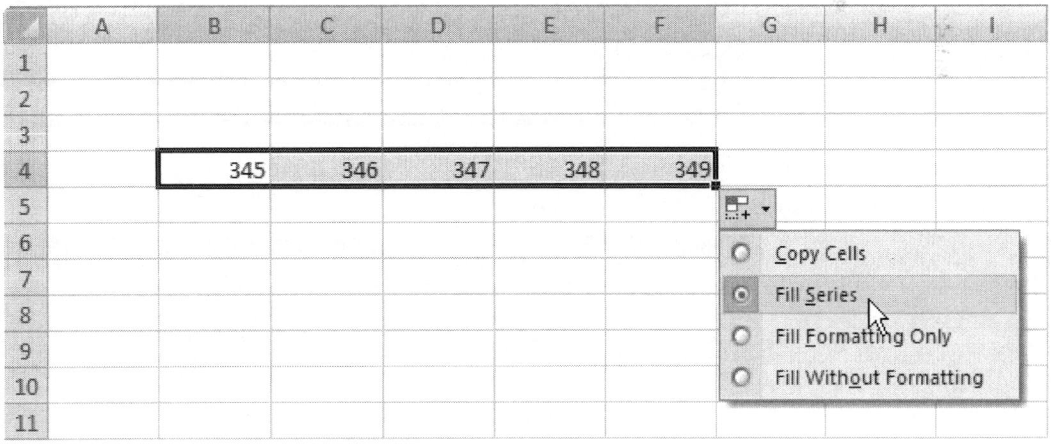

Figure 22.16 Using the Auto-Fill Options Menu to create a series of values.

Using the Auto-Fill Options Menu, you can select from the following items:

- Copy Cells—simply copies the value (and formatting) of the original cell into the new cells.
- Fill Series—increments the value in the original cell to create a series in the new cells.

- Fill Formatting Only—copies only the format of the original cell to the new cells; the values of the new cells are left unchanged.
- Fill Without Formatting—copies the value of the original cell into the new cells, but does not change the formatting of the new cells.

22.3.3 Creating a Linear Series with a Nonunity Increment

As shown in Figure 22.16, it is easy to use the Fill Handle to create a series in which the values are incremented by one. However, there are many instances where you need to increment a series by a value other than one. To specify a series increment, simply enter the first two values of the series before selecting the cells to be copied. This is illustrated in Figure 22.17.

	A	B	C	D	E	F	G
1							
2							
3							
4		345	350				
5							
6							

Figure 22.17 Preparing to create a series in which values are incremented by 5

Once the first two values of the series are selected, drag the Fill Handle with the left mouse button to complete the series (Figure 22.18).

	A	B	C	D	E	F	G
1							
2							
3							
4		345	350	355	360	365	
5							
6							

Figure 22.18 Completing the series using the Fill Handle.

22.3.4 Using the Fill Handle with the Right Mouse Button for Additional Options

If you drag the Fill Handle with the right mouse button, a menu of fill options will automatically pop up when the mouse button is released. The first four menu options, shown in Figure 22.19, are the same as the ones available through the Auto-Fill Options Menu. However, the right mouse button provides additional fill options.

The new fill options include a Linear Trend option that creates a linear series of values (with an increment of 5) and a Growth Trend option that creates an exponential growth series (fit to the two original values). The last menu item opens the Series dialog box, as shown in Figure 22.20.

This dialog box provides another way for you to specify an increment or step value for a series, as well as allowing you to create both linear and exponential growth series.

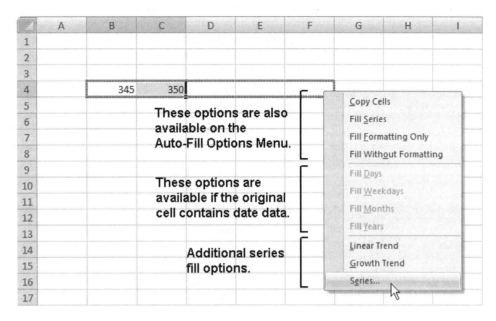

Figure 22.19   Fill options available with the right mouse button.

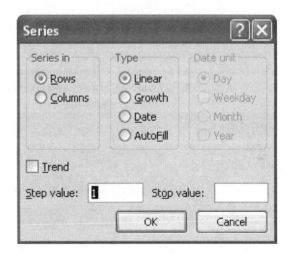

Figure 22.20   The Series dialog box.

Practice!

Practice using Fill Handles and creating Fill Series by performing the steps that follow. Note that sometimes you will be using the left mouse button and sometimes you will be using the right mouse button.

First, practice copying the contents of a cell:

1. Open a new worksheet.
2. Type the value 1.5 into cell A1. Grab the Fill Handle for cell A1 with the left mouse button and drag it over cells B1:G1.
3. When you release the mouse button, the value 1.5 will have been copied to cells B1:G1 as shown in Figure 22.21.

	A	B	C	D	E	F	G	H
1	1.5	1.5	1.5	1.5	1.5	1.5	1.5	
2								

Figure 22.21   The result after step 3.

Now try creating a linear series:

1. Type the values 1.5 and 1.7 into cells A3 and B3, respectively.
2. Select the region A3:B3 and grab the Fill Handle with the left mouse button.
3. Drag the fill handle over the cells C3:G3. When you release the mouse button, a linear series will have been created. (see Figure 22.22)

	A	B	C	D	E	F	G	H
3	1.5	1.7	1.9	2.1	2.3	2.5	2.7	
4								

Figure 22.22   The linear series created with the Fill Handle.

Note that Excel has created the linear Fill Series by using the difference between the first two cells (A3 and B3) as the increment. You can also control the increment value using the Series dialog, as illustrated with the following steps:

1. Type the value 1.5 into cell A5.
2. Grab the Fill Handle for cell A5 with the right mouse button and drag it over cells B5:G5.
3. When you release the mouse button, the Fill Series drop-down menu will appear.
4. Select "Series" from the drop-down menu. The Series dialog box will appear.
5. Check "Rows" in the box labeled **Series in**.
6. Check "Linear" in the box labeled **Type**.
7. Type "0.4" in the box labeled **Step value**.
8. Click **OK**.

The cells will be filled with a linear series in increments of 0.4, as shown in Figure 22.23.

	A	B	C	D	E	F	G	H
5	1.5	1.9	2.3	2.7	3.1	3.5	3.9	
6								

Figure 22.23   The linear series with an increment of 0.4 was created using the Series dialog box.

22.4   FORMATTING FOR APPEARANCE

Several formatting options are available to change the appearance of information in your worksheet. These include fonts, colors, borders, and text alignment. Careful application of these formatting options can help you create professional-looking worksheets, and help focus attention on the most important results.

Some appearance changes can be applied to selected cell ranges, while additional characteristics, such as column width or row height, apply only to selected columns or rows. Because of this, formatting for cells, columns and rows, and the entire worksheet will be presented separately.

22.4.1 Changing the Appearance of Cells

In previous sections, format options were selected from the Format Cells dialog box. This dialog box can also be used to change the appearance of cells; however, many of the most commonly used format changes are also available on the Ribbon's **Home tab** [Excel 2003: **Format bar**]. When possible, we will emphasize the use of the Ribbon.

The Ribbon can be customized, but typically the Home tab looks something like Figure 22.24. The amount of information displayed on the Ribbon changes as the size of the Excel window changes, so the Ribbon may look a little different on your computer.

Figure 22.24   The Excel Ribbon's Home Tab.

Home/Font group: Changing text attributes

Using the Ribbon, you can quickly change the appearance of your worksheet. Near the left side of the Home tab (Figure 22.24) is the *Font Group* (Figure 22.25) which contains drop-down lists you can use to select a font style and font size. The selected font style or size is applied to the cells that are selected when the font is changed.

Below the drop-down lists are three toggle buttons that allow you to apply and remove bold, italic, and underline attributes from the text in selected cells.

Figure 22.25   The Font Group on the Ribbon's Home tab.

NOTE: The term *toggle button* is used to indicate that you click the button once to activate the attribute, then click the same button again to deactivate it. For example, to show the displayed value in a cell in a bold font, first select the cell, then click the Bold toggle button on the Ribbon (Home tab, Font group). This activates the bold attribute for the cell. If you change your mind, simply select the cell and click the Bold button again to deactivate the bold attribute for the cell.

Home/Font group: Changing background and text colors

The Font Group on the Home tab also allows you to change cell background colors and text colors using the buttons indicated in Figure 22.26.

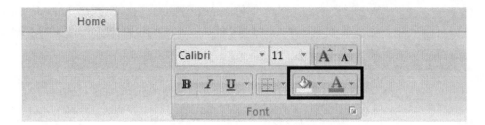

Figure 22.26   Cell fill color and text color buttons on the Font Group.

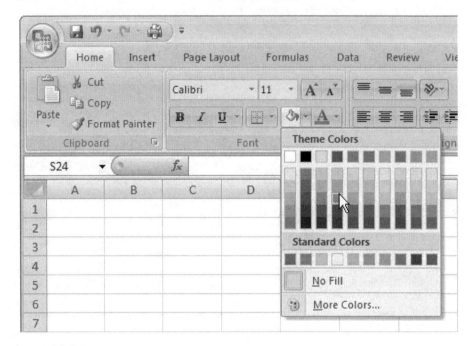

Figure 22.27   Selecting a new color from the color palette.

If you click either of the color selection buttons, the currently selected color (shown on the button) is applied to the selected cells. To use a different color, click the down-arrow on the right edge of the buttons. This causes a color palette to be displayed, as shown in Figure 22.27.

Home/Font group: Changing cell borders

The Format Toolbar also allows you to change cell borders using the button indicated in Figure 22.28.

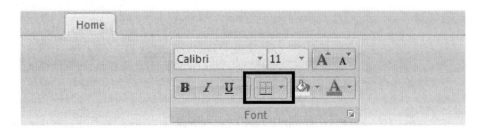

Figure 22.28   Changing cell borders.

Clicking the cell border button applies the border indicated on the button to the currently selected cell or cell range. To change the location or style of border, click the down-arrow on the border button to see a palette of border options, as shown in Figure 22.29.

NOTE: To get rid of an existing border, use the **No Border** option.

There are some limitations when using the Border Options Palette from the Format bar:

- The borders will always be drawn in the current border color (black, by default).
- There are border options such as "only interior borders" that are not available on the palette.

You have two options for greater control over cell borders. You can:

1. Activate **Draw Borders** from the Border Options Palette.
2. Click the **More Borders**. . . button on the Border Options Palette to open the Format Cells dialog, Border panel, shown in Figure 22.30.

Both of these options give you control over color, style, and placement of borders on selected cells and selected cell ranges.

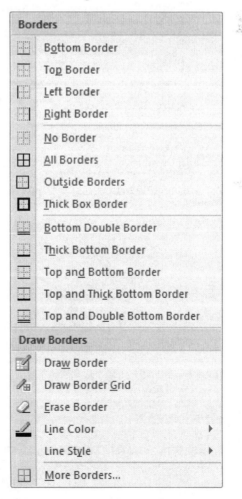

Figure 22.29   Border options palette.

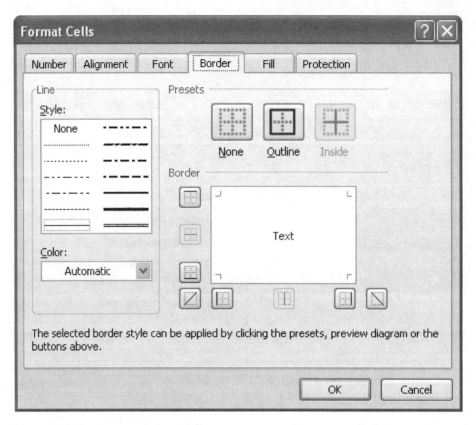

Figure 22.30   Changing the border characteristics using the Format Cells dialog, Border panel.

Home/Alignment group

The toggle buttons in the **Alignment group** (see Figure 22.31) allow you to specify how the cell contents are displayed within the cells.

You can set both vertical and horizontal alignments.

Vertical Alignment:

- Top Align
- Middle Align
- Bottom Align (default)

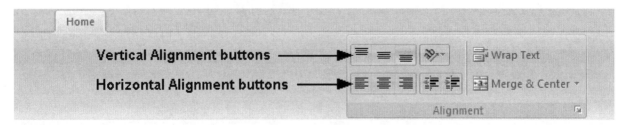

Figure 22.31   The Alignment group on the Ribbon's Home tab.

Horizontal Alignment:

- Left Justify (default for text)
- Center Justify
- Right Justify (default for numbers)

The effect of various alignments is illustrated in Figure 22.32.

The Alignment group on the Ribbon's Home tab also provides easy ways to wrap text within cells and center a heading in a number of merged cells (Figure 22.33).

	A	B	C	D	E	F
1						
2			Left Align	Center Align	Right Align	
3		Top Align	text	text	text	
4		Middle Align	text	text	text	
5		Bottom Align	text	text	text	
6						

Figure 22.32   Alignment options.

Figure 22.33   Buttons used to wrap text in cells and center a heading in multiple cells.

Both of these options are commonly used with table headings. For example, Figure 22.34 shows a loan table that can be used to determine how much you owe after each car payment, but the column headings in row 9 are pretty much unreadable because they are too long for the cells.

The improved table, shown in Figure 22.35, is easier to read because the heading text in row 9 has been wrapped, and the "Amounts in Dollars" label has been merged and centered over the values in columns B through E.

Home/Number group

The Number group on the Ribbon's Home tab provides access to number formats (General, Numeric, Currency, etc.) as well as some useful toggle buttons, as shown in Figure 22.36.

- The **currency toggle button** allows you to display a value with a dollar sign (or other currency symbol) and two decimal places.

	A	B	C	D	E	F	G
1	Car Loan Table						
2							
3	Amount Borrowed:	$ 15,000.00					
4	APR:	8%					
5	Term:	2	years				
6	Monthly Payment:	$678.41					
7							
8	Amounts in Dollars						
9	Payment	ore Payment	Paid on Inter	Paid on Princ	Loan Amount After Payment		
10	1	15000.00	100.00	578.41	14421.59		
11	2	14421.59	96.14	582.27	13839.33		
12	3	13839.33	92.26	586.15	13253.18		
13	4	13253.18	88.35	590.05	12663.12		
14	5	12663.12	84.42	593.99	12069.13		
30	21	2669.01	17.79	660.62	2008.39		
31	22	2008.39	13.39	665.02	1343.37		
32	23	1343.37	8.96	669.45	673.92		
33	24	673.92	4.49	673.92	0.00		
34							

Figure 22.34   Loan table before improving the headings.

	A	B	C	D	E	F
1	Car Loan Table					
2						
3	Amount Borrowed:	$ 15,000.00				
4	APR:	8%				
5	Term:	2	years			
6	Monthly Payment:	$678.41				
7						
8		Amounts in Dollars				
9	Payment Number	Loan Amount Before Payment	Paid on Interest	Paid on Principal	Loan Amount After Payment	
10	1	15000.00	100.00	578.41	14421.59	
11	2	14421.59	96.14	582.27	13839.33	
12	3	13839.33	92.26	586.15	13253.18	
13	4	13253.18	88.35	590.05	12663.12	
14	5	12663.12	84.42	593.99	12069.13	
30	21	2669.01	17.79	660.62	2008.39	
31	22	2008.39	13.39	665.02	1343.37	
32	23	1343.37	8.96	669.45	673.92	
33	24	673.92	4.49	673.92	0.00	
34						

Figure 22.35   Improved loan table with readable headings.

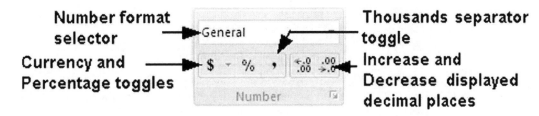

Figure 22.36   The Number group on the Ribbon's Home tab.

- The **percentage toggle** displays a value as a percentage by moving the decimal point two places to the right and showing the percent symbol. For example, the value 0.75 would be displayed as 75% if the percentage format has been toggled on.
- Clicking the **thousands separator button** causes the value to be displayed in Accounting format with thousands separators (commas) and two decimal places. For example, the value 12023.4 would be displayed as 12,023.40 if the thousands separator format has been toggled on.
- The toggle buttons to **increase** and **decrease** the number of displayed decimal places are self-explanatory.

The two buttons that increase and decrease the number of displayed decimal places can be very useful when you want all of the values in a list to show the same number of decimal places:

1. Select the entire set of values.
2. Increase or decrease the number of displayed decimal places on the first item in the list to display the desired number of decimal places.

All of the selected values will end up showing the same number of decimal places.

For example, when you create a column of values that are uniformly increasing by 0.2, the whole numbers will, by default, show one less decimal place. This is illustrated in Figure 22.37.

	A	B	C	D	E
1					
2					
3		1	← The currently active		
4		1.2	cell is a different color		
5		1.4	than the rest of the		
6		1.6	cells in the selection.		
7		1.8			
8		2			
9		2.2			
10		2.4			
11					

Figure 22.37   The selected list.

To make the entire list show two decimal places, do the following:

1.   Select the entire list, cells B3:B10.
2.   Click on the **Increase Decimal** button twice.

The number of displayed decimal places of the currently active cell (cell B3 in Figure 22.38) will be increased by two (because the button was clicked twice), and the entire list will be displayed with two decimal places.

	A	B	C	D	E
1					
2					
3		1.00			
4		1.20			
5		1.40			
6		1.60			
7		1.80			
8		2.00			
9		2.20			
10		2.40			
11					

Figure 22.38   The result - all values displayed with two decimal places.

EXAMPLE 22.2

EXAMPLE: FORMATTING A WORKSHEET

In the following example (Figure 22.39), the area of a triangle is being calculated from entered values for the length of the base, b, and the height, h, according to the following formula:

$$\text{Area} = \frac{1}{2}bh$$

	A	B	C	D	E	F	G
1	Area of a Triangle						
2							
3		b:	1	cm			
4		h:	3	cm			
5							
6		Area:	1.5	cm2			
7							

Figure 22.39   Formatting example.

To improve the appearance and readability of the worksheet, we will make the following formatting changes:

1. Make the title in cell A1 stand out by increasing the font size and adding the bold attribute.
2. Move the labels in column B closer to the values by right-justifying the labels.
3. Place a border around the calculated result in cell C6.
4. Superscript the 2 in cell D6.

First, format the title in cell A1:

1. Select cell A1.
2. Select 12-point font from the font size drop-down list in the Font Group on the Ribbon's Home tab (Figure 22.40).
3. Click the Bold button.

Right-justify the labels in column B:

1. Select the labels in cells B3:B6 as shown in Figure 22.41.
2. Click the Align Right button, to right-justify the labels.

Put a border around cells C6 and D6 to highlight the result:

1. Select the cell containing the calculated result, cell C6, and the cell containing the units, D6, as shown in Figure 22.42.
2. Click the drop-down arrow on the right side of the border button in the Font group.
3. Select a full outside border from the border options menu as shown in Figure 22.42.

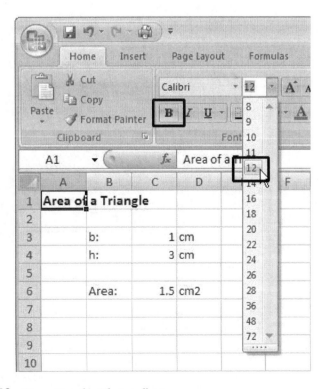

Figure 22.40   Formatting the title in cell A1.

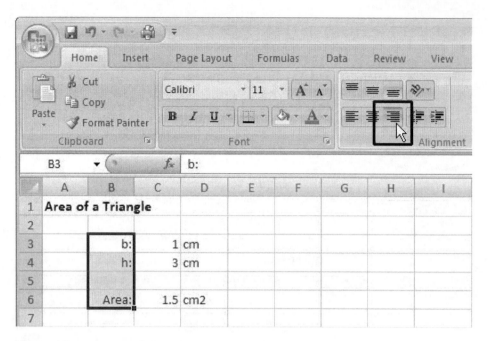

Figure 22.41   Right aligning the labels in column B.

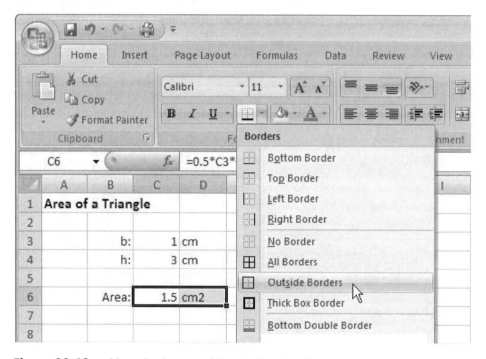

Figure 22.42   Adding a border around the calculated result.

The result of these format changes is shown in Figure 22.43.

The last desired format change, superscripting the 2 in cell D6, cannot be performed using buttons on the Ribbon. Instead, the change must be made from the Format Cells dialog box. You can open the Format Cells dialog box using the expansion button (indicated in Figure 22.44) on the Font group.

	A	B	C	D	E	F	G
1	Area of a Triangle						
2							
3		b:	1	cm			
4		h:	3	cm			
5							
6		Area:	1.5	cm2			
7							

Figure 22.43   The result of the formatting changes.

Figure 22.44   Accessing the Format Cells dialog box from the Font group.

Superscript the 2 in cm^2 in cell D6:

1. Double click on cell D6 and select just the 2 in cm2.
2. Click on the expansion button on the Font group to open the Format Cells dialog, shown in Figure 22.45.
3. Check the Superscript box in the **Effects** list, as illustrated in Figure 22.45.

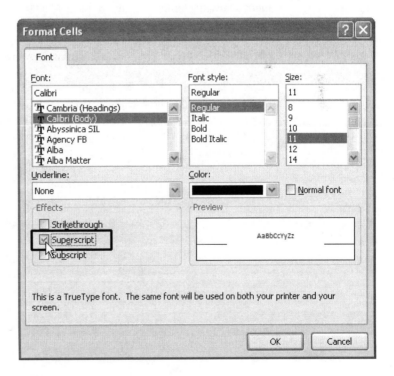

Figure 22.45   The Format Cells dialog box.

The final result is shown in Figure 22.46.

	A	B	C	D	E	F	G
1	Area of a Triangle						
2							
3		b:	1	cm			
4		h:	3	cm			
5							
6		Area:	1.5	cm^2			
7							

Figure 22.46　The final result.

While the formatting changes applied to this worksheet are purely superficial, they do make the worksheet easier to read and more professional in appearance, and they make the intent and result of the calculation more readily apparent.

APPLICATION

APPLICATION—ENGINEERING ECONOMICS

Engineering economics involves the study of interest, cash flow patterns, depreciation, inflation, and techniques for maximizing net value. This is an important area of study for all engineers, since engineers frequently serve as managers or executive officers of corporations.

The next example demonstrates how John can make a choice between two investment alternatives. One option is to place $10,000 in a very secure investment that will give him 6 percent annual growth. The other option is to put the $10,000 in the stock market, using a fund that has historically shown 11 percent growth. John knows that there is no guarantee that the stock fund will continue to return a rate of 11 percent, and he could even lose money. How should he decide which is the best investment for his money?

Well, the decision will ultimately be up to John, and he will make it on the basis of the level of risk that he is willing to accept. Excel, however, can help him to forecast the growth differential for the two options, and he can use this information to help him decide if it is worth it to take a chance on the stock market. The results of his calculations are shown in Figure 22.47.

John's analysis shows that, if the stock market fund does return 11 percent annual growth, in 40 years he will end up with over six times as much money as if he put the $10,000 in the low-risk, 6 percent fund. Now he has a decision to make!

Accumulated Capital		
Age	6% Growth	11% Growth
18	$ 10,000	$ 10,000
28	$ 17,908	$ 28,394
38	$ 32,071	$ 80,623
48	$ 57,435	$ 228,923
58	$ 102,857	$ 650,009

Figure 22.47　The results of John's analysis.

How'd he do That?

The future value of an amount invested in an interest-bearing fund can be calculated with the following equation:

$$F = P[1 + i]^N$$

Here, F is the future value, P is the amount initially deposited, i is the annual interest rate, and N is the number of years that the funds remain invested.

John built this equation into his worksheet and had Excel calculate future values for two different interest rates and four different values of N.

How'd he Make his Table Look so Good?

Initially, John's calculated results looked like Figure 22.48, but he made some formatting changes to improve the appearance. For practice, try making these format changes yourself. Begin by typing in the data shown in Figure 22.48, and then complete the steps to make your table look like the table in Figure 22.47.

	A	B	C	D
1	Accumulated Capital			
2	Age	6% Growth	11% Growth	
3	18	10000	10000	
4	28	17908	28394	
5	38	32071	80623	
6	48	57435	228923	
7	58	102857	650009	
8				

Figure 22.48   John's calculated results before formatting.

Add Dollar Signs to the Values.

To add dollar signs to the values in columns B and C, do the following:

1. Select the currency values in cell range B3:C7.
2. Choose **Accounting format** from the Ribbon [**Home tab → Number group → Number format drop-down list**]. This will add the currency symbols (dollar signs) and display the values with two decimal places.
3. While cell range B3:C7 is still selected, click the **Decrease Decimal** button [**Home tab → Number group**] twice to remove the displayed decimal places.

At this point the worksheet looks like Figure 22.49.

Center the Title Over the Entire Table.

To center the title over the table, we will merge cells A1 through C1, and then center the new merged cell by following these steps:

1. Select the region A1:C1.
2. Choose the **Merge & Center button** on the Ribbon [**Home tab → Alignment group → Merge & Center button**].

	A	B	C	D
1	Accumulated Capital			
2	Age	6% Growth	11% Growth	
3	18	$ 10,000	$ 10,000	
4	28	$ 17,908	$ 28,394	
5	38	$ 32,071	$ 80,623	
6	48	$ 57,435	$ 228,923	
7	58	$ 102,857	$ 650,009	
8				

Figure 22.49 Results table after adding dollar signs.

Make the Column Headings Boldface.

To make column headings in rows 1 and 2 boldface, do the following:

1. Select the column headings in rows 1 and 2 (cell range A1:C2)
2. Choose the **Bold** button on the Ribbon [**Home tab → Font group → Bold button**] (or press [Ctrl-B]).

Adjust the Width of the Columns.

AutoFit the column widths to the cell contents:

1. Select columns A, B, and C.
2. Position the mouse over the right edge of one of the columns (the mouse pointer will change to a vertical line with double-headed arrows).
3. Double-click the mouse.

The result is shown in Figure 22.50. Notice that column A was adjusted to fit the heading "Age" and not "Accumulated Capital". Merged cells are ignored when auto-fitting the column widths to the cell contents.

	A	B	C	D
1		Accumulated Capital		
2	Age	6% Growth	11% Growth	
3	18	$ 10,000	$ 10,000	
4	28	$ 17,908	$ 28,394	
5	38	$ 32,071	$ 80,623	
6	48	$ 57,435	$ 228,923	
7	58	$ 102,857	$ 650,009	
8				

Figure 22.50 Results table after adjusting column widths.

Center the Values.

To center the values in the each column, follow these steps:

1. Select the cell range containing the column headings and the values: A2:C7.
2. Click on the Center Alignment button on the Ribbon [**Home tab → Alignment group → Center Alignment button**].

Add Borders Around Each Cell.

To add borders around each cell, follow these steps:

1. Select the entire data set, cell range A1:C7.
2. Use the drop-down menu on the Borders button [**Home tab → Font group → Borders drop-down menu**].
3. Choose "All Borders" from the **Borders** menu.

Change the Cell Fill Color and Text Colors of the Title.

Follow these steps to change the background (fill) and text colors of the title:

1. Select the title (the merged cells A1:C1).
2. Use the drop-down menu on the Fill Color button [**Home tab → Font group → Fill Color drop-down menu**].
3. Choose a dark color for the cell background from the color palette. (Grey was selected in this example.)
4. Use the drop-down menu on the Font Color button [**Home tab → Font group → Font Color drop-down menu**].
5. Choose a light color for the title text. (White was selected in this example.)

Your completed table should now look like Figure 22.51.

	A	B	C	D
1	Accumulated Capital			
2	Age	6% Growth	11% Growth	
3	18	$ 10,000	$ 10,000	
4	28	$ 17,908	$ 28,394	
5	38	$ 32,071	$ 80,623	
6	48	$ 57,435	$ 228,923	
7	58	$ 102,857	$ 650,009	
8				

Figure 22.51   The formatted table.

22.4.2 Changing the Appearance of Columns and Rows

The primary formatting option that applies to an entire column is the column width. Similarly, you can set the height of entire rows. These values can be set in several ways:

- You can type the desired column width or row height directly into a dialog box.
- You can drag the edge of the column and row headings with the mouse to change their sizes.

- You can ask Excel to AutoFit the column width or row height to the contents of the column or row.

Using a dialog box to set the row height

Change the height of an entire row of cells:

1. Select the row or rows that you want to modify.
2. Use Ribbon options **Home tab → Cells group → [Format] drop-down menu** (see Figure 22.52) and then click the **Row Height ...** button.

The Row Height dialog box (Figure 22.53) will open. Enter the desired new row height in the **Row height** field. (The default row height is 15.)

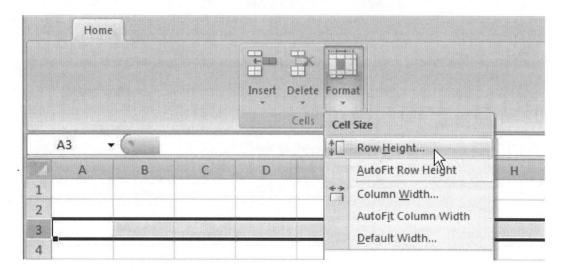

Figure 22.52   Accessing the Row Height dialog from the Cells group.

Figure 22.53   The Row Height dialog box.

Using the mouse to change column widths

Column widths are easy to change with the mouse:

1. Select the columns that you want to modify by clicking on the column headings. In Figure 22.54 columns B through D have been selected.
2. Position the mouse at the right edge of any selected column heading. The mouse cursor will change to a vertical bar with left and right arrows when positioned over the edge of the column (indicated in Figure 22.54).
3. To adjust the column widths, hold the left mouse button down and drag the vertical bar cursor to the desired column width (Figure 22.55). A Tool Tip will be displayed showing the actual column width.

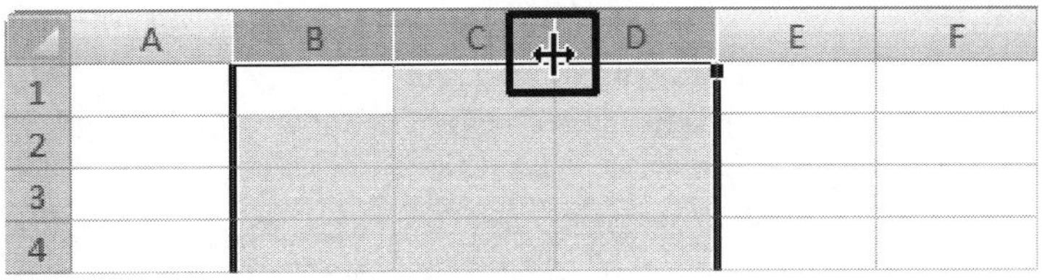

Figure 22.54   The mouse cursor is positioned over the edge of a column heading.

When you release the mouse button, the width of all selected columns will be changed (Figure 22.56).

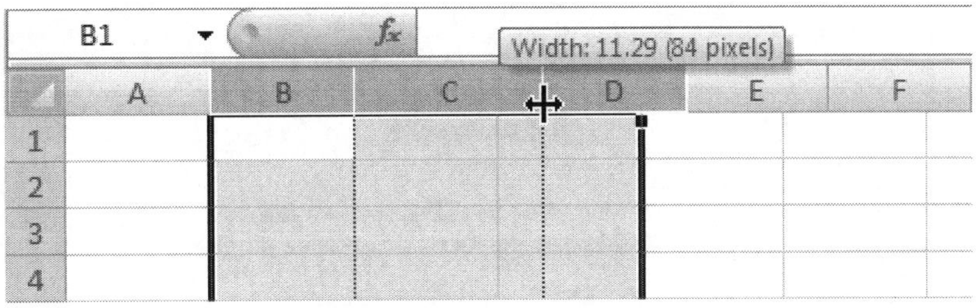

Figure 22.55   As the mouse cursor is dragged, only one column width is changed.

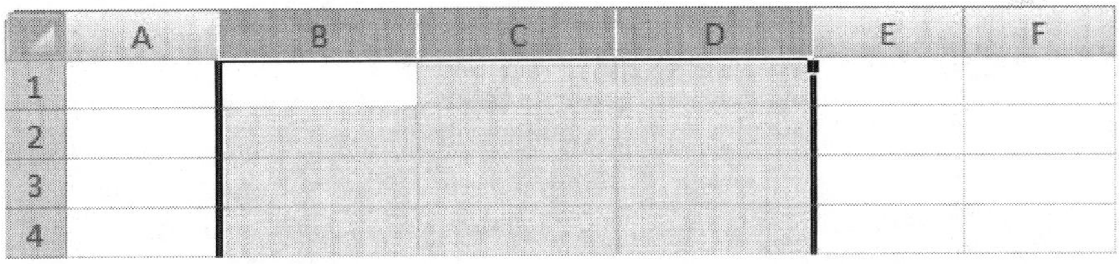

Figure 22.56   When you release the mouse button, all selected columns are widened.

Automatically fitting column widths to column contents

Excel will automatically adjust the width of selected columns (or the height of rows) to fit the contents of those columns (or rows). For example, in the worksheet shown in Figure 22.57, cell B2 contains a small number, and cell C2 contains a long text string.

Automatically adjust the width of columns to the columns' contents:

1. Select the column(s) to be adjusted.
2. Position the cursor over the right edge of any selected column's heading. The mouse cursor changes to a crossbar with left and right arrows (Figure 22.58) when it is positioned over the edge of the column heading.
3. Double-click the mouse's left button to adjust the column width to the column contents.

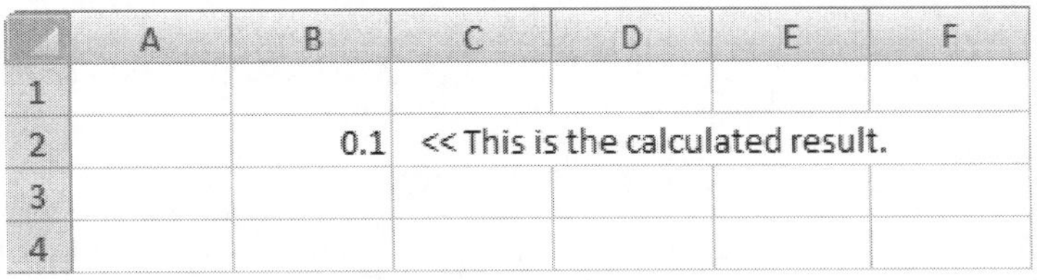

Figure 22.57   The column widths have not yet been adjusted.

The result is shown in Figure 22.59.

An alternative to step 3 is to select **AutoFit Column Width** from the Cell Size menu shown in Figure 22.52. [**Home tab** → **Cells group** → [**Format**] **drop-down menu**]

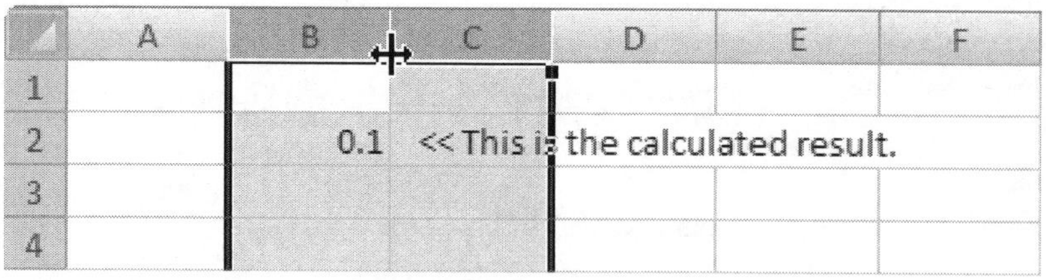

Figure 22.58   Preparing to change the column widths.

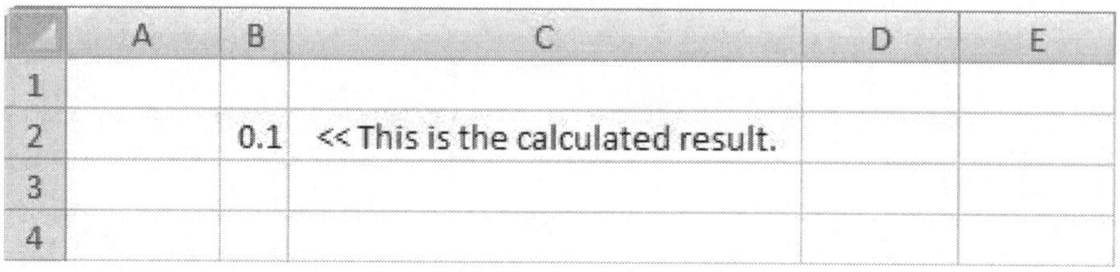

Figure 22.59   The column width has been adjusted to fit the column contents.

22.5   WORKING WITH WORKSHEETS

By default, an Excel workbook contains three worksheets named Sheet1, Sheet2, and Sheet3. Sometimes you will need more than three worksheets, and usually you should give the worksheets more descriptive names.

You can take the following common actions that apply to entire worksheets:

- Insert new worksheets into a workbook.
- Rename worksheets.
- Change the color of the worksheet tab.
- Hide a worksheet.
- Lock a worksheet.

22.5.1   Insert New Worksheets into a Workbook

Inserting a new worksheet into a workbook is a very common task, and there are several ways to do it:

1. Use the keyboard shortcut, [**Shift + F11**].
2. Click the [**Insert Worksheet**] button at the right end of the worksheet tabs (see Figure 22.60).
3. Use Ribbon options **Home tab** → **Cells group** → [**Insert**] **drop-down menu** and choose the **Insert Sheet** option.
4. Right-click on any worksheet tab and select **Insert ...**

22.5.2   Renaming a Worksheet

A workbook can easily grow into a collection of dozens of worksheets. It is helpful to distinguish among worksheets by giving them meaningful names. There are three ways to rename a worksheet:

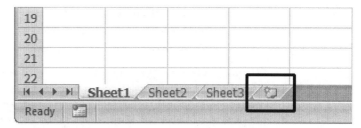

Figure 22.60 The [Insert Worksheet] button on the worksheet tab row.

1. Double-click on the worksheet tab.
2. Right-click on the worksheet tab and select **Rename** from the pop-up menu.
3. Use Ribbon options **Home tab → Cells group → [Format] drop-down menu** and choose the **Rename Sheet** option.

22.5.3 Changing the Color of the Worksheet Tab

You can also make specific worksheets easier to identify by changing the color of the worksheet's tab. There are two ways to change the color of a worksheet's tab:

1. Right-click on the worksheet tab and select **Tab Color** from the pop-up menu.
2. Use Ribbon options **Home tab → Cells group → [Format] drop-down menu** and choose the **Tab Color** option.

With either method, you can then select the new tab color from a color palette.

22.5.4 Hiding a Worksheet

It is also possible to hide a worksheet. When a worksheet is hidden, it is not visible but all of the cells are still updated and recalculated whenever a change is made in the visible parts of the workbook. The usual reasons for hiding worksheets are

- To get less-used calculations out of the way.
- To try to keep others from messing with your calculations.

There are two ways to hide a worksheet:

1. Right-click on the worksheet tab and select **Hide** from the pop-up menu.
2. Use Ribbon options **Home tab → Cells group → [Format] drop-down menu,** choose the **Hide & Unhide** menu, and select the **Hide Sheet** option.

Once you have a hidden worksheet, you may want to reveal or "unhide" it again. The same two approaches are used:

1. Right-click on *any* worksheet tab and select **Unhide** from the pop-up menu.
2. Use Ribbon options **Home tab → Cells group → [Format] drop-down menu,** choose the **Hide & Unhide** menu, and select the **Unhide Sheet** option.

A list of hidden worksheets will be displayed. Select the worksheet that you want to unhide.

22.5.5 Locking a Worksheet

A hidden worksheet is still available for editing; you just have to "unhide" it. If you really want to keep people from messing with your calculations, you need to lock and password protect the worksheet. The process is as follows:

1. Unlock all cells to which you want the user to have access after the worksheet is password protected.
2. Password protect the worksheet.

It may seem odd that you have to specify which cells should be unlocked, but by default, *all* cells in a worksheet are marked as "locked." The reason you can edit the cells in a worksheet is that locked cells are still available for editing until the worksheet is password protected. Before you password protect a worksheet, you need to think about how it will be used and which cells need to be available for editing. You must unlock all of the cells to which you want the user to have access after the worksheet is password protected.

As an example, let's return to the worksheet that calculates the area of a triangle (Figure 22.61).

	A	B	C	D	E	F
1	Area of a Triangle					
2						
3		b:	1	cm		
4		h:	3	cm		
5						
6		Area:	1.5	cm^2		
7						

Figure 22.61   Example worksheet: Calculating the area of a triangle.

The calculation is based on the values in cells C3 and C4, so those cells need to be unlocked before the worksheet is password protected. To unlock cells C3 and C4, follow these steps:

1. Select cells C3 and C4.
2. Use the Lock Cell toggle button from the Ribbon [**Home tab → Cells group → Format drop-down menu → Lock Cell toggle button**] to unlock the selected cells (Figure 22.62).

When you unlock cells C3 and C4, they will be available to a user after the worksheet is password protected.

There are two ways to password protect the worksheet:

1. Right-click on the worksheet tab and select **Protect Sheet...** from the pop-up menu.
2. Use Ribbon options [**Home tab → Cells group → Format drop-down menu → Protect Sheet ...**

Either way, the Protect Sheet dialog (Figure 22.63) will open. Be sure that the **Protect worksheet and contents of locked cells** checkbox is checked, and enter a password. Remember the password because you will need to know it if you ever need to remove the password protection.

There are a variety of options that you can choose when protecting a worksheet. By default, users can still select both locked and unlocked cells, but they cannot change the contents of locked cells.

When you click the [OK] button on the Protect Sheet dialog, you will be asked to confirm the password (Figure 22.64).

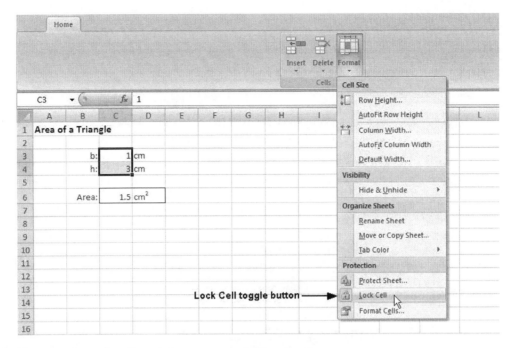

Figure 22.62   Using the Lock Cell toggle button to unlock selected cells.

Figure 22.63   The Protect Sheet dialog box.

Figure 22.64   Confirm Password dialog box.

Once you have password protected the worksheet, only those cells that were unlocked are available to the user.

22.6   FORMATTING A DATA SET AS AN EXCEL TABLE

A table is simply a collection of information arranged into a rectangular grid. Any range of cells in a worksheet can be used to hold a table. For example, temperature data from several monitoring stations can be collected in tabular form, as shown in Figure 22.65.

NOTE: This is not weather data; it gets hot in Miami, but not 72.6°C (163°F).

	A	B	C	D
1	Station	Temp. (°C)		
2	Newark	12.5		
3	Santa Fe	23.4		
4	Des Moines	53.2		
5	Miami	72.6		
6	Seattle	23.5		
7	Phoenix	34.6		
8				

Figure 22.65   Tabular data ready to be made into an Excel table.

22.6.1 Creating an Excel Table

Tables are even more powerful in Excel 2007. To turn data in cells into a table, you format the data as a table. This is done as follows:

1.   Select any cell in the data set (see Figure 22.66).

Note: If you do not have contiguous data (i.e., if there are empty cells in the data set), then you must select the entire data set (including headings).

2.   Use Ribbon options **Home tab → Styles group → Format as Table drop-down menu → Choose any style option**. (You can also create an Excel table from the Insert tab using these Ribbon options: **Insert tab → Tables group → Table button**. The table will be formatted using the Excel default table style, indicated in Figure 22.66.)

Excel will display the Create Table dialog box, as shown in Figure 22.67. The dialog box provides an opportunity to confirm the cell range for the data set (A1:B7 in this example) and indicate whether or not there are headings included with your data. In this example, we do have headings (Station, Temp. (°C)).

When you click the [OK] button on the Create Table dialog, Excel will convert the cell range to a table and apply formatting. The result is shown in Figure 22.68.

Notice that the headings in cells A1 and B1 are now drop-down menus—this is the power of Excel tables. From the menus behind the headings you can sort or filter the data.

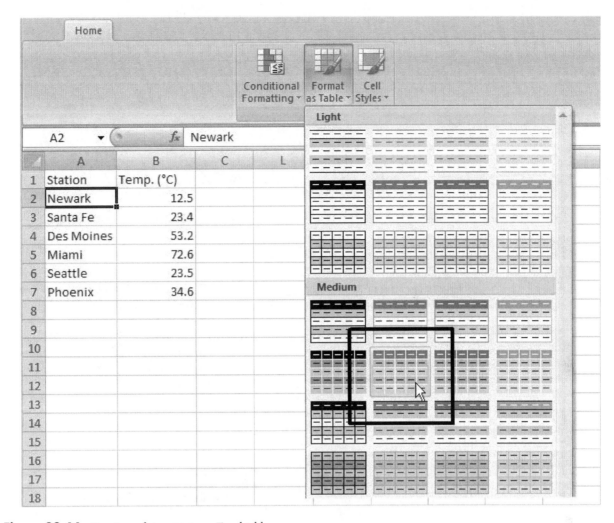

Figure 22.66 Turning a data set into an Excel table.

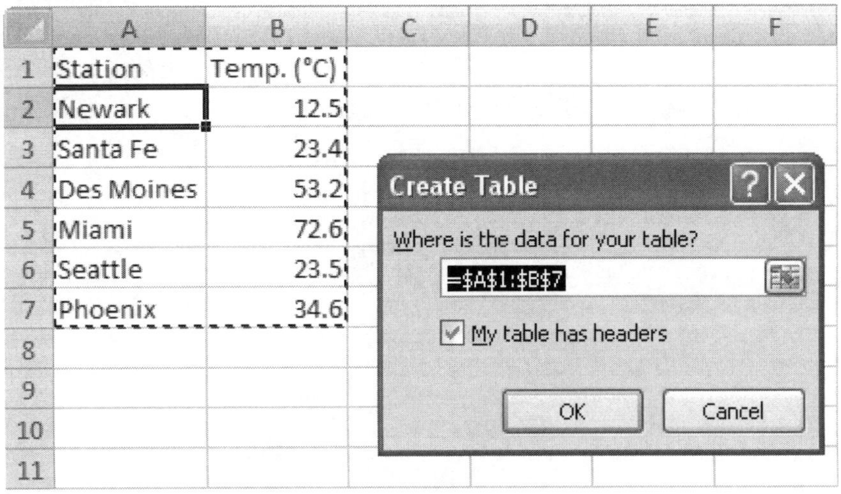

Figure 22.67 The Create Table dialog box.

	A	B	C	D
1	Station ▼	Temp. (°C) ▼		
2	Newark	12.5		
3	Santa Fe	23.4		
4	Des Moines	53.2		
5	Miami	72.6		
6	Seattle	23.5		
7	Phoenix	34.6		
8				

Figure 22.68   The Excel table.

22.6.2 Sorting Data in Excel Tables

To arrange the data in alphabetical order by station, use the drop-down menu on the **Station** heading (Figure 22.69) and choose **Sort A to Z**. The result is shown in Figure 22.70.

The drop-down menu indicator on the Station heading (see Figure 22.70) now has a small arrow pointing up; this indicates that the table has been sorted by station in ascending order.

Notice that Miami still has the highest temperature. When the stations were arranged in alphabetical order, the rows were rearranged, but the data on each row were kept together.

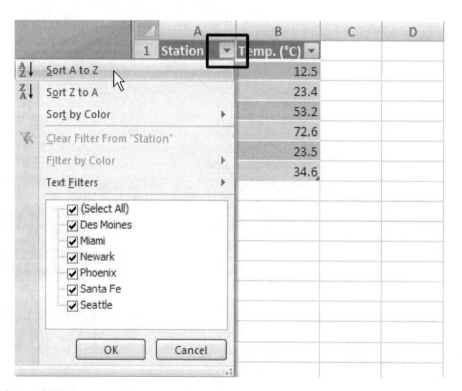

Figure 22.69   Sorting the Excel table.

	A	B	C	D
1	Station ↑	Temp. (°C) ▼		
2	Des Moines	53.2		
3	Miami	72.6		
4	Newark	12.5		
5	Phoenix	34.6		
6	Santa Fe	23.4		
7	Seattle	23.5		
8				

Figure 22.70   The table, sorted by Station.

22.6.3   Filtering Data in Excel Tables

We can also filter the data in tables to see only the portion of the data set that meets the filter criteria. For example, we might filter the data to see only the stations that are reporting temperatures greater than 50°C. To apply the filter, use the drop-down menu on the **Temp. (°C)** heading. Then choose **Number Filters** and **Greater Than ...** from the menus (see Figure 22.71.) The Custom AutoFilter dialog box will open (Figure 22.72).

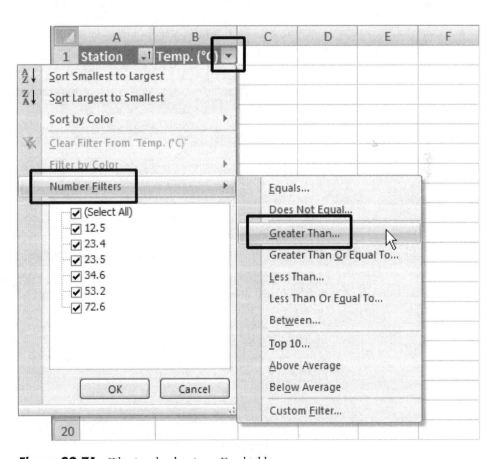

Figure 22.71   Filtering the data in an Excel table.

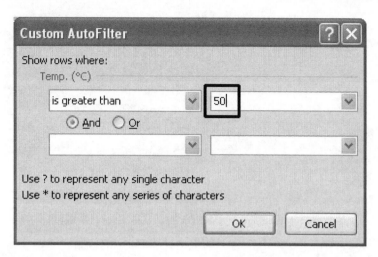

Figure 22.72   Custom AutoFilter dialog.

Enter the filter value (50 in this example) into the dialog box. Click **[OK]** to apply the filter. The result is shown in Figure 22.73. Notice that the drop-down menu indicator in cell B1 now includes a small funnel icon; this visually indicates that the table has been filtered on the temperature values. Also note (in Figure 22.73) that rows 5 through 7 are not visible. The rows containing temperatures less than or equal to 50°C have been hidden (not deleted).

To remove the filter, use the drop-down menu on the **Temp. (°C)** heading and choose **Clear Filter from Temp. (°C)**.

	A	B	C	D
1	Station	Temp. (°C)		
2	Des Moines	53.2		
3	Miami	72.6		
8				
9				

Figure 22.73   The filtered data.

22.6.4   Using a Total Row with Excel Tables

Excel will automatically add a row to the bottom of a table that can be used to show the totals in each column—but the *Total Row* can be used for a lot more than just showing totals.

To add a Total Row, right click anywhere on the table and select **Table → Totals Row** from the pop-up menu. The result is shown in Figure 22.74.

There is little point in summing the temperatures from the various stations, but the Total Row can be used in other ways. If you click on cell B8 (the total), a drop-down menu handle will appear, as shown in Figure 22.75.

If you open the drop-down menu (as shown in Figure 22.75) you see that the Total Row can be used to calculate any of the following:

- Sum (or total)
- Average

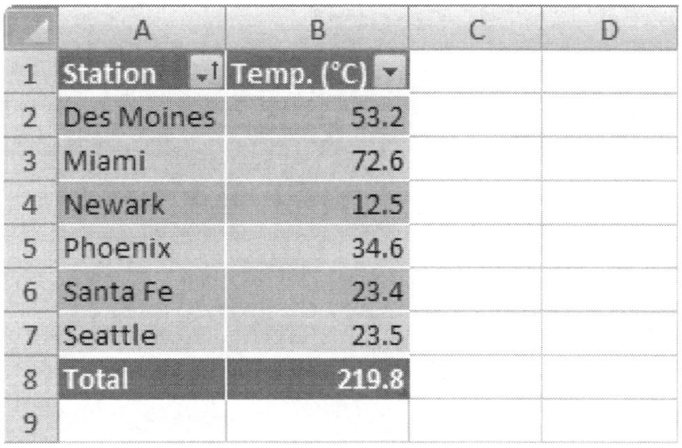

Figure 22.74 The example table with added Total Row.

- Count
- Maximum
- Minimum
- Standard Deviation
- Variance

If those don't meet your needs, you can use the **More Functions...** option.

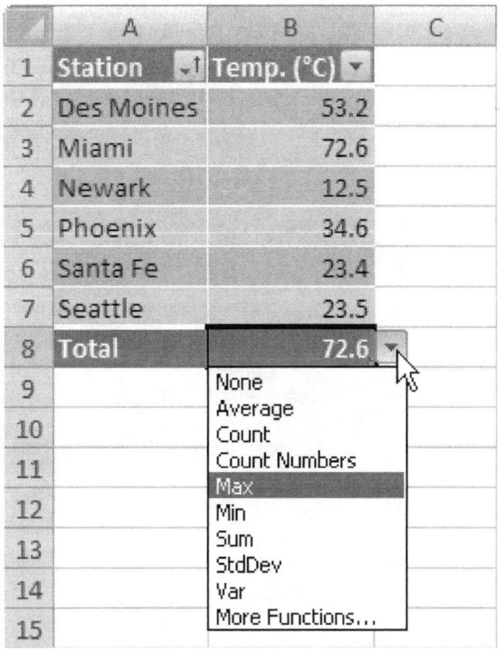

Figure 22.75 Options for the table's Total Row.

Practice!

Suppose that you have a data set that includes melting and boiling points of various gases, as shown in Figure 22.76.

	A	B	C	D
1	Symbol	Property	Temp. (°C)	
2	He	Boil	-268.9	
3	Xe	Melt	-112.0	
4	Ne	Melt	-248.6	
5	Ar	Boil	-185.8	
6	Rn	Boil	-61.8	
7	Ar	Melt	-189.3	
8	Kr	Boil	-152.9	
9	Kr	Melt	-157.0	
10	Rn	Melt	-71.0	
11	Ne	Boil	-245.9	
12				

Figure 22.76   Gas property data.

You want to sort the table so that

- All of the melting points appear first and the boiling points appear last, and
- The temperatures within each category are listed in descending order.

This can be accomplished as follows:

1. Click anywhere inside the data set.
2. Create an Excel table from the data using Ribbon options: **Home tab → Styles group → Format as Table drop-down menu → Choose a style option**.
3. Verify the cell range containing the data and indicate that the table has headings in the Create Table dialog, as shown in Figure 22.77. The result is shown in Figure 22.78.
4. Use the drop-down menu on the **Temp (°C)** heading and select **Sort Largest to Smallest**.

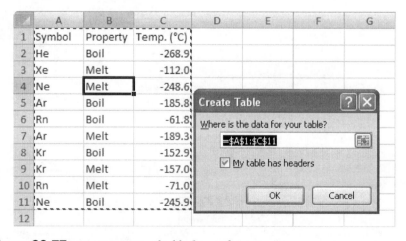

Figure 22.77   Creating an Excel table from a data set.

	A	B	C	D
1	Symbol ▾	Property ▾	Temp. (°C) ▾	
2	He	Boil	-268.9	
3	Xe	Melt	-112.0	
4	Ne	Melt	-248.6	
5	Ar	Boil	-185.8	
6	Rn	Boil	-61.8	
7	Ar	Melt	-189.3	
8	Kr	Boil	-152.9	
9	Kr	Melt	-157.0	
10	Rn	Melt	-71.0	
11	Ne	Boil	-245.9	
12				

Figure 22.78   The Excel table.

5.   Use the drop-down menu on the **Property** heading and select **Sort A to Z**. The result is shown in Figure 22.79.

	A	B	C	D
1	Symbol ▾	Property ▾↑	Temp. (°C) ▾	
2	Rn	Boil	-61.8	
3	Kr	Boil	-152.9	
4	Ar	Boil	-185.8	
5	Ne	Boil	-245.9	
6	He	Boil	-268.9	
7	Rn	Melt	-71.0	
8	Xe	Melt	-112.0	
9	Kr	Melt	-157.0	
10	Ar	Melt	-189.3	
11	Ne	Melt	-248.6	
12				

Figure 22.79   The sorted Excel table.

If, sometime later, you wanted to see only the boiling point values for argon and krypton, you could filter the table as follows:

1.   Use the drop-down menu on the **Symbol** heading and check the boxes for the "Ar" and "Kr" **Text Filters** as shown in Figure 22.80.
2.   Use the drop-down menu on the **Property** heading and check the "**Boil**" box as shown in Figure 22.81.

The filtered table is shown in Figure 22.82.

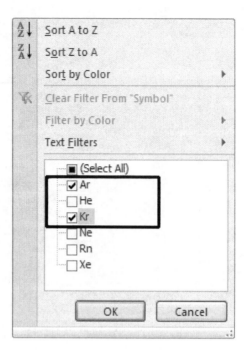

Figure 22.80 Setting the Symbol filter values.

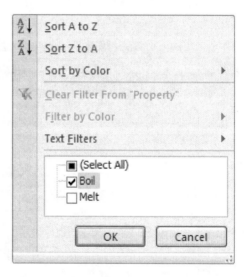

Figure 22.81 Setting the Property filter value.

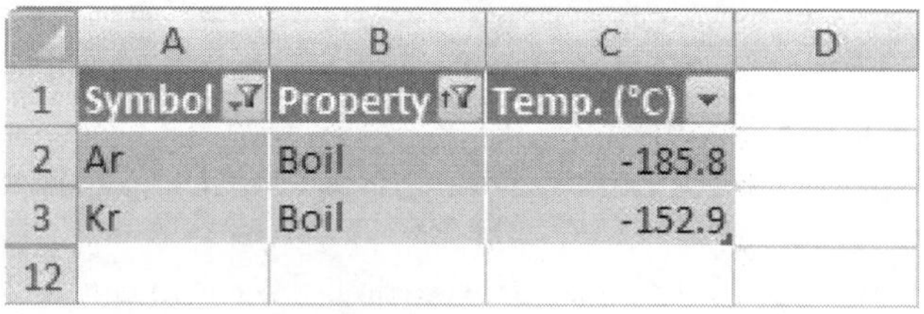

	A	B	C	D
1	Symbol	Property	Temp. (°C)	
2	Ar	Boil	-185.8	
3	Kr	Boil	-152.9	
12				

Figure 22.82 The result after filtering.

22.7   CONDITIONAL FORMATTING

Formatting options may be applied conditionally. The term *conditional formatting* means you may choose logical criteria to format cells.

For example, consider again the temperature data shown in Figure 22.83. Suppose that we want to emphasize high and low temperatures. We can use conditional formatting to make the cells with the temperature extremes stand out.

Create the worksheet shown in Figure 22.83. To initiate conditional formatting, select the cell range containing the temperature values, cells B2:B7, then click the Conditional Formatting button on the Ribbon [**Home tab → Styles group → Conditional Formatting button**]. A menu of options will be displayed as shown in Figure 22.84.

Excel 2007 has several new options for conditional formatting, including the data bars used in Figure 22.84. When you just want to visualize what's happening in your

	A	B	C
1	Station	Temp. (°C)	
2	Newark	12.5	
3	Santa Fe	23.4	
4	Des Moines	53.2	
5	Miami	72.6	
6	Seattle	23.5	
7	Phoenix	34.6	
8			

Figure 22.83   Temperatures at various monitoring locations.

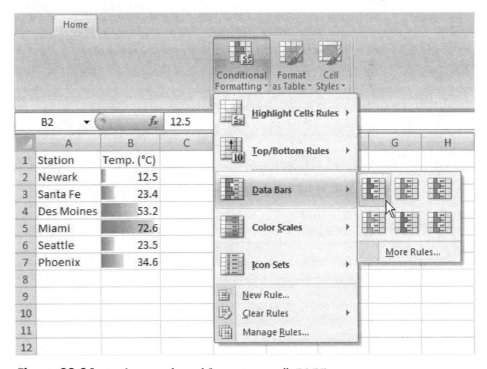

Figure 22.84   Applying conditional formatting to cells B2:B7.

data, the new formats work well. But you can still apply your own rules to highlight data values meeting your own criteria.

For example, to highlight all cells containing temperatures greater than 50°C, you would create a rule as follows:

1. Select the cells containing the data to be examined; cells B2:B7 in this example.

2. Open the Greater Than dialog box using Ribbon options **Home tab → Styles group → Conditional Formatting drop-down menu → Highlight Cells Rules option → Greater Than option**. This string of menu options is illustrated in Figure 22.85. The dialog box is shown in Figure 22.86.

3. To highlight cells containing temperature values greater than 50°C, enter a 50 in the condition field, as shown in Figure 22.86. Then select a highlight format from the drop-down list on the right side of the dialog box, or select "**Custom Format ...**" from the list to specify unique formatting for the highlighted cells.

The result is shown in Figure 22.87.

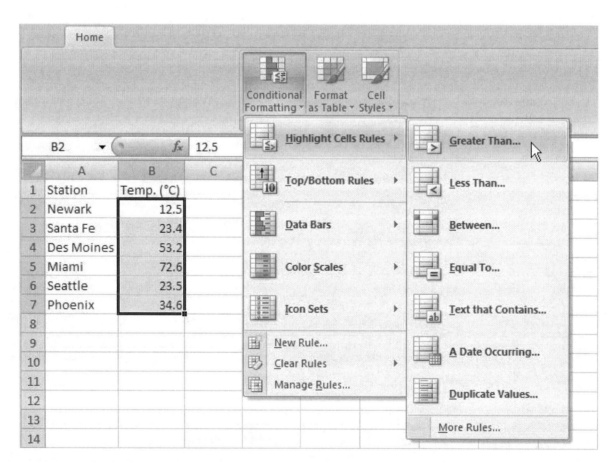

Figure 22.85   Ribbon options for creating a "greater than" rule.

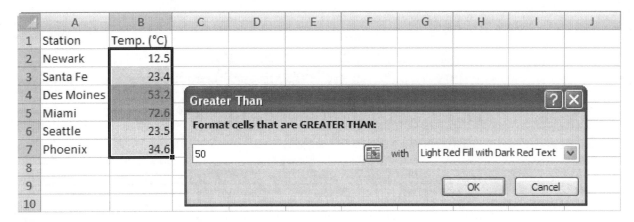

Figure 22.86 The Greater Than dialog box.

	A	B	C	D
1	Station	Temp. (°C)		
2	Newark	12.5		
3	Santa Fe	23.4		
4	Des Moines	53.2		
5	Miami	72.6		
6	Seattle	23.5		
7	Phoenix	34.6		
8				

Figure 22.87 The result of applying a conditional formatting rule to highlight temperatures above 50°C.

APPLICATION

APPLICATION—PROCESS MONITORING

A lot of engineers, especially young engineers, find themselves in jobs where they are responsible for keeping an eye on how a manufacturing facility is functioning. They must ensure that equipment is operating correctly, routine maintenance is getting done, and quality control goals are being met. A lot of data is collected in manufacturing facilities to allow this type of monitoring to take place, so wading through the data to check for problems can be a chore. Because Excel is such a universally available program, many companies provide this monitoring data as an Excel workbook. So, the engineer comes to work in the morning and opens the workbook in Excel to see how well things went overnight. Figure 22.88 illustrates what a very small daily data set might look like.

A quick look at the data shows a couple of temperatures that are below the 45°C minimum (5:15, 5:35), but finding problems would be easier if the values that are too low or too high were highlighted. Conditional formatting can make these values easy to spot.

The rule we will apply will instruct Excel to highlight values that are "not between" the minimum and maximum values listed in rows 4 and 6. You create a "not between" rule for the temperature values as follows:

	A	B	C	D	E	F
1	Date:	Tuesday, October 20				
2		Temperature	Speed	Power	Precision	Concentration
3	Units:	°C	RPM	Watt	mm	ppm
4	Min:	45	1195	1.12	1.28	72
5	Target:	47	1200	1.23	1.30	75
6	Max:	52	1205	1.35	1.3	76
7	Time	Temperature	Speed	Power	Precision	Concentration
8	5:00 PM	45	1200	1.11	1.22	75
9	5:05 PM	45	1198	1.33	1.22	75
10	5:10 PM	51	1197	1.10	1.30	75
11	5:15 PM	44	1196	1.39	1.32	75
12	5:20 PM	50	1200	1.31	1.36	75
13	5:25 PM	47	1201	1.34	1.29	75
14	5:30 PM	47	1200	1.05	1.33	75
15	5:35 PM	44	1202	1.37	1.24	75
16	5:40 PM	51	1198	1.38	1.34	75
17	5:45 PM	50	1194	1.40	1.26	75
18	5:50 PM	46	1201	1.14	1.35	75
19	5:55 PM	45	1195	1.31	1.36	75
20	6:00 PM	46	1196	1.08	1.28	75

Figure 22.88   Sample process monitoring data.

1. Select the temperature measurements, cells B8:B20.
2. Open the New Formatting Rule dialog box using Ribbon options **Home tab → Styles group → Conditional Formatting drop-down menu → New Rule... option**. The dialog box is shown in Figure 22.89.
3. Choose the type of rule: "Format only cells that contain"
4. Since we want to highlight cells that are outside the desired temperature range, select "not between" as the test condition.
5. Indicate the minimum (45°C, in cell B4) and maximum (52°C in cell B6) temperatures.
6. Click the [**Format...**] button to specify the format that should be used for the cells that are outside the desired temperature range. In this example they have been highlighted by using a dark background with bold, white text.

When you click the [**OK**] button, the rule will be applied to the selected cells and values outside the desired temperature range will be highlighted, as illustrated in Figure 22.90.

The same approach could be used to apply conditional formatting to the other types of measurements.

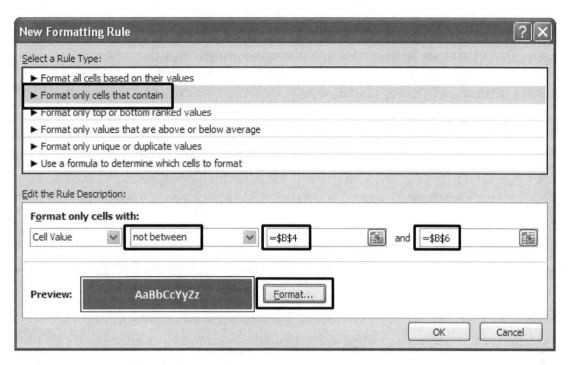

Figure 22.89 New Formatting Rule dialog box.

	A	B	C	D	E	F
1	Date:	Tuesday, October 20				
2		Temperature	Speed	Power	Precision	Concentration
3	Units:	°C	RPM	Watt	mm	ppm
4	Min:	45	1195	1.12	1.28	72
5	Target:	47	1200	1.23	1.30	75
6	Max:	52	1205	1.35	1.3	76
7	Time	Temperature	Speed	Power	Precision	Concentration
8	5:00 PM	45	1200	1.11	1.22	75
9	5:05 PM	45	1198	1.33	1.22	75
10	5:10 PM	51	1197	1.10	1.30	75
11	5:15 PM	44	1196	1.39	1.32	75
12	5:20 PM	50	1200	1.31	1.36	75
13	5:25 PM	47	1201	1.34	1.29	75
14	5:30 PM	47	1200	1.05	1.33	75
15	5:35 PM	44	1202	1.37	1.24	75
16	5:40 PM	51	1198	1.38	1.34	75
17	5:45 PM	50	1194	1.40	1.26	75
18	5:50 PM	46	1201	1.14	1.35	75
19	5:55 PM	45	1195	1.31	1.36	75
20	6:00 PM	46	1196	1.08	1.28	75

Figure 22.90 The process monitoring data after using conditional formatting to highlight temperatures outside desired operating conditions.

KEY TERMS

accounting format	font style	sort
AutoFit (column width)	general format	style
cell border	hide worksheet	table
column width	horizontal alignment	text format
conditional format	merge and center	thousands separator
currency format	protect (lock) worksheet	time format
date format	rename worksheet	vertical alignment
date–time value	ribbon	workbook
fill handle	row height	worksheet
filter	scientific format	worksheet tab
font size	series	

Summary

Common Data Formats

- **General format**—Excel will choose a format on the basis of the contents of the cell. It is the default format for cells containing numbers or text.
- **Currency format**—Excel will display the numeric data with a currency symbol.
- **Accounting format**—Excel will display the numeric data with a currency symbol aligned at the left side of the cell.
- **Date format**—Excel will display the data as a date.
- **Scientific format**—Excel will display the number in scientific notation.
- **Text format**—The contents of the cell will be treated as text.
- **Time format**—Excel will display the data as a time.

Assigning a Data Format to a Cell

Use Ribbon options **Home tab → Number group → Number format drop-down list**.

Date-Time Values

The digits to the left of the decimal point are used to indicate the number of days since the starting date. The digits to the right of the decimal point are used to indicate the time as a fraction of 24 hours.

Starting date defaults are as follows:

- PCs: January 1, 1900
- Apple computers: January 1, 1904

Change the starting date on a PC: **Microsoft Office button → Excel Options button → Advanced group → When Calculating this Workbook** section **→ Use 1904 Date System** check box.

Fill Handle

Use to quickly copy the contents of a cell across a column or row.

Creating a Linear Series

- Enter the first two series values in adjacent cells.
- Select the cells.
- Drag the Fill Handle with the left mouse button to create the series.

Drag the Fill Handle with the right mouse button for additional series options.

Formatting Cells

Most cell formatting options are located on the Ribbon's Home tab.

Home Tab → Font Group

- Font style and size
- Bold, Italic and Underline toggle buttons
- Cell Border (button and drop-down menu)
- Cell Fill Color (button and drop-down menu)
- Cell Font Color (button and drop-down menu)

Home Tab → Alignment Group

- Vertical Alignment toggle buttons
- Horizontal Alignment toggle buttons
- Merge and Center button

Home Tab → Number Group

- Number format selector (drop-down list)
- Currency format toggle button and drop-down menu
- Percentage format toggle button
- Thousands separator toggle button
- Increase and Decrease displayed digits buttons

Adjusting Row Height (three options)

- From a dialog box, **Home → Cells → Format drop-down menu → Row Height ... button**.
- Drag the edge of the row heading with the mouse.
- Double-click the edge of the row heading to AutoFit the row height.

Adjusting Column Width (three options)

- From a dialog box, **Home → Cells → Format drop-down menu → Column Width ... button.**
- Drag the edge of the column heading with the mouse.
- Double-click the edge of the column heading to AutoFit the column width.

Worksheet Options

- Insert a new worksheet: Right-click on any worksheet tab and select **Insert ...**
- Rename a worksheet: Double-click on the worksheet tab.
- Change the color of the worksheet tab: Right-click on the worksheet tab and select **Tab Color**.
- Hide a worksheet: Right-click on the worksheet tab and select **Hide**.

Locking a Worksheet

1. Unlock any cells that need to be available after locking the worksheet.

   - Select cells to be unlocked.
   - Click the **Lock Cell** toggle button [**Home tab → Cells group → Format drop-down menu → Lock Cell toggle button**].

2. Lock the worksheet by password protecting the worksheet.

   - ight-click on the worksheet tab and select **Protect Sheet ...**
   - Enter and confirm your chosen password.

Excel Tables

Formatting a Data Set as an Excel Table

1. Select any cell in the data set.
2. Use Ribbon options **Home tab → Styles group → Format as Table drop-down menu → Choose any style option** to create the table.

Sorting Data

- Use the drop-down menu on the column heading.
- Select the sort option (ascending or descending) from the menu.

Filtering Data

- Use the drop-down menu on the column heading.
- Choose the filter criteria from the menu.

Using a Total Row

- Insert the total row: Right click on the table and select **Table → Totals Row**.
- Click on a cell in the total row to see the drop-down list icon.
- Use the drop-down list to select the function applied to the total row cell.

Conditional Formatting

Use this function to highlight cells that meet certain criteria.

1. Select the cells that are to be assessed for conditional formatting.
2. Select or create a conditional format rule: **Home tab → Styles group → Conditional Formatting button**

Problems

1. When you use the General format, Excel attempts to interpret the type of data in your entry. Open a new workbook and type in the following items:

   1/2   _____
   1 1/2   _____
   $10.32   _____
   3E2   _____

To what types does Excel automatically convert your text? To see the type, select the cell (with the data already entered) and then look on the Ribbon's **Home tab → Number group**. The drop-down list that is used to select a number format is also used to indicate the format applied to the currently selected cell.

2. Use the online help features of Excel to determine how Excel dealt with the Y2K problem. Assume that you are entering dates of birth in an Excel spreadsheet. If you enter 5/23/19, does Excel record the year as 1919 or 2019? What about a date entered as 11/14/49?

3. Excel stores numbers with 15 digits of precision. Prove to yourself these limits of numerical precision.

First, select an empty cell and format the cell to the Number format with 20 decimal places. (Choose the Number format from the Ribbon [**Home tab → Number group**], then right-click on the cell and choose "**Format Cells ...**" from the pop-up menu to set the number of decimal places to 20.)

Then, type the following formula into the cell. This formula instructs Excel to calculate the square root of 2:

$$=SQRT(2)$$

Since the square root of 2 is an irrational number, the fractional part of its decimal representation has an unending number of nonrepeating digits. At what number of digits does Excel's accuracy stop?

4. The table in Figure 22.91 shows the temperatures recorded at several monitoring stations for the months of January and February 2008. The data are in no particular order. Create a worksheet that looks like Figure 22.91. Convert the data into an Excel table, then sort the data in your worksheet by station and then by date in

	A	B	C	D
1	Station	Date	Temp (°C)	
2	A02	2/1/2008	23.5	
3	A07	1/15/2008	14.6	
4	A02	2/15/2008	0.5	
5	B05	2/3/2008	20.0	
6	B05	1/12/2008	34.3	
7	C12	1/5/2008	20.2	
8	A02	2/23/2008	19.6	
9	B05	2/1/2008	22.3	
10				

Figure 22.91 Temperature data.

ascending order. The results should look like Figure 22.92. (The formatting of the table may be different, but the arrangement of the data values should be the same.)

5. Create a worksheet that looks like Figure 22.91. Use conditional formatting to highlight temperatures less than 20.0 degrees Celsius. Your result should be very similar to Figure 22.93.

6. Create a worksheet containing the table of noble gases shown in Figure 22.76. Create an Excel table, and then sort the table so that the elements are listed in alphabetical order. For each element, place the melting point first, followed by the boiling point. Your results should look like Figure 22.94.

Figure 22.92 The sorted Excel table.

Figure 22.93 Unsorted data highlighting temperatures less than 20°C.

7. Use conditional formatting to highlight the boiling points in the table of Figure 22.94 by applying conditional formatting to all cells containing the word "Boil". Your results should highlight the same items as in Figure 22.95.

8. Create and format a table that looks like Figure 22.96.

9. The median is the middle value in a sorted data list. Create the data table shown in Figure 22.97. Create an Excel table, and then sort the data to determine the median grade for this group of students.

10. Ben received a notice from his movie rental store on May 7 informing him that he failed to return a movie. After finding the movie under the couch cushion, he noticed that the due date was March 17. Use Excel's ability to subtract dates to determine whether it will be cheaper to pay the $1.29 per day late fee or to buy the movie for $69. If you set up your worksheet as shown in Figure 22.98, you can compute the number of late days by entering the formula

$$=C2 - C3$$

in cell C5.

	A	B	C	D
1	Symbol	Property	Temp. (°C)	
2	Ar	Melt	-189.3	
3	Ar	Boil	-185.8	
4	He	Boil	-268.9	
5	Kr	Melt	-157.0	
6	Kr	Boil	-152.9	
7	Ne	Melt	-248.6	
8	Ne	Boil	-245.9	
9	Rn	Melt	-71.0	
10	Rn	Boil	-61.8	
11	Xe	Melt	-112.0	
12				

Figure 22.94   Sorted properties of the noble gases.

	A	B	C	D
1	Symbol	Property	Temp. (°C)	
2	Ar	Melt	-189.3	
3	Ar	Boil	-185.8	
4	He	Boil	-268.9	
5	Kr	Melt	-157.0	
6	Kr	Boil	-152.9	
7	Ne	Melt	-248.6	
8	Ne	Boil	-245.9	
9	Rn	Melt	-71.0	
10	Rn	Boil	-61.8	
11	Xe	Melt	-112.0	
12				

Figure 22.95   Noble gas property table with boiling points highlighted.

	A	B	C	D	E	F	G
1	Name	Quiz 1	Quiz 2	Midterm	Quiz 3	Final	
2	Bob	23	12	43	21	54	
3	Maria	32	10	40	26	55	
4	Ralph	14	12	34	20	45	
5	Deepak	24	13	38	22	58	
6							

Figure 22.96   Student grades.

	A	B
1		
2	**Student**	**Score**
3	Sal	87
4	Sali	94
5	Sally	72
6	Sam	82
7	Sara	88
8	Sarah	78
9	Su Nee	95
10	Stewart	91
11	Stuart	68
12	Suri	84
13		

Figure 22.97   Grades.

	A	B	C	D
1				
2		Notice Date:	7-May	
3		Due Date:	17-Mar	
4				
5		Days Late:		
6				

Figure 22.98   Calculating the number of days between two dates.

NOTE: When Excel subtracts one date from another date, the result will be displayed with a Date format. You will need to format the cell containing the result as either *Number* or *General* type to see the number of days between the two dates.

11.   You can use Excel's Date format to find out the day of the week on which an event occurred. To do so, enter the date in a cell on a worksheet, then choose a Type for the Date format that includes the day of the week. The date you entered will then be displayed along with the day of the week.

For example, say your friend Anna was born on December 28, 1984. You could find out she was born on a Friday by entering 12/28/1984 into a cell, and then reformatting the cell to include the day of the week. The result is shown in Figure 22.99.

Find out the day of the week for each of these historical events:

(a) stock market crash, October 29, 1929
(b) first moon landing, July 20, 1969
(c) Cinco de Mayo (May 5), 2016
(d) your birthdate

	A	B	C
1			
2		Friday, December 28, 1984	
3			
4			

Figure 22.99 Long Date formatting used to determine the day of the week.

12. Use Excel to create a schedule for your classes.

Step 1: Enter Monday and Tuesday in adjacent cells.

Step 2: Select the cells containing Monday and Tuesday, and then use the Fill Handle to complete the headings for the class schedule. The result of this step is shown in Figure 22.100.

Step 3: Just below and to the left of the cell containing Monday, enter the time that your school's first class starts. Figure 22.101 assumes that classes begin at 8:00 A.M.

	A	B	C	D	E	F	G
1							
2		Monday	Tuesday	Wednesday	Thursday	Friday	
3							
4							
5							
6							
7							
8							
9							
10							
11							
12							

Figure 22.100 Day headings for a class schedule.

Step 4: Just below the time entered in Step 3, enter the time that the second class starts.

Step 5: Complete the remaining class start times in the time column. You may be able to use the Fill Handle to speed the process if your school has evenly spaced class times.

Step 6: Enter an abbreviation for each of your classes in the appropriate cell.

Step 7: Format the class schedule to make it easy to read. Figure 22.102 has been completed as an example.

	A	B	C	D	E	F	G
1							
2		Monday	Tuesday	Wednesday	Thursday	Friday	
3	8:00						
4	9:00						
5							
6							
7							
8							
9							
10							
11							
12							

Figure 22.101   First two Class Starting times entered in coloumn A.

	A	B	C	D	E	F	G
1							
2		Monday	Tuesday	Wednesday	Thursday	Friday	
3	8:00	MATH	MATH		MATH	MATH	
4	9:00	CHEM		CHEM		CHEM	
5	10:00						
6	11:00		HIST		HIST		
7	12:00		HIST		HIST		
8	1:00			Chem Lab			
9	2:00			Chem Lab			
10	3:00			Chem Lab			
11	4:00			Chem Lab			
12							

Figure 22.102   Completed class schedule.

Chapter 23
Formulas and Functions

23.1   INTRODUCTION

The ability to manipulate formulas, arrays, and mathematical functions is the most important feature of Excel for engineers. Engineers often test and refine potential solutions to a problem by using Excel. When they are satisfied that the solution works for small data sets, they might translate the solution to a programming language such as C or FORTRAN. The resulting program could then be executed on a powerful workstation or supercomputer that can handle large data sets. This use of a worksheet is called building a *prototype*. An application package such as Excel is useful for building prototypes because it allows users to quickly develop solutions and easily modify them.

This chapter will present the basics of using Excel to solve mathematical problems. Basics include writing formulas in a cell on the basis of values in other cells and using Excel's predefined functions to solve problems. Some examples of typical engineering calculations that can be performed using Excel's predefined functions will also be presented, including statistical calculations, trigonometric calculations, and matrix calculations.

In addition, you will be introduced to Excel macros—a method for recording and executing a series of actions. The use of macros can be a time-saving feature as you learn to solve problems that require a series of computations.

SECTIONS

OBJECTIVES

After reading this chapter, you should be able to perform the following tasks:

- Refer to cells and cell ranges in a worksheet.
- Create formulas in a worksheet.
- Locate and use Excel's predefined functions.
- Use absolute and relative cell references in formulas and functions.
- Perform simple matrix operations with Excel.
- Debug worksheet formulas that contain errors.
- Record and run a macro.

23.2   REFERENCING CELLS AND CELL RANGES

Calculations in Excel typically use values stored in various cells to calculate new values. The formulas (Fused to calculate the new values must refer to, or *reference*, the values in the other cells. The reference can be to the value in a single cell or to the set of values in a range of cells. References frequently use the cell location (e.g., B1 or A7) to identify a specific cell, but cells or cell ranges can also be given a name, and this can make formulas easier to understand. This will be presented in more detail in the following sections.

23.2.1   Cell References

A cell can be referenced by using its column letter and row number. The selected cell in Figure 23.1 can be referred to as cell B3. Notice in Figure 23.1 that the *Name Box* at the left end of the Formula bar displays the cell reference for the currently selected cell.

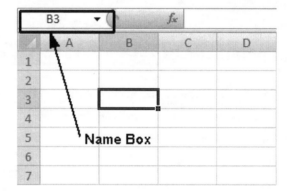

Figure 23.1   Reference a cell by using its row and column designations.

NOTE: The Formula bar is displayed by default, but it can be turned off. In Excel 2007, if the Formula bar is not displayed on your screen, use the following Ribbon options to cause it to be displayed: **View tab → Show/Hide group → check the Formula Bar box**. To turn it off uncheck the box. (In Excel 2003, choose View → Formula Bar from the main menu.)

NOTE: If the Formula bar is not being displayed when you open a new workbook, you can change the Excel 2007 default with these options: **Office button → Excel Options button → Advanced group → Display section →** check the box labeled **Show Formula Bar**.

If a value (number or text) is entered into cell B3, we can reference the contents of cell B3. For example, if we enter a value of 12 into cell B3 (as shown in Figure 23.2), we can say "cell B3 contains the value 12." In this way, we are referring to cell B3 to access the value 12.

If we put a simple formula into another cell, the formula can use the value of 12 by referencing B3. For example, if the formula =B3/2 is entered into cell B4, we can divide 12 by 2. The result is shown in Figure 23.3. Notice that the Formula bar displays the *contents* of cell B4 (the formula), while the *result* of the calculation is displayed in cell B4.

23.2.2   Referencing a Range of Cells

Some calculations are performed on multiple values, for example, calculating a sum or an average. In Excel, multiple values are typically stored in adjacent cells. When the group of values is referenced, it is termed a *cell range*. A rectangular cell range is identified by the top-left and bottom-right cell references, separated by a colon (:). The cell range selected in Figure 23.4 is referenced as A2:B6.

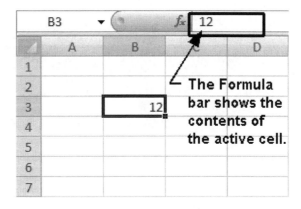

Figure 23.2   The Formula bar shows the contents of the currently selected cell.

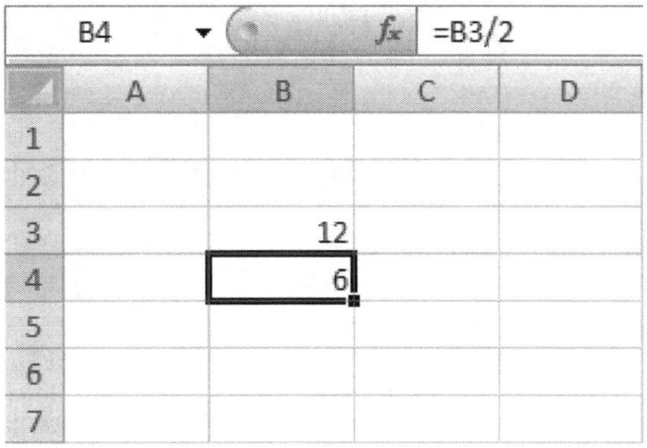

Figure 23.3   The formula in cell B4 references the value in cell B3.

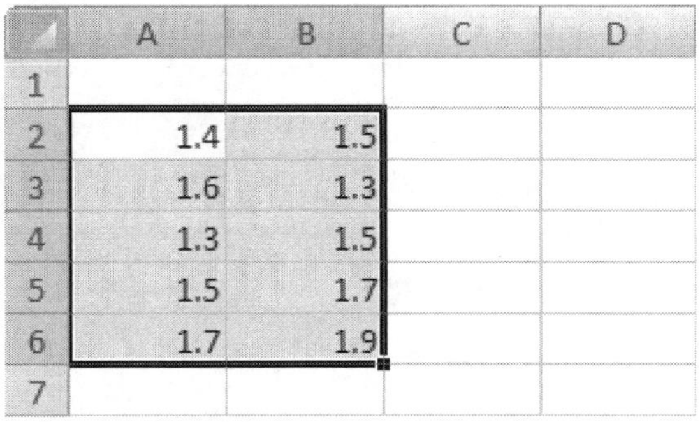

Figure 23.4   Selected cell range A2:B6.

A simple Excel function that uses a range of values is the *SUM* function. If =SUM(A2:B6) is entered into cell D2, the sum of the values in the cell range A2:B6 will be computed and displayed in cell D2, as shown in Figure 23.5.

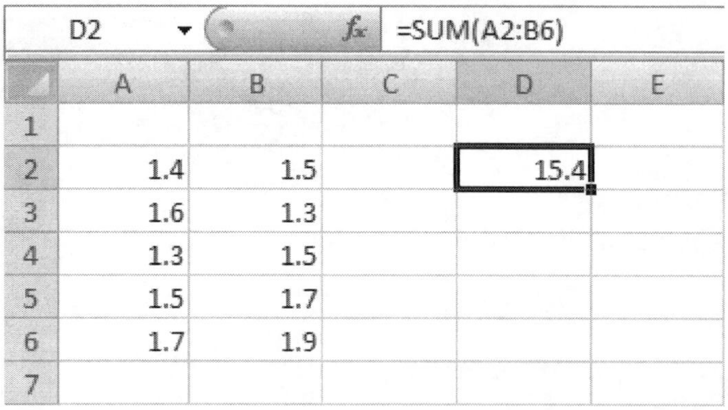

Figure 23.5 Example of a function (SUM) that references a cell range.

23.2.3 Naming a Cell or Range of Cells

It is often convenient to assign a name to a cell or range of cells. Once the name has been assigned, it can be used in formulas and functions to reference the cell or range of cells.

To assign a name to a range of cells, follow these steps:

1. Select the range of cells to be named (as shown in Figure 23.4).
2. Enter a name for the cell range in the Name box. In Figure 23.6, the range has been named MyValues.

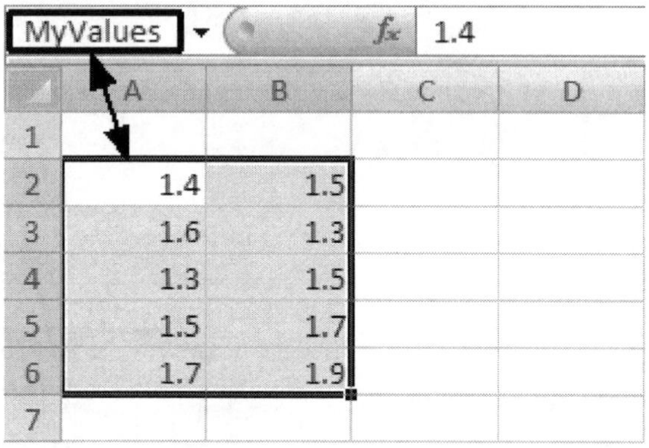

Figure 23.6 The cell range A2:B6 has been named MyValues.

Once the range has been named, the name can be used in the SUM function in cell D2, as shown in Figure 23.7.

Using names in formulas instead of row and column designations can make your worksheets easier to understand.

Once you have defined a named cell range, how do you "undefine" it if you need to? In Excel 2007 you can use the **Name Manager**, which is available from the Ribbon's Formulas tab, as indicated in Figure 23.8.

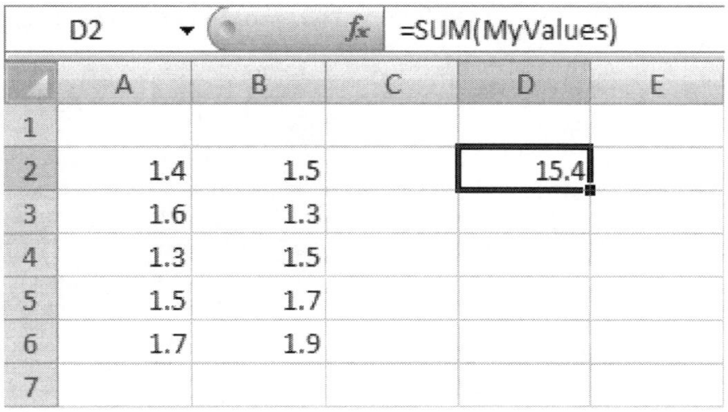

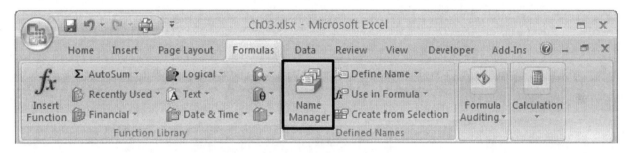

Figure 23.7   Example of using a named cell range in a formula.

Figure 23.8   Use the Name Manager to edit or delete a name.

23.3   CREATING AND USING FORMULAS

A formula in Excel consists of a mathematical expression. For the most part, the expression is defined using common mathematical operators:

+	Addition [+]
−	Subtraction [−]
*	Multiplication [*] or [Shift + 8]
/	Division [/]
^	Exponentiation [^] or [Shift + 6]

A cell containing a formula can display either the formula definition or the formula's calculated result. The default is to display the results in the cell. This is usually preferable since the formula definition for the currently active cell is displayed in the Formula bar.

To display formulas in cells, use the following options: **Formulas tab → Formula Auditing group → Show Formulas button**. (In Excel 2003: Tools → Options → choose the View panel on the Options dialog box → check the box labeled Formulas in the Window options area.)

In Figure 23.9, a formula has been entered in cell D1. The formula bar shows the formula definition to be

$$=A1*B1/C1$$

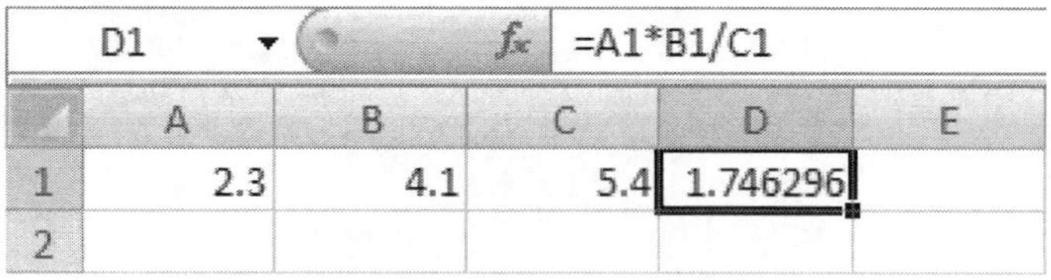

D1	▼	f_x	=A1*B1/C1	
	A	B	C	D	E
1	2.3	4.1	5.4	1.746296	
2					

Figure 23.9   An example of a formula in cell D1.

Like all formulas, the formula in cell D1 starts with an equal sign (=). The equal sign tells Excel that the cell contains a formula and not text. The result of applying this formula is displayed in cell D1 as 1.746296.

23.3.1   Formula Syntax

An Excel formula uses a strict *syntax*, or set of rules that govern how formulas must be entered, so that Excel can correctly interpret them. This means that you must learn the rules for entering a formula and adhere strictly to those rules. There is some good news here: The rules are not very hard to learn.

TABLE 23.1   Precedence of arithmetic operators

Precedence	Operator	Operation
1	%	Percentage
2	^	Exponentiation
3	*, /	Multiplication, Division
4	+, −	Addition, Subtraction

Rules:

- A formula can consist of operators, predefined function names, cell references, and cell names.
- A formula always begins with an equal sign (actually, Excel will also allow you to use a plus symbol).

  The equal sign is an indicator for Excel to evaluate the expression that follows as a formula, instead of simply interpreting the contents in the cell as a text phrase. Try removing the equal sign from a formula and see what happens.
- You can enter a formula into the Formula window on the Formula bar, or directly into the destination cell.
- You have to be careful about operator precedence. This is discussed in the next section.

23.3.2 Arithmetic Operators and Operator Precedence

Table 23.1 lists Excel's arithmetic operators. The operators are listed in order of *precedence*. Precedence indicates which operators are evaluated first; an operator that has higher precedence will always be evaluated before an operator of lower precedence. When operators have the same level of precedence, such as addition and subtraction, the operators are evaluated from left to right. If a different order of evaluation is needed, you must use parentheses to ensure that your formulas evaluate correctly.

Let's apply the rules of precedence to a few formulas and calculate the expected results.

EXAMPLE 1: = 8/2 + 2

The operator of highest precedence is the division symbol, so the first operation is 8/2 = 4. That result is used in the next operation, 4 + 2 = 6. The result of this formula should be 6, and that is what Excel calculated in cell B1, shown in Figure 23.10.

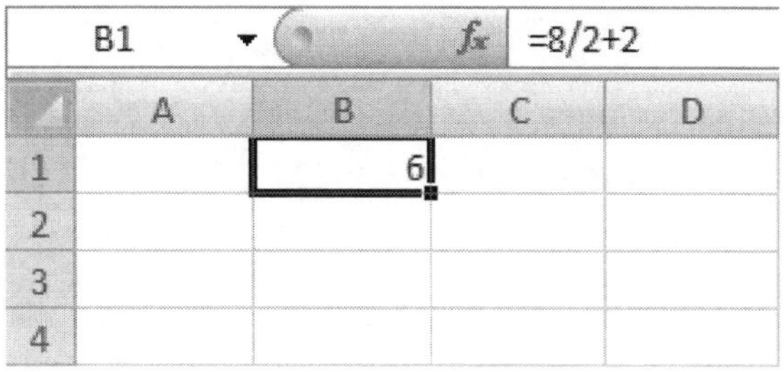

Figure 23.10   Excel's evaluation of the formula =8/2 + 2.

EXAMPLE 2: = 8/(2 + 2)

In Example 2, the operation in parentheses must be evaluated first, so 2 + 2 = 4. This result is used in the division, 8/4 = 2. The result of this formula should be 2, and that is what Excel calculated in cell B2, shown in Figure 23.11.

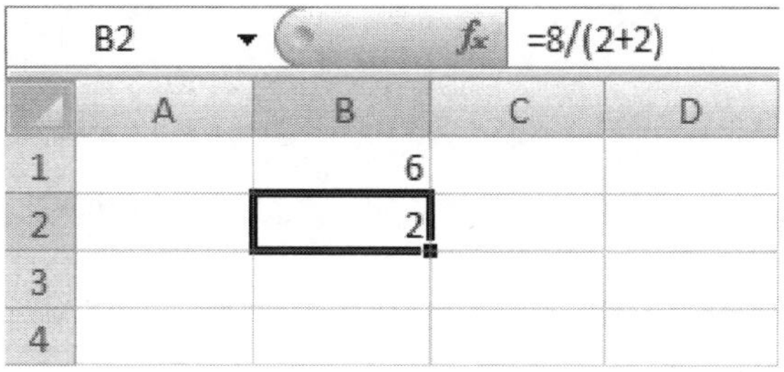

Figure 23.11   Excel's evaluation of the formula = 8/(2 + 2).

EXAMPLE 3: $= 3^2 + 24/2/4 + 3$

The exponentiation has the highest precedence and is evaluated first:

$$= [9] + 24/2/4 + 3$$

The divisions have the next highest priority and will be evaluated from left to right:

$$= [9] + [12]/4 + 3$$
$$= [9] + [3] + 3$$

The additions are then evaluated from left to right:

$$= [12] + 3$$
$$= [15]$$

The result of this formula should be 15, and that is what Excel calculated in cell B3, shown in Figure 23.12.

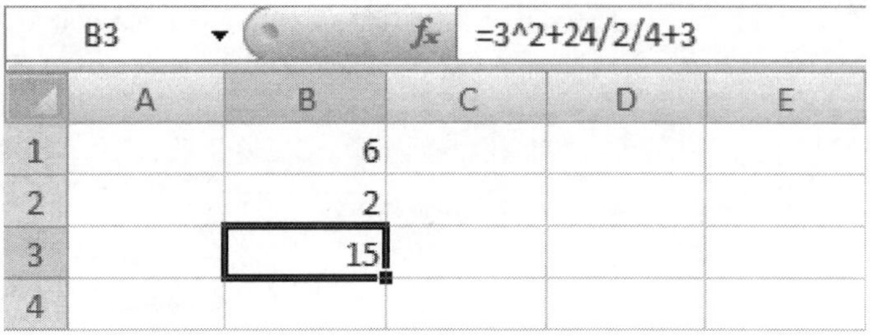

Figure 23.12   Excel's evaluation of the formula $= 3\char`\^2 + 24/2/4 + 3$.

There are other operators in Excel for operations like manipulating text and performing logical (Boolean) comparisons. Check out the online help system for precedence information on additional operators.

Practice!

Practice creating arithmetic expressions by following these instructions:

1. Select a cell.
2. Type the following arithmetic expression into the cell:

    $$= 6/2 + 3$$

    Try to figure out what the result will be before pressing the **Enter** key.
3. Do the same for the following expressions:

    $$= 6/(2 + 3)$$
    $$= 2\char`\^2 - 1$$
    $$= 2\char`\^(2 - 1)$$
    $$= 2 + 4/2/2 - 4$$

Answers

$= 6/2 + 3$	[6]
$= 6/(2 + 3)$	[1.2]
$= 2\char`\^2 - 1$	[3]
$= 2\char`\^(2 - 1)$	[2]
$= 2 + 4/2/2 - 4$	[−1]

23.4   USING EXCEL'S BUILT-IN FUNCTIONS

Excel has a large number of predefined or *built-in functions* available for immediate use. These functions are similar to functions in a programming language because they each require a specified number of arguments as input, and they each return a value. The built-in functions may be selected directly by choosing the **Insert Function** button from the Formula bar (indicated in Figure 23.13). When you click on the **Insert Function** button, the Insert Function dialog box will appear, as shown in Figure 23.14.

From the Insert Function dialog box, you can select functions in a variety of ways.

- **Search for a function.**   Type a topic in the box labeled **Search for a function**. The term "standard deviation" was used in the example shown in Figure 23.14.
- **Use categories.**   Select a category of functions from the drop-down menu, and then select a function from the **Select a function** list.
- **Reuse recently used functions.**   Once you have used several functions in a worksheet, you can quickly access them again by selecting the **Most Recently Used** item in the category drop-down list.

Most engineers will find lots of uses for functions from the **Math & Trig** and **Statistical** categories. Some engineers find functions in other categories very helpful as well. Several examples of available built-in functions will be presented later.

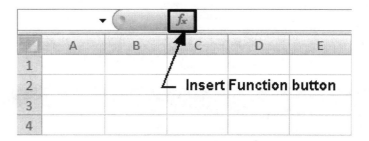

Figure 23.13   The Insert Function button is located on the Formula bar.

Once you have selected a function, the Function Arguments dialog box for that function will be displayed. As an example, the Function Arguments dialog box for the *SUM* function is shown in Figure 23.15.

The *SUM* function calculates the sum of a series of values. The values must be passed into the function as a *function argument* or input. The *SUM* function typically takes a cell range as the only argument, but you can have multiple arguments separated by commas, and the *SUM* function will add all of the input values. The **Number1** and **Number2** fields on the Function Arguments dialog box can hold a number, a reference to a single cell, or (most commonly) a reference to a range of cells. If you use the **Number1** and **Number2** fields on the dialog box, Excel will display additional fields so that you can sum additional values.

The most common use of the *SUM* function is to calculate the sum of a series of values stored in a cell range. The cell references must be passed into the *SUM* function.

Cell references can be entered as function arguments in one of two ways:

- A cell location or cell range can be typed into the formula.
- The cell or cell range can be selected by using the mouse.

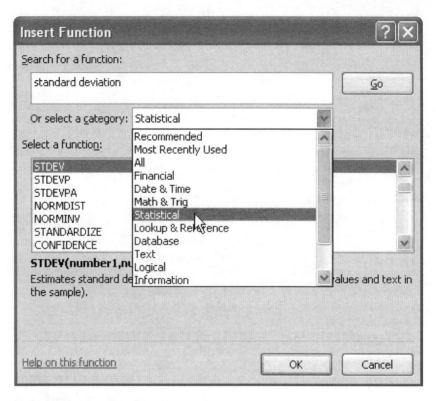

Figure 23.14 The Insert Function dialog box.

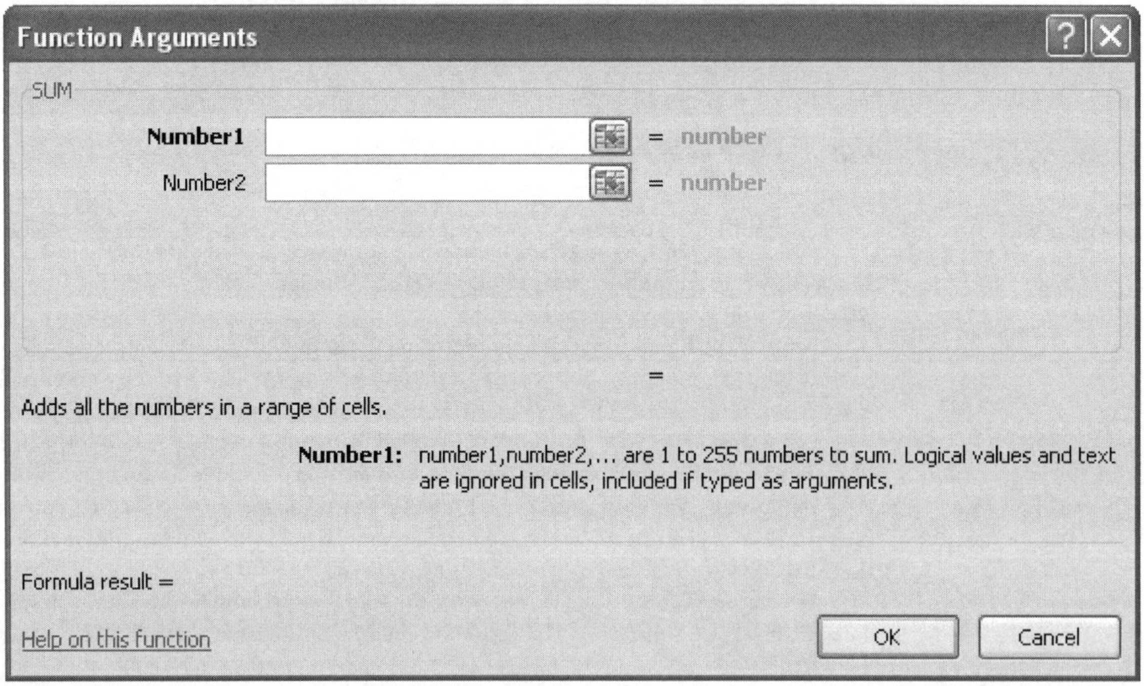

Figure 23.15 Functions Arguments dialog box for the *SUM* function.

Let's walk through an example, using the *SUM* function.

1. Type the values 7.5 and 6.2 into cells A3 and B3, respectively, as shown in Figure 23.16.

	A	B	C	D	E
1					
2					
3	7.5	6.2			
4					

Figure 23.16   Example: Values to be summed.

2. Select cell C3.
3. Choose the Insert Function button from the Formula bar. The Insert Function dialog box (Figure 23.14) will appear.
4. Choose the **SUM** function from the **Math & Trig** category.
5. The Function Arguments dialog box for the *SUM* function will appear, as shown in Figure 23.17.
6. You have two choices at this point. You can type the input cell range (A3:B3) into the box labeled **Number1**, or you can click the small button at the right of the data entry field. This button is called the *Select from Worksheet button*, and it has been indicated in Figure 23.17. The button represents a worksheet grid with an arrow pointing to a selection, and it is used to jump back to the work-

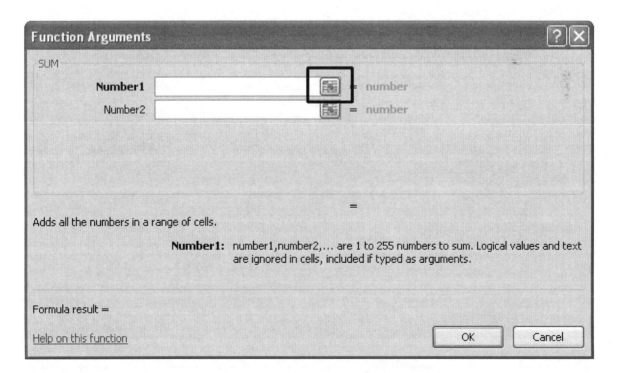

Figure 23.17   The Functions Arguments dialog for the *SUM* function with the Select from Worksheet button indicated.

sheet so that you can select a range of cells with the mouse. For now, click the **Select from worksheet** button. The Function Arguments dialog box will shrink so that the worksheet is visible, as shown in Figure 23.17. You can now select the input cell range (the values to be summed) by using the mouse. The selected range is indicated in the Function Arguments dialog box, in the cell containing the formula, and on the Formula bar (Figure 23.18).

7. When you are satisfied with the selection, click on the small button at the right side of the input field in the Function Arguments dialog box. This button, called the *Return to Dialog Box button*, is indicated in Figure 23.18. It is designed to look like a data entry field on a dialog box. The Return to Dialog Box button is used to jump back to the full-sized Function Arguments dialog box. When you return to the full-sized dialog box, the range you selected with the mouse will appear in the Number 1 data entry field. This is illustrated in Figure 23.19.

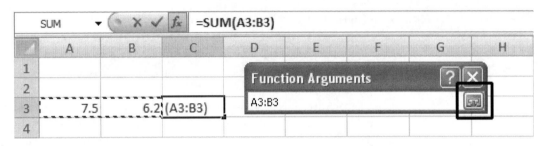

Figure 23.18   Selecting the input cell range for the *SUM* function with a mouse.

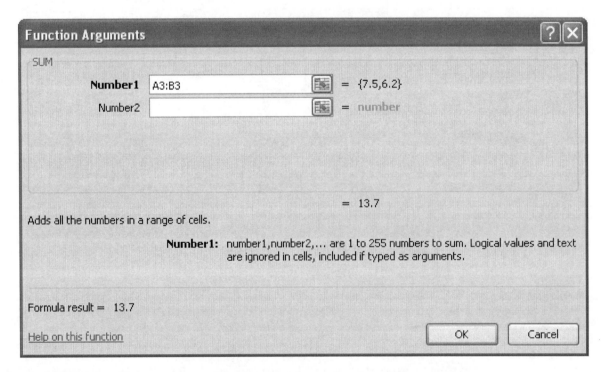

Figure 23.19   The Function Arguments dialog box after selecting the values to be summed.

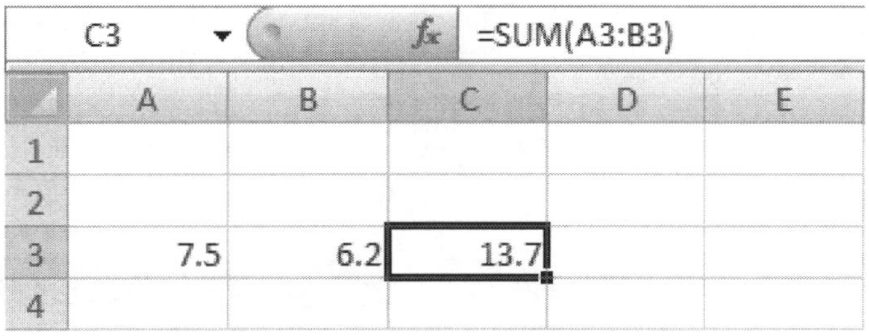

Figure 23.20   The result of summing the values in cells A3 and B3.

8. Click **OK** to complete the *SUM* formula in cell C3. The result is shown in Figure 23.20.

Be careful not to insert a range of cells into an expression that doesn't make sense mathematically. For example, it makes no sense to try to take the square root of a range of values, since the square root function, *SQRT*, accepts only a single value as an argument. If you attempted to send an invalid range into the *SQRT* function, such as =SQRT(A3:B3), Excel would respond by displaying the following error message in the cell containing the formula:

#VALUE

This error message is read "not a value" and indicates that you tried to pass into the *SQRT* function something other than a simple value.

23.4.1 Examples of Statistical Functions

The following steps will walk you through the use of two simple statistical functions that compute the mean and median of a list of numbers:

1. Enter the following seven midterm grades into the range A2:A8 as shown in Figure 23.21.

    32, 68, 93, 87, 75, 96, 82

2. Name the cell range **Midterm** by selecting the region A2:A8 and then entering the name in the Name box (illustrated in Figure 23.21.)

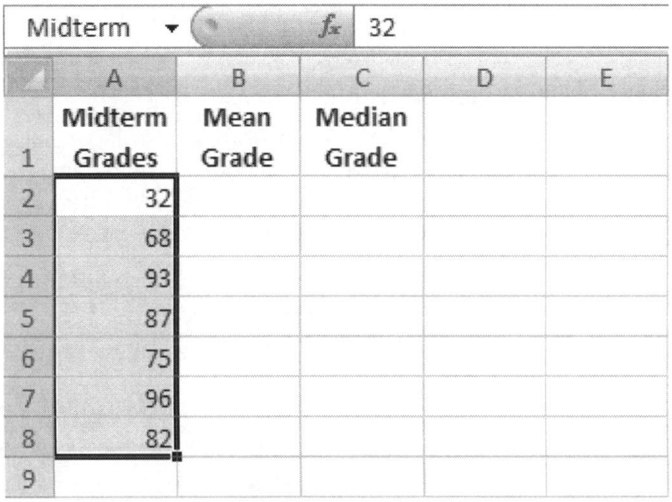

Figure 23.21   Entering midterm grades and assigning a name to the cell range.

3. Select cell B2, which will hold the mean (average) of the midterm grades and then select the **Insert Function** button from the Formula bar.

4. The Insert Function dialog box will appear. Select **Statistical** from the category list, and select **AVERAGE** from the function list, as illustrated in Figure 23.22. Click **OK**.

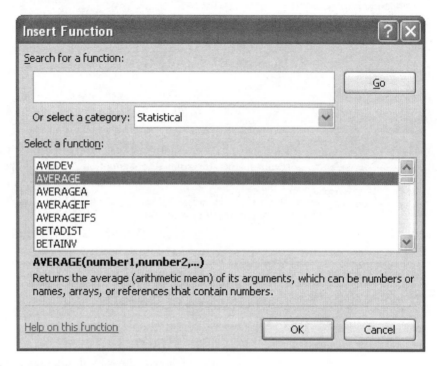

Figure 23.22 Selecting the *AVERAGE* function.

5. The Function Arguments dialog box will appear. Type **Midterm** in the box labeled **Number1**. The completed Function Arguments dialog box should resemble Figure 23.23.

6. Click **OK** to finish the operation. The result is shown in Figure 23.24.

A Quicker Way ...

Although the six-step process of selecting the *AVERAGE* function from the Insert Function dialog box and then completing the Function Arguments dialog for the *AVERAGE* function certainly works, after a while you will probably be looking for a quicker way to enter this commonly used function. Here is a quicker alternative:

1. Enter =AVERAGE(in cell B2.)
    Function names do not have to be entered in capital letters, but you do need to include the opening parenthesis to let Excel know you are entering a function name.

2. Select the midterm grades with the mouse.
    When you select cells A2:A8, Excel will recognize the named cell range and substitute **Midterm** for the cell range in the formula.

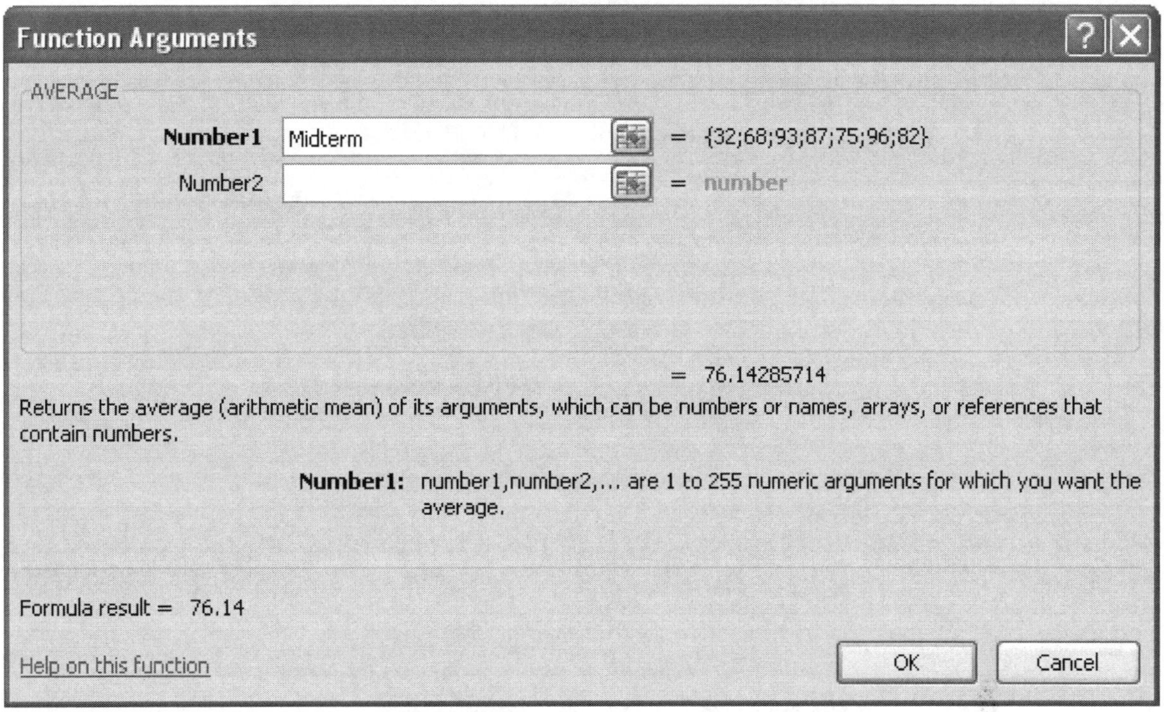

Figure 23.23   Indicating which values should be sent to the *AVERAGE* function.

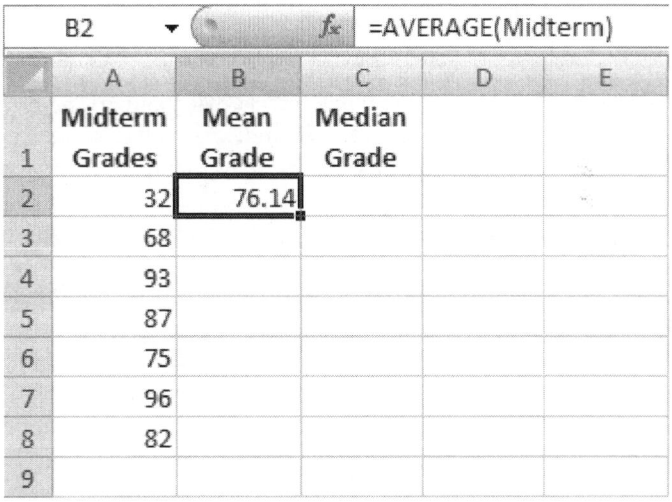

Figure 23.24   The completed *AVERAGE* formula.

3.   Press **Enter** to complete the formula.

You don't even need to enter the closing parenthesis; Excel will add that automatically.

Practice!

Use Excel's *MEDIAN* function to calculate the median grade in cell C2. Your finished worksheet should resemble Figure 23.25.

C2	▼			f_x	=MEDIAN(Midterm)

	A	B	C	D	E
1	Midterm Grades	Mean Grade	Median Grade		
2	32	76.14	82		
3	68				
4	93				
5	87				
6	75				
7	96				
8	82				
9					

Figure 23.25   Calculating mean and median grades.

23.4.2 Examples of Trigonometric Functions

Excel provides a full slate of standard trigonometric functions, including the hyperbolic varieties. In this example, we will calculate one of the angles of a right triangle from two known side lengths. The situation is illustrated in Figure 23.26.

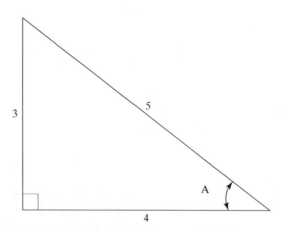

Figure 23.26   A 3-4-5 triangle, used to demonstrate Excel's trigonometric functions.

This is known as a 3-4-5 triangle and is a commonly used right triangle. Since we know the lengths of all three sides, there are several ways to determine angle A:

$$\sin(A) = 3/5, \text{ so } A = \text{asin}(3/5)$$
$$\cos(A) = 4/5, \text{ so } A = \text{acos}(4/5)$$
$$\tan(A) = 3/4, \text{ so } A = \text{atan}(3/4)$$

Any of these equations can be used. To demonstrate Excel's trigonometry functions, we will use them all.

NOTE: Excel's trigonometry functions express angles in *radians*; however, Excel provides the *DEGREES* function to easily convert radians to degrees.

1. Enter the known side lengths in cells B3:B5. Name cells B3, B4, and B5 "Opp", "Adj", and "Hyp", respectively. This is illustrated in Figure 23.27.
2. Use the arcsine function (*ASIN*) to compute angle A in radians (Figure 23.28).
3. Use the *DEGREES* function to convert radians to degrees (Figure 23.29).
4. Use the *ACOS* function to calculate the angle (Figure 23.30).
5. Use the *ATAN* function to calculate the angle (Figure 23.31).

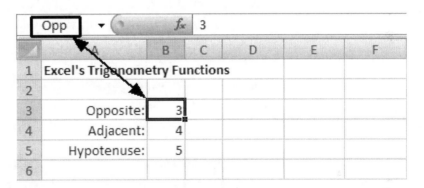

Figure 23.27   Known data for the trigonometry example.

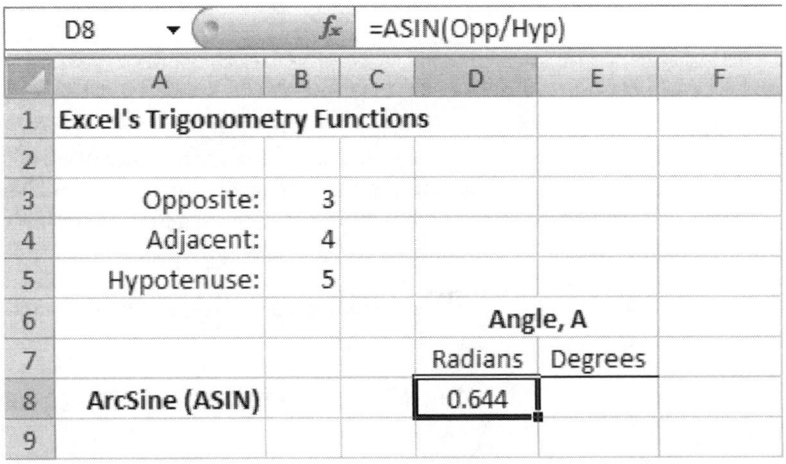

Figure 23.28   Using Excel's *ASIN* function to calculate an angle in radians.

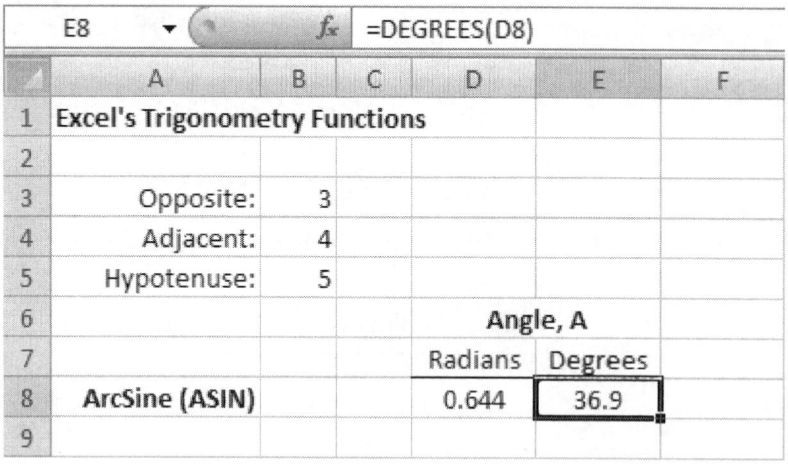

Figure 23.29　Converting an angle in radians to degrees.

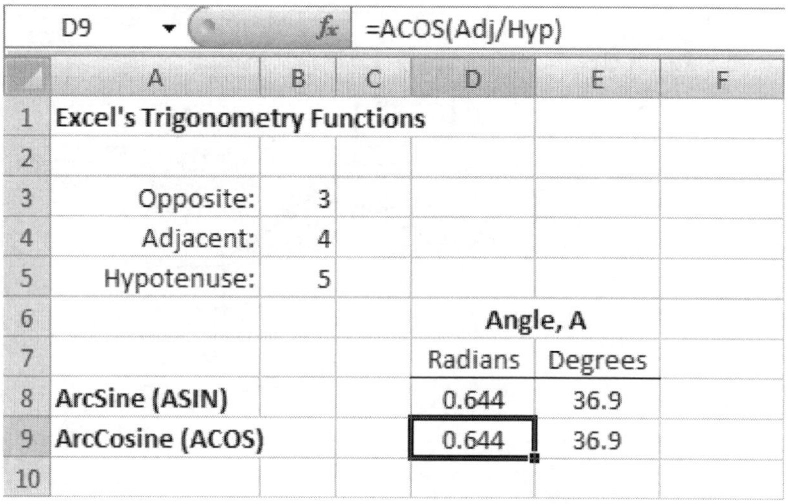

Figure 23.30　Using Excel's *ACOS* function to calculate an angle in radians.

23.4.3 Example of Matrix Operations

Matrices or arrays are frequently used in the formulation and solution of engineering problems. A *matrix* is a rectangular array of elements. Elements are referenced by row and column number. The grid structure of an Excel worksheet naturally lends itself to working with matrices. Excel has a number of built-in matrix operations that are included in the **Math & Trig** category of functions. These include the following:

MDETERM(array)—Returns the matrix determinant for the named array.

MINVERSE(array)—Returns the inverse of the named array.

MMULT(array1, array2)—Performs matrix multiplication on the two named arrays.

Some useful matrix functions are not found in the Math & Trig category—for example,

TRANSPOSE(array)—Interchanges the rows and columns of an array.

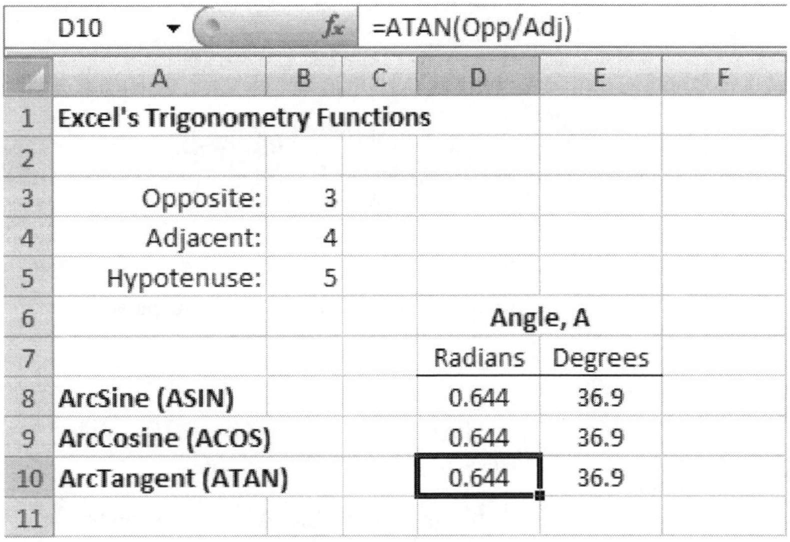

Figure 23.31   Using Excel's *ATAN* function to calculate an angle in radians.

Practice!

Identify the Excel functions that compute the following mathematical functions (use the Insert Function dialog box or the Excel Help system):

1. trigonometric sine
2. inverse hyperbolic tangent
3. natural logarithm
4. base 10 logarithm
5. raise e to a power
6. convert radians to degrees
7. convert degrees to radians

Answers:

SIN, ATANH, LN, LOG (or LOG10), EXP, DEGREES, RADIANS

Many other Excel functions take cell ranges as arguments and can be used to evaluate a matrix.

Matrix addition

Matrix addition is done by adding each of the corresponding cells of two matrices. The two matrices must be of the same *order*, which means that they both have the same number of rows and the same number of columns. *Matrix order* is often denoted as the number of rows by the number of columns, or (rows × columns).

As an example, let's define two matrices of order 2 × 2. Matrix A is stored in cells B2:C3, and that cell range has been named "A" as indicated in Figure 23.32. Matrix B is stored in cells F2:G3, and that cell range has been named "B".

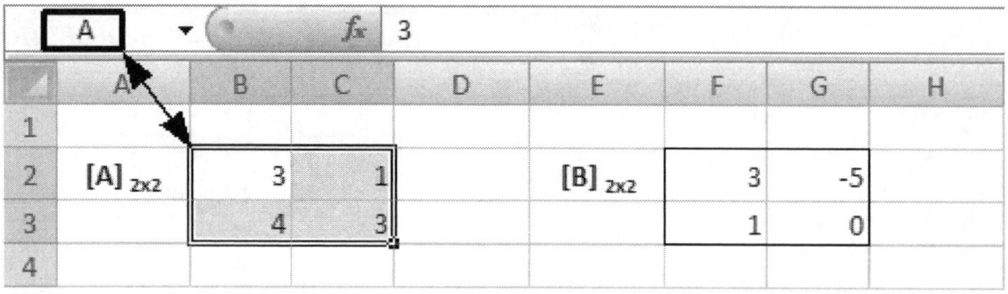

Figure 23.32   Defining matrices A and B.

After matrices A and B have been entered into the worksheet and named, add the matrices by following these steps:

1.   Select the region that will contain the result of the calculation, cells J2:K3 in this example.

2.   Type the following formula (using the named matrices A and B) into the selected region:

$$= A + B$$

The result of steps 1 and 2 is shown in Figure 23.33.

If you press **Enter** to complete the formula you will not get the desired result. When working with matrices you must indicate to Excel that you are asking for matrix addition. To complete an *array formula*, simultaneously press the following keys: **Ctrl + Shift + Enter**.

3.   Press **Ctrl + Shift + Enter** to complete the array formula and add the matrices.

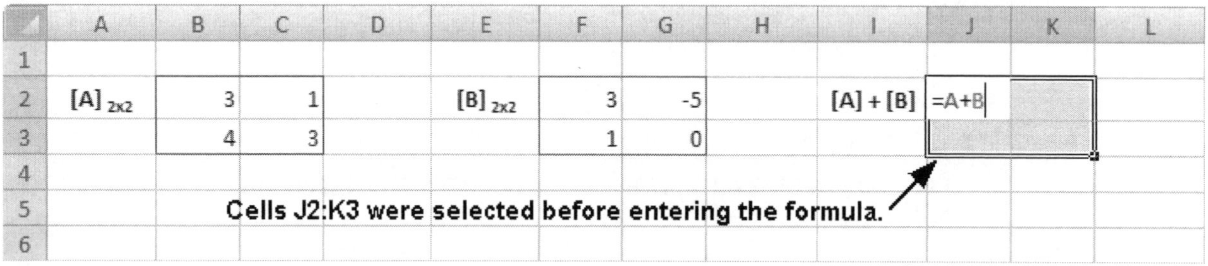

Figure 23.33   The not-quite-completed formula for adding matrices A and B.

When you press **Ctrl + Shift + Enter**, Excel puts the formula in every cell in the array (selected in step 1 of this example *before* entering the formula). The completed array formula is shown in Figure 23.34.

Notice in the Formula bar in Figure 23.34 that the formula is enclosed in curly braces. This is how Excel indicates that the formula is an array formula. Excel keeps all elements of an array together so you cannot edit or delete one cell in a cell range holding an array formula—you have to select the entire array before editing or deleting.

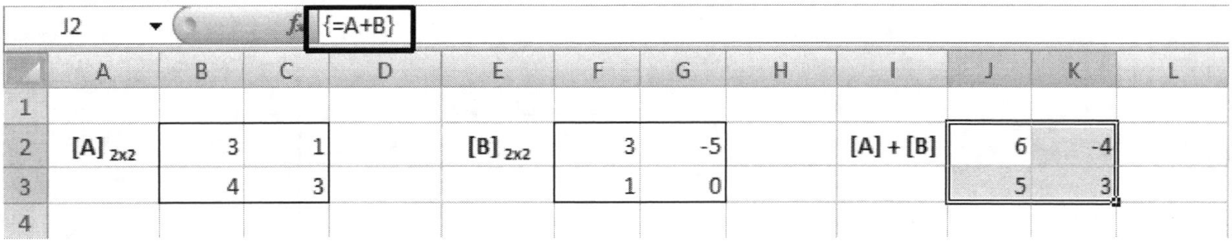

Figure 23.34   The sum of matrices A and B.

NOTE: You cannot type the braces to enter an array formula; you must use the **Ctrl + Shift + Enter** key sequence.

Matrix transpose

As a second example, we will transpose a matrix. The *transpose* of a matrix is the matrix that is formed by interchanging the rows and columns of the original matrix. To find the transpose of matrix B, follow these steps:

1. Select the range that will hold the result.
   The selected range must be the right size. Since matrix B is of order 2×2, the transpose of B will also be order 2×2. Cells F5:G6 have been selected in Figure 23.35.

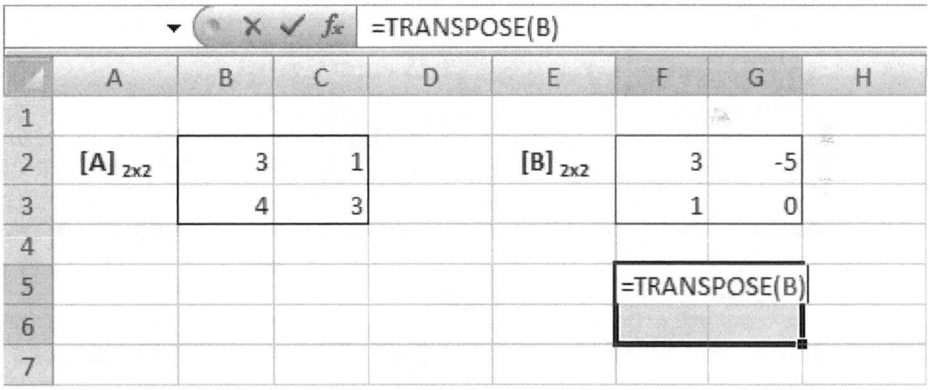

Figure 23.35   Entering the *TRANSPOSE* formula into cell range F5:G6.

2. Type the following formula: =TRANSPOSE(B)
3. Press **Ctrl + Shift + Enter** to complete the array formula.
4. Place appropriate borders and labels on your worksheet. The results should resemble Figure 23.36.

	A	B	C	D	E	F	G	H
1								
2	[A] $_{2x2}$	3	1		[B] $_{2x2}$	3	-5	
3		4	3			1	0	
4								
5					[B]^{T} $_{2x2}$	3	1	
6						-5	0	
7								

Figure 23.36 Computing the transpose of matrix B.

Multiplying matrices

Matrix multiplication is defined as follows: If $A = [a_{ij}]$ is an $m \times n$ matrix and $B = [b_{ij}]$ is an $n \times p$ matrix, then the product $AB = C = [c_{ij}]$ is an $m \times p$ matrix defined by

$$c_{ij} = \sum_{k=1}^{n} a_{ik} b_{kj}, \quad i = 1, 2, \ldots, m, \quad j = 1, 2, \ldots, p.$$

Using this equation, the product of A and B is calculated as

$$AB = \begin{bmatrix} 3 & 1 \\ 4 & 3 \end{bmatrix}\begin{bmatrix} 3 & -5 \\ 1 & 0 \end{bmatrix}$$

$$= \begin{bmatrix} (3 \cdot 3) + (1 \cdot 1) & (3 \cdot -5) + (1 \cdot 0) \\ (4 \cdot 3) + (3 \cdot 1) & (4 \cdot -5) + (3 \cdot 0) \end{bmatrix} = \begin{bmatrix} 10 & -15 \\ 15 & -20 \end{bmatrix}.$$

Excel has a built-in matrix multiplication function named *MMULT*. In Figure 23.37 we have used this function to verify the preceding results. You can practice using this function even if you have not yet studied matrix multiplication. Remember that matrix functions must be entered by using **Ctrl + Shift + Enter**.

J2		f_x	{=MMULT(A,B)}									
	A	B	C	D	E	F	G	H	I	J	K	L
1												
2	[A] $_{2x2}$	3	1		[B] $_{2x2}$	3	-5		[AB]	10	-15	
3		4	3			1	0			15	-20	
4												

Figure 23.37 Using *MMULT* to multiply two matrices.

23.4.4 Examples of Financial Functions

Suppose that you want to predict the future value of an investment at two different interest rates. The equation relating the *present value*, P, to the *future value*, F, is

$$F = P[1 + i]^N$$

The present value is the amount you invest, and the future value is what the investment will be worth N years later. The i in the equation is the annual interest rate.

NOTE: Officially, N is the number of compounding periods, and i is the interest rate per period—the period doesn't have to be a year. Monthly compounding is common. For example, for a five-year investment with a 12% annual presentage rate (APR) with monthly compounding, $N = 5 \times 12 = 60$ months and $i = 12\%/12 = 1\%$ per month.

Excel provides a set of financial functions that can solve this equation directly. In this example, John wants to know how much a $10,000 investment would be worth in 40 years if it were invested at 6 percent per year (assuming annual compounding). He also wants to compare that result with the future value if the funds were invested at 11 percent per year.

Case A: 6 Percent Interest (Compounded Annually)

From the equation, we can see that we need to know P, i, and N in order to solve for F. So, first we enter the known values into a worksheet, as shown in Figure 23.38.

	A	B	C	D	E
1	Calculating the Future Value of an Investment				
2					
3	Case A: 6% Interest				
4					
5	P:	-$10,000	expense		
6	I:	6%	per year		
7	N:	40	years		
8					

Figure 23.38   Entering known values before calculating the future value of an investment.

Notice that the present value was entered as a negative number. Excel uses a standard convention to distinguish incomes and expenses: Expenses are indicated as negative, and incomes are indicated as positive. Since you must put money out of your pocket into the investment, that is an expense and is entered as a negative value.

To calculate the future value, follow these steps:

1. Click in cell B9, and then click the **Insert Function** button on the Formula bar.
2. Select the *FV* (future value) function from the Insert Function dialog box (see Figure 23.39). The Function Arguments dialog box for the FV function will be displayed (Figure 23.40).
3. Fill in the data entry fields for function FV's arguments. The completed dialog box is shown in Figure 23.40.
4. Click **OK** to complete the calculation. The result is shown in Figure 23.41.

Notice that the Pmt (annual payment) field was left blank in Figure 23.40. This is necessary because there was no mention of any annual payments, just an initial investment of $10,000. This shows up in the formula in cell B9 as an unused argument (notice the two adjacent commas in the formula shown in Figure 23.41.) You could also put a value of zero in the Pmt field.

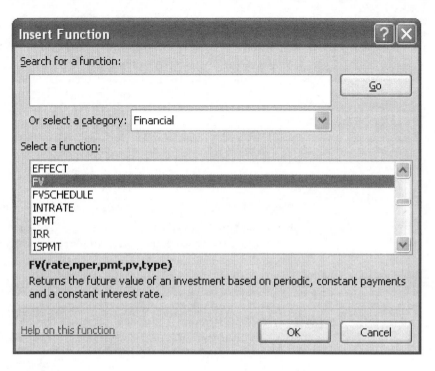

Figure 23.39   Selecting the *FV* function from the Financial category.

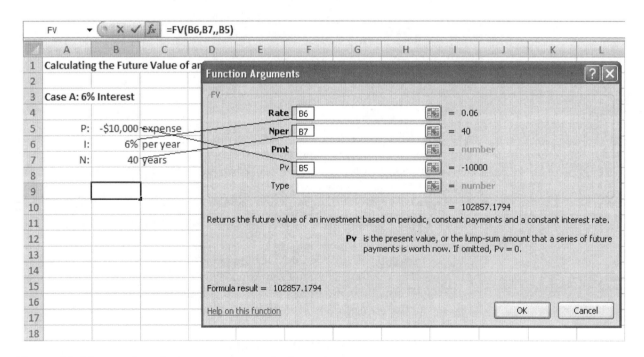

Figure 23.40   Specifying the function arguments for the *FV* function.

Case B: 11 Percent Interest (Compounded Annually)

Now, repeat these steps, using an 11 percent annual rate. The result is shown in Figure 23.42.

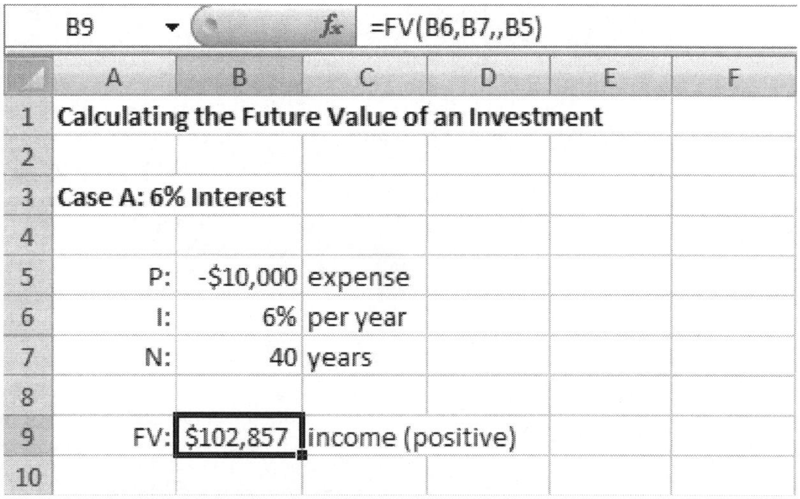

Figure 23.41   The calculated future value at 6% interest.

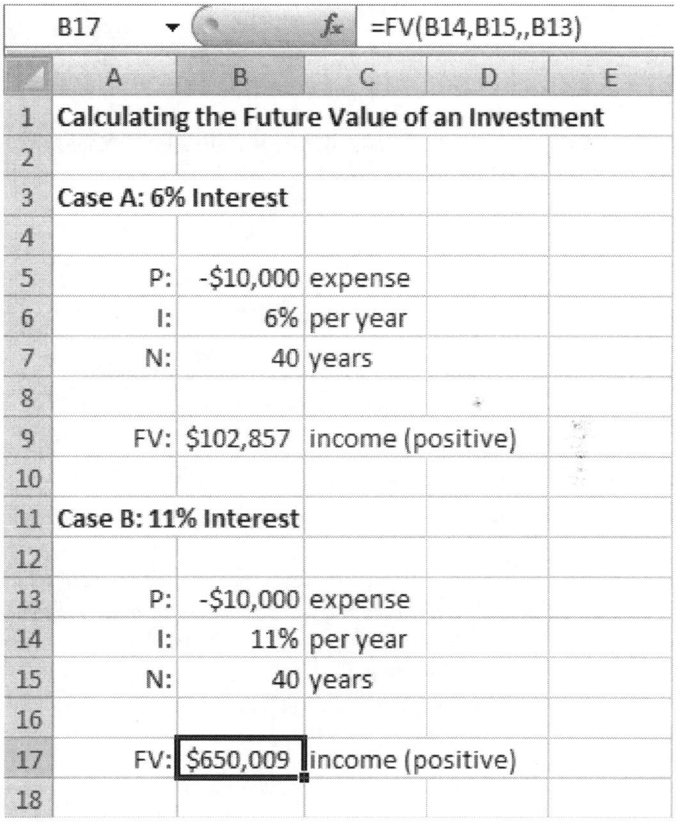

Figure 23.42   Calculating the future value at 11% interest.

23.5   ABSOLUTE AND RELATIVE CELL REFERENCES

Formulas may be copied from one location to another in a worksheet. Usually, you will want the cells that are referenced in the formula to follow the formula—this is called *relative referencing*.

For example, you may want to copy a formula that adds a row of numbers. Look at Figure 23.43. The formula in cell E1 adds the elements in cells A1 to C1. If you were to copy the formula in cell E1 to cell E2, what result would you want? Should the new formula compute the sum using values in row 1 or row 2?

E1				f_x	=SUM(A1:C1)	
	A	B	C	D	E	F
1	1	2	3	Sum =	6	
2	7	8	9	Sum =		
3						

Figure 23.43 Example of a formula with relative referencing.

If relative referencing is used, the copied formula in cell E2 will sum values in row 2 (cells A2 to C2). Try the following test:

1. Create the worksheet shown in Figure 23.43.
2. Copy the formula in cell E1 to cell E2 (you can use the Fill Handle to do this easily).

The result is shown in Figure 23.44. Note that the formula in cell E2 adds values on row 2, not row 1. The cell references have followed the formula (relative referencing).

E2				f_x	=SUM(A2:C2)	
	A	B	C	D	E	F
1	1	2	3	Sum =	6	
2	7	8	9	Sum =	24	
3						

Figure 23.44 Copying a formula that uses relative referencing.

There are times when you may want to copy a formula and *not* have the references follow the formula. This is called *absolute referencing*. A cell or range is denoted as an *absolute reference* by the placement of a dollar sign ($) in front of the row or column to be locked.

Look at Figure 23.45. This worksheet is the same as the worksheet in Figure 23.43, except that the formula uses absolute references, indicated by the dollar signs in the cell references.

E1				f_x	=SUM($A$1:$C$1)	
	A	B	C	D	E	F
1	1	2	3	Sum =	6	
2	7	8	9	Sum =		
3						

Figure 23.45 Example of a formula with absolute cell references ($).

When cell E1 is copied to cell E2 the results (Figure 23.46) are quite different with absolute cell referencing than with relative referencing. The formula in cell E2 sums values in row 1, not row 2! The references have not followed the formula.

E2	▼			f_x	=SUM($A$1:$C$1)	
	A	B	C	D	E	F
1	1	2	3	Sum =	6	
2	7	8	9	Sum =	6	
3						

Figure 23.46   The result of copying the formula in cell E1 to cell E2.

Each dollar sign (absolute reference symbol) acts like a lock on the cell reference.

- $A1 tells Excel not to change the A when the cell is copied (but the row reference can change).
- A$1 tells Excel not to change the 1 when the cell is copied (but the column reference can change).
- $A$1 tells Excel not to change either the A or the 1 when the cell is copied.

Practice!

There are times when you may want to make relative references to some cells and absolute references to other cells. For example, a formula may use a constant and several variables. You can use absolute referencing for the constant and relative referencing for the variables.

In the next example, we want to compute the areas of several circles with various radii. The formula uses the constant π (pi). When we copy the formula, we want the reference to π to remain absolute, but the reference to the radius to be relative. To practice with relative and absolute cell addresses, complete the following steps:

1. Create the worksheet shown in Figure 23.47. Notice that the formula for area in cell B6 uses absolute referencing for cell $B$3 (the constant, π) and relative referencing for cell A6 (the radius value).

2. Copy the formula in cell B6 by dragging the Fill Handle through cells B7:B10.

The result is shown in Figure 23.48. Because the formula in cell B6 used relative referencing for the radius value (A6), when the formula was copied the radius references were updated to use the values in cells A7 to A10. But because the reference to the cell containing the value of π used absolute referencing ($B$3), all of the copied formulas in cells B7 to B10 still refer to the value of π stored in cell B3.

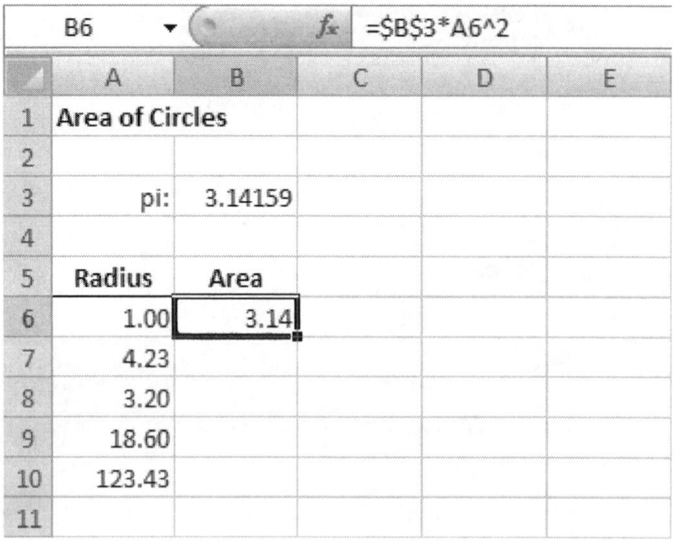

B6	▼	f_x	=$B$3*A6^2

	A	B	C	D	E
1	Area of Circles				
2					
3	pi:	3.14159			
4					
5	Radius	Area			
6	1.00	3.14			
7	4.23				
8	3.20				
9	18.60				
10	123.43				
11					

Figure 23.47   Using both absolute and relative cell references.

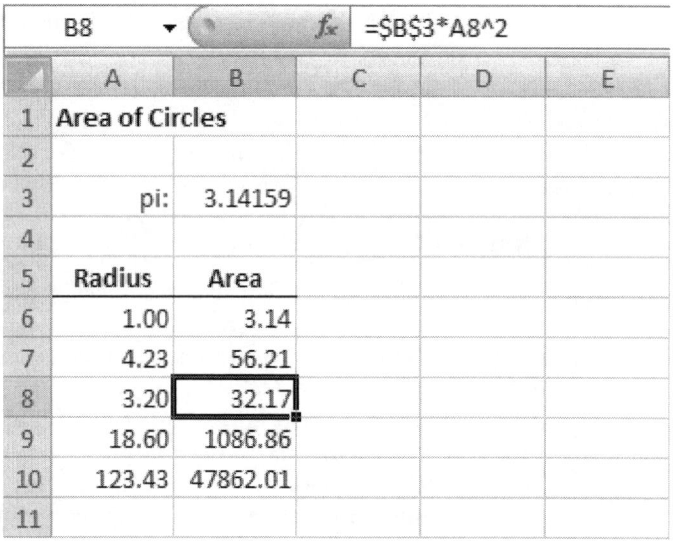

B8	▼	f_x	=$B$3*A8^2

	A	B	C	D	E
1	Area of Circles				
2					
3	pi:	3.14159			
4					
5	Radius	Area			
6	1.00	3.14			
7	4.23	56.21			
8	3.20	32.17			
9	18.60	1086.86			
10	123.43	47862.01			
11					

Figure 23.48   The result of copying the formula in cell B6 to B7:B10.

Practice!

An example of a slightly more complex use of formulas is the solution of *quadratic equations*. You may recall from high school algebra that if a quadratic equation is expressed in the form

$$ax^2 + bx + c = 0,$$

then the solutions for x are as follows:

$$x = -b \pm \frac{\sqrt{b^2 - 4ac}}{2a}, \quad (2a \neq 0)$$

Note that there are two solutions because of the $\pm$ in the equation. Since Excel does not directly recognize imaginary numbers, we must make the further restriction that

$$b^2 - 4ac \geq 0.$$

Practice working with Excel formulas by creating a worksheet that resembles Figure 23.49. Store coefficients in columns A, B, and C and enter the formulas for the two solutions in cells E5 and F5, respectively. The Excel formula for the first solution (in cell E5) is

$$=(-B5+SQRT(B5^2-4*A5*C5))/(2*A5)$$

The formula for the second solution (in cell F5) is

$$=(-B5-SQRT(B5^2-4*A5*C5))/(2*A5)$$

Verify that the constraints are being met by checking that $2a \neq 0$ (cell H5) and $b^2 - 4ac \geq 0$ (cell I5).

E5				f_x	=(-B5+SQRT(B5^2-4*A5*C5))/(2*A5)				
	A	B	C	D	E	F	G	H	I	J
1	Solving Quadatic Equations									
2										
3		Coefficients				Solutions			Checks		
4	a	b	c		Root 1	Root 2		2a	b^2 - 4ac	
5	1	2	1		-1.00	-1.00		2.00	0.00	
6	1	16	1							
7	-4	-8	24							
8	0	18	24							
9	-4	-8	4							
10										

Figure 23.49 Solving quadratic equations (partial).

Next, use the Fill Handle to copy the formulas in cells E5, F5, H5, and I5 down through rows 6 to 9. Your results should resemble Figure 23.50.

Notice how the row numbers in the formulas change because you are using relative references. Also, notice that an error is displayed for the solutions on row 8. The check calculation in cell H8 shows why; we have violated the constraint that $2a \neq 0$.

Figure 23.50 Solving quadratic equations (complete).

23.6 EXCEL ERROR MESSAGES

The formulas that we have presented so far are relatively simple. If you make an error when typing one of the example formulas, the location of the error is relatively easy to spot. As you begin to develop more complex formulas, locating and debugging errors becomes more difficult.

When a syntax error occurs in a formula, Excel will attempt to immediately catch the error and then display an error box that explains the error. However, formulas can be syntactically correct, but still produce errors when they are executed. If an expression cannot be evaluated, then Excel will denote the error by placing one of eight *error messages* in the target cell. These error messages are listed in Table 23.2.

TABLE 23.2 Excel error messages

Message	Description
######	The value is too wide to fit in the cell, or an attempt was made to display a negative date or time.
#VALUE	The wrong type of argument was used in a formula. This will occur, for example, if text was entered when an array argument was expected.
#DIV/0	An attempt was made to divide by zero in a formula. See the quadratic equation example in Figure 23.50 for an illustration.
# NAME	A name used in a formula is not recognized. Usually, the function or defined name was misspelled. Note that named ranges or functions may not contain spaces.
#REF	A referenced cell is not valid. This usually occurs when a cell is referenced in a formula and that cell is then deleted. It also occurs if an attempt is made to paste a cell over a referenced cell.
#NUM	The expression produces a numeric value that is out of range or invalid. Examples are extremely small, large, or imaginary numbers. To see this error, try this formula: $= SQRT(-1)$.
#NULL	An attempt was made to reference the intersection of two areas that don't intersect. This usually occurs when a space is inadvertently placed between two arguments, instead of a comma or colon, as in $=SUM(C2\ D3)$.

23.7   DEBUGGING EXCEL WORKSHEETS

When things go wrong and your worksheet is calculating values that can't be right, you have to find the error(s). This is called *debugging* the worksheet. With small worksheets you can select each cell and visually check to see if the formula is correct. But when worksheets get really large, checking every cell for an error is difficult, if not impossible. Fortunately, Excel provides some debugging tools that can help.

The worksheet shown in Figure 23.51 is a long-handed way of calculating the mean and standard deviation of a set of grades. Excel has a built-in function for calculating standard deviation (*STDEV*), but we need a worksheet that contains an error to show some debugging options. The worksheet in Figure 23.51 contains an error; finding it can be a challenge.

	A	B	C	D	E	F	G
1	Grade Calculations						
2							
3	Grades	Deviation	Dev^2			Results	
4	32	0.71	0.51				
5	14	-17.29	298.80		Mean:	31.29	
6	52	20.71	429.08		Sum(Dev^2):	1003.91	
7	26	-5.29	27.94		Std. Dev.:	11.93	
8	18	-13.29	176.51				
9	45	8.40	70.56				
10	32	0.71	0.51				
11							

Figure 23.51   A worksheet containing an error.

The standard deviation can be determined using the equation

$$\text{Std. Dev.} = \sqrt{\frac{\sum_{i=1}^{N}(x_i - \bar{x})^2}{N-1}}$$

where

$$Deviation = x_i - \bar{x}$$

23.7.1   Highlighting Formulas

A common worksheet error is the accidental replacement of a formula with a constant. A quick way to check for this is to have Excel highlight all cells that contain formulas. In Excel 2007 use Ribbon options **Home tab → Editing group→ Find & Select drop-down menu → Formulas option**. [Excel 2003: Edit → Go To → Select "Special" on the Go To dialog → Select "Formulas" on the Go To Special dialog.]

Excel will highlight all cells containing formulas, as illustrated in Figure 23.52. With the formulas highlighted it quickly becomes apparent that there is something wrong in cell B9; it doesn't contain a formula. Someone has typed 8.4 into cell B9, overwriting the formula.

Another option to check for this type of error is to have Excel display all of the formulas in the worksheet. In Excel 2007 this is done by toggling the **Show Formulas** button on the Ribbon (**Formulas tab** → **Formula Auditing group** → **Show Formulas button**.) When formulas are displayed (Figure 23.53), the error in cell B9 is again fairly easy to spot.

	A	B	C	D	E	F	G
1	Grade Calculations						
2							
3	Grades	Deviation	Dev^2			Results	
4	32	0.71	0.51				
5	14	-17.29	298.80		Mean:	31.29	
6	52	20.71	429.08		Sum(Dev^2):	1003.91	
7	26	-5.29	27.94		Std. Dev.:	11.93	
8	18	13.29	176.51				
9	45	8.40	70.56		Cell B9 does not		
10	32	0.71	0.51		contain a formula.		
11							

Figure 23.52   The grade calculation worksheet with all formulas highlighted.

Formulas

Trace Precedents   Show Formulas
Trace Dependents   Error Checking ▾
Remove Arrows ▾   Evaluate Formula
Watch Window

Formula Auditing

N29 f_x

	A	B	C	D	E	F	G
1	Grade Calcula						
2							
3	Grades	Deviation	Dev^2			Results	
4	32	=A4-$F$5	=B4^2				
5	14	=A5-$F$5	=B5^2		Mean:	=AVERAGE(A4	
6	52	=A6-$F$5	=B6^2		Sum(Dev^2):	=SUM(C4:C10)	
7	26	=A7-$F$5	=B7^2		Std. Dev.:	=SQRT(F6/COI	
8	18	=A8-$F$5	=B8^2				
9	45	8.4	=B9^2				
10	32	=A10-$F$5	=B10^2				
11							

Figure 23.53   Toggling the display of formulas to search for an error.

23.7.2 Tracing Dependents

A *dependent* is a value that is calculated after another calculation. In the grade calculations worksheet, you cannot calculate Deviation values until the Mean has been calculated, so the Deviation values are dependents of the Mean calculation.

You can have Excel display all of the dependents for any formula on the worksheet. In Excel 2007 this is done by selecting the formula you want to investigate and then clicking the **Trace Dependents** button on the Ribbon (**Formulas tab → Formula Auditing group → Trace Dependents button.**) This is illustrated in Figure 23.54. To clear the arrows from the display, click the **Remove Arrows** button on the Ribbon's Formulas tab.

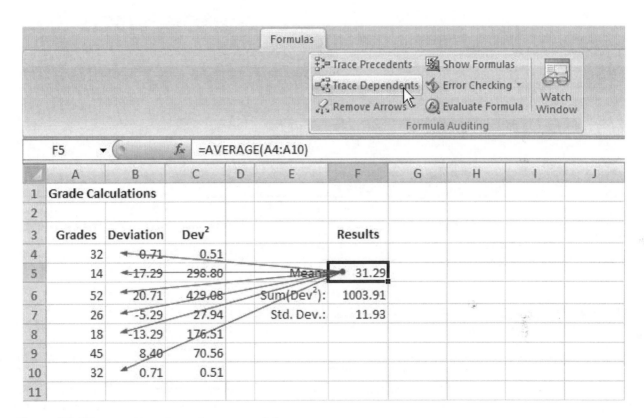

Figure 23.54   Using Trace Dependents to search for errors.

23.7.3 Tracing Precedents

A *precedent* is something that occurs before something else. In the grade worksheet, the Deviation values are calculated before the Dev^2 values, so the cells containing Deviation values are precedents for the cells containing the Dev^2 values. You can have Excel display all of the precedents for a particular formula by selecting the formula, then clicking the **Trace Precedents** button on the Ribbon's Formulas tab (**Formulas tab → Formula Auditing group → Trace Precedents button**). This is illustrated in Figure 23.55. To clear the arrows from the display, click the **Remove Arrows** button on the Ribbon's Formulas tab.

In Figure 23.55 we see that the calculation of the standard deviation depends on the value in cell F6 (the sum of the squared deviations) and all of the individual grades. It may seem odd that the individual grades are needed for this calculation, but Excel's *COUNT* function was used in the formula to determine the number of grades in the data set, and the *COUNT* function needed all of the grades to perform the count.

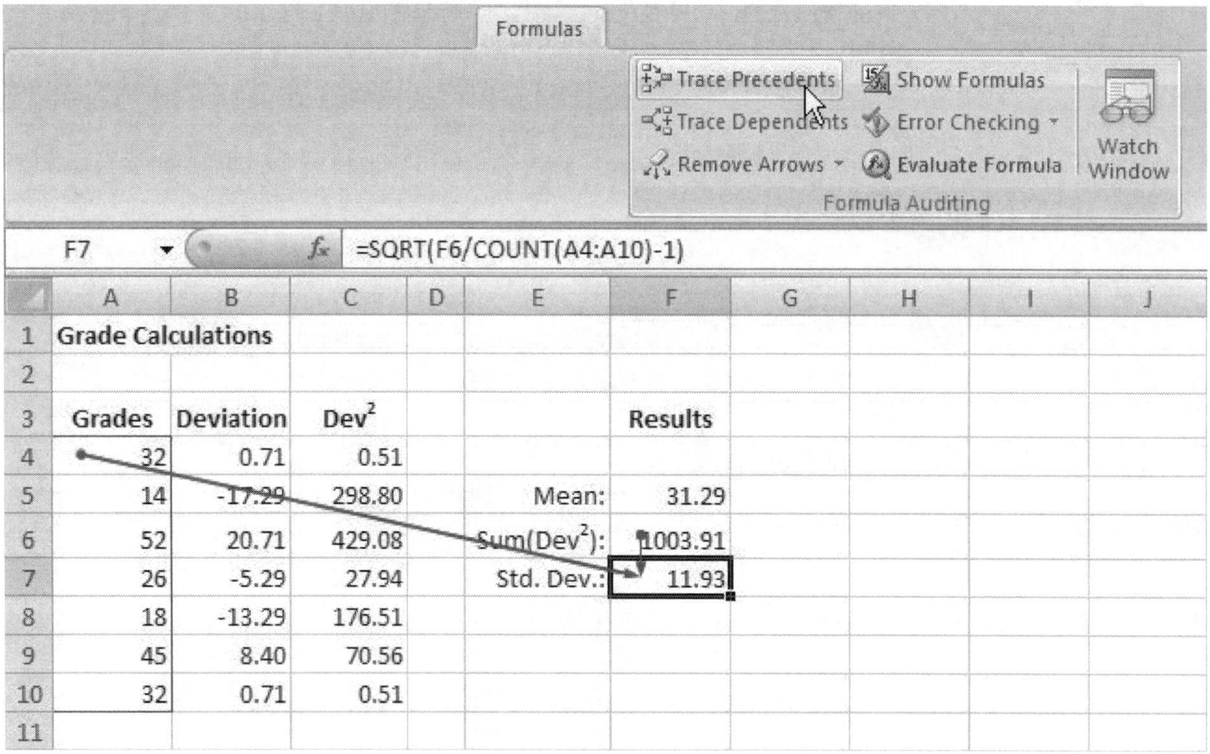

Figure 23.55 Checking the precedents of the standard deviation formula.

Column (or row) differences

Excel looks for unusual changes in row and column patterns and tries to let you know there may be a problem in an unobtrusive way. In Figure 23.56, the formula in cell C7 was entered as =B7^3 instead of =B7^2, which can happen if you make a simple typo while entering the formula. Excel noticed a change in pattern in that cell compared with its neighbors and marked the corner of the questionable cell with a colored triangle (indicated in Figure 23.56). These pattern changes may or may not represent errors, but they are usually worth checking out.

If you select the questionable cell and move your mouse over the warning indicator, a description of the potential error will be displayed (see Figure 23.57).

Excel's ability to watch out for row and column differences is a nice feature, but it has a couple of limitations:

- A value typed in over a formula (as in cell B9) is not detected.
- A change in pattern in the first or last cell of a column (or row) is not detected.

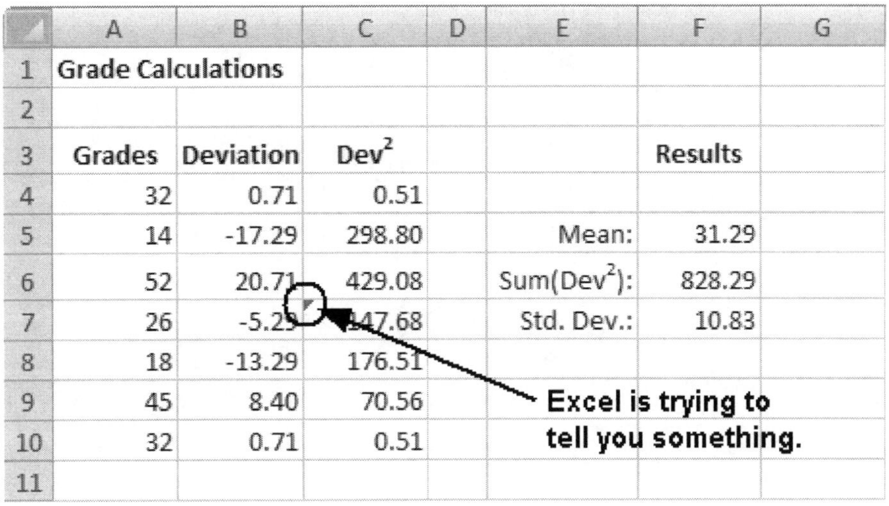

	A	B	C	D	E	F	G
1	Grade Calculations						
2							
3	Grades	Deviation	Dev^2			Results	
4	32	0.71	0.51				
5	14	-17.29	298.80		Mean:	31.29	
6	52	20.71	429.08		Sum(Dev^2):	828.29	
7	26	-5.2	47.68		Std. Dev.:	10.83	
8	18	-13.29	176.51				
9	45	8.40	70.56		Excel is trying to		
10	32	0.71	0.51		tell you something.		
11							

Figure 23.56   Excel marks the corner of cells when patterns seem to have changed.

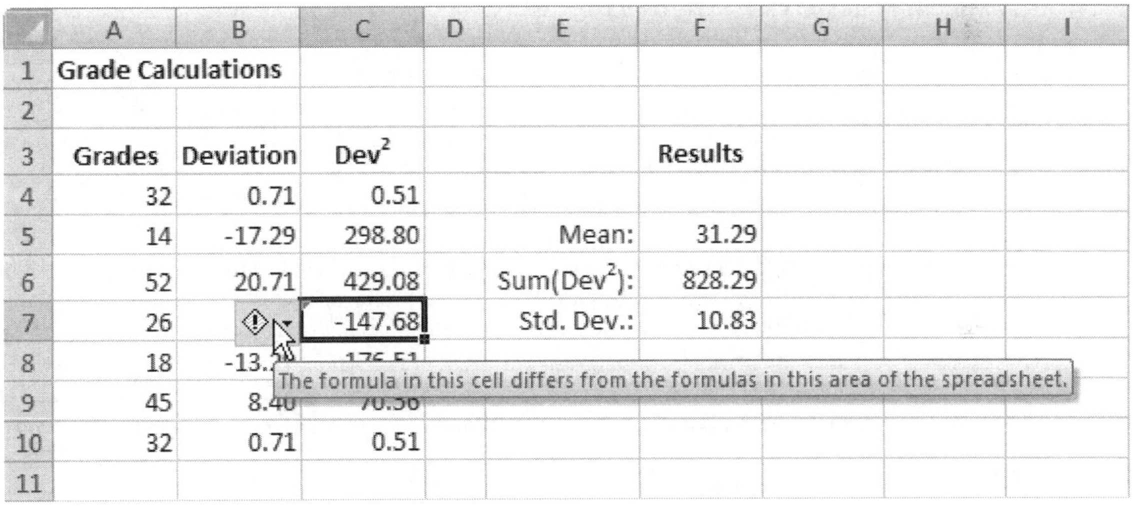

	A	B	C	D	E	F	G	H	I
1	Grade Calculations								
2									
3	Grades	Deviation	Dev^2			Results			
4	32	0.71	0.51						
5	14	-17.29	298.80		Mean:	31.29			
6	52	20.71	429.08		Sum(Dev^2):	828.29			
7	26		-147.68		Std. Dev.:	10.83			
8	18	-13.	176.51						
9	45	8.40	70.56						
10	32	0.71	0.51						
11									

The formula in this cell differs from the formulas in this area of the spreadsheet.

Figure 23.57   Move the mouse over the warning icon to see a description of the potential error.

The debugging methods described here helped identify an error in cell B9 (constant typed over a formula) and a second error (typo in a formula) inadvertently created while we were trying to find the first error. With those errors fixed, we can finally calculate the standard deviation of the grade data correctly (Figure 23.58).

The debugging tools prove their worth as the worksheet gets larger and more complex. Consider trying to find the same error without the debugging tool if column A contained 3,000 grades instead of 7 grades!

A	A	B	C	D	E	F	G
1	Grade Calculations						
2							
3	Grades	Deviation	Dev^2			Results	
4	32	0.71	0.51				
5	14	-17.29	298.80		Mean:	31.29	
6	52	20.71	429.08		Sum(Dev^2):	1121.43	
7	26	-5.29	27.94		Std. Dev.:	12.62	
8	18	-13.29	176.51				
9	45	13.71	188.08				
10	32	0.71	0.51				
11							

Figure 23.58   Corrected grade calculations worksheet.

23.8   USING MACROS TO AUTOMATE COMPUTATIONS

A *macro* is a stored collection of commands. If you type the same set of commands repeatedly, then using a macro can be a convenient, time-saving feature.

A macro is stored internally in a Visual Basic module. Visual Basic is a programming language. It is not within the scope of this text to teach you the Visual Basic language, and Excel allows you to record and execute macros without knowing Visual Basic. But because there is a programming language built into Excel (and other Microsoft Office programs), when you use macros you run the risk of contracting a computer virus (called a *macro virus*) that can be written in Visual Basic.

With Excel 2007, Microsoft has taken a big step towards minimizing the spread of macro viruses by using a new file name extension for most Excel workbooks, .xlsx. That final "x" is an indicator that macros cannot be stored in the workbook, and therefore the workbook cannot transmit a macro virus. You can write and use macros in any Excel workbook, but you can only save the macros if you use the new .xlsm file extension. This extension is available as part of the Save As procedure.

23.8.1   Recording a Macro

In Excel you can record a macro or write a macro program. The next sections will guide you through recording and running a macro. Then you will learn how to view the Visual Basic code that contains the macro commands. If you were to learn Visual Basic, then you could edit the code directly or write your own macros in the Visual Basic language.

Before recording a macro, it is wise to carefully plan the steps that you will be taking. When you are in recording mode, everything that you type is recorded—mistakes and all. In the next example, the major steps for computing several statistics for a set of data are listed. It is assumed that you are familiar with the use of Excel's built-in mathematical functions.

To prepare for recording the statistics macro, create the worksheet shown in Figure 23.59.

◢	A	B	C	D	E	F
1	Statistical Calculations					
2						
3		Data				
4		10				
5		12				
6		45				
7		32				
8		23				
9		23				
10		76				
11		21				
12		32				
13		21				
14						

Figure 23.59   Preparing to record a macro.

Next, decide whether you want to record the macro using *relative references* or *absolute references*. For example, we are going to calculate the mean value of the data set and put the result in cell E4, which is three cells to the right of the top of the column of data values. We have to tell Excel whether we want the result to appear "three cells to the right of the top of the column of data values" (relative reference), or "in cell E4" (absolute reference.) It is usually more useful to use relative referencing in macros.

To activate relative referencing, use the Ribbon's View tab with the following options: **View tab → Macros group → Macros drop-down menu → Click the Use Relative References toggle button.** The **Relative References** toggle button is highlighted (see Figure 23.60) when relative references are active.

One last step before recording the macro is choosing the cell that should be selected when macro recording begins. There are a few commonly used choices:

1. Select the cell at the top of the column of data. The advantage is that it is fairly easy to select the entire data set from this starting position.
2. Select the entire data set. This is commonly used if the macro will perform one calculation on the selected data (not so in this example).
3. Select the location where the result will be placed.

We will choose the first option in this example, although the other options could be used as well. Select cell B4 before recording the macro.

To record the sample macro, perform the following steps:

1. Turn on macro recording using the following Ribbon options: **View tab → Macros group → Macros drop-down menu → Record Macro... button**. [Excel 2003: Tools → Macro → Record New Macro.] The Record Macro dialog box will appear, as shown in Figure 23.61.

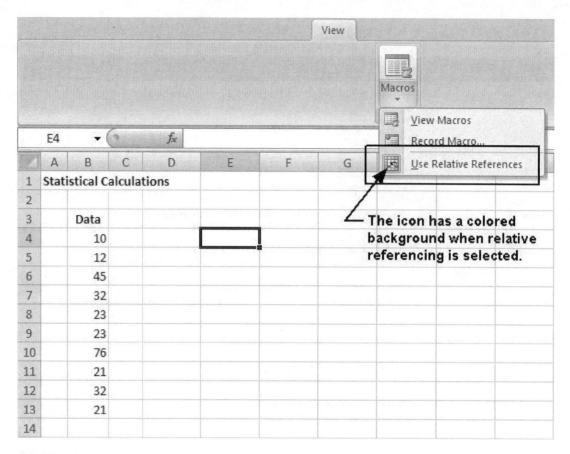

Figure 23.60   The icon on the Use Relative References toggle button has a colored background when it is selected.

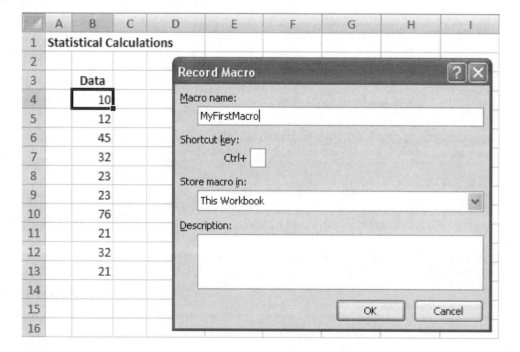

Figure 23.61   The Record Macro dialog box.

2. Give your macro a name—this example uses MyFirstMacro. This dialog box also allows you to assign a shortcut key and choose where to store the macro. When you are ready to record the macro, click **OK**.

NOTE: The "This Workbook" option is the default storage location, but your macro will not be stored with the workbook unless you use a macro-enabled workbook with the .xlsm file extension. If you try to save your workbook with the .xslx file extension after recording a macro, Excel will warn you that the macro cannot be stored.

Caution! Everything you now type will be recorded in the macro until you stop the recording process! To assist you in stopping the recording process, a Stop button is placed in the Status bar at the bottom of the Excel window, as indicated in Figure 23.62. [Excel 2003: The Stop button floats in a small dialog box.]

3. Enter the text "Results" in cell E3, then center and bold the font.
4. Enter the text "Mean:" in cell D4, right justified.

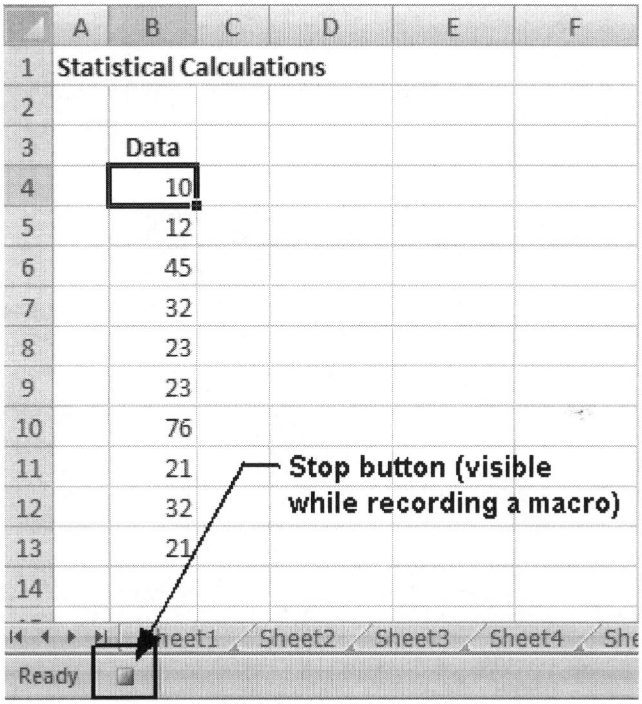

Figure 23.62 A Stop button appears in the Status bar while a macro is being recorded.

5. Enter the formula =AVERAGE(B4:B13) in cell E4.

    At this point your worksheet should resemble Figure 23.63.

6. Enter the text "Median:" in cell D5, right justified.
7. Enter the formula =MEDIAN(B4:B13) in cell E5.
8. Enter the text "Std. Dev.:" in cell D6, right justified.
9. Enter the formula =STDEV(B4:B13) in cell E6.

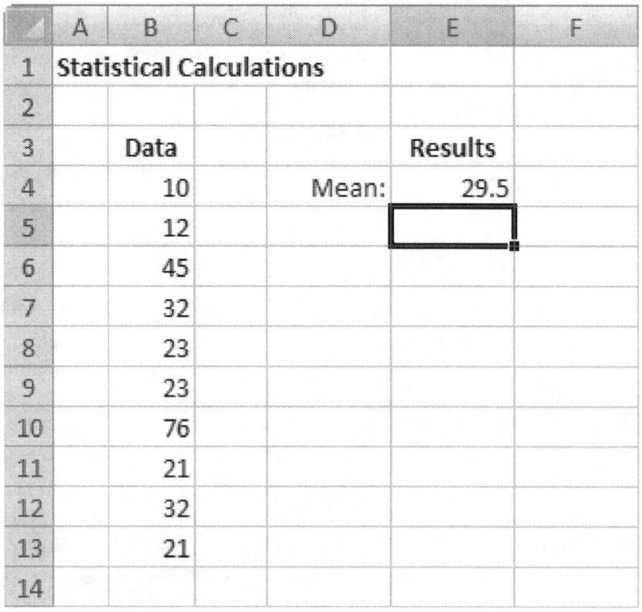

	A	B	C	D	E	F
1	Statistical Calculations					
2						
3		Data			Results	
4		10		Mean:	29.5	
5		12				
6		45				
7		32				
8		23				
9		23				
10		76				
11		21				
12		32				
13		21				
14						

Figure 23.63 The worksheet after the first set of results.

10. Check the formatting of the calculated values, adjusting the number of displayed digits as needed.
11. Press the **Stop** button to stop recording the macro. Congratulations—you have recorded a macro! Your worksheet should resemble Figure 23.64.

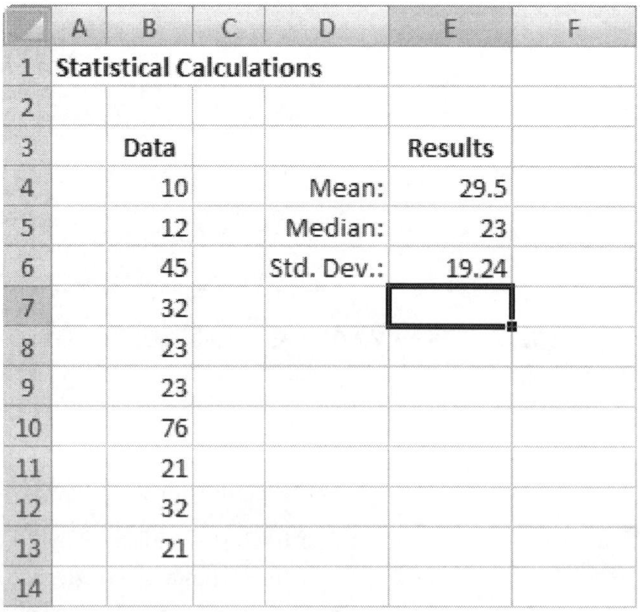

	A	B	C	D	E	F
1	Statistical Calculations					
2						
3		Data			Results	
4		10		Mean:	29.5	
5		12		Median:	23	
6		45		Std. Dev.:	19.24	
7		32				
8		23				
9		23				
10		76				
11		21				
12		32				
13		21				
14						

Figure 23.64 The worksheet after recording the macro.

23.8.2 Running a Macro

You can now retrieve and reuse your recorded macro whenever you need it. To see how powerful the use of macros can be, perform the following steps:

1. Clear the contents of all of the cells in columns D and E. First select columns D and E by clicking on the column headings, and then right-click and select **Clear Contents** from the Quick Edit menu.

2. Select the top value in the data set, cell B4.

3. Run your macro with the following Ribbon options: **View tab → Macros group → Macros drop-down menu → Select the View Macros option**. [Excel 2003: Tools → Macros → Macros.] The Macro dialog box will be displayed (Figure 23.65).

4. Select your macro's name from the list and then click the **Run** button. Voila! Your worksheet will automatically perform all of the commands that you previously recorded.

23.8.3 Editing a Macro

Several functions may be performed from the Macro dialog box (Figure 23.65).

- The **Step Into** button allows you to debug a macro.
- You can edit the macro (stored in a Visual Basic module.)
- The macro may be deleted by choosing the **Delete** button.
- A shortcut key may still be added for a macro by choosing the **Options** button.

Select your macro name from the list and choose the **Edit** button on the Macro dialog box. The Microsoft Visual Basic editor (where you can create, modify, and manage your

Figure 23.65 The Macro dialog box.

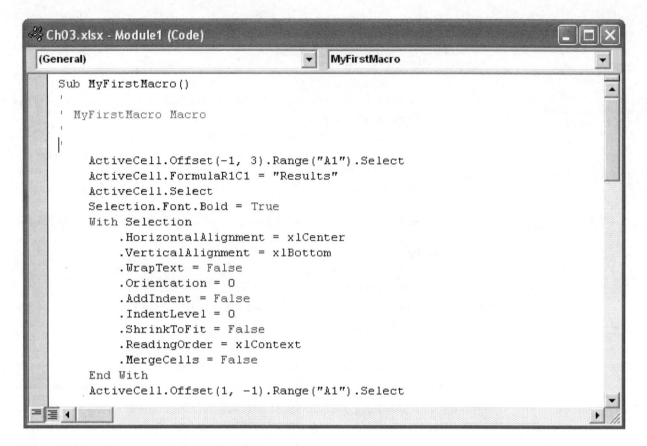

Figure 23.66 The macro code in the Visual Basic module.

macros) will open as depicted in Figure 23.66. Inside the editor, you can view and modify the Visual Basic code that was created when you recorded the macro.

For example, the following two lines of code placed the text "Results" in cell E3:

```
ActiveCell.Offset(-1, 3).Range("A1").Select

ActiveCell.FormulaR1C1 = "Results"
```

Practice!

Convince yourself that the code displayed in the Visual Basic editor is actually the same code contained in the macro. You can do this without knowing the Visual Basic language. Make a trivial change, such as changing the line

```
ActiveCell.FormulaR1C1 = "Mean:"
```

to

```
ActiveCell.FormulaR1C1 = "Average:"
```

Execute the modified macro by choosing the Run button on the Visual Basic editor standard toolbar. Your worksheet should change to reflect your code change as illustrated in Figure 23.67!

	A	B	C	D	E	F
1	Statistical Calculations					
2						
3		Data			Results	
4		10		Average:	29.5	
5		12		Median:	23	
6		45		Std. Dev.:	19.24	
7		32				
8		23				
9		23				
10		76				
11		21				
12		32				
13		21				
14						

Figure 23.67   The macro results after modifying the Visual Basic code.

APPLICATION

APPLICATION—CREATING TABLES OF COMPOUND AMOUNT FACTORS

Excel is a great tool for creating and displaying tables of information that are based on repetition of formulas. The next example shows how to create a table that shows the power of compound interest—a *compound amount factor table*. By using this table, an investor can see how the value of an initial investment will increase over time at different interest rates. For example, a person who invests $1,000 at 6 percent interest for 20 years will have $1,000 × 3.2017, or $3,207. A person who invests $1,000 at 11 percent interest for 20 years will have $1,000 × 8.0623, or $8,062.

To create the table, follow these steps:

1. Enter titles and headings as shown in Figure 23.68.

	A	B	C	D	E	F	G	H	I
1	Compound Amount Factors								
2									
3		Interest Rate:	6%	7%	8%	9%	10%	11%	
4									
5		Years							
6									

Figure 23.68   Titles and headings

2. Create the column of values indicating the duration of the investment in years. First, enter 0 in cell B6 and 10 in cell B7. Then select the region B6:B7 and drag the Fill Handle down seven more rows. For appearance, center justify the year values as shown in Figure 23.69.

3. Type 1 for year zero under each interest rate (cells C6:H6). Format region C6:H12 to display four decimal places. The result is shown in Figure 23.69.

4. The formula for single-payment compound factor is $[1 + i]^N$, where i is the interest rate and N is the number of interest periods—in this case, years. Enter the following formula for the single-payment compound amount factor in cell C7:

$$= (1+C\$3)^{\wedge}\$B7$$

Notice that dollar signs have been included to indicate that the interest rate is always in row 3 and the duration (number of interest periods) is always in column B.

5. Use the Fill Handle to copy the formula to cells C8:C12.

6. Select the region C7:C12. Drag the Fill Handle to the right until the whole table is populated. Your completed table should resemble Figure 23.70.

Notice that the equation for a compound amount factor was entered only once, in cell C7. All that was necessary to complete the rest of the table was to copy the equation in cell C7 to the rest of the cells in the table.

	A	B	C	D	E	F	G	H	I
1	Compound Amount Factors								
2									
3		Interest Rate:	6%	7%	8%	9%	10%	11%	
4									
5		Years							
6		0	1.0000	1.0000	1.0000	1.0000	1.0000	1.0000	
7		10							
8		20							
9		30							
10		40							
11		50							
12		60							
13									

Figure 23.69   Investment durations added in the Years column, and baseline factors (1.0000 in year zero) entered.

	A	B	C	D	E	F	G	H	I
1	Compound Amount Factors								
2									
3	Interest Rate:		6%	7%	8%	9%	10%	11%	
4									
5		Years							
6		0	1.0000	1.0000	1.0000	1.0000	1.0000	1.0000	
7		10	1.7908	1.9672	2.1589	2.3674	2.5937	2.8394	
8		20	3.2071	3.8697	4.6610	5.6044	6.7275	8.0623	
9		30	5.7435	7.6123	10.0627	13.2677	17.4494	22.8923	
10		40	10.2857	14.9745	21.7245	31.4094	45.2593	65.0009	
11		50	18.4202	29.4570	46.9016	74.3575	117.3909	184.5648	
12		60	32.9877	57.9464	101.2571	176.0313	304.4816	524.0572	
13									

Figure 23.70   The completed Single-Factor, Compound Amount Factor table.

APPLICATION

APPLICATION—INTERACTIVE DC CIRCUIT ANALYZER

When there is a sudden change in a DC circuit that includes a capacitor or an impedance, the current in the circuit varies with time (e.g., until the capacitor is charged). A general expression for the current I in a DC transient circuit is

$$I(t) = I_\infty + (I_0 - I_\infty)\, e^{-t/T},$$

where

I_0 is an initial value at the instant of sudden change,

I_∞ is the current at time $t = \infty$,

$T = RC$ is the time constant for a series R–C (resistance–capacitance) circuit,

and

$T = L/R$ is the time constant for a series R–L (resistance–impedance) circuit.

If switch S is closed at $t = 0$, then we can calculate the current in the circuit as a function of time. In this example we will determine the current in the circuit after a time equal to three time constants $(t = 3T)$. $I_0 = 0$ in this example (no current when the switch was open). We will create a worksheet that calculates $I\,(t = 3T)$ for any values of V and R entered by a user. If I_0, V, and R are entered into cells B5, B6, and B7, respectively, then the current at $t = \infty$ can be found from $I_\infty = V/R$. In our worksheet, the Excel formula for I_∞ is

$$=B5/B6$$

and the Excel formula for $I(t = 3T)$ is

$$=B9+(B4-B9)*EXP(B10)$$

If you enter the voltage (10 volts) and resistance (50 ohms) from the circuit displayed in Figure 23.71, then your calculated results should resemble those in Figure 23.72. The current at three time constants after the switch is closed equals 0.19 amps.

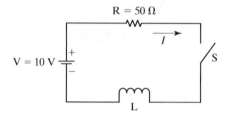

Figure 23.71   An R–L circuit.

You can use a worksheet like the one shown in Figure 23.72 to compute the current interactively by entering various values for V and R.

B11		f_x	=B9+(B4-B9)*EXP(B10)				
	A	B	C	D	E	F	G	H
1	Interactive DC Circuit Analyzer							
2						R = 50 Ω		
3	Inputs							
4	I(0):	0	amps					
5	V:	10	volts	V = 10 V			S	
6	R:	50	ohms					
7								
8	Calculated Results							
9	I(∞):	0.20	amps			L		
10	-t/T:	-3	no units					
11	I(t = 3T):	0.19	amps					
12								

Figure 23.72   Interactive calculator for finding the current in a DC transient circuit.

KEY TERMS

absolute cell referencing	error messages	named cell
ACOS function	Fill Handle	named cell range
ASIN function	formula	operator precedence
ATAN function	Formula bar	precedence
AVERAGE function	future value	precedent tracing
built-in functions	Insert Function button	present value
cell range	macro	prototype
compound amount factor	macro virus	radians
Ctrl + Shift + Enter	matrix	relative cell referencing
(array functions)	matrix order	Ribbon
debugging	matrix product	*STDEV* function
degrees	*MEDIAN* function	*SUM* function
DEGREES function	*MMULT* function	syntax
dependent tracing	Name box	transpose (matrix)

Summary

Referencing Cells

- Relative reference—cell addresses follow the formula when copied
- Absolute reference—cell addresses are fixed (use $ to create an absolute reference)
- Examples
  - $A$1 both row and column are absolute
  - $A1 column is absolute, row is relative
  - A$1 column is relative, row is absolute

Naming Cells and Cell Ranges

1. Select the cell or cell range.
2. Enter the name in the Name Box (left side of Formula bar).

Use the Name Manager [**Formula tab → Defined Names group → Name Manager**] to remove a name from a cell or cell range.

Formula Syntax

- Start a formula with an equal sign (=)
- Formulas can contain
  - math operators
  - values
  - cell references
  - function calls

Operator Precedence

- Formulas are generally interpreted from left to right, except
  - operator precedence rules (see the following table) sometimes alter the order, and
  - parentheses can be used to control how a function is interpreted

Built-In Functions

Precedence	Operator	Operation
1	%	Percentage
2	^	Exponentiation
3	*, /	Multiplication, Division
4	+, −	Addition, Subtraction

- Use the Insert Function button on the Formula bar to open the Insert Function dialog
- Search for a function (from the Insert Function dialog)
  - using a search
  - by category
- Function Arguments dialog boxes
  - identify all required and optional arguments
  - assist you in correctly using the functions
- The Excel Help system provides information on built-in functions

Commonly Used Excel Functions (only a small portion of Excel's built-in functions are listed here)

Basic Math Functions

- SUM
- LOG
- LN
- EXP
- FACT

Statistical Functions

- AVERAGE
- STDEV
- MEDIAN

Trigonometric Functions (angles are measured in radians)

- SIN
- COS
- TAN
- ASIN
- ACOS
- ATAN
- DEGREES (converts radians to degrees)
- RADIANS (converts degrees to radians)

Matrix Functions (enter an array function with Ctrl-Shift-Enter)

- MMULT
- MINVERSE
- MDETERM
- TRANSPOSE

Financial Functions

- PV
- FV
- PMT

Excel Error Messages

Message	Description
######	The value is too wide to fit in the cell, or an attempt was made to display a negative date or time.
#VALUE	The wrong type of argument was used in a formula. This will occur, for example, if text was entered when an array argument was expected.
#DIV/0	An attempt was made to divide by zero in a formula. See the quadratic equation example in Figure 23.50 for an illustration.
#NAME	A name used in a formula is not recognized. Usually, the function or defined name was misspelled. Note that named ranges or functions may not contain spaces.
#REF	A referenced cell is not valid. This usually occurs when a cell is referenced in a formula and that cell is then deleted. It also occurs if an attempt is made to paste a cell over a referenced cell.
#NUM	The expression produces a numeric value that is out of range or invalid. Examples are extremely small, large, or imaginary numbers. To see this error, try this formula: $=SQRT(-1)$
#NULL	An attempt was made to reference the intersection of two areas that don't intersect. This usually occurs when a space is inadvertently placed between two arguments, instead of a comma or colon, as in $=SUM(C2\ D3)$.

Debugging Worksheets

- Highlight Formulas [**Home tab → Editing group → Find & Select drop-down menu → Formulas option**]
- Display Formulas [**Formulas tab → Formula Auditing group → Show Formulas button**]
- Tracing Dependents [**Formulas tab → Formula Auditing group → Trace Dependents button**]
- Tracing Precedents [**Formulas tab → Formula Auditing group → Trace Precedents button**]
- Remove Arrows [**Formulas tab → Formula Auditing group → Remove Arrows button**]
- Pattern Errors—Excel marks the corners of cells that appear not to match the pattern of adjacent cells

Macros

- Recording a Macro [**View tab** → **Macros group** → **Macros drop-down menu** → **Record Macro... button**]
- Running a Macro [**View tab** → **Macros group**→ **Macros drop-down menu** → **Select the View Macros option**, then select the desired macro and click the **Run** button]
- Activating Relative Referencing [**View tab** → **Macros group** → **Macros drop-down menu** → **Click the Use Relative References toggle button**]

Problems

1. Place the number 10 in cell A1. Create an Excel formula that computes

    $$f(x) = x^2 - 4x + 3$$

    using the value in cell A1 as x.

2. Place the values for $x = 5$ and $y = 7$ in cells A1 and A2, respectively. Create an Excel formula that computes

    $$f(x, y) = y^3 - 10x^2$$

    using the values in cells A1 and A2.

3. Place the numbers 1, 2, ... 10 in cells A1:A10. Create an Excel formula in cell B1 that computes

    $$f(x) = \ln x + \sin x$$

    using the value in cell A1. Use the Fill Handle and drag the formula over cells B2:B10 to evaluate $f(x)$ for all ten values.

4. For a damped oscillation as depicted in Figure 23.73, the displacement of a structure is defined by the equation

    $$f(t) = 8\,e^{-kt} \cos(\omega t),$$

    where $k = 0.5$ and the frequency $\omega = 3$. Create an Excel formula for this equation. Compute $f(t)$ for t = 0.0, 0.1, 0.2, ... 4.0 seconds. What is the value of $f(t)$ for $t = 3.6$ seconds?

5. The formula that calculates the number of combinations of r objects taken from a collection of n objects is

    $$C(n, r) = \frac{n!}{(n - r)!r!}.$$

    The exclamation point is the mathematical symbol for the *factorial* operation. The factorial of a number $n = n \times (n - 1) \times (n - 2) \times, \ldots \times 3 \times 2 \times 1$. Thus, the factorial of

    $$4 = 4 \times 3 \times 2 \times 1 = 24.$$

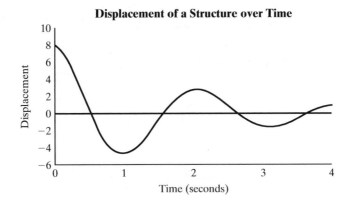

Figure 23.73   Damped oscillation representing displacement of a structure.

The Excel function for factorial is called *FACT*. The preceding formula can be used to compute the number of ways a committee of six people can be chosen from a group of eight people, as illustrated in Figure 23.74.

C6		f_x =FACT(C4)/(FACT(C4-C3)*FACT(C3))				
	A	B	C	D	E	F	G
1	Combinations						
2							
3		r:	6				
4		n:	8				
5							
6		combinations:	28				
7							

Figure 23.74   Calculating the number of possible combinations.

Write an Excel workbook to calculate combinations. Use it to compute how many 5-card hands may be drawn from a deck of 52 cards.

6.   Excel has a number of predefined logical functions. One of these, the *IF* function, has the following syntax:

$$=IF(TEST,T,F)$$

The effect of the function is to evaluate the expression *TEST*, which must be a logical expression. If the expression evaluates to "true," then *T* is returned. If the expression valuates to "false," then *F* is returned. For example, the *IF* function

```
IF (X < 200, X, "Cholesterol is too high')
```

tests to see if *X* is less than 200 (see Figure 23.75).

C4	▼			f_x	=IF(C3<200,C3,"Cholesterol is too high")	
	A	B	C	D	E	F	G
1	Cholesterol Check						
2							
3		X:	210				
4		Check:	Cholesterol is too high				
5							

Figure 23.75 Using the *IF* function.

- If *X* is less than 200, the *IF* function returns the value of *X*.
- If *X* is greater than or equal to 200, then the text statement "Cholesterol is too high" is returned (and displayed in the cell containing the *IF* function).

To try the *IF* function, expand the quadratic equation example (see Figure 23.50) to test for division by zero. If the expression $2a = 0$ is true, then display "Divide by Zero"; otherwise, return the value of $2a$.

Perform a similar test for $b^2 - 4ac \geq 0$. Display "Requires Complex Number" if the test is false.

7. Neglecting air resistance, the horizontal range of a projectile fired into the air at an angle of θ degrees is given by the formula

$$R = \frac{2V^2 \sin \theta \cos \theta}{g}.$$

Create a worksheet that computes *R* for a selected initial velocity *V* and firing angle θ. Use $g = 9.81$ meters/sec^2. Convert degrees to radians by using the *RADIANS* function. To test your results, an initial velocity of 150 meters/sec and firing angle of 25° should result in $R = 1,756$ meters.

8. Two frequently performed matrix operations are the calculation of the *determinant* of a matrix and the *inverse* of a matrix. The Excel functions for these operations are *MDETERM* and *MINVERSE*, respectively. Create matrices A and B as shown in Figure 23.32. Compute the matrix determinant and inverse of A and B.

9. Create a macro that computes, labels, and displays the determinant and inverse of a 3 × 3 matrix typed into cells A1:C3. Create a shortcut key to execute the macro.

10. Using trigonometry, you can calculate the height of a tall tree on a sunny day by measuring the length of the tree's shadow and the angle that the line between the tip of the shadow and the tip of the tree makes with the ground. The required variables are indicated in Figure 23.76.

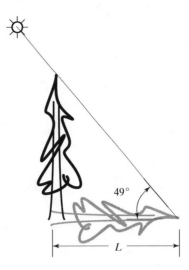

Figure 23.76 Determining the height of a tree on a sunny day.

If the length of the shadow is 22 meters and the angle is 49°, the height can be determined by using the tangent function:

$$height = L\,\text{TAN}(49°).$$

But remember, Excel's *TAN* function wants the angle in radians, not degrees. Use the *RADIANS* function to convert 49° to radians, then use Excel's *TAN* function to determine the height of the tree.

11. If a groundskeeper wants to apply 0.022 kg of fertilizer to each square meter of a football field, how much fertilizer should he or she purchase? Create an Excel worksheet to determine the answer.

Data

- A football field is 100 yards long and 50 yards wide.
- There are 3 feet per yard.
- There are 3.2808 feet per meter.

12. Any time you want to borrow money from a bank, credit union, or car dealer, you will have to pay back the loan in monthly payments with interest. The interest rate will be stated as an *annual percentage rate*, or *APR*. However, you will need a monthly interest rate to calculate the monthly payment. The monthly interest rate is simply the APR/12.

Create your own loan payment calculator in Excel. An example for a $10,000 loan with a 7 percent APR is shown in Figure 23.77. For this loan, the monthly payment will be about $309.

Follow these steps to create the loan payment calculator worksheet:

1. Enter the labels as shown in column B in Figure 23.77.

2. Enter an amount in cell C3. This is the amount you want to borrow. Format cell C3, using a Currency or Accounting format.

3. Enter the APR (from the bank) in cell C4. Format this cell with a Percentage format. (If you type 7% into the cell, Excel will automatically apply a Percentage format.)

	C8	▼	f_x	=PMT(C5,C6,C3)	
	A	B		C	D
1	Loan Payment Calculator				
2					
3		Amount borrowed (P):		$10,000	
4		Annual percentage rate (APR):		7%	
5		Monthly interest rate (i):		0.58%	
6		Number of monthly payments:		36	
7					
8		Amount of each payment (PMT):		-$308.77	
9					

Figure 23.77 Loan payment calculator.

4. In cell C5, enter the formula =C4/12 to compute the monthly interest rate from the annual rate. Format cell C5 with a Percentage format and display at least two decimal places.

5. Enter the number of monthly payments in cell C6.

6. Use Excel's *PMT* function in cell C8 to compute the required annual payment. The *PMT* function will use the values in cells C3, C5, and C6 as arguments. Use the Insert Function dialog box or the Help system to determine the proper syntax of the *PMT* function arguments.

Calculate the required payment for each of the following types of loans:

Loan Type	P	APR	N (months)
Car Loan	$ 21,000	8.0%	48
Student Loan	$ 24,000	4.3%	120
Home Loan	$250,000	6.5%	360

13. Calculate the mean, median, and mode for the grade data shown in Figure 23.78. The Excel functions used to compute these statistics are the *AVERAGE*, *MEDIAN*, and *MODE* functions, respectively.

14. A discount store sells two different brands of tire pressure gauges. Joseph wants to get the best tire gauge he can. He convinces the store manager to let him try two brands to see which one works better. He goes out to the parking lot and takes 10 pressure readings with each gauge on a single tire. The results (pressures in lb_f/in^2 or psi) are shown in Figure 23.79.

Use Excel's *AVERAGE* and *STDEV* functions to calculate the average pressure and the standard deviation for each column of data. Which gauge do you think Joseph should buy?

15. Matrix math can be used to solve systems of linear equations such as the following three equations:

$$1x_1 + 3x_2 + 5x_3 = 6$$
$$1x_1 + 4x_2 + 7x_3 = 4$$
$$2x_1 + 3x_2 + 1x_3 = 9$$

	A	B	C
1	**Grade Data**		
2			
3	**Student**	**Score**	
4	1	78	
5	2	88	
6	3	98	
7	4	88	
8	5	100	
9	6	95	
10	7	82	
11	8	96	
12	9	82	
13	10	98	
14	11	84	
15	12	64	
16	13	82	
17	14	77	
18	15	92	
19			
20	mean:		
21	median:		
22	mode:		
23			

Figure 23.78 Course scores.

	A	B	C
1	**Comparing Pressure Gauges**		
2			
3	**Gauge A**	**Gauge B**	
4	28	23	
5	28	32	
6	28	23	
7	25	27	
8	26	25	
9	26	32	
10	26	29	
11	28	23	
12	29	26	
13	28	29	
14			

Figure 23.79 Pressure readings on a single tire.

To solve these equations, collect the coefficients multiplying the x variables into a coefficient matrix C, and collect the constants on the right side of the equations into a vector (single-column matrix) r.

$$C = \begin{bmatrix} 1 & 3 & 5 \\ 1 & 4 & 7 \\ 2 & 3 & 1 \end{bmatrix} \quad r = \begin{bmatrix} 6 \\ 4 \\ 9 \end{bmatrix}$$

The x values (x_1, x_2 and x_3) are determined by inverting the C matrix and multiplying that result by the r vector.

$$x = C^{-1} r$$

In Excel, the process is carried out by using the *MINVERSE* function and the *MMULT* function. The results are shown in Figure 23.80.

	A	B	C	D	E	F	G	H
1	Solving Simultaneous Linear Equations							
2								
3	[C]	1	3	5		[r]	6	
4		1	4	7			4	
5		2	3	1			9	
6								
7	[C]inv	5.666667	-4	-0.33333		[x]	15	
8		-4.33333	3	0.666667			-8	
9		1.666667	-1	-0.33333			3	
10								

Figure 23.80 Solving simultaneous linear equations.

(a) Verify that the calculated results $x_1 = 15$, $x_2 = -8$ and $x_3 = 3$ do satisfy the simultaneous equations.

(b) Modify the worksheet to solve the following set of simultaneous equations:

$$1x_1 + 3x_2 + 5x_3 = 3$$
$$1x_1 + 4x_2 + 7x_3 = 5$$
$$2x_1 + 3x_2 + 1x_3 = 12$$

Chapter 24
Working with Charts

24.1 INTRODUCTION

With Excel 2007 the procedure for creating a basic graph, or *chart*, from a data set has changed. It is still easy, but the multistep dialog called the Chart Wizard used in earlier versions of Excel is gone. Now you create a basic chart from your data set and then refine the chart's features using various Ribbon options. When you are working with a chart, three new Ribbon tabs provide access to chart formatting options. These will be presented in detail later in the chapter.

The first sections of this chapter are organized to follow the typical steps that you will use in preparing a chart:

- Create the basic chart (Section 24.2).
- Select a chart layout (Section 24.3).
- Format features of the basic chart (Section 24.4).
- Preview and print the chart (Section 24.6).

Then, the chapter presents information on ways to add data to an existing chart and to prepare a chart with more than one curve. Finally, certain chart features that are particularly useful to engineers are examined.

OBJECTIVES

After reading this chapter, you should be able to perform the following tasks:

- Insert a basic chart on a worksheet.
- Use a chart layout to add additional features.
- Create Line charts and XY Scatter charts.
- Format chart legends, axes, and titles.
- Preview and print a chart.
- Add an additional data series to a chart.
- Scale axes and create error bars.

24.2   CREATING A BASIC CHART

Creating a basic chart in Excel is trivial:

1. Select the data to be charted.
2. Use the Ribbon's Insert tab.
3. Select the type of chart to be created from the Charts group.

That's it—the basic chart will be created and placed on the worksheet. Once the basic chart is created you can start modifying it to meet your needs.

Creating a chart in Excel is nearly automatic, but you need to understand that Excel is making the process easy by making some assumptions about how your data is organized. Your charting will be less stressful if you organize the data to be charted in ways that Excel can recognize.

- The data values for each *series* (each curve on a chart) should be in a single column or row. Columns are more common, but rows will work.
- If you want to name a data series, the name should be in a single cell at the top of the column or left end of the row.
- For an XY Scatter chart, which requires both x and y values for plotting, the x values should be in the left column or top row.

Figure 24.1 shows a typical data layout for creating an XY Scatter chart. The data to be plotted are in cells A3:B12, including the column headings. The potential values will be plotted on the x axis, and the current values on the y axis.

	A	B	C
1	Current - Potential Data		
2			
3	Potential (V)	Current (A)	
4	6.97	0.051	
5	5.96	0.044	
6	4.95	0.038	
7	3.98	0.032	
8	3.03	0.025	
9	1.91	0.018	
10	1.02	0.012	
11	0.50	0.008	
12	0.20	0.001	
13			

Figure 24.1   Data collected by measuring current across a 150 Ω resistor.

In this chapter we will cover XY Scatter charts first, because they are very commonly used in engineering.

24.2.1   Creating a Basic XY Scatter Chart

An *XY Scatter chart* shows the relationship between two variables, one plotted on the x axis and the other plotted on the y axis. This type of chart is useful for visualizing relationships among data: how one variable responds to changes in the other variable.

Before proceeding, create the worksheet shown in Figure 24.1 so that you can work through the examples in this chapter. The data in Figure 24.1 were collected by measuring current (I) in amperes (A) across a resistor for nine measured voltages (V). Ohm's law, which is

$$V = IR,$$

states that the relationship between V and I is linear if temperature is kept relatively constant. In this section we will create a basic XY Scatter chart from the data in Figure 24.1. An XY Scatter chart locates points using the x and y values associated with each data point. Because the x and y values for each point on the chart are paired, they are sometimes referred to as x, y *data pairs*.

Use the following steps to create an XY Scatter chart of the data in Figure 24.1:

1. Select the data to be charted (including the headings, if desired), cells A3:B12 in this example.
2. Insert the basic XY Scatter chart on your worksheet using Ribbon options: **Insert tab → Charts group → Scatter drop-down menu → Scatter with only markers style**. These Ribbon options are illustrated in Figure 24.2.

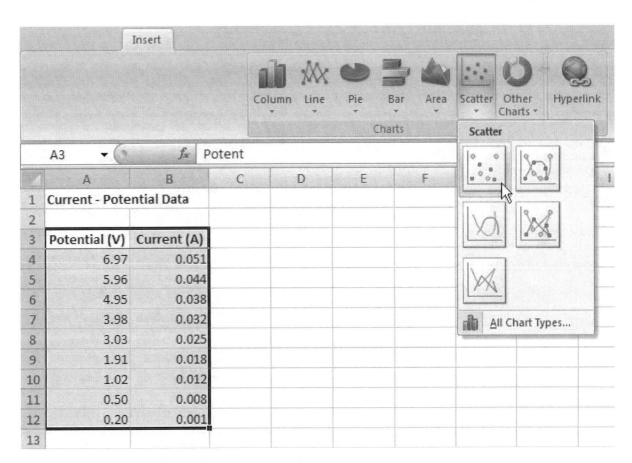

Figure 24.2   Inserting a basic XY Scatter chart on the worksheet.

Notice, in Figure 24.2, that there are five styles of XY Scatter chart available on the Scatter drop-down menu:

- Markers only, no connecting lines.
- Markers with smoothed connecting lines.
- Smoothed connecting lines, no markers.
- Markers and connecting lines, no line smoothing.
- Connecting lines, no line smoothing, no markers.

When you are inserting the basic chart, simply select the style you want Excel to use to create the chart. In this example we will use markers only. The basic XY Scatter chart created from our data is shown in Figure 24.3.

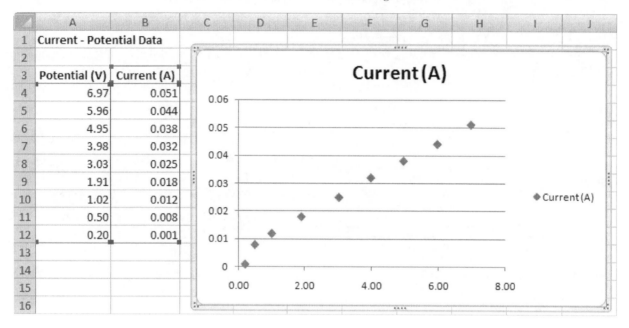

Figure 24.3   The basic XY Scatter chart on the worksheet.

Creating the basic chart is very easy, but there are no axis labels yet, and you may want to change the default title. Those changes will be described in the next section.

Following are some worksheet features (see Figure 24.3) that can be useful when working with charts:

- When a chart is selected, as in Figure 24.3, it is shown with a heavy border. If you need to move the chart, grab the border with the mouse and drag the chart to a new location.
- The chart border includes *handles* (small dots) on each corner and side. Those handles can be used (with the mouse) to change the size of the displayed chart.
- The data used to create the chart are indicated by colored boxes (around cells A4:A12 and B4:B12).
- The series heading that was selected before creating the graph ["Current (A)" in cell B3] was used as the series title in the legend (right side of chart) and as the chart title (top of chart).

The next step in creating a useful chart is getting axis labels on the chart. This is accomplished by selecting a chart layout, the subject of the next section.

24.3   SELECTING A CHART LAYOUT

Whenever a chart is selected, Excel makes additional chart tools available on the Ribbon in three new Chart Tool Tabs:

- **Design**—global aspects of the chart's design (chart type, layout, basic style).
- **Layout**—individual elements of a chart (axis labels, gridlines).
- **Format**—specific format details (shape line color, font color).

The Design tab (Figure 24.4) is the most general, while the Format tab gets much more detailed. You typically start editing your chart with the Design tab.

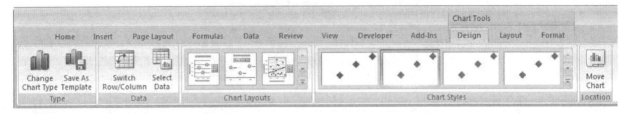

Figure 24.4   The Chart Tools: Design Tab on the Ribbon when a chart is selected.

When a basic XY Scatter chart is created, it is missing some key features, primarily the features used to describe what variable is being plotted on each axis and the units on the variable. The quickest way to add features to a chart is to select a *chart layout*. Various chart layouts are available from the Ribbon: **Chart Tools → Design tab → Chart Layouts group → Chart Layouts palette**. The Chart Layouts palette is shown in Figure 24.5. This is a very complex selection palette allowing you to choose various options, including

- Axis labels
- Legend location
- Gridline style
- Linear trendline

The good news is that Layout 1 (indicated in Figure 24.5) works for a lot of XY Scatter chart applications.

Apply a chart layout by following these steps:

1. Select the chart by clicking on some white space near the edge of the chart. You want the entire chart selected, not any of the elements of the chart such as an axis, a title, or a data point.
2. Click on the desired chart layout: **Chart Tools → Design tab → Chart Layouts group → Chart Layouts palette → select the desired layout**.

In Figure 24.6 Layout 1 has been applied to the chart. The only real change is that the words "Axis Title" now appear on the x and y axes.

To change the text of either an axis title or the chart title, simply select the title by clicking on it with the mouse, and start typing. The new text appears in the Formula bar (see Figure 24.7) until you press **Enter**; then the chart is updated.

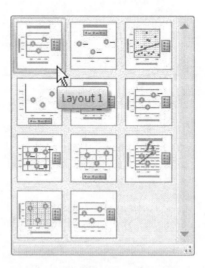

Figure 24.5   Chart Layouts palette.

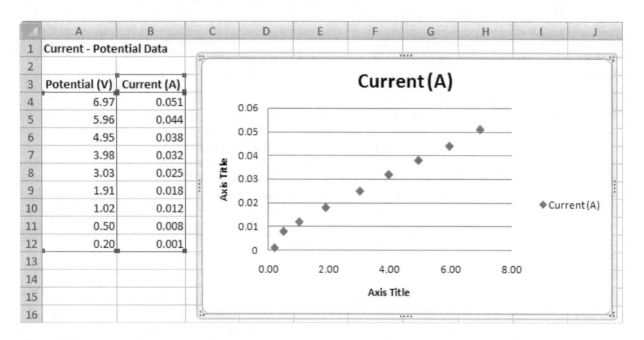

Figure 24.6   The XY Scatter chart after applying Layout 1.

Alternatively, you can edit a title "in place" with two careful mouse clicks on the title (see Figure 24.8):

1. Click once to select the title.
2. Click again to edit in place.

If there is a feature that you don't want, click on the feature to select it, then press **Delete**. For example, a *legend* is used to help the reader understand which curve is

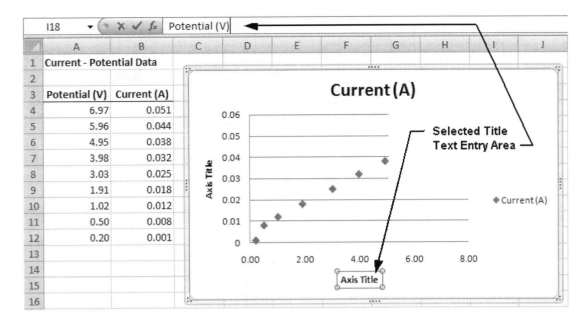

Figure 24.7   Entering an axis title using the Formula bar for text entry.

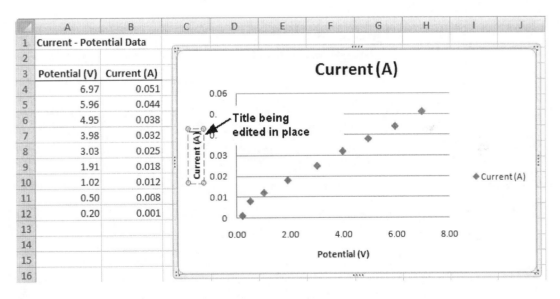

Figure 24.8   Editing a title in place.

associated with which data series. In this chart, the legend [♦ Current(A)] appears to the right of the graph. A legend isn't really necessary when there is only a single curve on the chart (as is the case in this example), so it can be deleted. See Figure 24.9 for an updated view of the chart.

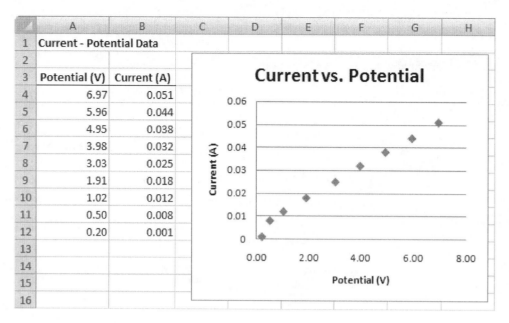

Figure 24.9   The XY Scatter chart after updating titles and deleting the legend.

24.4   FORMATTING CHART FEATURES

The chart is nearly ready to use. But the Layout tab on the Ribbon's Chart Tools (shown in Figure 24.10) allows you to update additional features, if needed.

Figure 24.10   The Chart Tools: Layout tab on the Ribbon when a chart is selected.

The Labels and Axes groups on the Layout tab allow you to quickly add chart features such as axis labels, a legend, or gridlines. If you want to annotate a chart, use a *text box* from the Insert group, as follows:

1. Select the chart (this causes the Chart Tools tabs to be available on the Ribbon).
2. Click the **Text Box** button: **Chart Tools → Layout tab → Insert group → Text Box button**. The mouse cursor will change to a vertical bar with a small crossbar showing the baseline of the text.
3. Position the mouse cursor on the chart where you want to place the text, then click the mouse. A text box will be placed on the chart and text entry will be initiated.
4. Type the desired text. (See Figure 24.11)
5. Click outside the text box to complete the text entry.

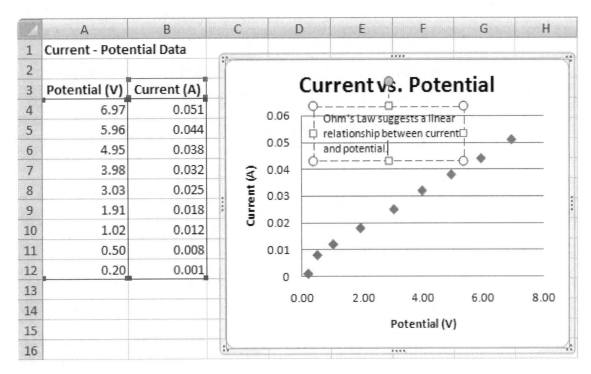

Figure 24.11   Adding text to a chart.

The text box is now an object associated with the chart, and it can be further modified. For example, we can assign a white background to the text box and add a dark border using the following steps:

1. Click the text box to select it. This causes the Drawing Tools: Format tab to be displayed on the Ribbon (Figure 24.12.)
2. Use the Shape Fill drop-down menu (indicated in Figure 24.12) to select a white background for the text box.
3. Use the Shape Outline drop-down menu (indicated in Figure 24.12) to select a dark color for the text box's border.

The result is shown in Figure 24.13.

24.4.1 Editing an Existing Chart Feature

In order to edit an existing chart feature, you usually need to open a dialog box for that feature. There are several ways to access these formatting dialog boxes:

*   Use the drop-down menus on the Ribbon, and select the "More" option at the bottom of the menu.

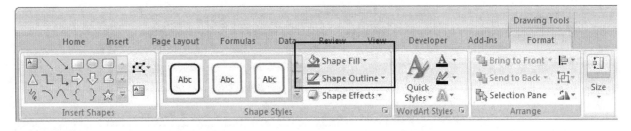

Figure 24.12   The Drawing Tools: Format tab is displayed when a text box has been selected.

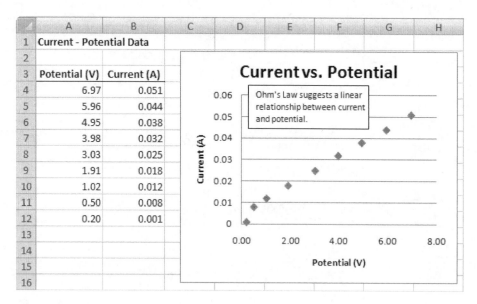

Figure 24.13 The annotated chart.

- Select the feature to be modified and click the **Format Selection** button on the Ribbon's Layout (or Format) tab: **Chart Tools → Layout (or Format) tab → Current Selection group → Format Selection button**.

- Right-click the feature and select the "Format" option for that feature from the pop-up menu.

As an example, we will give the *plot area* (the rectangle behind the data points) a dark border.

1. Select the plot area by clicking on one of the edges of the plot (e.g., one of the axis lines). Be careful to select the plot area and not gridlines or axis numeric values.

2. Click the **Format Selection** button on the Ribbon: **Chart Tools → Layout tab → Current Selection group → Format Selection**

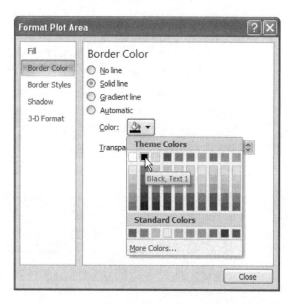

Figure 24.14 The Format Plot Area dialog box, Border Color panel.

button. The Format Plot Area dialog box will be displayed as shown in Figure 24.14.

3. Choose the Border Color panel.
4. Select the Solid Line option.
5. Choose a color from the Color drop-down palette.
6. Click the **Close** button when you are finished making changes to the plot area.

The result is shown in Figure 24.15.

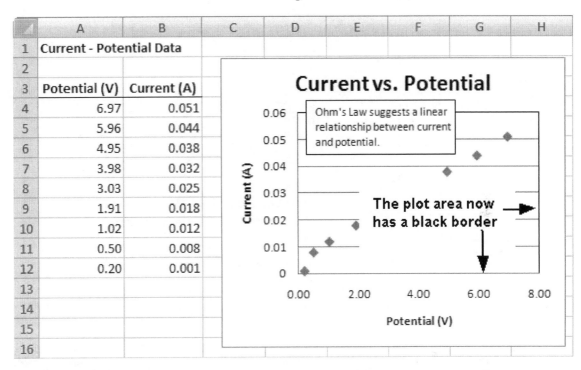

Figure 24.15   The reformatted chart.

Practice!

By default, Excel 2007 uses the format of the plotted data values to format the numbers on the axis. As a result, more digits than needed may display on an axis. For example, in Figure 24.15 the values on the x axis are shown with two decimal places that don't need to be there. To get rid of the extraneous decimal places we need to reformat the x axis. Try it with the following steps:

1. Select the x axis by clicking on any of the displayed axis numbers.
2. Click the Format Selection button on the Ribbon: **Chart Tools → Layout tab → Current selection group → Format Selection button**. The Format Axis dialog box will be displayed as shown in Figure 24.16.
3. Choose the Number panel.
4. Set the Decimal places to zero as shown in Figure 24.16.
5. Click the Close button when you are finished making changes to the axis.

The reformatted chart is shown in Figure 24.17.

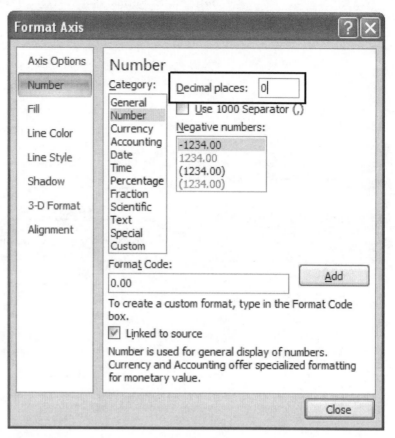

Figure 24.16   The Format Axis dialog box.

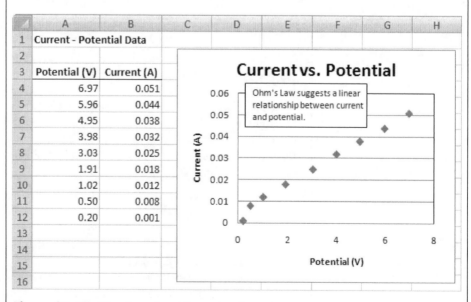

Figure 24.17   The chart after reformatting the *x* axis.

Practice!

Use the following data to practice creating an XY Scatter chart. Use a chart layout to get axis titles on the chart.

TABLE 24.1   Tank wash-out data

Time (s)	Conc. (mg/L)
0	100.0
10	36.8
20	13.5
30	5.0
40	1.8

Your chart should look something like Figure 24.18.

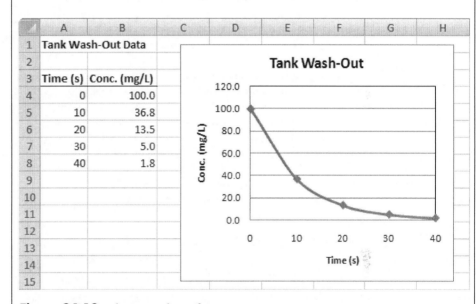

Figure 24.18   Plotting wash-out data.

24.5   CREATING A BASIC LINE CHART

The process for creating a Line chart is basically the same as for creating an XY Scatter chart:

1.   Select the data to be charted (including the headings, if desired).
2.   Insert the basic Line chart on your worksheet using Ribbon options: **Insert tab → Charts group → Line drop-down menu → Select a Line chart style.**

The difference between a *Line chart* and an XY Scatter chart in Excel is the way the x axis is handled. In an XY Scatter chart, the x location of each data point is along the x axis according to the magnitude of the x value associated with that point. In a Line chart there are no x *values*, just x *labels*. In a Line chart, the labels on the x axis are simply distributed uniformly across the chart from left to right.

As an example of creating a Line chart, consider the data shown in Table 24.2. These data represent the low-flow rates for two tributaries of the Pecos River. The lowest one-day flow rate (in cubic feet per second, or cfs) for each year is shown. We will create a Line chart that shows how the flow rates vary from year to year. First, create a worksheet that contains the data in Table 24.2.

TABLE 24.2   Annual low-flow rate of pecos river

Year	East Branch Flow (cfs)	West Branch Flow (cfs)
87	221	222
88	354	315
89	200	175
90	373	400
91	248	204
92	323	325
93	216	188
94	195	202
95	266	254
96	182	176

In this example, we are creating a Line chart with two data series, one for each tributary. A *data series* is a collection of related data points that are represented as a unit. Each data series will show up as a set of data points or a curve on the chart.

In preparation for creating a Line chart, the data in Table 24.2 is entered into an Excel worksheet, as shown in Figure 24.19.

	A	B	C	D	E
1	Annual Low-Flow Rate of the Pecos River				
2					
3	Year	East Branch Flow (cfs)	West Branch Flow (cfs)		
4	87	221	222		
5	88	354	315		
6	89	200	175		
7	90	373	400		
8	91	248	204		
9	92	323	325		
10	93	216	188		
11	94	195	202		
12	95	266	254		
13	96	182	176		
14					

Figure 24.19   Entering the flow data into a worksheet.

To create a basic Line chart with this data, follow these steps:

1. Select the data to be charted (including the headings), cells A3:C13 in this example.
2. Insert the basic Line chart on your worksheet using Ribbon options: **Insert tab → Charts group → Line drop-down menu → Select "Line with Markers" style** (indicated in Figure 24.20).

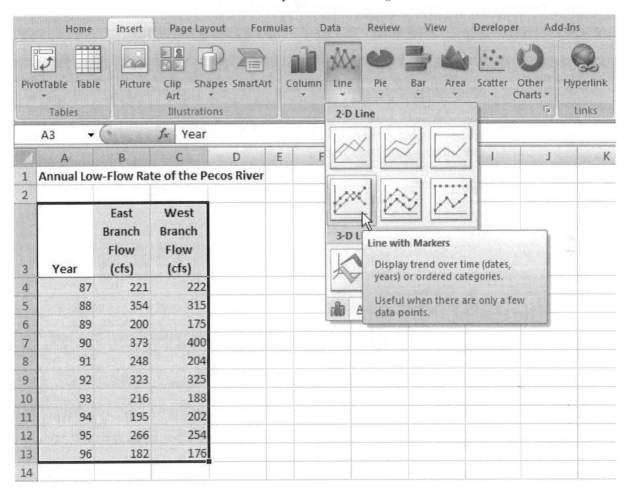

Figure 24.20 Inserting a Line chart with "Line with Markers" style.

The basic Line chart is shown in Figure 24.21.

Notice (in Figure 24.21) that we did not get quite the chart we wanted. We wanted two data series plotted with the years on the *x* axis as labels. Instead, Excel plotted the years as a third curve. It's easy to fix. First, select the "Year" curve on the plot and press the **Delete** key to remove the extra curve. The result is shown in Figure 24.22.

Next, to get the year values on the *x* axis, follow these steps:

1. Click on the chart to select it. This causes the Chart Tools tabs to be displayed on the Ribbon.
2. On the Design tab, click the Select Data button: **Chart Tools → Design tab → Data group → Select Data button**. This opens the Select Data Source dialog shown in Figure 24.23.

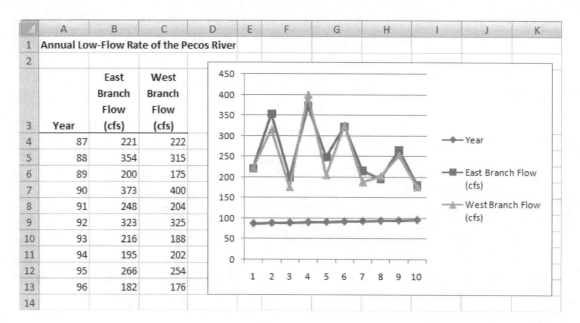

Figure 24.21   The basic Line chart (not quite what we wanted).

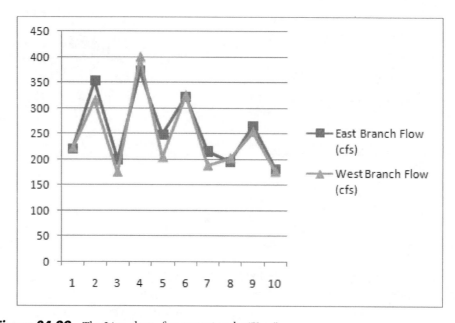

Figure 24.22   The Line chart after removing the "Year" curve.

In Figure 24.23 the default labels (1,2,3,4,5, . . .) have been indicated. We need to change those to the values in cells A4:A13.

3.   Click the Edit button in the Horizontal (Category) Axis Labels panel to change the *x* axis labels.
4.   Select cells A4:A13 as illustrated in Figure 24.24.
5.   Click **OK** to close the Axis Labels dialog and return to the Select Data Source dialog.
6.   Click **OK** to close the Select Data Source dialog.

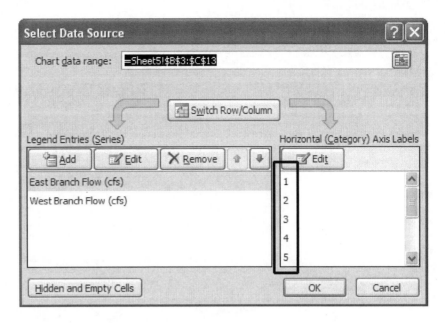

Figure 24.23   The Select Data Source dialog box.

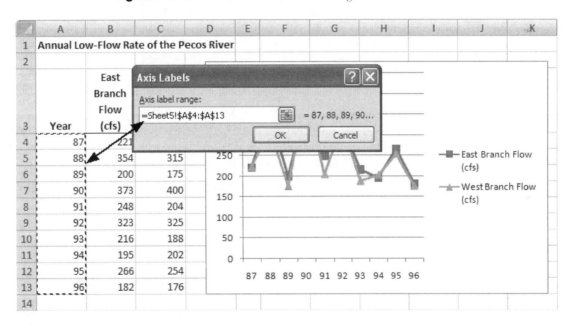

Figure 24.24   Selecting the year labels for the *x* axis.

A few more changes are appropriate:

- Select a Chart Layout (Layout 1 was used): **Chart Tools → Design tab → Chart Layouts group → Layout 1.**
- Add text for the chart title and *y* axis title.
- Add an *x* axis title: **Chart Tools → Layout tab → Labels group → Axis Titles drop-down menu → Primary Horizontal Axis Title → Title Below Axis button.** Add text to the *x* axis title.

The completed Line Graph is shown in Figure 24.25.

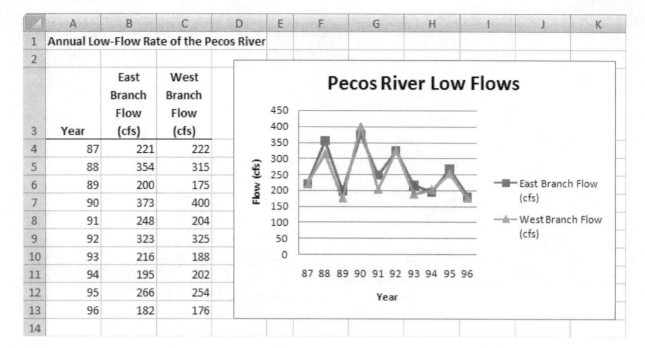

Figure 24.25   The completed Line chart.

Practice!

To observe the difference between an XY Scatter chart and a Line chart, create both types of chart using the data set shown in Figure 24.26. The nonuniformly spaced *x* values will show the difference between XY Scatter charts and Line charts.

	A	B	C
1	**X**	**Y**	
2	1	1	
3	2	2	
4	8	3	
5	9	4	
6			

Figure 24.26   XY data with nonuniformly spaced *x* values.

1.   Create the worksheet shown in Figure 24.26.
2.   Create an XY Scatter chart of the data. Your result should look like the left chart in Figure 24.27.
3.   Create a Line chart of the same data. Your result should look like the right chart in Figure 24.27.

Notice that, whenever you have nonuniformly spaced x values, the XY Scatter and Line chart types produce very different results. This is because the x values are considered numbers in the XY Scatter chart and category labels in the Line chart. That is why, on the Line chart, the x axis shows 1, 2, 8, and 9 as labels centered between the tick marks on the x axis.

Whenever you have numeric x values, you should use the XY Scatter chart type to correctly plot your data.

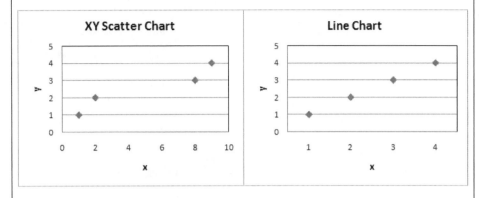

Figure 24.27   The same data, plotted with two different chart types.

Professional Success—Formatting Charts

The appearance of a chart in a document is important. A chart can make a lasting visual impression that summarizes or exemplifies the main points of your presentation or document. The following formatting guidelines will help you create a professional-looking chart:

- Choose a chart title that contains a clear, concise description of the chart contents.
- Create a label for each axis that contains, at a minimum, the name of the variable and the units of measurement that were used.
- Create a label for each data series. The lables can be consolidated in a legend if each data series is represented by a distinct color or style.
- Make sure that scale graduations are included for each axis. The graduation marks may take the form of gridlines (uniformly spaced horizontal and vertical lines) or tick marks. the choice of scale graduations can be controlled from the Axis Options panel on the Format Axis dialog box.
- Ideally, scale graduations should follow the *1, 2, 5 rule*. The 1, 2, 5 rule states that one should select scale graduations so that the smallest division of the axis is a positive or negative integer power of 10 times 1, 2, or 5. For example, a scale graduation of 10 follows the rule, but 0.33 does not.

Practice!

Practice formatting graphs for different purposes.

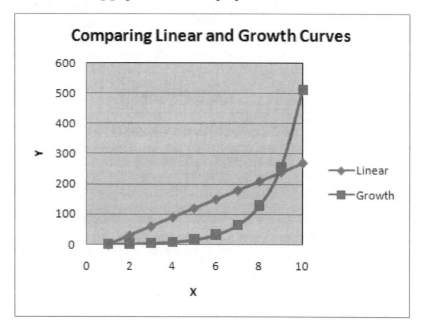

Figure 24.28   Linear and exponential growth curves.

The chart shown in Figure 24.28 was created from the data shown in Figure 24.29. The data set is easy to generate; just enter the first two values in each column,

	A	B	C	D
1	Linear and Exponential Growth Curves			
2				
3	X	Linear	Growth	
4	1	0	1	
5	2	30	2	
6	3	60	4	
7	4	90	8	
8	5	120	16	
9	6	150	32	
10	7	180	64	
11	8	210	128	
12	9	240	256	
13	10	270	512	
14				

Figure 24.29   Data for linear and exponential growth curves.

then use the Fill Handle to complete the series. You will need to use the right mouse button with the Fill Handle to create the exponential growth series.

First, create the XY Scatter chart from the data. Then format to the chart for two different purposes:

1. Format the chart to be readable using a black and white printer.

   - Use distinct markers for each curve.
   - Use black for both curves, but change the line styles to make the two curves clearly distinct.
   - Set the plot area color to white. (This is important for black and white printing because it allows the chart to be photocopied without the plot area covering up the curves.)

2. Format the chart to use only color to distinguish the curves.

   - Use no markers for either curve.
   - Use solid lines for both curves.
   - Choose a bright color for the plot area.
   - Choose two colors for the curves that clearly differentiate the two curves on the colored background. (In this example, a medium background was used so that the line colors could be lighter and darker than the background and the curves could be distinguished even when printed in black and white.)

Your results should look something like Figure 24.30 and Figure 24.31.

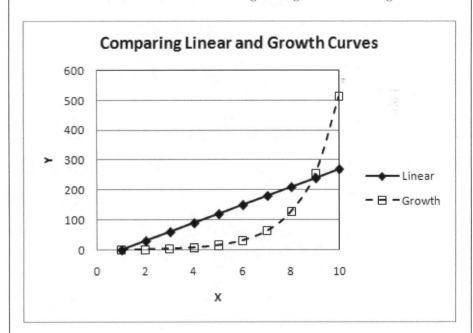

Figure 24.30   The XY Scatter chart formatted for a black and white printer.

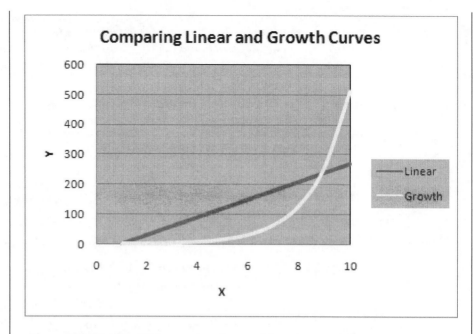

Figure 24.31 The XY Scatter chart formatted for color presentation.

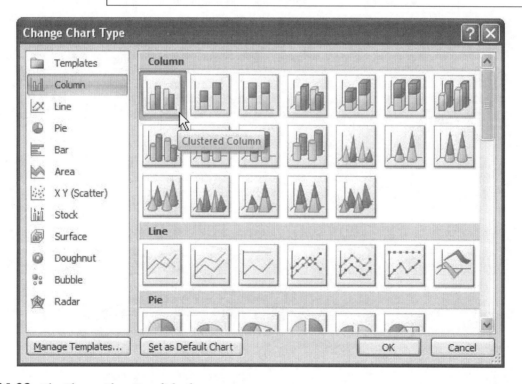

Figure 24.32 The Change Chart Type dialog box.

24.5.1 Changing Chart Types

The *chart type* can be changed after a chart has been created. Not all types of charts are appropriate for all data sets. For example, a pie chart is not appropriate for the Pecos River flow data used in this chapter (Table 24.2). But, a *Column chart* will work with the data. To change the chart type from Line chart (shown in Figure 24.25) to Column chart, do the following:

1. Click on the chart to select it.
2. Click on the Change Chart Type button on the Chart Tools: Design tab. (Ribbon options: **Chart Tools** → **Design tab** → **Type group** → **Change Chart Type button.** The Change Chart Type dialog box (Figure 24.32) will be displayed.
3. Select a Column chart style from the Column options. In this example, the "Clustered Column" style was selected.
4. Click **OK** to close the Change Chart Type dialog box.

The result is shown in Figure 24.33.

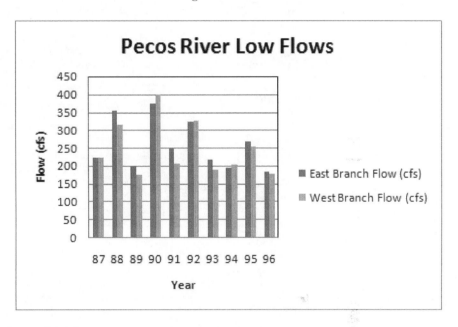

Figure 24.33 The Pecos River flow data as a Column chart.

24.6   PREVIEWING AND PRINTING CHARTS

You can print charts and worksheets without previewing them, but using the print preview feature allows you to control how the chart or worksheet will appear when printed.

24.6.1 Previewing Charts

There are two ways to preview charts:

- **Preview and print the worksheet with the embedded chart.** A chart is typically embedded in a worksheet, and if you preview or print the worksheet, the chart will also be visible.

- **Preview and print the chart only.** If you select an embedded chart before previewing or printing, then Excel will preview or print the chart only, without the rest of the worksheet. (A chart that was created as a separate page in the workbook will always preview and print separately.)

To preview a chart (only) before printing, do the following:

1. Click on the chart to select it.
2. Click the Print Preview button under the Office button: **Office button →
   Print submenu → Print Preview button.** (See Figure 24.34.)

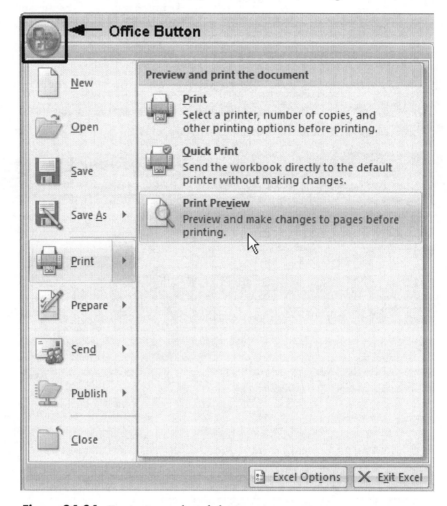

Figure 24.34   Previewing a selected chart.

The chart will be displayed as it will be printed. By default, when a chart is
previewed or printed without the rest of the worksheet, Excel scales the chart to fit
the page.

While you are in Print Preview, the Ribbon displays a Print Preview tab with some
useful options:

- The **Show Margins** check box allows you to see and adjust the page margins,
  as shown in Figure 24.35.
- The **Print** button sends the document to your printer.
- The **Page Setup** button opens the Page Setup dialog box, shown in Figure
  24.36.

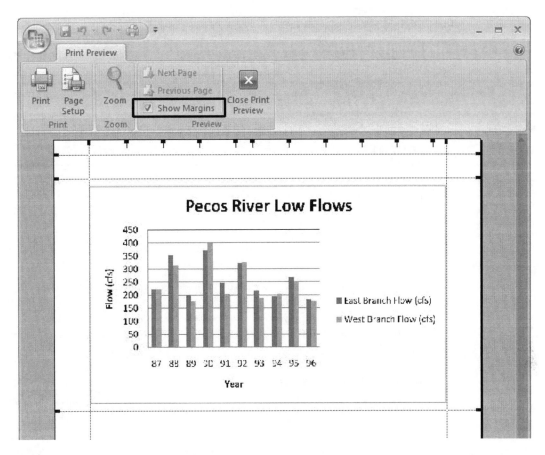

Figure 24.35   The previewed chart.

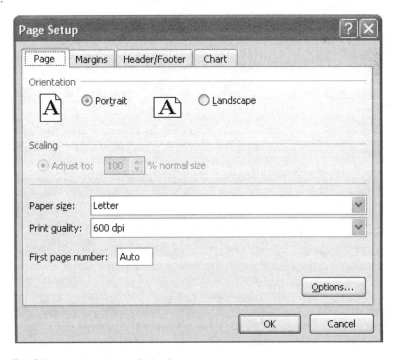

Figure 24.36   The Page Setup dialog box.

24.6.2 Printing Charts

You can print a chart by printing the worksheet that contains the chart, or you can print just the chart. To print the chart only, simply select the chart before printing.

Printing can be initiated from the Print Preview screen using the **Print** button visible in Figure 24.35, or directly from the **Office** button (**Office button** → **Print submenu** → **Print button**).

24.7 ADDING DATA TO CHARTS

When you are working with plotted data, you often may need to modify an existing chart to add additional data. You might have simply forgotten to type in a bit of data when creating the worksheet, or you might have collected additional data and need to include the new data on the existing chart. Excel makes either type of data addition easy.

24.7.1 Adding Data to an Existing Series

If you missed a row while typing in the data set, you might need to go back and add the missing data to the worksheet. When this happens, Excel makes it easy to update the chart as well. Procedurally, it makes a difference whether the missing data are being added to the middle of the data set or at the end, so each situation will be presented separately.

Adding Data in the Middle of the Data Set

Suppose there was another data point in the Current versus Potential data set (Figure 24.1) that was accidentally overlooked when the data set was entered on the worksheet. The missing item is 0.022 A at 2.47 V.

To add the data in the middle of the data range, simply make some space for the data by moving the lower data values down one row or inserting a new row. The result is shown in Figure 24.37.

In Figure 24.37, the data series has been selected (by clicking on any of the markers). When the data series is selected, the data used to create the series are outlined by colored boxes on the worksheet. So, the box around cells A4:A13 indicates the x values used to create the data series, and the box around cells B4:B13 shows the y values used in the series. Notice that the empty cells created to hold the additional data are enclosed by the colored boxes that show the data used to create the data series. When you insert values in the middle of a data set, Excel assumes you want the data included in the chart. Adding the data to the worksheet in the middle of the data set will cause the new values to be included in the chart—automatically.

When the new values are added to the worksheet, the new point appears on the chart, as shown in Figure 24.38.

Adding Data at the End of the Data set

When you add additional data at the end of the data set, Excel does not automatically include the new data in the plotted data set. For example, suppose that we repeated the experiment at the lowest potential because the data point at the left end of the data series seemed a little out of line and we were concerned that there might have been a data collection error. When we repeated the experiment, we got 0.150 V at a current of 0.001 A. We do not want to replace the last data value, but we want to add the new data to the plot.

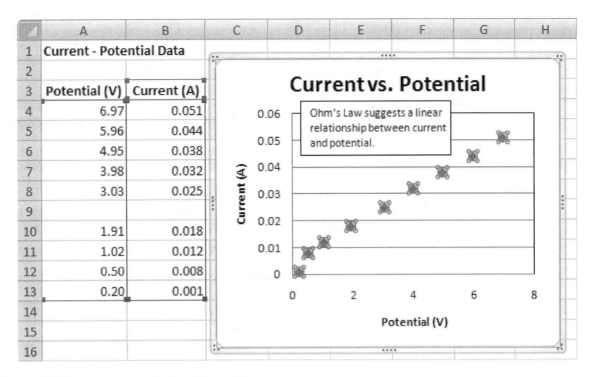

Figure 24.37   Making space for the additional data.

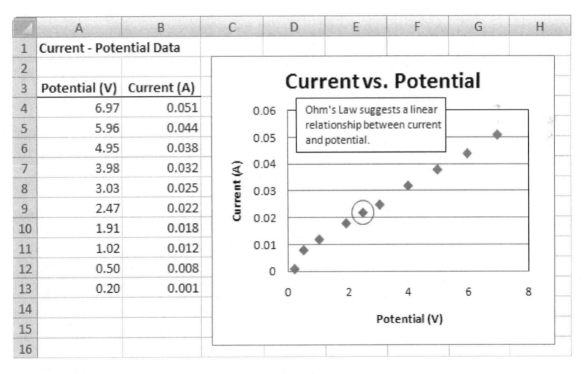

Figure 24.38   The XY Scatter chart with the new point indicated.

1. Add the new data to the worksheet in cells A14 and B14, as shown in Figure 24.39.
2. Click on any marker on the plotted data series to select the data series, as illustrated in Figure 24.39. Notice that the new data values in cells A14 and B14 are not included in the boxes that indicate the plotted data.
3. Position the mouse over either of the squares at the bottom edge of the Potential data box (the squares are called *handles*) and stretch the data box to include the new data value in cell A14. When the mouse is correctly positioned over the handle, the mouse icon changes to a double-headed arrow.
4. Repeat Step 3 to stretch the Current data box to include the new value in cell B14. The additional data point will be included on the Chart as part of the plotted data series.

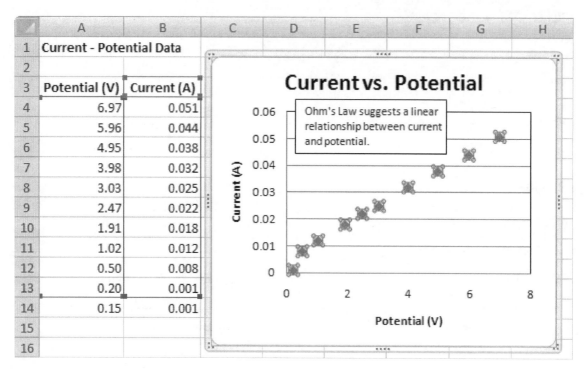

Figure 24.39 Data added at the end of the data set are not automatically plotted.

Adding a data point to the end of a data set by using the select data source dialog box

If the chart exists in its own sheet (not embedded in a worksheet), then the colored boxes that indicate the data used to create a data series are not available. However, any data added in the middle of the data set used to create the chart will still be added to the chart automatically. But if you need to add data to the end of the data set, you will need to use the Select Data Source dialog box, which is available using the **Select Data** button on the Ribbon: **Chart Tools → Design tab → Data group → Select Data button**.

The process for modifying the plotted data is as follows:

1. Click on the chart to select it. This causes the Ribbon to display the Chart Tools tabs. (This step is not needed if the chart is on its own page in the workbook; accessing the page selects the chart.)
2. Click the **Select Data** button on the Ribbon: **Chart Tools → Design tab → Data group → Select Data button**. This opens the Select Data Source dialog box shown in Figure 24.40.

3. Select the data series to be modified ("Current (A)" in this example).
4. Click the Edit button (indicated in Figure 24.40). This opens the Edit Series dialog box shown in Figure 24.41.
5. Select the cell ranges containing the data to be plotted.
6. Click **OK** to close the Edit Series dialog box.
7. Click **OK** to close the Select Data Source dialog box.

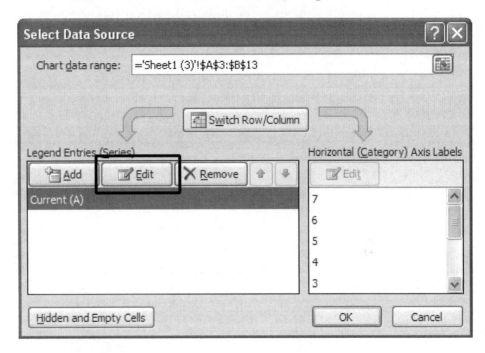

Figure 24.40   The Select Data Source dialog box.

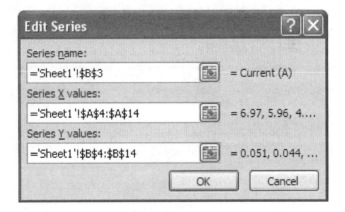

Figure 24.41   The Edit Series dialog box.

24.7.2 Adding a Data Series to an XY Scatter Chart

On a chart, each curve is a separate data series. On an XY Scatter chart, two data series may have differing y values, but share x values; or there may be two sets of x values and two sets of y values. The procedure for adding a data series is different for each situation, so each will be presented separately.

Adding a second data series—both series use the same x values

Repeating an experiment to test reproducibility is very common. For example, the experiment that generated the potential–current data shown in Figure 24.1 might be repeated. If it is possible to set exactly the same potential values across the resistor a second time, we could measure a new set of current values and obtain a data set containing one column of *x* values and two columns of *y* values. When plotted, the differences between the results from the two experiments would show how reproducible the experiment is (or isn't).

Repeating the experiment might generate a data set like that in Figure 24.42. In this figure, the chart has been selected to illustrate that the data from the second experiment has not yet been included on the chart.

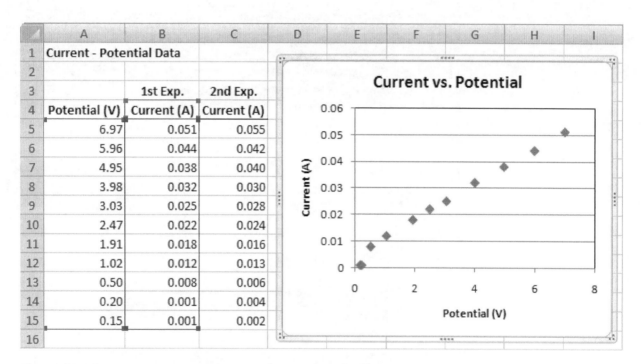

Figure 24.42   Preparing to add data from the second experiment to the chart.

In the new data set, shown in Figure 24.42, there are two columns of *y* values (columns B and C), and one column of *x* values (column A). If you have already created a chart of the results from the first experiment, adding the *y* values from the second experiment is very easy.

1. Select the chart. This causes the data used to create the chart to be shown in boxes on the worksheet (Figure 24.42).
2. Use the mouse to stretch the box containing the y values in column B to include the new *y* values in column C. This is illustrated in Figure 24.43. (The marker sizes were reduced so that the data points are more distinct.)

That's all it takes to add a new data series to a chart when the two data series use the same *x* values.

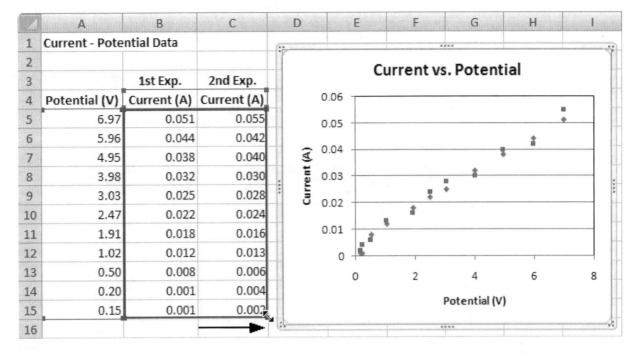

Figure 24.43   Expanding the *y* values cell range to include the second data series.

Adding a second data series—each series has its own x values

If it is not possible to exactly reproduce the potentials, we can still repeat the experiment over the same range of potentials (approximately 0 to 7 V). If we did so, we would create a new data set with new *x* and *y* values, as shown in Figure 24.44.

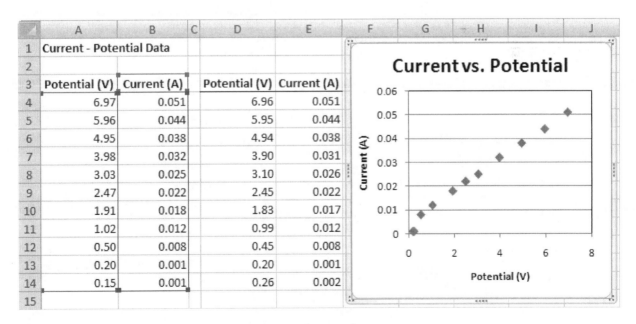

Figure 24.44   Preparing to plot the data from the second experiment.

If the new *y* values come with a new set of *x* values, then we can't just stretch the data boxes to create a second data series on the chart; we need to use the Select Data Source dialog box to add a new data series.

1. Click on the chart to select it. This causes the Ribbon to display the Chart Tools tabs.
2. Click the Select Data button on the Ribbon: **Chart Tools** → **Design tab** → **Data group** → **Select Data button**. This opens the Select Data Source dialog box shown in Figure 24.45.

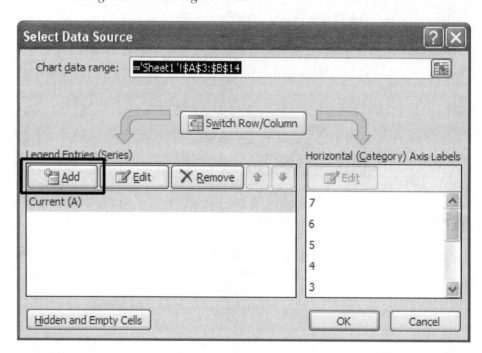

Figure 24.45   The Select Data Source dialog box used to add an additional data series to a chart.

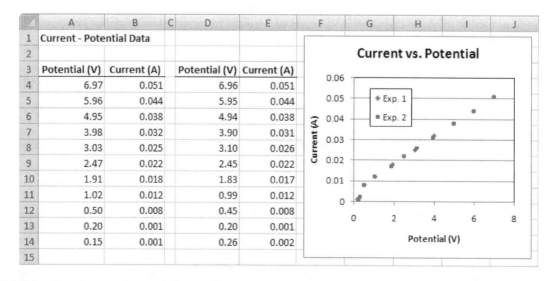

	A	B	C	D	E	F	G	H	I	J
1	Current - Potential Data									
2										
3	Potential (V)	Current (A)		Potential (V)	Current (A)					
4	6.97	0.051		6.96	0.051					
5	5.96	0.044		5.95	0.044					
6	4.95	0.038		4.94	0.038					
7	3.98	0.032		3.90	0.031					
8	3.03	0.025		3.10	0.026					
9	2.47	0.022		2.45	0.022					
10	1.91	0.018		1.83	0.017					
11	1.02	0.012		0.99	0.012					
12	0.50	0.008		0.45	0.008					
13	0.20	0.001		0.20	0.001					
14	0.15	0.001		0.26	0.002					
15										

Figure 24.46   The XY Scatter chart with the new data series plotted.

3. Click the **Add** button to add a new data series to the chart. This opens the Edit Series dialog box.
4. Select the cell ranges containing the new data to be plotted, cells D4:D14 and E4:E14 in this example.
5. Click OK to close the Edit Series dialog box.
6. Click OK to close the Select Data Source dialog box.

The result is shown in Figure 24.46.

APPLICATION

APPLICATION—GRAPHING TO EVALUATE A FUNCTION

Visualization can be a big help in trying to understand what your data means or how a function works. Excel can help with this by allowing you to quickly and easily graph data by evaluating a function. For example, exponentials and hyperbolic sines are commonly used functions for solving differential equations. When you solve these equations, you select the appropriate function on the basis of its characteristics. Being able to see a graph of a function is a big help in understanding how the function behaves. Figure 24.47 shows a plot of the hyperbolic sine function $(SINH(x))$ from $x = -10$ to 10.

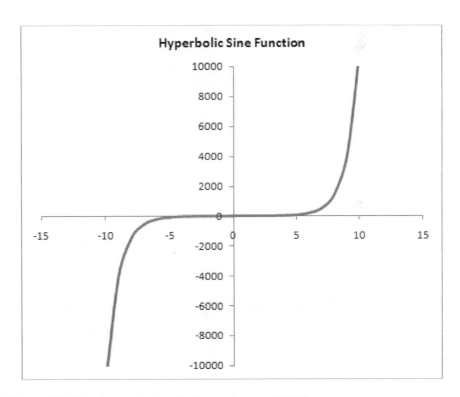

Figure 24.47   Plotting the hyperbolic sine function $(SINH)$.

How'd They do That?

To help visualize a function, first evaluate the function over a range of values in a worksheet, as shown in Figure 24.48.

Then create an XY Scatter plot of the evaluated results, select a chart layout, and enter the chart title. Set the axis formatting as desired.

B4 =SINH(A4)

	A	B	C	D	E
1	**Hyperbolic Sine**				
2					
3	x	sinh(x)			
4	-10	-11013			
5	-9	-4052			
6	-8	-1490			
7	-7	-548			
8	-6	-202			
9	-5	-74			
10	-4	-27			
11	-3	-10			
12	-2	-4			
13	-1	-1			
14	0	0			
15	1	1			
16	2	4			
17	3	10			
18	4	27			
19	5	74			
20	6	202			
21	7	548			
22	8	1490			
23	9	4052			
24	10	11013			
25					

Figure 24.48 Evaluation of the hyperbolic sine function, *SINH*.

24.8 CHARTING FEATURES THAT ARE USEFUL TO ENGINEERS

Excel has many advanced features for formatting charts. Some of the features are particularly useful for engineering applications. These include

- Trendlines
- Error bars
- Logarithmic axes
- Secondary axes

24.8.1 Adding a Trendline to a Chart

A *trendline* is a best fit line through a set of data points. Excel makes it very easy to add a trendline to an XY Scatter chart, and will present the equation of the trendline on the chart. Trendlines are available from the Chart Tools: Layout tab (Ribbon Options: **Chart Tools → Layout tab → Analysis group → Trendline drop-down menu**). (See Figure 24.49.)

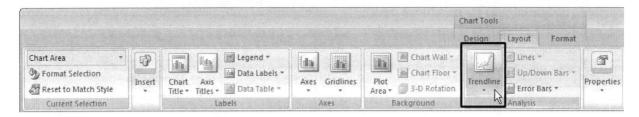

Figure 24.49   Trendlines are available from the Chart Tools: Layout tab.

Excel provides several commonly used trendline options, but only two are available from the Trendline drop-down menu on the Ribbon (Figure 24.50).

- Linear (straight line through the data)
- Exponential

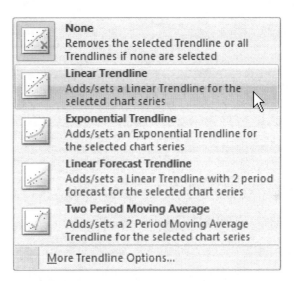

Figure 24.50   The Trendline drop-down menu provides quick access to commonly used trendlines.

Use the **More Trendline Options ...** button to open the Trendline dialog box for additional trendline options. The Trendline dialog box is also used to tell Excel to display the equation of the trendline on the chart.

Because Ohm's law predicts a linear relationship between potential and current, we will add a linear trendline to the potential–current data. To add a linear trendline follow these steps:

1. Click on any marker to select the data series.
2. Select Linear Trendline from the Trendline drop-down menu: **Chart Tools → Layout tab → Analysis group → Trendline drop-down menu → Linear Trendline option.**

Excel will show the trendline on the chart, as shown in Figure 24.51.

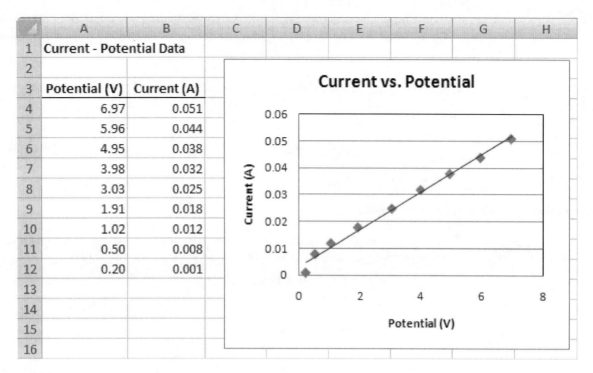

Figure 24.51 The current vs. potential data with a linear trendline added.

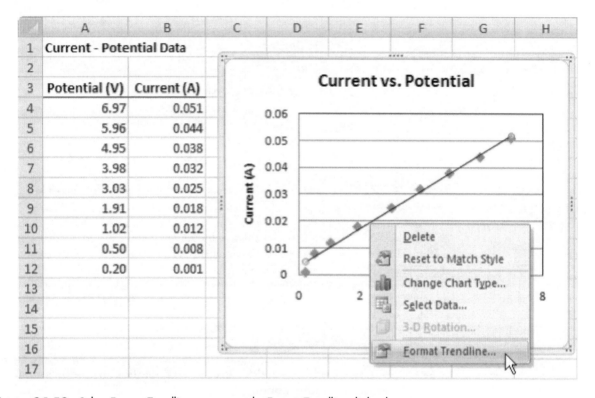

Figure 24.52 Select Format Trendline... to open the Format Trendline dialog box.

By default Excel does not show the equation of the trendline. To see the equation,

1. Right-click on the trendline (stay away from the markers) and select **Format Trendline ...** from the pop-up menu (Figure 24.52) (Or, use Ribbon options: **Chart Tools → Layout tab → Analysis group → Trendline drop-down menu → More Trendline Options...**) This opens the Format Trendline dialog box, shown in Figure 24.53.
2. Check the **Display Equation on chart** box.

The result is shown in Figure 24.54. Other commonly used options, indicated in Figure 24.53, allow you to

- Set the intercept of the trendline to a particular value (frequently zero).
- Display the R^2 value for the trendline on the chart. An R^2 value of 1 implies a perfect fit to the data. The lower the R^2 value, the poorer the fit.

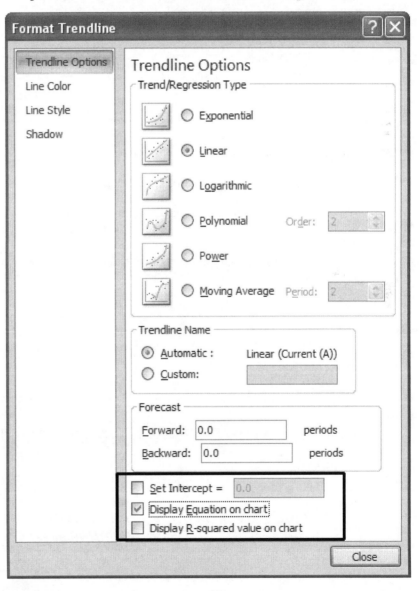

Figure 24.53   The Format Trendline dialog box.

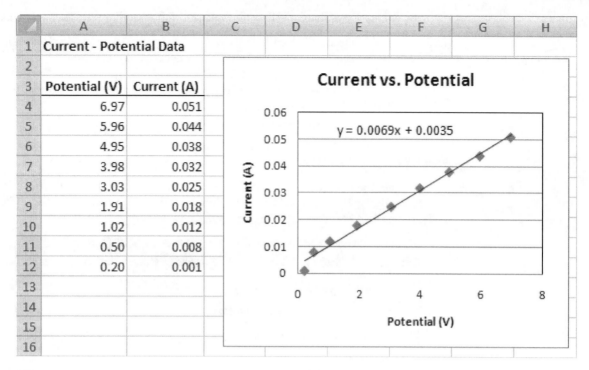

Figure 24.54   The XY Scatter chart with trendline and equation displayed.

24.8.2 Adding Error Bars to a Chart

Error bars represent the range of measured or statistical error in a data series. Error bars should not be used unless you understand their purpose.

The flow rates used in preparing the Annual Low Flows for Pecos River chart are only accurate to ±5% percent of each data value. We will use error bars to indicate this level of uncertainty. To add error bars to the East Branch data series shown in Figure 24.33, follow this procedure:

1. Select the series by clicking on any column of East Branch data.
2. Use the Error Bars drop-down menu from the Ribbon: **Chart Tools → Layout tab → Analysis group → Error Bars drop-down menu.**

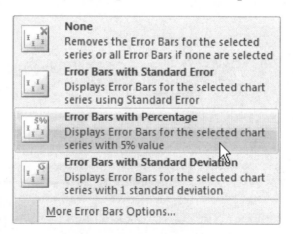

Figure 24.55   The Error Bars drop-down menu.

The Error Bars drop-down menu contains various options as shown in Figure 24.55. One of the options is error bars with 5% value (selected in Figure 24.55), so we can add the error bars we need with one click. Usually you will need to use the **More Error Bars Options ...** button to open the Error Bars dialog box.

The Column chart with 5% error bars is shown in Figure 24.56.

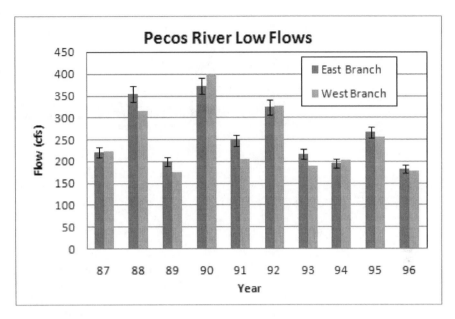

Figure 24.56   The Column chart with 5% error bars.

24.8.3 Using a Log Scale Axis

Excel will allow you to select a *logarithmic scale* on either the x or y axis as long as taking a logarithm of the values plotted on the axis is valid (no zero or negative values). If the exponential growth curve shown in Figure 24.28 is plotted with a logarithmic y axis, the data series should plot as a straight line.

To instruct Excel to use a log scale on the y axis, do the following:

1. Click on any number along the y axis to select the axis. This causes the Chart Tools tabs on the Ribbon to be displayed.
2. Use the Format Selection button on the Layout (or Format) tab to open the Format Axis dialog box (Figure 24.57). Ribbon options: **Chart Tools → Layout tab → Current Selection group → Format Selection button.**
3. Check the Logarithmic scale box, indicated in Figure 24.57.
4. Click Close to close the Format Axis dialog box.

The result is shown in Figure 24.58.

24.8.4 Using Secondary Axes

A *secondary axis* is a second y axis on the right side of the chart. It is typically used when two related but distinct data series are plotted on the same chart. That is, the two data series are both dependent upon the variable plotted on the x axis, but they have widely varying y values and usually different units. By plotting one series on each of the y axes (left and right), it can be easier to understand the chart.

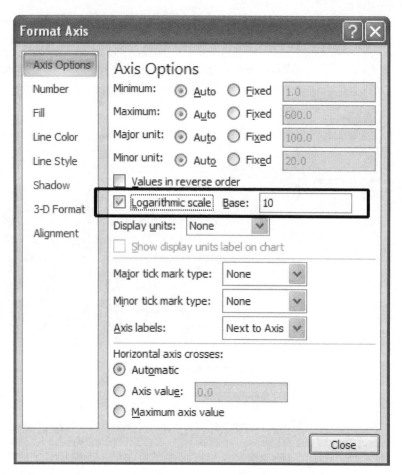

Figure 24.57   The Format Axis dialog box.

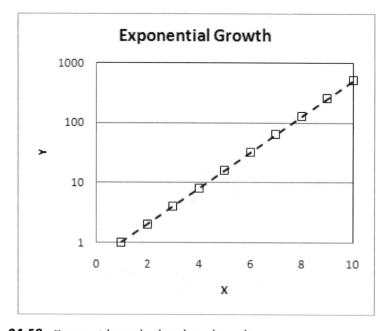

Figure 24.58   Exponential growth, plotted on a log scale.

To see how two related, but different data series can be plotted on the same graph, consider the (fictional) data set shown in Figure 24.59, which shows the low flows in the East Branch of the Pecos River and the average daily high temperature during the summer months. Presumably, there should be a relationship between a hot summer and low water.

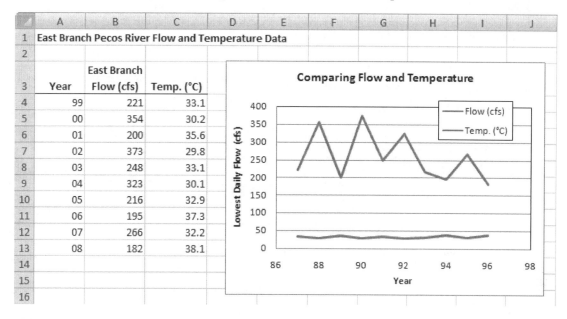

Figure 24.59 Pecos River flow and temperature data, before using a secondary axis.

The temperature values are ten times smaller than the flow values, so when they are plotted on the same scale, as in Figure 24.59, the temperature curve looks like a fairly flat line at the bottom of the chart. To see more detail in the temperature curve, we will plot it using a secondary axis:

1. Click on the temperature curve to select the data series.
2. Click the Format Selection button on the Layout tab: **Chart Tools → Layout (or Format) tab → Current Selection group → Format Selection button.** This opens the Format Series dialog shown in Figure 24.60.

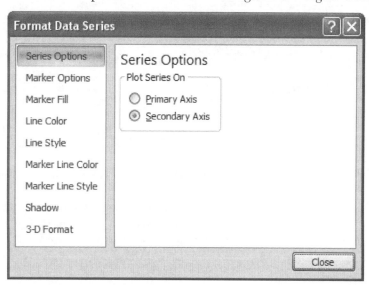

Figure 24.60 The Format Data Series dialog box.

3.   Select the Secondary Axis option in the Plot Series On list.
4.   Click Close to close the Format Series dialog box.

The chart with the secondary axis is shown in Figure 24.61.

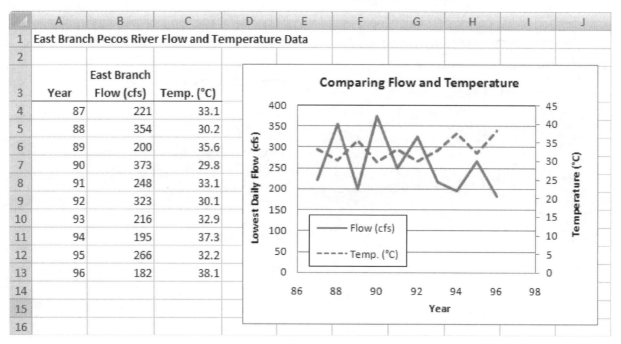

	A	B	C	D	E	F	G	H	I	J
1	East Branch Pecos River Flow and Temperature Data									
2										
3	Year	East Branch Flow (cfs)	Temp. (°C)							
4	87	221	33.1							
5	88	354	30.2							
6	89	200	35.6							
7	90	373	29.8							
8	91	248	33.1							
9	92	323	30.1							
10	93	216	32.9							
11	94	195	37.3							
12	95	266	32.2							
13	96	182	38.1							
14										
15										
16										

Figure 24.61   The Pecos River flow and temperature data, using a secondary axis.

KEY TERMS

1, 2, 5 rule	gridlines	secondary axis
axis labels	handles	series (data series)
chart	labels	smoothed lines
chart layout	legend	text box
chart type	Line chart	tickmark
Column chart	lines	trendline
data series	logarithmic axis	x axis
embedded chart	markers	XY Scatter chart
error bars	plot area	y axis

Summary

Creating an XY Scatter Chart

1.   Select the data to be plotted.
2.   Use the Ribbon's **Insert tab** → **Charts Group** → **Scatter drop-down menu.**
3.   Select the type of chart to be created from the Scatter drop-down menu.
4.   Select a Chart Layout: **Chart Tools** → **Design tab** → **Chart Layouts group** → **Chart Layouts palette**.
5.   Format individual chart features as needed.

Creating a Line Chart

Do not use a Line chart when your data includes numeric, nonuniformly spaced x values; use an XY Scatter plot instead.

1. Select the data to be plotted.
2. Use the Ribbon's **Insert tab** → **Charts Group** → **Line drop-down menu**.
3. Select the type of chart to be created from the Line drop-down menu.
4. Select a Chart Layout: **Chart Tools** → **Design tab** → **Chart Layouts group** → **Chart Layouts palette**.
5. Format individual chart features as needed.

Annotating a Chart by Adding a Text Box

1. Select the chart.
2. Click the **Text Box** button: **Chart Tools** → **Layout tab** → **Insert group** → **Text Box button**.
3. Position the mouse cursor on the chart where you want to place the text, then click the mouse.
4. Type the desired text.
5. Click outside the text box to complete the text entry.

Using a Dialog Box to Format a Chart Feature

1. Select the chart feature by clicking on it.
2. Click the **Format Selection** button on the Ribbon: **Chart Tools** → **Layout tab** → **Current Selection group** → **Format Selection button**. This opens the formatting dialog box for the chart feature.
3. Set the desired format options.
4. Click the **Close** button when you are done making changes.

Changing the Chart Type

1. Click on the chart to select it.
2. Click on the Change Chart Type: **Chart Tools** → **Design tab** → **Type group** → **Change Chart Type button**.
3. Select a chart style.
4. Click **OK** to close the Change Chart Type dialog box.

Previewing and Printing Charts

- **Preview and Print the Worksheet with the Embedded Chart**
- **Preview and Print the Chart Only** (Select chart before previewing or printing)

Previewing: **Office button** → **Print submenu** → **Print Preview button**.
Printing: **Office button** → **Print submenu** → **Print Preview button**.

Adding Data to Charts

Adding Data to an Existing Series–Data in the Middle of the Data Set

1. Insert one or more rows in the middle of the data set.
2. Enter the new data values. The chart will automatically include the new data values.

Adding Data to an Existing Series–Data at the End of the Data Set

1. Insert one or more rows in the middle of the data set.
2. Enter the new data values. The chart will not automatically include the new data values.
3. Select the chart to cause the data plotted on the chart to be indicated (colored boxes).
4. Adjust the size of the colored boxes to include the new data values.

Adding Data to an Existing Series Using the Select Data Source Dialog Box

1. Click on the chart to select it.
2. Click the **Select Data** button: **Chart Tools** → **Design tab** → **Data group** → **Select Data button**.
3. Select the data series to be modified.
4. Click the **Edit** button.
5. Select the cell ranges containing the data to be plotted.
6. Click **OK** to close the Edit Series dialog box.
7. Click **OK** to close the Select Data Source dialog box.

Adding a Second Data Series—Both Series Use the Same x Values

1. Select the chart.
2. Use the mouse to adjust the size of data box to include the new y values.

Adding a Second Data Series—Each Series Has Its Own x Values

1. Click on the chart to select it.
2. Click the **Select Data** button: **Chart Tools** → **Design tab** → **Data group** → **Select Data button**.
3. Click the **Add** button.
4. Select the cell ranges containing the new data to be plotted.
5. Click **OK** to close the Edit Series dialog box.
6. Click **OK** to close the Select Data Source dialog box.

Adding a Trendline

1. Right-click on a data series.
2. Select **Insert Trendline** from the pop-up menu.
3. Choose the Trendline type from the dialog box.

4. Set options as desired:

    (a) Set intercept value (if applicable)
    (b) Display equation of trendline on chart
    (c) Display the R^2 value of the regressed trendline

5. Click **Close** to close the dialog box.

Adding Error Bars

1. Click on a data series.
2. Use the Error Bars menu: **Chart Tools → Layout tab → Analysis group → Error Bars drop-down menu**.
3. Choose the type of error bar desired from the drop-down menu, or select **More Error Bar Options ...** to open the dialog box.

Using a Log Scale Axis

1. Click on any number along the y axis to select the axis.
2. Use the Format Selection button: **Chart Tools → Layout tab → Current Selection group → Format Selection button**.
3. Check the **Logarithmic scale** box.
4. Click **Close** to close the Format Axis dialog box.

Using a Secondary Axis

1. Click on the data series you wish to plot using the secondary axis.
2. Click the Format Selection button: **Chart Tools → Layout (or Format) tab → Current Selection group → Format Selection button**.
3. Select the **Secondary Axis** option in the **Plot Series On** list.
4. Click **Close** to close the Format Series dialog box.

Problems

1. Generate data points for the function

$$y = 4 \sin(x) - x^2$$

For $x = -5.0, -4.5, ..., 4.5, 5.0$ Chart the results by using an XY scatter plot. Add appropriate title and axis labels.

2. The equation for the plot of a circle is

$$x^2 + y^2 = r^2,$$

where r is the radius of the circle. For a radius of 5, the Excel equation for y is

$$y = \text{SQRT}(5 - x^{\wedge}2).$$

Generate points for y for $x = 0.0, ..., 2.2$ in increments of 0.1, and plot the results. Why does your plot show only ¼ of a circle? Can you create more data points to plot a full circle?

3.   The resolution of the data can dramatically change the appearance of a graph. If there are too few data points, the plot will not be smooth. If there are too many data points, the time and storage requirements become a burden. Generate two sets of data points for the following function:

$$f(x) = \sin(x)$$

For the first set use $x = 0.1, ..., 25.0$ in increments of 0.1 (250 data points). (You will definitely want to use the Fill Handle for this!) Generate another set with $x = 0, ..., 25$ in increments of 1 (25 data points). Plot both versions of $\sin(x)$. Does the plot with 25 data points give you a correct impression of the shape of the sine function?

4.   A graph that uses logarithmic scales on both axes is called a log–log graph. A log–log graph is useful for plotting power equations, since they appear as straight lines. A power equation has the following form:

$$y = ax^b$$

Table 24.3 presents data collected from an experiment that measured the resistance of a conductor for a number of sizes. The size (cross-sectional area) was measured in millimeters squared, and the resistance was measured in milliohms per meter. Create a scatter plot of these data.

TABLE 24.3   Resistance vs. area of a conductor

Area (mm²)	Resistance (milliohms/meter)
0.009	2000.0
0.021	1010.0
0.063	364.0
0.202	110.0
0.523	44.0
1.008	20.0
3.310	8.0
7.290	3.5
20.520	1.2

5.   Modify the x and y axes of the chart created in the previous problem to use a logarithmic scale. From viewing the resulting scatter plot, what can you infer about the relationship between resistance and size of a conductor in this experiment?

6.   Table 24.4 shows the average daily traffic flow at four different intersections for a five-year period. Create a worksheet and enter the table. Plot the data for intersections 1, 3, and 4, but not for intersection 2. Use different line types and markers for each of the three lines. Your graph should look like Figure 24.62.

7.   The Help system in Excel 2007 contains a topic entitled *Present your data in a scatter chart or a line chart*. Type the topic title into the Help system's search box, and then read the article. Summarize the differences between XY Scatter charts and Line charts.

8.   You can use a chart to find the solution to an equation. For example, the function

$$f(x) = 4x^3 + 12x^2 - 64x + 16 = 0$$

should have three solutions because of the For some equations, the solutions might not all be real and could be repeated, but for this particular equation, there are three distinct, real solutions, or *roots*. By simply evaluating the function over a range of x values and charting the results, you can see approxi-

TABLE 24.4   Average daily traffic flow at four downtown intersections

| | Average Daily Traffic Flow × 1,000) | | | |
| | Intersection # | | | |
Year	1	2	3	4
1996	25.3	12.2	34.8	45.3
1997	26.3	14.5	36.9	48.7
1998	28.6	14.9	42.6	43.2
1999	29.0	16.8	50.6	46.9
2000	32.4	17.6	70.8	54.9
2001	34.8	17.9	82.3	60.9

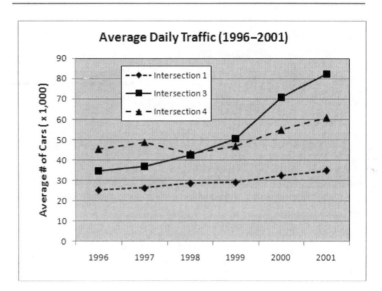

Figure 24.62   A plot of three of the columns in Table 24.3.

mate solutions on the graph. Figure 24.63 shows how this is done and indicates that $x = 0.25$ and $x = 2.6$ are approximate solutions.

Modify the x values in column A to try to

(a) find the value of the third solution
(b) get more precise values for the solutions.

9.   Create a chart to find approximate solutions of the following equation, then solve the quadratic equation to check your results:

$$3x^2 - 8x + 10 = 0$$

10.   Use a chart to find the values of x between 0.1 and 3 that satisfy the following equation:

$$4 \sin(x) + 12x^2 - 63 \ln(x) + 16 = 0$$

11.   Enthalpy and entropy data for saturated steam between 100 and 300°C are shown in Table 24.5.

(a) Prepare a chart of the enthalpy data as a function of temperature, and use it to estimate the enthalpy of saturated steam at 135°C.
(b) Prepare a chart of the entropy data as a function of temperature, and use it to estimate the entropy of saturated steam at 260°C.

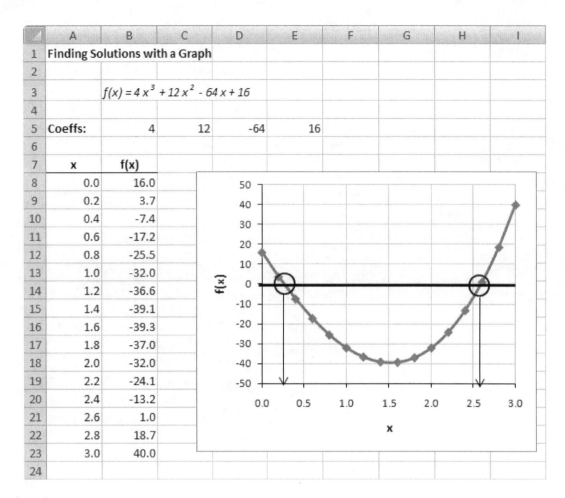

Figure 24.63 Using a chart to find solutions to an equation. Solutions are indicated.

TABLE 24.5 Properties of saturated steam

Temp.°C	Enthalpy kJ/kg	Entropy kJ/kg K
100	2680	7.4
150	2750	6.8
200	2790	6.4
250	2800	6.1
300	2750	5.7

12.   Finance majors often must adjust cost and revenue equations to try to maximize profit, which is the difference between revenue and cost $(P = R - C)$. The following cost and revenue equations are functions of x, the number of units produced and sold. Calculate the profit for a range of x values, and create a chart of profit versus units produced. What value of x produces the maximum profit? (Hint: It's less than 200.)

$$C = 1.2x^2 + 14x + 65$$

$$R = 527x - 0.015x^3$$

Chapter 25
Performing Data Analysis

25.1 INTRODUCTION

Engineers are routinely asked to make decisions and recommendations on the basis of data sets. The data sets may come from laboratory experiments or from a manufacturing plant's quality assurance tests. Either way, *data analysis* is the process used to get from raw data to the results that can be used to make decisions. Excel is commonly used for data analysis, in part because it provides a number of tools that can simplify the data analysis process. Some of those tools will be presented here, including those which perform the following functions:

- Creating a histogram from a data set.
- Calculating basic descriptive statistics about a data set.
- Checking for a correlation between two data sets.
- Performing a linear regression.
- Using a trend analysis to predict future values on the basis of historical values.

Also, engineers often use *iterative methods* to solve complex equations. To use an iterative method, solve the equation over and over again, changing the values of the input variables each time until the equation is satisfied. For example, the equation

$$3x^3 + 4x^2 - 2x - 3 = 0$$

OBJECTIVES

After reading this chapter, you should be able to perform the following tasks:

- Access and use the Analysis ToolPak.
- Create a histogram.
- Calculate descriptive statistics for a data series.
- Calculate the correlation between two data series.
- Perform a linear regression analysis on a set of data.
- Calculate linear and exponential trends for data series.
- Add trendlines to charts.
- Undertake the iterative solution of equations by using the Goal Seeker.
- Perform optimization by using the Solver tool.

637

can be solved in several ways. One option is to use an iterative method to simply try various values of x until you find the values that satisfy the equation. Two ways to solve problems using iterative methods in Excel are the *Goal Seek* and the *Solver*. The Solver can also be used to find the best solution; this process is called *optimization*.

25.2 USING THE ANALYSIS TOOLPAK

An add-in package is available for Excel that includes a number of statistical and engineering tools. This package, called the *Analysis ToolPak*, can be used to shorten the time that it usually takes to perform a complex analysis.

The Analysis ToolPak is typically installed as part of the Excel program, but not activated. Excel keeps program size down and performance up by not activating the add-ins that are not commonly used.

In Excel 2007, a quick glance at the Ribbon's Data tab (Figure 25.1) will show you if the Analysis ToolPak is ready for use on your system. If a button labeled **Data Analysis** appears on the Data tab in the Analysis group, then the Analysis ToolPak is installed and active on your system. If the button is missing, the Analysis ToolPak must either be activated or (less commonly) be installed from the Excel program CDs.

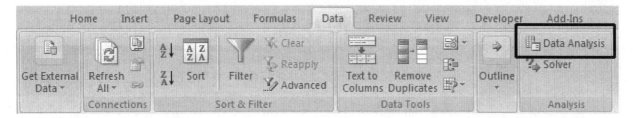

Figure 25.1 If the Data Analysis button appears on the Ribbon's Data tab, the Analysis ToolPak is installed and active.

(In Excel 2003, Choose Tools from the Menu bar. If the Data Analysis command does not appear on the Tools menu, then the Analysis ToolPak must be either activated or installed.)

25.2.1 Activating the Analysis ToolPak

If the **Data Analysis** button appears on the Ribbon's Data tab, you can skip this step.

In Excel 2007, add-ins like the Analysis ToolPak are managed using the Add-Ins panel on the Excel Options dialog box. To access the Excel Options dialog box, use the following options from the Office button: **Office button → Excel Options button** (this opens the Excel Options dialog box) **→ Add-Ins panel**. The Add-Ins panel of the Excel Options dialog box is shown in Figure 25.2.

Look for "Analysis ToolPak" in the **Inactive Application Add-Ins** list (highlighted in Figure 25.2.)

- If "Analysis ToolPak" is not listed in the **Inactive Application Add-Ins** list, it must be installed from the Excel program CDs (this is not common).
- If "Analysis ToolPak" is listed in the **Inactive Application Add-Ins** list, the Analysis ToolPak has been installed and you simply need to activate it.

The Analysis ToolPak can be activated with the following steps:

1. Select "Analysis ToolPak" in the **Inactive Application Add-Ins** list.
2. Click **Go ...** to open the Add-Ins dialog box, shown in Figure 25.3.

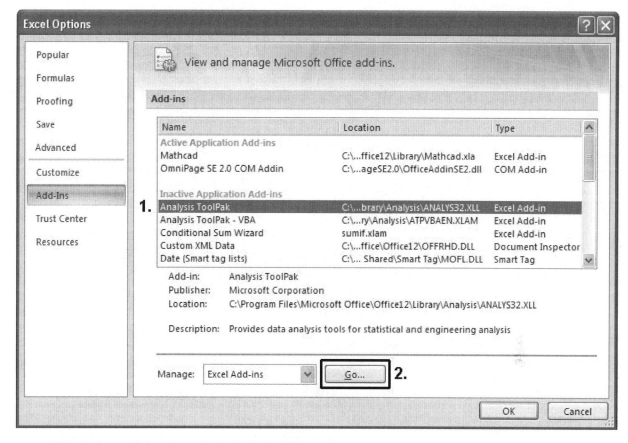

Figure 25.2   The Add-Ins panel on the Excel Options dialog box.

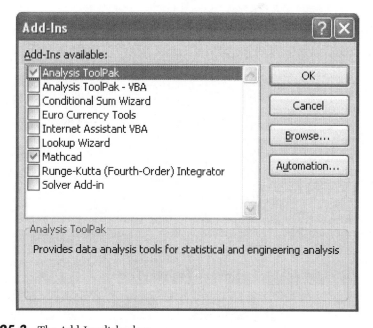

Figure 25.3   The Add-Ins dialog box.

3. Check the box labeled **Analysis ToolPak** (as illustrated in Figure 25.3).

4. Click **OK** to close the Add-Ins dialog box.

5. Click **OK** to close the Excel Options dialog box.

The Analysis ToolPak is now active on your system.

(In Excel 2003, open the Add-Ins dialog box using menu options: Tools → Add-Ins, then check the box labeled **Analysis ToolPak** as illustrated in Figure 25.3.)

25.2.2 Opening the Data Analysis Dialog Box

Once the Analysis ToolPak is active, click the **Data Analysis** button on the Ribbon's Data tab (see Figure 25.1) to open the Data Analysis dialog box, shown in Figure 25.4. (Excel 2003: Use menu options Tools → Data Analysis.)

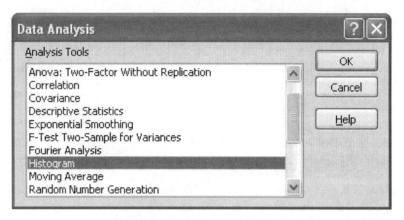

Figure 25.4   The Data Analysis dialog box.

The Data Analysis dialog box provides access to a wide assortment of analysis tools. Each tool requires a set of input parameters in a specific format, and dialog boxes are used to collect the required pieces of information. These usually include

- an input range (cells containing the data to be analyzed)
- an output range (a place for the tool to put the calculated results)
- option settings to control the data analysis process

The results of the data analysis are displayed in an output table. Additionally, some tools will generate a chart.

We will demonstrate how to use the Analysis ToolPak by using four of the available tools to perform these tasks:

- Create a histogram.
- Provide descriptive statistics.
- Compute a correlation.
- Perform a regression analysis.

It is beyond the scope of this text to interpret the results of these statistical analyses or to explain the meaning of statistical terms such as confidence interval, residuals, R square, standard error, etc.

25.3   CREATING A HISTOGRAM

We will first demonstrate the use of the Analysis ToolPak by creating a *histogram*. A histogram is a graph of the frequency distribution of a set of data. That is, it is a chart that shows how often certain values appear in a data set. Most students have seen histograms used by a teacher to show how many As, Bs, and so on were given on a particular assignment. An example of a grade distribution chart, or grade histogram, is shown in Figure 25.5.

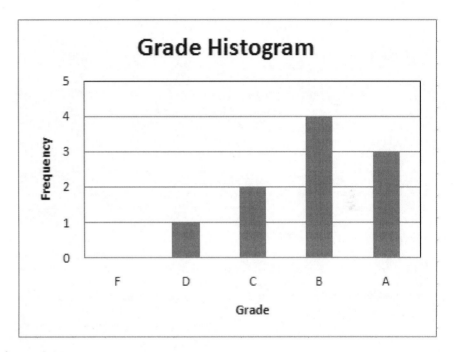

Figure 25.5   Grade histogram.

To create a histogram, the data are aggregated, or separated into groups, and the groups are graphed in a Column chart. A group is sometimes called a *bin*, since the process of creating a histogram can be visualized as follows:

1. Sort the data into bins.
2. Count the number of values in each bin.
3. Graph the bin names on the x axis and the number of values in the bins on the y axis.

In the grade example, each letter grade is assigned to a bin. To create the graph in Figure 25.1, we identify the bins (A to F), count the number of grades in each bin, and create the Column chart.

NOTE: The Histogram tool in Excel will create histograms only of numeric data, not of the letter grades used in this example. In the next example we will use numeric scores and the Histogram tool to create a grade histogram.

In a histogram, each column represents a bin, and the height of the bar represents the number of data values in that bin, which is called the *frequency* of data in the bin.

EXAMPLE 25.1 EXAMPLE: CREATING A GRADE HISTOGRAM

We begin by looking at a data set containing the student scores, Figure 25.6.

Next, we decide how the scores should be related to grades. A common grading method uses a 10-point interval between each grade level, or bin. Scores less than 60 receive a grade of F, less than 70 receive a D, and so on. This is indicated on the worksheet by defining bins as shown in column E in Figure 25.7.

	A	B	C
1	Grade Histogram		
2			
3	Student	Score	
4	Sal	87	
5	Sali	94	
6	Sally	72	
7	Sam	82	
8	Sara	88	
9	Sarah	78	
10	Su Nee	95	
11	Stewart	91	
12	Stuart	68	
13	Suri	84	
14			

Figure 25.6 Student score data.

	A	B	C	D	E	F
1	Grade Histogram					
2						
3	Student	Score		Grades	Bins	
4	Sal	87		F	60	
5	Sali	94		D	70	
6	Sally	72		C	80	
7	Sam	82		B	90	
8	Sara	88		A	100	
9	Sarah	78				
10	Su Nee	95				
11	Stewart	91				
12	Stuart	68				
13	Suri	84				
14						

Figure 25.7 Defining the upper limits of each grade bin.

The values in the bin column are the upper limits of each bin, so a score of 90 would be given a grade of B, not A. Since it is common for a score of 90 to receive an A grade, we can modify the values in the bins slightly, as shown in Figure 25.8.

	A	B	C	D	E	F
1	Grade Histogram					
2						
3	Student	Score		Grades	Bins	
4	Sal	87		F	59.99	
5	Sali	94		D	69.99	
6	Sally	72		C	79.99	
7	Sam	82		B	89.99	
8	Sara	88		A	100	
9	Sarah	78				
10	Su Nee	95				
11	Stewart	91				
12	Stuart	68				
13	Suri	84				
14						

Figure 25.8 Modified bin values.

To create a histogram from the scores and bins shown in Figure 25.8, follow these steps:

1. Open the Data Analysis dialog box (shown in Figure 25.9) with Ribbon options: **Data tab** → **Analysis group** → **Data Analysis button**. (Excel 2003: Use menu options Tools → Data Analysis.)

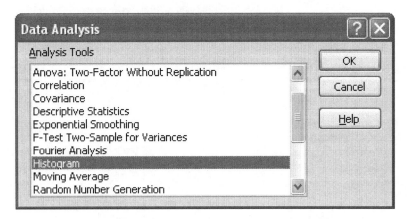

Figure 25.9   The Data Analysis dialog box with Histogram tool selected.

2. Select **Histogram** from the list of data analysis tools (illustrated in Figure 25.9).
3. Click **OK** to close the Data Analysis dialog box and open the Histogram dialog box (shown in Figure 25.10).
4. Select the score values (cells B4:B13) as the **Input Range** (shown in Figure 25.10).

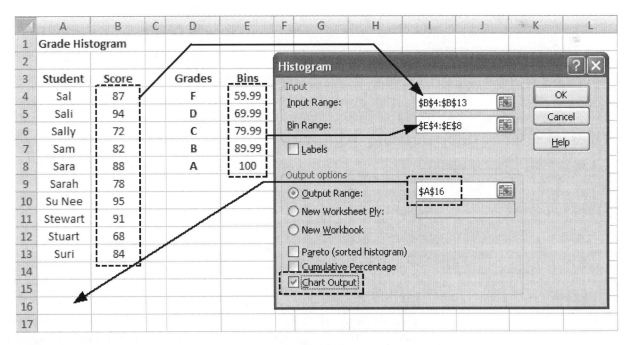

Figure 25.10   The histogram dialog box with required fields filled in.

5. Select the bin values (cells E4:E8) as the **Bin Range** (shown in Figure 25.10).
6. Select where you want the output to be located. In this example we have chosen to place the output below the data by entering A16 as the top-left cell of the **Output Range** (shown in Figure 25.10).
7. Request the histogram chart by checking the **Chart Output** box (shown in Figure 25.10).
8. Click **OK** to close the Histogram dialog box and create the histogram chart.

The result is shown in Figure 25.11.

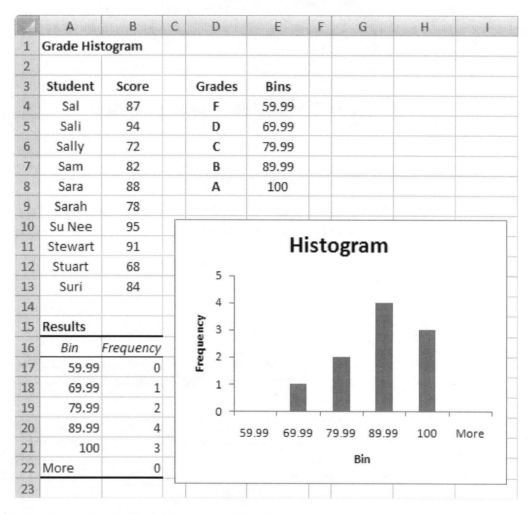

Figure 25.11 The resulting histogram (chart enlarged slightly).

If you want to replace the score values on the x axis with grade letters, just change the horizontal axis labels as follows:

1. Click the chart to select it. This causes the Ribbon to display the Chart Tools tabs.
2. Click the **Select Data** button on the Chart Tools: Design tab (Ribbon Options: **Chart Tools → Design tab → Data group → Select Data button**). This opens the Select Data Source dialog box shown in Figure 25.12.

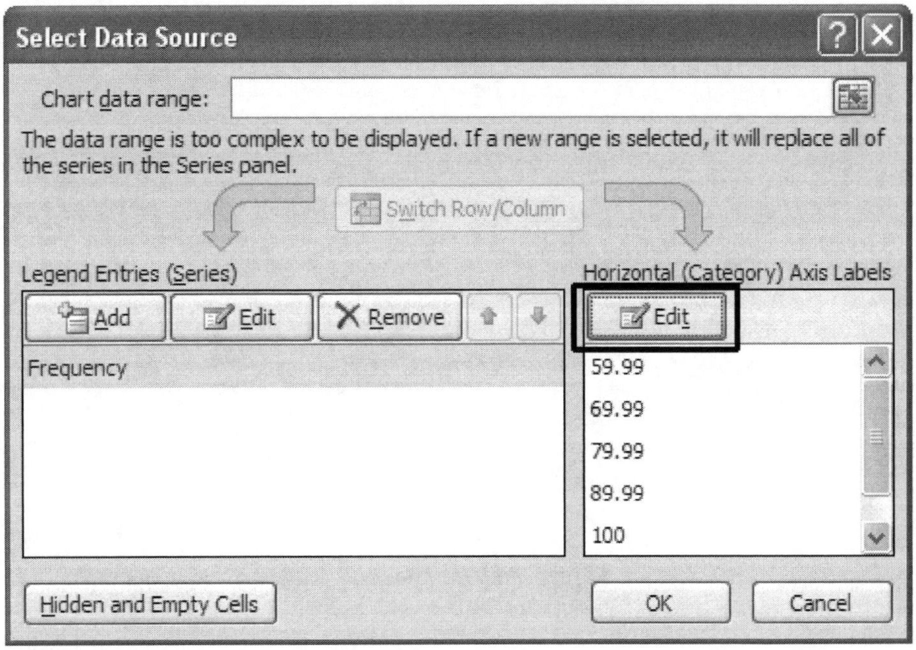

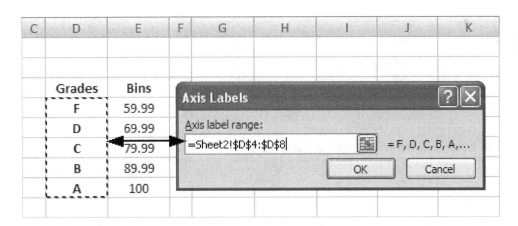

Figure 25.12   The Select Data Source dialog box.

3. Click the **Edit** button in the Horizontal (Category) Axis Labels area (indicated in Figure 25.12).
4. Select the cells containing the letter grades (cells D4:D8) as shown in Figure 25.13.

Grades	Bins
F	59.99
D	69.99
C	79.99
B	89.99
A	100

Axis Labels
Axis label range:
=Sheet2!$D$4:$D$8   = F, D, C, B, A,…

Figure 25.13   Select the new *x* axis labels.

5. Click **OK** to close the Axis Labels dialog box (Figure 25.13).
6. Click **OK** to close Select Data Source dialog box (Figure 25.12).

The resulting histogram, with the x axis title changed from "bin" to "Grade" is shown in Figure 25.14.

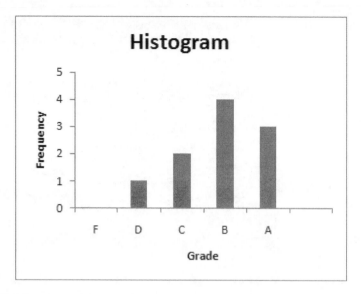

Figure 25.14   The completed grade histogram.

APPLICATION—HISTOGRAMS FOR QUALITY ASSURANCE

An example of the use of a histogram is to visualize the distribution of the tolerance errors of a test set of machine parts coming off of an assembly line. With a glance at the histogram, the quality assurance (QA) department can tell whether the tolerance errors are widely or narrowly distributed, as well as whether they are normally distributed or skewed.

The data in Figure 25.15 are the results of a test batch from an assembly line. The QA team collected 25 sample parts and measured their tolerances. The team noted that the test data typically range from about −5 to +5 thousandths of an inch from the correct size. The team created nine bins for the data.

To create a histogram of the data in Figure 25.15, perform the following steps:

1. Open the Data Analysis dialog box with Ribbon options: **Data tab** → **Analysis group** → **Data Analysis button**. (Excel 2003: Use menu options Tools → Data Analysis.)

2. Select **Histogram** from the list of data analysis tools.

3. Click **OK** to close the Data Analysis dialog box and open the Histogram dialog box.

4. Select the tolerance values (cells A3:A28) as the **Input Range** (shown in Figure 25.16).

5. Select the bin values (cells B3:B12) as the **Bin Range** (shown in Figure 25.16).

6. Notice that the cell ranges used as the Input Range and Bin Range included the column headings ("Tolerance" and "Bins"). Check the box labeled **Labels** (shown in Figure 25.16) to let Excel know that labels were included in the specified ranges.

	A	B	C	D	E	F
1	**Machine Parts Assembly Line 14**					
2						
3	Tolerance	Bins		Test Batch #	3201	
4	0.34	-3.5		Date:	2/1/2008	
5	1.03	-2.5		Units:	inches x 10^3	
6	-1.26	-1.5				
7	3.13	-0.5				
8	-0.1	0.5				
9	0.02	1.5				
10	-0.01	2.5				
11	2.12	3.5				
12	-1.4	4.5				
13	1.24					
14	2.29					
15	-0.71					
16	-1.38					
17	-1.13					
18	-1.34					
19	0.03					
20	-0.03					
21	-0.56					
22	-0.04					
23	-2.55					
24	-0.01					
25	0.56					
26	0.78					
27	0.99					
28	1.12					
29						

Figure 25.15   Tolerances of test batch machine parts.

7. Select where you want the output to be located. In this example we have chosen to send the output to a **New Worksheet Ply** (shown in Figure 25.16).

8. Request the histogram chart by checking the **Chart Output box** (shown in Figure 25.16).

9. Click **OK** to close the Histogram dialog box and create the histogram chart.

The result is shown in Figure 25.17. You could use the Chart Tools on the Ribbon to change the appearance of the histogram, if needed.

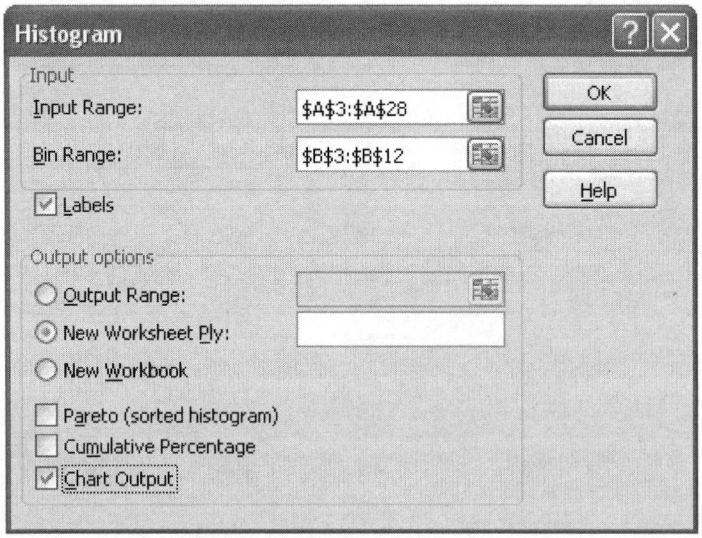

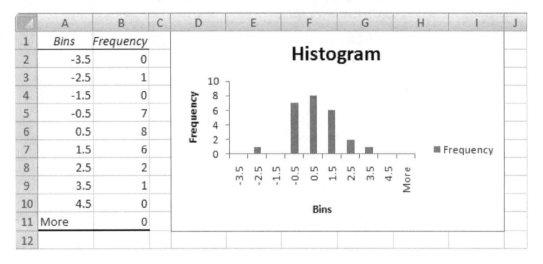

Figure 25.16 The Histogram dialog box filled in for the machine part tolerances histogram.

	A	B	C	D	E	F	G	H	I	J
1	*Bins*	*Frequency*								
2	-3.5	0								
3	-2.5	1								
4	-1.5	0								
5	-0.5	7								
6	0.5	8								
7	1.5	6								
8	2.5	2								
9	3.5	1								
10	4.5	0								
11	More	0								
12										

Figure 25.17 Histogram of tolerances of tested machine parts.

Several other features are available on the Histogram dialog box (see Figure 25.16). These include sorting the histogram (*Pareto*) and displaying a cumulative percentage (*Cumulative Percentage*).

The **Help** button on the Histogram dialog box displays detailed information about the input parameters and options for the Histogram tool.

25.4 PROVIDING DESCRIPTIVE STATISTICS

Excel provides a data analysis tool for computing common *descriptive statistics*, which are values calculated from a data set and used to describe some basic characteristics of the data set. You could calculate each of these values by using individual Excel built-in functions from the Insert Function dialog box, but the Descriptive Statistics tool conveniently aggregates the most common computations for you in a table.

As an example, we will go through the steps to compute the descriptive statistics of the machine-parts test data from Figure 25.15:

1. Open the Data Analysis dialog box with Ribbon options: **Data tab → Analysis group → Data Analysis button**. (Excel 2003: Use menu options Tools → Data Analysis.)

2. Select **Descriptive Statistics** from the list of data analysis tools.

3. Click **OK** to close the Data Analysis dialog box and open the Descriptive Statistics dialog box, shown in Figure 25.18.

4. Select the tolerance values (cells A3:A28) as the **Input Range** (shown in Figure 25.18).

5. Since the Input Range included a column heading, check the **Labels in First Row** box (shown in Figure 25.18).

6. Choose a location for the output table. In this example, we have opted to send the output to a **New Worksheet Ply**.

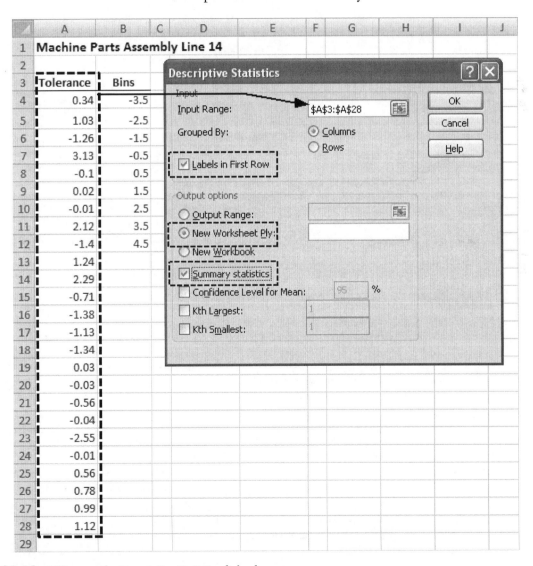

Figure 25.18 Filling out the Descriptive Statistics dialog box.

7. Check the **Summary statistics** box (shown in Figure 25.18) to tell Excel to calculate the descriptive statistics.
8. Click **OK** to close the Descriptive Statistics dialog box and calculate the statistic values.

The results are shown in Figure 25.19.

	A	B	C
1	*Tolerance*		
2			
3	Mean	0.1252	
4	Standard Error	0.261001	
5	Median	-0.01	
6	Mode	-0.01	
7	Standard Deviation	1.305004	
8	Sample Variance	1.703034	
9	Kurtosis	0.212016	
10	Skewness	0.296037	
11	Range	5.68	
12	Minimum	-2.55	
13	Maximum	3.13	
14	Sum	3.13	
15	Count	25	
16			

Figure 25.19   Descriptive statistics for the tested machine parts.

You are not expected to understand all of the terms in Figure 25.19. However, you can probably recognize some of them. Each statistic is described briefly in Table 25.1.

TABLE 25.1   The descriptive statistics

Statistic	Value*	Description
Mean	0.1252	The data set shows scatter around a central point, which is called the *mean*.
Standard Error	0.261001	The *standard error* is used to estimate how accurately the *sample mean* (0.1252 in this example) represents the *population mean*.
Median	−0.01	The *median* is the middle value of the sorted data set.
Mode	−0.01	The *mode* is the most commonly occurring value in the data set.
Standard Deviation	1.305004	The *standard deviation* is a measure of the data's variability.
Sample Variance	1.703034	The *sample variance* is the square of the *sample standard deviation*.
Kurtosis	0.212016	The *kurtosis* provides information about the "peakedness" of the data distribution compared with a normal distribution. Large positive values of kurtosis indicate that the data distribution is "tall and skinny" compared with the normal distribution.
Skewness	0.296037	The *skewness* provides information about the extent of asymmetry of the distribution about its *mean*.
Range	5.68	The *range* is the difference between the maximum and minimum values in the data set.
Minimum	−2.55	*Minimum* indicates the smallest value in the data set.
Maximum	3.13	*Maximum* indicates the largest value in the data set.
Sum	3.13	The *sum* is the result of adding all values in the data set.
Count	25	The *count* is the number of values in the data set.

*Values are from Figure 25.19.

From these results, the QA team can see that the measured tolerances ranged from −2.55 to +3.13 thousandths of an inch, with a mean tolerance close to zero (0.1252 thousandths of an inch). An important result for the team is the variability of the test data. The standard deviation (1.305 thousandths of an inch) is a measure of the data's variability. The standard deviation of the test data set, along with the size of the data set, can be used to make predictions about how many of the items on the assembly line eventually will be rejected.

APPLICATION

APPLICATION—COMPARING TWO ASSEMBLY LINES

Figure 25.15 presented test data for a single assembly line. In this example, we will compare the results from two assembly lines. The collected data are presented in Figure 25.20.

	A	B	C	D	E	F	G
1	**Machine Parts Tolerances**						
2							
3	Line 14	Line 17	Bins		Test Batch #	3201	
4	0.34	1.14	-10		Date:	2/1/2008	
5	1.03	0.2	-8		Units:	inches x 10³	
6	-1.26	-0.31	-6				
7	3.13	4.84	-4				
8	-0.1	-1.12	-2				
9	0.02	0.12	0				
10	-0.01	9.35	2				
11	2.12	-5.8	4				
12	-1.4	-0.31	6				
13	1.24	6.02	8				
14	2.29	0.21	10				
15	-0.71	-9.72					
16	-1.38	1.88					
17	-1.13	4.72					
18	-1.34	-1.01					
19	0.03	-5.72					
20	-0.03	1.86					
21	-0.56	-7.02					
22	-0.04	4.49					
23	-2.55	-5.27					
24	-0.01	-2.99					
25	0.56	-5.71					
26	0.78	2.36					
27	0.99	-5.76					
28	1.12	-1.14					
29							

Figure 25.20   Test data from two assembly lines.

In Figure 25.20, new bins have been assigned to cover the range of values from assembly line #17. Using this data, you can prepare a histogram for each line. The results are shown in Figure 25.21.

The histograms in Figure 25.21 clearly show that Line 17 is producing parts with a much wider range of tolerances. Therefore, there is a good chance that Line 17 is producing more rejected parts than Line 14. The engineer responsible for Line 17 will probably start looking for reasons why the distribution of tolerances is so wide, so that the equipment can be repaired.

To quantify the differences between the two data sets, you can calculate descriptive statistics for the two sets. To compare the values side by side, simply include both data sets in the Input Range on the Descriptive Statistics dialog box. This is illustrated in Figure 25.22. The calculated results are shown in Figure 25.23.

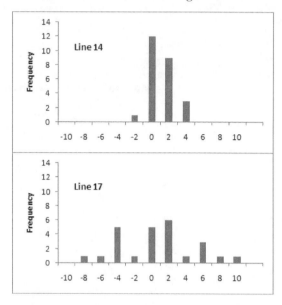

Figure 25.21   Histograms of the data from each assembly line.

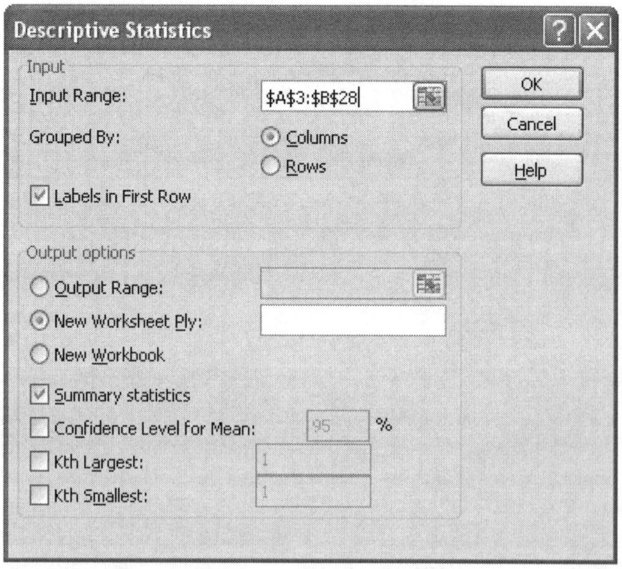

Figure 25.22   The Descriptive Statistics dialog box with two data columns in the Input Range.

In Figure 25.23 we see that the mean tolerances for the two assembly lines are different, and that the standard deviation of the values from Line 17 is much larger than the standard deviation from Line 14. Since the standard deviation is a measure of the data's variability, this result confirms (and quantifies) what was evident in the histograms: The distribution of tolerances in Line 17 is much wider.

	A	B	C	D	E
1	*Line 14*		*Line 17*		
2					
3	Mean	0.1252	Mean	-0.5876	
4	Standard Error	0.261001	Standard Error	0.92307	
5	Median	-0.01	Median	-0.31	
6	Mode	-0.01	Mode	-0.31	
7	Standard Deviation	1.305004	Standard Deviation	4.615351	
8	Sample Variance	1.703034	Sample Variance	21.30146	
9	Kurtosis	0.212016	Kurtosis	-0.32901	
10	Skewness	0.296037	Skewness	0.035812	
11	Range	5.68	Range	19.07	
12	Minimum	-2.55	Minimum	-9.72	
13	Maximum	3.13	Maximum	9.35	
14	Sum	3.13	Sum	-14.69	
15	Count	25	Count	25	
16					

Figure 25.23   Comparing the descriptive statistics for the two assembly lines.

25.5   COMPUTING A CORRELATION

The *correlation* of two data sets is a measure of how well the two ranges of data move together linearly. If large values of one set are associated with large values of the other, then a positive correlation exists. If small values of one set are associated with large values of the other (and vice versa), then a negative correlation exists.

In the left chart in Figure 25.24, the two curves increase together; these data sets are strongly and positively correlated. By contrast, the data sets shown in the right chart show a strong negative correlation; they move together, but not in the same direction.

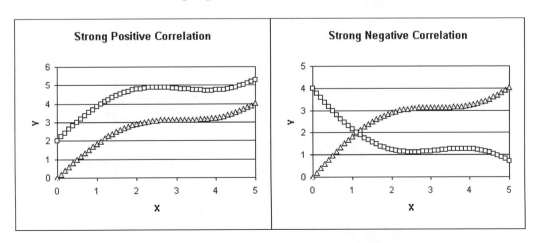

Figure 25.24   Examples of correlated data sets. Left panel: positive correlation. Right panel: negative correlation.

If the correlation is near zero, then the values in both sets are not linearly related (Figure 25.25).

Figure 25.26 shows the midterm grades and overall grade point averages (GPAs) for 20 students. We are interested in knowing whether there is a positive correlation between the midterm exam grades and the students' GPAs.

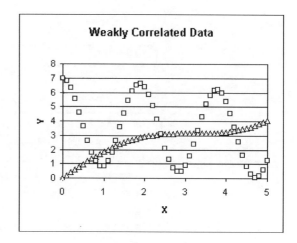

Figure 25.25   Weakly correlated data.

	A	B	C	D
1	Student #	Midterm Score	GPA	
2	1	45	1.7	
3	2	89	3.7	
4	3	90	3.9	
5	4	67	3.7	
6	5	88	2.4	
7	6	93	3.4	
8	7	32	1.8	
9	8	85	3.1	
10	9	68	2.4	
11	10	52	2.6	
12	11	77	3.5	
13	12	96	3.9	
14	13	54	2.1	
15	14	78	2.8	
16	15	83	2.4	
17	16	89	3.1	
18	17	79	2.9	
19	18	83	2.9	
20	19	72	3.1	
21	20	91	3.6	
22				

Figure 25.26   Midterm scores and GPAs for 20 students.

Once the data are available in an Excel worksheet, we can calculate the correlation between the students' midterm grades and GPAs with these steps:

1. Open the Data Analysis dialog box with Ribbon options: **Data tab → Analysis group → Data Analysis button**. (Excel 2003: Use menu options Tools → Data Analysis.)
2. Select **Correlation** from the list of data analysis tools.
3. Click **OK** to close the Data Analysis dialog box and open the Correlation dialog box, shown in Figure 25.27.

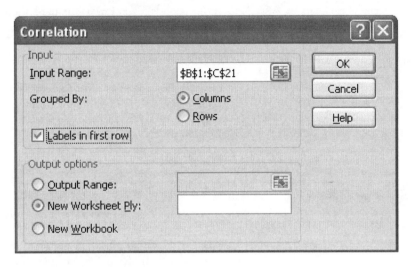

Figure 25.27   The Correlation dialog box.

4. Use the student midterm scores and GPAs (cells B1:C21, including the column headings) as the **Input Range** for the calculation (shown in Figure 25.27).
5. Since the Input Range included column headings, check the **Labels in First Row** box (shown in Figure 25.27).
6. Choose a location for the output table. In this example, we have opted to send the output to a **New Worksheet Ply**.
7. Click OK to close the Correlation dialog box and calculate the *correlation coefficient, r*.

The result is shown in Figure 25.28. Note that the correlation coefficient $r = 0.7354$ indicates that there is a positive correlation between midterm grades and GPAs for this group of students.

	A	B	C	D
1		Midterm Score	GPA	
2	Midterm Score	1		
3	GPA	0.7354	1	
4				

Figure 25.28   The correlation between midterm scores and GPAs.

25.6   PERFORMING A LINEAR REGRESSION

The *correlation coefficient* is a measure of whether a linear relationship exists between two sets of data. However, the correlation coefficient does not tell us what the relationship is, merely that it exists. A *linear-regression analysis* is an attempt to find the relationship among variables and express the relationship as a linear equation.

The Analysis ToolPak performs linear-regression analysis by using the least squares method to fit a curve through a set of observations. In this section, we will show you how to perform a regression that analyzes how a single dependent variable is affected by a single independent variable.

If the regression is a good fit to the data, then the regression allows us to predict future performance. For example, we might make a prediction about students' first-year college GPAs on the basis of their high school GPAs.

To do so, we would follow these steps:

1. Collect GPA data from a representative sample of college students. The data would include their high school GPAs and their first-year college GPAs.
2. Perform a linear regression, using the high school and college GPA data. The result of the regression would be a linear equation relating college GPA to high school GPA.
3. Use the regression equation with the GPAs of a group of recent high school graduates to predict how they would do in their first year of college.

If more than one independent variable is considered, then the analysis technique is called *multiple regression*. For example, students' SAT scores and IQs might both be tested as predictors, in addition to their high school GPAs.

Since we know that there is a positive relationship between overall GPA and midterm scores in the data in Figure 25.26, let's perform a regression analysis on the same data. We would like to know whether we can predict a student's midterm grade, given the student's GPA. We are making some strong assumptions about our collected data. These are assumptions about our sampling technique and the underlying distribution of the student GPAs. We will ignore these ramifications here, but you will study them if you take a statistics course.

To perform a regression analysis, follow these steps:

1. Open the Data Analysis dialog box with Ribbon options: **Data tab → Analysis group → Data Analysis button**. (Excel 2003: Use menu options Tools → Data Analysis.)
2. Select **Regression** from the list of data analysis tools.
3. Click **OK** to close the Data Analysis dialog box and open the Regression dialog box, shown in Figure 25.29.
4. Use the student midterm scores (cells B1:B21, including the column heading) as the **Input Y Range** for the calculation (shown in Figure 25.29).
5. Use the student GPAs (cells C1:C21, including the column heading) as the **Input X Range** for the calculation (shown in Figure 25.29).

NOTE: In regression analysis, x is used to predict y. Since we are trying to predict midterm score from GPA, the midterm scores are the **Input Y Range** and the GPAs are the **Input X Range**.

6. Since the input ranges included column headings, check the **Labels** box (shown in Figure 25.29).

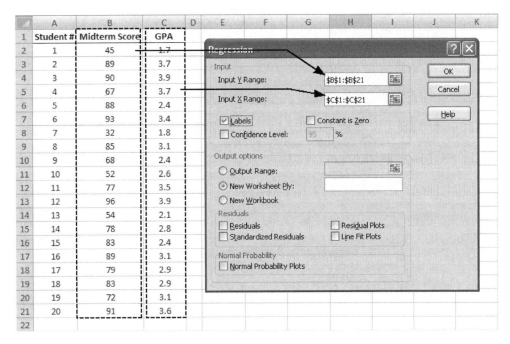

Figure 25.29   The Regression dialog box being filled in.

7. Choose a location for the output table. In this example, we have opted to send the output to a **New Worksheet Ply**.

8. Click OK to close the Regression dialog box and perform the regression analysis.

The results are shown in Figure 25.30.

Figure 25.30 presents a lot more information than you probably care to know. One of the important results is the significance of the F statistic (Significance F = 0.0002). This means that there is a very low probability that the results are from chance.

The regression coefficients (Intercept and GPA) are listed in the *Coefficients* column. We use these to build a predictive equation:

$$\text{Predicted Midterm Grade} = 19.272 \times \text{GPA} + 18.696$$

The R^2 value (R Square = 0.541) is a pretty low value, considering that $R^2 = 1.000$ indicates that the regression line is a perfect fit to the data. Also, notice that the *standard error of the intercept* (12.648) is almost as great as the value of the coefficient (18.696). Ideally, you would like to see standard errors much smaller than the coefficients. Finally, look at the *P-values* associated with the coefficients in Figure 25.30. The P-values represent the probability that you could get the calculated result by random chance. Ideally, you would want very small P-values associated with your coefficients, such as the P = 0.0002 on the GPA. This indicates that the probability that the GPA coefficient could be obtained by random chance is only 0.02 percent. However, the probability that the intercept coefficient could be obtained by random chance is 15.7 percent. That's pretty high, and it suggests that there is a lot of uncertainty associated with the intercept coefficient in the regression.

When a coefficient has a high P-value, you have to wonder if the coefficient needs to be included in the model at all. We can rework the regression analysis without an intercept (actually, setting the intercept to zero) to see if it makes a difference in the results. To do so, follow the same check, but check the **Constant is Zero** box on the

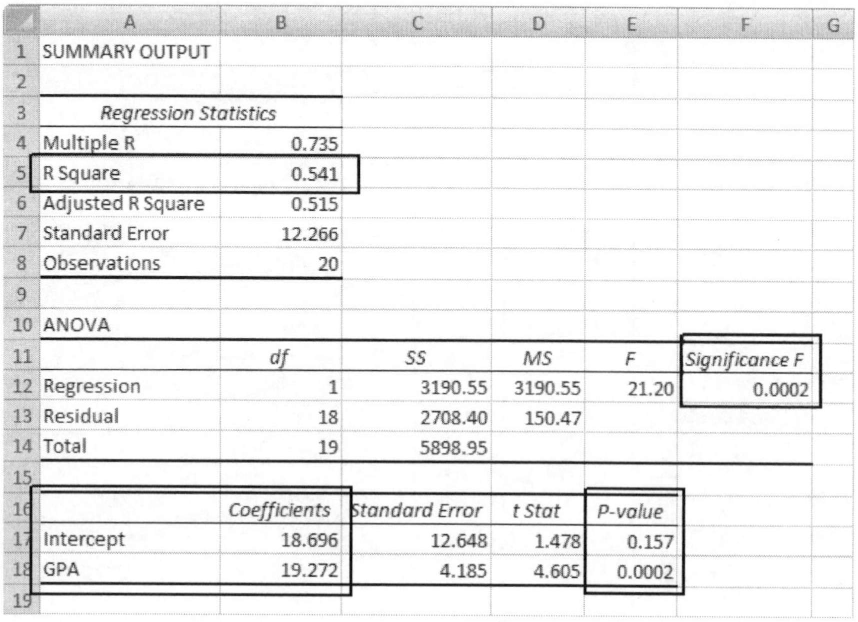

SUMMARY OUTPUT					
Regression Statistics					
Multiple R	0.735				
R Square	0.541				
Adjusted R Square	0.515				
Standard Error	12.266				
Observations	20				
ANOVA					
	df	*SS*	*MS*	*F*	*Significance F*
Regression	1	3190.55	3190.55	21.20	0.0002
Residual	18	2708.40	150.47		
Total	19	5898.95			
	Coefficients	*Standard Error*	*t Stat*	*P-value*	
Intercept	18.696	12.648	1.478	0.157	
GPA	19.272	4.185	4.605	0.0002	

Figure 25.30 Regression analysis results.

Regression dialog box, as shown in Figure 25.31. The results of performing the regression with the intercept forced to be equal to zero are shown in Figure 25.32.

Notice that the R^2 value is much closer to 1.0, and the Significance F and P-value for the GPA coefficient are miniscule. This appears to be a better result. The predictive equation is now

$$\text{Predicted Midterm Grade} = 25.312 \times \text{GPA}$$

Figure 25.33 shows both regression equations superimposed on a graph of the original data.

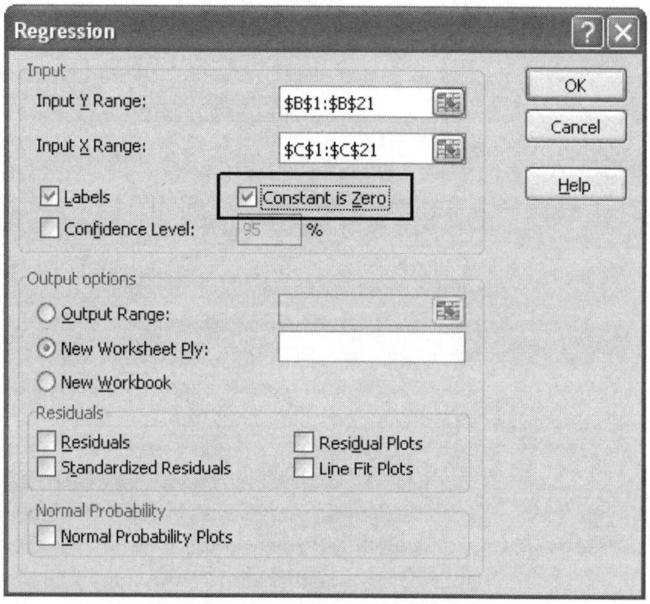

Figure 25.31 Forcing the intercept equal to zero on the Regression dialog box.

⬚	A	B	C	D	E	F	G
1	SUMMARY OUTPUT						
2							
3	*Regression Statistics*						
4	Multiple R	0.987					
5	R Square	0.975					
6	Adjusted R Square	0.922					
7	Standard Error	12.643					
8	Observations	20					
9							
10	ANOVA						
11		*df*	*SS*	*MS*	*F*	*Significance F*	
12	Regression	1	117017.79	117017.79	732.03	4.952E-16	
13	Residual	19	3037.21	159.85			
14	Total	20	120055				
15							
16		*Coefficients*	*Standard Error*	*t Stat*	*P-value*		
17	Intercept	0	#N/A	#N/A	#N/A		
18	GPA	25.312	0.936	27.056	1.23E-16		
19							

Figure 25.32   Regression results with intercept set equal to zero.

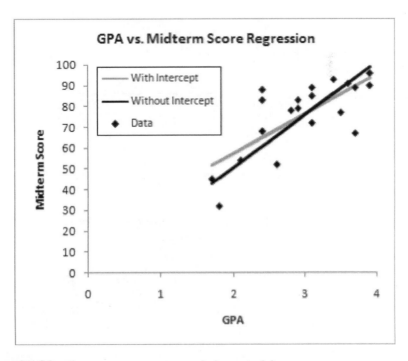

Figure 25.33   The regression equations with the original data.

25.7 TREND ANALYSIS

Trend analysis is the science of forecasting or predicting future elements of a data series on the basis of historical data. Trend analysis is used in many areas, such as financial forecasting, epidemiology, capacity planning, and criminology. Excel has the ability to calculate linear and exponential growth trends for data series. Excel can also calculate and display various trendlines for charts.

A *linear trend* consists of fitting known *x* and *y* values to a linear equation. Unknown *y* values may then be predicted by extending the *x* values and using the equation to calculate new *y* values. This is called *linear extension*. An exponential trend can be created in a similar manner, except that the data are fit to an exponential equation. The graph of a trend is called a *trendline*.

25.7.1 Trend Analysis with Data Series

A trend analysis can either extend or replace a series of data elements. The simplest method for extending a data series with a linear regression is to drag the Fill Handle past the end of the data series. For example, Figure 25.34 shows the number of occurrences of a hypothetical disease for the years 2001 to 2004.

By assuming a linear rate of increase in the disease, you can estimate the number of occurrences for 2005 to 2009. To calculate the *linear trend*,

1. Select the known data (A5:D5).
2. Drag the Fill Handle to the right so that the fill box covers cells (E5:I5).

When you release the mouse, cells (E5:I5) will contain the data elements predicted by a linear regression of the original data. This result is shown in Figure 25.35. Notice that the date values in row 4 were never used when calculating the linear trend and filling cells E5:I5 by using the Fill Handle. Excel assumes that the known

	A	B	C	D	E	F	G	H	I	J
1	Occurrence of Disease X (in thousands)									
2										
3		Known Values				Predicted Values				
4	2001	2002	2003	2004	(2005)	(2006)	(2007)	(2008)	(2009)	
5	1.1	1.9	3.0	3.8						
6										

Figure 25.34 Disease data.

	A	B	C	D	E	F	G	H	I	J
1	Occurrence of Disease X (in thousands)									
2										
3		Known Values				Predicted Values				
4	2001	2002	2003	2004	(2005)	(2006)	(2007)	(2008)	(2009)	
5	1.1	1.9	3.0	3.8	4.8	5.7	6.6	7.5	8.4	
6										

Figure 25.35 Disease data and projected disease occurrences.

values (A5:D5) are separated by equal intervals (one year in this example) and that the new values will have the same interval. So, you can predict what will happen in 2005, 2006, and 2007, but you cannot use the Fill Handle to predict what will happen in 2005, 2010, and 2050 (unless you calculate all intervening years as well.)

The *Fill Series command* can be used for somewhat more sophisticated trend analysis. To extend or replace a data series by using the Fill Series command, first select the region of data over which the analysis is to occur. This includes the original data and the new cells that are to hold the predicted data. Let's try some of the Fill Series functions, using the sample data in Figure 25.34:

1. Create a worksheet with the titles and headers shown in Figure 25.36.
2. Type the numbers 1.1, 1.9, 3.0, and 3.8 into cells B6:E6.
3. Copy the values to rows 8, 10, 12, and 14. The same known values will be used for each trend analysis.

25.7.2 Trend Analysis: Linear Extension

To extend the known values with a linear regression and leave the original values unchanged, follow these steps:

1. Select cells B8:J8, the known data points and the unknown (to be calculated) points.
2. Open the Series dialog box (shown in Figure 25.37) using Ribbon options: **Home tab → Editing group → Fill drop-down menu → Series ... button**. (Excel 2003: Edit → Fill → Series.)

Note that a step value (the amount by which a series is increased or decreased) has been calculated by Excel. The step value can be modified manually to set the increment value for x in the linear equation

$$y = mx + b.$$

	A	B	C	D	E	F	G	H	I	J	K
1	**Using the Fill Series Command**										
2				**Occurrence of Disease X (in thousands)**							
3			**Known Values**				**Predicted Values**				
4	**Type of Series**	2001	2002	2003	2004	(2005)	(2006)	(2007)	(2008)	(2009)	
5											
6	**Original Known Values**	1.1	1.9	3.0	3.8						
7											
8	**Linear Extension**	1.1	1.9	3.0	3.8						
9											
10	**Linear Replacement**	1.1	1.9	3.0	3.8						
11											
12	**Exponential Replacement**	1.1	1.9	3.0	3.8						
13											
14	***TREND* Function**	1.1	1.9	3.0	3.8						
15											
16											

Figure 25.36 Preparing to use the Fill Series command.

	A	B	C	D	E	F	G	H	I	J	K	L
1	Using the Fill Series Command											
2				Occurrence of Disease X (in thousands)								
3			Known Values				Predicted Values					
4	Type of Series	2001	2002	2003	2004	(2005)	(2006)	(2007)	(2008)	(2009)		
5												
6	Original Known Values	1.1	1.9	3.0	3.8							
7												
8	Linear Extension	1.1	1.9	3.0	3.8							
9												
10	Linear Replacement	1.1	1.9	3.0	3.8							
11												
12	Exponential Replacement	1.1	1.9	3.0	3.8							
13												
14	TREND Function	1.1	1.9	3.0	3.8							
15												
16												
17												
18												
19												
20												

Series dialog box:

Series in: ⦿ Rows ○ Columns

Type: ○ Linear ○ Growth ○ Date ⦿ AutoFill

Date unit: ● Day ○ Weekday ○ Month ○ Year

☐ Trend

Step value: 0.92   Stop value:

[OK] [Cancel]

Figure 25.37 The Series dialog box in use.

	A	B	C	D	E	F	G	H	I	J	K
1	Using the Fill Series Command										
2				Occurrence of Disease X (in thousands)							
3			Known Values				Predicted Values				
4	Type of Series	2001	2002	2003	2004	(2005)	(2006)	(2007)	(2008)	(2009)	
5											
6	Original Known Values	1.1	1.9	3.0	3.8						
7											
8	Linear Extension	1.1	1.9	3.0	3.8	4.8	5.7	6.6	7.5	8.4	
9											
10	Linear Replacement	1.1	1.9	3.0	3.8						
11											
12	Exponential Replacement	1.1	1.9	3.0	3.8						
13											
14	TREND Function	1.1	1.9	3.0	3.8						
15											
16											

Figure 25.38 After performing the linear extension trend analysis.

A stop value (the value at which the series is to end) may be entered if you want to set an upper limit to the trend.

3. Check the box labeled "Rows" in the **Series in** group.
4. Check the box labeled AutoFill.
5. Clear all other checkboxes.

The results are depicted in Row 8 in Figure 25.38 (labeled Linear Extension). Note that these results are identical to the results obtained by dragging the Fill Handle in Figure 25.35.

25.7.3 Trend Analysis: Linear Replacement

Follow these steps to calculate a linear trend and replace the original data values with best-fit data:

1. Select cells B10:J10, the known data points and the unknown (to be calculated) points.
2. Open the Series dialog box using Ribbon options: **Home tab → Editing group → Fill drop-down menu → Series . . . button**. (Excel 2003: Edit → Fill → Series.)
3. Check the box labeled "Rows" in the **Series in** group.
4. Check the box labeled **Linear**.
5. Check the box labeled **Trend**. This causes the original data points to be replaced by values calculated using the linear trend equation.

The results are depicted in Row 10 in Figure 25.39 (labeled Linear Replacement). Note that the predicted values are the same as in the previous example, but some of the known values have been modified.

	A	B	C	D	E	F	G	H	I	J	K
1	**Using the Fill Series Command**										
2						**Occurrence of Disease X (in thousands)**					
3			**Known Values**			**Predicted Values**					
4	**Type of Series**	2001	2002	2003	2004	(2005)	(2006)	(2007)	(2008)	(2009)	
5											
6	**Original Known Values**	1.1	1.9	3.0	3.8						
7											
8	**Linear Extension**	1.1	1.9	3.0	3.8	4.8	5.7	6.6	7.5	8.4	
9											
10	**Linear Replacement**	1.1	2.0	2.9	3.8	4.8	5.7	6.6	7.5	8.4	
11											
12	**Exponential Replacement**	1.1	1.9	3.0	3.8						
13											
14	***TREND* Function**	1.1	1.9	3.0	3.8						
15											
16											

Figure 25.39   After linear replacement trend analysis.

25.7.4 Trend Analysis: Exponential Replacement

To create a trend using exponential growth series, follow these steps:

1. Select cells B12:J12, the known data points and the unknown (to be calculated) points.
2. Open the Series dialog box using Ribbon options: **Home tab → Editing group → Fill drop-down menu → Series ... button**. (Excel 2003: Edit → Fill → Series.)
3. Check the box labeled "Rows" in the **Series in** group.

4. Check the box labeled **Growth**.

5. Check the box labeled **Trend**. This causes the original data points to be replaced by values calculated using the growth trend equation.

The results are depicted in Row 12 in Figure 25.40 (labeled Exponential Replacement).

25.7.5 Trend-Analysis Functions

Excel provides two trend-analysis functions, one for linear trend calculation and another for calculating exponential trends. These are useful if the known dependent data may change and the trendline must be recalculated frequently. The linear trend function *TREND* uses the least squares method for its calculation. The syntax for *TREND* is

TREND(Known_y's, Known_x's, New_x's, Const).

	A	B	C	D	E	F	G	H	I	J	K
1	Using the Fill Series Command										
2		Occurrence of Disease X (in thousands)									
3		Known Values				Predicted Values					
4	Type of Series	2001	2002	2003	2004	(2005)	(2006)	(2007)	(2008)	(2009)	
5											
6	Original Known Values	1.1	1.9	3.0	3.8						
7											
8	Linear Extension	1.1	1.9	3.0	3.8	4.8	5.7	6.6	7.5	8.4	
9											
10	Linear Replacement	1.1	2.0	2.9	3.8	4.8	5.7	6.6	7.5	8.4	
11											
12	Exponential Replacement	1.2	1.8	2.7	4.1	6.3	9.5	14.5	22.0	33.3	
13											
14	*TREND* Function	1.1	1.9	3.0	3.8						
15											
16											

Figure 25.40 After exponential growth replacement trend analysis.

The arguments are as follows:

- **Known_y's.** The known y values are the known dependent values in the linear equation $y = mx + b$. In Figure 25.40, the known y values are 1.1, 1.9, 3.0, and 3.8.

- **Known_x's.** The known x values are the values of the independent variable for which the y values are known. In Figure 25.40, these are the values 2001, 2002, 2003, and 2004. If the known x values are omitted, then the argument is assumed to be $\{1, 2, 3, 4 \ldots\}$.

- **New_x's.** The new x values are the values of the independent variable for which you want new y values to be calculated. If you want the predictions for years 2005 to 2009, then select the range (F14:J14). If you want to calculate the linear trend for the whole time span (2001–2009), then select the range (B14:J14).

- **Const.** If the const argument is set to FALSE, then b is set to zero, so the equation describing the relationship between y and x becomes $y = mx$. If the const argument is set to TRUE or omitted, then b is computed.

To use the *TREND* function without replacing the original known values, follow this procedure:

1. Select cells F14:J14, the unknown (to be calculated) points only.
2. Choose the **Insert Function** button on the Formula bar and select the Statistical category.
3. Choose the *TREND* function from the function list. The Function Arguments dialog box will appear, as shown in Figure 25.41.
4. Select or type the range (B14:E14) for the Known_y's.
5. Select or type the range (B4:E4) for the Known_x's (the years 2001–2004).

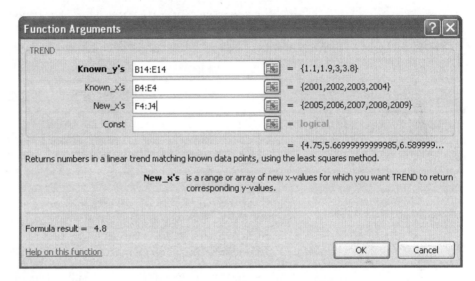

Figure 25.41   The Function Arguments dialog box for the *TREND* function.

	A	B	C	D	E	F	G	H	I	J	K
1	Using the Fill Series Command										
2			Occurrence of Disease X (in thousands)								
3			Known Values				Predicted Values				
4	Type of Series	2001	2002	2003	2004	2005	2006	2007	2008	2009	
5											
6	Original Known Values	1.1	1.9	3.0	3.8						
7											
8	Linear Extension	1.1	1.9	3.0	3.8	4.8	5.7	6.6	7.5	8.4	
9											
10	Linear Replacement	1.1	2.0	2.9	3.8	4.8	5.7	6.6	7.5	8.4	
11											
12	Exponential Replacement	1.2	1.8	2.7	4.1	6.3	9.5	14.5	22.0	33.3	
13											
14	*TREND* Function	1.1	1.9	3.0	3.8	4.8	5.7	6.6	7.5	8.4	
15											
16											

Figure 25.42   The result of using the *TREND* function.

6. Select or type the range (F4:J4) as the New_x's (the years 2005–2009).
7. Don't click **OK**. Since we want the output to be an array rather than a single value, press **Ctrl + Shift + Enter**.

The results can be seen in line 14 of the worksheet shown in Figure 25.42 (labeled TREND Function.)

There is a corresponding Excel function for producing an exponential growth trend, named *GROWTH*. The arguments for the *GROWTH* function are similar to the arguments for *TREND*.

Practice!

Practice using the *TREND* function to interpolate tabulated data.

Because the *TREND* function allows you to specify the x values at which to predict new y values, you can use it to interpolate between values in a table. For example, consider a table that contains information on various properties of water in the vapor state as functions of temperature and pressure (Table 25.2).

TABLE 25.2 Properties of saturated steam

Temp.°C	Enthalpy kJ/kg	Entropy kJ/kg K
100	2680	7.4
150	2750	6.8
200	2790	6.4
250	2800	6.1
300	2750	5.7

Invariably, you will need to know the enthalpy at a temperature that is not included in the table, so you will have to interpolate. For example, let's find the enthalpy of saturated steam at 218°C.

To use the *TREND* function to interpolate, do the following:

1. Enter the temperature and enthalpy data for 200°C and 250°C into a worksheet, as shown in Figure 25.43.

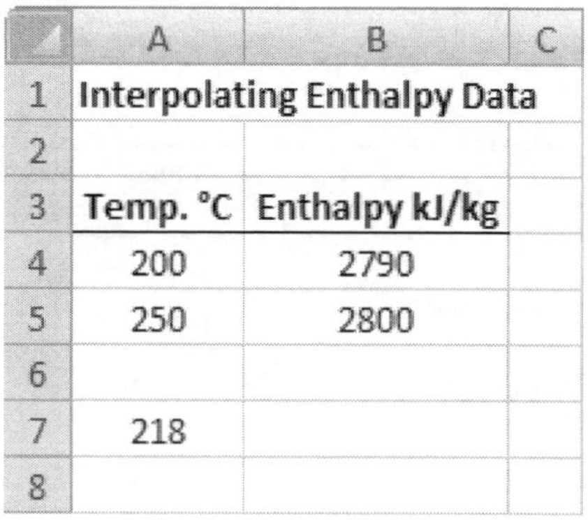

	A	B	C
1	Interpolating Enthalpy Data		
2			
3	Temp. °C	Enthalpy kJ/kg	
4	200	2790	
5	250	2800	
6			
7	218		
8			

Figure 25.43 Preparing to interpolate enthalpy data.

2. Enter the desired temperature, 218°C, in the worksheet, as shown in Figure 25.43.
3. Enter the TREND function in cell B7 as follows:

=TREND(B4:B5,A4:A5,A7)

The result is shown in Figure 25.44.

	B7	▼	f_x	=TREND(B4:B5,A4:A5,A7)	
	A	B	C	D	E
1	**Interpolating Enthalpy Data**				
2					
3	**Temp. °C**	**Enthalpy kJ/kg**			
4	200	2790			
5	250	2800			
6					
7	218	2794			
8					

Figure 25.44   The result of the linear interpolation.

Practice interpolating for the following saturated steam values:

- Entropy at 218°C (Answer: 6.3 kJ / kg K)
- Enthalpy at 140° (Answer: 2736 kJ / kg)
- Enthalpy at 350°C (Answer: 2700 kJ / kg)

25.7.6 Trend Analysis for Charts

Excel will calculate and display graphic representations of trends on a chart with the use of *trendlines*. Five types of regression trendlines, plus a moving average trendline, can be added. Each type of trendline is described in Table 25.3.

Trendlines cannot be added to all types of charts. For example, trendlines cannot be added to data series in pie charts, 3-D charts, stacked charts, or doughnut charts. Trendlines can be added to Column charts, XY Scatter plots, and Line charts. If a trendline is added to a chart and the chart type is subsequently changed to one of the exempted types, then the trendline is lost.

TABLE 25.3   Excel trendline types

Trendline Type	Formula
Linear	Calculates the least squares fit by using $y = mx + b$. (m is the slope and b is a constant.)
Logarithmic	Calculates least squares by using $y = c \cdot \ln(x) + b$ (c and b are constants.)
Polynomial	Calculates least squares for a line by using $$y = b + c_x + c_x \cdots + c_n x^n.$$ ($b, c_1, c_2, \ldots, c_n$ are constants, the order can be set in the Add Trendline dialog box, and the maximum order is 6.)
Exponential	Calculates least squares by using $y = ce^{bx}$. (c and b are constants.)
Power	Calculates least squares by using $y = cx^b$. (c and b are constants.)
Moving Average	Calculates the series of moving averages by using $$F_{(t+1)} = \frac{1}{N} a_1^N A_{(t-j+1)}.$$ Keep in mind that each data point in a moving average is the average of a specified number of previous data points. N is the number of prior periods to average, A_t is the value at time t, and F_t is the forecasted value at time t.

To create a trendline, first generate a chart of an acceptable type. As an example, we will make an XY Scatter chart by using the data in Figure 25.45. These data represent the growth of a certain type of algae in the Great Salt Lake. It has been predicted that, if left undisturbed, the algae would multiply exponentially.

	A	B	C
1	Algae Growth		
2			
3	Day	Population (millions)	
4	1	1.00	
5	2	1.12	
6	3	1.92	
7	4	2.65	
8	5	4.12	
9	6	6.41	
10	7	8.66	
11	8	14.36	
12	9	23.34	
13	10	34.22	
14			

Figure 25.45   Data set: Growth of algae.

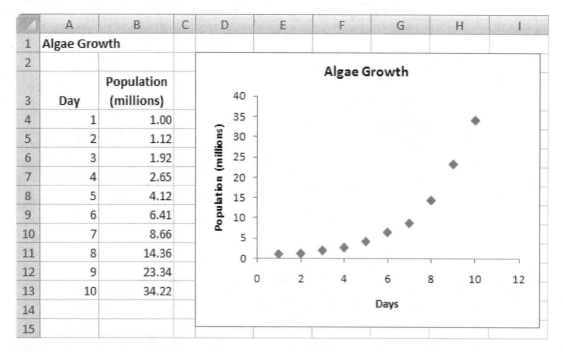

Figure 25.46   The algae growth data plotted on an XY Scatter chart.

Here are the steps used to add a trendline to a chart:

1. Create a worksheet containing the data in Figure 25.45.
2. Create an XY Scatter chart from the data.
3. Add a chart layout with titles to the chart, as shown in Figure 25.46.
4. Right-click on the data series (right-click on any marker).
5. Select **Add Trendline . . .** from the pop-up menu. The Format Trendline dialog box (Figure 25.47) will open.

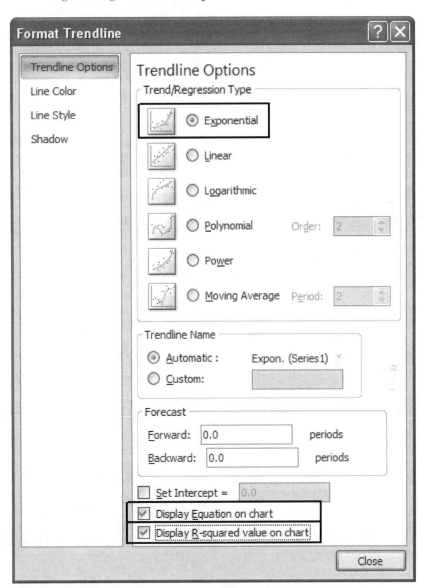

Figure 25.47   The Format Trendline dialog box.

6. Select the following options (indicated in Figure 25.47):

- Exponential Type
- Display Equation on chart
- Display R-squared value on chart

7. Click the **Close** button to close the Format Trendline dialog box.

The results are shown in Figure 25.48.

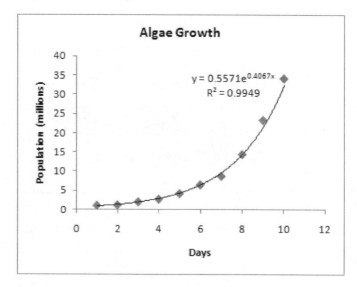

Figure 25.48   The algae growth data with exponential trendline.

Practice!

Practice adding trendlines to charts and modifying trendline options.

First, create the worksheet of student score data shown in Figure 25.49. Then create an XY Scatter chart of the data.

Add a linear trendline to the chart as follows:

1. Right-click on the data series (right-click on any marker).
2. Select **Add Trendline ...** from the pop-up menu. The Format Trendline dialog box will open.
3. Select the following options:

   - Linear Type
   - Set Intercept = 0
   - Display Equation on chart
   - Display R-squared value on chart

4. Forecast Backward 1.7 periods.
5. Click the **Close** button to close the Format Trendline dialog box.

Your graph should look like Figure 25.50.

Next, try a polynomial trendline with a high order.

1. Right-click on the trendline.
2. Select **Format Trendline ...** from the pop-up menu. The Format Trendline dialog box will open.

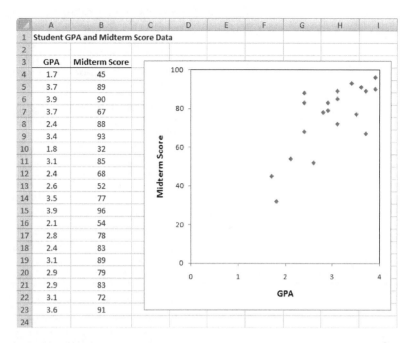

	A	B	C	D	E	F	G	H	I
1	Student GPA and Midterm Score Data								
2									
3	GPA	Midterm Score							
4	1.7	45							
5	3.7	89							
6	3.9	90							
7	3.7	67							
8	2.4	88							
9	3.4	93							
10	1.8	32							
11	3.1	85							
12	2.4	68							
13	2.6	52							
14	3.5	77							
15	3.9	96							
16	2.1	54							
17	2.8	78							
18	2.4	83							
19	3.1	89							
20	2.9	79							
21	2.9	83							
22	3.1	72							
23	3.6	91							
24									

Figure 25.49   Student score data for trendline practice.

3.   Select the following options:

- Polynomial Type
- Order set to 6

4.   Click the **Close** button to close the Format Trendline dialog box.

What does the trendline look like when a high-order polynomial is used with noisy data?

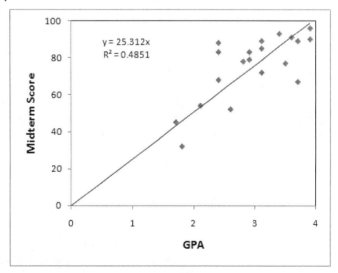

Figure 25.50   The student score data with linear trendline.

Finally, use the moving average trendline.

1. Right-click on the trendline.
2. Select **Format Trendline ...** from the pop-up menu. The Format Trendline dialog box will open.
3. Select the following options:

    *   Moving Average Type
    *   Period set to 2

4. Click the **Close** button to close the Format Trendline dialog box.

What does the moving average trendline look like when the data are not sorted before plotting?

25.8   USING THE GOAL SEEK TOOL

The next two sections introduce a technique for solving complex equations called *iterative solutions*. Iterative solutions use an initial guess for each variable in the equation and then solve both sides of the equation. Unless you are very lucky, the two sides of the equation evaluated by using the guess will not be equal. If they are not equal, try another guess. This process continues until a value is found that satisfies the equation, or until the allowed number of guesses has been met.

The trick to getting solutions by using iterative methods is coming up with good guesses. The next two sections present different methods. The *Goal Seek tool* (this section) uses a simple method that is easy to use, but that may fail to find a solution. The *Solver* (section 25.9) uses a more powerful technique to choose guesses and can usually find a solution, but it is a bit harder to learn to use.

The Goal Seek tool is used to find the input values of an equation when the results are known. It takes an initial guess for an input value and uses iterative refinement to attempt to locate the real input value.

As an example, we will use the Goal Seek tool to find the solution of a polynomial equation:

$$f(x) = 3x^3 + 2x^2 + 4 = 0.$$

The equation $f(x)$ has a real solution, which is approximately $x = -3$. We can use the initial guess of $x = 1$ to start the Goal Seek process, which will then attempt to converge on a more accurate value for x.

Caution: The Goal Seek tool does not always converge. With some functions, the initial guess must closely approximate the real solution if Goal Seek is to converge.

To see how the Goal Seeker works, use the following steps:

1. Create a worksheet that resembles Figure 25.51. Note the coding for $f(x)$ in the Formula box. The formula should be placed in cell B3.
2. Place 1, which is our initial guess for x, in cell B4. This results in $f(x)$ evaluating to a value of 9, which is displayed in cell B3.
3. Open the Goal Seek dialog box (shown in Figure 25.52) by using these Ribbon options: **Data tab → Data Tools group → What-If Analysis drop-down menu → Goal Seek ... button.** (Excel 2003: Tools → Goal Seek.)

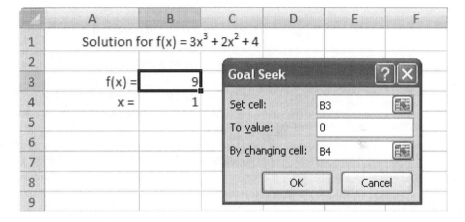

| B3 | ▼ | f_x | =3*B4^3+2*B4^2+4 |

	A	B	C	D
1	Solution for $f(x) = 3x^3 + 2x^2 + 4$			
2				
3	f(x) =	9		
4	x =	1		
5				

Figure 25.51   Solving a polynomial using the Goal Seek tool.

	A	B	C	D	E	F
1	Solution for $f(x) = 3x^3 + 2x^2 + 4$					
2						
3	f(x) =	9				
4	x =	1				
5						
6						
7						
8						
9						

Goal Seek [?][X]

Set cell: B3

To value: 0

By changing cell: B4

[OK]   [Cancel]

Figure 25.52   The Goal Seek dialog box in use.

4. Set the Goal Seek fields as follows:

a. Set cell → B3 (this is the *target cell*, or the goal of the goal seek operation)

b. To value → 0 (this is the result value that we want Goal Seek to find)

c. By changing cell → B4 (this is the cell where the value is changed to try to meet the goal).

5. Click **OK** to start the Goal Seek operation.

The Goal Seek tool will try many values in cell B4, trying to meet the goal of a value of 0 in cell B3. The Goal Seek tool might find a pretty good answer and quit, or it

Goal Seek Status [?][X]

Goal Seeking with Cell B3 found a solution.   [Step]

Target value: 0   [Pause]

Current value: 3.74866E-05

[OK]   [Cancel]

Figure 25.53   The Goal Seek Status box.

could stop after a large number of attempts. In Excel 2007 the Goal Seek Status box (Figure 25.53) tells you whether or not a solution was found. In our example, a solution was found. The result is shown in Figure 25.54. Goal Seek found that a value of $x = -1.37347$ produces a solution, $f(x) = 0.0000375$, that is pretty close to zero.

	A	B	C	D
1	Solution for f(x) = 3x³ + 2x² + 4			
2				
3	f(x) =	3.75E-05		
4	x =	-1.37347		
5				

Figure 25.54   The solution after using the Goal Seek tool.

25.9   USING SOLVER FOR OPTIMIZATION PROBLEMS

Excel's *Solver* is designed to solve constrained nonlinear optimization problems. Solving these complex problems is an important task for engineers in petroleum, defense, financial, agricultural, and process-control industries.

While the Solver is capable of handling complex optimization problems, you can also use it for more mundane problems. We will take a look at constrained optimization problems later in this section, but first let's introduce the Solver by using the same polynomial that was solved by using the Goal Seek tool in the last section, namely,

$$f(x) = 3x^3 + 2x^2 + 4 = 0.$$

The Solver is an Excel add-in that must be installed and activated before it can be used. To see if Solver is active on your system, look on the Ribbon for a **Solver Button**: Data tab → Analysis group → Solver button. (Excel 2003: Tools → Solver.) If the button is present, the Solver is ready to use. If not, the Solver must either be activated (common) or installed (uncommon).

25.9.1   Activating the Excel Solver

If the **Solver** button appears on the Ribbon's Data tab, you can skip this step.

In Excel 2007, add-ins like the Solver are managed using the Add-Ins panel on the Excel Options dialog box. To access the Excel Options dialog box, use the following options from the Office button: **Office button → Excel Options button** (this opens the Excel Options dialog box) → **Add-Ins panel**. The Add-Ins panel of the Excel Options dialog box is shown in Figure 25.55.

Look for "Solver Add-In" in the **Inactive Application Add-Ins** list (highlighted in Figure 25.55).

- If "Solver Add-In" is not listed in the **Inactive Application Add-Ins** list, it must be installed from the Excel program CDs (this is not common).
- If "Solver Add-In" is listed in the **Inactive Application Add-Ins** list, the Solver has been installed and you simply need to activate it.

The Solver can be activated with the following steps:

1. Select "Solver Add-In" in the **Inactive Application Add-Ins** list.
2. Click **Go ...** to open the Add-Ins dialog box, shown in Figure 25.56.

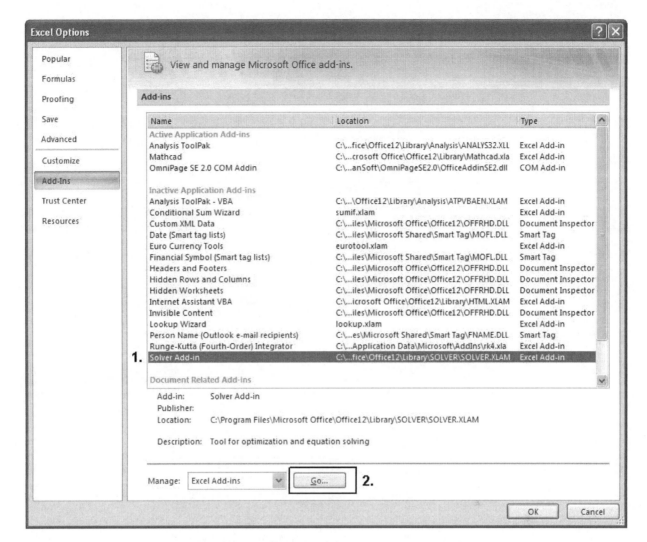

Figure 25.55   The Add-Ins panel on the Excel Options dialog.

3.   Check the box labeled **Solver Add-In** (as illustrated in Figure 25.56).
4.   Click **OK** to close the Add-Ins dialog box.
5.   Click **OK** to close the Excel Options dialog box

The Solver is now active on your system.

[In Excel 2003, open the Add-Ins dialog box using menu options: Tools → Add-Ins, and then check the box labeled **Solver Add-In** (or, on older systems, just "Solver"), as illustrated in Figure 25.56.]

25.9.2 Using the Solver

To find a solution to the example polynomial

$$f(x) = 3x^3 + 2x^2 + 4 = 0.$$

we first set up the same worksheet used in section 25.8. This is shown in Figure 25.57.

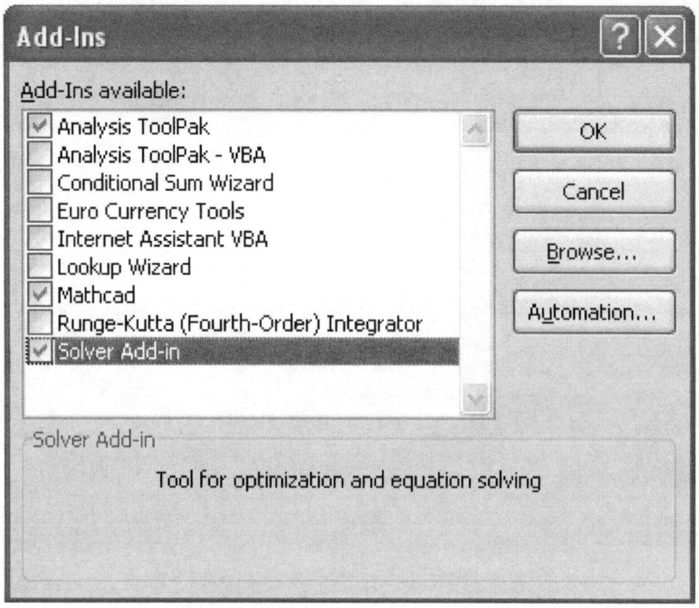

Figure 25.56 The Add-Ins dialog box.

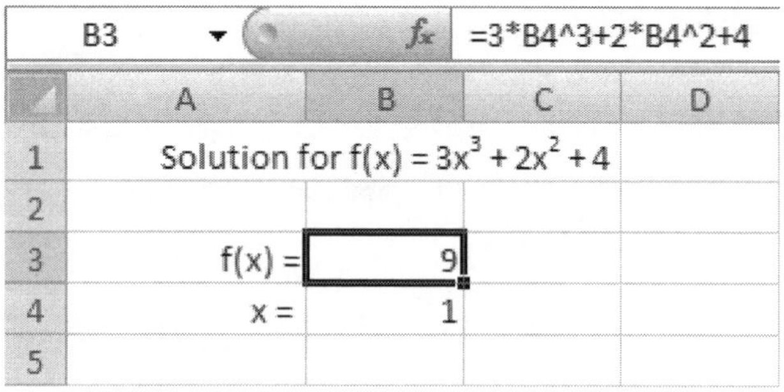

Figure 25.57 Preparing to solve a polynomial using the Solver.

Then follow these steps to solve this problem using the Solver:

1. Open the Solver Parameters dialog box (shown in Figure 25.58) using these Ribbon options: **Data tab → Analysis group → Solver button**. (Excel 2003: Tools → Solver.)

2. Set the following Solver parameters:

    a. Set Target Cell → B3

    b. Equal to → Value of → 0

    c. By Changing Cells → B4

3. Click the **Solve** button to activate the Solver.

The Solver will try various values in cell B4, trying to find an x value that makes $f(x) = 0$. It usually succeeds, and it tells you when it finds a solution by displaying the Solver Result box shown in Figure 25.59. The result of using the Solver to solve the polynomial is shown in Figure 25.60. The solutions found with Goal Seek and the Solver are identical to at least six decimal places (shown in Figure 25.54 and Figure 25.60.)

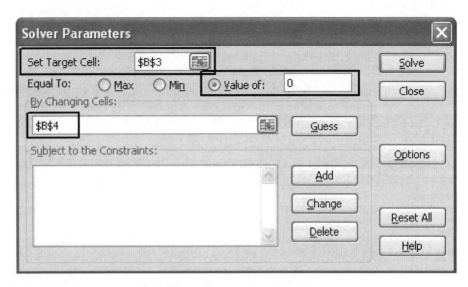

Figure 25.58 The Solver Parameters dialog box.

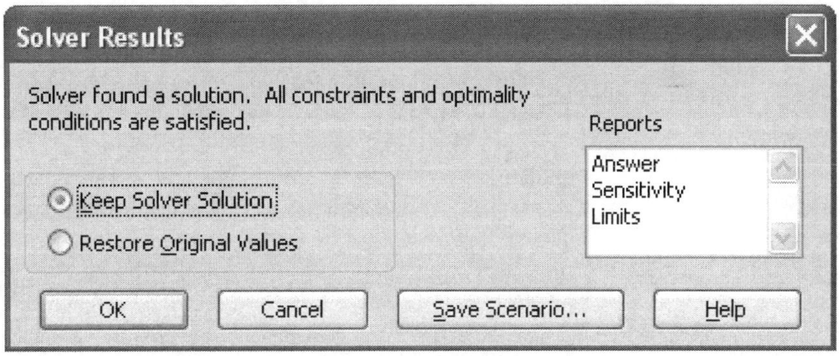

Figure 25.59 The Solver Results box.

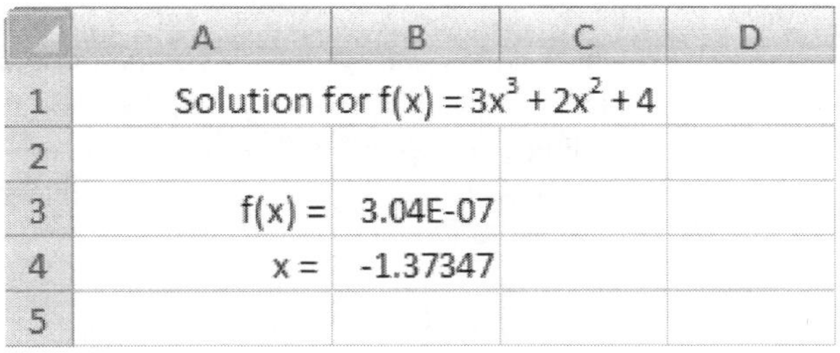

	A	B	C	D
1	Solution for $f(x) = 3x^3 + 2x^2 + 4$			
2				
3	f(x) =	3.04E-07		
4	x =	-1.37347		
5				

Figure 25.60 The solution found with the Solver.

25.9.3 Setting Up an Optimization Problem in Excel

What is an optimization problem? Many engineering problems have more than one solution, so engineers look for the best, or optimal, solution.

Engineers choose among a range of possible solutions by first specifying any limits to the input parameters of the problem (availability of raw materials or labor, for example). Given the limitations, the problem becomes one of finding the best solution, which in mathematical terms is a minimum or maximum solution. Engineers often seek solutions that maximize the strength of a load-bearing structure subject to a weight limit, or designs that minimize the weight of an aircraft while making sure it can handle the stresses of flight and landing.

The equation that is to be maximized (or minimized) is called the *objective function*. The limitations to the input parameters of the objective function are called *constraints*. Problems of this type—finding a minimum or maximum, given multiple constraints—are called *optimization problems*.

The most difficult part of solving an optimization problem is setting up the objective function and identifying the constraints. An objective function takes the form

$$y = f(x_1, x_2, \ldots, x_n).$$

The independent variables (x) are limited by m constraints, which take the form

$$c_i(x_1, x_2, \ldots, x_n) = 0 \text{ for } i = 1, 2, \ldots, m.$$

The constraints may also be expressed as inequalities. Excel Solver can handle both linear and nonlinear constraints. However, nonlinear constraints must be continuous functions. Although the constraints are expressed as functions, they are always evaluated within a range of precision called the *tolerance*. A constraint such as $x^1 < 0$, if the tolerance is large enough, may be evaluated as TRUE when $x^2 = 0.0000003$.

Nonlinear optimization problems may have multiple minima or maxima. In a minimization problem, all solutions, except the absolute minimum, are called *local minima*. The solution that is chosen by Solver is dependent on the initial starting point for the solution. The initial guess should be as close to the real solution as possible. These are challenges with optimization in general, not just with Excel Solver.

This has probably been rather confusing. A couple of examples will make things clearer. Let's proceed by setting up examples of both a linear and a nonlinear optimization problem.

25.9.4 Linear Optimization Example

Assume that you wish to maximize the profit for producing widgets. The widgets come in two models: economy and deluxe. The economy model sells for $49.00, and the deluxe model sells for $79.00. The cost of production is determined primarily by labor costs, which are $14.00 per hour. The union limits the workers to a total of 2,000 hours per month. The economy widget can be built in 3 person-hours and the deluxe widget can be built in 4 person-hours. The management believes that it can sell up to 600 deluxe widgets per month and up to 1,200 economy widgets. Since you have a limited workforce, the main variable under your control is the ability to balance the number of economy units versus deluxe units that are built. Your job is to determine how many economy widgets and how many deluxe widgets should be built to maximize the company's profit.

The independent variables are as follows:

w_1 = the number of economy widgets produced each month

w_2 = the number of deluxe widgets produced each month.

The target that you wish to maximize is the profit, p. It is described mathematically by the following objective function:

$$p = (\$49 - (3 \text{ person-hours} * \$14/\text{hour})) \, w_1$$
$$+ (\$79 - (4 \text{ person-hours} * \$14/\text{hour})) \, w_2$$
$$= 7w_1 + 23w_2$$

The constraints can be expressed mathematically as limitations on ω_1 and ω_2. The maximum number of widgets to be produced is limited both by sales and by labor availability. The sales limitations (imposed by management) can be expressed as

$$w_1 \leq 1{,}200 \text{ widgets}$$

and

$$w_2 \leq 600 \text{ widgets.}$$

The availability of labor is limited by the labor union and can be expressed as

$$3w_1 + 4w_2 \leq 2000.$$

Finally, the general constraint of nonnegativity is imposed on ω_1 and ω_2, since you cannot produce a negative number of widgets:

$$w_1 + w_2 \geq 0$$

Figure 25.61 shows how to set up the widget problem in a worksheet. Cells C4 and C5 have been named *Weconomy* and *Wdeluxe*, respectively, to make the formulas more readable. The formulas in cells C8 and C11 are displayed in cells D8 and D11.

	A	B	C	D	E
1	Widget Profit Optimization Worksheet				
2					
3	Independent Variables				
4		Economy Widgets:	0	units per month	
5		Deluxe Widgets:	0	units per month	
6					
7	Objective Function				
8		Profit, P:	0	=7*Weconomy+23*Wdeluxe	
9					
10	Constraints				
11		Labor Constraint:	0	=3*Weconomy+4*Wdeluxe	
12					

Figure 25.61   Worksheet for linear optimization example.

You have already completed the hardest part of using the Solver, which is setting up the worksheet. To run the Solver, perform these steps:

1. Open the Solver Parameters dialog box (shown in Figure 25.62) using these Ribbon options: **Data tab → Analysis group → Solver button**. (Excel 2003: Tools → Solver.)
2. Set the following Solver parameters:

    a. Set Target Cell → C8 (the cell holding the objective function, aka the profit function)

    b. Equal to → Max (we want to maximize the profit)

    c. By Changing Cells → C4:C5 (the number of each type of widget).

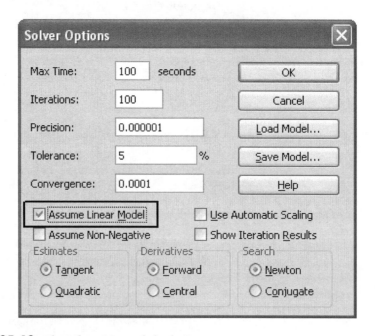

Figure 25.62 The Solver Parameters for the linear optimization problem.

3. Add each of the following five constraints (shown in Figure 25.62):

    a. C11 < = 2000 (this is the labor constraint)
    b. Weconomy < = 1200
    c. Weconomy > = 0
    d. Weconomy < = 600
    e. Weconomy > = 0

4. Click the **Options** button to open the Solver Options dialog box, shown in Figure 25.63.

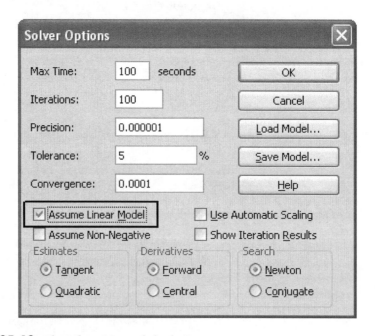

Figure 25.63 The Solver Options dialog box.

5. As a general rule, don't mess with the Solver options unless you understand the methods used by the Solver, but this is a linear optimization problem so it is OK to check the **Assume Linear Model** box.
6. Click **OK** to close the Solver Options dialog box.
7. Click the Solve button to activate the Solver.

The Solver Results dialog box will appear, as depicted in Figure 25.64.

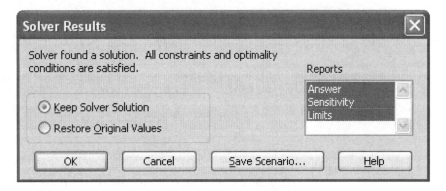

Figure 25.64   The Solver Results box is displayed when the solution has been found.

The Solver Results box should show that Solver has found a solution. There are three types of reports available from Solver: Answer, Sensitivity, and Limits.

1. Select all three types of reports.
2. Click **OK** to close the Solver Results box and see the solution.

The worksheet will now contain modified values for the input parameters and objective function, as shown in Figure 25.65. The optimized worksheet shows that the maximum profit, $11,500 per month, is achieved by producing only deluxe widgets. Only 500 deluxe widgets can be produced per month, but the company can sell 600 per month; thus, the available labor pool is a limiting constraint.

	A	B	C	D	E
1	**Widget Profit Optimization Worksheet**				
2					
3	**Independent Variables**				
4		Economy Widgets:	0	units per month	
5		Deluxe Widgets:	500	units per month	
6					
7	**Objective Function**				
8		Profit, P:	11500	=7*Weconomy+23*Wdeluxe	
9					
10	**Constraints**				
11		Labor Constraint:	2000	=3*Weconomy+4*Wdeluxe	
12					

Figure 25.65   The optimized solution.

The Solver placed three new worksheets in the workbook:

- The **Answer report** summarizes the initial and final values of the input parameters and the optimized variable.
- The **Sensitivity report** describes information about the marginal effects of making small changes in the constraints. Sometimes, a small constraint change can make a large difference in the output. For nonlinear models, these are called *Lagrange multipliers*. For linear models, these are called either *dual values* or *shadow prices*.
- The **Limits report** shows the effect on the solution as each input parameter is set to its minimum or maximum limit.

As a manager, you can easily modify the constraints and rerun Solver to see how the optimal solution might change. You can rapidly observe the effect on profit of

- hiring more laborers
- modifying prices
- adjusting the widget mix

25.9.5 Nonlinear Optimization Example

As an example of nonlinear optimization, we will use an optimization problem for which the solution is obvious. This will familiarize you with the process of setting up a nonlinear optimization problem and convince you that the results are correct.

The objective function that we wish to minimize is

$$y = 100\left(x_2 - x_1^2\right)^2 + (1 - x_1)^2,$$

with the nonnegativity constraints

$$x_1 \geq 0$$

and

$$x_2 \geq 0.$$

Since the terms $\left(x_2 - x_1^2\right)^2$ and $(1 - x_1)^2$ must be positive for real numbers x_1 and x_2, we know the answer. The minimum y is zero when $x_1 = 1$ and $x_2 = 1$. The worksheet for this example is shown in Figure 25.66.

C8		f_x	=100*(x_2-x_1^2)^2+(1-x_1)^2		
	A	B	C	D	E	F
1	Nonlinear Optimization					
2						
3	Input Parameters					
4		x1:	0			
5		x2:	0			
6						
7	Objective Function					
8		y:	1			
9						

Figure 25.66 Worksheet for nonlinear optimization example.

Complete the following steps to use the Solver to perform nonlinear optimization:

1. Open the Solver Parameters dialog box (shown in Figure 25.67) using these Ribbon options: **Data tab → Analysis group → Solver button**. (Excel 2003: Tools → Solver.)

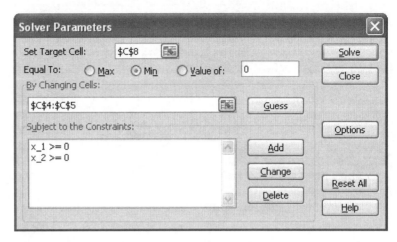

Figure 25.67   The Solver Parameters dialog box for the nonlinear optimization example.

2. Set the following Solver parameters:

   a. Set Target Cell → C8 (the cell holding the objective function)

   b. Equal to → Min (we want to Minimize the function)

   c. By Changing Cells → C4:C5 (x_1 and x_2).

3. Add each of the following nonnegativity constraints (shown in Figure 25.67):

   a. x_1 > = 0

   b. x_2 > = 0

4. Click the **Options** button to open the Solver Options dialog box.

5. Make sure the **Assume Linear Model** box is not checked.

6. Click **OK** to close the Solver Options dialog box.

7. Click the **Solve** button to activate the Solver.

The result is shown in Figure 25.68; the results produced by Solver are good approximations of the true minimum.

	A	B	C	D	E	F
1	**Nonlinear Optimization**					
2						
3	**Input Parameters**					
4		x1:	0.999977			
5		x2:	0.999962			
6						
7	**Objective Function**					
8		y:	6.5E-09			
9						

Figure 25.68   The optimized solution.

There are other local minima for this objective function. Try setting the initial parameters to $x_1 = 5$ and $x_2 = 3$ and rerunning the Solver. The results produced by Solver (Figure 25.69) show that the algorithm is stuck in a local minimum.

	A	B	C	D	E	F
1	Nonlinear Optimization					
2						
3	Input Parameters					
4		x1:	0.630967			
5		x2:	0.400659			
6						
7	Objective Function					
8		y:	0.13683			
9						

Figure 25.69   Solver results when started with $x_1 = 5$ and $x_2 = 3$.

APPLICATION

APPLICATION—YIELD STRENGTH OF MATERIALS

Materials science is an important field of study for engineers that covers the electronic, optical, mechanical, chemical, and magnetic properties of metals, polymers, composite materials, and ceramics.

Crystalline materials are subject to *slip deformation* when a shear stress is applied to the material. The deformation occurs when atomic planes slide along the directions of densest atomic packing, as shown in Figure 25.70.

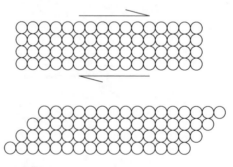

Figure 25.70   Slip deformation.

When crystalline materials such as metals and alloys are formed by cooling molten metal, separate crystals form in the melt and grow together. The boundaries between the growing crystals form barriers to slip deformation, increasing the observed *yield strength* of the metal. The relationship between grain size (i.e., the size of the individual crystals in the metal) and observed yield strength, σ_y, is described by the Hall–Petch equation,

$$\sigma_y = \sigma_o + k_y \frac{1}{\sqrt{d}},$$

where σ_o is the yield strength of the pure metal (i.e., single crystal, $d = \infty$). The value of the proportionality factor, k_y, depends on the material and can be obtained by regression analysis from experimental data (see Figure 25.71).

	A	B	C	D	E	F
1	**Regression for Hall-Petch Coefficients**					
2				**Plotting Variables**		
3	**Grain Size, d (μm)**	**Yield Strength, σ_y (MN/m^2)**		**1/SQRT(d)**	**σ_y**	
4	406	93		0.050	93	
5	106	129		0.097	129	
6	75	145		0.115	145	
7	43	158		0.152	158	
8	30	189		0.183	189	
9	16	233		0.250	233	

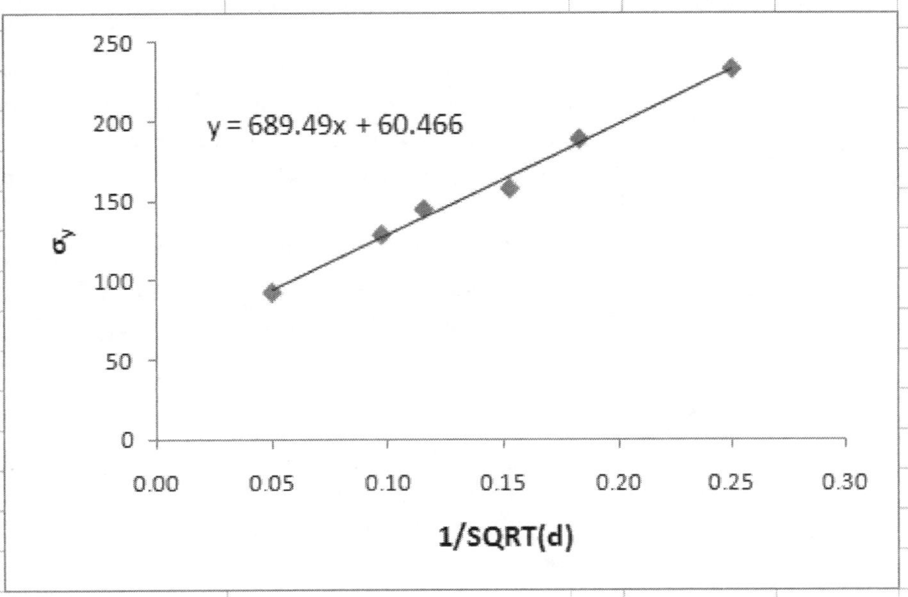

Figure 25.71   Table of carbon–steel data and results of regression analysis.

For the carbon–steel data shown here, the coefficients for the Hall–Petch equation can be found by using Excel:

$$\sigma_y = 60.466 \frac{MN}{m^2} + 689.49 \frac{MN\mu m^{0.5}}{m^2} \frac{1}{\sqrt{d}}.$$

The value of the proportionality factor would typically be reported as

$$k_y = 0.689 \frac{MN}{m^{3/2}}.$$

How'd They Do That?

The Hall–Petch equation is an example of an equation that can be written in linear form

$$y = ax + b,$$

where a is the slope of the line through the data values and b is the y-intercept. Comparing terms with the Hall–Petch equation, you see that

$$\sigma_y = y,$$
$$\sigma_o = b, \text{ and}$$
$$\frac{1}{\sqrt{d}} = x.$$

A plot of $\dfrac{1}{\sqrt{d}}$ on the x axis against σ_y on the y axis shows the desired linear relationship.

We can use an Excel trendline to determine the equation of the line through the data, using the following steps:

1. Create a worksheet by using the carbon–steel data shown in Figure 25.71.
2. Add a third column to your worksheet that contains 1/SQRT(d).
3. Create the XY Scatter chart like the one shown in Figure 25.71.
4. Right-click on one of the data points and select **Add Trendline ...** from the pop-up menu. The Format Trendline dialog box will open.
5. Choose a **Linear** trendline and check the box labeled **Display equation on chart**.
6. Click the **Close** button to close the Format Trendline dialog box.

Excel will determine the regression fit through the data points and display the equation of the regression line on the graph, as shown in Figure 25.71.

KEY TERMS

Analysis ToolPak	GROWTH function	objective function
bin	growth trend	optimization
constraint	histogram	regression
correlation	iterative methods	Solver
correlation coefficient, r	linear regression	standard deviation
data analysis	linear trend	statistics
descriptive statistics	mean	trend analysis
exponential growth	median	TREND function
frequency	mode	trendline
Goal Seek	multiple regression	

Summary

Creating a Histogram

1. Open the Data Analysis dialog box: **Data tab → Analysis group → Data Analysis button**.
2. Select **Histogram** from the list of data analysis tools.
3. Click **OK** to close the Data Analysis dialog box and open the Histogram dialog box.

4. Set the **Input Range**.
5. Set the **Bin Range**. (Excel will assign default bin values if you skip this step.)
6. Select the output location.
7. Request the histogram chart by checking the **Chart Output** box.
8. Click **OK** to close the Histogram dialog box and create the histogram chart.

Calculating Descriptive Statistics

1. Open the Data Analysis dialog box: **Data tab → Analysis group → Data Analysis button**.
2. Select **Descriptive Statistics** from the list of data analysis tools.
3. Click **OK** to close the Data Analysis dialog box and open the Descriptive Statistics dialog box.
4. Select the data values as the **Input Range** (shown in Figure 25.18).
5. Check the **Labels in First Row** box if your data include a column heading.
6. Choose a location for the output table.
7. Check the **Summary statistics** box.
8. Click **OK** to close the Descriptive Statistics dialog box and calculate the statistic values.

Statistic	Description
Mean	The data set shows scatter around a central point, which is called the *mean*.
Standard Error	The *standard error* is used to estimate how accurately the *sample mean* represents the *population mean*.
Median	The *median* is the middle value of the sorted data set.
Mode	The *mode* is the most commonly occurring value in the data set.
Standard Deviation	The *standard deviation* is a measure of the data's variability.
Sample Variance	The *sample variance* is the square of the *sample standard deviation*.
Kurtosis	The *kurtosis* provides information about the "peakedness" of the data distribution compared with a normal distribution.
Skewness	The *skewness* provides information about the extent of asymmetry of the distribution about its *mean*.
Range	The *range* is the difference between the maximum and minimum values in the data set.
Minimum	*Minimum* indicates the smallest value in the data set.
Maximum	*Maximum* indicates the largest value in the data set.
Sum	The *sum* is the result of adding all values in the data set.
Count	The *count* is the number of values in the data set.

Computing a Correlation

1. Open the Data Analysis dialog box: **Data tab → Analysis group → Data Analysis button**.
2. Select **Correlation** from the list of data analysis tools.
3. Click **OK** to close the Data Analysis dialog box and open the Correlation dialog box.
4. Set the **Input Range** for the calculation.
5. Check the **Labels in First Row** box if your data set included a column heading.
6. Choose a location for the output table.
7. Click **OK** to close the Correlation dialog box and calculate the *correlation coefficient, r*.

Performing a Linear Regression

Two ways to perform a linear regression in Excel include

- Adding a trendline (except for the moving average type) to a chart and
- Using the Regression tool in the Analysis ToolPak.

Adding a Trendline to a Chart

1. Create an XY Scatter chart from your data.
2. Right-click on the data series.
3. Select **Add Trendline …** from the pop-up menu. The Format Trendline dialog box will open.
4. Select the type of trendline desired.
5. Set desired options:

   - Set intercept value
   - Display Equation on chart
   - Display R-squared value on chart

6. Click the Close button to close the Format Trendline dialog box and create the trendline.

Types of Trendlines

Trendline Type	Formula
Linear constant.)	Calculates the least squares fit by using $y = mx + b$. (m is the slope and b is a
Logarithmic	Calculates least squares by using $y = c \cdot ln(x) + b$. (c and b are constants.)
Polynomial	Calculates least squares for a line by using ($b, c_1, c_2, \ldots, c_n$ are constants, the order can be set in the Add Trendline dialog box, and the maximum order is 6.)
Exponential	Calculates least squares by using $y = ce^{bx}$. (c and b are constants.)
Power	Calculates least squares by using $y = cx^b$. (c and b are constants.)
Moving Average	Not a regression trendline. Calculates the series of moving averages by using $$F_{(t+1)} = \frac{1}{N} \sum_{1}^{N} A_{t-j+1}.$$ N is the number of prior periods to average, A_t is the value at time t, and F_t is the forecasted value at time t.

Using the Regression Tool in the Analysis ToolPak

1. Open the Data Analysis dialog box: **Data tab → Analysis group → Data Analysis button**.
2. Select **Regression** from the list of data analysis tools.
3. Click **OK** to close the Data Analysis dialog box and open the Regression dialog box.
4. Set the **Input Y Range** for the regression analysis.
5. Set the **Input X Range** for the regression analysis.
6. Check the **Labels** box if you included column (or row) headings in the input ranges.
7. Choose a location for the output table.
8. Click **OK** to close the Regression dialog box and perform the regression analysis.

Trend Analysis with the Series Dialog Box

Linear Extension (preserves known values)

1. Select known data points and the unknown (to be calculated) points.
2. Open the Series dialog box: **Home tab → Editing group → Fill drop-down menu → Series ... button**.
3. Select **Rows** or **Columns** as appropriate for your data.
4. Select the **AutoFill** type.
5. Clear the **Trend** box.
6. Click **OK** to calculate the series values.

Linear Replacement (replaces known values with calculated trend values)

1. Select known data points and the unknown (to be calculated) points.
2. Open the Series dialog box: **Home tab → Editing group → Fill drop-down menu → Series ... button**.
3. Select **Rows** or **Columns** as appropriate for your data.
4. Select the **Linear** type.
5. Check the **Trend** box.
6. Click **OK** to calculate the series values.

Exponential Growth Replacement (replaces known values with calculated trend values)

1. Select known data points and the unknown (to be calculated) points.
2. Open the Series dialog box: **Home tab → Editing group → Fill drop-down menu → Series ... button**.
3. Select **Rows** or **Columns** as appropriate for your data.
4. Select the **Growth** type.
5. Check the **Trend** box.
6. Click **OK** to calculate the series values.

Using the TREND Function (preserves known values)

1. Select the unknown (to be calculated) points only.
2. Choose the **Insert Function** button on the Formula bar and select the Statistical category.
3. Choose the *TREND* function from the function list. The Function Arguments dialog box will appear.
4. Enter the **Known_y's** cell range.
5. Enter the **Known_x's** cell range.
6. Enter the **New_x's** cell range.
7. Press **Ctrl + Shift + Enter** to enter the formula in multiple cells.

Iterative Solutions

Excel provides two iterative solvers:

- Goal Seek – simple to use, can fail to find roots.
- Solver – a little more complicated, can handle constraints and optimization, finds most roots.

Using Goal Seek

1. Create a worksheet that provides a cell for an initial value and a cell for the calculated result (aka target cell). (There can be many additional calculations between the initial value and the target cell, but Goal Seek uses two cells.)

2. Enter an initial guess.

3. Open the Goal Seek dialog box: **Data tab → Data Tools group → What-If Analysis drop-down menu → Goal Seek ... button.**

4. Set the Goal Seek fields as follows:

   (a) Set cell → (this is the *target cell*, or the goal of the goal seek operation)

   (b) To value → (this is the result value that we want Goal Seek to find)

   (c) By changing cell → (this is the cell where the value is changed to try to meet the goal).

5. Click **OK** to start the Goal Seek operation.

Using Solver

1. Create a worksheet that provides one or more cells for initial values, and a cell for the calculated result (aka target cell). (There can be many additional calculations between the initial values and the target cell, but Solver requires at least two cells.)

2. Open the Solver Parameters dialog box: **Data tab → Analysis group → Solver button**.

3. Set the following Solver parameters:

   (a) Set Target Cell

   (b) Equal to → Options:

      i.   Value of → <value>

      ii. Max

      iii. Min

   (c) By Changing Cells (Solver will vary the values in multiple cells, if needed)

4. Click the **Solve** button to activate the Solver.

Problems

1. Use the Analysis ToolPak Histogram feature and the data in Figure 25.26 to create a cumulative percentage histogram of the students' midterm exam grades. What percent of the students earned a score of 80 or lower on the midterm exam?

2. Use the Descriptive Statistics selection from the Analysis ToolPak to find the mean and standard deviation for the student GPAs in Figure 25.26. Compute how many GPAs are within one standard deviation of the mean. Compute this by adding the standard deviation to the mean and then subtracting the standard deviation from the mean. How many GPAs lie within the range of the two numbers? What percentage of the GPAs lie within one standard deviation of the mean?

3. Look at the traffic-study data in Table 25.4. Perform a regression analysis for intersection 3. What is the linear equation that best fits the data? Use your linear equation to predict the traffic flow at this intersection in 2003.

TABLE 25.4 Average daily traffic flow at four downtown intersections

	Average Daily Traffic Flow (x 1,000)			
	Intersection #			
Year	1	2	3	4
1996	25.3	12.2	34.8	45.3
1997	26.3	14.5	36.9	48.7
1998	28.6	14.9	42.6	43.2
1999	29.0	16.8	50.6	46.9
2000	32.4	17.6	70.8	54.9
2001	34.8	17.9	82.3	60.9

4. Generate a Scatter plot for the 11% column in Figure 25.72. Add an exponential growth trendline to the chart. Then, using the Format Trendline dialog box, forecast forward 20 periods (20 more years). By looking at the projected trendline, determine John's approximate nest egg at age 68 if he invests $10,000 at age 18 (assuming he hasn't started spending it).

	A	B	C	D	E	F	G	H	I
1	Compound Amount Factors								
2									
3	Interest Rate:		6%	7%	8%	9%	10%	11%	
4									
5		Year							
6		0	1.0000	1.0000	1.0000	1.0000	1.0000	1.0000	
7		10	1.7908	1.9672	2.1589	2.3674	2.5937	2.8394	
8		20	3.2071	3.8697	4.6610	5.6044	6.7275	8.0623	
9		30	5.7435	7.6123	10.0627	13.2677	17.4494	22.8923	
10									

Figure 25.72 Single-payment compound amount factors.

5. Using an XY Scatter chart, graph the function

$$f(x) = x^3 + \sin(x/2) + 2x - 4$$

for $x = [-2, 2]$ in increments of 0.1. Add a trendline to the chart. What type of trendline best fits the data? Display the equation and R^2 value on the chart.

6. Evaluate the function

$$y = \ln(2x) + \sin(x)$$

for $x = [1, 10]$ in increments of 0.1. Chart the results using an XY Scatter chart. From looking at the plot, what do you think is the minimum of the function in this range?

7. Compute values of
$$f(x) = 2x^3 - 13x - 9$$
for $x = -3, 3]$ in increments of 0.1. Plot the function by using an XY Scatter plot. You can see from the plot that $f(x) = 0$ near $x = -2.1, -0.8$, and 2.8. Use these three guesses and the Goal Seek tool to find more accurate solutions for $f(x) = 0$.

8. Use the Solver to minimize the objective function
$$f(x) = (x_1 + 2x_2 - 7)^2 + (2x_1 + x_2 - 5)^2$$
with the constraints $-10 " x_1, x_2 " 10$. What are the values of x_1 and x_2 when $f(x)$ is at its minimum?

9. A cylindrical chemical petroleum tank must hold 6.8 m3 of hazardous waste. Your task is to design the tank in a cost-effective manner by minimizing its surface area. Ignore the thickness of the walls in your design. Recall that the surface area S of a right-angled cylinder is
$$S = 2\pi r^2 + 2\pi rh \text{ square meters,}$$
and the volume V of a cylinder is
$$V = \pi r^2 h \text{ cubic meters.}$$
Use the Solver to minimize r and h.

10. Enthalpy and entropy data for saturated steam between 100 and 300°C are shown in Table 25.5. Prepare a chart of the enthalpy data as a function of temperature, and add a trendline to the chart that fits the data well. Report the equation of the trendline and the R^2 value.

TABLE 25.5 Properties of saturated steam

Temp. (°C)	Enthalpy kJ/kg	Entropy kJ/kg K
100	2680	7.4
150	2750	6.8
200	2790	6.4
250	2800	6.1
300	2750	5.7

TABLE 25.6 Viscosity of water

Temp. (°C)	μ(cP)
0	1.8
5	1.5
10	1.3
15	1.1
20	1.0
25	0.9
30	0.8
35	0.7
40	0.6

11. The viscosity of a liquid varies greatly as the temperature of the liquid changes. An engineer simulating a hydroelectric power plant must account for the effect of temperature on the viscosity of water in his simulation. Create a chart of the viscosity and temperature data listed in Table 25.6, and find a trendline that fits the data. Report the equation of the line and the R^2 value.

12. The values charted in Figures 25.24 and 25.25 were computed by using the following equations:

Figure 25.24, left panel

$$y_1 = x + \sin(x)$$
$$y_2 = 2 + 0.9x + \sin(x)$$

Figure 25.24, right panel

$$y_1 = x + \sin(x)$$
$$y_3 = 4 - 0.9x - \sin(x)$$

Figure 25.25

$$y_1 = x + \sin(x)$$
$$y_4 = 4 - 0.2x + 3\cos(x/3)$$

Use these equations to calculate y values (i.e., $y1, y2, y3, y4$, values) for x values between 0 and 5, with an interval of 0.2. Use these values with Excel's Correlation tool to determine the correlation coefficients for the following cases:

(a) $y1, y2$—Figure 25.24, left panel
(b) $y1, y3$—Figure 25.24, right panel
(c) $y1, y4$—Figure 25.25

Chapter 26

Database Management within Excel

26.1 INTRODUCTION

Microsoft Excel implements a rudimentary *database management system* (DBMS) by treating lists in a worksheet as database records. A database management system is a collection of programs that enables you to store, extract, and modify information from a database. Excel's system is helpful for organizing, sorting, and searching through worksheets that contain many related items. You can import complete databases from external database management systems such as Microsoft Access, Oracle, dBase, Microsoft FoxPro, and text files. You can create structured queries by using Microsoft Query to retrieve selected information from external sources.

If you require a relational DBMS, then you are encouraged to use another, more complete software application such as Microsoft Access. However, the database functions within Excel are adequate for many problems. An example of one way that an engineer might use this functionality is to import experimental data that have been stored in a relational DBMS in order to perform analysis on the data, using Excel's built-in functions.

OBJECTIVES

After reading this chapter, you should be able to perform the following tasks

- Create a database within Excel
- Enter data into an Excel database
- Sort a database on one or more keys
- Use filters to query databases

26.1.1 Database Terminology

A database within Excel is sometimes called a *list*. A *database* can be thought of as an electronic file cabinet that contains a number of folders. Each folder contains similar information for different objects. For example, each folder might contain the information about a student at a college of engineering. The database is the collection of all student folders.

The data in each folder are organized in a similar fashion. For example, each folder might include a student's

- last name
- first name
- college identification number
- address
- department
- class

and other pertinent information.

Using database terminology, each folder is called a *record*. Each data item is stored within a *field*. The title for each data item is called a *field name*.

Any region in an Excel worksheet can be defined as a database. Excel represents each record as a separate row. Each cell within the row is a field. The heading for each column is the field name.

Figure 26.1 depicts a small student database. Rows 3 through 12 each represent a student record. Each record has five fields. The field names are the column headings (e.g., **Last Name**).

	A	B	C	D	E	F	G
1							
2		**Last Name**	**First Name**	**GPA**	**Department**	**Class**	
3		Phillips	Casey	3.51	Electrical	Junior	
4		Noland	Rudy	2.98	Chemical	Senior	
5		Murray	Susie	3.92	Electrical	Senior	
6		Carter	Christine	2.78	Civil	Junior	
7		Madison	Richard	3.41	Mechanical	Junior	
8		Carter	Frank	3.12	Chemical	Senior	
9		Kirk	William	3.35	Civil	Sophmore	
10		Hahn	Eric	3.87	Mechanical	Junior	
11		Garcia	Rob	3.21	Electrical	Sophmore	
12		Ault	Linda	3.78	Chemical	Senior	
13							

Figure 26.1 Example of a student database.

26.2 CREATING DATABASES

Most database management systems store records in one or more separate files. The file delimits the boundaries of the database. Excel, however, stores a database as a region in a worksheet.

Excel must have some way of knowing where the database begins and ends in the worksheet. There are two methods for associating a region with a database.

- Leave a perimeter of blank cells around the database region.
- Explicitly name the region.

Because of the unique way that Excel delimits a database, the following tips are recommended:

- Maintain only one database per worksheet. This will speed up access to the sorting and filtering functions, and you will not need to name the database regions.

- Make sure that each column heading in the database is unique. If there were two headings for **Last Name**, for example, a logical query such as

Find all records with **Last Name** *equal to* **Smith**

would not make sense.

- Leave an empty column to the right of the database and an empty row at the bottom of the database (and to the left and top if the database does not include cell A1.). Excel uses the empty row and column to mark the edge of the database. An alternative method is to assign a name to the region of the database. One disadvantage of assigning a name is that the allocated region may have to be redefined when records are added or deleted.

- Do not use cells to the right of the database for other purposes. Filtered rows may inadvertently hide these cells.

26.3 ENTERING DATA

Once the field names for the database have been created in the column headings, data may be entered by using several methods. One method of data entry is to type data directly into a cell. A database field may contain any legitimate Excel value, including a number, date, text, or formula. For example, you might add a column to the database in Figure 26.1 that is titled **Full Name**. Instead of copying or retyping the first and last names of each student, the new field could concatenate the **First Name** and **Last Name** entries by using the following formula:

```
=CONCATENATE(B2,", ",A2)
```

The result is shown in Figure 26.2.

A second method for entering data is to use a form. The data entry form is readily available from the menus in Excel 2003 (Data → Form), but it is not part of the Ribbon in Excel 2007. You can still use the form, but with Excel 2007 you must first add the **Form...** button to the Quick Access Toolbar using the following steps:

1. Click the small down arrow next to the Quick Access Toolbar (illustrated in Figure 26.3).
2. Select **More Commands** from the Customize Quick Access Toolbar menu (see Figure 26.3). This opens the Excel Options dialog to the Customize panel as shown in Figure 26.4.
3. Select **Commands Not in the Ribbon** in the **Choose commands from** drop-down list.
4. Select **Form...** from the list of available commands (left panel).
5. Click **Add >>>** to add the **Form...** button to the Quick Access Toolbar.
6. Click **OK** to close the Excel Options dialog box.

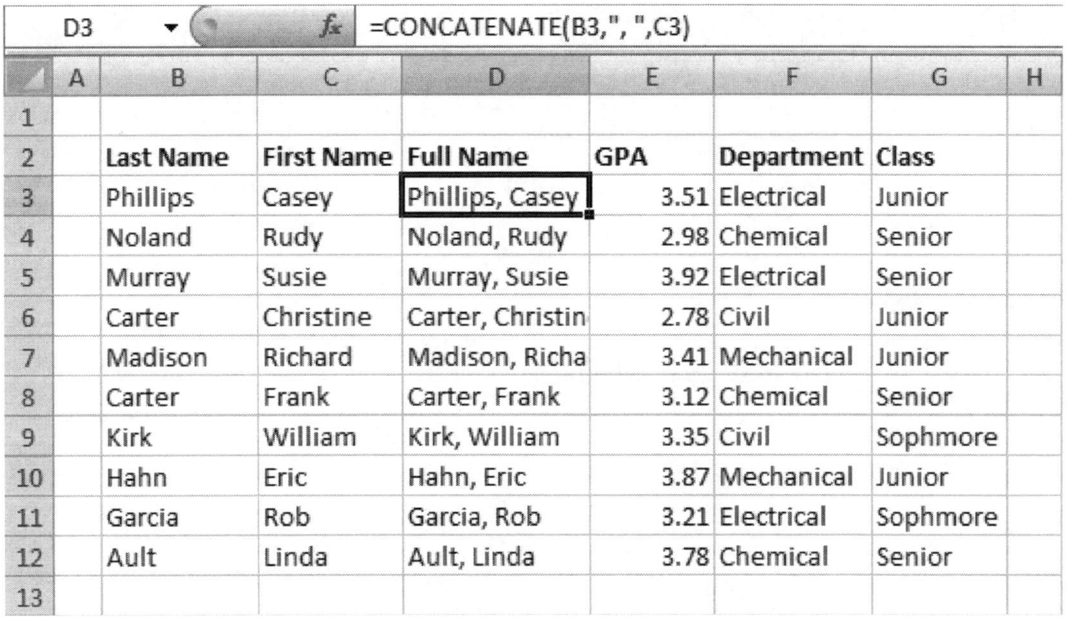
D3
=CONCATENATE(B3,", ",C3)
A B C D E F G H
1
2 Last Name First Name Full Name GPA Department Class
3 Phillips Casey Phillips, Casey 3.51 Electrical Junior
4 Noland Rudy Noland, Rudy 2.98 Chemical Senior
5 Murray Susie Murray, Susie 3.92 Electrical Senior
6 Carter Christine Carter, Christin 2.78 Civil Junior
7 Madison Richard Madison, Richa 3.41 Mechanical Junior
8 Carter Frank Carter, Frank 3.12 Chemical Senior
9 Kirk William Kirk, William 3.35 Civil Sophmore
10 Hahn Eric Hahn, Eric 3.87 Mechanical Junior
11 Garcia Rob Garcia, Rob 3.21 Electrical Sophmore
12 Ault Linda Ault, Linda 3.78 Chemical Senior
13

Figure 26.2 Inserting a Full Name field.

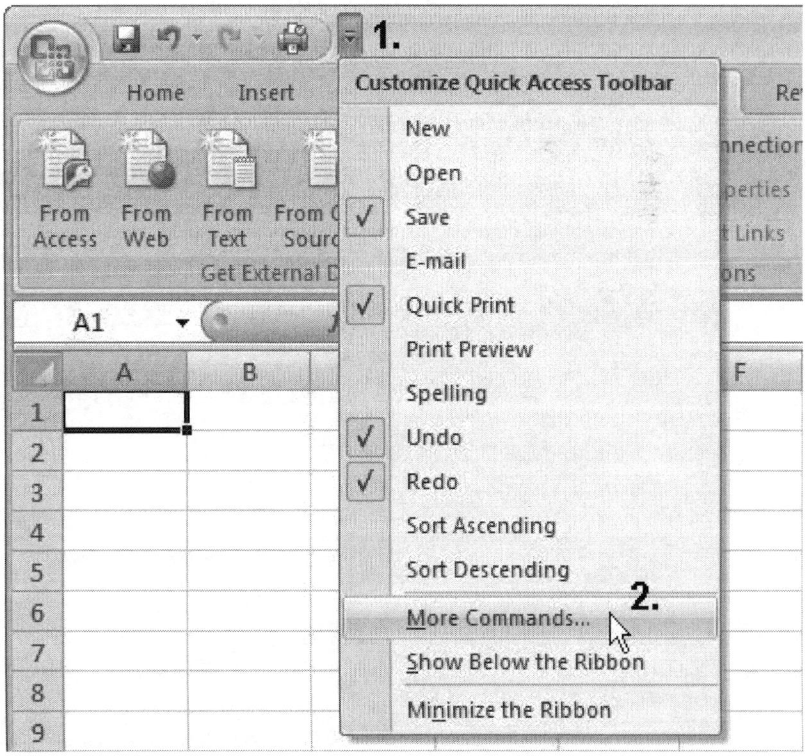
1.
Customize Quick Access Toolbar
Home
Insert
From Access
From Web
From Text
Get External D
New
Open
Save
E-mail
Quick Print
Print Preview
Spelling
Undo
Redo
Sort Ascending
Sort Descending
More Commands...
2.
Show Below the Ribbon
Minimize the Ribbon
A1

Figure 26.3 Adding a button to the Quick Access Toolbar.

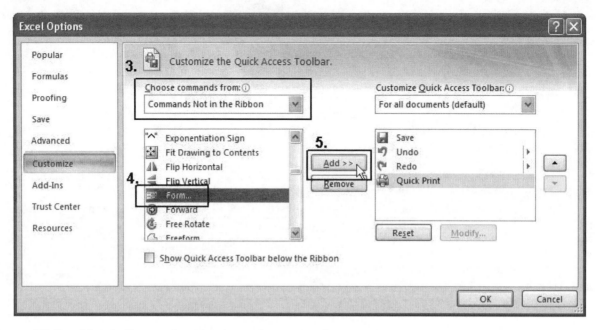

Figure 26.4 Adding the **Form...** button to the Quick Access Toolbar.

Once the **Form...** button is available, you can use it for data entry by following these steps:

1.   Select any data cell in the database.
2.   Click the **Form...** button.

The Data Entry form will appear, as depicted in Figure 26.5. The title of the Data Entry form will be the same as the name of the current worksheet, *Student Database* in this example.

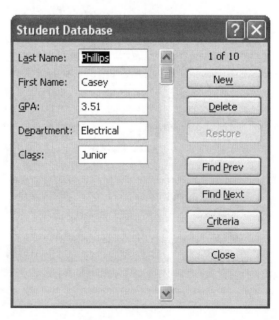

Figure 26.5 The Form dialog (Student Database is the name of the worksheet containing the database).

Practice!

Before proceeding, it will be helpful for you to create the database depicted in Figure 26.1. This database will be used for the examples in the rest of the chapter. Practice entering some of the data by using the Data Entry form. Enter some of the data by typing directly into the worksheet. Which method is more resistant to typing errors?

From the Data Entry form you can

- Create a new record by clicking the **New** button.
- Scroll through the database with the slider control.
- Select adjacent records with the **Find Prev** and **Find Next** buttons.
- **Delete** records.
- Modify existing records.

26.4   SORTING A DATABASE

The power of a database management system lies in its ability to search for information, rearrange data, and filter information.

To sort a database, follow this procedure:

1.   Select any data cell in the database.
2.   Open the Sort dialog box using any of these methods:

   a.   From the Ribbon's Home tab: **Home tab → Editing group → Sort & Filter drop-down menu → Custom Sort... button**.

   b.   From the Ribbon's Data tab: **Data tab → Sort & Filter group→ Sort button**.

   c.   Excel 2003: Data → Sort.

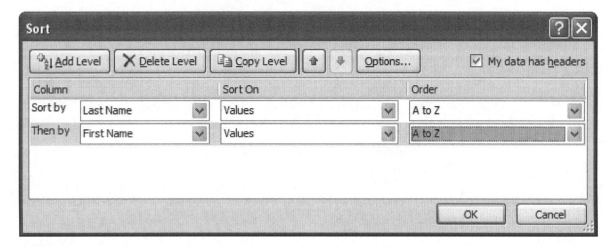

Figure 26.6   The Sort dialog box.

The Sort dialog box will appear, as depicted in Figure 26.6. The field on which the sort is made is called the *sort key*. Excel allows you to sort on multiple keys. In this example we will sort on **Last Name** and **First Name**.

3. Choose **Last Name** in A to Z (ascending) order as the first key.
4. Click **Add Level**, then choose **First Name** in A to Z order as the second key.
5. Make sure that the **My data has headers** box is checked.
6. Click **OK** to close the Sort dialog box and perform the sort.

The result is an alphabetical listing, by last name, of the student database as shown in Figure 26.7.

	A	B	C	D	E	F	G
1							
2		Last Name	First Name	GPA	Department	Class	
3		Ault	Linda	3.78	Chemical	Senior	
4		Carter	Christine	2.78	Civil	Junior	
5		Carter	Frank	3.12	Chemical	Senior	
6		Garcia	Rob	3.21	Electrical	Sophmore	
7		Hahn	Eric	3.87	Mechanical	Junior	
8		Kirk	William	3.35	Civil	Sophmore	
9		Madison	Richard	3.41	Mechanical	Junior	
10		Murray	Susie	3.92	Electrical	Senior	
11		Noland	Rudy	2.98	Chemical	Senior	
12		Phillips	Casey	3.51	Electrical	Junior	
13							

Figure 26.7 The sorted database.

Caution   If you select a portion of the database before asking Excel to perform a sort, Excel will show a warning box that there are nonempty adjacent cells. Sorting a portion of the database will misalign the data in the various fields, and Excel tries to warn you not to do it. If you accidentally scramble the database, immediately click the **Undo** button on the Quick Access toolbar.

If you follow the procedure listed above and click in a single cell before performing any database operations, Excel will automatically select the entire database before sorting or filtering.

Practice!

Sort the student database in ascending order by Department and descending order by GPA within each department. Your results should resemble Figure 26.8.

	A	B	C	D	E	F	G
1							
2		Last Name	First Name	GPA	Department	Class	
3		Ault	Linda	3.78	Chemical	Senior	
4		Carter	Frank	3.12	Chemical	Senior	
5		Noland	Rudy	2.98	Chemical	Senior	
6		Kirk	William	3.35	Civil	Sophmore	
7		Carter	Christine	2.78	Civil	Junior	
8		Murray	Susie	3.92	Electrical	Senior	
9		Phillips	Casey	3.51	Electrical	Junior	
10		Garcia	Rob	3.21	Electrical	Sophmore	
11		Hahn	Eric	3.87	Mechanical	Junior	
12		Madison	Richard	3.41	Mechanical	Junior	
13							

Figure 26.8   Sorted student database (Department A to Z, GPA largest to smallest).

26.5   FILTERING DATA

Excel has several mechanisms for locating records that match specified criteria. For example, you may be interested in reviewing the students with Chemical Engineering majors. After you select **Chemical** as the desired criterion, Excel displays only those records with Department field equal to "Chemical."

The process of limiting the visible records on the basis of some criteria is called *filtering*. There are three methods for filtering a database in Excel:

- AutoFilter
- Custom AutoFilter
- Advanced Filter

Filtering does not delete records from a database; it only hides records that do not meet the filter criteria.

26.5.1 Using the AutoFilter

The *AutoFilter* allows you to filter records while viewing the database on the worksheet. It is very quick and intuitive.

To activate the AutoFilter feature, follow these steps:

1. Select a data cell within the database.
2. Use any of these methods:
   a. From the Ribbon's Home tab: **Home tab → Editing group → Sort & Filter drop-down menu → Filter button.**
   b. From the Ribbon's Data tab: **Data tab → Sort & Filter group → Filter button.**
   c. Excel 2003: **Data → Filter → AutoFilter.**

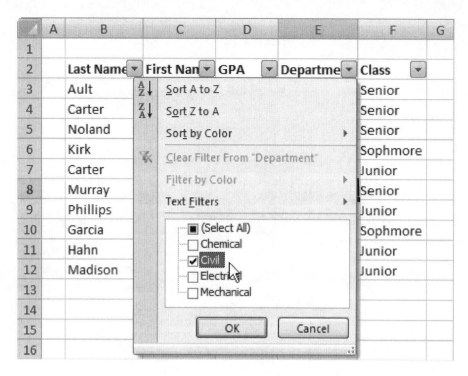

Figure 26.9 The AutoFilter, preparing to filter on Department = "Civil".

A small arrow will appear in the heading of each column (see Figure 26.9). When you click on one of the arrows, a small drop-down menu will appear that contains the possible choices for that field. Figure 26.9 depicts the student database with the AutoFilter option turned on. The drop-down menu for the Department field is shown, with the filter criterion set for **Civil**.

When the **OK** button is clicked, only the records with Department equal to **Civil** will be displayed (see Figure 26.10). The small arrow at the head of the Department column now shows a small funnel icon to signify that this column is filtering some records.

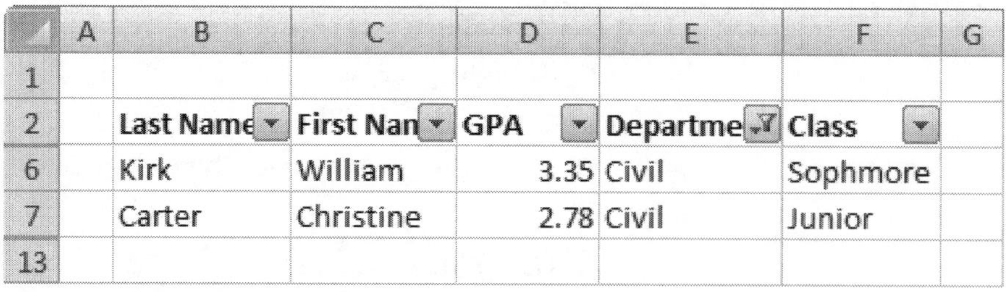

	A	B	C	D	E	F	G
1							
2		Last Name ▾	First Nan ▾	GPA ▾	Departme ⏷	Class ▾	
6		Kirk	William	3.35	Civil	Sophmore	
7		Carter	Christine	2.78	Civil	Junior	
13							

Figure 26.10 The filtered database showing only records where Department = "Civil".

To remove the filter and display all records, use one of these methods:

- From the Ribbon's Home tab: **Home tab → Editing group → Sort & Filter drop-down menu → Clear button**.
- From the Ribbon's Data tab: **Data tab → Sort & Filter → group Clear button**.
- Excel 2003: Data → Filter → Show All.

Practice!

Practice using the AutoFilter. Use the AutoFilter to select all students in electrical engineering. Your result should look like Figure 26.11.

	A	B	C	D	E	F	G
1							
2		Last Name ▾	First Nam ▾	GPA ▾	Departme ⧩	Class ▾	
8		Murray	Susie	3.92	Electrical	Senior	
9		Phillips	Casey	3.51	Electrical	Junior	
10		Garcia	Rob	3.21	Electrical	Sophmore	
13							

Figure 26.11   Filtering for Electrical Engineering majors.

When you are done filtering, use any of these approaches to deactivate (toggle) the AutoFilter.

- From the Ribbon's Home tab: **Home tab → Editing group → Sort & Filter drop-down menu → Filter button**.
- From the Ribbon's Data tab: **Data tab → Sort & Filter group → Filter button**.
- Excel 2003: Data → Filter → AutoFilter.

26.5.2 Using the Custom AutoFilter

The AutoFilter options that you have learned so far are fine if you want to make an exact match. However, in many cases, you will want to specify a range. For example, you may want to view the students who have GPAs greater than 3.5. One way to specify ranges is to use the *Custom AutoFilter* dialog box. To use the Custom AutoFilter option to specify students with a GPA > 3.5, follow this procedure:

1. Select a data cell within the database.
2. Activate the AutoFilter using any of the methods listed above.
3. Open the AutoFilter menu for the GPA column (using the arrow icon in the column heading).
4. Select **Number Filters...** from the GPA drop-down menu (see Figure 26.12).
5. Select **Custom Filter...** as shown in Figure 26.12. The Custom AutoFilter dialog box will open as shown in Figure 26.13.
6. Complete the Custom AutoFilter dialog box data entry fields as shown in Figure 26.13 to filter for GPAs > 3.5:

   a. Left drop-down list, choose **is greater than**
   b. Right text field, enter **3.5**

7. Click **OK** to close the Custom AutoFilter dialog box and filter the data.

   The result of applying the custom filter is shown in Figure 26.14.

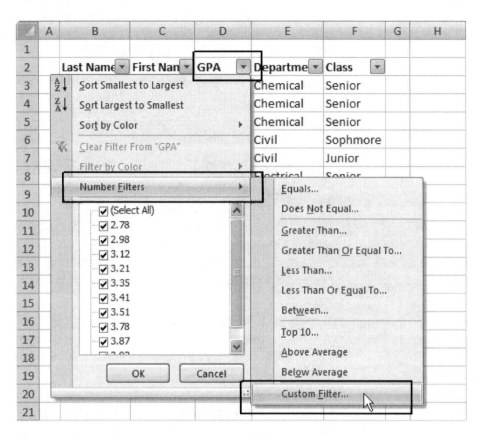

Figure 26.12   Requesting a custom filter on GPA.

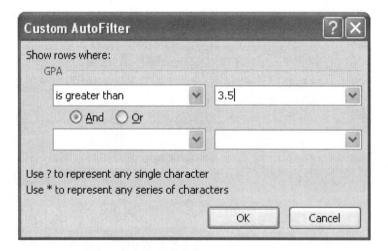

Figure 26.13   Custom AutoFilter dialog box.

	A	B	C	D	E	F	G
1							
2		Last Name ▾	First Nan ▾	GPA ▾	Departme ▾	Class ▾	
3		Ault	Linda	3.78	Chemical	Senior	
8		Murray	Susie	3.92	Electrical	Senior	
9		Phillips	Casey	3.51	Electrical	Junior	
11		Hahn	Eric	3.87	Mechanical	Junior	
13							

Figure 26.14   The database filtered for GPAs > 3.5.

Practice!

Practice using the Custom AutoFilter function. You can use it to specify a simple logical expression. The Custom AutoFilter dialog box allows you to join two logical conditions with an *And* operator or an *Or* operator.

If you choose **And**, then both conditions must be true for the record to be displayed. If you choose **Or**, then the record will be displayed if either of the conditions is met.

Use a Custom AutoFilter to select all students with GPAs between 3.0 and 3.5. The Custom AutoFilter dialog box for this filter is illustrated in Figure 26.15. The filtered result is shown in Figure 26.16.

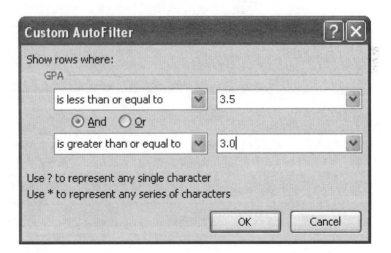

Figure 26.15   Creating a custom filter to find students with GPAs between 3.0 and 3.5.

	A	B	C	D	E	F	G
1							
2	Last Name ▾	First Nan ▾	GPA ▾	Departme ▾	Class ▾		
4		Carter	Frank	3.12	Chemical	Senior	
6		Kirk	William	3.35	Civil	Sophmore	
10		Garcia	Rob	3.21	Electrical	Sophmore	
12		Madison	Richard	3.41	Mechanical	Junior	
13							

Figure 26.16   The filtered database: Students with GPA between 3.0 and 3.5.

Next, clear the GPA filter and create a custom filter to display all students from either Electrical or Chemical Engineering. Your result should look like Figure 26.17.

	A	B	C	D	E	F	G
1							
2	Last Name ▾	First Nan ▾	GPA ▾	Departme ▾	Class ▾		
3		Ault	Linda	3.78	Chemical	Senior	
4		Carter	Frank	3.12	Chemical	Senior	
5		Noland	Rudy	2.98	Chemical	Senior	
8		Murray	Susie	3.92	Electrical	Senior	
9		Phillips	Casey	3.51	Electrical	Junior	
10		Garcia	Rob	3.21	Electrical	Sophmore	
13							

Figure 26.17   The filtered database: Chemical or Electrical engineering majors.

To remove the filter and display all records, use one of these methods:

- From the Ribbon's Home tab: **Home tab → Editing group → Sort & Filter drop-down menu → Clear button**.
- From the Ribbon's Data tab: **Data tab → Sort & Filter group → Clear button**.
- Excel 2003: Data → Filter → Show All.

26.5.3 Using Wild-Card Characters

A greater range of choices may be made by using the question mark or asterisk character as a wild-card character. A *wild-card character* is a placeholder that can be filled by any legitimate character.

The question mark is used to represent any single character. For example, the logical expression

```
Department=????ical
```

will return all departments with exactly four characters followed by *ical*. In our student database, Chemical would be displayed, but Mechanical, Electrical, and Civil would not, as they do not contain exactly four characters followed by *ical*.

The asterisk is used to represent the replacement of zero or more characters. For example, the logical expression

```
Department=*ical
```

will return all departments ending in *ical*, no matter how many letters precede *ical* (including zero letters). In our student database, Chemical, Electrical, and Mechanical would be displayed, but Civil would not.

Some wild-card functions can also be performed by using the following conditions in the Custom AutoFilter dialog:

- begins with
- ends with
- contains
- does not begin with
- does not end with
- does not contain

Practice!

Practice using the wild-card characters and menu selections in the Custom AutoFilter dialog box. Be sure to clear the filter between each exercise.

Here are two methods of selecting all students whose last name begins with an S:

Method 1.

```
Last Name begins with S
```

Method 2.

```
Last Name equals S*
```

Here are two methods for selecting all students whose last name ends in an N and does not contain an H:

Method 1.

```
Last Name ends with N
And
Last Name does not contain H
```

Method 2.

```
Last Name equals *N
And
Last Name does not equal *H*
```

Note that the Custom AutoFilter box is not case sensitive.

Try creating a Custom AutoFilter for selecting all students whose last name ends in an N and does not contain an H. Your result should look like Figure 26.18.

◢	A	B	C	D	E	F	G
1							
2		Last Name ▼	First Nan ▼	GPA ▼	Departme ▼	Class ▼	
12		Madison	Richard	3.41	Mechanical	Junior	
13							

Figure 26.18 Results after filtering.

26.5.4　Using the Advanced Filter

The filtering methods that you have been shown so far allow a great deal of flexibility. By adding filters to multiple fields and by using the Custom AutoFilter, wild cards, and logical operators, you can build relatively complex filters.

However, there are some cases that can't be handled by these methods. Suppose that the engineering departments have different GPA requirements. We want to find students who meet the following criteria:

```
Electrical Engineering with GPA > 3.6
Or
Chemical Engineering with GPA > 3.0
Or
Civil Engineering with GPA > 3.2
Or
Mechanical Engineering with GPA > 3.4
```

You can't create a filter that solves this request by using the AutoFilter. You will need to use the *Advanced Filter*, which allows you to build more complex queries.

The term *query* can be used as a noun or a verb. As a verb, it means to ask a question. When we query a database, we are asking the database program to return all records that meet our criteria. As a noun, the query is the list of criteria that we want the database program to use to identify applicable records.

To use the Advanced Filter, you must first set up a Criteria table. A *Criteria table* is just what it sounds like, a table of criteria that must be met for a filter to occur. To create a Criteria table, perform these steps:

1.　Copy the field names from your database to another location in the same worksheet. (Leave at least one blank row of cells between the Criteria table and the database.)

2.　Type in the criteria that must be met for your filter.

26.5.5　Logic within Rows

All criteria within a single row must be met for a match to occur. This is equivalent to a logical *And* operator.

26.5.6　Logic between Rows

A Criteria table may have more than one active row. A match on any row in a criteria table may be met for a match to occur. This is equivalent to a logical *Or* operator.

As an example, Figure 26.19 shows a criteria table to select students in each major who meet the department's GPA requirement.

Now that we have set up the criteria table, we can use the Advanced Filter dialog box to build a filter by using the criteria table. To use the Advanced Filter, follow these steps:

1.　Click on any data cell in the database to select it. Excel will automatically detect all of the database records.

2.　Open the Advanced Filter dialog box with Ribbon options: **Data tab → Sort & Filter group → Advanced button**. (Excel 2003: Data → Filter → Advanced Filter.) The Advanced Filter dialog box is shown in Figure 26.20.

3.　Indicate the cell range containing the criteria table, including the column headings. (Cells B3:F7 in this example.)

	Criteria Table				
	Last Name	**First Name**	**GPA**	**Department**	**Class**
			>3.6	Electrical	
			>3.0	Chemical	
			>3.2	Civil	
			>3.4	Mechanical	

	Database				
	Last Name	**First Name**	**GPA**	**Department**	**Class**
	Ault	Linda	3.78	Chemical	Senior
	Carter	Frank	3.12	Chemical	Senior
	Noland	Rudy	2.98	Chemical	Senior
	Kirk	William	3.35	Civil	Sophmore
	Carter	Christine	2.78	Civil	Junior
	Murray	Susie	3.92	Electrical	Senior
	Phillips	Casey	3.51	Electrical	Junior
	Garcia	Rob	3.21	Electrical	Sophmore
	Hahn	Eric	3.87	Mechanical	Junior
	Madison	Richard	3.41	Mechanical	Junior

Figure 26.19 Criteria table and database before filtering.

Figure 26.20 The Advanced Filter dialog box.

4. Select the **Action: Filter the list, in-place**.

5. Click **OK** to close the Advanced Filter dialog box and filter the data.

The results are shown in Figure 26.21.

◢	A	B	C	D	E	F	G
1							
2		**Criteria Table**					
3		Last Name	First Name	GPA	Department	Class	
4				>3.6	Electrical		
5				>3.0	Chemical		
6				>3.2	Civil		
7				>3.4	Mechanical		
8							
9		**Database**					
10		Last Name	First Name	GPA	Department	Class	
11		Ault	Linda	3.78	Chemical	Senior	
12		Carter	Frank	3.12	Chemical	Senior	
14		Kirk	William	3.35	Civil	Sophmore	
16		Murray	Susie	3.92	Electrical	Senior	
19		Hahn	Eric	3.87	Mechanical	Junior	
20		Madison	Richard	3.41	Mechanical	Junior	
21							

Figure 26.21 The database after applying the Advanced Filter.

KEY TERMS

Advanced Filter
And operator
AutoFilter
criteria
criteria table
Custom AutoFilter

database
database management
system (DBMS)
data entry form
field
field name

filtering
Or operator
query
record
sort
wild-card character (?, *)

Summary

Delimiting a Database in Excel

- Leave a perimeter of blank cells around the database region.
- Explicitly name the region.

Recommendations for Using Databases within Excel

- Maintain only one database per worksheet.
- Use unique column headings.

- Leave an empty column to the right of the database and an empty row at the bottom of the database.
- Do not use cells to the right or left of the database for other purposes.

Sorting a Database

1. Select any data cell in the database.
2. Open the Sort dialog box: **Data tab** → **Sort & Filter group** → **Sort button**. The Sort dialog box will open.
3. Select the field name and sort order.
4. Click **Add Level** if more than one field is included in the sort, then select the next field name and sort order.
5. If your database includes column headings, be sure that the **My data has headers** box is checked.
6. Click **OK**.

Filtering a Database

There are three methods for filtering a database in Excel:

- AutoFilter
- Custom AutoFilter
- Advanced Filter

Activating and Deactivating the AutoFilter (toggles)

1. Select a data cell within the database.
2. **Data tab** → **Sort & Filter group** → **Filter button**.

Filtering with the AutoFilter

1. Click on the small arrow on the desired column heading.
2. Select the desired filter criterion from the drop-down menu.

Clearing the AutoFilter

- **Data tab** → **Sort & Filter group** → **Clear button**

Filtering with the Custom AutoFilter

1. Select a data cell within the database.
2. Activate the AutoFilter.
3. Open any AutoFilter menu (using the arrow icon in the column heading).
4. Select **Number Filters...** or **Text Filters...** from the drop-down menu.
5. Select **Custom Filter....** The Custom AutoFilter dialog box will open.
6. Complete the Custom AutoFilter dialog box.
7. Click **OK**.

Wild-Card Characters

- ? - replacement of any single character
- * - replacement of zero or more characters

Filtering with the Advanced Filter

1. Create a Criteria Table

    (a) Logic within rows is equivalent to a logical *And* operator.
    (b) Logic between rows is equivalent to a logical *Or* operator.

2. Click on any data cell in the database to select it.
3. Open the Advanced Filter dialog box: **Data tab → Sort & Filter group → Advanced button**.
4. Indicate the cell range containing the criteria table, including the column headings.
5. Select the **Action. Filter the list, in-place** is the more commonly used choice.
6. Click **OK**.

Problems

1. Figure 26.22 shows the thermal properties of sundry materials. The construction column indicates whether or not the material is used in typical residential construction. Type this data into a worksheet, or download the worksheet from the author's website:

    http://www.chbe.montana.edu/IntroExcel

    From the web page, select the item labeled *Thermal Properties*.

	A	B	C	D	E	F
1	Thermal Properties of Various Materials (at 20°C)					
2						
3	Material	Construction	Density - ρ (kg/m³)	Specific Heat - c_p (J/kg.K)	Conductivity - k (J/s.m.°C)	
4	Aluminum	yes	2700	896	237.00	
5	Bronze	no	8670	343	26.00	
6	Concrete	yes	500	840	0.13	
7	Copper	no	8930	383	400.00	
8	Glass	yes	2800	800	0.81	
9	Ice	no	910	57	202.00	
10	Plaster	yes	1800	112	0.81	
11	Polystyrene	yes	1210		0.04	
12	Wood (pine)	yes	420	2700	0.15	
13	Wool Insulation	yes	200		0.04	
14						

Figure 26.22   Thermal properties of various materials.

Use this worksheet to solve the following:

(a) Sort the worksheet by **Specific Heat** in ascending order. Where do the blank entries get placed after the sort?

(b) Sort the worksheet by the **Construction** field with the **yes** category at the top. Within each Construction category, sort in descending order of **Density**.

(c) Use the AutoFilter to show only **Construction** materials.

(d) Use the Custom AutoFilter to show only construction materials with a **Density** > 1000 and **Conductivity** < 1.00.

(e) Use the Advanced Filter to show **Construction** materials with a **Specific Heat** > 800 and non-construction materials (**Construction** = no) with a **Specific Heat** > 300. Show your criteria table.

(e) Can you solve the last problem using only the AutoFilter, not the Advanced Filter?

Describe the actions you performed to solve each part of this problem.

2. A common database used by many people is an address book. It contains names, addresses, phone numbers, and sometimes other information such as birth dates and anniversaries. But paper-based address books can be hard to keep in alphabetical order as names are added and deleted, and sometimes they don't have enough fields for all of the phone numbers and email addresses we use today.

Create an address book database in Excel containing the fields listed below. You can add other fields if you like to keep track of additional information.

- Last Name
- First Name
- Street Address
- City
- State
- Postal Code
- Email
- Home Phone
- Work Phone
- Cell Phone

Add at least three people to the address book, and sort the data by last name.

3. When students need to work together on projects, conflicts can arise because some students like to wait until the last possible minute, some like to get the projects done as soon as possible, and some like to work at a slow and steady pace. Also, scheduling meetings can be a problem because some students like to get together in the afternoons to work on projects, some like evenings, and others want to do the work only on the weekends.

Enter the database shown in Figure 26.23, and use Excel's database filtering to identify the following:

(a) Groups of students who all like to get projects "done and over with" as soon as possible.

(b) Groups of students who all like to work on group projects in the afternoons.

4. Most data tables can be treated as databases and sorted or filtered. For example, consider the properties of liquid water tabulated in Figure 26.24.

◢	A	B	C	D
1	**Student Preferences Database**			
2				
3	**Name**	**Preferred Work Style**	**Preferred Work Time**	
4	Seth	Done and Over With	Evenings	
5	Alicia	Slow and Steady	Afternoons	
6	Allyson	Last Minute	Evenings	
7	Terry	Last Minute	Afternoons	
8	Sam	Done and Over With	Weekends	
9	Brittany	Last Minute	Weekends	
10	Treair	Slow and Steady	Evenings	
11	Rob	Last Minute	Afternoons	
12				

Figure 26.23 Student work preferences database.

◢	A	B	C	D	E
1	**Properties of Liquid Water**				
2					
3	**T (°C)**	**Visc. (cP)**	**SG**	**Th. Cond. (W/m K)**	
4	0	1.8	1.000	0.554	
5	5	1.5	1.000	0.565	
6	10	1.3	1.000	0.577	
7	15	1.1	0.999	0.587	
8	20	1.0	0.998	0.597	
9	25	0.9	0.997	0.606	
10	30	0.8	0.996	0.615	
11	35	0.7	0.994	0.623	
12	40	0.6	0.992	0.630	
13					

Figure 26.24 Properties of liquid water (approximate values).

Create the data table shown in Figure 26.24, then perform these tasks:

(a) Filter the database to show data for temperatures greater than or equal to 10°C and less than 20°C.

(b) Filter the database to show data with thermal conductivities greater than 0.6 W/m K.

5. One problem with having lots of books is keeping track of them. The database shown in Figure 26.25 is one way to keep records.

List the steps you would use in Excel to filter the database to display only reference books that are out on loan.

	A	B	C	D	E
1	**Book**	**Type**	**Status**	**Loaned To**	
2	Popular Myths about Engineers	Humor	In Library		
3	10,000 Engineer Jokes	Humor	On Loan	Paula	
4	Statics and Dynamics for Dummies	Text	In Library		
5	Complete and Concise Steam Tables	Reference	On Loan	Max	
6	Properties of Liquid Water	Reference	In Library		
7					

Figure 26.25   Personal library management database.

6.   Figure 26.26 shows the initial stages of a database for holding a grocery list. If this list were maintained, any of your roommates could easily filter the database to show only needed items and quickly print a grocery list.

	A	B	C	D	E	F
1	**Grocery List**					
2						
3	**Item**	**Category**	**Size**	**On Hand**	**Status**	
4	Bread	Bakery	Loaf	0	Needed	
5	Lunch Meat, Turkey	Deli	1 pound, sliced	2	Not Needed	
6	Lunch Meat, Beef	Deli	1 pound, sliced	1	Not Needed	
7	Mayo	Condiments	Jar, 8 oz.	0	Needed	
8						

Figure 26.26   Grocery list database.

Create your own grocery list database and practice filtering, as follows:
   (a) Filter for **Needed** items.
   (b) Filter for items that are running low by filtering for **On Hand** < 2.

Chapter 27

Collaborating with Other Engineers

27.1 THE COLLABORATIVE DESIGN PROCESS

Engineering design is the process of devising an effective, efficient solution to a problem. The solution may take the form of a component, a system, or a process. Engineers generally solve problems by collaborating with others as members of a team. As a student, you will undoubtedly be asked to participate in collaborative projects with other students.

You may or may not have experience working on a team. If a team works together effectively, then more can be accomplished by the team than through any individual effort (or even the sum of individual efforts). If team members do not work together effectively, however, the group can become mired in power struggles and dissension. When this occurs, one of two things usually happens. Either the team makes little progress toward its goals, or a small subgroup of the team takes charge and does all of the work. Some guidelines for being an effective team member are presented at the end of this chapter, in the "Professional Success" section.

OBJECTIVES

After reading this chapter, you should be able to perform the following tasks

- Track revisions in an Excel document
- Share workbooks among team members
- Insert comments in an Excel document
- Transfer worksheet data to and from other applications
- Use a password to restrict ability to open a file
- Use a password to restrict ability to write to a file
- Use a password to restrict access to a worksheet

27.1.1 Microsoft Excel and Collaboration

The ability to work well on a team can best be learned by participating in a successful team effort. Microsoft Excel includes several tools that can help to solve one of the most burdensome technical tasks of group collaboration—the preparation of the team workbook. In the past, collaborative workbook preparation has been extremely difficult. The result has been that the task is usually assigned to one or two team members. New features of Microsoft Excel make it feasible for the whole team to participate in the composition and revision of a workbook. With Office 2007, the new Ribbon includes a *Review tab* that is all about working with others. Learning to use these features will require some time and practice on your team's part. The rewards, however, will be well worth the effort.

27.2   TRACKING CHANGES

One problem that arises in workbook preparation by a team is keeping track of revisions. For example, one team member may be given the task of revising a portion of the team project. After the revisions are made, the team will meet and approve some, or all, of the revisions. Then one of the team members will incorporate the accepted changes into the workbook.

Excel has a feature called *Tracking Changes* that will not only mark revisions, but will also keep track of who is making each revision. The worksheet may be printed showing both the original text and the revisions. Revisions may then be globally accepted or selectively accepted into the workbook.

27.2.1 Highlighting Changes

To activate the tracking changes feature, follow these steps:

1. Open the Highlight Changes dialog box (shown in Figure 27.1) using Ribbon options: **Review tab → Changes group → Track Changes drop-down menu → Highlight Changes ... button**. (Excel 2003: Tools → Track Changes → Highlight Changes.)

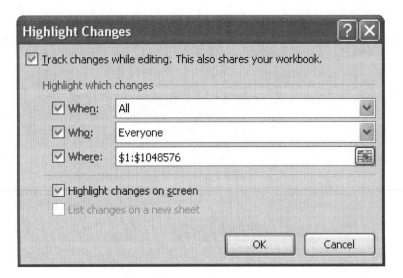

Figure 27.1   The Highlight Changes dialog box.

2. Check the **Track Changes while editing** box. This will make the workbook available to others (*shared*), and it will turn on *history tracking*. You will now have access to the next three boxes and drop-down lists, which allow you to limit the changes that are highlighted by time, user, and worksheet region.

3. Check the **When** box and select **All** from the drop-down list. All subsequent changes to the workbook will be tracked.

4. Check the **Who** box and select **Everyone** from the drop-down list to track changes by every user of the worksheet.

5. Check the **Where** box and use the **Jump to Worksheet** button to select the entire worksheet. (Select the entire worksheet by clicking the corner of the cell headings, between the A and 1 headings as illustrated in Figure 27.2.)

6. Check the **Highlight changes on screen** box so that all changes to the worksheet will be easy to see.

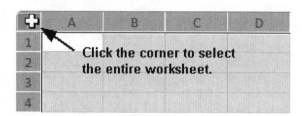

Figure 27.2 Selecting the entire worksheet.

NOTE: The alternative is to list changes on a new sheet. This can be useful when there are extensive changes.

7. Click **OK** to close the Highlight Changes dialog box.

Make a change on your worksheet and note what happens. Any modified cells are outlined in blue, and a small blue tab is placed in the upper left corner of the cell. These are called revision marks. (See Figure 27.3.)

	A	B	C	D	E	F	G	H
1	Body Mass Index (BMI) Calculations							
2								
3	Height (in)	Weight (lb)	BMI	Status			Status Codes	
4	62	136	24.9	Normal		0.0	Underweight	
5	74	195	25.0	Overweight		18.5	Normal	
6	68	155	23.6	Normal		25.0	Overweight	
7	71	130	18.1	Underweight		30.0	Obese	
8	65	160	26.6	Overweight				
9	58	114						
10	76	195	◄— Revision mark					
11								

Figure 27.3 Revision mark in cell B10.

27.2.2 Creating an Identity

As you review a document that other team members have revised, you can see who made the revision, the date and time of the revision, and the previous contents of the cell. The identity feature works only if each reviewer has provided an identity to the Excel application. To identify yourself to Excel, do the following:

1. Open the Excel Options dialog box shown in Figure 27.4: **Office button →
    Excel Options button**. (Excel 2003: Tools → Options.)
2. Use the **Popular** panel, and the **Personalize your copy of Microsoft
    Office** section. (Excel 2003: General tab.)
3. Enter your name in the **User name** box.
4. Click OK to close the Excel Options dialog box.

Your identity will now be attached to any revisions that you make to a worksheet. You can test the feature by making a change. If you move the mouse over the revision mark, a comment is displayed (shown in Figure 27.5) that indicates who made the change, and when.

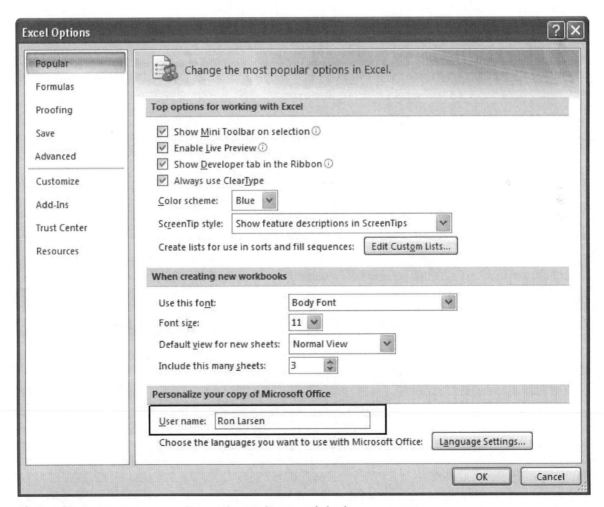

Figure 27.4 Identifying yourself using the Excel Options dialog box.

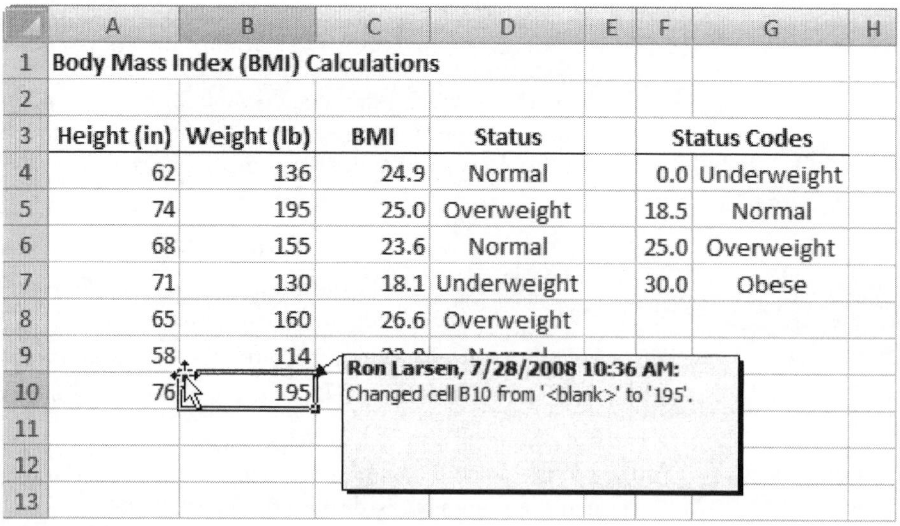

	A	B	C	D	E	F	G	H
1	Body Mass Index (BMI) Calculations							
2								
3	Height (in)	Weight (lb)	BMI	Status		Status Codes		
4	62	136	24.9	Normal		0.0	Underweight	
5	74	195	25.0	Overweight		18.5	Normal	
6	68	155	23.6	Normal		25.0	Overweight	
7	71	130	18.1	Underweight		30.0	Obese	
8	65	160	26.6	Overweight				
9	58	114						
10	76	195						
11								
12								
13								

Ron Larsen, 7/28/2008 10:36 AM:
Changed cell B10 from '<blank>' to '195'.

Figure 27.5 Example of a revision mark with information about who made the change, and when.

27.2.3 Incorporating or Rejecting Revisions

Revision marks are not wholly incorporated into the document until they are reviewed and then accepted or rejected. Revision marks can be reviewed by using the Accept or Reject Changes dialog box. To accept or reject changes, follow these steps:

1. Open the Select Changes to Accept or Reject dialog box (shown in Figure 27.6) using Ribbon options: **Review tab → Changes group → Track Changes drop-down menu → Accept/Reject Changes ... button**. (Excel 2003: Tools → Track Changes → Accept or Reject Changes.)

2. Check the **When** box and select **Not Yet Reviewed** from the drop-down list. This will allow you to review all new (not-yet-reviewed) changes.

3. Check the **Who** box and select **Everyone** from the drop-down list to see the changes made by all worksheet users.

4. Check the **Where** box and select the entire worksheet.

5. Click **OK** to close the Select Changes to Accept or Reject dialog box.

Select Changes to Accept or Reject

Which changes

☑ When: Not yet reviewed

☑ Who: Everyone

☑ Where: $1:$1048576

OK   Cancel

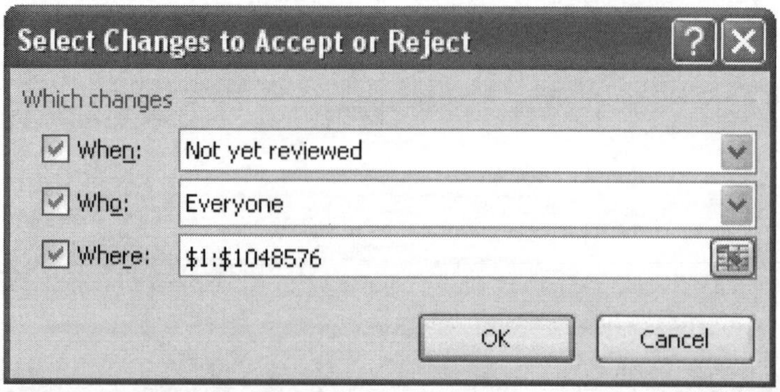

Figure 27.6 Select Changes to Accept or Reject dialog box.

Excel will now guide you through each selected revision and give you the opportunity to accept or reject the revision. The Accept or Reject Changes dialog box will appear, as shown in Figure 27.7. You will be guided through the revisions one at a time, unless you select Accept All or Reject All.

Accept or Reject Changes

Change 1 of 1 made to this document:

Ron Larsen, 7/28/2008 10:59 AM:

Changed cell B10 from '<blank>' to '195'.

| Accept | Reject | Accept All | Reject All | Close |

Figure 27.7   The Accept or Reject Changes dialog box.

27.3   ADDING COMMENTS TO A DOCUMENT

At times, a reviewer may want to attach notes or *comments* to a cell without changing the contents of the cell. To add a comment to a cell, follow this procedure:

1.   Select the cell that you want to comment on.
2.   Click the **New Comment** button on the Review tab: **Review tab → Comments group → New Comment button**. (Excel 2003: Insert → Comment.)
3.   Type in the text of the comment, then click outside the comment box when you are finished.

A cell that is attached to a comment will be marked with a small red tab in the upper right-hand corner of the cell (see cell B3 in Figure 27.8). When the mouse cursor is moved over the red tab, the comment will be displayed.

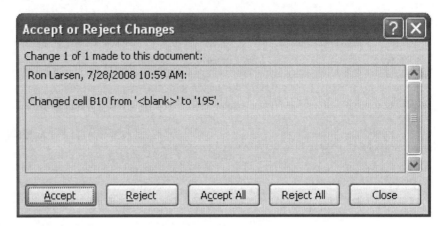

	A	B	C	D	E	F	G	H
1	Body Mass Index (BMI) Calculations							
2								
3	Height (in)	Weight (lb)	Dave Kuncicky: Should we be using metric units here?				Status Codes	
4	62	136				0.0	Underweight	
5	74	195				18.5	Normal	
6	68	155	23.6	Normal		25.0	Overweight	
7	71	130	18.1	Underweight		30.0	Obese	
8	65	160	26.6	Overweight				
9	58	114	23.8	Normal				
10	76	195	23.7	Normal				
11								

Figure 27.8   Example of a comment added to cell B3.

Displayed comments may be viewed, edited, or deleted. You can view comments one at a time by moving the mouse cursor over each comment tab (Figure 27.8), or you can also toggle the **Show All Comments** button on the Ribbon's Review tab to see all comments on a worksheet. (Excel 2003: **Show/Hide All Comments** button on the Reviewing toolbar.)

To edit or delete a displayed comment in Excel 2007, follow these stops:

1.   Click on the comment to select it.
2.   Use the **Edit Comment** or **Delete Comment** buttons on the Review tab.

In Excel 2003, use these steps (these steps work in Excel 2007, too):

1.   Right-click on the cell containing the comment.
2.   Select **Edit Comment** or **Delete Comment** options from the pop-up menu.

27.4   MAINTAINING SHARED WORKBOOKS

Excel provides a mechanism that allows several users to simultaneously *share* a workbook over a network. A shared workbook must reside in a shared folder on the network. Other access restrictions may apply, depending on your local network setup.

Once you are able to share a workbook, different users can view and modify the workbook at the same time. Sharing a workbook clearly requires the group to follow some protocol so that users do not overwrite one another's work. Sharing a workbook is most effective if simultaneous users edit different parts of the workbook. Excel can be set up to keep a history of changes to a shared workbook, and previous versions may be recalled if necessary.

27.4.1   Sharing a Workbook

Follow these steps to share a workbook:

1.   Click the **Share Workbook** button on the Review tab to open the Share Workbook dialog box (Figure 27.9): **Review tab → Changes group → Share Workbook button**. (Excel 2003: Tools → Share Workbook.)

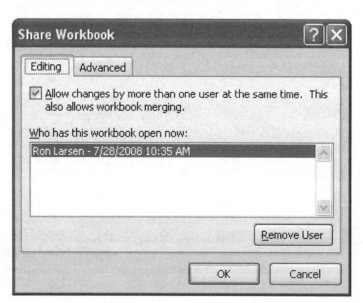

Figure 27.9   The Share Workbook dialog box.

2. Select the Editing tab.

3. Check the box labeled **Allow changes by more than one user at the same time**.

Once the workbook is shared, this tab can be used to see who is currently editing the workbook.

27.4.2 Keeping a Change History

Excel can keep a log of changes made by each user of a shared workbook. The log of changes is called a *change history*. To set the options for a change history, follow this procedure:

1. Click the Share Workbook button on the Review tab to open the Share Workbook dialog box (Figure 27.9): **Review tab → Changes group → Share Workbook button**. (Excel 2003: Tools → Share Workbook.)

2. Select the Advanced tab, as shown in Figure 27.10.

3. In the section labeled **Track Changes**, set the length of time to keep a change history.

If you decide not to keep a history of changes, select the **Track changes** option labeled **Don't keep change history**.

One reason to turn off the change history or to keep the time duration low is to limit the size of the workbook. A change history can significantly increase the disk space required

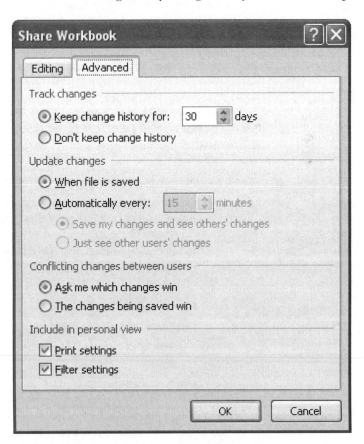

Figure 27.10   The Advanced tab on the Share Workbook dialog box.

to store a workbook. There is a trade-off between being cautious and limiting the storage requirements of the project. The use of the change-history feature is not a substitute for regularly backing up a workbook to some other medium, such as a removable disk or tape.

27.4.3 Managing Conflicts

If you are about to save a workbook, some of your changes may conflict with pending changes from another user. The **Conflicting changes between users** section of the Advanced tab allows you to specify how you want to resolve conflicts, if at all. If you choose the first option, **Ask me which changes win**, then the Resolve Conflicts dialog box will appear when you attempt to save the file.

You will be prompted to resolve each conflict. If you don't want to resolve conflicts when you save a shared workbook, then select the option labeled **The changes being saved win**. The last user to save conflicting changes wins.

27.4.4 Personal Views

The **Include in personal view** section of the Advanced tab allows you to use personal printer or filter settings. When the workbook is saved, a separate personal view is saved for each user.

27.4.5 Merging Workbooks

Group members do not always have access to the same network. One scenario that occurs when groups collaborate on a workbook is that each member takes a copy of the workbook home for the evening. Each group member works separately on the workbook, and later the workbooks are merged back into a single document.

Copies of a workbook can be revised and merged only if a change history is being maintained. Be sure to set a sufficient length of time for the change history so that the history doesn't expire before the workbook copies are merged. The number of days is set in the Share Workbook dialog box as shown in Figure 27.10.

Before you can merge workbooks in Excel 2007, you need to put the Compare and Merge Workbooks button on the Quick Access Toolbar with these steps (not needed in Excel 2003):

1. Click the **Customize Quick Access Toolbar** button (small down arrow) at the right side of the Quick Access Toolbar.
2. Select **More Commands . . .** from the Customize Quick Access Toolbar menu. The Excel Options dialog box, Customize panel will open as shown in Figure 27.11.
3. Select **Commands Not in the Ribbon** from the **Choose Commands from** drop-down list.
4. Select **Compare and Merge Workbooks** from the left selection list.
5. Click the **Add** button.
6. Click **OK** to close the Excel Options dialog box.

Once the **Compare and Merge Workbooks** button is available, follow these steps to merge several copies of a workbook:

1. Open the first copy and then click the **Compare and Merge Workbooks** button on the Quick Access Toolbar. (Excel 2003: Tools → Compare and Merge Workbooks.) You will be prompted to choose a file to merge.
2. Continue to merge files until all copies have been merged into one workbook.

After the workbooks have been merged, you will need to view the change history and selectively choose the changes that you want in the merged workbook.

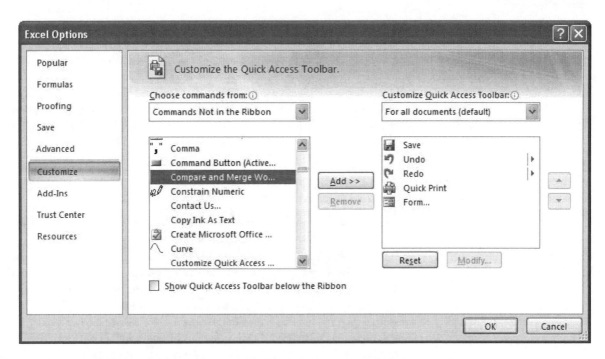

Figure 27.11   Adding the Compare and Merge Workbooks button to the Quick Access toolbar.

27.4.6 Restrictions for Shared Workbooks

Some features of Excel cannot be used while a workbook is being shared. However, all features can be used if the workbook has sharing turned off. The disadvantage of turning off sharing is that the change history is deleted. When a workbook is shared, a good rule of thumb is to use sound judgment, as not all worksheets or workbooks are meant to be shared. Here's a list of some of the features of Excel that cannot be used when sharing is in effect:

- Creation, modification, or deletion of passwords. Passwords should be set up before the workbook is shared.
- Deletion of worksheets.
- Insertion or modification of charts, pictures, or hyperlinks.
- Insertion or deletion of regions of cells. (Single rows or columns can be deleted.)
- Creation of data tables or pivot tables.
- Insertion of automatic subtotals.

27.5   PASSWORD PROTECTION

Several levels of *protection* exist for workbooks. Your personal file space may be protected by the network operating system. The folder in which your workbook resides may be protected. These methods are outside the scope of this section. The methods that are discussed here apply only to a single workbook or parts of a workbook.

The methods that follow, in and of themselves, will not prevent another user from copying your workbook; but one of the methods (open access) can prevent another user from viewing the copied workbook.

One way to limit access to a shared workbook is with *password protection*. A variety of password types will be discussed next. In every case, be sure to write down or memorize your password. If you lose a password, you will not be able to retrieve your work.

27.5.1 Open Protection

A password can be set that restricts a user from opening a file. This means that an unauthorized user cannot read or print the file by using Excel. This type of access is called *open access*, since it protects a file from being opened. A user will still be able to copy the file. The password protection for open access will also apply to the copied file.

NOTE: You cannot restrict open access on a shared workbook.

To set a password for open access, follow this procedure:

1. Choose Save As → Excel Workbook from the Office button: **Office button → Save As submenu → Excel Workbook option**. (Excel 2003: File → Save As.) The Save As dialog box will open.

2. Choose **Tools → General Options ...** from the Save As dialog box. The General Options dialog box will open, as shown in Figure 27.12.

3. Choose the **Always create backup** option. This option specifies that Excel should create a backup copy of your workbook every time it is saved. Unless you are extremely short of disk space, this is an excellent option!

4. To restrict others from opening your workbook file, type a password in the box labeled **Password to open,** as illustrated in Figure 27.12.

5. You will be prompted to confirm the password by entering it a second time (Figure 27.13.) Note that Excel uses case-sensitive passwords.

Hint: One of the most common reasons that a password seems to suddenly stop working is that you have the caps-lock key turned on.

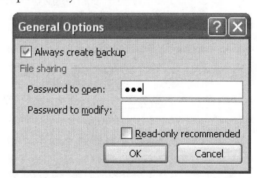

Figure 27.12 The General Options dialog box.

Figure 27.13 The Confirm Password dialog box.

27.5.2 Modify or Write Protection

There may be times when you want to allow others to read your workbook (read access), but you do not want anyone to be able to save changes to the workbook. This type of protection is called *modify access* or *write access* because others are not allowed to write the changed file to a storage device. To set a modify password, follow these steps:

1. Choose Save As → Excel Workbook from the Office button: **Office button → Save As sub-menu → Excel Workbook option**. (Excel 2003: File → Save As.) The Save As dialog box will open.
2. Choose **Tools → General Options ...** from the Save As dialog box. The General Options dialog box will open, as shown in Figure 27.12.
3. Type a password in the box labeled **Password to modify** (see Figure 27.12).
4. You will be prompted to confirm the password by entering it a second time.

The next time you attempt to open the file, the Password dialog box will appear, as depicted in Figure 27.14. You will be prompted for a password if you want to open the file for write access. A password is not needed to open the file for reading only.

Figure 27.14 The Password dialog is used to access a password-protected workbook.

NOTE: A user can open a write-protected file as a read-only file and then save it under a different name. The new file can be modified by the user without a password. So, modify access protects your workbook file from changes, but does not protect you from having others use your work.

27.5.3 Sheet Protection

Protection can be finely tuned. Once you have completed part of a worksheet, you may want to protect it merely to prevent yourself from inadvertently modifying that section. One example of the use of *sheet protection* is to lock cells that contain formulas, while allowing cells that contain input data to be modified.

By default, all cells are locked (but locking cells has no effect until the worksheet is password protected). Before activating worksheet protection, you must unlock the cells that you want to be available after the worksheet is protected. The general procedure for locking down a worksheet is as follows:

1. Unlock the cells that you wish to make available after the worksheet is locked.
2. Protect the worksheet.

For example, Figure 27.15 shows a worksheet that can be used to solve quadratic equations. The formulas for the two solutions are in cells C9 and C10. The user inputs the three coefficients a, b, and c in cells A2, B2, and C2, respectively. We need to unlock

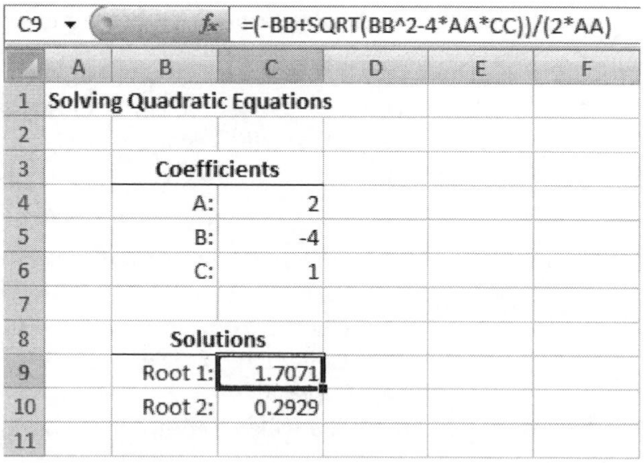

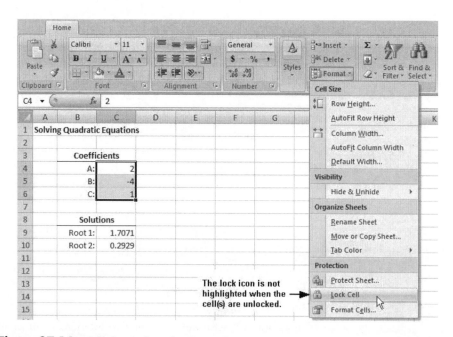

Figure 27.15   Worksheet for solving quadratic equations.

the cells containing the coefficients so that they can still be used after locking the worksheet.

NOTE: The cells holding the coefficient values have been named AA, BB, and CC to make the formulas easier to read. CC was used rather than C because C is a reserved variable name in Excel; it stands for "column."

Follow this procedure to unlock a region of cells within a workbook:

1.   Select the cells to be unlocked, cells C4:C6 in this example. (Remember: All cells are locked, by default.)
2.   Unlock the cells by clicking the Lock Cell toggle button as illustrated in Figure 27.16: **Home tab → Cells group → Format drop-down menu → Lock Cell toggle button**. (Excel 2003: Format → Cells → Protection tab → Clear the Locked checkbox.)

Figure 27.16   Unlocking selected cells.

Whether the cells are locked or unlocked makes no difference until the worksheet is protected. To activate worksheet protection, follow these steps:

1. Activate worksheet protection using one of these methods:
    a. Use Ribbon options: **Home tab → Cells group → Format drop-down menu → Protect Sheet . . . option**.
    b. Right-click on the worksheet tab and select **Protect Sheet ...**
    c. Excel 2003: Tools → Protection → Protect Sheet.

The Protect Sheet dialog box will be displayed (Figure 27.17).

2. Verify that the **Protect worksheet and contents of locked cells** box is checked.
3. Enter a password if you wish. If you enter a password,
    *   You will be prompted to confirm it.
    *   You will neezd to use this password to make changes to the worksheet in the future.

Figure 27.17   The Protect Sheet dialog box.

4. In the **Allow all users of this worksheet to** list,
    a. Check the box labeled Select unlocked cells
    b. Clear all other check boxes
5. Click **OK** to close the Protect Sheet dialog box. (You will be prompted to confirm the password if you entered one.)

After protecting the worksheet you can enter values for the coefficients in cells C4:C6 and the calculated results will change. However, you cannot select or modify any other cells.

You might want to allow users to **Select locked cells** as well (Figure 27.17). There are pros and cons to this:

*   PRO: Users can click on the cells containing formulas to verify the math.
*   CON: Users can get frustrated because they can select cells, but are not allowed to modify them.

27.6   IMPORTING AND EXPORTING DATA FROM EXTERNAL FILE FORMATS

One problem of working as part of a team is that team members may use different application software. In addition, a large and complex project may require the team to use several software packages, such as Word, Access, and HTML. You may have to move data from one application to another in the process of completing a project.

Excel provides several methods for importing data. In this section, we will discuss two methods for importing external files: File Open and the Text Import Wizard.

- File Open—used when Excel has built-in methods for importing the type of file you are using.
- Text Import—used when you need to get basic text loaded into an Excel workbook.

Whenever Excel has built-in methods for importing the type of file you are using, you should use the File Open method to preserve as much of the original content as possible.

27.6.1   Importing Data Using the File Open Option

A number of types of file formats may be imported directly into Excel. To import files, follow these steps:

1. Open the Open dialog box (see Figure 27.18) from the Office button as: **Office button → Open button**. (Excel 2003: File → Open.)
2. Use the **Files of type** drop-down menu to select the file name extension of the file you want to import into Excel.

A few of the importable file types are shown in Figure 27.18. These include text files, XML files, Microsoft Access files, dBase files, etc.

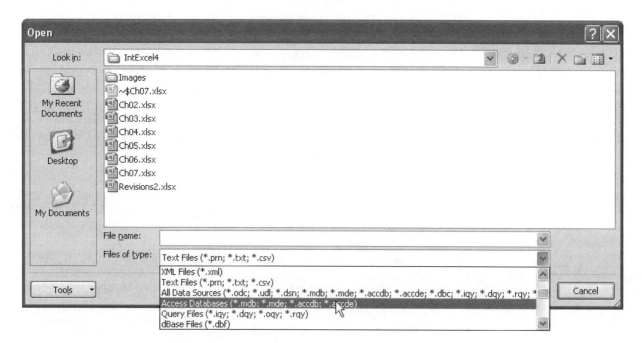

Figure 27.18   The Files of type drop-down menu.

You may open and view an external file type within Excel. If you modify the file, Excel will ask if you want to save the file in its original format or in Excel format.

- If the file is saved in Excel format, then the external program (e.g., dBase) will not be able to view the changes.
- If the file is saved in the external format (e.g., dBase), then some Excel formatting may be lost. For example, formulas and macros may not be translated into the external format.

Excel supports a wide range of file formats, but not all. When Excel does not support the file format used by your other software, sometimes a text file can be a useful intermediary.

27.6.2 Importing Text Data by Using the Text Import Wizard

Most applications will let you export data (using the **Save As** menu item) as tab- or space-delimited text. (A *delimiter* is a character that separates data values.) In addition, you may produce data from a computer program that you have written. In either case, the *Text Import Wizard* helps you align and import the data. When you import a text file you will get alphanumeric characters only. Formatting, colors, font size, etc., cannot be imported by using this method.

NOTE: A *Wizard* is a multi-step dialog box that leads the user through a multi-step process. Most of the Excel 2003 wizards are gone in Excel 2007, but the Text Import Wizard is still used.

To demonstrate how to import a text file, we created a text file using a text editor (Notepad in this example, but WordPad or Word could also be used). The contents of the text file are shown in Figure 27.19. On each row the values have been separated by tabs.

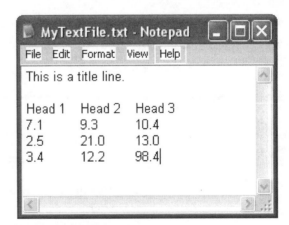

Figure 27.19   Creating the MyTextFile.txt file using Notepad.

We begin the text import process by attempting to open the file in Excel.

1. Open the Open dialog box: **Office button → Open button**. (Excel 2003: File → Open.)
2. Select **Text Files** in the **Files of type** drop-down menu (see Figure 27.18).
3. Browse for the MyTextFile.txt file.
4. Click **Open** to attempt to open the file.

Excel will recognize that it is dealing with a text file and will automatically start the Text Import Wizard. Step 1 is illustrated in Figure 27.20.

To import the file into Excel using the Text Import Wizard, follow these steps:

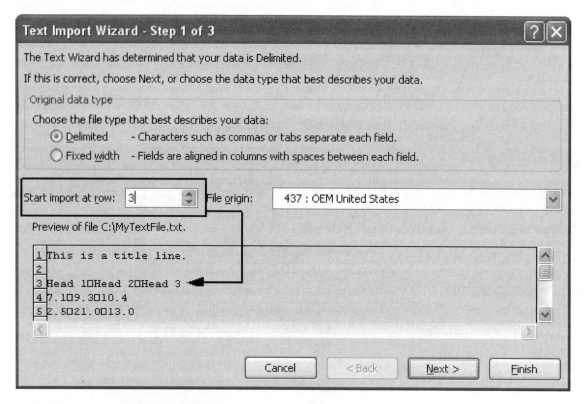

Figure 27.20   Text Import Wizard, Step 1 of 3.

Text Import Wizard, Step 1 of 3

1. Indicate the type of data in the file. In this example, the data has been delimited with tabs.
    a. Delimited—values are separated by delimiters (such as the tabs we used).
    b. Fixed width—each column of values has the same number of characters.
2. Decide where you want Excel to begin importing the data. Many text files have some title text at the top of the file. Importing text files is cleaner when only the data is imported. We will skip the title line and begin the import at row 3.
3. Click **Next >** to go to Step 2 of 3, as shown in Figure 27.21.

Text Import Wizard, Step 2 of 3

1. Select the type(s) of delimiters used in the file. In this example, only tabs were used.
2. Click **Next >** to go to Step 3 of 3, as shown in Figure 27.22.

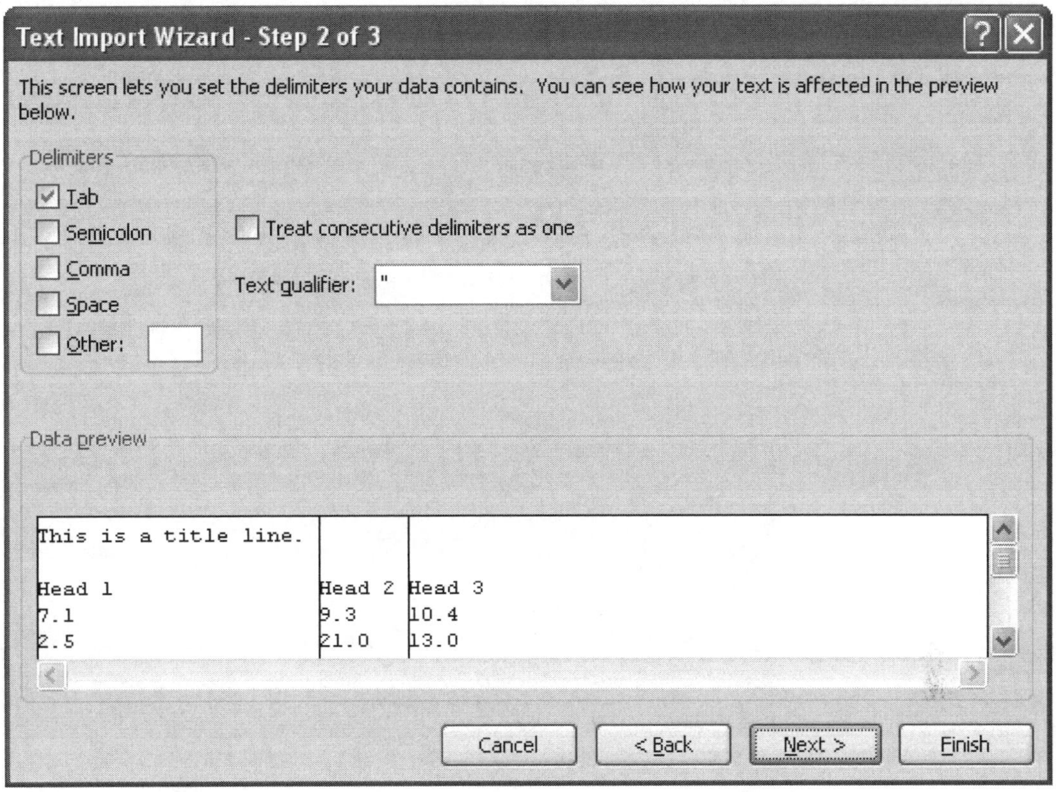

Figure 27.21   Text Import Wizard, Step 2 of 3.

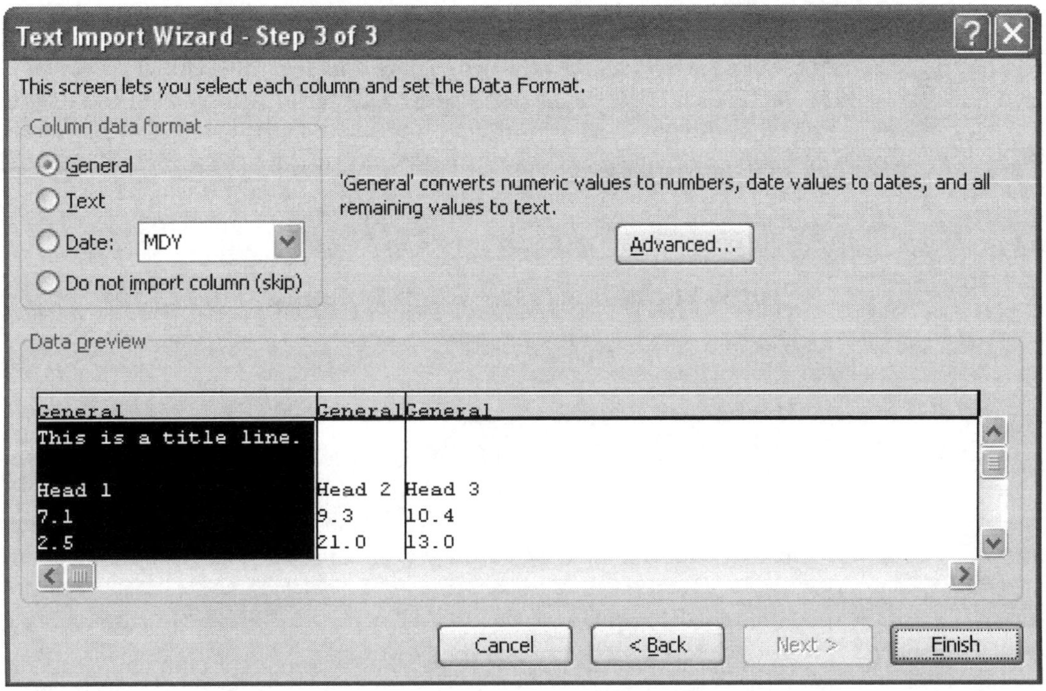

Figure 27.22   Text Import Wizard, Step 3 of 3.

Text Import Wizard, Step 2 of 3

1. Verify the data format that will be used to import each column of data. In this example, the General format will be used. If you need to change a column data format:
    a. Select the column. (The selected column is shown in black with white text.)
    b. Choose a **Column data format** from the options list.

2. Click the **Finish** button to import the data into Excel.

The imported data are shown in Figure 27.23. Notice that the title line was not imported because we asked that the import start in row 3 of the text file (in step 1 of the Text Import Wizard).

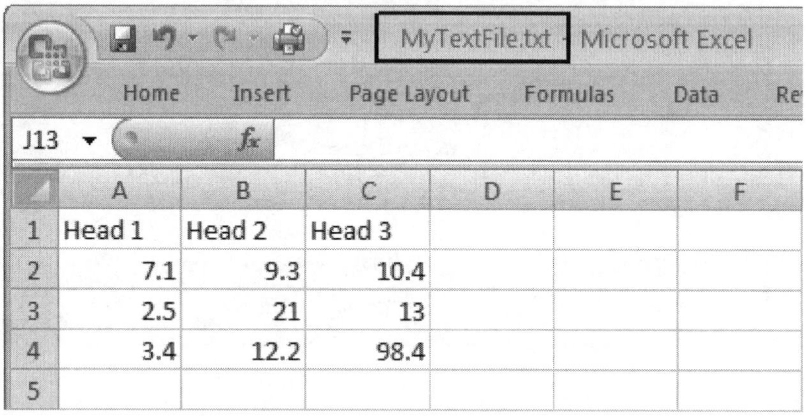

Figure 27.23   The imported text data.

Also, note that the file name shown in the Title bar in Figure 27.23 is still MyTextFile.txt. Excel does not automatically change the file extension to .xlsx. You should save the worksheet with the .xlsx extension to ensure that Excel features (e.g., formatting, formulas) are saved correctly. Excel will display a warning message if you attempt to save the worksheet with the .txt file extension.

Professional Success—Team Meeting Guidelines

Read the following job listings:

Mechanical Engineer

We have an immediate need for an engineer to interface an engineering automation & optimization environment with a variety of CAD and CAE systems ... B.S./M.S. in mechanical engineering ... Good communication skills and *a strong interest in interacting with customers in problem-solving situations are required.*

Electrical Engineer

Perform audio subsystem validation to verify prototypes throughout the product-development program cycle. *Must work well in a team environment.*

Aerospace Engineer

Applicant selected may be subject to a government security investigation and must meet eligibility requirements for access to classified information. *Must be a team player* and possess excellent written and oral communication skills.

Industrial Engineer

Investigate manufacturing processes in continuous-improvement environment; recommend refinements. Design process equipment to improve processes. Must be highly skilled at planning/managing and be *able to sell ideas to team members* and company management.

Extrusion Engineer

This manufacturer of fiber optics is seeking an Extrusion Engineer who can handle the majority of the technical issues in production. The successful candidate must be *able to work with other disciplines in a team atmosphere* of mutual support.

Software Engineer

Looking for a well-rounded software engineer with strong experience in object-oriented design and GUI development. Must be a highly motivated self-starter who *works well in a team environment.*

All of the positions listed were taken from actual job postings. What do the position announcements have in common? Teamwork! The ability of an engineer to work well in the team environment has as much to do with professional success as do scientific and technical skills. Few engineering accomplishments are produced in isolation. The following guidelines may help as you begin to conduct and participate in team meetings:

Decision Making

At first, attempt to make decisions by consensus. If that fails due to a single member who continually disagrees, then move to a consensus minus one approach. If consensus minus one fails, then move to a majority rule. Be aware that, as you lose the consensus of team members, the ability of the team to succeed is weakened. Time spent on gaining consensus by winning all team members over to an idea is time well spent!

Confidentiality

Respect the other members' right to confidentiality. Lay ground rules about what material, if any, is to be treated confidentially. In the world of business and government contracts, you may be asked to sign a confidentiality agreement. These legal documents specify which of your employer's materials are protected from disclosure.

Attention

Actively listen—ask questions or request clarification of other members' comments. Create a summary of important points that other team members have made. Acknowledge that you have understood. Try not to mentally rehearse what you are going to say while others are speaking.

Preparation

Be adequately prepared for the meeting.

Punctuality

Be on time. If you are 10 minutes late and there are six other members in the group, then you are wasting one person-hour of time!

Ensure Active Contribution

If not all team members are contributing and actively participating, then something is wrong with the group process. Stop the meeting and take time to get everyone involved before proceeding.

Record Keeping

Someone on the team should keep records of team meetings.

Flexibility

One of the aspects of working on a team is that you win some and you lose some. Not every one of your ideas will be accepted by the group. Be prepared to think of creative solutions that every team member can accept.

Dynamics

Help improve relationships among the team members. Do not dominate the meeting or let another member dominate the meeting. If this cannot be resolved within the group, enlist the help of an outside facilitator. A facilitator is a nongroup member who does not contribute to the content of the group discussion, but helps smooth the group process. One of the roles of a facilitator is to prevent any single team member from dominating the others.

Quorum

Establish at the onset of meetings what a team quorum will be. Do not hold team meetings unless a quorum is present.

APPLICATION

APPLICATION—USING TEAMWORK TO SOLVE A PROBLEM

Three students—Sara, Justin, and Allison—were assigned a group project. Their assignment was to determine the energy required to pump water through a packed-bed filter for a local industrial facility (see Figure 27.24).

Here's what the team knew:

- Water flows at a rate of 400 liters per minute from a holding tank that is open to the atmosphere (pressure at point a = 1 atm = 1.01×10^5 Pa) and into a centrifugal pump (25 HP, 60% efficiency).
- The water then flows through the packed-bed filter and into an elevated, pressurized storage tank (pressure at point b = 3.00×10^5 Pa).

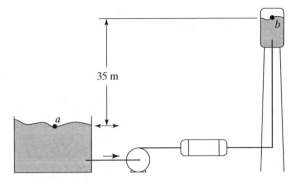

Figure 27.24   Water pumped through a packed-bed filter.

- The elevation change between the water level in the open tank (point a) and the water level in the pressurized tank (point b) is 35 m.
- The equation used to solve problems of this type is called the mechanical energy balance equation and is shown in Figure 27.25.
- The pump energy term on the left side of the equation represents the energy added to the system by the pump [expressed in *head* (height) of fluid—civil-engineering style].
- The terms on the right side represent the energy required to change the pressure of the fluid, to lift the fluid from H_a to H_b (potential energy), to accelerate the fluid from V_a to V_b and to overcome friction (F). The group's task is to find F, which can be pretty significant with a packed bed in the flow line.

$\dfrac{\eta W_p}{g}$ =	$\dfrac{(P_b - P_a)}{\rho g}$ +	$(H_b - H_a)$ +	$\dfrac{1}{2g}\left(\alpha_b V_b^2 - \alpha_a V_a^2\right)$ +	F
pump energy term	pressure energy term	potential energy term	acceleration term	friction term

Figure 27.25   Mechanical energy balance.

The team devised the following strategy to solve the problem:

1. The first thing they did was to throw out the acceleration term, since the fluid velocity at the surface of each tank (at points a and b) is very small. When those small velocities are squared, the acceleration term will be insignificant.
2. That left the pump energy term, the pressure energy term, and the potential energy term.
3. The students decided to each take one piece of the equation. They each solved a piece of the larger problem in a separate workbook. Then they combined their results by linking to each workbook to find F. Sara took the pump term, Justin took the pressure term, and Allison took the potential energy term.

Sara's Part

Sara's part was the most difficult. She was to find the pump energy term, or $\dfrac{\eta W_p}{g}$.

W_p is the energy per unit mass to the pump (usually from a motor), and is ηW_p the energy per unit mass from the pump to the fluid. Sara knew that the efficiency, η, is 60% or 0.60.

But she didn't know the energy per unit mass to the pump, W_p, She did know the power rating of the pump. Power is related to through the mass flow rate through the pump:

$$Power = m_{flow} W_p$$

Mass flow rate is related to the stated volumetric flow rate through the fluid density,

$$m_{flow} = V_{flow}\, \rho.$$

The acceleration due to gravity $g = 9.8$ m/sec^2 at sea level. So Sara developed her worksheet, which looked like Figure 27.26. Sara saved her worksheet with the name PumpEnergy.xlsx.

	A	B	C	D	E
1	Pump Term				
2		Power:	25	HP	
3		η:	0.60		
4		V flow:	400	liters/min	
5		ρ:	1000	kg/m^3	
6		g:	9.8	m/sec^2	
7					
8	Converting to SI units				
9		Power:	18642.5	Joules/sec	
10		η:	0.60		
11		V flow:	0.00667	m^3/sec	
12		ρ:	1000	kg/m^3	
13		g:	9.8	m/sec^2	
14					
15	Calculated Values				
16		m flow:	6.667	kg/sec	
17		Wp:	2796.4	Joules/kg	
18					
19		Pump Term:	171.2	J s^2 / m kg = m	
20					

Figure 27.26   Sara's worksheet to find the pump energy term.

The equations in Sara's worksheet are as follows:

C9:	=C2*745.7	(the constant is 745.7 Watts/HP)
C11:	=C4/1000/60	(the 1000 converts liters m^3 to and the 60 converts minutes to seconds)
C16:	=C11*C12	(density times volumetric flow rate)
C17:	=C9/C16	(pump power rating divided by mass flow rate)
C19:	=C10*C17/C13	$\left(\dfrac{\eta\, W_p}{g}\right)$

Justin's Part

Justin's spreadsheet is a bit simpler, since there were fewer conversions and calculations required. He was to find the pressure–energy term = $(P_b - P_a)/p.g$. Justin's worksheet is shown in Figure 27.27. Justin saved his worksheet with the name PressureEnergy.xlsx.

The equation in Justin's worksheet is

C7: =(C3-C2)/(C4*C5)

	A	B	C	D	E
1	Pressure Term				
2		P_a:	1.01E+05	Pa = n/m^2	
3		P_b:	3.00E+05	Pa = n/m^2	
4		ρ:	1000	kg/m^3	
5		g:	9.8	m/sec^2	
6					
7		Pressure Term:		20.3 J s^2 / m kg = m	
8					

Figure 27.27 Justin's worksheet finds the pressure energy term.

Allison's Part

Allison's task was the easiest of all. She was to find the potential energy term $H_b - H_a$ Allison's worksheet is shown in Figure 27.28. Allison saved her worksheet with the name Potential.xlsx.

The equation in Allison's worksheet is

C5: C3-C2

	A	B	C	D	E
1	Potential Energy Term				
2		H_a:	0	m	
3		H_b:	35	m	
4					
5	Potential Energy Term:		35	m	
6					

Figure 27.28 Allison's worksheet finds the potential energy term.

Combining the Results

Once each of the members had completed the assigned portion, the group got together and quickly finished the project. They created a summary workbook and created links to cells in their individual worksheets. Figure 27.29 shows the results.

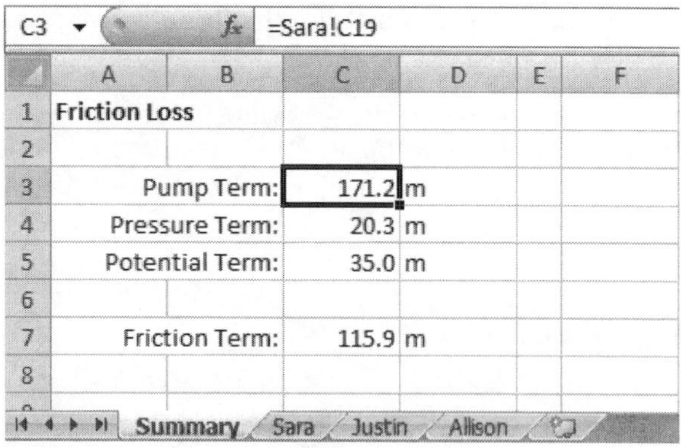

Figure 27.29 Summary worksheet used to find the friction term.

Sara combined all of their worksheets into a single workbook. The links that refer to other worksheets are shown next.

C3: =Sara!C19
C4: =Justin!C7
C5: =Allison!C5
C7: =C3-C4-C5

NOTE: The external links can also refer to separate workbooks. The format for a remote cell reference is the workbook file name in square brackets, then worksheet name followed by an exclamation point, followed by the cell number.

```
[FileName]SheetName!CellRef
```

If a reference is made to a workbook in another directory, then the file name must contain the full pathname.

While this is a very simple example of using a spreadsheet to collaborate on a group assignment, it does illustrate how easily the results from different members can be combined to complete a project.

KEY TERMS

change history	open protection	tab-delimited text
comment	password protection	Text Import Wizard
delimiter	protection	tracking changes
history tracking	revision mark	write access
locked cells	shared workbook	write protection
modify access	sheet protection	
open access	space-delimited text	

Summary

Tracking Changes

Identifying Yourself to Microsoft Office

1. Open the Excel Options dialog box: **Office button → Excel Options button**.

2. Use the **Popular** panel, and the **Personalize your copy of Microsoft Office** section.

3. Enter your name in the User name box.

4. Click **OK** to close the Excel Options dialog box.

Activating Change Tracking

1. Open the Highlight Changes dialog box: **Review tab → Changes group → Track Changes drop-down menu → Highlight Changes ... button**.

2. Check the **Track Changes while editing** box.

3. Check the **When** box and select **All**.

4. Check the **Who** box and select **Everyone**.

5. Check the **Where** box and select the entire worksheet.

6. Check the **Highlight changes on screen** box.

7. Click **OK**.

Incorporating or Rejecting Revisions

1. Open the Select Changes to Accept or Reject dialog box: **Review tab → Changes group → Track Changes drop-down menu → Accept/ Reject Changes ... button**.

2. Check the **When** box and select **Not Yet Reviewed**.

3. Check the **Who** box and select **Everyone**.

4. Check the **Where** box and select the entire worksheet.

5. Click **OK** to close the Select Changes to Accept or Reject dialog box. The Accept or Reject Changes dialog box will open.

6. Accept or reject each change as it is presented, or use the **Accept All** or **Reject All** buttons to process all changes at once.

Adding a Comment to a Cell

1. Select the cell that you want to comment on.

2. Click the **New Comment** button on the Review tab: **Review tab → Comments group → New Comment button**.

3. Type in the text of the comment. Then click outside the comment box when you are finished.

Sharing a Workbook

1. Click the Share Workbook button to open the Share Workbook dialog box: **Review tab → Changes group → Share Workbook button**.

2. Select the Editing tab.

3. Check the box labeled **Allow changes by more than one user at the same time**.

Setting Open Access Protection

Open access protection requires a password to open a workbook.

1. Choose Save As → Excel Workbook from the Office button: **Office button → Save As submenu → Excel Workbook option**.

2. Choose **Tools → General Options ...** from the Save As dialog box. The General Options dialog box will open.

3. Type a password in the box labeled **Password to open**.

4. Confirm the password.

Setting Modify or Write Access Protection

Modify or write access protection requires a password to save changes to a workbook.

1. Choose Save As → Excel Workbook from the Office button: **Office button → Save As submenu → Excel Workbook option**.

2. Choose **Tools → General Options . . .** from the Save As dialog box. The General Options dialog box will open.

3. Type a password in the box labeled **Password to modify**.

4. Confirm the password.

Worksheet Protection

The general procedure for locking down a worksheet is as follows:

1. Unlock the cells that are to be available after the worksheet is locked.

2. Protect the worksheet.

Unlocking Cells

1. Select the cells to be unlocked.

2. Unlock the cells by clicking the Lock Cell toggle button: **Home tab → Cells group → Format drop-down menu → Lock Cell toggle button**.

Protect Worksheet

1. Right-click on the worksheet tab and select **Protect Sheet ...** The Protect Sheet dialog box will be displayed.

2. Verify that the **Protect worksheet and contents of locked cells** box is checked.

3. Enter a password if you wish.

4. Set desired access properties in the **Allow all users of this worksheet to** list.

5. Click **OK**.

Text Import Wizard

1. Open the Open dialog box: **Office button → Open button**.

2. Select **Text Files** in the **Files of type** drop-down menu.

3. Browse for the text file.

4. Click **Open** to attempt to open the file. The Text Import Wizard will open.

Text Import Wizard, Step 1 of 3

1. Indicate the type of data in the file.
   (a) Delimited
   (b) Fixed width

2. Decide on the row into which you want Excel to begin importing the data.

3. Click **Next >**.

Text Import Wizard, Step 2 of 3

1. Select the type(s) of delimiters used in the file.
2. Click **Next >**.

Text Import Wizard, Step 3 of 3

1. Verify the data format that will be used to import each column of data. If you need to change a column data format,
    (a) Select the column.
    (b) Choose a **Column data format** from the options list.
2. Click the **Finish** button to import the data into Excel.

Problems

1. Practice merging workbooks with the following steps:
    (a) Create a workbook with the data shown in Figure 27.3.
    (b) Make two copies of the workbook.
    (c) Make changes to each of the three documents.
    (d) Merge the revised documents into a single document by opening the copy of the shared workbook into which you want to merge changes from another workbook file on disk.
    (e) Merge the workbooks.
    (f) Work through the process of accepting and rejecting the revisions.

2. Consider how passwords can be used to protect your Excel workbooks:
    (a) Do the password-protection mechanisms discussed in this chapter prevent another student from making a copy of your Excel workbook? If so, which ones?
    (b) Do any of the protection methods presented in the chapter prevent someone from printing your document without knowing the password? If so, which ones?

3. Turn sharing on and create a change history for a workbook. Then turn sharing off and see if the change history is actually deleted.

4. Set the change-history timer in the Share Workbook dialog box for one day. Wait more than 24 hours and see if the history really expires.

5. Create three workbooks, one for each of Sara's, Justin's, and Allison's parts of the Pump application in this chapter. Create a fourth, summary workbook that references cells in the other three workbooks and produces the final result (the friction term).

6. Create the quadratic equation solving tool shown in Figure 27.15. Then
    • Unlock the cells containing the coefficients.
    • Protect the worksheet so that only the cells containing the three coefficients are available.

Use your worksheet to find solutions to the following quadratic equations:
    (a) $2x^2 - 4x + 1 = 0$ (Solution shown in Figure 27.30)
    (b) $4x^2 - 5x + 1 = 0$
    (c) $4x^2 - 8x - + = 0$

	A	B	C	D	E	F
1	**Solving Quadratic Equations**					
2						
3		**Coefficients**				
4		A:	2		multiplies x^2	
5		B:	-4		multiplies x	
6		C:	1		constant	
7						
8		**Solutions**				
9		Root 1:	1.7071			
10		Root 2:	0.2929			
11						

Figure 27.30   Quadratic equation solving tool.

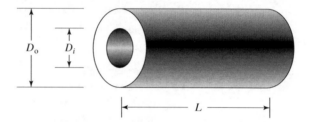

Figure 27.31   Schematic of the cylinder.

7.   Delegating assignments to team members and then recombining the individual results to create the final product takes some practice, but it can work well if all do their part. As a practice problem, work with two other people to solve this problem: Find the total surface area of a hollow cylinder (Figure 27.31).

	A	B	C	D	E	F	G	H
1	**Surface Area of a Hollow Cylinder**							
2								
3	Outside Diameter:							
4	Inside Diameter:							
5	Length:							
6								
7								
8		Outside Surface Area:				<< Team Member 1		
9								
10								
11								
12		Inside Surface Area:				<< Team Member 2		
13								
14								
15								
16		Total End Area:				<< Team Member 3		
17								
18								

Figure 27.32   The labeled worksheet, before any formulas have been entered.

First, create the worksheet shown in Figure 27.32. There are no formulas in this worksheet, just labels (for now).

Once the labeled worksheet has been created, share the workbook so that it can be used by more than one person at a time. Next, save the workbook with three different names, one for each team member. Then have each team member add a formula to his or her own worksheet, as follows:

Team Member 1: Cell D8   = PI()*C3*C5
Team Member 2: Cell D12   = PI()*C4*C5
Team Member 3: Cell D16   = 2*PI()*((C3/2)^2 − (C4/2)^2)

NOTE: None of the formulas will return a numeric result yet, because the dimensions of the cylinder have not been specified. The team members can test their own portions with the following test dimensions if they wish:

$$\text{Test dimensions: } D_o = 3 \quad D_i = 1 \quad L = 7$$

After each team member has added a formula to his or her own worksheet, merge the three worksheets. Then, in the merged workbook, enter the last formula to cell G3 (=D8+D12+D16) to add the area calculated by each team member.

Finally, enter the test dimensions in cells C3:C5, and see if all of the pieces came together correctly. The result is shown in Figure 27.33.

	A	B	C	D	E	F	G	H
1	Surface Area of a Hollow Cylinder							
2								
3		Outside Diameter:	3					
4		Inside Diameter:	1			Total Area:	100.5	
5		Length:	7					
6								
7								
8		Outside Surface Area:		66.0		<< Team Member 1		
9								
10								
11								
12		Inside Surface Area:		22.0		<< Team Member 2		
13								
14								
15								
16		Total End Area:		12.6		<< Team Member 3		
17								
18								

Figure 27.33 Combining workbooks to calculate the surface area of a hollow cylinder.

Chapter 28

Excel and the World Wide Web

28.1 ENGINEERING AND THE INTERNET

The *Internet* is one of the primary means of communication for scientists and engineers. Correspondence through electronic mail, the transfer of data and software via electronic file transfer, and research by using online search engines and databases are everyday tasks for engineers. The *World Wide Web* (*WWW* or simply *Web*) is a collection of technologies for publishing, sending, and obtaining information by using the Internet. Using the Internet requires every engineering student to learn two new essential skills. First, every student must gain fluency in searching, locating, and retrieving relevant technical information from the Web. Second, every engineering student must learn how to post written documents to the Web. The ability to present technical results via the Web is an essential communication skill for modern engineers.

OBJECTIVES

After reading this chapter, you should be able to perform the following tasks:

- Access the World Wide Web from within an Excel worksheet.
- Retrieve files from HTTP servers into a local worksheet.
- Use the Web Query feature to import Excel data from the Internet.
- Create hyperlinks in a worksheet.
- Convert Excel documents to HTML.

Professional Success

The World Wide Web holds a wealth of information about your new profession. Take some time to visit the professional societies that represent your discipline. The following URLs represent a few of the national and international organizations that are online:

Accreditation Board for Engineering and Technology (ABET)	www.abet.org
American Institute of Aeronautics and Astronautics (AIAA)	www.aiaa.org
American Institute of Chemical Engineers (AICHE)	www.aiche.org
American Society of Civil Engineers (ASCE)	www.asce.org
American Society for Engineering Education (ASEE)	asee.org
American Society of Mechanical Engineers (ASME)	www.asme.org
American Society of Naval Engineers (ASNE)	www.navalengineers.org
Engineers Without Borders (EWB)	www.ewb-usa.org
Institute of Electrical and Electronics Engineers (IEEE)	www.ieee.org
National Society of Black Engineers (NSBE)	www.nsbe.org
National Society of Professional Engineers (NSPE)	www.nspe.org
Society of Women Engineers (SWE)	society of women engineers. swe.org

28.2 ACCESSING THE WORLD WIDE WEB FROM WITHIN EXCEL

To access the Internet from within Excel, your computer must be connected to the Internet. If you are in a computer lab at school, then the computer may be connected to a local area network (LAN) through a network card. The LAN may or may not be connected to the Internet. Ask your lab manager or instructor for details. During the rest of this chapter, it is assumed that your computer is connected to the Internet.

Excel works well with the Web. Here are some basic Web-related tasks that will be covered in this chapter:

- Creating hyperlinks in Excel worksheets.
- Using Excel-related websites.
- Getting data from the Web into Excel.

- Opening Excel files stored on the Web.
- Copying and pasting Web data into an Excel file.
- Using a Query to obtain Web data.
- Saving an Excel worksheet as a Web document.

28.3   CREATING HYPERLINKS IN A WORKSHEET

A *hyperlink*, or simply *link*, can be thought of as a pointer to another location. When you click on a hyperlink, the contents at that location are immediately displayed. The hyperlink may point to

- A cell in another worksheet in your Excel workbook.
- Another Excel worksheet on your local computer.
- A document from another application, such as Microsoft Word.
- A Web-based file stored on the other side of the planet.
- A remote document that is retrieved from the world wide web using a transfer protocol.

You are probably familiar with the "http" that precedes most Web addresses; it stands for *hypertext transfer protocol* and is one of the methods used to transfer information around the Web. The "http" is in web addresses (aka *URLs*, or *uniform resource locators*) to tell the browsers how to transfer the contents, but if you leave it out, modern browsers will determine an appropriate transfer protocol. Commonly used transfer protocols include

- http—hypertext transfer protocol, for web pages.
- ftp—file transfer protocol, for file exchange.
- smtp—simple mail transfer protocol, for email.

28.3.1   Typing a Web Address in a Cell

The simplest way to insert a hyperlink in an Excel worksheet is to type a Web address in a cell. Excel will recognize the syntax and create the hyperlink. As an example, enter the Web address for Engineers Without Borders, **www.ewb-usa.org,** in a cell, as shown in Figure 28.1. When you move the mouse over the hyperlink, the "finger" pointer is displayed. If you click on the link, a browser will open to display the Engineers Without Borders - USA website so that you can read about what engineering students are doing to improve people's lives around the world. (There are EWB organizations around the world; check out **www.ewb-international.org** to see a list of countries.)

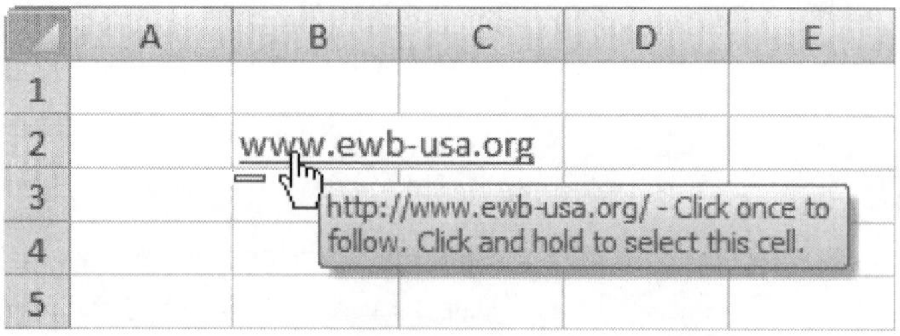

Figure 28.1   Inserting a hyperlink in a cell.

28.3.2 Using the Insert Hyperlink Dialog Box

There is also an Insert Hyperlink dialog box to assist in creating a hyperlink. This can be helpful when you are not certain of the exact Web address, because you can search for the website you want using a browser. To use the Insert Hyperlink dialog box, follow these steps:

1. Right-click in the cell where the link will be placed. A pop-up menu will open.
2. Select **Insert Hyperlink...** from the pop-up menu. The Insert Hyperlink dialog box (Figure 28.2) will open.
    Alternate method: select the cell and use Ribbon options: **Insert tab →** **Link group → Insert Hyperlink button**.
3. In the **Text to display** field, enter the text that you want displayed as the link. If you leave this field blank, the actual web address will be displayed.
4. Click the **Browse the Web** button to search for the website you want to link to. The web address will appear in the **Address** field.
    Alternate method: simply type the web address in the **Address** field.
5. Click **OK** to close the Insert Hyperlink dialog box.

The link will be created in the cell, as illustrated in Figure 28.3.

28.3.3 Links within Your Excel Workbook

Another use for hyperlinks is providing quick access to other locations in the same workbook. For example, the worksheet shown in Figure 28.4 provides an overview of the anticipated profit on a project, but readers are almost certainly going to want to see how the total revenue and total cost values were calculated. Links provide a quick way for the reader to get to the detailed calculations.

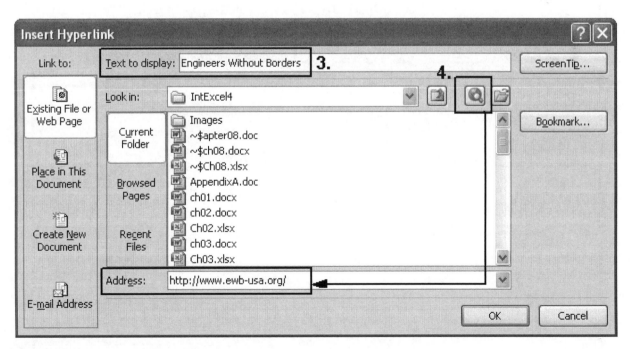

Figure 28.2 The Insert Hyperlink dialog box.

	A	B	C	D	E
1					
2					
3		Engineers Without Borders			
4					
5					

Figure 28.3   The link created using the Insert Hyperlink dialog box.

	A	B	C	D	E	F
1	Project Summary Page					
2					Details...	
3		Total Revenues:	$ 1,230,000		Revenue Data	
4		Total Costs:	$ 847,328		Cost Data	
5						
6		Net Profit:	$ 382,672			
7						

Figure 28.4   Links to other locations in the same workbook.

The workbook contains three worksheets, named Summary, Costs, and Revenues. To insert the link to the revenue data (on the Revenues worksheet), use these steps:

1. Right-click in cell E3, where the revenue data link will be placed. A pop-up menu will open.

2. Select **Insert Hyperlink...** from the pop-up menu. The Insert Hyperlink dialog box (Figure 28.5) will open.

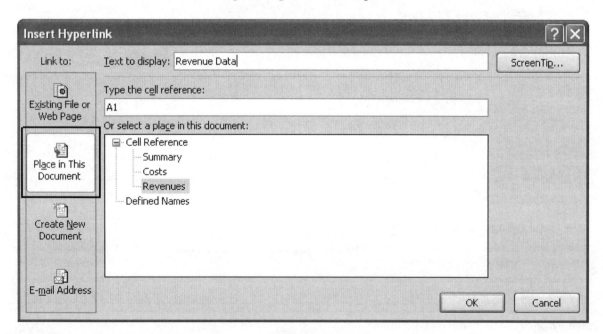

Figure 28.5   The Insert Hyperlink dialog box that appears when you insert a link within a worksheet.

3. Click the **Place in This Document button** in the **Link to:** list (indicated in Figure 28.5).
4. Enter *Revenue Data* in the **Text to display** field.
5. Select the **Revenues** sheet in the **Or select a place in this document** list. The default is to link to cell A1 on the selected sheet, and we will leave that default unchanged.
6. Click **OK** to close the Insert Hyperlink dialog box.

When you click on the Revenue Data link, Excel displays the Revenues sheet as shown in Figure 28.6.

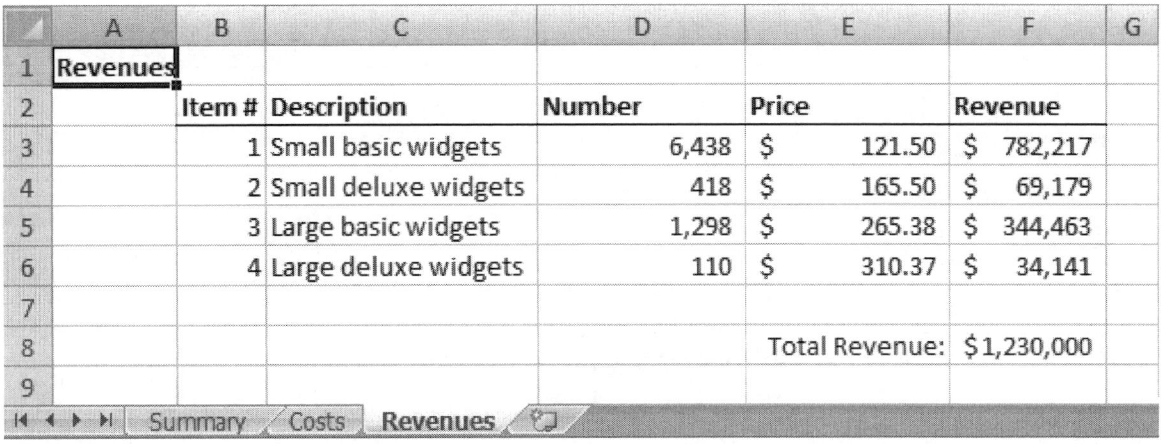

	A	B	C	D	E	F	G
1	Revenues						
2		Item #	Description	Number	Price	Revenue	
3		1	Small basic widgets	6,438	$ 121.50	$ 782,217	
4		2	Small deluxe widgets	418	$ 165.50	$ 69,179	
5		3	Large basic widgets	1,298	$ 265.38	$ 344,463	
6		4	Large deluxe widgets	110	$ 310.37	$ 34,141	
7							
8					Total Revenue:	$1,230,000	
9							

⏮ ◀ ▶ ⏭   Summary / Costs / **Revenues** /

Figure 28.6   The result of following the Revenue Data link.

28.4   USING WEBSITES RELATED TO EXCEL

Excel is such a commonly used program that there are a huge number of websites related to its use. These fall into two basic categories:

- How to use the Excel program.
- How to use Excel to accomplish some task.

Microsoft maintains a section of web pages specifically for Excel users. The primary page for Microsoft is located at the following URL:

http://www.microsoft.com

Within the Microsoft site are Excel tutorials, product information, and a number of free add-ins, patches, and templates. It is important to periodically check for updates to your programs, since security problems are frequently found in the most popular applications.

There are many other websites available that provide instruction on using Excel for myriad of tasks. A good way to search for these sites is to enter a topic into a search engine such as Google (Google is a trademark of Google, Inc.). For example, you could search for "Hyperlinks in Excel" and see results similar to those shown in Figure 28.7.

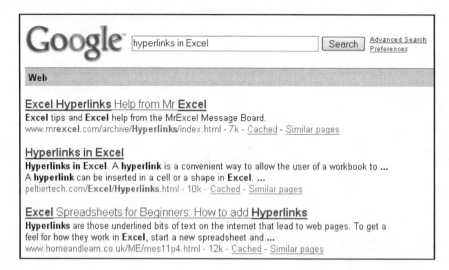

Figure 28.7 Partial results of a Google search on "hyperlinks in Excel."

28.5   USING WEB DATA IN EXCEL

The Web is a huge source of information for engineers. The way you access that information depends on how the information is stored.

- Data in tables on web pages can be copied and pasted into Excel.
- Excel workbooks can be accessed over the Web.
- Web queries can be used to retrieve data over the Web.

    We'll consider each of these ways of accessing data from the Web.

28.5.1 Copying and Pasting Web Data into Excel

A lot of engineering data is published to the Web for others to use. For example, the U.S. Department of Energy's Energy Information Administration (EIA) provides a wealth of data on energy-related topics. Oil price information is available at

    http://www.eia.doe.gov/emeu/mer/petro.html

A portion of the website is shown in Figure 28.8.

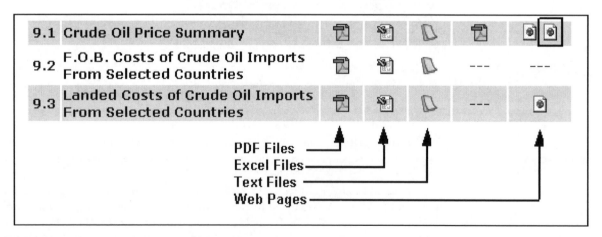

Figure 28.8 EIA data on oil prices (partial).

Notice that the data is provided in four different formats:

- PDF files
- Excel files
- Text files
- Web pages

We'll start by opening the web page containing a crude oil price summary (indicated with a box in Figure 28.8). This data set lists crude oil prices since 1968. The table is quite large; only a portion of the table is shown in Figure 28.9.

http://www.eia.doe.gov/emeu/aer/txt/ptb0521.html

Table 5.21 Crude Oil Refiner Acquisition Costs, 1968-2007
(Dollars per Barrel)

Year	Domestic	
	Nominal [1]	Real [2]
1968 [E]	3.21	12.88
1969 [E]	3.37	12.89
1970 [E]	3.46	12.57
1971 [E]	3.68	12.73
1972 [E]	3.67	12.17
1973 [E]	4.17	13.09
1974	7.18	20.68
1975	8.39	22.08
1976	8.84	21.99

Figure 28.9   Crude oil cost data (part of Web table).

To copy the data to the Windows clipboard, follow these steps:

1. Click inside the table.
2. Select the entire table using browser options **Edit → Select All** (or the shortcut, **Ctrl + A**).
3. Use browser menu options **Edit → Copy** (or the shortcut, **Ctrl + C**).

To paste the data into Excel, follow these steps:

1. Click in the cell that will hold the top-left corner of the table.
2. Paste the table into Excel using Ribbon Options **Home tab → Clipboard group → Paste button** (or the shortcut **Ctrl + V**).

The result of the paste operation is shown in Figure 28.10. To demonstrate that the pasted values can be used in Excel, the real (adjusted for inflation) price of crude oil has been plotted using an Excel Line chart.

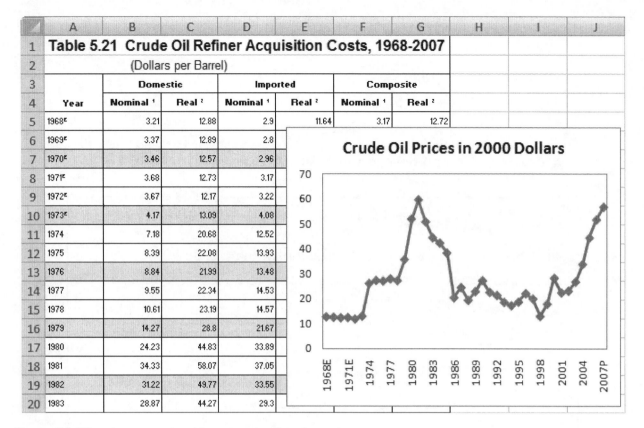

Table 5.21 Crude Oil Refiner Acquisition Costs, 1968-2007						
(Dollars per Barrel)						
	Domestic		Imported		Composite	
Year	Nominal [1]	Real [2]	Nominal [1]	Real [2]	Nominal [1]	Real [2]
1968E	3.21	12.88	2.9	11.64	3.17	12.72
1969E	3.37	12.89	2.8			
1970E	3.46	12.57	2.96			
1971E	3.68	12.73	3.17			
1972E	3.67	12.17	3.22			
1973E	4.17	13.09	4.08			
1974	7.18	20.68	12.52			
1975	8.39	22.08	13.93			
1976	8.84	21.99	13.48			
1977	9.55	22.34	14.53			
1978	10.61	23.19	14.57			
1979	14.27	28.8	21.67			
1980	24.23	44.83	33.89			
1981	34.33	58.07	37.05			
1982	31.22	49.77	33.55			
1983	28.87	44.27	29.3			

Figure 28.10   After pasting the table into Excel and graphing.

Some Web tables paste into Excel more cleanly than others. Here are some pointers to improve your ability to copy and paste values into Excel:

- Select the entire table before copying.
- Use Paste Special, As Text if needed.

Tables on websites are presented using complex HTML (hypertext mark-up language) formatting codes that include codes to start and conclude various formatting options, such as table layout. By selecting the entire table you ensure that you are copying all of the HTML codes associated with the table, which will help when Excel converts the table formats.

If the Paste operation fails, then try using Paste Special and pasting as Text or Unicode text. Pasting as text strips out the HTML codes.

But the Energy Information Administration provides a better option: downloading the data as Excel files.

28.5.2 Downloading Excel Files from the Web

If the data you need is available as an Excel file, then you can download the file and open it in Excel. As an example, let's open the Excel file (actually, it's an .asp file, but Excel can open it) labeled Fuel Ethanol and Biodiesel Overview, 1981–2007 in the EIA website (indicated in Figure 28.11, and located at www.eia.doe.gov/emeu/aer/renew.html).

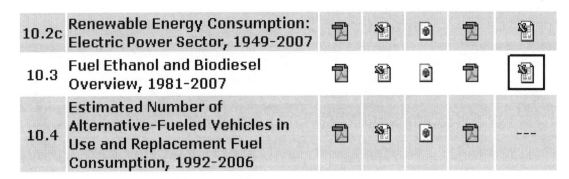

10.2c	Renewable Energy Consumption: Electric Power Sector, 1949-2007					
10.3	Fuel Ethanol and Biodiesel Overview, 1981-2007					
10.4	Estimated Number of Alternative-Fueled Vehicles in Use and Replacement Fuel Consumption, 1992-2006					---

Figure 28.11   EIA data on renewable energy (partial).

When you click on the link, your browser will likely display a dialog box asking you if you want to save the file or open it in Excel. Open the file in Excel. The result is shown in Figure 28.12. A chart of renewable energy use since 1973, created from the EIA data, is shown in Figure 28.13.

	A	B	C	D
9	Table 10.1 Renewable Energy Production and Consumption by Source			
10				
11				
12	Year	Biofuels Production	Total Biomass Energy Production	Total Renewable Energy Production
13		(Trillion Btu)	(Trillion Btu)	(Trillion Btu)
14	1973 January	Not Available	129.787	405.6
15	1973 February	Not Available	117.338	362.38
16	1973 March	Not Available	129.938	401.695
17	1973 April	Not Available	125.636	382.261
18	1973 May	Not Available	129.834	393.811
19	1973 June	Not Available	125.611	379.147
20	1973 July	Not Available	129.787	369.356
21	1973 August	Not Available	129.918	355.671

Figure 28.12   Partial display of downloaded Excel file.

28.5.3 Using a Web Query to Retrieve Web Data

A *Web Query* retrieves data from an external source over the web and places the data in a local Excel worksheet. In this example we will use a Web query to get current currency exchange rates from the file rates.asp at http://moneycentral.msn.com. This is one of several sample queries that are provided with a standard Excel installation.

To run a Web Query, follow these steps:

1.   Open a new blank Excel workbook.
2.   Open the Existing Connections dialog box (Figure 28.14) using Ribbon options: **Data tab → Get External Data group → Existing Connections button**.

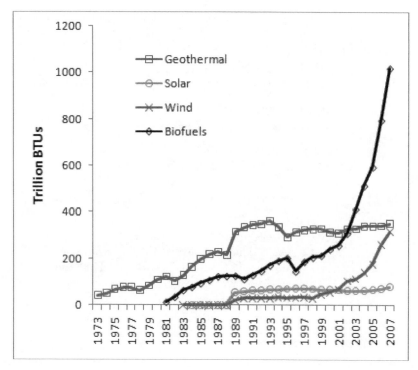

Figure 28.13   A plot of renewable energy use since 1973, created using data from the EIA website.

Figure 28.14   The Existing Connections dialog box.

(Excel 2003: Open the Select Data Source dialog box using Data → Import External Data → Import Data.)

3. Select **MSN MoneyCentral Investor Currency Rates** (as shown in Figure 28.14).

4. Click **Open**. The Import Data dialog box will open, as shown in Figure 28.15.

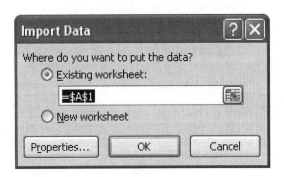

Figure 28.15 The Import Data dialog box.

5. Choose a location for the imported query results (cell A1 in the existing worksheet by default).

6. Click **OK** to retrieve the data.

The results are shown in Figure 28.16.

	A	B	C	D	E	F
1	-->-->					
2	Currency Rates Provided by MSN Money					
3	Click here to visit MSN Money					
4						
5	Name	In US$	Per US$			
6	Argentine Peso to US Dollar	0.33014	3.029			
7	Australian Dollar to US Dollar	0.95202	1.05			
8	Bahraini Dinar to US Dollar	2.6486	0.378			
9	Bolivian Boliviano to US Dollar	0.14134	7.075			
10	Brazilian Real to US Dollar	0.63512	1.575			
11	British Pound to US Dollar	1.9786	0.505			
12	Canadian Dollar to US Dollar	0.97609	1.025			

Figure 28.16 The query results.

A Web Query is a formatted text file. The contents of the MSN query used to access the data in the previous example are displayed in Figure 28.17. The effect of executing the query is to access the web server at the URL and execute the command named. The results are returned and displayed in your local Excel worksheet.

```
WEB
1
http://moneycentral.msn.com/investor/external/excel/rates.asp

Selection=EntirePage
Formatting=All
PreFormattedTextToColumns=True
ConsecutiveDelimitersAsOne=True
SingleBlockTextImport=False
```

Figure 28.17   The query used to retrieve the currency values.

You can ask Excel to refresh the data periodically. This could be important if your business handles a lot of different currencies. To set the query refresh period,

1. Click the **Properties** button on the Import Data dialog box. This opens the External Data Range Properties dialog box shown in Figure 28.18.

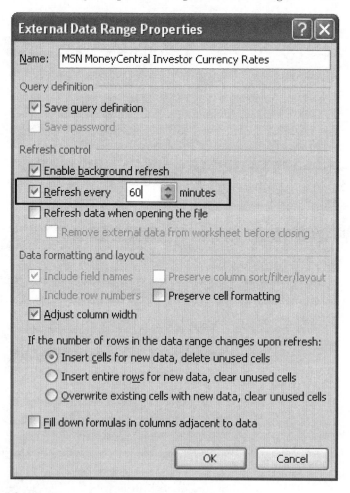

Figure 28.18   The External Data Range Properties dialog box.

2. Check the **Refresh every** box and set the interval to 60 minutes, or whatever refresh interval is needed.

3. Click **OK** to close the dialog box.

As long as you have your worksheet open and you are connected to the Internet, the Web Query will automatically run every 60 minutes and update the currency rates.

28.6   SAVING AN EXCEL WORKBOOK AS A WEB PAGE

Once you have created an Excel workbook you can save it as an HTML *web page*. Not all Excel features are supported by HTML (*hypertext markup language*), so you want to save your work as an Excel file (.xlsx or .xlsm) first, and then create the web page.

The basic steps involved are as follows:

1. Choose a web page format.

   a. Web Page (*.htm, *.html)

   b. Single File Web Page (*.mht; *.mhtml)

   The **Web Page format** creates a web page of your workbook, plus a folder containing supporting materials (graphics, mostly). This format minimizes the size of the web page, but requires that the supporting folder be maintained.

   The **Single File Web Page format** (not available in Excel 2003) puts everything needed to display the web page in a single file. It is convenient because you don't have to worry about the supporting folder, but the file can be large.

2. Choose a file name.

3. Assign a page title.

4. Select whether to create a web page of the entire workbook, or just the current worksheet.

5. Create the web page.

These basic steps will be demonstrated using the workbook shown in Figure 28.4 that presents cost and revenue data for a project. We will create a Web page for the entire workbook.

To save this workbook as a web page, follow these steps:

1. Open the Save As dialog box (Figure 28.19) using the Office button: **Office button → Save As submenu → Other Formats button**. (Excel 2003: File → Save as Web Page.)

2. Choose the **Save as type** format. Standard **Web Page (*.htm, *.html)** format was selected in this example.

3. Enter the file name **ProjectData.htm** in the **File name** field.

4. Use the **Change Title...** button to assign the title **Project Cost and Revenue Data** to the web page.

5. Use the **Save** option **Entire Workbook** to create a web page of the entire Excel workbook.

6. Click the **Save** button to save the workbook as a Web page.

   Alternative: The **Publish** button allows you to to republish the Web page each time the Excel file is saved.

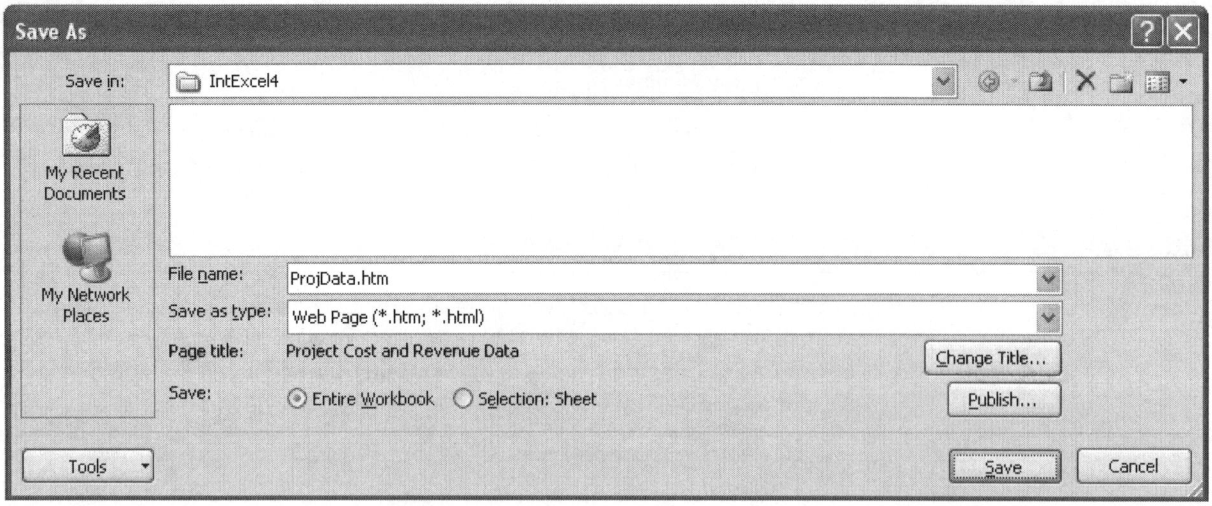

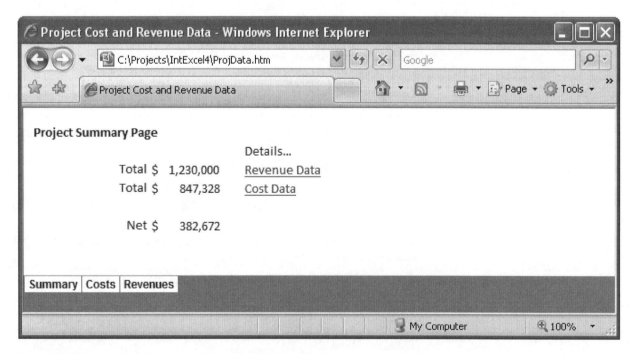

Figure 28.19   The Save As dialog box, filled in.

The result of saving the workbook as a web page includes the following:

- A web page with the file name **ProjData.htm**, shown in Figure 28.20.
- A folder named **ProjData_Files** containing an .htm file for each of the three worksheets in the workbook, plus the tab strip (shown in Figure 28.20) and supporting materials.

Figure 28.20   The Web page created from the Excel workbook.

KEY TERMS

copy and paste
HTML (hypertext
markup language)
http (hypertext transfer
protocol)

hyperlink
link
URL (uniform resource
locator)

web page
web query
World Wide Web

Summary

Creating Hyperlinks
Two Methods

1. Type a web address into a cell.
2. Use the Insert Hyperlink dialog box.

Using the Insert Hyperlink Dialog Box to Create an External Link

1. Right-click in the cell where the link will be placed.
2. Select **Insert Hyperlink...** from the pop-up menu.
3. In the **Text to display** field, enter the text that you want displayed as the link. If you leave this field blank, the actual web address will be displayed.
4. Click the **Browse the Web** button to search for the website to which you want to link. The web address will appear in the **Address** field.
   Alternate method: simply type the web address in the **Address** field.
5. Click **OK** to close the Insert Hyperlink dialog box.

Using the Insert Hyperlink Dialog Box to Create a Link within Your Excel Workbook

1. Right-click in the cell where the link will be placed.
2. Select **Insert Hyperlink...** from the pop-up menu.
3. Click the **Place in This Document button** in the **Link to:** list.
4. Enter the link label text in the **Text to Display** field.
5. Select the link location (sheet and/or cell location).
6. Click **OK** to close the Insert Hyperlink dialog box.

Using Data from the Web
Common Ways to Access Web Data:

- Data in tables on web pages can be copied and pasted into Excel.
- Excel workbooks can be accessed over the Web.

Copying and Pasting Web Data into Excel
To Copy the Data to the Windows Clipboard,

1. Click inside the Web table.
2. Select the entire table using browser options **Edit → Select All** (or the shortcut, **Ctrl + A**).
3. Use browser menu options **Edit → Copy** (or the shortcut, **Ctrl + C**).

To Paste the Data into Excel,

1. Click in the cell that will hold the top-left corner of the table.
2. Paste the table into Excel using Ribbon Options **Home tab → Clipboard group → Paste button** (or the shortcut **Ctrl + V**).

Downloading Excel Files from the Web

1. Click the Web link to the Excel file.
2. Indicate whether the file should be saved or opened (if asked).

Saving a Worksheet as a Web Page

1. Open the Save As dialog box using the Office button: **Office button → Save As submenu → Other Formats button**.
2. Choose the **Save as type** format (Web Page, or Single File Web Page).
3. Enter the file name in the **File name** field.
4. Use the **Change Title...** button to assign a title to the web page.
5. Use the **Save** options to choose to save the entire workbook or just the current worksheet.
6. Click the **Save** button to save the workbook as a Web page.

Web Format Options

- The **Web Page format** creates a web page of your workbook, plus a folder containing supporting materials (graphics, mostly). This format minimizes the size of the web page, but requires that the supporting folder be maintained.
- The **Single File Web Page format** (not available in Excel 2003) puts everything needed to display the web page in a single file. It is convenient because you don't have to worry about the supporting folder, but the file can be large.

Problems

1. Create a workbook named SI Units.xlsx. Enter the label SI Base Unit Definitions in a cell and create a hyperlink from this cell to

    http://physics.nist.gov/cuu/Units/current.html

2. Use the Help feature to read about the HYPERLINK function (another method of creating a hyperink, not covered in this chapter). One advantage of using the HYPERLINK function is that the link can depend on a conditional expression. Create an IF expression that links to www.mozilla.com if cell $A1 = Firefox$ and that links to www.microsoft.com if cell $A1 = Explorer$.

3. One use of hyperlinks in Excel worksheets is to provide quick access to online reference materials. As an example, perform a Google® search to find the equation used to calculate the surface area of a cone. Then finish the worksheet shown in Figure 28.21 by using the equation to calculate the surface area and adding a hyperlink to the site that provided the equation.

4. The British have long used the stone as a unit of mass, and it continues to be used in everyday speech, even though the United Kingdom switched to the SI

	A	B	C	D	E
1	**Surface Area of a Cone**				
2					
3		Base Radius:	2	cm	
4		Height:	6	cm	
5					
6		Surface Area:		cm^2	
7					
8		Link to Reference:			
9					

Figure 28.21 Partially completed worksheet for computing the surface area of a cone.

system of units many years ago. Search the web to find out how many pounds are equal to 1 stone, then create a worksheet that accomplishes the following:

(a) Computes the mass of a 150-pound individual, in stones.

(b) Provides a hyperlink to the website that was used to find out how pounds and stones are related.

5. An online search has revealed that a plasma television can be purchased from Store A for 650 US$ + 50 US$ s/h, or from Store B for 700 C$ + 63 C$ s/h. After a bit of searching, you figure out that US$ stands for U.S. dollars, C$ means Canadian dollars, and s/h stands for shipping and handling. Create a worksheet that performs these tasks:

(a) Computes the total cost of each system, and converts all costs to the same currency, either U.S. or Canadian.

(b) Provides a hyperlink to a website that provides currency exchange rates, such as http://www.xe.com/ucc/.

Which store has the better price?

6. After searching an online auction site for a new rug, you have found exactly the item you want. You submit a bid and win the item, and then notice that the rug is in Pakistan and you just agreed to pay 22,000 Pakistani rupees. Furthermore, after the auction you learn that the seller is happy to ship to your country, at an additional cost of 34,000 rupees.

Create a worksheet to compute exactly what the rug is going to cost you, including shipping. Provide a hyperlink to the website you used to find the exchange rate between Pakistani rupees and your currency.

Section 6

Appendix: Commonly Used Functions

ABS(*n*)	Returns the absolute value of a number
AND(*a, b, ...*)	Returns the logical AND of the arguments (TRUE if all arguments are TRUE, otherwise FALSE)
ASIN(*n*)	Returns the arcsine of *n* in radians
AVEDEV(*n1, n2, ...*)	Returns the average of the absolute deviations of the arguments from their mean
AVERAGE(*n1, n2, ...*)	Returns the arithmetic mean of its arguments
BIN2DEC(*n*)	Converts a binary number to decimal
BIN2HEX(*n*)	Converts a binary number to hexadecimal
BIN2OCT(*n*)	Converts a binary number to octal
CALL(...)	Calls a procedure in a DLL or code resource
CEILING(*n, sig*)	Rounds a number *n* up to the nearest integer (or nearest multiple of significance, *sig*)
CHAR(*n*)	Returns the character represented by the number *n* in the computer's character set
CHIDIST(*x, df*)	Returns the one-tailed probability of the chi-squared distribution, using *df* degrees of freedom
CLEAN(*text*)	Removes all nonprintable characters from *text*
COLUMN(*ref*)	Returns the column number of a reference
COLUMNS(*ref*)	Returns the number of columns in a reference
COMBIN(*n, r*)	Returns the number of combinations of *n* items, choosing *r* items
COMPLEX(*real, imag, suffix*)	Converts real and imaginary coefficients into a complex number
CONCATENATE(*str1, str2, ...*)	Concatenates the string arguments
CORREL(**A1, A2**)	Returns the correlation coefficients between two data sets
COS(*n*)	Returns the cosine of an angle

COUNTBLANK(*range*)	Counts the number of empty cells in a specified range
DEC2BIN(*n, p*)	Converts the decimal number *n* to binary, using *p* places (or characters)
DELTA(*n1, n2*)	Tests whether two numbers are equal
ISERROR(*v*)	Returns TRUE if value *v* is an error
ISNUMBER(*v*)	Returns TRUE if value *v* is a number
FACT(*n*)	Returns the factorial of *n*
FORECAST(*x, known x's, known y's*)	Predicts a future value based on a linear trend
LN(*n*)	Returns the natural logarithm of *n*
MDETERM(**A**)	Returns the matrix determinant of array **A**
MEDIAN(*n1, n2, ...*)	Returns the median of its arguments
MOD(*n, d*)	Returns the remainder after *n* is divided by *d*
OR(*a, b, ...*)	Returns the logical OR of its arguments (TRUE if any argument is TRUE, FALSE if all arguments are FALSE)
PI()	Returns the value of *pi* to 15 digits of accuracy
POWER(*n, p*)	Returns the value of *n* raised to the power of *p*
PRODUCT(*n1, n2, ...*)	Returns the product of its arguments
QUOTIENT(*n, d*)	Returns the integer portion of *n* divided by *d*
RADIANS(*d*)	Converts degrees to radians
RAND()	Returns an evenly distributed pseudorandom **number** $> = 0$ and < 1
ROUND(*n, d*)	Rounds *n* to *d* digits
ROW(*ref*)	Returns the row number of a reference
SIGN(*n*)	Returns the sign of a number *n*
SQRT(*n*)	Returns the square root of a number *n*
STDEVP(*n1, n2, ...*)	Calculates the standard deviation of its arguments
SUM(*n1, n2, ...*)	Returns the sum of its arguments
SUMSQ(*n1, n2, ...*)	Returns the sum of the squares of its arguments
TAN(*n*)	Returns the tangent of an angle
TRANSPOSE(**A**)	Returns the transpose of an array
TREND(*known y's, known x's, new x's, constant*)	Returns values along a linear trend by fitting a straight line, using the least squares method
VARP(*n1, n2, ...*)	Calculates the variance of its arguments

Section 7
Introduction to MATLAB®

Chapter 29
Getting Started with MATLAB

ENGINEERING ACHIEVEMENT: WIND TUNNELS

Wind tunnels are test chambers built to generate precise wind speeds. Accurate scale models of new aircraft and missiles can be mounted on force-measuring supports in the test chamber, and then measurements of the forces acting on the models can be made at many different wind speeds and angles of the models relative to the wind direction. Some wind tunnels can operate at hypersonic velocities, generating wind speeds of thousands of miles per hour. The sizes of wind tunnel test sections vary from a few inches across to sizes large enough to accommodate a fighter jet. At the completion of a wind tunnel test series, many sets of data have been collected that can be used to determine the lift, drag, and other aerodynamic performance characteristics of a new aircraft at its various operating speeds and positions. Wind tunnels are also used to test the performance of sports equipment like composite skis, snowboards, bicycles, and racing cars. In this chapter, we give examples of using MATLAB to analyze wind tunnel results.

SECTIONS

OBJECTIVES

After reading this chapter, you should be able to

- understand the MATLAB screen layout, windows, and interactive environments,
- initialize and use scalars, vectors, and matrices in computations,
- write simple programs using MATLAB, and
- create and use script M-files.

29.1   INTRODUCTION TO MATLAB AND MATLAB WINDOWS

MATLAB is one of a number of commercially available, sophisticated mathematical computation tools, such as Maple, Mathematica, and MathCad. Despite what their proponents may claim, none of these tools is "the best." They all have strengths and weaknesses. Each will allow you to perform basic mathematical computations, but they differ in the ways that they handle symbolic calculations and more complicated mathematical processes. MATLAB excels at computations involving matrices. In fact, its name, **MATLAB**, is short for **Mat**rix **Lab**oratory. At a very basic level, you can think of these programs as sophisticated, computer-based calculators. They can perform the same functions as your scientific calculator, but they can also do much more. In many engineering programs, students are learning to use mathematical computational tools like MATLAB, in addition to also learning a high-level language such as JAVA, C, or C++. This then gives you the option of choosing the right tool or language for the problem that you are solving.

Today's MATLAB has capabilities far beyond the original MATLAB and is an interactive system and programming language for general scientific and technical computation. Because MATLAB commands are similar to the way that we express engineering steps in mathematics, writing computer solutions in MATLAB can be much quicker than writing solutions in a high-level language. It is important to understand when to use a computational program such as MATLAB and when to use a general purpose, high-level programming language. MATLAB excels at numerical calculations, especially matrix calculations, and graphics. Usually, high-level programs do not offer easy access to graphing. The primary area of overlap between MATLAB and high-level programs is in "number crunching"—programs that require repetitive calculations or processing of large quantities of data. Both MATLAB and high-level languages are good at processing numbers. It is usually easier to write a "number crunching" program in MATLAB, but it usually executes faster in C or C++. The one exception to this rule is with matrices. Because MATLAB is optimized for matrices, if a problem can be formulated with a matrix solution, MATLAB executes substantially faster than a similar program in a high-level language.

Hint   A number of examples are presented in this text. We encourage you to type the example problems into MATLAB as you read the book, and observe the results. You may think that some of the examples are too simple to type in yourself—that just reading the material is sufficient. However, you will remember the material much better if you both read it and type it.

To begin MATLAB, use your mouse to click on the MATLAB icon (which should be located on the desktop) or use the start menu. If you are using a UNIX operating system, type **matlab** at the **prompt**. You should see the MATLAB prompt >> (or **EDU** >> if you are using the Student Edition), which tells you that MATLAB is waiting for you to enter a command. To exit MATLAB, type **quit** or **exit** at the MATLAB prompt, or choose **EXIT MATLAB** from the file menu, or select the close icon (x) from the upper right-hand corner of the screen. (See Figure 29.1.) The start button is located in the lower left-hand corner of the MATLAB window, and it offers alternative access to the MATLAB toolboxes and to the various MATLAB windows, help function, and Internet products. Toolboxes provide additional MATLAB functionality for specific content areas, but they will not be discussed in this text.

MATLAB uses display windows. The default view shown in Figure 29.1 includes a large command window in the center, the current folder window on the left, and the workspace and command history windows on the right. In addition, document windows, graphics windows, and editing windows will automatically open when needed.

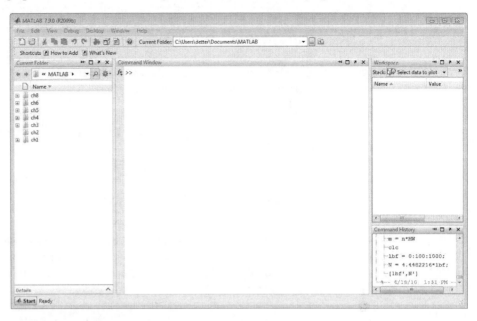

Figure 29.1   MATLAB opening window.

29.1.1 Command Window

You can use MATLAB in two basic modes. The **command window** offers an environment similar to a note pad. Using the command window allows you to save the values you calculate, but not the commands used to generate those values. If you want to save the command sequence, you will need to use the editing window to create an **M-file**. (M-files are presented in Section 29.4.) Both approaches are valuable. In this chapter, we will concentrate on using the command window so that you become comfortable with it. In the later chapters, we will use M-files to store programs that we develop with MATLAB.

You can perform calculations in the command window in a manner very similar to the way you perform calculations on a scientific calculator. Most of the syntax is even the same. For example, to compute the value of 5 squared, type the command

5^2

The answer will be displayed in the following manner:

ans =

0.25

Or, to use a trigonometric function to find the value of $\cos(\pi)$, type

cos(pi)

which results in the following output:

ans =

-1

We will cover MATLAB functions in Chapter 30.

Hint: You may find it frustrating to discover that when you make a mistake, you cannot just overwrite your command on the same line after you have executed it. This is because the command window is creating a list of all the commands you have entered. Instead, you can enter the correct command on a new line, and then execute your new version. MAT-LAB also offers another way to make it easier to update commands. You can use the arrow keys, usually located on the right-hand side of your keyboard. The **up arrow**, , allows you to move through the list of commands you have executed. Once you find the appropriate command, you can edit it, and then execute your new version. This can be a real time-saver.

MATLAB includes extensive help tools. To use the command-line help function, type **help** in the command window. A list of help topics will appear. To use the windowed help screen, select **Help** $\rightarrow$ **MATLAB Help** from the menu bar. A windowed version of the help list will appear.

29.1.2 Command History Window

The **command history window** records the commands you issued in the command window. When you exit MATLAB, or when you issue the **clc** command to clear all commands, the command window is cleared. However, the command history window retains a list of all of your commands. You may clear the command history using the edit menu if you need to. If you work on a public computer, as a security precaution, MATLAB's defaults may be set to clear the history when you exit MATLAB. If you entered the example commands above, notice that they are repeated in the command history window. This window is valuable for a number of reasons. It allows you to review previous MATLAB sessions, and it can be used to transfer commands to the command window. For example, in the command window, type

    clc

This should clear the command window, but leave the data in the command history window intact. You can transfer any command from the command history window to the command window by double clicking (which also executes the command) or by clicking and dragging the line of code into the command window. Try double clicking

    cos(pi)

which should return

    ans =
        -1

Click and drag

    5^2

from the command history window into the command window. The command will not execute until you press the enter key, and then you'll get the following result:

    ans =
        25

You will find the command history useful as you perform more and more complicated calculations in the command window.

29.1.3 Workspace Window

The **workspace window** keeps track of the variables you have defined as you execute commands in the command window. As you do the examples, the workspace window should just show one variable, **ans**, and it should also tell us that it has a value of 25, as shown below:

Name	Value
▦ **ans**	25

The workspace window can be cleared using the command **clear** or by using the edit menu.

Set the workspace window to show more about this variable by right-clicking on the bar with the column labels. Check **size** and **bytes**, in addition to **name**, **value**, and **class**. Your workspace window should now display:

Name	Value	Size	Bytes	Class
▦ **ans**	25	1×1	8	double

The yellow grid-like symbol indicates the variable **ans** is an array. The size, 1×1, tells us that it is a single value (one row by one column) and therefore a scalar. The array uses 8 bytes of memory. MATLAB was written in C, and the class designation tells us that in the C language **ans** is a double precision, floating point array. For our needs it is enough to know that the variable **ans** can store a floating point number (one with a decimal point). MATLAB considers every number you enter to be a floating point number, whether you put a decimal in the number or not.

You can define additional variables in the command window and they will be listed in the workspace window. For example, type

```
A = 5
```

which returns

```
A =
    5
```

Notice that the variable A has been added to the workspace window, which lists variables in alphabetical order. Variables beginning with capital letters are listed first, followed by variables starting with lowercase letters:

Name	Value	Size	Bytes	Class
▦ **A**	5	1×1	8	double
▦ **ans**	25	1×1	8	double

Entering matrices into MATLAB is not discussed in detail in this section. However, you can enter a simple one-dimensional matrix by typing

```
B = [1, 2, 3, 4]
```

which returns

```
B =
    1   2   3   4
```

The commas are optional. You would get the same result with

```
B = [1 2 3 4]
```

Notice that the variable B has been added to the workspace window and that it is a 1×4 array:

Name	Value	Size	Bytes	Class
⊞ **A**	5	1×1	8	double
⊞ **B**	[1 2 3 4]	1×4	32	double
⊞ **ans**	25	1×1	8	double

We define two-dimensional matrices in a similar fashion. Semicolons are used to separate rows. For example,

```
C = [1,2,3,4; 10,20,30,40; 5,10,15,20]
```

displays

```
C =

    1    2    3    4
   10   20   30   40
    5   10   15   20
```

Notice that C appears in the workspace window as a 3×4 matrix. You can recall the values for any variable by just typing in the variable name. For example, entering

```
A
```

displays

```
A =

    5
```

The information that is shown in the workspace window is the following:

Name	Value	Size	Bytes	Class
⊞ **A**	5	1×1	8	double
⊞ **B**	[1 2 3 4]	1×4	32	double
⊞ **C**	< 3×4 double >	3×4	96	double
⊞ **ans**	25	1×1	8	double

Although we have only introduced variables that are matrices, other types of variables, such as symbolic variables, are possible.

If you prefer to have a less cluttered desktop, you may close any of the windows (except the command window) by selecting the x in the upper right-hand corner of each window. You can also personalize which windows you prefer to keep open by selecting **View** from the menu bar and checking the appropriate windows. If you suppress the workspace window, you can still find out what variables have been defined by using the command

```
whos
```

which returns

Name	Size	Bytes	Class
A	1×1	8	double
B	1×4	32	double
C	3×4	96	double
ans	1×1	8	Double

29.1.4 Current Folder Window

When MATLAB either accesses files or saves information onto your computer, it uses the current folder, which is shown in the **current folder window**. The default for the current folder varies, depending on your version of the software and how it was installed. However, the current folder is listed at the top of the main window. The current folder can be changed by selecting another folder from the drop-down list located next to the folder listing, or by browsing through your computer files using the browse button located next to the drop-down list.

29.1.5 Document Window

Double clicking on any variable listed in the workspace window automatically launches a **document window** containing the **array editor**. Values stored in the variable are displayed in a spreadsheet format. You can change values in the array editor, or you can add new values. For example, if you have not already entered the two-dimensional matrix **C**, enter the following command in the command window:

```
C = [1,2,3,4; 10,20,30,40; 5,10,15,20];
```

Placing a semicolon at the end of the command suppresses the output so that it is not repeated back in the command window; however, C should now be listed in the workspace window. Double click it. A document window will open above the workspace window, as shown in Figure 29.2. (Only a portion of the MATLAB screen is shown in Figure 29.2.) You can now add additional values to the C matrix or change existing values.

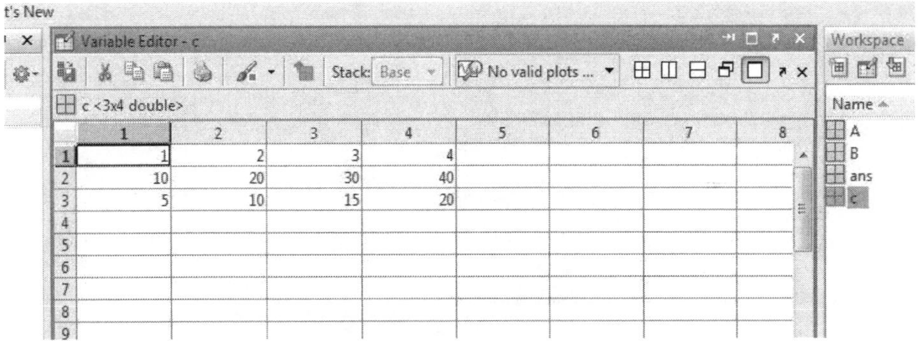

Figure 29.2 Document window with the array editor.

The document window that displays the array editor can also be used in conjunction with the workspace window to create entirely new arrays. Run your mouse slowly over the icons in the shortcut bar at the top of the workspace window. The function of each icon should appear, if you are patient. The new-variable icon looks like a page with an asterisk at its upper-left corner. Select the new-variable icon. A new variable called **unnamed** should appear on the variable list. You can change its name by right-clicking and selecting **rename** from the pop-up menu. To add values to this new variable, double click on it and add your data from the document window.

29.1.6 Graphics Window

The **graphics window** launches automatically when you request a graph. To create a simple graph first, create an array of **x** values:

```
x = [1,2,3,4,5];
```

(Remember, the semicolon suppresses the output from this command; however, a new variable **x** appears in the workspace window.) Now create a list of **y** values:

y = [10,20,30,40,50];

To create a graph, use the **plot** command:

plot(x,y)

The graphics window opens automatically. (See Figure 29.3.) Notice that a new window label also appears on the task bar at the bottom of the screen indicating that this plot is Figure 1. Any additional graphs you create will overwrite Figure 1 unless you specifically command MATLAB to open a new graphics window. MATLAB makes it easy to modify graphs by adding titles, x and y labels, multiple lines, and more.

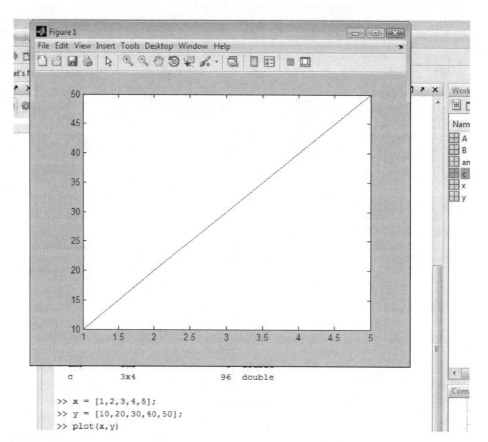

Figure 29.3 MATLAB graphs.

29.1.7 Edit Window

The **edit window** is opened by choosing **File** from the menu bar, then **New**, and finally **m-file (File → New → m-file)**. This window allows you to type and save a series of commands without executing them. You may also open the edit window by typing **edit** at the command prompt. The last section in this chapter will give an example of creating and executing an M-file.

29.2 SIMPLE OPERATIONS

The command window environment is a powerful tool for solving engineering problems. To use it effectively, you will need to understand more about how MATLAB stores information, and then performs operations on that information. In Chapter 30, we cover the wide range of functions that are also available in MATLAB.

29.2.1 Defining Variables

When solving engineering problems, it is important to visualize the data related to the problem. Sometimes the data is just a single number, such as the radius of a circle. Other times, the data may be a coordinate on a plane that can be represented as a pair of numbers, with one number representing the x-coordinate and the other number representing the y-coordinate. In another problem, we might have a set of four x-y-z coordinates that represent the four vertices of a pyramid with a triangular base in a three-dimensional space. We can represent all of these examples using a special type of data structure called a matrix. A **matrix** is a set of numbers arranged in a rectangular grid of rows and columns. Thus, a single point can be considered a matrix with one row and one column—often referred to as a **scalar**. An x-y coordinate can be considered a matrix with one row and two columns, and is often called a **vector**. A set of four x-y-z coordinates can be considered a matrix with four rows and three columns. Examples are the following:

$$\mathbf{A} = [3.5] \qquad \mathbf{B} = [1.5 \quad 3.1] \qquad \mathbf{C} = \begin{bmatrix} -1 & 0 & 0 \\ 1 & 1 & 0 \\ 1 & -1 & 0 \\ 0 & 0 & 2 \end{bmatrix}$$

Note that the data within a matrix are written inside brackets.

In MATLAB, we assign names to the scalars, vectors, and matrices we use. The following rules apply to these **variable names**:

- Variable names must start with a letter.
- Variable names are case sensitive. The names **time**, **Time**, and **TIME** all represent different variables.
- Other than the first letter, variable names can contain letters, digits, and the underscore (_) character. To test whether a name is a legitimate variable name, use the **isvarname** command. The answer **1** means true, and the answer **0** means false. For example,

```
isvarname Vector
ans =
     1
```

means that **Vector** is a legitimate variable name.

- Variable names can be any length, but only the first N characters are used by MATLAB. The value of N varies, depending on the version of MATLAB that you are using. For Version 7, R2009b, the value of N is 63. You can see the value of N on your system by typing

```
namelengthmax
```

- Variables cannot have the same name as any of MATLAB's keywords. To see a list of all MATLAB keywords, type

      `iskeyword`

- MATLAB allows you to use the names of its built-in functions as variable names. This is a dangerous practice since you can overwrite the meaning of a function, such as cos. To check whether a name is a built-in function, use the **which** command. For example, typing

      `which cos`

returns

      `built-in`

together with the function's directory location.

MATLAB also contains a number of predefined constants and special values that are available to our programs. These values are described in the following list:

ans   Represents a value computed by an expression but not stored in a variable name.

clock Represents the current time in a six-element row vector containing year, month, day, hour, minute, and seconds.

date   Represents the current date in a character-string format, such as 20-Jun-10.

eps   Represents the floating-point precision for the computer being used. This epsilon precision is the smallest amount with which two values can differ in the computer.

i,j   Represents the value $\sqrt{-1}$.

Inf   Represents infinity, which typically occurs as a result of a division by zero. A warning message will be printed when this value is computed.

NaN   Represents Not-a-Number and typically occurs when an expression is undefined, as in the division of zero by zero.

pi   Represents π.

29.2.2 Scalar Operations

The arithmetic **operations** between two scalars are shown in Table 29.1. They include addition, subtraction, multiplication, division, and exponentiation. The command

      `a = 1 + 2`

Table 29.1 Arithmetic operations between two scalars

Operation	Algebraic Form	MATLAB Form
Addition	$a + b$	**a + b**
Subtraction	$a - b$	**a − b**
Multiplication	$a \times b$	**a * b**
Division	$\dfrac{a}{b}$	**a/b**
Exponentiation	a^b	**a^b**

should be read as **a** is assigned a value of 1 plus 2, which is the addition of two scalar quantities. Assume, for example, that you have defined **a** in the previous statement and that **b** has a value of 5:

```
b = 5
```

Then

```
x = a + b
```

will return the following result:

```
x =
    8
```

The equal sign in MATLAB is called the **assignment operator**. The assignment operator causes the result of your calculations to be stored in a computer memory location. In the example above, **x** is assigned a value of eight, and is stored in computer memory. If you enter the variable name

```
x
```

into MATLAB, you get the result

```
x =
    8
```

which should be read as "**x** is assigned a value of 8." If we interpret assignment statements in this way, we are not disturbed by the valid MATLAB statement

```
x = x + 1
```

which, since the value stored in **x** was originally 8, returns

```
x =
    9
```

indicating that the value stored in the memory location named **x** has been changed to 9. Clearly, this statement is not a valid algebraic statement, but is understandable when viewed as an assignment rather than as a statement of equality. The assignment statement is similar to the familiar process of saving a file. When you first save a word processing document, you assign it a name. Subsequently, when you've made changes, you resave your file, but still assign it the same name. The first and second versions are not equal; you've just assigned a new version of your document to an existing memory location.

Because several operations can be combined in a single arithmetic expression, it is important to know the **precedence** of arithmetic operations, or the order in which operations are performed. Table 29.2 contains the precedence of arithmetic operations performed in MATLAB. Note that this precedence follows the standard algebraic precedence rules.

Table 29.2   Precedence of arithmetic operations

Precedence	Operation
1	Parentheses, innermost first
2	Exponentiation, left to right
3	Multiplication and division, left to right
4	Addition and subtraction, left to right

To illustrate the precedence of arithmetic operations, assume that we want to calculate the area of a trapezoid, where the base is horizontal and the two edges are vertical. Assume that values have been entered into variables using these commands:

```
base = 5;
height_1 = 12;
height_2 = 6;
```

Now you can compute the area by entering the equation for area in MATLAB:

```
area = 0.5*base*(height_1 + height_2)
```

This equation returns

```
area =
      45
```

Understanding the order of operation is important. Because of the parentheses, MATLAB will first add the two height values together, and then perform the multiplication operations, starting from the left.

Neglecting the parentheses will result in the wrong answer. For example,

```
area = 0.5*base*height_1 + height_2
```

gives

```
area =
      36
```

In this case, MATLAB will first perform the multiplications and then add the result to **height_2.** Clearly, it is important to be very careful when converting equations into MATLAB statements. Adding extras parentheses is an easy way to ensure that computations are performed in the order you want.

If an expression is long, break it into multiple statements. For example, consider the equation

$$f = \frac{x^3 - 2x^2 + x - 6.3}{x^2 + 0.05005x - 3.14}$$

The value could be computed with the following MATLAB statements:

```
numerator = x^3 - 2*x^2 + x - 6.3;
denominator = x^2 + 0.05005*x - 3.14;
f = numerator/denominator;
```

It is better to use several statements that are easy to understand than to use one statement that requires careful thought to figure out the order of operations.

Hint   MATLAB does not read "white space," so it does not matter if you add spaces to your commands. It is easier to read a long expression if you add a space before and after plus and minus signs, but not after multiplication and division signs.

The variables stored in a computer can assume a wide range of values. For most computers, the range extends from 10^{-308} to 10^{308} which should be enough to accommodate most computations. However, it is possible for the result of an expression to be outside of this range. For example, suppose that we execute the following commands:

```
x = 2.5e200;
y = 1.0e200;
z = x*y
```

MATLAB responds with

```
z =
    Inf
```

because the answer (2.5e400) is outside of the allowable range. This error is called **exponent overflow**, because the exponent of the result of an arithmetic operation is too large to store in the computer's memory.

Exponent underflow is a similar error, caused by the exponent of the result of an arithmetic operation being too small to store in the computer's memory. Using the same allowable range, we obtain an exponent underflow with the commands

```
x = 2.5e-200;
y = 1.0e200
z = x/y
```

which together return

```
z =
    0
```

The result of an exponent underflow is zero.

We also know that the division by zero is an invalid operation. If an expression results in a division by zero, the result of the division is infinity:

```
z = y/0
z =
    Inf
```

MATLAB may also print a warning telling you that division by zero is not possible.

EXAMPLE 29.1   WIND TUNNEL ANALYSIS

Wind tunnels are used to evaluate high performance aircraft. (See Figure 29.4.) To interpret wind tunnel data, the engineer needs to understand how gases behave. The basic equation describing gas properties is the ideal gas law,

$$PV = nRT$$

where

P = pressure, kPa

V = volume, m^3

n = number of kmoles of gas in the sample

R = ideal gas constant, 8.314 kPa m^3/kmole K

T = temperature, expressed on an absolute scale (i.e., in degrees K)

In addition, we know that the number of kmoles of gas is equal to the mass of gas divided by the molar mass (also known as the molecular weight); that is,

$$n = m/\text{MW}$$

where

m = mass, kg

MW = molar mass, kg/kmole

Different units can be used in the equations, if the value of R is changed accordingly. Assume that the volume of air in the wind tunnel is 1000 m³. Before the wind tunnel is turned on, the temperature of the air is 300 K and the pressure is 100 kPa. The molar mass (molecular weight) of air is approximately 29 kg/kmole. Find the mass of air in the wind tunnel.

Figure 29.4   Wind tunnels used to test aircraft designs.

SOLUTION

1. Problem Statement

Find the mass of air in the wind tunnel.

2. Input/Output Description

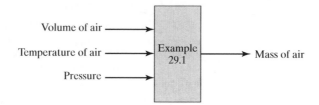

3. Hand Example

Working the problem by hand (or with a calculator) allows you to outline an algorithm, which you can translate to MATLAB code later. You should choose simple data that make it easy to check your work. In this example, we want to solve the ideal gas law for n, and plug in the given values. This results in

$$n = PV/RT$$
$$= (100 \text{ kPa} \times 1000 \text{ m}^3)/(8.314 \text{ kPa m}^3/\text{kmole K} \times 300 \text{ K})$$
$$= 40.0930 \text{ kmoles}$$

Convert moles to mass by multiplying by the molar mass:

$$m = n \times \text{MW} = 40.0930 \text{ kmoles} \times 29 \text{ kg/kmole}$$
$$m = 1162.70 \text{ kg}$$

4. MATLAB Solution

The solution to this problem is really just entering data, and then computing two equations. The command window in Figure 29.5 shows the commands, together with their corresponding MATLAB output. Notice also the use of parentheses in the denominator computation; they are necessary for the correct calculation of the denominator value.

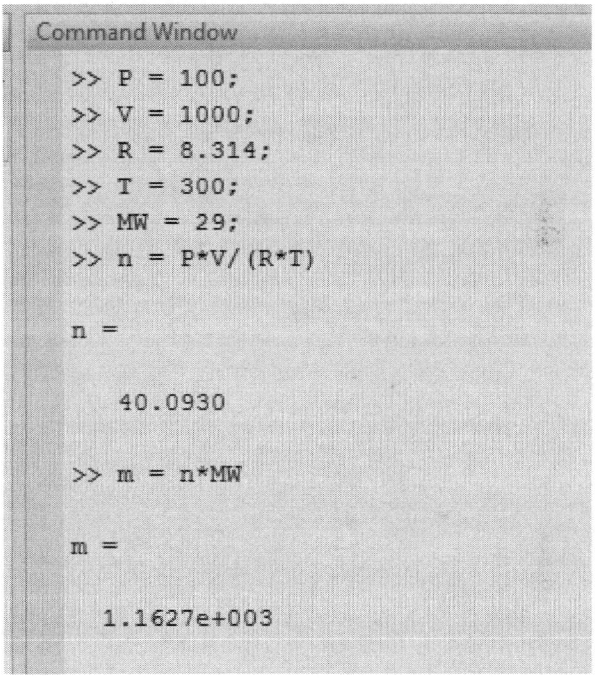

```
Command Window
    >> P = 100;
    >> V = 1000;
    >> R = 8.314;
    >> T = 300;
    >> MW = 29;
    >> n = P*V/(R*T)

    n =

        40.0930

    >> m = n*MW

    m =

        1.1627e+003
```

Figure 29.5 Wind tunnel air mass.

5. Testing

In this case, comparing the result to the hand result is sufficient. More complicated problems solved in MATLAB should use a variety of input data to confirm that your solution works in a variety of cases. Notice that the variables defined in the command window are listed in the workspace window. Also notice that the command history lists the commands executed in the command window. If you were to scroll up in the command history window, you would see commands from previous MATLAB sessions. All of these commands are available for you to move to the command window.

29.2.3 Element-By-Element Operations

Using MATLAB simply as a calculator can be useful, but its real strength is in matrix manipulations. (Remember that when we use the term matrix, we can be referring to a scalar, a vector, or a matrix with rows and columns.) As described previously, the easiest way to define a matrix is to use a list of numbers called an explicit list. The command

```
X = [1,2,3,4];
```

defines a row vector with four values. Recall that when defining this vector, you may either list the values with or without commas. A new row is indicated by a semicolon, so that a column vector is specified as

```
Y = [1; 2; 3; 4];
```

and a matrix that contains both rows and columns would be created with the statement

```
A = [1,2,3,4; 2,3,4,5; 3,4,5,6];
```

Hint: You can also keep track of how many values you have entered into a matrix if you enter each row on a separate line. Thus, another way to enter values into the matrix **A** above would be:

```
A = [1,2,3,4;
     2,3,4,5;
     3,4,5,6]
```

While a complicated matrix might have to be entered by hand, evenly spaced matrices can be entered much more readily. The command

```
B = 1:5;
```

or the command

```
B = [1:5];
```

defines a row matrix with the five values 1, 2, 3, 4, 5. The square brackets are optional. The default increment is 1, but if you want to use a different increment, put it between the first and final values. For example,

```
C = 1:2:5
```

indicates that the increment between values will be 2 and displays

```
C =
   1   3   5
```

If you want MATLAB to calculate the increment between values, you can use the linspace command. Specify the initial value, the final value, and how many total values you want. For example,

```
D = linspace(1,10,3)
```

initializes a vector with three values, evenly spaced between 1 and 10, as shown below:

```
D =
   1.0000   5.5000   10.0000
```

Matrices can be used in many calculations with scalars. If **A** = [1 2 3], we can add 5 to each value in the matrix with the calculation

```
B = A + 5
```

which displays

```
B =
   6   7   8
```

This works well for addition and subtraction; however, multiplication and division are slightly different. In matrix mathematics, the multiplication operator has a very specific meaning. If you want to do an element-by-element multiplication, the operator must be preceded by a period. For example,

    A.*B

results in the first element of **A** multiplied by the first element of **B**, the second element of **A** multiplied by the second element of **B**, and so on. For the example of **A** (which is [1,2,3]) and **B** (which is [6,7,8]),

    A.*B

returns

    ans =
          6   14   24

(Be sure to do the math to convince yourself why these are the correct answers.)

Using just an asterisk (instead of a period and an asterisk) specifies matrix multiplication which is discussed in Chapter 32. If you get error messages in computation statements, be sure to see if you have forgotten to include the period for **element-by-element operations**.

The same syntax holds for element-by-element division and exponentiation, as shown in these statements:

    A./B

    A.^2

As an exercise, predict the values resulting from the preceding two expressions, then test out your predictions by executing the commands in MATLAB.

The matrix capability of MATLAB makes it easy to do repetitive calculations. For example, assume you have a list of angles in degrees that you would like to convert to radians. First, put the values into a matrix. For angles of 10, 15, 70, and 90, enter

    D = [10,15,70,90];

To change the values to radians, you must multiply by $\pi/180$:

    R = D*pi/180;

This command returns a matrix **R**, with the values in radians. (In the next chapter, we will show you easier ways to convert degrees to radians, or from radians to degrees, using built-in functions.)

Hint   The value of π is built into MATLAB as a floating point number, called **pi**. Because π is an irrational number, it cannot be expressed exactly with a floating point representation, and the MATLAB constant, **pi**, is really an approximation.

Another useful matrix operator is transposition. The **transpose operator** basically changes rows to columns or vice versa. For example, using the matrix D defined above,

    D'

displays

    ans =

          10
          15
          70
          90

This makes it easy to create tables. For example, to create a table of degrees to radians, enter

```
table = [D',R']
```

which tells MATLAB to create a matrix named **table**, where the first column is **D'**, and the second column is **R'**:

```
table =
        10.0000    0.1745
        15.0000    0.2618
        70.0000    1.2217
        90.0000    1.5708
```

EXAMPLE 29.2

SCIENTIFIC DATA CONVERSION

Scientific data, such as that collected from wind tunnels, are usually in SI (system international) units. However, much of the manufacturing infrastructure in the United States has been tooled in English (sometimes called American Engineering or American Standard) units. Engineers need to be fluent in both systems, and especially careful when sharing data with other engineers. Perhaps the most notorious example of unit confusion problems occurred in the flight of the *Mars Climate Orbiter*, the second flight of the NASA Mars Surveyor Program. (See Figure 29.6.) The spacecraft burned up in the orbit of Mars in September 1999 because of a look-up table embedded in the spacecraft's software. The table, probably generated from wind tunnel testing, used pounds force (lbf), when the program expected values in newtons (N).

Use MATLAB to create a conversion table of pounds force (lbf) to newtons (N). Your table should start at 0 and go to 1000 lbf, at 100 lbf intervals. Use the conversion

Figure 29.6 Mars Climate Orbiter.

1. Problem Statement

Create a table converting pound force (lbf) to newtons (N).

$$1 \text{ lbf} = 4.4482216 \text{ N}$$

2. Input/Output Description

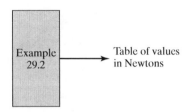

Example 29.2 → Table of values in Newtons

3. Hand Example

Here are a few conversions that we compute by hand so that we can then compare them to the entries in the table generated by MATLAB:

$$0 \times 4.4482216 = 0$$
$$100 \times 4.4482216 = 444.82216$$
$$1000 \times 4.4482216 = 4448.2216$$

4. MATLAB Solution

It is always a good idea to clear the command space and the workspace before beginning a new problem solution. The **clc** command clears the command window and the command **clear** removes all variables from memory. The command **clf** clears the current figure and thus clears the graph window.

See Figure 29.7 for the commands entered, and the table computed by MATLAB. Notice in the workspace window that lbf and N are 1×11 matrices, and that **ans** (which is where the table we created is stored) is an 11×2 matrix. The output from the first two commands was suppressed by adding a semicolon at the end of each line. It would be very easy to create a table with more entries by changing the increment to 10 or even to 1. Also notice that you will need to multiply the table results by 1000 to get the correct answers. MATLAB tells you this is necessary directly above the table.

5. Testing

Comparing the results of the MATLAB solution to the hand solution shows the same results. Once we have verified that our solution works, it is easy to use the same algorithm to create other conversion tables. For example, modify this example to create a conversion table of newton (N) to pound force, with an increment of 10 N, from 0 N to 1000 N.

29.2.4 Additional Ways to Define Matrices

As you solve more and more complicated problems with MATLAB, you will find that you need to combine small matrices into larger matrices, extract information from large matrices, create very large matrices, and use matrices with special properties. In this section, we demonstrate some of the techniques for performing these operations.

```
Command Window

>> lbf = 0:100:1000;
>> N = 4.4482216*lbf;
>> [lbf',N']

ans =

  1.0e+003 *

         0         0
    0.1000    0.4448
    0.2000    0.8896
    0.3000    1.3345
    0.4000    1.7793
    0.5000    2.2241
    0.6000    2.6689
    0.7000    3.1138
    0.8000    3.5586
    0.9000    4.0034
    1.0000    4.4482
```

Figure 29.7   Command window with solution to Example 29.1.

We know that a matrix can be defined by typing in a list of numbers enclosed in square brackets. The numbers can be separated by spaces or commas; we prefer to use commas to make the numbers easier to read. New rows are indicated with a semicolon within the brackets:

```
A = [3.5];
B = [1.5, 3.1];
C = [-1,0,0; 1,1,0; 0,0,2];
```

A matrix can also be defined by listing each row on a separate line, as in the following set of MATLAB commands:

```
C = [-1,0,0;
      1,1,0;
      1,-1,0;
      0,0,2];
```

If there are too many numbers in a row to fit in one line, you can continue the statement in the next line, but a comma and an **ellipsis** (three dots) are needed at the end of the line to indicate that the row is to be continued. (You can also use the ellipsis to continue long assignment statements in MATLAB.) For example, if we want to define **F** with 10 values, we could use either of the following statements:

```
F = [1,52,64,197,42,-42,55,82,22,109];
```

or

```
F = [1,52,64,197,42,-42, ...
      55,82,22,109];
```

MATLAB also allows you to define a matrix by using another matrix that has already been defined. For example, the following statements

```
B = [1.5, 3.1];
S = [3.0, B]
```

define a new vector **S**, and its value is displayed as the following:

```
S =
    3.0000    1.5000    3.1000
```

Similarly,

```
T = [1,2,3; S]
```

displays

```
T =
    1.0000    2.0000    3.0000
    3.0000    1.5000    3.1000
```

We can also change values in a matrix, or include additional values, by using a reference to specific locations. Thus, the command

```
S(2) = -1.0;
```

changes the second value in the matrix **S** from 1.5 to −1. If you then type the matrix name **S** into the command window—that is,

```
S
```

then MATLAB displays

```
S =
    3.0000   -1.0000    3.1000
```

We can also extend a matrix by defining new elements. If we execute the command

```
S(4) = 5.5;
```

we extend the matrix **S** to four elements instead of three. If we define element **S(8)** using the following statement

```
S(8) = 9.5;
```

then the matrix S will have eight values, and the values of **S(5), S(6), and S(7)** will be set to zero. Thus, entering the matrix name in the command line will display the following:

```
S =
    3   -1   3.1000   5.5000   0   0   0   9.5000
```

The **colon operator** is a very powerful operator for defining new matrices and modifying existing matrices. An evenly spaced matrix can be defined with the colon operator. Thus,

```
H = 1:8
```

will define a matrix and display it as follows:

```
H =
    1   2   3   4   5   6   7   8
```

The default spacing for the colon operator is 1. However, when colons are used to separate three numbers, the middle value becomes the spacing. For example,

```
time = 0.0:0.5:2.0
```

will define the vector and display it as follows:

```
time =
        0    0.5000    1.0000    1.5000    2.0000
```

The colon operator can also be used to extract data from matrices, which becomes very useful in data analysis. When a colon is used in a matrix reference in place of a specific subscript, the colon represents the entire row or column. To illustrate, assume that we define a matrix with the following statement:

```
M = [1,2,3,4,5;
     2,3,4,5,6;
     3,4,5,6,7];
```

We can then extract the first column with this command

```
x = M(:,1)
```

which defines a matrix **x**, and displays the following:

```
x =
    1
    2
    3
```

You can extract any of the columns in a similar manner. To extract the fourth column, we can use the following statement:

```
y = M(:,4)
```

The output displayed is the following:

```
y =
    4
    5
    6
```

Similarly, to extract a row, use the following:

```
z = M(1,:)
```

which displays

```
z =
    1    2    3    4    5
```

In all of the preceding examples, read the colon as "all of the rows," or "all of the columns." You do not have to extract an entire row or an entire column. The colon operator can also be used to select values "from row i to row j" or "from column m to column n." For example, to extract the two bottom rows of the M matrix, we can enter the following:

```
w = M(2:3,:)
```

which defines a new matrix w and displays its contents:

```
w =
    2    3    4    5    6
    3    4    5    6    7
```

Similarly, to extract just the four numbers in the lower right-hand corner of matrix **M**, use

```
w = M(2:3,4:5)
```

which displays

```
w =

    5    6
    6    7
```

In MATLAB, it is valid to have a matrix that is empty. For example, the following statements will each generate an **empty matrix**:

```
a = [];
b = 4:-1:5;
```

Finally, using the matrix name with a single colon, as in

```
x = M(:);
```

transforms **M** into one long column matrix that is formed from selecting column 1, followed by column 2, then column 3, then column 4, and then column 5. It is important to recognize that any matrix can be represented as a single column matrix using this notation. Therefore, if you reference a matrix using only a single subscript, as in M(8), this reference will always assume that you are using the single column matrix representation. Thus, in this example, **M(8)** is the value in the second row and third column, or a 4.

29.3   OUTPUT OPTIONS

MATLAB gives us a number of options for displaying information. We can choose to have numbers displayed in a variety of forms (for example, use a specific number of decimal positions or use a scientific format). We can also use MATLAB statements within our programs to display information in different ways. In this section we first present the ways in which numbers can be displayed, and then we present two MATLAB commands that give us additional control over the output of information.

29.3.1   Number Display

In this section, we present the options that we have to display information in MATLAB. These options include a scientific notation, and then a number of ways of displaying numeric information.

Although you can enter any number in decimal notation, it is not always the best way to represent very large or very small numbers. For example, a number that is used frequently in chemistry is Avogadro's constant, whose value to four significant digits is 602,200,000,000,000,000,000,000. The diameter of an iron atom is approximately 140 picometers, which is .000000000140 meters. **Scientific notation** expresses a value as a number between 1 and 10 (the mantissa) multiplied by a power of 10 (the exponent). In scientific notation, Avogadro's number becomes 6.022×10^{23} and the diameter of an iron atom becomes 1.4×10^{-10} meters. In MATLAB, values in scientific notation are designated with an e between the mantissa and the exponent, and it is referred to as an **exponential notation**. For example,

```
Avogadros_constant = 6.022e23;
Iron_diameter = 140e12;
Iron_diameter = 1.4e10;
```

It is important to omit blanks between the mantissa and the exponent. For example, MATLAB will interpret

```
6.022    e23
```

as two different values (6.022 and 10^{23}).

When elements of a matrix are displayed in MATLAB, integers are always printed as integers. However, values with decimal fractions are printed using a default format that shows four decimal digits. Thus,

```
A = 5
```

returns

```
A =
    5
```

but

```
A = 51.1
```

returns

```
A =
   51.1000
```

MATLAB allows you to specify other formats that show more significant digits. For example, to specify that we want values to be displayed in a decimal format with 14 decimal digits, we use the command

```
format long
```

which changes all subsequent displays. For example,

```
A
```

now returns

```
A =
   51.10000000000000
```

We can return the format to four decimal digits by using the command

```
format short
A
A =
   51.1000
```

Two decimal digits are displayed when the format is specified as **format bank**. No matter what display format you choose, MATLAB uses double precision floating-point numbers in its calculations. Exactly how many digits are used in these calculations depends upon your computer. However, changing the display format does not change the accuracy of your results. When numbers become too large or too small for MATLAB to display using the default format, the program automatically expresses them in scientific notation. For example, if you enter Avogadro's constant into MATLAB in decimal notation,

```
avo = 602000000000000000000000
```

the program returns

```
avo =
   6.0200e+023
```

You can force MATLAB to display all numbers in scientific notation with **format short e** (with 5 significant digits) or **format long e** (with 14 significant digits). Thus,

```
format short e
x = 10.356789
```

returns

```
x =
   1.0357e+001
```

Another format command is **format+**. When a matrix is displayed with this format, the only characters printed are plus and minus signs. If a value is positive, a plus sign will be displayed; if a value is negative, a minus sign will be displayed. If a value is zero, nothing will be displayed. This format allows us to view a large matrix in terms of its signs:

```
format +
B = [1,-5,0,12; 10005,24,-10,4]
B =
   +-++
   +-++
```

For long and short formats, a common scale factor is applied to the entire matrix if the elements become very large or very small. This scale factor is printed along with the scaled values.

Finally, the command **format compact** suppresses many of the line feeds that appear between matrix displays and allows more lines of information to be seen together on the screen. The command **format loose** will return the command window to the less compact display mode. The examples in this text use the compact format to save space. Table 29.3 contains a summary of the numeric display formats.

Table 29.3 Numeric display formats

MATLAB Command	Display	Example
format short	4 decimal digits	15.2345
format long	14 decimal digits	15.23453333333333
format short e	4 decimal digits	1.5234e+01
format long e	15 decimal digits	1.523453333333333e+01
format bank	2 decimal digits	15.23
format +	+, −, blank	+

29.3.2 Display function

The display (**disp**) function can be used to display the contents of a variable without printing the variable's name. Consider these commands:

```
x = 1:5;
disp(x)
```

returns

```
1   2   3   4   5
```

The display command can also be used to display a string (text enclosed in single quote marks). This can be useful when displaying information from M-files, which are discussed later in this chapter. An example of using this command to give a header to a set of data that is printed from an M-file is shown below:

```
disp('The values in the x matrix are:');
disp(x);
```

These statements return the following:

```
The values in the x matrix are:
1   2   3   4   5
```

The semicolon at the end of the **disp** statement is optional. Notice that the output from the two **disp** statements is displayed on separate lines.

29.3.3 Formatted Output

The **fprintf** function gives you even more control over the output than you have with the **disp** function. In addition to displaying both text and matrix values, you can specify the format to be used in displaying the values, and you can specify when to skip to a new line. If you are a C programmer, you will be familiar with the syntax of this function. With few exceptions, the MATLAB **fprintf** functions use the same formatting specifications as the C **fprintf** function.

The general form of this command contains a string and a list of matrices:

```
fprintf(format-string,var, . . .)
```

Consider the following example:

```
temp = 98.6;
fprintf('The temperature is %f degrees F \n',temp);
```

The character string in single quote marks, which is the first argument inside the **fprintf** function, contains the percent character to begin a formatting operator that will specify the format of the value to be printed at that location. In this example, the formatting is defined by the conversion character, **f**, which tells MATLAB to display the temperature value in a default fixed-point format. Note in the output generated below that the default precision in the printed output has six digits after the decimal point:

```
The temperature is 98.600000 degrees F
```

The final character sequence in the formatting string, **\n**, inserts a special character in the printed output that causes MATLAB to start a new line. Format operations usually end with **\n** so that subsequent output will start on a new line, rather than the current one.

There are many other conversion characters (such as **%e** and **%g**) and special characters that can be used in the formatting operator to produce the output that is desired. Some of these characters are shown in Tables 29.4 and 29.5.

Table 29.4 Type field format

Type Field	Result
%**f**	fixed point, or decimal notation
%**e**	exponential notation
%**g**	whichever is shorter, %**f** or %**e**

Table 29.5 Special format commands

Format Command	Resulting Action
\n	linefeed
\r	carriage return (similar to linefeed)
\t	tab
\b	backspace

You can further control how the variables are displayed by using the optional width field and precision field with the format command. The **width field** controls the minimum number of characters to be printed. It must be a positive decimal integer. The **precision field** is preceded by a period and specifies the number of decimal places after the decimal point for exponential and fixed-point types. For example, **% 8.2f** specifies that the minimum total width available to display your result is 8 digits, two of which are after the decimal point:

```
fprintf('The temperature is %8.2f degrees F\n',temp);
```

returns

```
The temperature is 100.10 degrees F
```

Many times when you use the **fprintf** function, your variable will be a matrix. For example,

```
temp = [98.6, 100.1, 99.2];
```

MATLAB will repeat the string in the **fprintf** command until it uses all of the values in the matrix:

```
fprintf('The temperature is %8.2f degrees F\n',temp);
```

returns

```
The temperature is 98.60 degrees F
The temperature is 100.10 degrees F
The temperature is 99.20 degrees F
```

If the variable is a two-dimensional matrix, MATLAB uses the values one column at a time, going down the first column, then the second, and so on. Here is a more complicated example:

```
patient = 1:3;
temp = [98.6, 100.1, 99.2];
```

Combine these two matrices:

```
history = [patient; temp]
```

returns

```
history =
        1.0000    2.0000    3.0000
       98.6000  100.1000   99.2000
```

Now we can use the **fprintf** function to create a table that is easier to interpret:

```
fprintf('Patient %f3 had a temperature of %7.2f \n',
history)
```

sends the following output to the command window:

```
Patient 1 had a temperature of 98.60
Patient 2 had a temperature of 100.10
Patient 3 had a temperature of 99.20
```

As you can see, the **fprintf** function allows you to have a great deal of control over the output form.

29.4 SAVING YOUR WORK

Working in the command window is similar to performing calculations on your scientific calculator. When you turn off the calculator, or when you exit the program, your work is gone. It is possible to save the values of the variables that you defined in the command window and that are listed in the workspace window. Although this may be useful, it is more likely that you will want to save the list of commands that generated your results. We will show you how to save and retrieve variables (the results of the assignments you made and the calculations you performed) to **MAT-files** or to **DAT-files**. Then, we will show you how to generate **M-files**, or **script files**, containing MATLAB commands that are created in the edit window. These files can then be retrieved at a later time to give you access to the commands, or programs, that are contained in them. All example programs in the rest of this text will be generated as M-files so that you have the flexibility of working on the programs, and coming back at a later time to continue your work without reentering the commands.

29.4.1 Saving Variables

To preserve the variables you created in the command window (check the workspace window on the left-hand side of the MATLAB screen for the list of variables) between sessions, you must save the contents of the workspace window to a file. The default format is a binary file called a MAT-file. To save the workspace (remember, this is just the set of variables, not the list of commands in the command window) to a file, use the **save** command:

```
save file_name
```

Although **save** is a MATLAB command, **file_name** is a user-defined file name. The file name can be any name you choose, as long as it conforms to the variable naming conventions for MATLAB. If you execute the **save** command without a filename, MATLAB names the file **matlab.mat**. You could also choose **File → Save Workspace As** from the menu bar, which will then prompt you to enter a file name for your data.

To restore the values of variables to the workspace, type

```
load file_name
```

Again, **load** is a MATLAB command, but **file_name** is the user-defined file name. If you just type **load**, MATLAB will look for the default **matlab.mat** file.

The file you save will be stored in the current directory. To illustrate, type

```
clear, clc
```

This will clear the workspace and the command window. Verify that the workspace is empty by checking the workspace window, or by typing

```
whos
```

Now define several variables, such as:

```
A = 5;
B = [1,2,3];
C = [1,2; 3,4];
```

Check the workspace window once again to confirm that the variables have been stored. Now, save the workspace to a file called **my_example_file**:

```
save my_example_file
```

Confirm that this new file has been stored in the current directory. If you prefer to save the file to another directory (for instance, onto a thumb drive), use the browse button to navigate to the directory of your choice. Remember that in a public computer lab, the current directory is probably purged after each user logs off the system.

Now, clear the workspace and command window again by typing

```
clear, clc
```

The workspace window should be empty. Now load the file back into the workspace:

```
load my_example_file
```

Again, the file you want to load must be in the current directory, or else MATLAB will not be able to find it. In the command window, type the variable names. You should see the names and the values of the variables displayed.

MATLAB can also store individual matrices or lists of matrices into the current directory via the command

```
save file_name variable_list
```

where **file_name** is the user-defined file name where you wish to store the information, and **variable_list** is the list of variables to be stored in the file. For example,

```
save file1 A B
```

would save just the variables **A** and **B** into **file1.mat**.

If your saved data will be used by a program other than MATLAB (such as C or C++), the MAT format is not appropriate, because MAT files are unique to MATLAB. The **ASCII** format is standard between computer platforms and is more appropriate if you need to share files. MATLAB allows you to save files as ASCII files by modifying the save command:

```
save file_name.dat variable_list −ascii
```

The command -**ascii** tells MATLAB to store the data in a standard 8-digit text format. ASCII files should be saved into a DAT file instead of a MAT file, so be sure to add **.dat** to your file name—if you do not, it will default to **.mat**.

If more precision is needed, the data can be stored with a 16-digit text format:

```
save file_name.dat variable_list -ascii −double
```

It is also possible to delimit, or separate, the elements (numbers) with tabs:

```
save file_name.dat variable_list -ascii −double −tabs
```

For example, to create the matrix **Z** and save it to the file **data_2.dat** in 8-digit text format, use the following commands:

```
Z = [5,3,5; 6,2,3];
save data_2.dat Z −ascii
```

This command causes each row of the matrix **Z** to be written to a separate line in the data file. You can view the **data_2.dat** file by double clicking the file name in the current directory window. Follow the directions in the import wizard, which will automatically launch, to load the data into the workspace with the same name as the data file.

You can use this same technique to import data from other programs, including Excel spreadsheets, or you can select File and then **import data** from the menu bar.

Perhaps, the easiest way to retrieve data from an ASCII DAT file is to enter the **load** command followed by the file name. This will cause the information to be read into a matrix with the same name as the data file.

29.4.2 Creating and Using M-Files

In addition to providing an interactive computational environment using the command window, MATLAB can also be used as a powerful programming language. The MATLAB commands that you write represent a program that you can create and save in a file called an **M-file**. An M-file is a text file similar to a C or C++ source-code file. An M-file can be created and edited using the MATLAB M-file Editor/Debugger, or you can use another text editor of your choice. The MATLAB editing window is shown in Figure 29.8. To use the MATLAB editing window, choose File → New → BlankM-File If you choose **a different text editor, make sure the files you save are in the ASCII format**.

Figure 29.8 The editing window—also called the Editor/Debugger.

When you save an M-file, it is stored in the current directory. You will need to name your file with a MATLAB variable name; that is, the name must start with a letter and contains only letters, numbers, and the underscore (_). Spaces are not allowed.

There are two types of M-files, called scripts and functions; we discuss scripts here and Chapter 30 will discuss functions. A **script** M-file is simply a list of MATLAB statements that are saved in a file (with a **.m** file extension). The script has access to workspace variables. Any variables created in the script are accessible to the workspace when the script finishes. A script created in the MATLAB editor window can be executed by selecting the save and run option from the Debug menu bar. (See Figure 29.8.) Alternately, a script can be executed by typing a filename or by using the **run** command from the command window.

Assume you have created a script file named **example1.m**. You can either run the script from the edit window or use one of the following three equivalent ways of executing the script from the command window, as shown in Table 29.6.

Table 29.6 Executing M-files from the command window

MATLAB Command	Comments
example1	Type the file name. The .m file extension is assumed.
run example1	Use the **run** command with the file name.
run('example1')	This method uses the functional form of the **run** command.

You can find out what M-files are in the current directory by typing

what

into the command window. You can also simply browse through the current directory by looking in the current directory window.

Using M-files allows you to work on a project and to save the list of commands for future use. Because you will be using these files in the future, it is a good idea to add comments to the commands to help you remember the step in the solution, or algorithm. **Comments** are indicated by a percent sign, and they can be on a line by themselves, or at the end of a command line. MATLAB will ignore any comments when it is executed. We now present an example in which the solution is developed as an M-file. Most of the problem solutions in the rest of this text will be developed as M-files. We suggest that you use M-files when you are using MATLAB for homework solutions (in this and other courses) because you often will want to go back and rerun the program with new data, or you will want to make small changes in the statements. If you have not used an M-file to store the program, you will need to reenter the complete program when you need it in another work session.

EXAMPLE 29.3

UNDUCTED FAN ENGINE PERFORMANCE

An advanced turboprop engine, called an **unducted fan** (UDF), is one of the promising new propulsion technologies being developed for future transport aircraft. (See Figure 29.9.) Turboprop engines, which have been in use for decades, combine the power and reliability of jet engines with the efficiency of propellers. They are a significant improvement over earlier piston-powered propeller engines. Their application has been limited to smaller commuter-type aircraft, however, because they are not as fast or powerful as the fan-jet engines used on larger airliners. The UDF engine employs significant advancements in propeller technology, narrowing the performance gap between turboprops and fan-jets. New materials, blade shapes, and higher rotation speeds enable UDF-powered aircraft to fly almost as fast as fan-jets, and with greater fuel efficiency. The UDF is also significantly quieter than the conventional turboprop.

During the test flight of a UDF-powered aircraft, the pilot has set the engine power level at 40,000 N, which causes the 20,000 kg aircraft to attain a cruise speed of 180 m/s. The engine throttles are then set to a power level of 60,000 N, and the aircraft begins to accelerate. As the speed of the plane increases, the aerodynamic drag increases in proportion to the square of the air speed. Eventually, the aircraft reaches a new cruise speed, where the thrust from the UDF engines is just offset by the drag. The equations used to estimate the velocity and acceleration of the aircraft from the time the throttle is reset to the time the plane reaches new cruise speed (at approximately 120 s) are the following:

$$\text{velocity} = 0.00001 \text{ time}^3 - 0.00488 \text{ time}^2 + 0.75795 \text{ time} + 181.3566$$
$$\text{acceleration} = 3 - 0.000062 \text{ velocity}^2$$

Write a MATLAB program, using a script M-file, that calculates the velocity and acceleration of the aircraft at times from 0 to 120 seconds, and at increments of 10 seconds. Assume that time zero represents the point at which the power level was increased. Display the results in a table of time, velocity, and acceleration.

Figure 29.9   An unducted fan (UDF) engine.

SOLUTION

1. Problem Statement

Calculate the velocity and acceleration, using a script M-file.

2. Input/Output Description

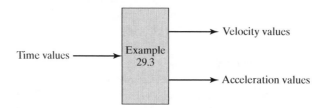

3. Hand Example

Solve the equations stated in the problem for time = 100 seconds;

4. MATLAB Solution

Create a new script M-file using the **File → New → script** menu selection. Enter these commands:

```
%-----------------------------------------------------------
% Example 29_3 This program generates velocity
% and acceleration values for a UDF aircraft test.
%
clear, clc
%
```

```
% Define the time matrix.
time = 0:10:120;
%
% Calculate the velocity and acceleration values.
velocity = 0.00001*time.^3 - 0.00488*time.^2 ...
+ 0.75795*time + 181.3566;
acceleration = 3 - 6.2e-05*velocity.^2;
%
% Display the results in a table.
disp('Time, Velocity, Acceleration Values');
disp([time',velocity',acceleration']);
%-----------------------------------------------------------
```

Save the file with a name of your choice, using the file selection from the menu bar. Remember that the file name needs to be a legitimate variable name. For example, you might save the file as **Example29_3 or ch29_ex3**.

5. Testing

Execute the file by selecting the run icon from the menu bar. The following results will be displayed in the command window.

```
Time, Velocity, Acceleration Values
        0    181.3566     0.9608
  10.0000    188.4581     0.7980
  20.0000    194.6436     0.6511
        :
 100.0000    218.3516     0.0440
 110.0000    218.9931     0.0266
 120.0000    219.3186     0.0178
```

The command window does not contain the commands executed in the script M-file. The hand example values match those computed by MATLAB. It will now be easy to modify the M-file to make changes to the program to solve other similar problems.

29.4.3 User Input from M-Files

We can create more general programs by allowing the user to input variable values from the keyboard while the program is running. The **input** command allows us to do this. It displays a text string in the command window and then waits for the user to provide the requested input. For example,

```
z = input('Enter a temperature value')
```

displays

```
Enter a temperature value
```

in the command window. If the user enters a value such as

```
5
```

the program assigns the value of 5 to the variable **z**. If the input command does not end with a semicolon, the value entered is displayed on the screen.

The same approach can be used to enter a one- or two-dimensional matrix. The user must provide the appropriate brackets and delimiters (commas and semicolons). For example,

```
z = input('Enter values in 2 rows and 3 columns');
```

requests the user to input a matrix such as:

```
[1,2,3; 4,5,6]
```

Since there is not a semicolon after the **input** statement, the following is displayed:

```
z =
   1   2   3
   4   5   6
```

We will give examples using the **input** statement in some of the problem solutions that follow in later chapters.

Summary

In this chapter, we introduced you to the MATLAB environment. In particular, we explored the window structure and solved problems in the command window. The primary data structure in MATLAB is a matrix, which can be a single point (a scalar), a list of values (a vector), or a rectangular grid of values with rows and columns. Values can be entered into a matrix by explicitly listing the values or by loading them from MAT files or ASCII files. In addition, we learned how to save values in both MAT files and ASCII files. We explored the various mathematical operations that are performed in an element-by-element manner. Finally, we learned how to use a script M-file to record the sequence of commands used to solve a MATLAB problem.

Matlab Summary

This MATLAB summary lists all the special constants, special characters, commands, and functions that were defined in this chapter:

Special Constants	
ans	value computed
clock	current time
date	current date
eps	smallest difference recognized
i	imaginary number, $\sqrt{-1}$
Inf	infinity
j	imaginary number, $\sqrt{-1}$
Nan	not-a-number
pi	mathematical constant, π

Special Characters

[ ]	forms matrices
( )	used in statements to group operations and used with a matrix name to identify specific elements
. . .	used to indicate a command continued on the next line
'	indicates the transpose of a matrix (apostrophe)
,	separates subscripts or matrix elements (comma)
;	separates rows in a matrix definition and suppresses output when used in commands
:	used to generate matrices and indicates all rows or all columns
=	assignment operator—assigns a value to a memory location—not the same as an equality
%	indicates a comment in an M-file and used in formatting output
+	scalar and element-by-element addition
−	scalar and element-by-element subtraction
°	scalar multiplication
.°	element-by-element multiplication
/	scalar division
./	element-by-element division
^	scalar exponentiation
.^	element-by-element exponentiation
\n	new line

Functions

clc	clears command screen
clear	clears workspace
disp	displays strings and variables
edit	opens the edit window
exit	terminates MATLAB
format +	sets format to plus and minus signs only
format bank	sets format to 2 decimal places
format compact	sets format to compact form
format long	sets format to 14 decimal places
formal long e	sets format to 14 exponential places
format loose	sets format back to default, noncompact form
format short	sets format back to default, four decimal places
format short e	sets format to four exponential places
fprintf	displays formatted output
help	invokes help utility
input	allows user to enter values from the keyboard
iskeyword	prints a list of keywords
isvarname	determines whether a name is a valid variable name
linspace	linearly spaced vector function
load	loads matrices from a file
namelengthmax	displays the number of characters used by MATLAB in a variable name
quit	terminates MATLAB
save	saves variables in a file
what	displays M-files in the current directory
which	specifies whether a function is built-in or user-defined
who	lists variables in memory
whos	lists variables and their sizes

KEY TERMS

array editor	operations	precedence
ascii	ellipsis	precision field
assignment operator	empty matrix	prompt
colon operator	exponent overflow	scalar
command history window	exponent underflow	scientific notation
command window	exponential notation	script file
comment	graphics window	transpose operator
current folder window	import data	up arrow
DAT-file	M-file	variable name
document window	MAT-files	vector
edit window	matrix	width field
element-by-element	operation	workspace window

Problems

Which of the following are legitimate variable names in MATLAB? Test your answers by trying to assign a value to each name by using, for example,

```
3vars = 3
```

or by using **isvarname**, as in

```
isvarname 3vars
```

Remember, **isvarname** returns a 1 if the name is legal and a 0 if it is not.

1. `3vars`
2. `global`
3. `help`
4. `My_var`
5. `sin`
6. `X+Y`
7. `_input`
8. `input`
9. `tax-rate`
10. `example1.1`
11. `example1_1`
12. Although it is possible to reassign a function name as a variable name, it is not a good idea, so checking to see if a name is also a function name is also recommended. Use **which** to check whether the preceding names are function names, as in

```
which cos
```

Are any of the names in Problems 1 to 11 also MATLAB function names?

Predict the outcome of the following MATLAB calculations. Check your results by entering the calculations into the command window.

13. `1+3/4`
14. `5*6*4/2`
15. `5/2*6*4`

16.   **5^2*3**
17.   **5^(2*3)**
18.   **1+3+5/5+3+1**
19.   **(1+3+5)/(5+3+1)**

Create MATLAB code to perform the following calculations. Remember that the square root of a value is equivalent to raising the value to the ½ power. Check your code by entering it into MATLAB.

20. 5^2

21. $\dfrac{5 + 3}{5.6}$

22. $\sqrt{4 + 6^3}$

23. $9\dfrac{6}{12} + 7 \cdot 5^{3+2}$

24. $1 + 5 \cdot 3/6^2 + 2^{2-4} \cdot 1/5 \cdot 5$

25.   The area of a circle is πr^2. Define r as 5, and then find the area of a circle.

26.   The surface area of a sphere is $4\pi r^2$. Find the surface area of a sphere with a radius of 10 ft.

27.   The volume of a sphere is $\dfrac{4}{3}\pi r^3$. Find the volume of a sphere with a radius of 2 ft.

28.   The volume of a cylinder is $\pi r^2 h$. Define r as 3 and h as the matrix

h = [1,5,12]

Find the volume of the cylinders.

29.   The area of a triangle is ½ base × height. Define the base as the matrix

b = [2,4,6]

and the height h as 12, and find the area of the triangles.

30.   The volume of a right prism is base area x vertical_dimension. Find the volumes of prisms with triangles of Problem 29 as their bases, for a vertical dimension of 10.

31.   Generate an evenly spaced vector of values from 1 to 20, in increments of 1. (Use the **linspace** command.)

32.   Generate a vector of values from zero to 2π in increments of $\pi/100$ (Use the **linspace** command.)

33.   Generate a vector containing 15 values, evenly spaced between 4 and 20. (Use the **linspace** command.)

34.   Generate a table of conversions from degrees to radians. The first line should contain the values for $0°$, the second line should contain the values for $10°$, and so on. The last line should contain the values for $360°$.

35.   Generate a table of conversions from centimeters to inches. Start the centimeters column at 0 and increment by 2 cm. The last line should contain the value 50 cm.

36.   Generate a table of conversions from mi/h to ft/s. The initial value in the mi/h column should be 0 and the final value should be 100. Print 14 values in your table.

37.   The general equation for the distance that a free falling body has traveled (neglecting air friction) is

$$d = \tfrac{1}{2}gt^2$$

Assume that $g = 9.8$ m/s^2 Generate a table of time versus distance traveled, for time from 0 to 100 sec. Be sure to use element-by-element operations, and not matrix operations.

38. Newton's law of universal gravitation tells us that the force exerted by one particle on another is

$$F = G\frac{m_1 m_2}{r^2}$$

where the universal gravitational constant is found experimentally to be

$$G = 6.673 \times 10^{-11} \text{ Nm}^2/\text{kg}^2$$

The mass of each object is m_1 and m_2, respectively, and r is the distance between the two particles. Use Newton's law of universal gravitation to find the force exerted by the Earth on the Moon, assuming that:

the mass of the Earth is approximately 6×10^{24} kg
the mass of the Moon is approximately 7.4×10^{22} kg, and
the Earth and the Moon are an average of 3.9×10^8 apart.

39. We know the Earth and the Moon are not always the same distance apart. Find the force the Moon exerts on the Earth for 10 distances between and 3.8×10^8 m and 4.0×10^8 m

Matrix Analysis

Create the following matrix **A**:

$$\mathbf{A} = \begin{bmatrix} 3.4 & 2.1 & 0.5 & 6.5 & 4.2 \\ 4.2 & 7.7 & 3.4 & 4.5 & 3.9 \\ 8.9 & 8.3 & 1.5 & 3.4 & 3.9 \end{bmatrix}$$

40. Create a matrix **B** by extracting the first column of matrix **A**.
41. Create a matrix **C** by extracting the second row of matrix **A**.
42. Use the colon operator to create a matrix **D** by extracting the first through third columns of matrix **A**.
43. Create a matrix **F** by extracting the values in rows 2, 3, and 4, and combining them into a single column matrix.
44. Create a matrix **G** by extracting the values in rows 2, 3, and 4, and combining them into a single row matrix.

Chapter 30

MATLAB Functions

ENGINEERING ACHIEVEMENT: WEATHER PREDICTION

Weather satellites provide a great deal of information to meteorologists to use in their predictions of the weather. Large volumes of historical weather data is also analyzed and used to test models for predicting weather. In general, meteorologists can do a reasonably good job of predicting overall weather patterns. However, local weather phenomena, such as tornadoes, water spouts, and microbursts, are still very difficult to predict. Even predicting heavy rainfall or large hail from thunderstorms is often difficult. Although Doppler radar is useful in locating regions within storms that could contain tornadoes or microbursts, the radar detects the events as they occur and thus allows little time for issuing appropriate warnings to populated areas or aircraft passing through the region. Accurate and timely prediction of weather and associated weather phenomena still provides many challenges for engineers and scientists. In this chapter, we present several examples related to analysis of weather phenomena.

OBJECTIVES

After reading this chapter, you should be able to

- use a variety of mathematical and trigonometric functions,
- use statistical functions,
- generate uniform and Gaussian random sequences, and
- write your own MATLAB functions.

30.1   INTRODUCTION TO FUNCTIONS

Arithmetic expressions often require computations other than addition, subtraction, multiplication, division, and exponentiation. For example, many expressions require the use of logarithms, exponentials, and trigonometric functions. MATLAB includes a **built-in** library of these useful functions. For example, if we want to compute the square root of **x** and store the result in **b**, we can use the following commands:

```
x = 9;
b = sqrt(x);
```

If **x** is a matrix, the function will be applied element-by-element to the values in the matrix, as shown in these statements:

```
x = [4,9,16];
b = sqrt(x)
b =
    2   3   4
```

All **functions** can be thought of as having three components: a name, input, and output. In this example, the name of the function is **sqrt**, the required input (also called the **argument**) goes inside the parentheses and can be a scalar or a matrix, and the output is a calculated value or values. The output was assigned the variable name **b**.

Some functions require multiple inputs. For example, the remainder function, **rem**, requires two inputs—a dividend and a divisor. We represent this as **rem(x,y)**. The function computes the remainder of the division, and returns that as the output of the function as shown in this example:

```
rem(10,3)
ans =
    1
```

The **size** function is an example of a function that returns two outputs. This function determines the number of rows and columns in a matrix, and returns the two values as a vector that represents the function output. For example,

```
d = [1,2,3; 4,5,6];
size(d)
ans =
    2   3
```

You can also assign scalar variable names to each of the outputs by representing the left-hand side of the assignment statement as a vector, as in

```
[nrows,ncols] = size(d)
x =
    2
y =
    3
```

You can create **nested functions**, as shown in this example that computes the square root of the sine of the variable x:

```
g = sqrt(sin(x))
```

When one function is used to compute the argument of another function, be sure to enclose the argument of each function in its own set of parentheses. Nesting of functions is also called **composition** of functions.

MATLAB includes extensive help tools, which are especially useful for interpreting function syntax. To use the command-line help function, type **help** in the command window. A list of help topics will appear; the following list is the first few lines of information:

```
HELP topics:
matlab\general    - general purpose commands
matlab\ops        - operators and special characters
matlab\lang       - programming language constructs
matlab\elmat      - elementary matrices and matrix
                    manipulation
matlab\randfun    - random number generating functions
matlab\elfun      - elementary math functions
matlab\specfun    - specialized math functions
```

To get help on a particular topic, type **help <topic>**. For example, to get help on the tangent function, type

```
help tan
```

The following should be displayed:

```
TAN  Tangent of argument in radians.
  TAN(X) is the tangent of the elements of X.
  See also atan, tand, atan2.
```

To use the windowed help screen, select **Help → MATLAB Help** from the menu bar. A windowed version of the help list will appear. This help function includes a MATLAB tutorial that you will find extremely useful. As shown in Figure 30.1, the list in the left-hand window is a table of contents. Notice also that the table of contents includes a link to a list of functions, organized both by category and alphabetically by name. You can use this link to find out what MATLAB functions are available to solve most problems. For example, you probably are not familiar with a mathematical function called the "error

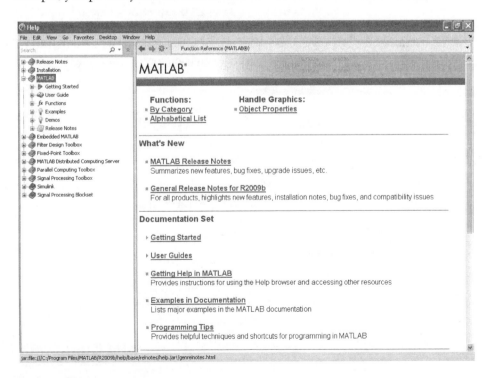

Figure 30.1 The MATLAB Help environment.

function." One place the error function occurs is in the solution to transient heat transfer problems. We will illustrate how to use the MATLAB help window to determine if a MATLAB function is available for the error function.

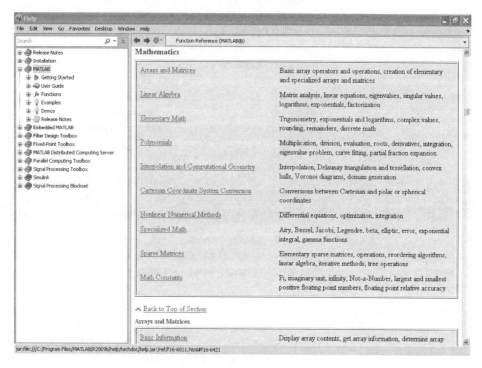

Figure 30.2   Mathematical functions Help window.

Select the **MATLAB Functions Listed by Category** link, then the Mathematics link. (See Figure 30.2.) Near the bottom of the page is the category Specialized Math, which lists the error function. Follow the links to the error function description.

The MATLAB function for the error function is **erf**, and it requires a single input. For example,

```
erf(0.8)
```

returns

```
ans =
    0.7421
```

Finally, if you are connected to the Internet, use the start button in the lower left-hand corner of the MATLAB window to access MATLAB's online content. You will also want to check The MathWorks Web site at www.mathworks.com.

30.2   ELEMENTARY MATHEMATICAL FUNCTIONS

The elementary math functions include functions to perform a number of common computations, such as computing the absolute value and the square root of a number. In addition, in this section we include a group of functions used to perform rounding:

abs(x)	Computes the absolute value of x.

```
abs(-3)
ans =
    3
```

sqrt(x)	Computes the square root of **x**. **sqrt(85)** **ans =** **9.2195**
round(x)	Rounds **x** to the nearest integer. **round(8.6)** **ans =** **9**
fix(x)	Rounds (or truncates) **x** to the nearest integer toward zero. **fix(8.6)** **ans =** **8**
floor(x)	Rounds **x** to the nearest integer toward $-$infinity. **floor(-8.6)** **ans =** **$-$9**
ceil(x)	Rounds **x** to the nearest integer toward $+$infinity. **floor(-8.6)** **ans =** **$-$8**
sign(x)	Returns a value of -1 if **x**<0, and returns a value of 0 if **x**$=0$, and returns a value of $+1$ if **x**>0. **sign(-8)** **ans =** **$-$1**
rem(x,y)	Computes the remainder of **x/y**. **rem(25,4)** **ans =** **1**
exp(x)	Computes the value of e^x where e is the base for natural logarithms or approximately 2.718282. **exp(10)** **ans =** **2.2026e+004**
log(x)	Computes ln(**x**), the natural logarithm of **x** to the base e. **log(10)** **ans =** **2.3026**
log10(x)	Computes $\log_{10}$(**x**), the common logarithm of **x** to the base 10. **log10(10)** **ans =** **1**
log2(x)	Computes $\log_2$(**x**), the logarithm of **x** to the base 2. **log2(8)** **ans =** **3**

Logarithms deserve special mention in this section. As a rule, the function **log** in all computer languages means the **natural logarithm**. Although not the standard in mathematics textbooks, this is the standard in computer programming. This is a common source of errors, especially for new users. If you want the log base 10, you'll need to use the **log10** function. A **log2** function is also included in MATLAB, but logarithms to any other base will need to be computed; there is no general logarithm function that allows the user to input the base.

You can find the syntax for other common mathematical functions by selecting **Help** from the tool bar, and following the **Mathematics** link.

EXAMPLE 30.1   ATMOSPHERIC ANALYSIS

Meteorologists study the atmosphere in an attempt to understand and ultimately predict the weather. Weather prediction is a complicated process, even with the best data. Meteorologists study chemistry, physics, thermodynamics, and geography, in addition to specialized courses about the atmosphere. (See Figure 30.3.) One equation used by meteorologists is the Clausius–Clapeyron equation, which is usually introduced in chemistry classes and examined in more detail in thermodynamics classes.

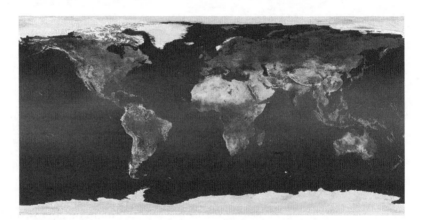

Figure 30.3   View of the Earth's weather from space.

In meteorology, the Clausius–Clapeyron equation is used to determine the relationship between saturation water-vapor pressure and the atmospheric temperature. The saturation water-vapor pressure can be used to calculate relative humidity, an important component of weather prediction, when the actual partial pressure of water in the air is known.

The Clausius–Clapeyron equation is:

$$\ln(P^{\circ}/6.11) = \left(\frac{\Delta H_v}{R_{\text{air}}}\right) * \left(\frac{1}{273} - \frac{1}{T}\right)$$

where

P° is the saturation vapor pressure for water, in mbar, at temperature T;

ΔH_v is the latent heat of vaporization for water, 2.453×10^6 J/kg;

R_{air} is the gas constant for moist air, 461 J/kg; and

T   is the temperature in degrees K.

It is rare that temperatures on the surface of the Earth are lower than $-60°F$ or higher than $120°F$. Use the Clausius–Clapeyron equation to find the saturation vapor pressure for temperatures in this range. Present your results as a table of temperature in Fahrenheit and saturation vapor pressure.

SOLUTION

1. Problem Statement

Find the saturation vapor pressure at temperatures from $-60°F$ to $120°F$, using the Clausius–Clapeyron equation.

2. Input/Output Description

Temperature values $\longrightarrow$ Example 30.1 $\longrightarrow$ Vapor pressures

3. Hand Example

The Clausius–Clapeyron equation requires all the variables to have consistent units. That means that temperature (T) needs to be in degrees K. To change Fahrenheit to Kelvin, use

$$T_k = (T_f + 459.6)/1.8$$

(There are many places to find unit conversions. The Internet is one source, as are science and engineering textbooks.)

Now we need to solve the Clausius–Clapeyron equation for the saturation vapor pressure $(P°)$. We have

$$\ln(P°/6.11) = \left(\frac{\Delta H_v}{R_{air}}\right) * \left(\frac{1}{273} - \frac{1}{T}\right)$$

$$P° = 6.11 * \exp\left(\left(\frac{\Delta H_v}{R_{air}}\right) * \left(\frac{1}{273} - \frac{1}{T}\right)\right)$$

Solve for one temperature, for example, let $T = 0°F$:

$$T = (0 + 459.6)/1.8 = 255.3333$$

$$P° = 6.11 * \exp\left(\left(\frac{2.453 \times 10^6}{461}\right) * \left(\frac{1}{273} - \frac{1}{255.3333}\right)\right) = 1.5836 \text{ mbar}$$

4. MATLAB Solution

Create the MATLAB solution in an M-file, and then run it in the command environment:

```
%-------------------------------------------------------------
% Example 30_1 This program computes the saturation
% vapor pressure for water at different temperatures.
%
clear, clc
%
% Define the temperature matrix in F and convert to K.
TF = [-60:10:120];
TK = (TF + 459.6)/1.8;
%
% Define latent heat constant and ideal gas constant.
Delta_H = 2.45e6;
R_air = 461;
```

```
%
% Calculate the vapor pressures.
Vapor_Pressure = 6.11*exp((Delta_H/R_air)*(1/273 -
1./TK));
%
% Display the results in a table.
disp('Temp(k) and Vapor Pressure');
disp([TF',Vapor_Pressure'])
%-----------------------------------------------------
```

When creating a MATLAB program, it is a good idea to comment liberally. This makes your program easier for others to understand, and may make it easier for you to debug. Notice that most of the lines of code end with a semicolon, which suppresses the output. Therefore, the only information that displays in the command window is the output table.

5. Testing

The output from this program is shown below:

```
Temp(k) and Vapor Pressure
-60.0000      0.0698
-50.0000      0.1252
-40.0000      0.2184
-30.0000      0.3714
-20.0000      0.6163
-10.0000      1.0000
      0       1.5888
      :
100.0000     65.5257
110.0000     88.4608
120.0000    118.1931
```

The hand solution and the MATLAB solution match for $T = 0°F$. The Clausius–Clapeyron equation can be used for more than just humidity problems. By changing the value of ΔH and R, you could generalize the program to any condensing vapor.

30.3   TRIGONOMETRIC FUNCTIONS

The trigonometric functions **sin, cos,** and **tan** all assume that angles are represented in radians. The trigonometric functions **sind, cosd**, and **tand** all assume that angles are represented in degrees. To convert radians to degrees, or degrees to radians, use the following conversions, which utilize the fact that 180° is equal to π radians:

```
angle_degrees = angle_radians*(180/pi);
angle_radians = angle_degrees*(pi/180);
```

In trigonometric calculations, the value of π is often needed, so a constant, **pi**, is built into MATLAB. However, since π cannot be expressed as a floating-point number, the constant **pi** in MATLAB is only an approximation of the mathematical quantity π. Usually, this is not important; however, you may notice some surprising results—for example,

```
sin(pi)
ans =
    1.2246e-016
```

We expected an answer of zero; we got a very small answer, but not zero.

Access the Help function from the menu bar and follow the instructions in Section 30.1 for a complete list of trigonometric functions available in MATLAB. Note that there are function for arguments in radians, and functions for arguments in degrees; some of these are listed here:

sin(x)   Computes the sine of **x**, where **x** is in radians.
```
sin(pi/2)
ans =
     1
```

sind(x)   Computes the sine of **x**, where **x** is in degrees.
```
sind(90)
ans =
     1
```

cos(x)   Computes the cosine of **x**, where **x** is in radians.
```
cos(pi)
ans =
    -1
```

tan(x)   Computes the tangent of **x**, where **x** is in radians.
```
tan(pi)
ans =
    -1.2246e-016
```

asin(x)   Computes the arcsine, or inverse sine, of **x**, where x must be between -1 and 1. The function returns an angle in radians between $\pi/2$ and $-\dfrac{\pi}{2}$.
```
asin(-1)
ans =
    -1.5708
```

sinh(x)   Computes the hyperbolic sine of **x**, where **x** is in radians.
```
sinh(pi)
ans =
    11.5487
```

EXAMPLE 30.2

COMPUTING DISTANCES USING GPS

The GPS (Global Positioning System) coordinates that specify a location on the Earth are the latitude and longitude values for the position. In this section, we develop an algorithm and MATLAB program to determine the distance between two objects given their latitudes and longitudes. Before developing the programs, we need to briefly discuss latitudes and longitudes and develop an equation to determine the distance between the two points using these coordinates.

Assume that Earth is represented by a sphere with a radius of 3960 miles. A **great circle** is formed by the intersection of this sphere and a plane that passes through the center of the sphere. If the plane does not pass through the center of the sphere, it will be a circle with a smaller circumference and hence is not a great circle. The **prime meridian** is a north-south great circle that passes through Greenwich, just outside London, and

Figure 30.4   Rectangular Coordinate System for the Earth.

through the North Pole. The **equator** is an east-west great circle that is equidistant from the North Pole and the South Pole. Thus, we can define a **rectangular coordinate** system such that the origin is the center of the Earth, the z-axis goes from the center of the Earth through the North Pole, and the x-axis goes from the center of the Earth through the point where the prime meridian intersects the equator. (See Figure 30.4.) The **latitude** is an angular distance, is measured in degrees, and extends northward or southward from the equator (as in 25 N); and the **longitude** is an angular distance, is measured in degrees, and extends westward or eastward from the prime meridian (as in 120 W).

The **Global Positioning System (GPS)**, originally developed for military use, uses 24 satellites circling the Earth to pinpoint a location on the surface. Each satellite broadcasts a coded radio signal indicating the time and the satellite's exact position 11,000 miles above the Earth. The satellites are equipped with an atomic clock that is accurate to within one second every 70,000 years. A GPS receiver picks up the satellite signal and measures the time between the signal's transmission and its reception. By comparing signals from at least three satellites, the receiver can determine the latitude, longitude, and altitude of its position.

The shortest distance between two points on a sphere is known to be on the arc of the great circle containing them. If we know the angle between vectors from the center of the Earth to the two points defining the arc, we can then estimate the distance as a proportion of the Earth's circumference. To illustrate, suppose that the angle between two vectors from the center of the Earth is 45°. Then the angle is 45/360, or 1/8 of a complete revolution. Hence, the distance between the two points is 1/8 of the Earth's circumference (pi times twice the radius) or 3110 miles.

The best way to compute the shortest distance between two points that are specified in latitude (α) and longitude (β) is through a series of coordinate transformations. Recall that the **spherical coordinates** (ρ, φ, θ) of a point P in a rectangular coordinate system represents the length ρ (rho) of the vector connection the point to the origin, the angle φ (phi) between the positive z-axis and the vector, and the angle θ (theta) between the x-axis and the projection of the vector in the xy-plane. (See Figure 30.5.)

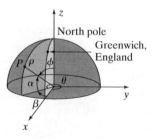

Figure 30.5   Spherical Coordinate System for the Earth.

We then convert the spherical coordinates to rectangular coordinates (x,y,z). Finally a simple trigonometric equation computes the angle between the points (or vectors) in rectangular coordinates. Once we know the angle between the points, we can then use the technique described in the previous paragraph to find the distance between the two points.

We need to use equations that relate latitude and longitude to spherical coordinates, that convert spherical coordinates to rectangular coordinates, and that compute the angle between two vectors. Figure 30.5 is useful in relating the notation to the following equations:

- Latitude/longitude and spherical coordinates:

$$\alpha = 90° - \varphi, \beta = 360° - \theta$$

- Spherical and rectangular coordinates:

$$x = \rho \sin \varphi \cos \theta, y = \rho \sin \varphi \sin \theta, z = \rho \cos \theta$$

- Angle γ between two vectors a and b:

$$\cos \gamma = a \cdot b/(|a||b|)$$

where $a \cdot b$ is the dot product (defined below) of a and b and where $|a|$ is the length of the vector a (also defined below)

- Dot product of two vectors (xa, ya, za) and (xb, yb, zb) in rectangular coordinates:

$$a \cdot b = xa \cdot xb + ya \cdot yb + za \cdot zb$$

- Length of a vector (xa, yz, za) in rectangular coordinates:

$$\sqrt{(xa^2 + ya^2 + za^2)}$$

- Great circle distance:

$$\text{distance} = (\gamma/(2\pi))(\text{Earth's circumference}) = (\gamma/(2\pi))(\pi \cdot 2 \text{ radius}) = \gamma \cdot 3960.$$

Pay close attention to the angle units in these equations. Unless otherwise specified, it is assumed that the angles are measured in radians.

Write a MATLAB program that asks the user to enter the latitude and longitude coordinates for two points in the Northern Hemisphere. Then compute and print the shortest distance between the two points.

1. Problem Statement

Compute the shortest distance between two points in the Northern Hemisphere.

2. Input/Output Description

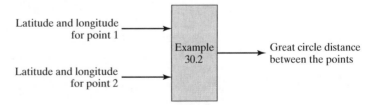

3. Hand Example

For a hand example, we will compute the great circle distance between New York and London. The latitude and longitude of New York is 40.75°N and 74°W, respectively, and the latitude and longitude of London is 51.5° N and 0° W, respectively.

The spherical coordinates for New York are

$$\varphi = (90 - 40.75)° = 4925(\pi/180) = 0.8596$$
$$\theta = (360 - 74)° = 286(\pi/180) = 4.9916$$
$$\rho = 3960.$$

The rectangle coordinates for New York (to two decimal places) are

$$x = \rho \sin \varphi \cos \theta = 826.90$$
$$y = \rho \sin \varphi \sin \theta = -2883.74$$
$$z = \rho \cos \theta = 2584.93.$$

Similarly, the rectangular coordinates for London can be computed to be

$$x = 2465.16, y = 0, z = 3099.13.$$

The cosine of the angle between the two vectors is equal to the dot product of the two vectors divided by the product of their lengths, or 0.6408. Using an inverse cosine function, g can be determined to be 0.875 radians. Finally, the distance between New York and London is

$$0.875 \cdot 3960 = 3466 \text{ miles.}$$

4. MATLAB Program

```
%-------------------------------------------------------------
% Example 30_2 This program determines the distance
between
% two points that are specified with latitude and longitude
% values that are in the Northern Hemisphere.
%
clear, clc
%
% Get locations of two points.
lat1 = input('Enter latitude north for point 1: ');
long1 = input('Enter longitude west for point 1: ');
lat2 = input('Enter latitude north for point 2: ');
long2 = input('Enter longitude west for point 2: ');
%
% Convert latitude and longitude to rectangular coordinates.
rho = 3960;
phi = (90 - lat1)*(pi/180);
theta = (360 - long1)*(pi/180);
x1 = rho*sin(phi)*cos(theta);
y1 = rho*sin(phi)*sin(theta);
z1 = rho*cos(phi);
phi = (90 - lat2)*(pi/180);
theta = (360 - long2)*(pi/180);
x2 = rho*sin(phi)*cos(theta);
y2 = rho*sin(phi)*sin(theta);
z2 = rho*cos(phi);
%
% Compute the angle between vectors.
dot = x1*x2 + y1*y2 + z1*z2;
```

```
dist1 = sqrt(x1*x1 + y1*y1 + z1+z1);
dist2 = sqrt(x2*x2 + y2*y2 + z2*z2);
gamma = acos(dot/(dist1*dist2));
%
% Compute and print the great circle distance.
display('Great Circle Distance in miles:');
fprintf(%8.0f \n',gamma*rho)
%-------------------------------------------------
```

5. Testing

We start testing with the hand example, which gives the following interaction:

```
Enter latitude north for point 1: 40.75
Enter longitude west for point 1: 74
Enter latitude north for point 2: 51.5
Enter longitude west for point 2: 0
Great Circle Distance in miles:
    3466
```

This matches our hand example. Try this with some other locations, but remember that you need to choose points that are in the northern latitude and western longitude. The equations need to be slightly modified for points in other parts of the world.

30.4   DATA ANALYSIS FUNCTIONS

Analyzing data is an important part of evaluating test results. MATLAB contains a number of functions that make it easier to evaluate and analyze data. We first present a number of simple analysis functions, and then functions that compute more complicated measures or metrics related to a data set.

30.4.1 Simple Analysis

The following groups of functions are frequently used in evaluating a set of test data: maximum and minimum, mean and median, sums and products, and sorting. We now cover each group separately.

The **max** and **min** function can be used in a number of ways to determine not only the maximum and minimum values, but also their locations in a matrix. Here are a set of examples to illustrate the various ways to use these functions.

max(x)	Returns the largest value in the vector **x**.

```
x = [1,5,3];
max(x)
ans =
     5
```

max(x)	Returns a row vector containing the maximum value from each column of the matrix **x**.

```
x = [1,5,3;
     2,4,6];
max(x)
ans =
     2   5   6
```

`[a,b] = max(x)`	Returns a vector containing the largest value in a vector **x** and its location in the vector **x**.
	
	`x = [1,5,3];`
	`[a,b] = max(x)`
	`a =`
	`    5`
	`b =`
	`    2`

`[a,b] = max(x)`	Returns a row vector a containing the maximum element from each column of the matrix **x**, and returns a row vector **b** containing location of the maximum in each column of the matrix **x**.
	
	`x = [1,5,3;`
	`     2,4,6];`
	`[a,b] = max(x)`
	`a =`
	`    2  5  6`
	
	`b =`
	`    2  1  2`

`max(x,y)`	Returns a matrix the same size as **x** and **y**. (Both **x** and **y** must have the same number of rows and columns.) Each element in the resulting matrix contains the maximum value from the corresponding positions in **x** and **y**.
	
	`x = [ 1,5,3; 2,4,6];`
	`y = [10,2,4; 1,8,7];`
	`max(x,y)`
	`ans =`
	`      10  5 4`
	`       2  8 7`

`min(x)`	Returns the smallest value in the vector **x**.
	
	`x = [1,5,3];`
	`min(x)`
	`ans =`
	`       3`

`min(x)`	Returns a row vector containing the minimum value from each column of the matrix **x**.
	
	`x = [1,5,3;`
	`2,4,6];`
	`min(x)`
	`ans =`
	`    1  4  3`

`[a,b] = min(x)`	Returns a vector containing the smallest value in a vector **x** and its location in the vector **x**.
	
	`x = [1,5,3];`
	`[a,b] = max(x)`
	`a =`
	`     1`
	`b =`
	`     1`

`[a,b] = min(x)`	Returns a row vector **a** containing the minimum element from each column of the matrix **x**, and returns a row vector **b** containing location of the maximum in each column of the matrix **x**.

```
x = [1,5,3;
     2,4,6];
[a,b] = min(x)
a =
    1   4   3
b =
    1   2   1
```

`min(x,y)`	Returns a matrix the same size as x and y. (Both x and y must have the same number of rows and columns.) Each element in the resulting matrix contains the maximum value from the corresponding positions in x and y.

```
x = [ 1,5,3; 2,4,6];
y = [10,2,4; 1,8,7];
min(x,y)
ans =
    1   2   3
    1   4   6
```

The **mean** of a group of values is the average of the values. The Greek symbol μ (mu) represents the value of the mean in many mathematics and engineering applications:

$$\mu = \frac{\sum_{k=1}^{N} x_k}{N}$$

$$\sum_{k=1}^{N} x_k = x_1 + x_2 + x_3 + \cdots + x_N$$

In simple terms, to find the mean, just add up all the values and divide by the total. The **median** is the value in the middle of the group, assuming that the values are sorted. If there is an odd number of values, the median is the value in the middle position. If there is an even number of values, then the median is the mean of the two middle values. The functions for computing the mean and the median are as follows:

`mean(x)`	Computes the mean value (or average value) of a vector x.

```
x = [1,5,3]
mean(x)
ans =
       3.0000
```

`mean(x)`	Returns a row vector containing the mean value from each column of a matrix **x**.

```
x = [1,5,3;
     2,4,6];
mean(x)
ans =
       1.5000   4.5000   4.5000
```

`median(x)`	Finds the median of the elements of a vector x.

```
x = [1,5,3]
median(x)
```

```
          ans =
                3
```

median(x)
Returns a row vector containing the median of each column of a matrix **x**.
```
x = [1,5,3;
     2,4,6];
median(x)
ans =
      1.5000   4.5000   4.5000
```

MATLAB also contains functions for computing the sums and products of vectors (or of the columns in a matrix) and functions for computing the cumulative sums and products of vectors (or the elements of a matrix):

sum(x)
Computes the sum of the elements the vector **x**.
```
x = [1,5,3];
sum(x)
ans =
      9
```

sum(x)
Computes a row vector containing the sum of the elements from each column of the matrix **x**.
```
x = [1,5,3;
     2,4,6];
sum(x)
ans =
      3  9  9
```

prod(x)
Computes the sum of the elements the vector **x**.
```
x = [1,5,3];
prod(x)
ans =
      15
```

prod(x)
Computes a row vector containing the product of the elements from each column of the matrix **x**.
```
x = [1,5,3;
     2,4,6];
product(x)
ans =
      2  20  18
```

cumsum(x)
Computes a vector of the same size as **x** containing the cumulative sums of the elements of **x** from each column of the matrix **x**.
```
x = [1,5,3;
     2,4,6];
cumsum(x)
```

```
               ans =
                    1   5   3
                    3   9   9
```

cumprod(x)   Computes a vector of the same size as **x** containing the cumulative products of the elements of **x** from each column of the matrix **x**.

```
               x = [1,5,3;
                    2,4,6];
               cumprod(x)
               ans =
                    1    5    3
                    2   20   18
```

The **sort** command arranges the values of a vector **x** into ascending order. If **x** is a matrix, the command sorts each column into ascending order:

sort(x)   Computes the sum of the elements the vector **x**.

```
               x = [1,5,3];
               sort(x)
               ans =
                    1   3   5
```

sort(x)   Computes a row vector containing the sum of the elements from each column of the matrix **x**.

```
               x = [1,5,3;
                    2,4,6];
               sort(x)
               ans =
                    1   4   3
                    2   5   6
```

Hint: All of the functions in this section work on the columns in two-dimensional matrices. If your data analysis requires you to evaluate data in rows, the data must be transposed—in other words, the rows must become columns and the columns must become rows. The transpose operator is a single quote ('). For example, if you want to find the maximum value in each row of matrix **x**, use this command:

```
x = [1,5,3;
     2,4,6];
max(x')
ans =
        5   6
```

MATLAB offers two functions that allow us to determine the size of a matrix: **size** and **length**:

size(x)   Determines the number of rows and columns in the matrix **x**.

```
               x = [1,5,3;
                    2,4,6];
               size(x)
               ans =
                    2   3
```

`[a,b] = size(x)`	Determines the number of rows in **x** and assigns that value to **a**, and determines the number of columns in **x** and assigns that value to **b**.

```
x = [1,5,3;
     2,4,6];
[a,b] = size(x)
a =
    2
b =
    3
```

`length(x)`	Determines the largest dimension of the matrix x; this is also the value of **max(size(x))**.

```
x = [1,5,3;
     2,4,6];
length(x)
ans =
    3
```

EXAMPLE 30.3

PEAK WIND SPEEDS FROM MOUNT WASHINGTON OBSERVATORY

Rising to 6288 ft., New Hampshire's Mount Washington is not among the world's highest mountains. Nevertheless, it lays claim to being the "Home of the World's Worst Weather." Extreme cold, freezing fog, snow, and wind . . . especially wind . . . are commonplace here, as shown in Figure 30.6.

Figure 30.6 Mount Washington Observatory.

On April 10, 1934, weather maps showed a weak storm developing well to the west of New Hampshire, another system off the coast of North Carolina, and a high pressure ridge building over eastern Canada and the North Atlantic. The high pressure ridge strengthened the following day, blocking the systems approaching from the west and south, causing them to converge on Mount Washington and the research station at its summit. As night came, winds were already well over 100 mph and the research team at the Observatory prepared for superhurricane conditions. April 12 brought even more strengthening with gusts frequently over 220 mph, until 1:21 p.m., when the peak of 231 mph was recorded. It remains today the highest surface wind speed ever officially recorded on Earth.

Mount Washington Observatory collects extensive weather data, some of which can be obtained from their Web site, www.mountwashington.org. Analyzing large amounts of such data can be confusing, so it is a good idea to start with a smaller data set, develop an approach that works, and then apply it to larger data sets. Table 30.1 provides one such set of monthly peak wind data from four successive years, recorded by the Observatory. Enter the data in an Excel file named **Wind_Data**, such that each row of the file represents one month and each column represents a year. The Excel file should contain only the data shown in Table 30.1, not the text information.

TABLE 30.1   Peak monthly peak wind speed (mph)

	2005	2006	2007	2008
January	113	142	121	110
February	117	137	127	118
March	117	119	117	145
April	95	110	156	118
May	90	88	113	93
June	58	86	89	84
July	61	99	72	88
August	82	97	94	85
September	129	96	95	93
October	136	158	110	97
November	110	92	110	110
December	104	102	124	129

1. Problem Statement

Using the data in the file **Wind_Data.xls**, find the average peak wind speed by month, the average peak wind speed by year, and the month and year that recorded the highest peak wind speed.

2. Input/Output Description

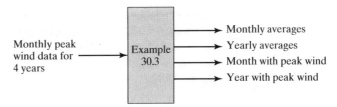

3. Hand Example

The data set is small enough to allow us to find some of the results we expect to obtain later with our MATLAB solution. For example, the average of the peak wind speeds for the month of January is

$$(113 + 142 + 121 + 110)/4 = 121.5 \text{ mph}$$

The average peak wind speed for the year 2005 is

$$(113 + 117 + 117 + 95 + 90 + 58 + 61 + 82 + \\ 129 + 136 + 110 + 104) = 101 \text{ mph}$$

Finally, we can see by inspecting the data in the table that the highest overall peak wind speed was 158 mph, occurring in October, 2006. This hand example will help us develop the MATLAB solution for the data set and ensure it is working correctly for this set as well as larger ones.

4. MATLAB Solution

First, we will put the data file into the MATLAB workspace as a matrix. Since it is an Excel spreadsheet, the easiest approach is to use the import wizard (shown in Figure 30.7) by choosing **File → Import Data**, and then selecting **Wind_Data**. Once the import

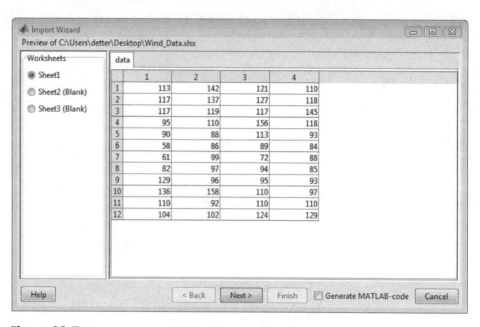

Figure 30.7   MATLAB Import Wizard.

wizard has completed the import, the variable name **data** will appear in the workspace window. We now write the script M-file to solve the problem:

```
%-------------------------------------------------
% Example 30_3 This program calculates statistics
% from a set of data from Mount Washington.
%
clc
%
% Use the import wizard to copy the wind data from
% an excel spread sheet into the variable data.
% Then copy the data into wd.
wd = data;
%
% Find the monthly averages (stored in the rows).
disp('Monthly Averages')
```

```
disp(sum(wd')/4)
%
% Find the yearly averages (stored in the columns).
disp('Yearly Averages')
disp(sum(wd)/12)
%
% Find the month in which the peak wind occurred
disp('Peak Wind and Corresponding Month')
[peak,month] = max(max(wd'))
%
% Find the year in which the peak wind occurred
disp('Peak Wind and Corresponding Year')
disp('Peak Wind and Corresponding Year')
[peak,year] = max(max(wd))
%-----------------------------------------------
```

Notice that the code did not start with our usual **clear, clc** commands, because that would clear the workspace, effectively deleting the **data** variable. Next, we rename **data** to **wd**, to make the name more unique as well as shorter. We will be using this variable frequently, so it is a good idea to make it short to minimize the chance of errors caused by mistyping.

Next, the matrix **wd** is transposed, so that the data for each month is in a column instead of a row. That allows us to use the **sum** command to add up all the wind values for the month. Dividing by 4 will calculate the averages for each month. Similarly, we can add up all the monthly totals to get the total for the year and divide by 12 to get the averages for each year.

The transpose of the matrix is used for determining the overall peak wind value and the month in which it occurred. Understanding this command line is easier if we break the command into two commands. The first part of the command, **max(wd')**, computes a vector with the maximum value for each month. Thus, **max(max(wd;))** will determine the maximum of all 12 months and will also determine which month. A similar operation with **wd**, instead of **wd'**, will allow us to determine the year in which the peak wind occurred. We can see already from this output that the maximum speed of 158 mph occurred in the tenth month (October) and second year (2006).

5. Testing

The output from this program is shown in below:

```
Monthly Averages
  121.5000  124.7500  124.5000  119.7500   96.0000   79.2500
   80.0000   89.5000  103.2500  125.2500  105.5000  114.7500

Yearly Averages
  101.0000  110.5000  110.6667  105.8333

Peak Wind and Corresponding Month
peak =
     158
month =
       10
Peak Wind and Corresponding Year
peak =
     158
year =
     2
```

Compare the MATLAB output to the hand example computation done earlier to confirm that the averages, the maximum, and the corresponding month and year were correctly determined. Once you have confirmed that the M-file works properly, you can use it to analyze other data sets, especially much larger ones where hand examples may not be easy to perform.

There are several things you should notice after executing this M-file. In the workspace window, both **data** and **wd** are listed. All of the variables created when the M-file **Example30_3** is executed are available for additional calculations, to be entered in the command window, if desired. Also notice that the original Excel file, **Wind_Data.xls**, is still in the current directory. Finally, notice that the command history window only reflects commands issued from the command window. It does not show commands executed from an M-file.

30.4.2   Variance and Standard Deviation

Two of the most important statistical measurements of a set of data are the **variance** and the **standard deviation**. Before we give their mathematical definitions, it is useful to develop an intuitive understanding of these values. Consider the values of vectors **data_1** and **data_2**, plotted in Figures 30.8(a) and 30.8(b).

If we attempt to draw a line through the middle of the values in the plots, this line would be at approximately 3.0 in both plots. Thus, we would assume that both vectors have approximately the same mean value of 3.0. However, the data in the two vectors clearly have some distinguishing characteristics. The data values in **data_2** vary more, or deviate more, from the mean. Thus, measures of variance and deviation for the values in **data_2** will be greater than measures of variance and deviation for **data_1**. An intuitive understanding of variance (or deviation) relates to the variance of the values from the mean. The larger the variance, the further the values fluctuate from the mean value.

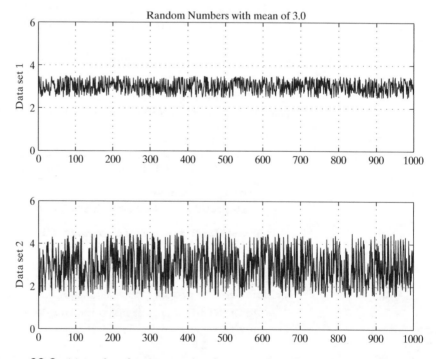

Figure 30.8   (a) Random data (**data_1**) with a mean of 3.0. (b) Random data (**data_2**) with a mean of 3.0.

Mathematically, the variance σ^2 of a set of data values (which we will assume are stored in a vector **x**) can be computed with the following equation:

$$\sigma^2 = \frac{\displaystyle\sum_{k=1}^{N}(x_k - \mu)^2}{N - 1}.$$

This equation is a bit intimidating at first, but if you look at it closely it seems much simpler. The term $x_k - \mu$ is the difference, or deviation, of x_k from the mean. This value is squared so that we will always have a positive value. We then add together the squared deviations for all of the data points. This sum is then divided by N-1, which approximates an average. (The equation for variance sometimes uses a denominator of N, but the form here has statistical properties that make N-1 generally more desirable.) Thus, the variance is the average squared deviation of the data from the mean.

The standard deviation is defined as the square root of the variance, or

$$\sigma = \sqrt{\sigma^2}$$

where σ is the Greek symbol sigma. In a normal (Gaussian) distribution of a large amount of data, approximately 68 percent of the data falls within one sigma variation of the mean ($\pm$ one sigma). If you extend the range to a two-sigma variation ($\pm$ two sigma), approximately 95 percent of the data should fall inside these bounds, and if you go out to three sigma, over 99 percent of the data should fall in this range. (See Figure 30.9.)

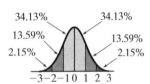

Figure 30.9 Normal distribution of data.

The function for calculating standard deviation is shown below. (MATLAB does not have a built-in function for variance, but to compute the variance we just square the standard deviation.

std(x)	Computes the standard deviation of the elements of a vector x.

```
x = [1,5,3]
std(x)
ans =
    2
```

std(x)	Returns a row vector containing the standard deviation of each column of a matrix **x**.

```
x = [1,5,3;
     2,4,6];
std(x)
ans =
     0.7071  0.7071  2.1213
```

30.5 RANDOM NUMBER GENERATING FUNCTIONS

There are many engineering problems that require the use of random numbers in the development of a solution. In some cases, the random numbers are used to develop a simulation of a complex problem. The simulation can be tested over and over to analyze the results, and each test represents a repetition of the experiment. We also use random numbers to approximate noise sequences. For example, the static we hear on a radio is a noise sequence. If we are testing a program that uses an input data file that represents a radio signal, we may want to generate noise and add it to a speech signal or music signal to provide a more realistic sound.

30.5.1 Uniform Random Numbers

Random numbers are not defined by an equation; instead, they can be characterized by a distribution of values. For example, random numbers that are equally likely to be any value between an upper and lower limit are called **uniform random numbers**.

The **rand** function in MATLAB generates random numbers uniformly distributed over the interval 0 to 1. A **seed** value is used to initiate a random sequence of values. This seed value is initially set to zero, but it can be changed with the **rand** function. The actual random values depend on the seed value, so the value you see when you run these statements may differ.

rand(n)	Returns a matrix with **n** rows and **n** columns. Each value in the matrix is a uniform random number between 0 and 1.
	
	`rand(2)`
	`ans =`
	`    0.9501    0.6068`
	`    0.2311    0.4860`

rand(m,n)	Returns a matrix with **m** rows and **n** columns. Each value in the matrix is a uniform random number between 0 and 1.
	
	`rand(3,2)`
	`ans =`
	`    0.8913    0.0185`
	`    0.7621    0.8214`
	`    0.4565    0.4447`

rand('seed',n)	Sets the value of the seed to the value of **n**. The value of **n** is initially set to 0. This allows you to specify a different starting point in the random number calculations.

rand('seed')	Returns the current value of the random seed. This allows you to start generating random numbers with the same seed in order to get the same sequence of values.
	
	`rand('seed')`
	`ans =`
	`        1.1647e+009`

Random sequences with values that range between values other than 0 and 1 are often needed. Suppose we want to generate values between $+5$ and -5. First, we generate random numbers between 0 and 1, and store them in the matrix **r**:

`r = rand(100,1);`

Because the difference between $+5$ and -5 is 10, we know that we want our random numbers to vary over a range of 10, so we will need to multiply everything by 10:

```
r = r*10;
```

Now our random numbers vary from 0 to 10. If we add the lower bound (-5) to our matrix, with this command

```
r = r - 5;
```

the result will be random numbers varying from -5 to 5. We can generalize these results with the equation

$$x = (b - a) \cdot r + a$$

where

a is the lower bound,
b is the upper bound, and
r is a set of random numbers.

30.5.2 Gaussian Random Numbers

When we generate a random number sequence with a uniform distribution, all values are equally likely to occur. However, we sometimes need to generate random numbers using distributions in which some values are more likely to be generated than others. For example, suppose that a random number sequence represents outdoor temperature measurements taken over a period of time. We would find that the temperature measurements have some variation, but typically are not equally likely. For example, we might find that the values vary only a few degrees, although larger changes would occasionally occur because of storms, cloud shadows, and day-to-night changes.

Random number sequences that have some values that are more likely to occur than others are often modeled as **Gaussian random numbers** (also called **normal random numbers**). An example of a set of values with a Gaussian distribution is shown in Figure 30.9. Although a uniform random variable has specific upper and lower bounds, a Gaussian random variable is not defined in terms of upper and lower bounds; it is defined in terms of the mean value and the variance, or standard deviation, of the values. For Gaussian random numbers, approximately 68 percent of the values will fall with one standard deviation, 95 percent with two standard deviations, and 99 percent within three standard deviations from the mean.

MATLAB will generate Gaussian values with a mean of 0 and a variance of 1.0 if we specify a normal distribution. The functions for generating Gaussian values are as follows:

randn(n)   Returns a matrix with n rows and n columns. Each value in the matrix is a Gaussian, or normal, random number with a mean of 0 and a variance of 1.

```
randn(2)
ans =
    -0.4326   0.1253
    -1.6656   0.2877
```

rand(m,n)   Returns a matrix with m rows and n columns. Each value in the matrix is a Gaussian, or normal, random number between 0 and 1.

```
randn(3,2)
```

```
ans =
        -1.1465    0.0376
         1.1909    0.3273
         1.1892    0.1746
```

The functions already presented to specify the value of the seed, or to save the value of the seed, work independently of whether the random numbers are uniform or Gaussian.

To modify Gaussian values with a mean of 0 and a variance of 1 to another Gaussian distribution, multiply the values by the standard deviation of the desired distribution, and add the mean of the desired distribution. Thus, if r is a random number sequence with a mean of 0 and a variance of 1.0, the following equation will generate a new random number with a standard deviation of a and a mean of b:

$$x = a \cdot r + b$$

For example, to create a sequence of 500 Gaussian random variables with a standard deviation of 2.5 and a mean of 3, use

```
x = randn(1,500)*2.5 + 3;
```

EXAMPLE 30.4

PEAK WIND STANDARD DEVIATION FROM MOUNT WASHINGTON OBSERVATORY

Climatologists examine weather data over long periods of time, trying to find patterns. Weather data have been kept reliably in the United States since the 1850s; however, most reporting stations have only been in place since the 1930s and 1940s. Climatologists perform statistical analyses on the data they collect to detect recurring patterns, trends, and anomalies. Although the data in **Wind_Data.xls** (discussed in Example 30.3) only represent one location for four years, we can use the data to practice statistical calculations. Find the standard deviation for each month and for each year, and then find the standard deviation for the entire data set.

1. Problem Statement

Find the standard deviation for each month, each year, and for the entire data set.

2. Input/Output Description

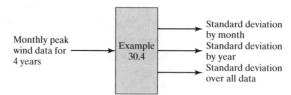

3. Hand Example

The standard deviation is found with the equation from page 829. Using only the month of January, first calculate the sum of the squares of the difference between the mean value of 121.5 and the actual value:

$$(113 - 121.5)^2 + (142 - 121.5)^2 + (121 - 121.5)^2 + (110 - 121.5)^2 = 625$$

Divide this sum by the number of data points minus 1:

$$625/(4 - 1) = 208.3333$$

Finally, take the square root to get 14.4338 mph.

4. MATLAB Solution

```
%-----------------------------------------------------------------------------------------
% Example 30_4 This program calculates the mean
% peak wind speed by month and by year, and finds the
% standard deviation of the peak speeds by month,
% by year, and for all four years.
%
clc
% Use the import wizard to copy the wind data from
% an excel spread sheet into the variable data.
% Then copy the data into wd.
load wd;
%
% Find the standard deviation for each month
disp('Monthly Standard Deviation')
disp(std(wd'))
%
% Find the standard deviation for each year
disp('Yearly Standard Deviation')
disp(std(wd))
%
% Find the standard deviation for all months and years
disp('Overall Standard Deviation')
disp(std(wd(:)))
%-----------------------------------------------------------------------------------------
```

The transpose operator is used in this example to find the mean values by month. When we use the matrix again without the transpose, it finds the mean values by year. Finally, recall that

```
wd(:)
```

converts the two-dimensional matrix **wd** into a one-dimensional vector, thus making it possible to find the standard deviation of all the entire data set in one command.

5. Testing

When we execute this M-file, the following results appear in the command window:

```
Monthly Standard Deviation
14.4338   9.3229  13.6991  25.9792  11.5181  14.3149
16.8325   7.1414  17.2119  27.1953   9.0000  13.7447
Yearly Standard Deviation
24.7203  23.4889  21.6179  19.1588
Total Standard Deviation
21.9894
```

First, check the results visually to make sure they make sense. Notice that the mean values and that the standard deviations vary much more from month-to-month than they do from year-to-year, which is what we would expect. Also compare the MATLAB output to the hand example done earlier to confirm that the standard deviations were correctly determined. As before, once you have confirmed the M-file works properly, you can use it to analyze other data sets.

EXAMPLE 30.5

FLIGHT SIMULATOR

Computer simulations are used to generate situations that model or emulate a real world situation. Some computer simulations are written to play games such as checkers, poker, and chess. To play the game, you indicate your move, and the computer will select an appropriate response. Other animated games use computer graphics to develop an interaction as you use the keys or a mouse to play the game. In more sophisticated computer simulations, such as those in a flight simulator, the computer not only responds to the input from the user, but also generates values, such as temperatures, wind speeds, and the locations of other aircraft. The simulators also model emergencies that occur during the flight of an aircraft. If all of this information generated by the computer were always the same set of information, the value of the simulator would be greatly reduced. It is important that there be randomness to the generation of the data. Simulations that use random numbers to generate values that model events are called **Monte Carlo simulations**.

Write a program to generate a random-number sequence to simulate one hour of wind speed data that are updated every 10 seconds. Assume that the wind speed will be modeled as a uniform distribution, random number that varies between a lower limit and an upper limit. Let the lower limit be 5 mph and the upper limit be 10 mph. Save the data to an ASCII file named **windspd.dat**.

SOLUTION

1. Problem Statement

Generate one hour of wind speed data using a lower limit of 5 mph and an upper limit of 10 mph.

2. Input/Output Description

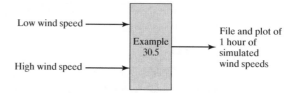

3. Hand Example

This simulation uses MATLAB's random-number generator to generate numbers between 0 and 1. We then modify these values to be between a lower limit (5) and an upper limit (10). Using the equation developed in Section 30.1.5,

$$x = (b - a) \cdot r + a$$

we first multiply the range (10–5) times the random numbers, and then add the lower bound (5). Hence, the value 0.1 would be converted to this value:

$$x = (10 - 5) \cdot 0.1 + 5 = 5.5$$

4. MATLAB Solution

```
%------------------------------------------------------------------------------------
% Example 30_5 This program generates and plots
% one hour of simulated wind speeds.
%
clear, clc
```

```
%
% Specify high and low speeds and a seed value.
low_speed = input('Enter low speed: ');
high_speed = input('Enter high speed: ');
seed = input('enter seed: ');
rand('seed',seed);
%
% Define the time matrix.
t = 0:10:3600;
%
% Convert time to hours.
t = t/3600;
%
% Determine how many time values are needed.
num = length(t);
%
% Calculate the speed values.
speed = (high_speed - low_speed)*rand(1,num) +
low_speed;
%
% Create a table.
table = [t',speed'];
save windspd.dat table -ascii
subplot(2,1,1),plot(t,speed),title('Simulated Wind
Speed'),
xlabel('Time, s'),ylabel('Wind Speed, mph'),grid
%-------------------------------------------------------------------------------------
```

Notice that we used the **length** command to determine how many elements were in the **t** matrix; this function returns the maximum dimension of a matrix, and since **t** has 1 row and 361 columns, the result was 361.

5. Testing

We can see from Figure 30.10 that the wind speed does indeed vary between 5 mph and 10 mph.

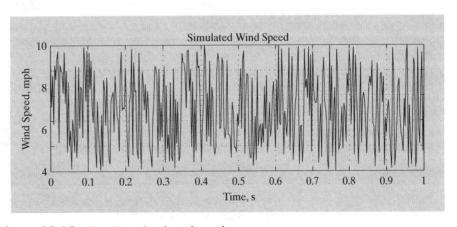

Figure 30.10 Plot of simulated wind speeds.

30.6   USER-DEFINED FUNCTIONS

The MATLAB programming language is built around functions. A function is simply a piece of computer code that accepts an input argument from the user and provides output to the program. Functions allow us to program efficiently, since we do not need to rewrite the computer code for calculations that are performed frequently. For example, most computer programs contain a function that calculates the sine of a number. In MATLAB, **sin** is the function name used to call up a series of commands that perform the necessary calculations. The user needs to provide an angle, and MATLAB returns a result. It is not necessary for the user to even know that MATLAB uses an approximation to an infinite series to find the value of **sin**.

We have already explored many of MATLAB's **built-in functions**, but you may wish to define your own functions that are used commonly in your programming. **User-defined functions** are stored as M-files, and can be accessed by MATLAB if they are in the current directory.

30.6.1 Syntax

User defined MATLAB functions are written in M-files. Access a new function M-file the same way a script M-file is created: select **File → New → m -file** from the menu bar. To explain how M-file functions work, we will use several examples.

Here is a simple function to begin:

```
function s=f(x)
% This function adds 3 to each value in an array.
s = x + 3;
```

These lines of code define a function called **f**. Notice that the first line starts with the word **function**. This is a requirement for all user-defined functions. Next, an output variable that we have named **s** is set equal to the function name, with the input arguments enclosed in parentheses **(x)**. A comment line follows that will be displayed if a user types:

```
help f
```

once the function has been saved in the current directory. The file name must be the same as the function name, so in this case it must be stored as an M-file named **f**, which is the default suggestion when the save icon is selected from the menu bar. Finally, the output, **s**, is defined as **x + 3**.

From the command window, or inside a **script M-file**, the function **f** is now available. Now type

```
f(4)
```

and the program returns

```
ans =
     7
```

More complicated functions can be written that require more than one input argument. For example, these lines of code define a function called **g**, with two inputs, **x** and **y**:

```
function output=g(x,y)
% This function multiplies x and y together
% Be sure that x and y have the same size.
a = x.*y;
output = a;
```

You can use the comment lines to let users know what kind of input is required and to describe the function. In this example the function returns the values in the matrix named **output**.

You can also create functions that return more than one output variable. Many of the predefined MATLAB functions return more than one result. For example, **max** returns both the maximum value in a matrix and the element number where the maximum occurs. To achieve a similar result in a user-defined function, make the output a matrix of answers, instead of a single variable. For example,

```
function [dist,vel,accel] = motion(t)
% This function calculates the distance,
% velocity and acceleration of a car.
accel = 0.5.*t;
vel = accel.* t;
dist = vel.*t;
```

Once saved as **motion** in the current directory, you can use the function to find values of **distance**, **velocity**, and **acceleration** at specified times:

```
[distance,velocity,acceleration] = motion(10)
distance =
          500
velocity =
           50
acceleration =
            5
```

If you call the **motion** function without specifying all three outputs, only the first output will be returned:

```
motion(10)
ans =
     500
```

Remember, all variables in MATLAB are matrices, so it is important in the example above to use the `.*` operator, which specifies element-by-element multiplication:

```
time = 0:10;
[distance,velocity,acceleration] = motion(time);
disp('Time, Distance, Velocity, Acceleration')
fprintf('%4.1f %7.1f %7.1F %9.1f\n', ...
        [time',distance',velocity',acceleration'])
```

returns

Time,	Distance,	Velocity,	Acceleration
0.0	0.0	0.0	0.0
1.0	0.5	0.5	0.5
2.0	4.0	2.0	1.0
.			
.			
.			
3.0	13.5	4.5	1.5
8.0	256.0	32.0	4.0
9.0	365.5	40.5	4.5
10.0	5000.0	50.0	5.0

Because **time, distance, velocity**, and **acceleration** were row vectors, the transpose operator was used to print them in columns.

30.6.2 Local Variables

The variables used within function M-files are known as **local variables**. The only way that a function can communicate with the workspace is through input arguments and the output returned. Any variables defined within the function only exist for the function to use. For example, consider the **g** function previously described:

```
function output=g(x,y)
% This function multiplies x and y together
% Be sure that x and y are the same size matrices
a = x .*y;
output = a;
```

The variable **a** is a local variable. It can be used for additional calculations inside the function **g**, but it is not stored in the workspace. To confirm this, clear the workspace and the command window, then call the **g** function:

```
clear, clc
g(10,20)
```

returns

```
g(10,20)
ans =
      200
```

Notice that the only variable stored in the workspace window is **ans**. Not only is **a** not there, but neither is **output**, which is also a local variable:

Just as calculations performed in the command window, or from a script M-file, cannot access variables defined in functions, functions cannot access the variables defined in the workspace. That means that functions must be completely self-contained. The only way they can get information from your program is through the input arguments, and the only way they can deliver information is through the function output.

30.6.3 Naming User-defined Functions

A function M-file must have the same file name as its function name defined in the first line. For example,

```
function results = velocity(t)
```

might be the first line of a user-defined function. The function's name is **velocity**, and it must be stored in the current directory as **velocity**. Function names need to conform to the same naming conventions as variable names: They must start with a letter; they may only contain letters, numbers and the underscore; and they must not be reserved names. It is possible to give a function the same name as a predefined MATLAB function, in which case the user-defined function will become the default until it is removed from the current directory or the current directory is changed. The MATLAB predefined function is not overwritten; MATLAB just looks in the current directory first for function definitions before it looks into the predefined function files. In general, it is not a good idea to use the same name for a user-defined function as for an existing MATLAB function.

30.6.4 Rules for Writing and Using User-defined Functions

Writing and using an M-file function require the user to follow very specific rules. These rules are summarized as follows:

- The function must begin with a line containing the word function, which is followed by the output argument, an equals sign, and the name of the function.

The input arguments to the function follow the name of the function and are enclosed in parentheses. This line distinguishes the function file from a script M-file:

```
function output_name = function_name(input)
```

- The first few lines of the function should be comments because they will be displayed if help is requested for the function name:

```
% Add comments to your function for users
```

- The only information returned from the function is contained in the output arguments, which are, of course, matrices. Always check to be sure that the function includes a statement that assigns a value to the output argument.
- A function that has multiple input arguments must list the arguments in the function statement, as shown in the following example, which has two input arguments:

```
function error = mse(w,d)
```

- A function that is going to return more than one value should show all values to be returned as a vector in the function statement, as in

```
function [dist,vel,accel] = motion(x)
```

All output values need to be computed within the function.

- The same matrix names can be used in both a function and the program that references it. No confusion occurs as to which matrix is referenced, because the function and the program are completely separate. However, any values computed in the function, other than the output arguments, are not accessible from the program.
- The special functions **nargin** and **nargout** can be used to determine the number of input arguments and the number of output arguments for a function. Both require a string containing the function name as input. For the **motion** function described earlier,

```
nargin('motion')
```

returns

```
ans =
     1
```

and

```
nargout('motion')
```

returns

```
ans =
     3
```

EXAMPLE 30.6

A FUNCTION TO CONVERT DEGREES CELSIUS TO DEGREES FAHRENHEIT

When working with temperatures, some computations will be easier to perform using degrees Celsius, and other computations will be easier to perform using degrees Fahrenheit. Write a function that will convert degrees Celsius to degrees Fahrenheit.

SOLUTION

1. Problem Statement

Create and test a function called **celsius** to convert degrees Celsius to degrees Fahrenheit.

2. Input/Output Description

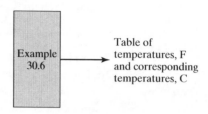

3. Hand Example

The equation for converting temperatures in Celsius to Fahrenheit is:

$$T_f = 9/5\,T_c + 32$$

If we choose $T_c = 0°$ C, then $T_f = 32°$ F. If we choose $T_c = 20°$ F, then $T_f = 68°$ C.

4. MATLAB Solution

```
%----------------------------------------------------------
% Example 30_6 This program converts temperatures from
% Fahrenheit to Celsius using a user-defined function.
%
clear, clc
%
% Define a vector of temperatures Fahrenheit
Tf = 0:10:200;
%
% Use a function to convert temperature to Celsius.
Tc = Celsius(Tf);
%
% Generate an output table
disp('A Conversion Table')
disp('degrees F degrees C')
fprintf('%5.0f %9.2f\n',Tc)
%----------------------------------------------------------
```

The function called by the program is shown below:

```
%----------------------------------------------------------
function deg_c = Celsius(Tf)
% This function converts Fahrenheit to Celsius.
%
deg_c = 9/5.*Tf + 32;
%----------------------------------------------------------
```

Remember that, in order for the script M-file to find the function, it must be in the current directory and must be named **Celsius.m**. The program generates the following results in the command window:

```
A Conversion Table
degrees F    degrees C
      0        32.00
     10        50.00
     20        68.00
      .
      .
      .
    180       356.00
    190       374.00
    200       392.00
```

5. Testing

Compare the MATLAB solution to the hand solution. Since the output is a table, it is easy to see that the conversions generated by MATLAB correspond to those calculated by hand. Notice that the titles and column headings were generated with the **disp** function. We could have used the **fprintf** function:

```
fprintf('A table of radians to degrees \n')
```

A common error is to forget the **\n**, in which case there would be no carriage return.

Summary

In this chapter, we explored the various predefined MATLAB functions. These functions included general mathematical functions, trigonometric functions, data analysis functions, and random number generation. These functions give us the power to perform operations through a simple function reference. We also learned to write our own functions. This allows us to use operations that we want to repeat without having to repeat the code each time we want to use the operation. It also allows us to keep our MATLAB program shorter, and that is important in maintaining readability.

Matlab Summary

The following MATLAB summary lists and briefly describes the functions presented in this chapter:

Functions	
abs	computes the absolute value
asin	computes the inverse sine (arcsine)
ceil	rounds to the nearest integer toward positive infinity
cos	computes the cosine
cumprod	computes a cumulative product of the values in an array
cumsum	computes a cumulative sum of the values in an array

(continued)

Functions (*continued*)

`erf`	calculates the error function
`exp`	computes the value of e^x
`fix`	rounds to the nearest integer toward zero
`floor`	rounds to the nearest integer toward minus infinity
`help`	opens the help function
`help win`	opens a help window
`length`	determines the largest dimension of an array
`log`	computes the natural log
`log10`	computes the log base 10
`log2`	computes the log base 2
`max`	finds the maximum value in an array, and determines which element stores the maximum value
`mean`	computes the average of the elements in an array
`median`	finds the median of the elements in an array
`min`	finds the minimum value in an array, and determines which element stores the minimum value
`prod`	multiplies the values in an array
`rand`	generates evenly distributed random numbers
`randn`	generates normally distributed (Gaussian) random numbers
`rem`	calculates the remainder in a division problem
`round`	rounds to the nearest integer
`sign`	determines the sign (positive or negative)
`sin`	computes the sine
`sinh`	computes the hyperbolic sine
`size`	determines the number of rows and columns in an array
`sort`	sorts the elements of a vector into ascending order
`sqrt`	calculates the square root of a number
`std`	determines the standard deviation
`sum`	sums the values in an array
`tan`	computes the tangent

KEY TERMS

argument	local variable	random number
built-in functions	Monte Carlo simulation	seed
composition of functions	mean	standard deviation
computer simulation	nested functions	uniform random number
function	natural logarithm	user-defined function
Gaussian random numbers	normal random numbers	median

Problems

1. Sometimes it is convenient to have a table of sine, cosine, and tangent values instead of using a calculator. Create a table of all three of these trigonometric functions for angles from 0 to 2π in increments of 0.1 radians. Your table should contain a column for the angle, followed by the three trigonometric function values.

2. The range of an object shot at an angle θ with respect to the x axis and an initial velocity v_0 is given by

$$R(\theta) = \frac{v^2}{g}\sin(2\theta) \text{ for } 0 \le \theta \le \frac{\pi}{2} \text{ and neglecting air resistance.}$$

Use $g = 9.9$ m/s^2 and an initial velocity of 100 m/s. Show that the maximum range is obtained at $\theta = \pi/4$ by computing the range in increments of 0.05 from $0 \le \theta \le \pi/2$. Because you are using discrete angles, you will only be able to determine θ to within 0.05 radians. Remember, **max** can be used to return not only the maximum value in an array, but also the element number where the maximum value is stored.

3. MATLAB contains functions to calculate the natural log **(log)**, the log base 10 **(log10)** and the log base 2 **(log2)**. However, if you want to find a logarithm to another base, for example base b, you will have to do the math yourself:

$$\log_b(x) = \frac{\log_e(x)}{\log_e(b)}.$$

What is the log of 10 to the base b, when b is defined from 1 to 10 in increments of 1?

4. Populations tend to expand exponentially:

$$P = P_0 e^{rt}$$

where P is the current population,

P_0 is the original population,
r is the rate, expressed as a fraction,
and t is the time.

If you originally have 100 rabbits that breed at a rate of 90 percent (0.9) per year, find how many rabbits you will have at the end of 10 years.

5. Chemical reaction rates are proportional to a rate constant, k, which changes with temperature according to the Arrhenius equation

$$k = k_0 e^{-Q/RT}$$

For a certain reaction

$$Q = 8{,}000 \text{ cal/mole}$$
$$R = 1.987 \text{ cal/mole K}$$
$$k_0 = 1200 \text{ min}^{-1}$$

find the values of k for temperatures from 100K to 500K, in 50-degree increments. Create a table of your results.

6. The vector **G** represents the distribution of final grades in a statics course. Compute the mean, median, and standard deviation of G. Which better represents the "most typical grade," the mean or the median? Why?

```
G = [68,83,70,75,82,57,5,76,85,62,71,96,78,76,72,75,83,93]
```

Use MATLAB to determine the number of grades in the array. (Do not just count them.).

7.   Generate 10,000 Gaussian random numbers with a mean of 80 and standard deviation of 23.5. Use the **mean** function to confirm that your array actually has a mean of 80. Use the **std** function to confirm that your standard deviation is actually 23.5.

Rocket Analysis

A small rocket is being designed to make wind shear measurements in the vicinity of thunderstorms. Before testing begins, the designers are developing a simulation of the rocket's trajectory. They have derived the following equation, which they believe will predict the performance of the test rocket, where t is the elapsed time, in seconds:

$$\text{height} = 2.13t^2 - 0.0013t^4 + 0.000034t^{4.751}$$

8.   Compute and print a table of time versus height, at 2-second intervals, up through 100 seconds. (The equation will actually predict negative heights. Obviously, the equation is no longer applicable once the rocket hits the ground. For now, do not worry about this physical impossibility; just do the math.)

9.   Use MATLAB to find the maximum height achieved by the rocket.

10.   Use MATLAB to find the time the maximum height is achieved.

Sensor Data

Suppose that a file named **sensor.dat** contains information collected from a set of sensors. Each row contains a set of sensor readings, with the first row containing values collected at 0 seconds, the second row containing values collected at 1.0 seconds, and so on.

16.   Write a program to read the data file and print the number of sensors and the number of seconds of data contained in the file. (Hint: use the **size** function.)

17.   Find both the maximum value and minimum value recorded on each sensor. Use MATLAB to determine at what times they occurred.

18.   Find the mean and standard deviation for each sensor, and for all the data values collected. Remember, column 1 does not contain sensor data; it contains time data.

Temperature Data

Suppose you are designing a container to ship sensitive medical materials between hospitals. The container needs to keep the contents within a specified temperature range. You have created a model predicting how the container responds to exterior temperature, and now need to run a simulation.

19.   Create a normal distribution of temperatures (Gaussian distribution) with a mean of 70°F, and a standard deviation of 2 degrees, corresponding to 2 hours duration. You will need a temperature for each time value from 0 to 120 minutes.

20.   Plot the data on an x-y plot. Recall that the MATLAB function for plotting is **plot(x,y).**

21.   Find the maximum temperature and the minimum temperature.

Chapter 31

Control Structures

ENGINEERING ACHIEVEMENT: SIGNAL PROCESSING

Computer algorithms for word recognition are complicated algorithms that work best when the speech signals are "clean." However, when speech signals are collected by microphones, the background noise is also collected. Therefore, preprocessing steps are often used to remove some of the background noise before attempting to identify the words in the speech signals. These preprocessing steps may require a number of operations that fall into the area of signal processing, such as analyzing the characteristics of a signal, decomposing a signal into sums of other signals, coding a signal in a form that is easy to transmit across a communication channel, and extracting information from a signal. Some of the functions commonly used in signal processing are used in examples in this chapter.

OBJECTIVES

After reading this chapter, you should be able to

- use relational and logical operators in conditions that are true or false,
- use the conditions with the **find** function to select values from vectors and matrices, and
- implement for loops and while loops in MATLAB.

31.1   RELATIONAL AND LOGICAL OPERATORS

The MATLAB programs that we have developed have been based on performing mathematical operations, using functions, and printing or plotting the results of these computations. These programs have had a **sequential structure**; that is, the commands were executed one after another in a serial fashion. There are two other types of structures called selection structures and repetition structures. Definitions of these three **control structures** are now given; Figure 31.1 shows a graphical depiction of these structures.

- Sequences are lists of commands that are executed one after another.
- A **selection structure** allows the programmer to execute one command (or group of commands) if some criteria is true, and a second set of commands if the criteria is false. A selection statement provides the means of choosing between these paths based on a **logical condition**. The **conditions** that are evaluated often contain **relational** and **logical** operators or functions.
- A **repetition structure**, or **loop**, causes a group of statements to be executed zero, one, or more times. The number of times a loop is executed depends on either a counter or the evaluation of a logical condition.

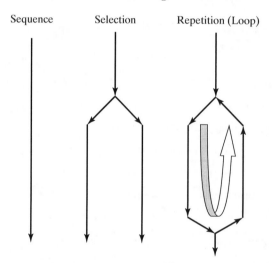

Figure 31.1   Sequence, selection, and loop control structures.

Before presenting the MATLAB commands for selection statements and loops, we first need to define **relational operators** and **logical operators**. MATLAB has six relational operators for comparing two matrices of equal size, as shown in Table 31.1. Comparisons are either true or false, and most computer languages (including MATLAB) use the number 1 for true and 0 for false.

TABLE 31.1   Relational operators

Relational Operator	Interpretation
<	less than
<=	less than or equal to
>	greater than
>=	greater than or equal to
==	equal to
~ =	not equal to

Assume we define two scalars as shown:

```
x = 5;
y = 1;
```

and use a relational operator such as < (for less than) with the two variables, as in:

```
x<y
```

This new expression (**x<y**) is evaluated to be either true or false. In this case, **x** is not less than **y**, so MATLAB responds

```
ans =
     0
```

indicating the comparison was not true. MATLAB uses this answer in selection statements and in repetition structures to make decisions.

Of course, variables in MATLAB usually represent entire matrices. If we redefine **x** and **y**, we can see how MATLAB handles comparisons between matrices:

```
x = 1:5;
y = x-4;
x<y
ans =
     0    0    0    0    0
```

MATLAB compares corresponding elements and creates an answer matrix of zeros and ones. In the previous example, **x** was greater than **y** for every element comparison, so every comparison was false, and the answer was a string of zeros. Consider these statements:

```
x = [ 1, 2, 3, 4, 5];
y = [-2, 0, 2, 4, 6];
x<y
ans =
     0    0    0    0    1
```

The result tells us that the comparison was false for the first four elements, but true for the last. In order for MATLAB to decide that a comparison is true for an entire matrix, it must be true for every element in the matrix. In other words, all of the results must be one.

MATLAB also allows us to combine comparisons with logical operators; **and**, **not**, and **or**, as shown in Table 31.2.

TABLE 31.2 Logical operators

Logical Operator	Interpretation
&	and
~	not
|	or

Consider the following commands and corresponding output:

```
x = [ 1, 2, 3, 4, 5];
y = [-2, 0, 2, 4, 6];
```

```
z = [ 8, 8, 8, 8, 8];
z>x & z>y
ans =
     1   1   1   1   1
```

Since z is greater than both x and y for every element, the condition is true for each corresponding set of values. The statement

```
x>y | x>z
```

is read as "x is greater than y or x is greater than z" and would return an answer as the following:

```
ans =
     1   1   1   0   0
```

This result is interpreted to mean that the condition is true for the first three elements and false for the last two.

These relational and logical operators are used in both selection structures and loops to determine what commands should be executed.

31.2 SELECTION STRUCTURES

MATLAB offers two kinds of selection structures: the function **find**, and a family of **if** structures.

31.2.1 The **find** Function

The **find** command is unique to MATLAB, and can often be used instead of both **if** and **loop** structures. It returns a vector composed of the indices of the nonzero elements of a vector x. Those indices can then be used in subsequent commands. The usefulness of the **find** command is best described with examples.

Assume that we have a vector containing a group of distance values that represent the distances of a cable car from the nearest tower. We want to generate a vector containing velocities of the cable at those distances. If the distance of the cable car from the tower is less than or equal to 30 ft., we use this equation to compute the velocity:

$$\text{velocity} = 0.425 + 0.00175\,d^2$$

If the cable car is farther than 30 ft. from the tower, we use the following equation:

$$\text{velocity} = 0.625 + 0.12\,d - 0.00025\,d^2$$

We can use the **find** function to find the distance values greater than 30 ft. and the distance values less than or equal to 30 ft. Because the **find** function identifies the subscripts for each group of values, we can compute the corresponding velocities with these statements:

```
lower = find(d<=30);
velocity(lower) = 0.425 + 0.00175*d(lower).^2;
upper = find(d>=30);
velocity(upper) = 0.625 + 0.12*d - 0.00025*d.^2;
```

If all the values of d are less than or equal to 30, the vector **upper** will be an empty vector, and the reference to **d(upper)** and **velocity(upper)** will not cause any values to change.

Our next example assumes that you have a list of temperatures measured in a manufacturing process. If the temperature is less than 95°F, the items produced will be faulty. Assume that the temperatures for a set of items are the following:

```
temp = [100,98,94,101,93];
```

Use the **find** function to determine which items are faulty:

```
find(temp<95)
```

returns a vector of element numbers:

```
ans =
     3    5
```

which tells us that items 3 and 5 will be faulty. MATLAB first evaluated **temp < 95**, which resulted in a vector of zeros and ones. We can see this by typing the comparison into MATLAB:

```
temp<95
```

which returns a vector indicating when the comparison was true (1) and when it was false (0):

```
ans =
     0    0    1    0    1
```

The **find** command identified the elements for which the comparison was true (where the **ans** vector reported ones).

It is also sometimes useful to name these element lists. For example,

```
faulty = find(temp<95);
pass = find(temp>=95);
```

makes it possible to create a results table:

```
failtable = [faulty',temp(faulty)']
```

which returns a table of elements and the corresponding temperatures:

```
failtable =
     3    94
     5    93
```

When the **find** command is used with a two-dimensional matrix, a single element number is returned. As discussed before, MATLAB is a column dominant language and considers two-dimensional matrices as one long list of numbers. Just as **fprintf** works down one column at a time, the **find** function uses an element numbering scheme that works down each column one at a time. For example, consider a 10-by-3 matrix. The element numbers are shown in Figure 31.2.

An alternate way to use **find** returns the row and column designation of an element:

```
[row, column] = find(expression)
```

For example, consider the following two-dimensional matrix, and use **find** to determine the location of all elements greater than 9:

```
x = [1,2,3; 10,5,1; 12,3,2; 8,3,1]
element = find(x>9)
```

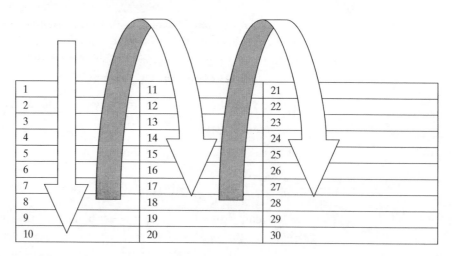

Figure 31.2   Element numbering sequence for a 10 × 3 matrix.

```
[row,column] = find(x>9)
```

returns

```
x =
     1     2     3
    10     5     1
     3    12     2
     8     3     1
element =
           2
           7
row =
       2
       3
column =
           1
           2
```

Notice that the numbers 10 and 12 are the only two values greater than 9. By counting down the columns, we see that they are elements 2 and 7 respectively. Using the alternative designation, 10 is in row 2, column 1, and 12 is in row 3, column 2.

EXAMPLE 31.1

THE SINC FUNCTION

The **sinc** function is used in many engineering applications, but especially in signal processing applications. Unfortunately, there are two widely accepted definitions for this function:

$$f_1(x) = \frac{\sin(\pi x)}{\pi x} \quad \text{and} \quad f_2(x) = \frac{\sin x}{x}$$

Both of these functions have an indeterminate form of 0/0 when x is equal to 0. In this case, L'Hôpital's theorem from calculus can be used to prove that both functions are equal to 1 when x is equal to 0. For values of x not equal to 0, these two functions have a similar form. The first function, $f_1(x)$, crosses the x-axis when x is an integer; the second function crosses the x-axis when x is a multiple of π.

MATLAB does not include a **sinc** function. Assume that you would like to define a function called **sinc1** that uses the first definition, and a function called **sinc2** that uses the second definition. Test your functions by calculating values of x from -5π to $+5\pi$, and plotting the results.

SOLUTION

1. Problem Statement

Create and test functions for the two definitions of the sinc function:

$$f_1(x) = \frac{\sin(\pi x)}{\pi x} \quad \text{and} \quad f_2(x) = \frac{\sin x}{x}$$

2. Input/Output Description

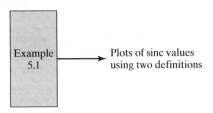

Example 5.1 → Plots of sinc values using two definitions

3. Hand Example

The following table computes a few values of these sinc functions

x	sin(πx)/(πx)	sin(x)/x
0	0/0 = 1	0/0 = 1
1	0	sin(1) /1 = 0.8415
2	0	sin(2)/2 = 0.4546
3	0	sin(3)/3 = 0.0470

4. MATLAB Solution

First, create the functions **sinc1** and **sinc2**:

```
%-----------------------------------------------------------
function output = sinc1(x)
%  This function calculates the value of sinc
%  using the definition of sin(pi*x)/(pi*x).
%
%  Determine the elements in x that are close to zero.
set1 = find(abs(x)<0.0001);
%
```

```
%  Set those elements in the output array to 1.
output(set1) = 1;
%
%  Determine elements in x that are not close to 0.
set2 = find(abs(x)>=0.0001);
%
%  Calculate sin(pi*x)/(pi*x) for the elements not close to 0.
output(set2) = sin(pi*x(set2))./(pi*x(set2));
%------------------------------------------------------------
%------------------------------------------------------------
function output = sinc2(x)
%  This function calculates the value of sinc
%  using the definition of sin(x)/x.
%
%  Determine the elements in x that are close to zero.
set1 = find(abs(x)<0.0001);
%
%  Set those elements in the output array to 1.
output(set1) = 1;
%
%  Determine elements in x that are not close to 0.
set2 = find(abs(x)>=0.0001);
%
%  Calculate sin(x)/x for the elements not close to 0.
output(set2) = sin(x(set2))./x(set2);
%------------------------------------------------------------
```

Once we have created the functions in M-files, we can test them in the command window using the inputs from the hand example:

```
sinc1(0)
ans =
     1
sinc1(1)
ans =
     0
sinc2(0)
ans =
     1
sinc2(1)
ans =
     0.8415
```

When we compare the results with the hand example, we see that the answers match. (Although you will see when you run this example that instead of zero, you will get very small values in some cases.)

5. Testing

We now use the functions in our M-file solution to Example 31.1 with confidence.

```
%-------------------------------------------------------
%  Example 5_1 This program plots the sinc function
%  using two definitions for the sinc function.
%
clear, clc
%
%  Define an array of angles
x = -5*pi:pi/100:5*pi;
%
%  Calculate sinc1 and sinc2.
y1 = sinc1(x);
y2 = sinc2(x);
%
%  Create the plot.
subplot(2,1,1),plot(x,y1),
    title('Two Definitions for sinc Function'),
    ylabel('sin(pi*x)/(pi*x)'),grid,
    axis([-5*pi,5*pi,-0.5,1.5]),
subplot(2,1,2),plot(x,y2),xlabel('angle, radians'),
    ylabel('sin(x)/x'),grid,
    axis([-5*pi,5*pi,-0.5,1.5])
%-------------------------------------------------------
```

This program generates the plot shown in Figure 31.3. The plots indicate that the function is working properly. Testing the functions with one value at a time validated its answers for a scalar input; however, the program that generated the plots sent a vector argument to the functions. The plots confirm that it also performs properly with vector input.

If you have trouble understanding how this function works, remove the semicolons that are suppressing the output, and run the program. Understanding the output from each line will help you understand the program logic better.

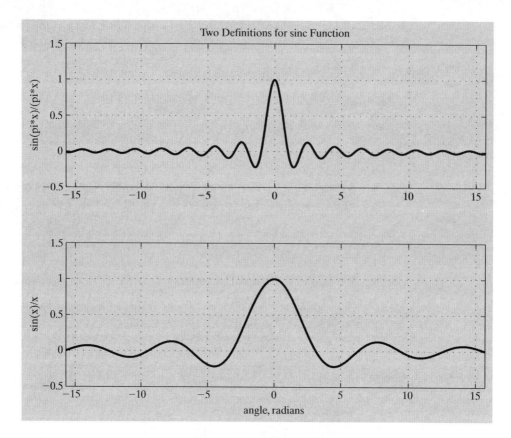

Figure 31.3 Plots of alternative definitions for the **sinc** function.

31.2.2 The Family of **if** Statements

There are situations when the **find** statement does not do what we need to do. In these cases, we can use the **if** statement which has the following form:

```
if comparison
    statements
end
```

If the logical expression (the comparison) is true, the statements between the **if** statement and the **end** statement are executed. If the logical expression is false, program control jumps immediately to the statement following the **end** statement. It is good programming practice to indent the statements within an **if** structure for readability. For example,

```
if G<50
    count = count +1;
    disp(G);
end
```

This statement (from **if** to **end**) is easy to interpret if **G** is a scalar. For example, if **G** has a value of 25, then **count** is incremented by 1 and **G** is displayed on the screen.

However, if **G** is not a scalar, then the **if** statement considers the comparison true only if it is true for every element. If **G** is defined as:

```
G = 0:10:80;
```

then the comparison is false, and the statements inside the **if** statement are not executed. In general, **if** statements work best when dealing with scalars.

An **if** statement can also contain an **else** clause that allows us to execute one set of statements if the comparison is true, and a different set of statements if the comparison is false. To illustrate this feature, assume that we have a variable **interval**. If the value of **interval** is less than 1, we set the value of **x_increment** to **interval/10**; otherwise, we set the value of **x_increment** to 0.1. The following statement performs these steps:

```
if interval < 1
    x_increment = interval/10;
else
    x_increment = 0.1;
end
```

When **interval** is a scalar, this is easy to interpret. However, when **interval** is a matrix, the comparison is only true if it is true for every element in the matrix. So, if

```
interval = 0:0.5:2;
```

the elements in the matrix are not all less than 1. Therefore, MATLAB skips to the **else** portion of the statement, and all values in the **x_increment** vector are set equal to 0.1. Again, **if/else** statements are probably best used with scalars, although you may find limited use with vectors.

When we need more levels of **if-else** statements, it may be difficult to determine which logical expressions must be true (or false) to execute each set of statements. In these cases, the **elseif** clause is often used to clarify the program logic, as illustrated in the following statement:

```
if temperature>100
    disp('Too hot—equipment malfunctioning')
elseif temperature>90
    disp('Normal operating temperature')
elseif temperature>50
    disp('Temperature below desired operating range')
else
    disp('Too cold—turn off equipment')
end
```

In this example, temperatures above 90°F and below or equal to 100°F are in the normal operating range. Temperatures outside of this range generate an appropriate message. Notice that a temperature of 101°F does not trigger all of the responses; it only displays the first message. Also notice that the final **else** does not require a comparison. In order for the computation to reach the final **else**, the temperature must be less than or equal to 50°F. Again, this structure is easy to interpret if **temperature** is a scalar. If it is a matrix, the comparison must be true for every element in the matrix.

As before, **elseif** structures work well for scalars, but **find** is probably a better choice for matrices. Here is an example with an array of temperatures that generates a table of results in each category using the **find** statement:

```
temperature = [90,45,68,84,92,95,101];
%
set1 = find(temperature>100);
disp('Too Hot—Equipment Malfunctioning')
disp('Element, Temperature')
table1 = [set1; temperature(set1)];
fprintf('%1.0f    %8.0f \n',table1)
%
set2 = find(temperature>90 & temperature<=100);
disp('Normal Operating Temperature')
disp('Element, Temperature')
table2 = [set2; temperature(set2)];
fprintf('%1.0f    %8.0f \n',table2)
%
set3 = find(temperature>50 & temperature<=90);
table3 = [set3; temperature(set3)];
disp('Temperature Below Desired Operating Range')
disp('Element, Temperature')
fprintf('%1.0f    %8.0f \n',table3)
%
set4 = find(temperature<=50);
table4 = [set4; temperature(set4)];
disp('Too Cold-Turn Off Equipment')
disp('Element, Temperature')
fprintf('%1.0f    %8.0f \n',table4)
```

The output is:

```
Too Hot—Equipment Malfunctioning
Element, Temperature
7         101
Normal Operating Temperature
Element, Temperature
5          92
6          95
Temperature Below Desired Operating Range
Element, Temperature
1          90
3          68
4          84
Too Cold-Turn Off Equipment
Element, Temperature
2          45
```

EXAMPLE 31.2

ASSIGNING PERFORMANCE QUALITY SCORES

The **if** statement is used most effectively when the input is a scalar. Create a function to determine performance quality based on a quality score, assuming a single input to the function. The quality grades should be based on the following criteria:

Quality Grade	Score
A	>=90 to 100
B	>=80 and <90
C	>=70 and <90
D	>= 60 and <70
F	<60

SOLUTION

1. Problem Statement

Determine the performance quality based on a numeric score.

2. Input/Output Description

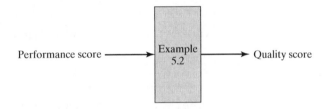

Performance score ──────▶ Example 5.2 ──────▶ Quality score

3. Hand Example

For example, a score of 85 should be a B.

4. MATLAB Solution

First, create the function:

```
%-----------------------------------------------------------
function results = quality(x)
%  This function requires a scalar input
%
if(x>=90)
    results = 'A';
elseif(x>=80)
    results = 'B';
elseif(x>=70)
    results = 'C';
elseif(x>=60)
    results = 'D';
```

```matlab
else
    results = 'E';
end
%---------------------------------------------------------
```

5. Testing

We can now test the function in the command window:

```matlab
quality(25)
ans =
     F
quality(80)
ans =
     B
quality(-52)
ans =
     F
quality(108)
ans =
     A
```

Notice that, although the function seems to work properly, it returns quality scores for values over 100 and less than 0. You can now go back and add the logic to exclude those values using nested **if** structures:

```matlab
%---------------------------------------------------------
function results = grade(x)
%  This function converts a scalar input to a score
%  that is a quality score.
if(x>=0 & x<=100)
    if(x>=90)
        results = 'A';
    elseif(x>=80)
        results = 'B';
    elseif(x>=70)
        results = 'C';
    elseif(x>=60)
        results = 'D';
    else
        results = 'F';
    end
else
    results = 'Illegal Input';
end
%---------------------------------------------------------
```

In the command window, we can test the function again:

```
grade(-10)
ans =
      Illegal Input
grade(108)
ans =
      Illegal Input
```

This function will work well for scalars, but if you send a vector to the function, you may get some unexpected results of the vector comparisons in the function:

```
score = [95,42,83,77];
grade(score)
ans =
     F
```

31.3 LOOPS

A loop is a structure that allows you to repeat a set of statements. In general, you should avoid loops in MATLAB because they are seldom needed, and they can significantly increase the execution time of a program. If you have previous programming experience, you may be tempted to use loops extensively. Try instead to formulate a solution using **find**. However, there are occasions when loops are needed, so we give a brief introduction to **for** loops and **while** loops.

31.3.1 For Loops

In general, it is possible to use either a **for** or a **while** loop in any situation that requires a repetition structure. However, **for** loops are the easier choice when you know how many times you want to repeat a set of instructions. The general format is

```
for index = expression
    statements
end
```

Each time through the **for** loop, the index has the value of one of the elements in the expression matrix. This can be demonstrated with a simple **for** loop:

```
for k=1:5
    k
end
```

returns

```
k =
    1
k =
    2
k =
    3
```

```
k =
    4
k =
    5
```

The rules for writing and using a **for** loop are the following:

a.   The index of a **for** loop must be a variable. Although **k** is often used as the symbol for the index, any variable name can be used. The use of **k** is strictly a style issue.

b.   If the expression matrix is the empty matrix, the loop will not be executed. Control will pass to the statement following the **end** statement.

c.   If the expression matrix is a scalar, the loop will be executed one time, with the index containing the value of the scalar.

d.   If the expression is a row vector, each time through the loop the index will contain the next column in the matrix.

e.   If the expression matrix is a matrix, each time through the loop the index will contain the next column in the matrix. This means that the index will be a column vector.

f.   Upon completion of a **for** loop, the index contains the last value used.

g.   The colon operator can be used to define the expression matrix using the following format:

```
for k = initial:increment:limit
```

h.   All index variables in **nested loops** must be different variables.

   In an example in the previous section, we used the **find** function to find distances greater than 30 ft. and distances less than or equal to 30 ft. We then computed the corresponding velocities. Another way to perform these steps uses a **for** loop. In the following statements, the value of **k** is set to 1, and the statements inside the loop are executed as many times as there are values in the vector **d**. The value of **k** is incremented to 2, and the statements inside the loop are executed again. This continues until the value of **k** is greater than the length of the **d** vector.

```
for k=1:length(d)
   if d(k)<=30
      velocity(k) = 0.425 + 0.00175*d(lower).^2;
   else
      velocity(k) = 0.625 + 0.12*d - 0.00025*d.^2;
   end
end
```

Although these statements perform the same operations as the previous steps using the **find** function, the solution without a loop will execute much faster.

31.2.4 While Loops

The **while** loop is a structure for repeating a set of statements as long as a specified condition is true. The general format for this control structure is:

```
while expression
      statements
end
```

If the expression is true, the statements are executed. After these statements are executed, the condition is retested. If the condition is still true, the group of statements is executed again. When the condition is false, control skips to the statement following the **end** statement. The variables modified within the loop should include the variables in the expression, or the value of the expression will never change. If the expression is always true (or is a value that is nonzero), the loop becomes an **infinite loop**. (You can exit an infinite loop by typing Ctrl c.)

We used a **for** loop to compute velocities for a cable car in the previous section. We now use a **while** loop to perform the same steps. Recall that we have one equation to use to compute velocity if the distance of the cable car is less than or equal to 30 ft. from a tower; otherwise we use a different equation to compute the velocity. Here is the **while** loop solution:

```
k = 1;
while k<=length(d)
   if d(k)<=30
      velocity(k) = 0.425 + 0.00175*d(k).^2;
   else
      velocity(k) = 0.625 + 0.12*d - 0.00025*d(k).^2;
   end
end
```

Although these statements perform the same operations as the previous steps using the **find** function, the solution without a loop will execute much faster.

31.3.3 Loop Timing

To demonstrate that a solution without loops is much faster to execute than one with a **for** loop or a **while** loop, consider the following statements. We generate an array of ones that has 200 rows and 200 columns. We then multiply each element in the array by pi. This computation is computed three times—once without a loop, once with a for loop, and once with a **for** loop. Here are the statements that use the **tic** and **toc** functions to compute the execution times of each segment of code. Use the help feature to review these two useful functions.

```
%  Compute an array of ones that is 200x200.
a = ones(200);
%
%  Determine time without a loop.
tic
b = a*pi;
toc
%
%  Determine time with a for loop.
tic
for k=1:length(a(:))
   b(k) = a(k)*pi;
end
```

```
toc
%
%  Determine time for while loop.
tic
k = 1
while k<=length(a(:))
   b(k) = a(k)*pi;
   k = k+1;
end
toc
```

The output from these statements is the following:

```
Elapsed time is 0.000204 seconds.
Elapsed time is 0.005703 seconds.
Elapsed time is 0.076786 seconds.
```

The solution with a **for** loop takes nearly 30 times more computer time than the solution without a loop; the solution with a **while** loop takes over 350 times more computer time than the solution without a loop.

Summary

In this chapter, we expanded our set of programming tools through the addition of relational and conditional operators. These operators allow us to describe conditions that can be evaluated to be true or false. The **find** command uses conditions to select elements in matrices; this command is one of the most powerful commands in MATLAB. We also introduced **if** loops, **for** loops, and **while** loops.

MATLAB SUMMARY   This MATLAB summary lists and briefly describes all of the special characters, commands, and functions that were defined in this chapter:

Special Characters	
<	less than
<=	less than or equal to
>	greater than
>=	greater than or equal to
==	equal to
~=	not equal to
&	and
|	or
~	not

Commands and Functions

`clock`	determines the current time on the CPU clock
`else`	defines the path if the result of an **if** statement is false
`elseif`	defines the path if the result of an **if** statement is false, and specifies a new logical test
`end`	identifies the end of a control structure
`find`	determines which elements in a matrix meet the input criteria
`for`	generates a loop structure
`if`	tests a logical expression
`tic`	starts a timing sequence
`toc`	stops a timing sequence
`while`	generates a loop structure

KEY TERMS

conditions
control structures
logical condition
logical operator

loop
nested loops
relational operator
repetition structure

selection structure
sequential structure

Problems

Distances to the Horizon

The distance to the horizon increases as you climb a mountain (or a hill). The expression

$$d = \sqrt{2rh + h^2}$$

where

d = distance to the horizon,
r = radius of the Earth, and
h = height of the hill,

can be used to calculate that distance. The distance depends on how high the hill is and the radius of the Earth. Of course, on other planets the radius is different. For example, the Earth's diameter is 7,926 miles and Mars' diameter is 4,217 miles.

1. Create a MATLAB program to find the distance in miles to the horizon both on Earth and on Mars for hills from 0 to 10,000 ft., in increments of 500 ft. Remember to use consistent units in your calculations. Use the **meshgrid** function to solve this problem. Report your results in a table. Each column should represent a different planet, and each row should represent a different hill height. Be sure to provide a title for your table and column headings. Use **disp** for the title and headings; use **fprintf** for the table values.

2. Create a function called **distance** to find the distance to the horizon. Your function should accept two input vectors, **radius** and **height**, and should return a table similar to the one in Problem 1. Use the results of Problem 1 to validate your calculations.

Currency Conversions

Use your favorite Internet search engine and World Wide Web browser to identify recent currency conversions for British pounds sterling, Japanese yen, and the European euro to U.S. dollars. Use the conversion tables to create the following tables. Use the **disp** and **fprintf** commands in your solution, which should include a title, column labels, and formatted output.

3. Generate a table of conversions from yen to dollars. Start the yen column at ¥5 and increment by ¥5. Print 25 lines in the table.

4. Generate a table of conversions from the euro to dollars. Start the euro column at €1 and increment by €2. Print 30 lines in the table.

5. Generate a table with four columns. The first should contain dollars, the second the equivalent number of euros, the third the equivalent number of pounds, and the fourth the equivalent number of yen.

Temperature Conversions

This set of problems requires you to generate temperature conversion tables. Use the following equations, which describe the relationships between temperatures in degrees Fahrenheit (T_F), degrees Celsius (T_C), degrees Kelvin (T_K), and degrees Rankine (T_R), respectively:

$$T_F = T_R - 459.67°\text{R}$$

$$T_F = \frac{9}{5}T_C + 32°\text{F}$$

$$T_R = \frac{9}{5}T_K$$

You will need to rearrange these expressions to solve some of the problems.

6. Generate a table with the conversions from Fahrenheit to Kelvin for values from 0°F to 200°F. Allow the user to enter the increments in degrees F between lines.

7. Generate a table with the conversions from Celsius to Rankine. Allow the user to enter the starting temperature and increment between lines. Print 25 lines in the table.

8. Generate a table with the conversions from Celsius to Fahrenheit. Allow the user to enter the starting temperature, the increment between lines, and the number of lines for the table.

Rocket Trajectory

Suppose a small rocket is being designed to make wind sheer measurements in the vicinity of thunderstorms. The height of the rocket can be represented by the following equation:

$$\text{height} = 2.13t^2 - 0.0013t^4 + 0.000034t^{4.751}$$

9. Create a function called **height** that accepts time as an input and returns the height of the rocket. Use the function in your solutions for the next two problems.

10. Compute, print, and plot the time and height of the rocket from the time it launches until it hits the ground, in increments of 2 seconds. If the rocket has not

hit the ground within 100 seconds, print values only up through 100 seconds. (Use the function from Problem 9.)

11. Modify the steps in Problem 10 so that, instead of a table, the program prints the time at which the rocket begins to fall back to the ground and the time at which it hits the ground (when the elevation becomes negative).

Suture Packaging

Sutures are strands or fibers used to sew living tissue together after an injury or an operation. Packages of sutures must be sealed carefully before they are shipped to hospitals so that contaminants cannot enter the packages. The substance that seals the package is referred to as the sealing die. Generally, sealing dies are heated with an electric heater. For the sealing process to be a success, the sealing die is maintained at an established temperature and must contact the package with a predetermined pressure for an established period of time. The period of time during which the sealing die contacts the package is called the dwell time. Assume that the ranges of parameters for an acceptable seal are the following:

Temperature :	150−170°C
Pressure:	60−70 psi
Dwell Time:	2.0−2.5 sec

12. Assume that a file named **suture.dat** contains information on batches of sutures that have been rejected during a one-week period. Each line in the data file contains the batch number, the temperature, the pressure, and the dwell time for a rejected batch. A quality-control engineer would like to analyze this information to determine

- the percent of the batches rejected due to temperature,
- the percent rejected due to pressure, and
- the percent rejected due to dwell time.

If a specific batch is rejected for more than one reason, it should be counted in all applicable totals. Give the MATLAB statements to compute and print these three percentages. Use the following data to create **suture.dat**.

Batch Number	Temperature	Pressure	Dwell Time
24551	145.5°F	62.3	2.23
24582	153.7°F	63.2	2.52
26553	160.3°F	58.9	2.51
26623	159.5°F	58.9	2.01
26642	160.3°F	61.2	1.98

13. Modify the solution developed in Problem 12 so that it also prints the number of batches in each rejection category and the total number of batches rejected. (Remember that a rejected batch should appear only once in the total, but could appear in more than one rejection category.)

14. Confirm that the data in **suture.dat** relates only to batches that should have been rejected. If any batch should not be in the data file, print an appropriate message with the batch information.

Timber Regrowth

A problem in timber management is to determine how much of an area to leave uncut so that the harvested area is reforested in a certain period of time. It is assumed that reforestation takes place at a known rate per year, depending on climate and soil conditions. A reforestation equation expresses this growth as a function of the amount of timber standing and the reforestation rate. For example, if 100 acres are left standing after harvesting and the reforestation rate is 0.05, then 105 acres are forested at the end of the first year. At the end of the second year, the number of acres forested is 110.25 acres. If $year_0$ is the acreage forested, then

$$year_1 = year_0 + rate*year_0 = year_0*(1+rate)$$
$$year_2 = year_1 + rate*year_1 = year_1*(1+rate)$$
$$= year_0*(1+rate)*(1+rate) = year_0*(1+rate)^2$$
$$year_3 = year_2 + rate*year_2 = year_2*(1+rate)$$
$$= year_0*(1+rate)^3$$
$$year_n = year_0*(1+rate)^n$$

15. Assume that there are 14,000 acres total, with 2500 uncut acres and that the reforestation rate is 0.02. Print a table showing the number of acres reforested at the end of each year for a total of 20 years. You should also present your results in a bar graph, labeled appropriately.

16. Modify the program developed in Problem 15 that the user can enter the number of years to be used for the table.

17. Modify the program developed in Problem 15 so that the user can enter a number of acres, and the program will determine how many years are required for the number of acres to be forested. (You will need a loop for this one.)

18. Suppose that a file named **sensor.dat** contains information collected from a set of sensors. Each row contains a set of sensor readings, with the first row containing values collected at 0 seconds, the second row containing values collected at 1.0 seconds, and so on. Write a program to print the subscripts of sensor data values with an absolute value greater than 20.0, using the **find** command.

Power Plant Output

The power output in megawatts from a power plant over a period of 8 weeks has been stored in a data file named **plant.dat**. Each line in the file represents data for one week and contains the output for day 1, day 2, through day 7.

19. Write a program that uses the power-plant output data and prints a report that lists the number of days with greater-than-average power output. The report should give the week number and the day number for each of these days, in addition to printing the average power output for the plant during the 8-week period.

20. Write a program that uses the power-plant output data and prints the day and week during which the maximum and minimum power output occurred. If the maximum or minimum power output occurred on more than one day, the program should print all the days involved.

21. Write a program that uses the power-plant output data to print the average power output for each week. Also print the average power output for day 1, day 2, and so on.

Chapter 32

Matrix Computations

ENGINEERING ACHIEVEMENT: MANNED SPACE FLIGHT

Some of the greatest achievements of engineering over the last few decades have included manned space flight. These achievements began with the first manned space flight that occurred on April 12, 1961, when the Russians launched a spacecraft manned by Yuri Gagarin that orbited the Earth. The first American manned space flight occurred on May 5, 1961, when Alan Shepard completed a suborbital flight. On February 20, 1962, John Glenn became the first American to orbit the Earth. The first Moon landing occurred on July 20, 1969. The Moon landing was probably the most complex and ambitious engineering project ever attempted. Major breakthroughs were required in the design of the Apollo spacecraft, the lunar lander, and the three-stage Saturn V rocket. Even the design of the space suit was a major engineering project, resulting in a system that included a three-piece space suit and backpack, which together weighed 190 pounds. In this chapter, we include problems to show how matrices are useful in analyzing the weight of spacecraft components and in solving equations needed for the design of electrical circuits used in spacecraft sensors.

SECTIONS

OBJECTIVES

After reading this chapter, you should be able to

- use MATLAB functions to generate special matrices,
- perform operations that apply to an entire matrix as a unit, and
- solve simultaneous equations using MATLAB matrix operations.

32.1   SPECIAL MATRICES

In this chapter, we present matrix operations that use the entire matrix, such as matrix multiplication. (In Chapter 29, we presented element-by-element operations that used only one element from the matrix at a time.) We will show how these matrix operations can be used to solve a number of different types of problems, from computing dot products and matrix products, to solving systems of linear equations. However, before we do that, we present a group of MATLAB functions that generate special matrices. Some of these functions will be used in later sections of this chapter.

32.1.1 Matrices of Zeros and Ones

We often need to create a matrix that is filled with zeros, or that is filled with ones. MATLAB has two functions to make that an easy task to perform. The **zeros** function generates a matrix containing all zeros. If the argument to the function is a scalar, as in **zeros(6)**, the function will generate a square matrix using the argument as both the number of rows and the number of columns. If the function has two scalar arguments, as in **zeros(m,n)**, the function will generate a matrix with **m** rows and **n** columns. Because the **size** function returns two scalar arguments that represent the number of rows and columns in a matrix, we can use the **size** function to generate a matrix of zeros that is the same size as another matrix. The following MATLAB statements and the corresponding values displayed illustrate these various cases:

```
A = zeros(3)
A =
   0   0   0
   0   0   0
   0   0   0
B = zeros(3,2)
B =
   0   0
   0   0
   0   0
C = [1,2,3; 4,2,5]
C =
   1   2   3
   4   2   5
D = zeros(size(C))
D =
   0   0   0
   0   0   0
```

The **ones** function generates a matrix containing all ones, just as the **zeros** function generates a matrix containing all zeros. If the argument to the function is a scalar, as in **ones(6)**, the function will generate a square matrix using the argument as both the number of rows and the number of columns. If the function has two scalar arguments, as in **ones(m,n)**, the function will generate a matrix with **m** rows and **n** columns. To generate a matrix of ones that is the same size as another matrix, use the **size** function to determine the correct number of rows and columns. The following MATLAB statements illustrate these various cases:

```
A = ones(3)
A =
    1    1    1
    1    1    1
    1    1    1
B = ones(3,2)
B =
    1    1
    1    1
    1    1
C = [1,2,3; 4,2,5]
C =
    1    2    3
    4    2    5
D = ones(size(C))
D =
    1    1    1
    1    1    1
```

32.1.2 Identity Matrix

An **identity matrix** is a matrix with ones on the main diagonal and zeros everywhere else. For example, the following matrix is an identity matrix with four rows and four columns:

$$\begin{bmatrix} 1 & 0 & 0 & 0 \\ 0 & 1 & 0 & 0 \\ 0 & 0 & 1 & 0 \\ 0 & 0 & 0 & 1 \end{bmatrix}$$

Note that the **main diagonal** is the diagonal containing elements in which the row number is the same as the column number. Therefore, the subscripts for elements on the main diagonal in this example are (1,1), (2,2), (3,3), and (4,4).

In MATLAB, identity matrices can be generated using the **eye** function. The arguments of the **eye** function are similar to those for the **zeros** and the **ones** functions. If the argument to the function is a scalar, as in **eye(6)**, the function will generate a square matrix using the argument as both the number of rows and the number of columns. If the function has two scalar arguments, as in **eye(m,n)**, the function will generate a matrix with **m** rows and **n** columns. To generate an identity matrix that is the same size as another matrix, use the **size** function to determine the correct number of rows and columns. Although most applications use a square identity matrix, the definition can be extended to nonsquare matrices. The following statements illustrate these various cases:

```
A = eye(3)
A =
    1    0    0
    0    1    0
    0    0    1
```

```
B = eye(3,2)
B =
    1    0
    0    1
    0    0
C = [1,2,3; 4,2,5]
C =
    1    2    3
    4    2    5
D = eye(size(C))
D =
    1    0    0
    0    1    0
```

Hint: We recommend that you do not name an identity matrix i, because i will no longer represent $\sqrt{-1}$ in any statements that follow.

32.1.3 Diagonal Matrices

The **diag** function can be used to extract one of the diagonals of a matrix, or to create a **diagonal matrix**. To extract the main diagonal from a matrix, consider the following statements and values displayed:

```
A = [1,0,5; 7,4,-2; 3,-1,1];
diag(A)
ans =
    1
    4
    1
```

Other diagonals can be specified by passing a second parameter k to the function that denotes the position of the diagonal from the main diagonal ($k = 0$). We illustrate this using the example matrix **A**:

```
diag(A,1)
ans =
    0
   -2
```

If the first argument to **diag** is a vector **V**, then this function generates a square matrix. If the second parameter **k** is equal to zero, then the elements of **V** are placed on the main diagonal, and if $k > 0$, they are placed above the main diagonal. If $k < 0$, they are placed below the main diagonal. Thus, we have

```
B = [1,2,3]
B =
    1    2    3
diag(B)
```

```
ans =
      1    0    0
      0    2    0
      0    0    3
diag(B,1)
ans =
      0    1    0    0
      0    0    2    0
      0    0    0    3
      0    0    0    0
```

There are two additional functions that are often useful when extracting diagonals from a matrix. The **fliplr** function flips a matrix from left to right; the **flipud** function flips a matrix from up to down. For example, these statements display the matrix C, and the matrix generated by these functions:

```
C = [1,2,3; 4,2,5]
C =
      1    2    3
      4    2    5
D = fliplr(C)
D =
      3    2    1
      5    2    4
E = flipud(C)
E =
      4    2    5
      1    2    3
```

We will illustrate the use of one of these functions in the next section.

32.1.4 Magic Squares

MATLAB includes a matrix function called **magic** that generates a **magic square**—one in which the sum of all of the columns is the same, as is the sum of all of the rows. For example, consider the following statements that generate a magic square with four rows and four columns, and then computes the sums of the columns:

```
A = magic(4)
A =
     16    2    3   13
      5   11   10    8
      9    7    6   12
      4    4   15    1
sum(A)
ans =
     34   34   34   34
```

To find the sum of the rows, we need to transpose the matrix:

```
sum(A')
ans =
    34   34   34   34
```

Not only is the sum of all of the columns and rows the same; but also the sum of the left-to-right main diagonal is the same as the sum of the right-to-left main diagonal. The diagonal from left to right is

```
diag(A)
ans =
    16
    11
     6
     1
```

Finding the sum of the diagonal reveals the same number as the sum of the rows and columns:

```
sum(diag(A))
ans =
    34
```

Finally, to find the diagonal from lower left to upper right, we first have to flip the matrix and then find the sum of the diagonal:

```
fliplr(A)
ans =
    13    3    2   16
     8   10   11    5
    12    6    7    9
     1   15   14    4
diag(ans)
ans =
    13
    10
     7
     4
sum(ans)
ans =
    34
```

One of the earliest documented examples of a magic square is in a woodcut (shown in Figure 32.1) by Albrecht Dürer, created in 1514. Scholars believe the square was a reference to alchemical concepts popular at the time. The date of the woodcut is included in the two middle squares of the bottom row. Magic squares have fascinated

Figure 32.1   Melancholia, by Albrect Dürer, 1514, and a close-up of an embedded magic square.

both professional and amateur mathematicians for centuries. For example, Benjamin Franklin experimented with magic squares. You can create magic squares of any size greater than 2×2, using MATLAB. However, other magic squares are possible – MATLAB's solution is not the only one.

32.2   MATRIX OPERATIONS AND FUNCTIONS

Many engineering computations use a matrix as a convenient way to represent a set of data and to perform operations on that data. In this chapter, we are primarily interested in matrices that are not vectors; that is, they have more than one row and more than one column. In Chapter 29, we presented scalar operations that are performed element-by-element. In this section, we present matrix operations and matrix multiplication.

32.2.1   Transpose

The **transpose** of a matrix is a new matrix in which the rows of the original matrix are the columns of the new matrix. Mathematically, we use a superscript $\mathbf{T}$ after the name of a matrix to refer to the transpose of the matrix. For example, consider the following matrix and its transpose:

$$\mathbf{A} = \begin{bmatrix} 2 & 5 & 1 \\ 7 & 3 & 8 \\ 4 & 5 & 21 \\ 16 & 13 & 0 \end{bmatrix} \quad \mathbf{A^T} = \begin{bmatrix} 2 & 7 & 4 & 16 \\ 5 & 3 & 5 & 13 \\ 1 & 8 & 21 & 0 \end{bmatrix}$$

If we consider a couple of the elements, we see that the value in position $(3,1)$ of $\mathbf{A}$ has now moved to position $(1,3)$ of $\mathbf{A^T}$, and the value in position $(4,2)$ of $\mathbf{A}$ has now moved to position $(2,4)$ of $\mathbf{A^T}$. In general terms, the row and column subscripts are interchanged to form the transpose; hence, the value in position (i, j) is moved to position (j, i).

In MATLAB, the transpose of the matrix **A** is denoted by **A'**. Observe that the transpose will have a different size than the original matrix if the original matrix is not a square matrix. We frequently use the transpose operation to convert a row vector to a column vector or a column vector to a row vector.

32.2.2 Dot Product

The **dot product** is a scalar computed from two vectors of the same size. This scalar is the sum of the products of the values in corresponding positions in the vectors, as shown in the following summation equation, which assumes that there are n elements in the vectors **A** and **B**:

$$\text{dot product} = \mathbf{A} \cdot \mathbf{B} = \sum_{i=1}^{n} a_i b_i$$

In MATLAB, we can compute the dot product with the following statement:

```
dot_product = sum(A.*B);
```

Recall that **A.*B** contains the results of an element-by-element multiplication of **A** and **B**. When **A** and **B** are both row vectors or are both column vectors, **A.*B** is also a vector. We then sum the elements in this vector, thus yielding the dot product. The **dot** function may also be used to compute the dot product:

```
dot(A,B);
```

To illustrate, assume that **A** and **B** are the following vectors:

$$\mathbf{A} = \begin{bmatrix} 4 & -1 & 3 \end{bmatrix} \qquad \mathbf{B} = \begin{bmatrix} -2 & 5 & 2 \end{bmatrix}$$

The dot product is then

$$\begin{aligned} \mathbf{A} \cdot \mathbf{B} &= 4 \cdot (-2) + (-1) \cdot 5 + 3 \cdot 2 \\ &= (-8) + (-5) + 6 \\ &= -7 \end{aligned}$$

You can test this result by defining the two vectors, and then typing

```
dot(A,B)
```

EXAMPLE 32.1

CALCULATING MASS OF A SPACECRAFT

The mass of space vehicles, such as the one shown in Figure 32.2, is extremely important. Entire groups of people in the design process keep track of the location and mass of every nut and bolt. This information is used to determine the center of gravity of the vehicle in addition to its total mass. One reason the center of gravity is important is that rockets tumble if the center of gravity is behind the center of pressure. You can demonstrate this with a paper airplane. Put a paperclip on the tail of the paper airplane and observe how the flight pattern changes.

Although finding the center of gravity is a fairly straightforward calculation, it becomes more complex when you realize that the mass of the vehicle and the distribution of mass changes as the fuel is burned.

In this example, we will only find the total mass of some of the components used in a complex space vehicle, as shown below:

Item	Amount	Mass (g)
Bolt	3	3.50
Screw	5	1.50
Nut	2	0.79
Bracket	1	1.75

The total mass is really a dot product. You need to multiply each amount times the corresponding mass, and then add them up. Write a MATLAB program to find the mass of this list of components, using matrix math.

Figure 32.2   A Titan satellite launch vehicle.

SOLUTION

1. Problem Statement

Find the total mass for a set of specified components.

2. Input/Output Description

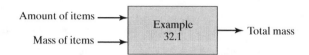

3. Hand Example

Here is a table of items, how many of these items are being used, and the mass of each individual item:

Item	Amount		Mass (g)	Totals (g)
Bolt	3	×	3.50	= 10.50
Screw	5	×	1.50	= 7.50
Nut	2	×	0.79	= 1.58
Bracket	1	×	1.75	= 1.75
				21.33

At the end of each row, we compute the mass for that item, and then add these up at the end of the table.

4. MATLAB Solution

We use an M-file for our solution so that it will be easy to store, and easy to modify for additional data sets. We demonstrate two ways to compute the total mass—using vector computations and using the dot product function.

```
%-----------------------------------------------------
%  Example 32_1 - This program determines the mass
%  for a set of items given the quantity and mass
%  of each individual item.
%
clear, clc
%
% Define the item and mass vectors.
amount = [3,5,2,1];
mass = [3.5,1.5,0.79,1.75];
%
% Compute the mass using vector computations.
total_mass_1 = sum(amount.*mass)
%
% Compute the mass with the dot product function.
total_mass_2 = dot(amount,mass)
%-----------------------------------------------------
```

5. Testing

The output for this program is:

```
total_mass_1 =
    21.3300
total_mass_2 =
    21.3300
```

Both approaches give the same result and agree with the hand example. Now that we know the program works, we can use it for any number of items.

32.2.3 Matrix Multiplication

Matrix multiplication is not accomplished by multiplying corresponding elements of the matrices. In matrix multiplication, the value in position $c(i,j)$ of the product **C** of two matrices **A** and **B** is the dot product of row i of the first matrix and column j of the second matrix, as shown in the following summation equation:

$$c_{i,j} = \sum_{k=1}^{N} a_{ik} b_{kj}$$

Because the dot product requires that the vectors have the same number of elements, the first matrix **A** must have the same number of elements N in each row as there are in each column of the second matrix **B**. Thus, if **A** and **B** both have five rows and five columns, their product has five rows and five columns respectively. Furthermore, for these matrices, we can compute both **AB** and **BA**, but in general they will not be equal.

If **A** has two rows and three columns and **B** has three rows and three columns, the product **AB** will have two rows and three columns. To illustrate, consider the following matrices:

$$\mathbf{A} = \begin{bmatrix} 2 & 5 & 1 \\ 0 & 3 & -1 \end{bmatrix} \quad \mathbf{B} = \begin{bmatrix} 1 & 0 & 2 \\ -1 & 4 & -2 \\ 5 & 2 & 1 \end{bmatrix}$$

The first element in the product $\mathbf{C} = \mathbf{AB}$ is

$$c_{1,1} = \sum_{k=1}^{3} a_{1k} b_{k1}$$
$$= a_{1,1} b_{1,1} + a_{1,2} b_{2,1} + a_{1,3} b_{3,1}$$
$$= 2 \cdot 1 + 5 \cdot (-1) + 1 \cdot 5$$
$$= 2$$

Similarly, we can compute the rest of the elements in the product of **A** and **B**:

$$\mathbf{AB} = \mathbf{C} = \begin{bmatrix} 2 & 22 & -5 \\ -8 & 10 & -7 \end{bmatrix}$$

In this example, we cannot compute **BA**, because **B** does not have the same number of elements in each row as **A** has in each column.

An easy way to decide whether a matrix product exists is to write the sizes of the two matrices side by side. Then, if the two inside numbers are the same, the product exists, and the size of the product is determined by the two outside numbers. To illustrate, in the previous example, the size of **A** is 2×3, and the size of **B** is 3×3. Therefore, if we want to compute **AB**, we write the sizes side by side:

$$2 \times 3, \ 3 \times 3$$

The two inner numbers are both the value 3, so **AB** exists, and its size is determined by the two outer numbers, 2×3. If we want to compute **BA**, we again write the sizes side by side:

$$3 \times 3, \ 2 \times 3$$

The two inner numbers are not the same, so **BA** does not exist. If the two inner numbers are the same, then **A** is said to be **conformable** for multiplication to **B**.

In MATLAB, matrix multiplication is denoted by an asterisk. Thus, the command to perform matrix multiplication of matrices **A** and **B** is

```
A*B;
```

For example, to generate the matrices in our previous example, and then compute the matrix product, we can use the following MATLAB statements:

```
A = [2,5,1; 0,3,-1 ];
B = [1,0,2; -1,4,-2; 5,2,1 ];
C = A*B
C =

    2   22   -5
   -8   10   -7
```

Note that **B*A** does not exist, because the number of columns of **B** does not equal the number of rows of **A**. In other words, **B** is not conformable for multiplication with **A**. Execute this MATLAB command:

```
C = B*A;
```

You will get the following warning message:

```
???  Error using ==> mtimes
Inner matrix dimensions must agree.
```

In general, the matrix product **AB** is not equal to the matrix product **BA**. However, the products **AB** and **BA** are equal if one of the matrices is an identity matrix. We demonstrate this with the following MATLAB statements and their corresponding values:

```
A = [1,0,2; -1,4,-2; 5,2,1];
I = eye(3)
I =
    1   0   0
    0   1   0
    0   0   1
```

```
A*I
ans =
       1    0    2
      -1    4   -2
       5    2    1
I*A
ans =
       1    0    2
      -1    4   -2
       5    2    1
```

EXAMPLE 32.2

COMPUTING MASS FOR SEVERAL VENDORS

Suppose you would like to know which commercial vendor offers the least overall mass total for the items you'll use. Your list of items stays the same, but the mass of each item is different because they are purchased from different vendors. An example is shown below:

Item	Amount	Mass (g) Vendor A	Mass (g) Vendor B	Mass (g) Vendor C
Bolt	3	3.50	2.98	2.50
Screw	5	1.50	1.75	1.60
Nut	2	0.79	1.25	0.99
Bracket	1	1.75	0.95	1.25

The total mass for each vendor is a dot product. You need to multiply each amount times the corresponding mass, and then add them up. But it would be nice to do just one calculation. Matrix multiplication is the answer. We will need to define the amount vector as a row, but the mass matrix will be a 4 × 3 matrix.

SOLUTION

1. Problem Statement

Find the total mass for each vendor.

2. Input/Output Description

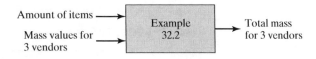

3. Hand Example

In the table below we compute the mass for vendor A:

Item	Amount		Mass (g)	Totals (g)
Bolt	3	×	3.50	= 10.50
Screw	5	×	1.50	= 7.50
Nut	2	×	0.79	= 1.58
Bracket	1	×	1.75	= 1.75
				21.33

Similar computations give the mass for other two vendors:

$$\text{mass for vendor B} = 21.14\,\text{g}$$
$$\text{mass for vendor C} = 18.73\,\text{g}$$

4. MATLAB Solution

We use an M-file for our solution. As we convert our hand solution into a MATLAB solution, we need to think about the matrix sizes. The item matrix will have one row and four columns; the vendor matrix will have four rows and three columns. If we check the size of the matrix multiplication result, we have $(1 \times 4)\,(4 \times 3)$, which gives a (1×3) solution which contains the total mass for each of the three vendors.

```
%------------------------------------------------------------
%  Example 32_2 - This program determines the mass
%  for a set of items given the quantity and mass
%  of each individual item, for a group of vendors.
%
clear, clc
%
% Define the item and mass vectors
amount = [3, 5, 2, 1];
vendor_1 = [3.50, 1.50, 0.79, 1.75]';
vendor_2 = [2.98, 1.75, 1.25, 0.95]';
vendor_3 = [2.50, 1.60, 0.99, 1.25]';
vendor_matrix = [vendor_1, vendor_2, vendor_3];
%
%  Compute the values for the three vendors.
vendor_mass = amount*vendor_matrix;
disp('Vendor Mass Amounts')
disp(vendor_mass)
%------------------------------------------------------------
```

5. Testing

The output for the this program is shown below

Vendor Mass Amounts

21.3300   21.1400   18.7300

Based on this solution, vendor C is the best choice in terms of mass. (The best choice overall may not be vendor C because of other factors, including quality and cost.)

EXAMPLE 32.3

COMPARING MASS FOR COMPETING DESIGNS

Assume that two engineers are promoting competing designs, as shown below:

Item	Amount Design A	Amount Design B	Mass (g) Vendor A	Mass (g) Vendor B	Mass (g) Vendor C
Bolt	3	5	3.50	2.98	2.50
Screw	5	2	1.50	1.75	1.60
Nut	2	3	0.79	1.25	0.99
Bracket	1	2	1.75	0.95	1.25

Now, for each design, we need to multiply each amount times the corresponding mass. Again, matrix multiplication is a good choice for computing the answers.

SOLUTION

1. Problem Statement

Find the total mass for each vendor.

2. Input/Output Description

3. Hand Example

In the previous problem, we computed the mass for the first design for the three vendors. In the table below, we compute the mass for the second design, for vendor A.

Item	Amount		Mass (g)	Totals (g)
Bolt	5	×	3.50	= 17.50
Screw	2	×	1.50	= 3.00
Nut	3	×	0.79	= 2.37
Bracket	2	— ×	1.75	= 3.50
				26.37

Similar computations give the mass for other two vendors, for the second design:

$$\text{mass for vendor B} = 24.0500 \text{ g}$$

$$\text{mass for vendor C} = 21.1700 \text{ g}$$

4. MATLAB Solution

We use an M-file for our solution. As we convert our hand solution into a MATLAB solution, we need to think about the matrix sizes. The "amount matrix" will have two rows (one for each design) and four columns (to represent the number of items in each design). The "vendor matrix" will have four rows (one for the mass of each of the four items) and three columns (one for each vendor). If we check the size of the matrix multiplication result, we have $(2 \times 4)\,(4 \times 3)$, which gives a (2×3) solution which contains the mass of the three vendors, for each design.

```
%-----------------------------------------------------------
% Example 32_3 - This program determines the mass
% for competing designs.  It does this by specifying
% the amounts of each item for each design, and
% then specifying the mass for each item
% for a group of vendors.
%
clear, clc
%
% Define the item amounts and mass vectors
design_1_items = [3, 5, 2, 1];
design_2_items = [5, 2, 3, 2];
designs = [design_1_items; design_2_items];
vendor_1 = [3.50, 1.50, 0.79, 1.75}';
vendor_2 = [2.98, 1.75, 1.25, 0.95]';
vendor_3 = [2.50, 1.60, 0.99, 1.25]';
vendor_matrix = [vendor_1, vendor_2, vendor_3];
%
%  Compute the design values for the three vendors.
mass = designs*vendor_matrix;
%
design_1 = mass(1:)
design_2 = mass(2:)
%-----------------------------------------------------------
```

5. Testing

The output for this program is shown below

```
design_1
   21.3300    21.1400    18.7300
design_2
   26.3700    24.0500    21.1700
```

It is important in this program to be sure to identify which numbers go with each design, and thus we printed these separately. If we had just printed the matrix of values, it would not necessarily be clear which ones went with each design.

32.2.4 Matrix Powers

Recall that if **A** is a matrix, then the expression **A.^2** squares each element in **A**. If we want to square the matrix—that is, compute **A*A**—we can use the operation **A^2**. Thus, **A^4** is equivalent to **A*A*A*A**. To perform a matrix multiplication between two matrices, the number of rows in the first matrix must be the same value as the number of columns in the second matrix. Therefore, to raise a matrix to a power, the number of rows must equal the number of columns, and thus the matrix must be a square matrix. For example, consider the following statements and corresponding display:

```
A = [1 2; 3,4];
C = A^2
C =
     7    10
    15    22
D = A.^2;
D =
     1     4
     9    16
```

Thus, it is always important when multiplying matrices to be sure that we distinguish between element-by-element multiplication and actual matrix multiplication.

32.2.5 Matrix Inverse

By definition, the **inverse** of a square matrix **A** is the matrix $\mathbf{A}^{-1}$ such that the matrix products $\mathbf{A}\mathbf{A}^{-1}$ and $\mathbf{A}^{-1}\mathbf{A}$ are both equal to the identity matrix. For example, consider the following two matrices **A** and **B**:

$$\mathbf{A} = \begin{bmatrix} 2 & 1 \\ 4 & 3 \end{bmatrix} \qquad \mathbf{B} = \begin{bmatrix} 1.5 & -0.5 \\ -2 & 1 \end{bmatrix}$$

If we compute the products **AB** and **BA**, we obtain the following matrices (do the matrix multiplications by hand to be sure you follow the steps):

$$\mathbf{AB} = \begin{bmatrix} 1 & 0 \\ 0 & 1 \end{bmatrix} \qquad \mathbf{BA} = \begin{bmatrix} 1 & 0 \\ 0 & 1 \end{bmatrix}$$

Therefore, **A** and **B** are inverses of each other, or $\mathbf{A} = \mathbf{B}^{-1}$ and $\mathbf{B} = \mathbf{A}^{-1}$.

Computing the inverse of a matrix is a tedious process; fortunately, MATLAB contains an **inv** function that performs the computations for us. (We do not present the steps for computing an inverse in this text. Refer to a linear algebra text if you are interested in the techniques for computing an inverse.) Thus, if we execute **inv(A)** using the matrix **A** defined previously, the result will be another matrix containing the inverse. If we then invert that matrix, the result should be the original matrix **A**. Also, recall that the product of a matrix with its inverse equals the identity matrix. We can illustrate these relationships with the following statements:

```
A = [1,0,2; -1,4,-2; 5,2,1]
A =
     1     0     2
    -1     4    -2
     5     2     1
```

```
B = inv(A)
B =
    -0.2222   -0.1111    0.2222
     0.2500    0.2500    0.0000
     0.6111    0.0556   -0.1111
A*B
ans =
     1.0000    0.0000    0.0000
    -0.0000    1.0000    0.0000
    -0.0000    0.0000    1.0000

B*A
ans =
     1.0000    0.0000    0.0000
     0.0000    1.0000    0.0000
    -0.0000    0.0000    1.0000
```

There are matrices for which an inverse does not exist; these matrices are called **singular** or **ill-conditioned matrices**. When you attempt to compute the inverse of an ill-conditioned matrix in MATLAB, an error message is printed.

32.2.6 Determinants

A **determinant** is a scalar value computed from the entries in a square matrix. Determinants have various applications in engineering, including computing inverses and solving systems of simultaneous equations. For a 2×2 matrix $\mathbf{A}$, the determinant is defined to be

$$|\mathbf{A}| = a_{1,1}\,a_{2,2} - a_{2,1}\,a_{1,2}$$

Therefore, the determinant of $\mathbf{A}$, or $|\mathbf{A}|$, is equal to 8 for the following matrix:

$$\mathbf{A} = \begin{bmatrix} 1 & 3 \\ -1 & 5 \end{bmatrix}$$

For a 3×3 matrix $\mathbf{A}$, the determinant is defined to be

$$|\mathbf{A}| = a_{1,1}a_{2,2}a_{3,3} + a_{1,2}a_{2,3}a_{3,1} + a_{1,3}a_{2,1}a_{3,2}$$
$$- a_{3,1}a_{2,2}a_{1,3} - a_{3,2}a_{2,3}a_{1,1} - a_{3,3}a_{2,1}a_{1,2}$$

If

$$\mathbf{A} = \begin{bmatrix} 1 & 3 & 0 \\ -1 & 5 & 2 \\ 1 & 2 & 1 \end{bmatrix}$$

then $|\mathbf{A}|$ is equal to $5 + 6 + 0 - 0 - 4 - (-3)$, or 10.

A more involved process is necessary for computing determinants of matrices with more than three rows and columns. We do not include a discussion of the process for computing a general determinant here, because MATLAB will automatically compute a determinant using the **det** function, with a square matrix as its argument, as in **det(A)**.

32.3   SOLUTIONS TO SYSTEMS OF LINEAR EQUATIONS

Consider the following system of three equations with three unknowns:

$$
\begin{aligned}
3x + 2y - z &= 10 \\
-x + 3y + 2z &= 5 \\
x - y - z &= -1
\end{aligned}
$$

We can rewrite this system of equations using the following matrices:

$$
\mathbf{A} = \begin{bmatrix} 3 & 2 & -1 \\ -1 & 3 & 2 \\ 1 & -1 & -1 \end{bmatrix} \quad \mathbf{X} = \begin{bmatrix} x \\ y \\ z \end{bmatrix} \quad \mathbf{B} = \begin{bmatrix} 10 \\ 5 \\ -1 \end{bmatrix}
$$

Using matrix multiplication, the **system of equations** can then be written as $\mathbf{AX} = \mathbf{B}$. Go through the multiplication to convince yourself that this matrix equation yields the original set of equations.

To simplify the notation, we designate the variables as x_1, x_2, x_3, and so on. Rewriting the initial set of equations using this notation, we have

$$
\begin{aligned}
3x_1 + 2x_2 - x_3 &= 10 \\
-x_1 + 3x_2 + 2x_3 &= 5 \\
x_1 - x_2 - x_3 &= -1
\end{aligned}
$$

This set of equations is then represented by the matrix equation $\mathbf{AX} = \mathbf{B}$, where $\mathbf{X}$ is the column vector $[x_1, x_2, x_3]^{\mathrm{T}}$. We now present two methods for solving a system of N equations with N unknowns.

32.3.1   Solution Using the Matrix Inverse

One way to solve a system of equations is by using the matrix inverse. For example, assume that $\mathbf{A}$, $\mathbf{X}$, and $\mathbf{B}$ are the matrices defined earlier in this section:

$$
\mathbf{A} = \begin{bmatrix} 3 & 2 & -1 \\ -1 & 3 & 2 \\ 1 & -1 & -1 \end{bmatrix} \quad \mathbf{X} = \begin{bmatrix} x_1 \\ x_2 \\ x_3 \end{bmatrix} \quad \mathbf{B} = \begin{bmatrix} 10 \\ 5 \\ -1 \end{bmatrix}
$$

Then $\mathbf{AX} = \mathbf{B}$. If we premultiply both sides of this matrix equation by $\mathbf{A}^{-1}$, we have $\mathbf{A}^{-1}\mathbf{AX} = \mathbf{A}^{-1}\mathbf{B}$. However, because $\mathbf{A}^{-1}\mathbf{A}$ is equal to the identity matrix $\mathbf{I}$, we have $\mathbf{IX} = \mathbf{A}^{-1}\mathbf{B}$, or $X = \mathbf{A}^{-1}\mathbf{B}$. In MATLAB, we can compute this solution with the following command:

```
X = inv(A)*B;
```

As an example, we will solve the following system of equations:

$$
\begin{aligned}
3x_1 + 5x_2 &= -7 \\
2x_1 - 4x_2 &= 10
\end{aligned}
$$

Type the following MATLAB commands to define **A** and **B,** and then solve the system of equations:

```
A = [3,5; 2,-4];
B = [-7,10]';
X = inv(A)*B
```

X =
   1.0000
  -2.0000

Note that **B** is defined to be a column matrix. Substitute these values for **X** back into the original equations to convince yourself that these values represent the solution to the system of equations.

EXAMPLE 32.4

SOLVING ELECTRIC CIRCUIT EQUATIONS

Solving an electrical circuit problem can often result in a set of simultaneous equations to solve. For example, consider the electrical circuit in Figure 32.3. It contains a single

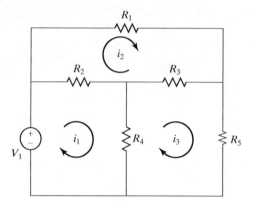

Figure 32.3 An electrical circuit.

voltage source and five resistors. You can analyze this circuit by dividing it up into smaller pieces and applying two basic electrical facts:

$$\sum voltage \text{ around a circuit must be zero}$$

$$\text{Voltage} = \text{current} \times \text{resistance}, V = iR$$

Following the lower left-hand loop results in our first equation:

$$-V_1 + R_2(i_1 - i_2) + R_4(i_1 - i_3) = 0$$

Following the upper loop results in our second equation:

$$R_1 i_2 + R_3(i_2 - i_3) + R_2(i_2 - i_1) = 0$$

Finally, following the lower right-hand loop results in the last equation:

$$R_3(i_3 - i_2) + R_5 i_3 + R_4(i_3 - i_1) = 0$$

Since we know all the resistances (R values) and the voltage, we have three equations and three unknown currents. Now we need to rearrange the equations so that they are in a form where we can perform a matrix solution—in other words, we need to isolate the current variables:

$$(R_2 + R_4)i_1 + (-R_2)i_2 + (-R_4)i_3 = V_1$$

$$(-R_2)i_1 + (R_1 + R_2 + R_3)i_2 + (-R_3)i_3 = 0$$

$$(-R_4)i_1 + (-R_3)i_2 + (R_3 + R_4 + R_5)i_3 = 0$$

Write a MATLAB program to solve these equations, using the matrix inverse method. Allow the user to enter the five values of R and the voltage from the keyboard.

SOLUTION

1. Problem Statement

Find the three currents for the circuit shown in Figure 32.3.

2. Input/Output Description

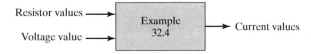

3. Hand Example

For a hand example, assume that all the resistor values are 1 ohm, and that the voltage source is 5 volts. The set of equations then becomes the following:

$$2\,i_1 - i_2 - i_3 = 5$$
$$-i_1 + 3\,i_2 - i_3 = 0$$
$$-i_1 - i_2 + 3\,i_3 = 0$$

To solve this set of equations without MATLAB, you can either do it by hand, or use your calculator. In either case, you should get an answer of $i_1 = 5, i_2 = 2.5, i_3 = 2.5$. A negative value for current indicates that the current is flowing in a direction opposite to the one we chose as positive.

4. MATLAB Solution

We develop the solution as an M-file in order to be able to store it and to easily modify it for additional problem solutions.

```
%-----------------------------------------------------------
-     -      -       -       -        -
%   Example 32_4 - This program reads resistor and voltage
%   values and then computes the corresponding current
%   values for a specified electrical circuit.
%
clear, clc
%
%   Enter resistor values.
R1 = input('Input resistor value R1 in ohms:');
R2 = input('Input resistor value R2 in ohms:');
R3 = input('Input resistor value R3 in ohms:');
R4 = input('Input resistor value R4 in ohms:');
R5 = input('Input resistor value R5 in ohms:');
V = input('Input the value of voltage in volts, V:');
%
```

```
%  Initialize the matrix A and vector B using AX = B
form.
A = [(R2+R4), -R2, -R4;
      -R2, (R1+R2+R3), -R3;
      -R4, -R3, (R3+R4+R5)]
B = [V, 0, 0]';
current = inv(A)*B
disp('Current:')
disp(current)
%-------------------------------------------------------
```

5. Testing

If we test this program using the data from our hand example, the interaction will be the following:

```
Input resistor value R1 in ohms:   1
Input resistor value R2 in ohms:   1
Input resistor value R3 in ohms:   1
Input resistor value R4 in ohms:   1
Input resistor value R5 in ohms:   1
Input the value of voltage V in volts: 5
Current:
   5.0000
   2.5000
   2.5000
```

These values should match those you computed for the hand example. We now test the program with a different set of values:

```
Input resistor value R1 in ohms:   2
Input resistor value R2 in ohms:   4
Input resistor value R3 in ohms:   6
Input resistor value R4 in ohms:   8
Input resistor value R5 in ohms:   10
Input the value of voltage V in volts: 10
Current:
   1.6935
   0.9677
   0.8065
```

32.3.2 Solution Using Matrix Left Division

Another way to solve a system of linear equations is to use the **matrix left division** operator:

```
X = A\B;
```

This method produces the solution using Gaussian elimination, without forming the inverse. Using the matrix division operator is more efficient than using the matrix inverse and produces a greater numerical accuracy.

As an example, we will solve the same system of equations used in the previous example:

$$3x_1 + 5x_2 = -7$$
$$2x_1 - 4x_2 = 10$$

However, now solve for **X** by using matrix left division:

```
A = [3,5; 2,-4];
B = [-7,10]';
X = A\B
X =
   1
  -2
```

To confirm that the values of **X** do indeed solve each equation, we can multiply **A** by **X** using the expression **A*X**. The result is the column vector **[-7, 10]'**.

If there is not a unique solution to a system of equations, an error message is displayed. The solution vector may contain values of NaN, ∞, or $-\infty$, depending on the values of the matrices **A** and **B**.

Summary

In this chapter, we presented matrix functions to create matrices of zeros, matrices of ones, identity matrices, diagonal matrices, and magic squares. We also defined the transpose, the inverse, and the determinant of a matrix, and presented functions to compute them. We also presented functions for flipping a matrix from left to right, and for flipping it from top to bottom. We defined the dot product (between two vectors) and a matrix product (between two matrices), and presented functions to compute these. Two methods for solving a system of N equations with N unknowns using matrix operations were presented. One method used the inverse of a matrix, and the other used matrix left division.

MATLAB SUMMARY

This MATLAB summary lists and briefly describes all of the special characters, commands, and functions that were defined in this chapter:

Special Characters	
'	indicates a matrix transpose
*	matrix multiplication
\	matrix left division

Commands and Functions

---

det	computes the determinate of a matrix
dot	computes the dot product of two vectors
diag	extracts the diagonal from a matrix, or generates a matrix with the input on the diagonal
eye	generates an identity matrix
fliplr	flips a matrix from left to right
flipud	flips a matrix from up to down
inv	computes the inverse of a matrix
magic	generates a magic square
ones	generates a matrix composed of ones
zeros	generates a matrix composed of zeros

KEY TERMS

conformable
determinant
diagonal matrix
dot product
identity matrix

ill-conditioned matrix
inverse
magic square
main diagonal
matrix left division

matrix multiplication
singular matrix
system of equations
transpose

Problems

1. Compute the dot product of the following pairs of vectors, and then show that

$$\mathbf{A} \cdot \mathbf{B} = \mathbf{B} \cdot \mathbf{A}$$

(a) $\mathbf{A} = [1\ 3\ 5]$, $\mathbf{B} = [-3\ -2\ 4]$

(b) $\mathbf{A} = [0\ -1\ -4\ -8]$, $\mathbf{B} = [4\ -2\ -3\ 24]$

2. Compute the total mass of the following components, using a dot product:

Component	Density, g/cm³	Volume, cm³
Propellant	1.2	700
Steel	7.8	200
Aluminum	2.7	300

3. Bomb calorimeters are used to determine the energy released during chemical reactions. The total heat capacity of a bomb calorimeter is defined as the sum of the product of the mass of each component and the specific heat capacity of each component. That is,

$$CP = \sum_{i=1}^{n} m_i C_i$$

where

m_i is the mass of each component, g;
C_i is the heat capacity of each component, J/gK; and
CP is the total heat capacity, J/K.

Find the total heat capacity of a bomb calorimeter with the following components:

Component	Mass, g	Heat Capacity, J/gK
Steel	250	0.45
Water	100	4.2
Aluminum	10	0.90

4. Compute the matrix product $\mathbf{A} * \mathbf{B}$ of the following pairs of matrices:

(a) $\mathbf{A} = [12\ 4;\ 3\ -5]$, $\mathbf{B} = [2\ 12;\ 0\ 0]$

(b) $\mathbf{A} = [1\ 3\ 5;\ 2\ 4\ 6]$, $\mathbf{B} = [-2\ 4;\ 3\ 8;\ 12\ -2]$

5. A series of experiments were performed with the bomb calorimeter from Problem 3. In each experiment, a different amount of water was used, as shown in the following table:

Experiment #	Mass of Water, g
1	110.0
2	100.0
3	101.0
4	98.6
5	99.4

Calculate the total heat capacity for the calorimeter for each of the experiments.

6. Given the array $\mathbf{A} = [-1\ 3;\ 4\ 2]$, raise each element of $\mathbf{A}$ to the second power. Raise $\mathbf{A}$ to the second power by matrix exponentiation. Explain why the answers are different.

7. Given the array $\mathbf{A} = [-1\ 3;\ 4\ 2]$, compute the determinant of A.

8. If $\mathbf{A}$ is conformable to $\mathbf{B}$ for addition, then a theorem states that $(\mathbf{A}+\mathbf{B})^{\mathrm{T}} = \mathbf{A}^{T}+\mathbf{B}^{T}$. Use MATLAB to test this theorem on the following matrices:

$$A = \begin{bmatrix} 2 & 12 & -5 \\ -3 & 0 & -2 \\ 4 & 2 & -1 \end{bmatrix} \quad B = \begin{bmatrix} 4 & 0 & 12 \\ 2 & 2 & 0 \\ -6 & 3 & 0 \end{bmatrix}$$

9. Given that matrices $\mathbf{A}$, $\mathbf{B}$, and $\mathbf{C}$ are conformable for multiplication, the associative property holds; that is, $\mathbf{A}(\mathbf{BC}) = (\mathbf{AB})\mathbf{C}$. Test the associative property using matrices $\mathbf{A}$ and $\mathbf{B}$ from Problem 8, along with matrix $\mathbf{C}$:

$$C = \begin{bmatrix} 4 \\ -3 \\ 0 \end{bmatrix}$$

10. Recall that not all matrices have an inverse. A matrix is singular (i.e., it does not have an inverse) if $|A| = 0$. Test the following matrices using the determinant function to see if each has an inverse:

$$A = \begin{bmatrix} 2 & -1 \\ 4 & 5 \end{bmatrix}, \quad B = \begin{bmatrix} 4 & 2 \\ 2 & 1 \end{bmatrix}, \quad C = \begin{bmatrix} 2 & 0 & 0 \\ 1 & 2 & 2 \\ 5 & -4 & 0 \end{bmatrix}$$

If an inverse exists, compute it.

11.   Solve the following systems of equations using both the matrix left division and the inverse matrix methods:

(a)
$$-2x_1 + x_2 = -3$$
$$x_1 + x_2 = 3$$

(b)
$$10x_1 - 7x_2 + 0x_3 = 7$$
$$-3x_1 + 2x_2 + 6x_3 = 4$$
$$5x_1 + x_2 + 5x_3 = 6$$

(c)
$$x_1 + 4x_2 - x_3 + x_4 = 2$$
$$2x_1 + 7x_2 + x_3 - 2x_4 = 16$$
$$x_1 + 4x_2 - x_3 + 2x_4 = -15$$
$$3x_1 - 10x_2 - 2x_3 + 5x_4 = -15$$

12.   Time each method you used in Problem 11 for part c by using the **clock** function and the **etime** function, the latter of which measures elapsed time. Which method is faster, left division or inverse matrix multiplication?

```
t0 = clock;
(code to be timed)
etime(clock, t0)
```

13.   In Example 32.4, we showed that the circuit shown in Figure 32.3 could be described by the following set of linear equations:
$$(R_2 + R_4)i_1 + (-R_2)i_2 + (-R_4)i_3 = V_1$$
$$(-R_2)i_1 + (R_1 + R_2 + R_3)i_2 + (-R_3)i_3 = 0$$
$$(-R_4)i_1 + (-R_3)i_2 + (R_3 + R_4 + R_5)i_3 = 0$$

We solved this set of equations using the matrix inverse approach. Redo the problem, but this time use the left division approach.

14.   **Amino Acids.** The amino acids in proteins contain molecules of oxygen (O), carbon (C), nitrogen (N), sulfur (S), and hydrogen (H), as shown in Table 32.1. The molecular weights for oxygen, carbon, nitrogen, sulfur, and hydrogen are as follows:

Oxygen	15.9994
Carbon	12.011
Nitrogen	14.00674
Sulfur	32.066
Hydrogen	1.00794

(a) Write a program in which the user enters the number of oxygen atoms, carbon atoms, nitrogen atoms, sulfur atoms, and hydrogen atoms in an amino acid. Compute and print the corresponding molecular weight. Use a dot product to compute the molecular weight.

(b) Write a program that computes the molecular weight of each amino acid in Table 32.1, assuming that the numeric information in this table is contained in a data file named **elements.dat**. Generate a new data file named **weights.dat** that contains the molecular weights of the amino acids. Use matrix multiplication to compute the molecular weights.

TABLE 32.1   Amino acid molecules

Amino Acid	O	C	N	S	H
Alanine	2	3	1	0	7
Arginine	2	6	4	0	15
Asparagine	3	4	2	0	8
Aspartic	4	4	1	0	6
Cysteine	2	3	1	1	7
Glutamic	4	5	1	0	8
Glutamine	3	5	2	0	10
Glycine	2	2	1	0	5
Histidine	2	6	3	0	10
Isoleucine	2	6	1	0	13
Leucine	2	6	1	0	13
Lysine	2	6	2	0	15
Methionine	2	5	1	1	11
Phenylanlanine	2	9	1	0	11
Proline	2	5	1	0	10
Serine	3	3	1	0	7
Threonine	3	4	1	0	9
Tryptophan	2	11	2	0	11
Tyrosine	3	9	1	9	11
Valine	2	5	1	0	11

Section 8

Maple User Manual

33 Preface

33.1 Maple Software

Maple™ software is a powerful system that you can use to solve mathematical problems from simple to complex. You can also create professional quality documents, presentations, and custom interactive computational tools in the Maple environment.

You can access the power of the Maple computational engine through a variety of interfaces.

Interface	Description
Standard (default)	A full-featured graphical user interface that helps you create electronic documents to show all your calculations, assumptions, and any margin of error in your results. You can also hide the computations to allow your reader to focus on the problem setup and final results. The advanced formatting features lets you create the customized document you need. Because the documents are *live*, you can edit the parameters and, with the click of a button, compute the new results. The Standard interface has two modes: *Document* mode and *Worksheet* mode. An interactive version of this manual is available in the Standard Worksheet interface. From the **Help** menu, select **Manuals, Resources, and more → Manuals → User Manual**.
Classic	A basic worksheet environment for older computers with limited memory. The Classic interface does not offer all of the graphical user interface features that are available in the Standard interface. The Classic interface has only one mode, *Worksheet* mode.
Command-line version	A command-line interface for solving very large complex problems or batch processing with scripts. No graphical user interface features are available.
Maplet™ Applications	Graphical user interfaces containing windows, textbox regions, and other visual interfaces, which gives you point-and-click access to the power of Maple. You can perform calculations and plot functions without using the worksheet.
Maplesoft™ Graphing Calculator	A graphical calculator interface to the Maple computational engine. Using it, you can perform simple computations and create customizable, zoomable graphs. This is available on Microsoft® Windows® only.

This manual describes how to use the Standard interface. As mentioned, the Standard interface offers two modes: *Document* mode and *Worksheet* mode. Using either mode, you can create high quality interactive mathematical documents. Each mode offers the same features and functionality, the only difference is the default input region of each mode.

33.2 Shortcut Keys by Platform

This manual will frequently refer to context menus and command completion when entering expressions. The keyboard keys used to invoke these features differ based on your operating system.

This manual will only refer to the keyboard keys needed for a Windows operating system. The shortcut keys for your operating system can be viewed from the **Help** menu (**Help → Manuals, Resources, and more → Shortcut Keys**).

Context Menus

- **Right-click**, Windows and UNIX®

- **Control-click**, Macintosh®

That is, place the mouse over the input or output region and press the right button on the mouse or press and hold the **Control** key and click the mouse key for Macintosh.

For more information on Context Menus, see *Context Menus (page 937)*.

Command Completion

- **Esc**, Macintosh, Windows, and UNIX

- **Ctrl + Space**, Windows

- **Ctrl + Shift + Space**, UNIX

Begin entering a command in a Maple document. Press the **Esc** key. Alternatively, use the platform-specific keys. For Windows, press and hold the **Ctrl** key and then press the **Space** bar.

For more information on Command Completion, see *Command Completion (page 945)*.

33.3 In This Manual

This manual provides an introduction to the following Maple features:

- Ease-of-use when entering and solving problems

- Point-and-click interaction with various interfaces to help you solve problems quickly

- Maple commands and standard math notation

- Clickable Calculus

- The help system

- Online resources

- Performing computations

- Creating plots and animations

- The Maple programming language

- Using and creating custom Maplet applications

- File input and output, and using Maple with third party products

- Data structures

For a complete list of manuals, study guides, toolboxes, and other resources, visit the Maplesoft web site at **http://www.maplesoft.com**

33.4 Audience

The information in this manual is intended for first-time Maple users and users looking for a little more information.

33.5 Conventions

This manual uses the following typographical conventions.

- **bold** font - Maple command, package name, option name, dialog, menu, or text field
- *italics* - new or important concept
- **Note** - additional information relevant to the section
- **Important** - information that must be read and followed

33.6 Customer Feedback

Maplesoft welcomes your feedback. For suggestions and comments related to this and other manuals, contact **doc@maplesoft.com**.

34 Getting Started

Don't worry about your difficulties in Mathematics. I can assure you mine are still greater.

~Albert Einstein

Mathematics touches us every day—from the simple chore of calculating the total cost of our purchases to the complex calculations used to construct the bridges we travel.

To harness the power of mathematics, Maplesoft provides a tool in an accessible and complete form. That tool is Maple.

34.1 In This Chapter

Section	Topics
Introduction to Maple (page 902) - The main features of Maple's Standard Interface	• Starting the Standard Document Interface • Entering commands and mathematical expressions • Toolbars • Context menus • Copy and drag keys • Saving Maple documents
Entering Expressions (page 917) - Methods of entering expressions in 1-D and 2-D Math	• Execution groups • Math Mode and Text Mode • Palettes • Symbol names • Toolbar icons
Point-and-Click Interaction (page 929) - An introduction to the point-and-click features in Maple	• Assistants • Tutors • Context menus • Task templates • Exploration Assistant
Commands (page 943) - An introduction to the commands of the Maple language	• Using commands from the Maple library • Entering commands • Document blocks
The Maple Help System (page 950) - Accessing help on commands, packages, point-and-click features, and more	• How to access help for Maple features • Interacting with help pages • Viewing and interacting with examples

Section	Topics
Available Resources (page 953) - Both online and from within Maple	• New user resources, including the Maple Tour and the Maple Portal • Examples • Online help • Maple web site resources

34.2 Introduction to Maple

Working in Maple

With Maple, you can create powerful interactive documents. The Maple environment lets you start solving problems right away by entering expressions in 2-D Math and solving these expressions using point-and-click interfaces. You can combine text and math in the same line, add tables to organize the content of your work, or insert images, sketch regions, and spreadsheets. You can visualize and animate problems in two and three dimensions, format text for academic papers or books, and insert hyperlinks to other Maple files, web sites, or email addresses. You can embed and program graphical user interface components, as well as devise custom solutions using the Maple programming language.

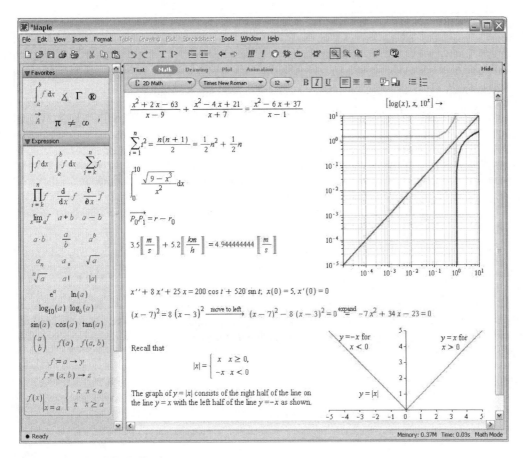

Figure 34.1: The Maple Environment

Starting the Standard Document Interface

To start Maple on:

Windows	From the **Start** menu, select **All Programs** → **Maple 15** → **Maple 15**.
	Alternatively:
	Double-click the **Maple 15** desktop icon.

Macintosh	1. From the Finder, select **Applications** and **Maple 15**.
	2. Double-click **Maple 15**.
UNIX	Enter the full path, for example, **/usr/local/maple/bin/xmaple**
	Alternatively:
	1. Add the Maple directory (for example, **/usr/local/maple/bin**) to your command search path.
	2. Enter **xmaple**.

The first Maple session opens with a **Startup** dialog explaining the difference between *Document Mode* and *Worksheet Mode*. Using either mode, you can create high quality interactive mathematical documents. Each mode offers the same features and functionality; the only difference is the default input region of each mode.

Document Mode

Document mode uses *Document Blocks* as the default input region to hide Maple syntax. A Document Block region is indicated by two triangles located in the vertical Markers column along the left pane of the Maple Document, ⊠⌊. If the Markers column is not visible, open the **View** menu and select **Markers**. This allows you to focus on the problem instead of the commands used to solve the problem. For example, when using context menus on Maple input in Document mode (invoked by right-clicking or **Control**-clicking for Macintosh), input and output are connected using an arrow or equal sign with self-documenting text indicating the calculation that had taken place. The command used to solve this expression is hidden.

$$\boxtimes \quad x^2 + 7x + 10 \xrightarrow{\text{solve}} \{x = -2\}, \{x = -5\}$$

When starting Standard Maple, the default mode is Document mode.

Worksheet Mode

Worksheet mode uses a Maple prompt as the default input region. The Maple input prompt is a red angle bracket, $\lfloor >$. When using context menus on input in Worksheet mode, all commands are displayed.

$$\lfloor > \quad x^2 + 7x + 10$$
$$\lfloor > \quad solve(\{ x^2 + 7^*x + 10 = 0 \})$$
$$\{x = -2\}, \{x = -5\}$$

To work in Worksheet mode, select **File → New → Worksheet Mode**.

Document and Worksheet Modes

Regardless of which mode you are working in, you have the opportunity to show or hide your calculations. You can hide commands in Worksheet Mode by adding a document block from the **Format** menu, **Format → Create Document Block** (see *Document Blocks (page 948)*), or you can show commands in Document mode by adding a Maple prompt from the **Insert** menu, **Insert → Execution Group → Before / After Cursor** (see *Input Prompt (page 972)*).

This chapter discusses features common to both modes. Specific aspects of Document mode are explained in *Document Mode (page 957)*, and aspects of Worksheet mode are explained in *Worksheet Mode (page 971)*.

The Startup dialog also contains links to items, such as various document options, help resources including updates and other introductory help pages, and application resources on the Maplesoft web site. Subsequent sessions display **Tip of the Day** information.

To start a Maple session:

1. In the **Startup** dialog, select **Blank Document** or **Blank Worksheet**. A blank document displays.

or

1. Close the **Startup** dialog.

2. From the **File** menu, select **New**, and then either **Document Mode** or **Worksheet Mode**. A blank document displays.

Every time you open a document, Maple displays a **Quick Help** pop-up list of important shortcut keys. To invoke **Quick Help** at any time, press the **F1** key.

Entering 2-D Math

In Maple, the default format for entering mathematical expressions is 2-D Math. This results in mathematical expressions that are equivalent to the quality of math found in textbooks. Entering 2-D Math in Maple is done using common key strokes or palette items. For more information on palettes, see *Palettes (page 919)*. An example of entering an expression using common key strokes is presented in the following section. An example of entering an expression using palette items is presented in *Example 3 - Enter an Expression Using Palettes (page 924)*.

Common Operations

Entering mathematical expressions, such as $\dfrac{35}{99} + \dfrac{1}{9}$, $x^2 + x$, and $x \cdot y$ is natural in 2-D Math.

To enter a fraction:

1. Enter the numerator.

2. Press the forward slash (/) key.

3. Enter the denominator.

4. To leave the denominator, press the right arrow key.

To enter a power:

1. Enter the base.

2. Press the caret (^) key.

3. Enter the exponent, which displays in math as a superscript.

4. To leave the exponent, press the right arrow key.

To enter a product:

1. Enter the first factor.

2. Press the asterisk (*) key, which displays in 2-D Math as a dot, $\cdot$.

3. Enter the second factor.

Implied Multiplication:

In most cases, you do not need to include the multiplication operator, $\cdot$. Insert a space character between two quantities to multiply them.

Note: In some cases, you do not need to enter the multiplication operator or a space character. For example, Maple interprets a number followed by a variable as multiplication.

Important: Maple interprets a sequence of letters, for example, xy, as a single variable. To specify the product of two variables, you must insert a space character (or multiplication operator), for example, $x\,y$ or $x\cdot y$. For more information, refer to the **2DMathDetails** help page.

Shortcuts for Entering Mathematical Expressions

Table 34.1: Common Keystrokes for Entering Symbols and Formats

Symbol/Formats	Key	Example
implicit multiplication	**Space** key	$\left(x^2 - 7xy + 3y^2\right)xy$
explicit multiplication [1]	* (asterisk)	$2\cdot3$
fraction [2]	/ (forward slash)	$\dfrac{1}{4}$
exponent (superscript) [2]	^ (**Shift + 6** or caret key)	x^2
subscript [2]	_ (**Shift** + underscore)	x_a
navigating expressions	Arrow keys	
command / symbol completion [3]	• **Esc**, Macintosh, Windows, and UNIX • **Ctrl + Space**, Windows • **Ctrl + Shift + Space**, UNIX	ab
square root	*sqrt* and then command completion	$\sqrt{25}$

Symbol/Formats	Key	Example
exponential function [2]	*exp* and then command completion	e^x
enter / exit 2-D Math	• **F5** key • **Math** and **Text** icons in the toolbar	$\frac{1}{4}$ versus 1/4
[1] required for products of numbers			
[2] use the right arrow key to leave a denominator, superscript, or subscript region			
[3] for more information, see *Command Completion (page 925)*.			

For a complete list of shortcut keys, refer to the **2-D Math Shortcut Keys and Hints** help page. To access this help page in the Maple software, in Math mode enter **MathShortcuts** and then press **Enter**. For information on the Maple Help System, see *The Maple Help System (page 950)*.

Example 1 - Enter and Evaluate an Expression Using Keystrokes

Review the following example:

$$\frac{x^2 + y^2}{2}$$

In this example, you will enter $\dfrac{x^2 + y^2}{2}$ and evaluate the expression.

Action	Result in Document
To enter the expression: 1. Enter **x**.	x
2. Press **Shift + 6** (the ^ or caret key). The cursor moves to the superscript position.	x
3. Enter **2**.	x^2
4. Press the right arrow key. The cursor moves right and out of the superscript position.	x^2
5. Enter the + symbol.	$x^2 +$
6. Enter **y**.	$x^2 + y$
7. Press **Shift + 6** to move to the superscript position.	$x^2 + y$

Action	Result in Document
8. Enter **2** and press the right arrow key.	$x^2 + y^2$
9. With the mouse, select the expression that will be the numerator of the fraction.	$x^2 + y^2$
10. Enter the / symbol. The cursor moves to the denominator, with the entire expression in the numerator.	$\dfrac{x^2 + y^2}{1}$
11. Enter **2**.	$\dfrac{x^2 + y^2}{2}$
12. Press the right arrow key to move right and out of the denominator position.	$\dfrac{x^2 + y^2}{2}$
To evaluate the expression and display the result inline: 13. Press **Ctrl + =** (**Command + =**, Macintosh).	$\dfrac{x^2 + y^2}{2} = \dfrac{1}{2}x^2 + \dfrac{1}{2}y^2$

To execute 2-D Math, you can use any of the following methods.

- Pressing **Ctrl + =** (**Command + =**, for Macintosh). That is, *press and hold* the **Ctrl** (or **Command**) key, and then press the equal sign (=) key. This evaluates and displays results inline.

- Pressing the **Enter** key. This evaluates and displays results on the next line and centered.

- Right-click (**Control**-click for Macintosh) the input to invoke a context menu item. From the context menu, select **Evaluate and Display Inline**. See *Context Menus (page 937)* for more details.

- Using the **Edit** menu items **Evaluate** and **Evaluate and Display Inline**.

Toolbar Options

The Maple toolbar offers several buttons to assist you when interacting with Maple. See **Table 34.2**.

Table 34.2: Maple Toolbar Options

Basic Usage	Icon	Equivalent Menu Option or Command
Inserts plain text after the current execution group.	T	From the **Insert** menu, select **Text**.
Inserts Maple Input after the current execution group. For details, refer to *Execution Groups (page 917)*.	[>	From the **Insert** menu, select **Execution Group** and then **After Cursor**.
Encloses the selection in a subsection. For details, refer to page 296 of the **Maple 15 User Manual**.		From the **Format** menu, select **Indent**.
Removes any section enclosing the selection.		From the **Format** menu, select **Outdent**.

Basic Usage	Icon	Equivalent Menu Option or Command
Executes all commands in the worksheet or document	*!!!*	From the **Edit** menu, select **Execute** and then **Worksheet**.
Executes a selected area.	*!*	From the **Edit** menu, select **Execute** and then **Selection**.
Clears Maple's internal memory. For details, refer to the **restart** help page.	↻	Enter *restart*.
Add and edit Maple code that is executed each time the worksheet is opened. For details, refer to the **startupcode** help page.	✿°	From the **Edit** menu, select **Startup Code**.
Adjusts the display size of document content. **Note:** plots, spreadsheets, images, and sketches remain unchanged.	🔍 🔍 🔍	From the **View** menu, select **Zoom Factor** and then a zoom size.
Opens the Maple help system. For details, refer to *The Maple Help System (page 950)*.	📖	From the **Help** menu, select **Maple Help**.

For 1-D Math and text regions, the **Tab** icon in the toolbar allows you to set the **Tab** key to move between placeholders (or cells in a table) or to indent text.

Table 34.3: Tab Icon Description

Tab Icon	Description
⇥	Tab icon **off**. Allows you to move between placeholders using the **Tab** key.
⇥	Tab icon **on**. Allows you to indent in the worksheet using the **Tab** key.
Text Math	The Tab icon is disabled when using 2-D Math (**Math** mode), and as such, the **Tab** key allows you to move between placeholders.

Toolbar icons are controlled by the location of the cursor in the document. For example, place the cursor at an input region and the **Text** and **Math** icons are accessible while the others are dimmed. See **Table 34.4** for a list of the tools available in each icon.

Table 34.4: Toolbar Icons and their Tools

Toolbar Icon Options
Text tools

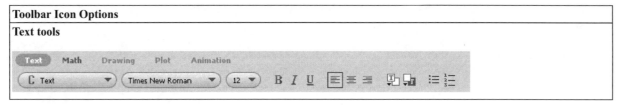

Toolbar Icon Options

Math tools

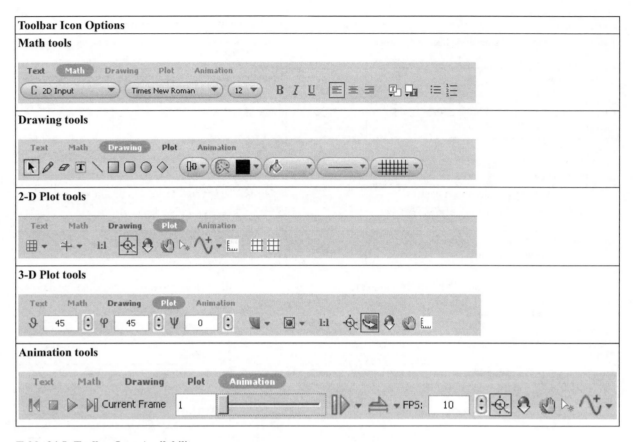

Drawing tools

2-D Plot tools

3-D Plot tools

Animation tools

Table 34.5: Toolbar Icon Availability

Region	Available Tools
Input region	Text and Math icons
Plot region	Drawing and Plot icons
Animation region	Drawing, Plot, and Animation icons
Canvas and Image regions	Drawing icon

The **Text** and **Math** icons allow you to enter text and math in the same line by choosing the appropriate input style at each stage when entering the sentence.

The derivative of $\sin(x)$ is $\cos(x)$.

For an example, see *Example 6 - Enter Text and 2-D Math in the Same Line Using Toolbar Icons (page 928)*.

Using the tools available in these icons, you can customize the input style of the text and 2-D Math. For the **Text** and **Math** icons, the icon that is selected remains in that state until prompted otherwise; therefore, if the **Text** icon is selected and you press the **Enter** key, the new input region remains a Text region.

The **Text** and **Math** icons differ while at a Maple input prompt. The Math icon displays input as 2-D Math, whereas the Text icon displays Maple input. For details, refer to *Math Mode vs. Text Mode (page 917)*.

$$> \quad \frac{x^2}{2}$$

```
>  x^2/2;
```

To access the tools available in the **Plot** and **Drawing** icons, click a plot region. These tools allow you to manipulate the plot or draw shapes and enter text on the plot region. By clicking an animation region, you have the same features available for a plot region, in addition to tools for playing the animation in the **Animation** icon. For details on plots and animations, refer to page 241 of the **Maple 15 User Manual**.

For the remaining icons, hover the mouse over the icon to display the icon description.

Context Menus and Copy & Drag

Context Menus

Maple dynamically generates a context menu of applicable options when you right-click an object, expression, or region. The options available in the context menu depend on the selected input region. For example, you can manipulate and graph expressions, enhance plots, format text, manage palettes, structure tables, and more. When using context menus to perform an action on an expression, the input and output are connected with a self-documenting arrow or equal sign indicating the action that had taken place. For more information, see *Context Menus (page 937)*.

Copy & Drag

With Maple, you can drag input, output, or curves in a plot region into a new input region. This is done by highlighting the input or selecting the curve and dragging it with your mouse into a new input region. Dragging the highlighted region will cut or delete the original input. To prevent this, use the copy and drag feature.

- **Ctrl** + drag, Windows and UNIX
- **Command** + drag, Macintosh

That is, highlight the region you want to copy. Press and hold the **Ctrl** key while you drag the input to the new region using the mouse. The steps are the same for Macintosh with the exception of pressing the **Command** key.

Example 2 - Solve and Plot an Equation Using Context Menus and Copy & Drag

Review the following example:

$$5x - 7 = 3x + 2$$

In this example, we will enter the equation and then solve and plot the equation using context menus and Maple's copy & drag feature. This example will only refer to the keystrokes needed on a Windows operating system to invoke the context menus and the copy & drag feature. For your operating system, refer to the Preface of the **Maple 15 User Manual** for the equivalent keystrokes.

To solve the equation:

1. Enter the equation.

2. Right-click the equation and select **Move to Left**.

Input:

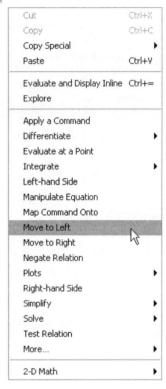

$5x - 7 = 3x + 2$

Cut	Ctrl+X
Copy	Ctrl+C
Copy Special	▶
Paste	Ctrl+V
Evaluate and Display Inline	Ctrl+=
Explore	
Apply a Command	
Differentiate	▶
Evaluate at a Point	
Integrate	▶
Left-hand Side	
Manipulate Equation	
Map Command Onto	
Move to Left	
Move to Right	
Negate Relation	
Plots	▶
Right-hand Side	
Simplify	▶
Solve	▶
Test Relation	
More...	▶
2-D Math	▶

Result:

$$5x - 7 = 3x + 2 \xrightarrow{\text{move to left}} 2x - 9 = 0$$

A brief description, "move to left" is displayed above the arrow that connects the input and output.

3. Right-click the output from the previous action, $2x - 9 = 0$, and select **Solve → Isolate Expression for → x**.

Input:

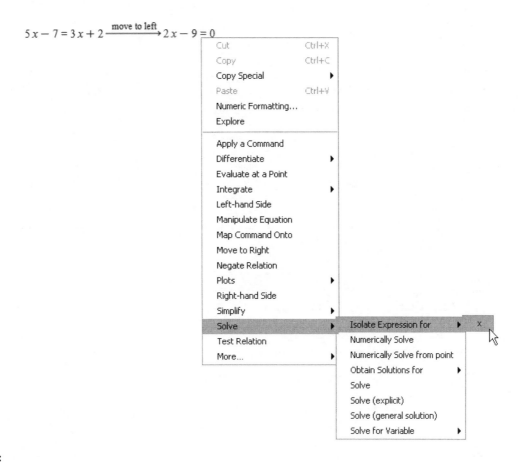

$$5x - 7 = 3x + 2 \xrightarrow{\text{move to left}} 2x - 9 = 0$$

Result:

$$5x - 7 = 3x + 2 \xrightarrow{\text{move to left}} 2x - 9 = 0 \xrightarrow{\text{isolate for x}} x = \frac{9}{2}$$

Now that we have solved the equation, we can plot it. To do this, we will copy the equation $2x - 9 = 0$ to a new document block and use context menus again.

4. From the **Format** menu, select **Create Document Block**.

5. To copy the expression $2x - 9 = 0$, highlight only this expression from the previous result. Press and hold the **Ctrl** key and drag the expression to the new document block region.

Result:

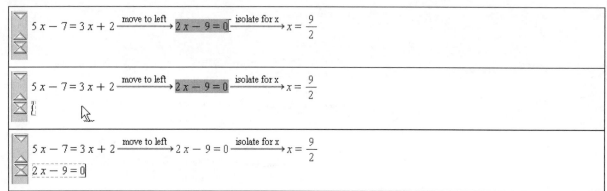

To plot the expression:

6. Right-click the equation, and select **Left-hand Side**.

Input:

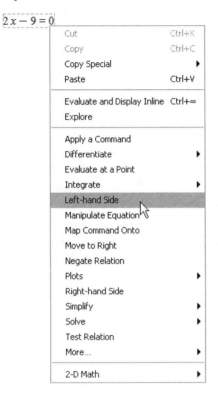

Result:

$$2x - 9 = 0 \quad \xrightarrow{\text{left hand side}} \quad 2x - 9$$

7. Right-click the expression and select **Plots → 2-D Plot**.

Input:

Result:

$2x - 9 \quad \rightarrow$

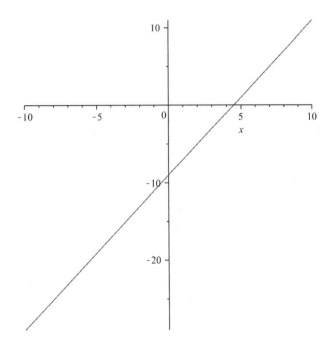

Saving a Maple Document

To save these examples you created, from the **File** menu, select **Save**. Maple documents are saved as **.mw** files.

34.3 Entering Expressions

Execution Groups

An execution group is a grouping of Maple input with its corresponding Maple output. It is distinguished by a large square bracket, called a *group boundary*, at the left. An execution group may also contain any or all of the following: a plot, a spreadsheet, text, embedded components, and a drawing canvas.

Execution groups are the fundamental computation and documentation elements in the document. If you place the cursor in an input command and press the **Enter** or **Return** key, Maple executes all of the input commands in the current execution group.

Math Mode vs. Text Mode

The default mode of entry in Document or Worksheet mode is Math Mode, which displays input in 2-D Math. In earlier releases of Maple, commands and expressions were entered using Maple Input or 1-D Math.

Important: With Maple input, you must terminate commands with a semicolon or colon.

```
> cos(alpha)^2+sin(alpha)^2;
```

$$\cos(\alpha)^2 + \sin(\alpha)^2$$

```
> a*int(exp(sqrt(2)*x),x);
```

$$\frac{1}{2} a \sqrt{2} \, e^{\sqrt{2}\,x}$$

```
> limit(f(x),x=infinity);
```

$$\lim_{x \to \infty} f(x)$$

```
> sum(a[k]*x^k, k=0..m)=product(b[j]*x^j, j=0..n);
```

$$\sum_{k=0}^{m} a_k x^k = \prod_{j=0}^{n} \left(b_j x^j \right)$$

In Document Mode, to enter input using Maple Input mode, insert a Maple prompt by clicking [> in the toolbar, and then click the **Text** button in the toolbar. In Worksheet Mode, simply click the **Text** button. See **Figure 34.2**.

Figure 34.2: Text and Math Buttons on the Toolbar

Table 34.6: Math Mode vs. Text Mode

Math Mode	Text Mode
Maple's default setting. Executable standard math notation. This is also referred to as **2-D Math Input**.	Executable Maple notation. This is also referred to as **1-D Math Input** or **Maple Input**.
> $\int x^2 + 2x + 1 \, dx$ $\frac{1}{3} x^3 + x^2 + x$	```> int(x^2+2*x+1, x);``` $\frac{1}{3} x^3 + x^2 + x$
Access from the **Insert → 2-D Math** menu.	Access from the **Insert → Maple Input** menu.
When using 2-D Math, the **Math** mode icon is highlighted in the toolbar, Text Math.	When entering Maple Input or text in a text region, the **Text** mode icon is highlighted in the toolbar, Text Math.

Math Mode	Text Mode
In Document Mode (or a document block), input is entered in a document block with a slanted cursor, $\boxtimes$ l .	In Document Mode (or a document block), input is entered with a vertical cursor, as plain text, $\boxtimes$ Enter some text .
In Worksheet Mode, input is made at an input prompt with a slanted cursor, $\boxed{>}$ l .	In Worksheet Mode, input is made at an input prompt with a vertical cursor, $\boxed{>}$ $\mid$.
To convert a 2-D Math expression to 1-D Math, right-click the expression (**Command**-click, Macintosh) and select **2-D Math** → **Convert To** → **1-D Math Input**.	To convert a 1-D Math expression to 2-D Math, right-click the expression (**Command-click**, Macintosh) and select **Convert To** → **2-D Math Input**.
No termination symbol is required.	All input must end with a semi-colon (;) or a colon (:).
Palettes make entering expressions in familiar notation easier than entering foreign syntax and reduces the possibility of introducing typing errors.	Using palettes while in 1-D Math teaches you the related Maple command syntax.

If you prefer 1-D Math input, you can change the default math input notation.

To change math input notation for a session or globally across all documents:

1. From the **Tools** menu, select **Options**. The **Options Dialog** opens.

2. Click the **Display** tab.

3. In the **Input Display** drop-down list, select **Maple Notation**.

4. Click the **Apply to Session** or **Apply Globally** button.

Important: The new input display becomes the default setting *after* pressing the **Enter** key.

Palettes

Palettes are collections of related items that you can insert into a document by clicking or drag-and-dropping. The Maple environment provides access to over 20 palettes containing items such as symbols (∞) , layouts $\left(A^{b}\right)$, mathematical operations $\left(\displaystyle\int_{a}^{b} f \, dx\right)$, and much more.

By default, palettes are displayed in the left pane of the Maple environment when you launch Maple. If the palettes are not displayed,

1. From the **View** menu, select **Palettes**.

2. Select **Expand Docks**.

3. Right-click (**Control**-click, Macintosh) the palette dock. From the context menu, select **Show All Palettes**.

Alternatively, from the main menu, select **View** → **Palettes** → **Arrange Palettes** to display specific palettes.

You can create a **Favorites** palette of the expressions and entities you use often by right-clicking (**Control**-click, Macintosh) the palette template you want to add and selecting **Add To Favorites Palette** from the context menu.

Table 34.7: Palette Categories

Palette Category	Palette Description
Expression Palettes 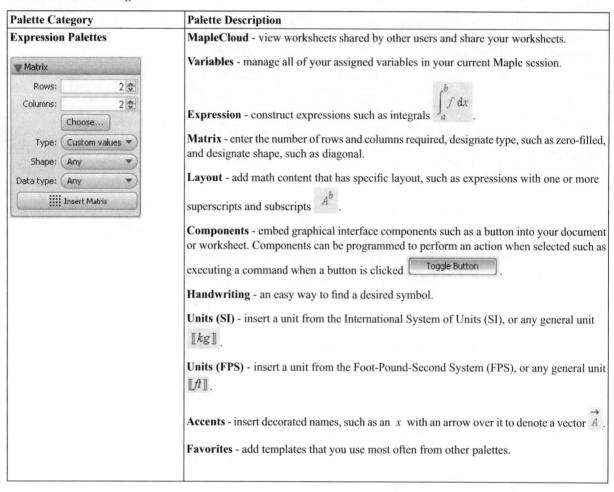	**MapleCloud** - view worksheets shared by other users and share your worksheets. **Variables** - manage all of your assigned variables in your current Maple session. **Expression** - construct expressions such as integrals $\int_{a}^{b} f \, dx$. **Matrix** - enter the number of rows and columns required, designate type, such as zero-filled, and designate shape, such as diagonal. **Layout** - add math content that has specific layout, such as expressions with one or more superscripts and subscripts A^{b}. **Components** - embed graphical interface components such as a button into your document or worksheet. Components can be programmed to perform an action when selected such as executing a command when a button is clicked Toggle Button. **Handwriting** - an easy way to find a desired symbol. **Units (SI)** - insert a unit from the International System of Units (SI), or any general unit $[\![kg]\!]$. **Units (FPS)** - insert a unit from the Foot-Pound-Second System (FPS), or any general unit $[\![ft]\!]$. **Accents** - insert decorated names, such as an x with an arrow over it to denote a vector $\vec{A}$. **Favorites** - add templates that you use most often from other palettes.

Palette Category	Palette Description
Mathematical Palettes ▼ Common Symbols π e i j I ∞ Σ Π ∫ d ∩ ∪ ≥ > ≯ ≱ ≤ < ≮ ≰ α ≈ ~ = ≠ ≡ ≢ ∈ ∉ ⊆ \ ∅ ∃ ∀ ¬ ∧ ∨ ⊻ ⇒ ℂ ℝ ℕ ℚ ℤ ℜ ℑ := ‖ ′ + − × / ± ∓ ∘ ∗ • · ∇ ! ℵ ℏ ℓ ⊥	Palettes for constructing expressions **Common Symbols**, **Relational** $\geq$, **Relational Round** $\geq$, **Operators** $\div$, **Large Operators** $\oint$, **Negated** $\neq$, **Fenced** $\langle\!\langle$, **Arrows** $\nrightarrow$, **Constants and Symbols** ∞. **Punctuation** - insert punctuation symbols, such as inserting the registered trademark and copyright symbols © into text regions **Miscellaneous** - insert miscellaneous math and other symbols outside the above categories $\Box$.
Alphabetical Palettes ▼ Greek A B Γ Δ E Z H Θ I K Λ M N Ξ O Π P Σ T Υ Φ X Ψ Ω α β γ δ ε ε ζ η θ ϑ ι κ ϰ λ μ ν ξ o π ϖ ρ ϱ σ ς τ υ φ ϕ χ ψ ω	**Greek**, **Script** $\mathcal{A}$, **Fraktur** $\mathfrak{A}$, **Open Face** $\mathbb{C}$, **Cyrillic** Ж, **Diacritical Marks** ′, **Roman Extended Upper Case** Æ, **Roman Extended Lower Case** æ.

Viewing and Arranging Palettes

By default, palettes display in palette docks at the right and left sides of the Maple window. To view and manage palettes and palette docks, see **Table 34.8**.

Table 34.8: Managing Palettes

To view palette docks:	
• From the **View** menu, select **Palettes**, and then **Expand Docks**. There are docks on the far right and left of the window.	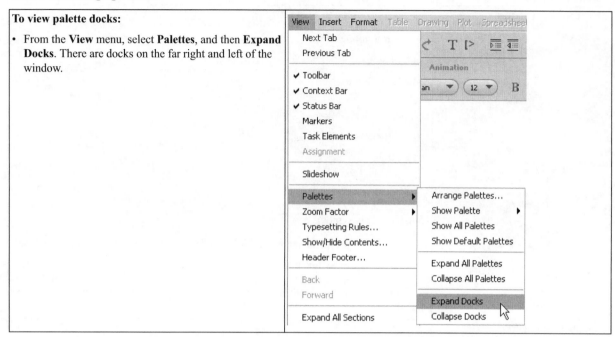

To add a palette: 1. Right-click the palette dock. Maple displays a context menu near the palette. 2. From the context menu, select **Show Palette** and then select the palette.	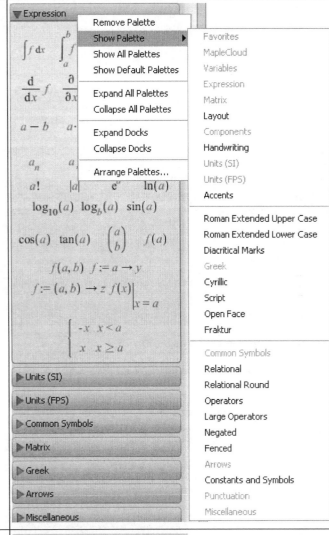
To expand or collapse a palette in the palette dock: • Click the triangle at the left of the palette title.	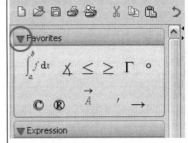

To move a palette in the palette dock:	
• Move the palette by clicking the title and dragging the palette to the new location.	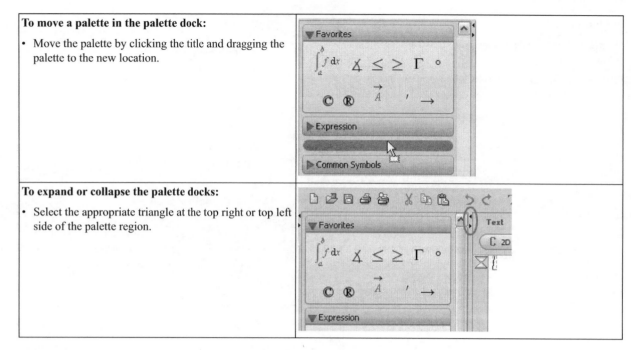
To expand or collapse the palette docks:	
• Select the appropriate triangle at the top right or top left side of the palette region.	

Example 3 - Enter an Expression Using Palettes

Review the following example:

$$\sum_{i=1}^{10} \left(7\,i^2 - 5\,i \right) = 2420$$

In this example, we will enter $\displaystyle\sum_{i=0}^{10} \left(7\,i^2 - 5\,i \right)$ and evaluate the expression.

Action	Result in Document
1. Place the cursor in a new document block. In the **Expression** palette, click the summation template $\sum_{i=k}^{n} f$. Maple inserts the summation symbol with the range variable placeholder highlighted.	$\displaystyle\sum_{i=k}^{n} f$
2. Enter **i** and then press **Tab**. The left endpoint placeholder is selected. Notice that the color of the range placeholder has changed to black. Each placeholder must have an assigned value before you execute the expression. The **Tab** key advances you through the placeholders of an inserted palette item.	$\displaystyle\sum_{i=k}^{n} f$

Action	Result in Document
3. Enter **1** and then press **Tab**. The right endpoint placeholder is selected.	$$\sum_{i=1}^{n} f$$
4. Enter **10** and then press **Tab**. The expression placeholder is selected.	$$\sum_{i=1}^{10} f$$
5. Enter $\left(7 i^2 - 5 i\right)$. For instructions on entering this type of expression, see *Example 1 - Enter and Evaluate an Expression Using Keystrokes (page 907)*.	$$\sum_{i=1}^{10} \left(7 i^2 - 5 i\right)$$
6. Press **Ctrl + =** (**Command + =** for Macintosh) to evaluate the summation.	$$\sum_{i=1}^{10} \left(7 i^2 - 5 i\right) = 2420$$

Handwriting Palette

The **Handwriting** palette provides another way to find and insert desired symbols easily.

1. Draw the symbol with your mouse in the space provided.

2. Click the **recognize** button, [$\overline{n}_\to \pi$]. Maple matches your input against symbols available in the system. See **Figure 34.3**.

3. To view more symbols (where indicated with a box around the result), click the displayed symbol and choose one of the selections from the drop-down menu.

4. To insert a symbol, click the displayed symbol.

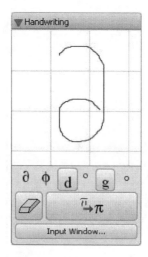

Figure 34.3: Handwriting Palette

For more information, refer to the **handwritingpalette** help page.

Symbol Names

Each symbol has a name and some have aliases. By entering its name (or an alias) in Math mode, you can insert the symbol in your document. All common mathematical symbols, including all Greek characters, π , and   the square root symbol ($\sqrt{}$), are recognized by Maple.

Note: If you hover the mouse pointer over a palette item, a tooltip displays the symbol's name.

To insert a symbol, enter the first few characters of a symbol name using a keyword that is familiar to you and then press the completion shortcut key, **Esc** (refer to the Preface of the **Maple 15 User Manual**). Symbol completion works in the same way as command completion (see *Command Completion (page 945)*).

- If a unique symbol name matches the characters entered, Maple inserts the corresponding symbol.
- If multiple symbol names match the characters entered, Maple displays the completion list, which lists all matches, including commands. To select an item, click its name or symbol.

Example 4 - Square Root

To find the square root of 603729 :

Action	Result in Document
1. In a new document block, enter *sqrt*.	sqrt
2. Press the symbol completion shortcut key, **Esc**. Maple displays a pop-up list of exact matches.	sqrt
3. In the completion list, select sqrt. Maple inserts the symbol with the x placeholder selected.	$\sqrt{x}$
4. Enter 603729.	$\sqrt{603729}$
5. Press **Ctrl + = (Command + =**, Macintosh).	$\sqrt{603729} = 777$

Example 5 - Complex Numbers

When you simply type the letter i in Math mode, it is in italics. This letter is just a variable, and is not the same as the imaginary unit $\sqrt{-1}$, denoted by I or i in Maple.

Multiply two complex numbers, $-0.123 + 0.745\,i$ **and** $4.2 - i$:

Action	Result in Document
1. In a new document block, enter $(-0.123 + 0.745\,i$.	$(-0.123 + 0.745\,i$
2. Press the symbol completion shortcut key, **Esc**. Maple displays a pop-up list of partial and exact matches, including symbols and commands.	$(-0.123 + 0.745\,i$
3. Select the imaginary unit, i (imaginary).	$(-0.123 + 0.745\,i$

Action	Result in Document
4. Close the parentheses, enter a space (for implicit multiplication), and type the second expression in parentheses, using symbol completion for the second imaginary number.	$(-0.123 + 0.745\,\mathrm{i})\,(4.2 - \mathrm{i})$
5. Press **Ctrl + =** (**Command + =**, Macintosh) to evaluate the product.	$(-0.123 + 0.745\,\mathrm{i})\,(4.2 - \mathrm{i}) \; = \; 0.2284 + 3.2520\,\mathrm{I}$

For more information on entering complex numbers, refer to the **HowDoI** help page.

Toolbar Icons

In the introduction section, you learned about the toolbar icons and context toolbars available in Maple (see *Toolbar Options (page 908)*). The toolbar can be used to format your document, alter plots and animations, draw in a canvas, write in both Math and Text modes in one line and much more. The last of these is demonstrated in the next example.

Example 6 - Enter Text and 2-D Math in the Same Line Using Toolbar Icons

Enter the following sentence:

Evaluate

$$\int_{1}^{5} \left(3\,x^2 + 2\sqrt{x} + 3\sqrt[3]{x} \right)\, dx \quad \text{and write in simplest terms.}$$

Action	Result in Document
To enter this sentence: 1. Select the **Text** icon and enter **Evaluate**.	Text ▢ Math ▢ Dra C Text ▾ ☒ Evaluate|
2. Select the **Math** icon. 3. From the **Expression** palette, select the definite integra-tion template, $\int_{a}^{b} f\, dx$. The expression is displayed with the first placeholder highlighted.	Text ▢ Math ▢ Dra C 2D Math ▾ Evaluate $\int_{a}^{b} f\, dx$
4. With the first placeholder highlighted, enter **1**, then press **Tab**. 5. Enter **5** and press **Tab** to highlight the integrand region.	Text ▢ Math ▢ Dra C 2D Math ▾ Evaluate $\int_{1}^{5} f\, dx$

Action	Result in Document
6. Enter **(3x^2** and press the right arrow to leave the super-script position. 7. Enter **+ 2**.	Evaluate $\displaystyle\int_{1}^{5}\left(3\,x^2 + 2\right)dx$
8. Press the **Space** bar for implicit multiplication. Enter **sqrt** and press **Esc** to show the command completion options. Maple displays a pop-up list of exact matches. Select the square root symbol, $\sqrt{x}$. Maple inserts the symbol with the x placeholder selected. Alternatively, select the square root symbol from the **Expression** palette.	Evaluate $\displaystyle\int_{1}^{5}\left(3\,x^2 + 2\ \text{sqrt}\,dx\right.$
9. Enter **x**, then press the right arrow to leave the square root region. 10. Enter **+ 3**, and then press the **Space** bar. 11. Select the **n-th root** symbol from the Expression palette, $\sqrt[n]{a}$.	Evaluate $\displaystyle\int_{1}^{5}\left(3\,x^2 + 2\sqrt{x} + 3\sqrt[n]{a}\ \ dx\right.$
12. Enter **3**, then press **Tab**. 13. Enter **x)**, then press **Tab**. 14. Enter **x** for the integration variable.	Evaluate $\displaystyle\int_{1}^{5}\left(3\,x^2 + 2\sqrt{x} + 3\sqrt[3]{x}\right)dx$
15. Click the **Text** icon in the toolbar, then enter the rest of the sentence: "and write in simplest terms."	Evaluate $\displaystyle\int_{1}^{5}\left(3\,x^2 + 2\sqrt{x} + 3\sqrt[3]{x}\right)dx$ and write in simplest terms.

34.4 Point-and-Click Interaction

Maple contains many built-in features that allow you to solve problems quickly without having to know any commands.

Assistants

Maple offers a set of assistants in the form of graphical user interfaces to perform many tasks without the need to use any syntax. An example of an assistant is shown in **Figure 34.4**.

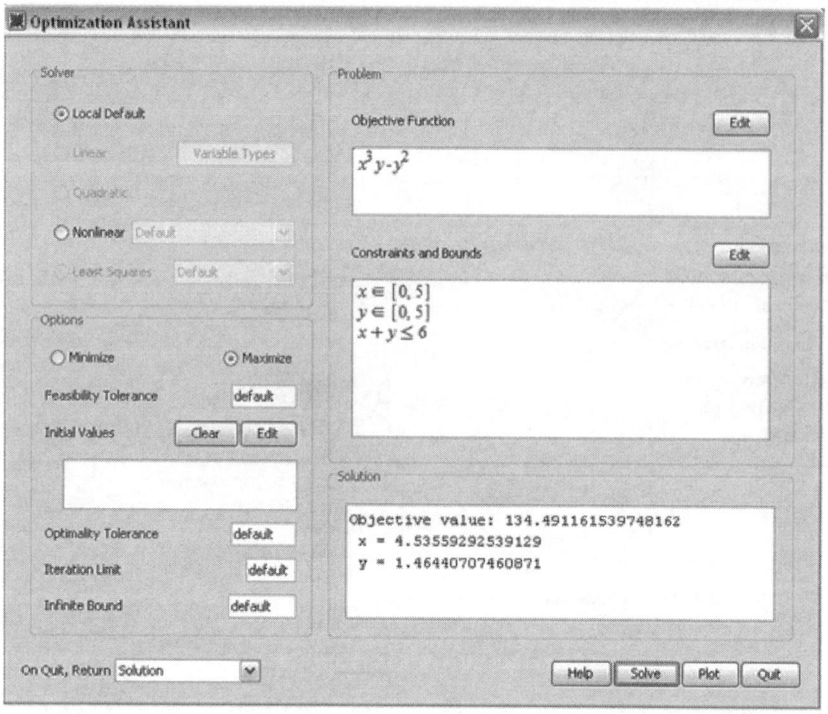

Figure 34.4: Optimization Assistant

Using the **Tools → Assistants** menu, you can access tools to help you accomplish various tasks. See **Figure 34.5**. In some cases, you can launch an assistant by entering an expression and selecting the assistant from the context menu that displays.

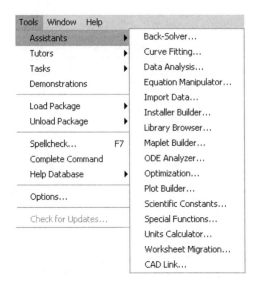

Figure 34.5: Accessing the Assistants from the Tools Menu

Example 7 - Curve Fitting Assistant

Enter a data sample and use the **Curve Fitting Assistant** to find the best approximation of a function to fit the data.

Action	Result in Document
1. From the **Tools** menu, select **Assistants → Curve Fitting**. The first dialog in the **Curve Fitting Assistant** appears.	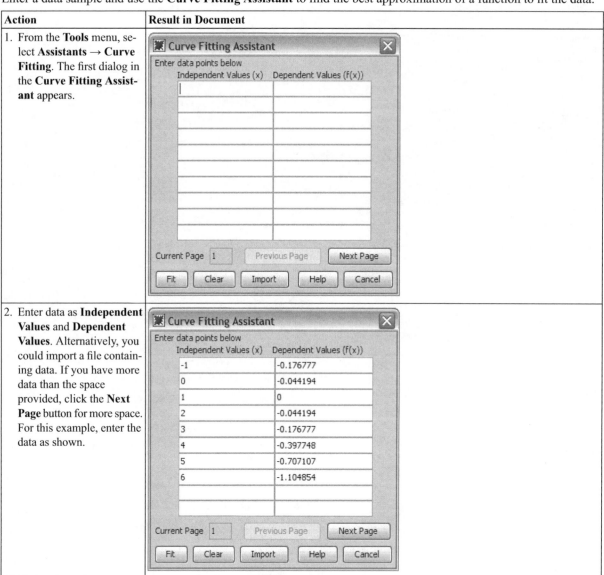
2. Enter data as **Independent Values** and **Dependent Values**. Alternatively, you could import a file containing data. If you have more data than the space provided, click the **Next Page** button for more space. For this example, enter the data as shown.	

Action	Result in Document
3. Once you have entered the data, click the **Fit** button. The second dialog of the **Curve Fitting Assistant** appears.	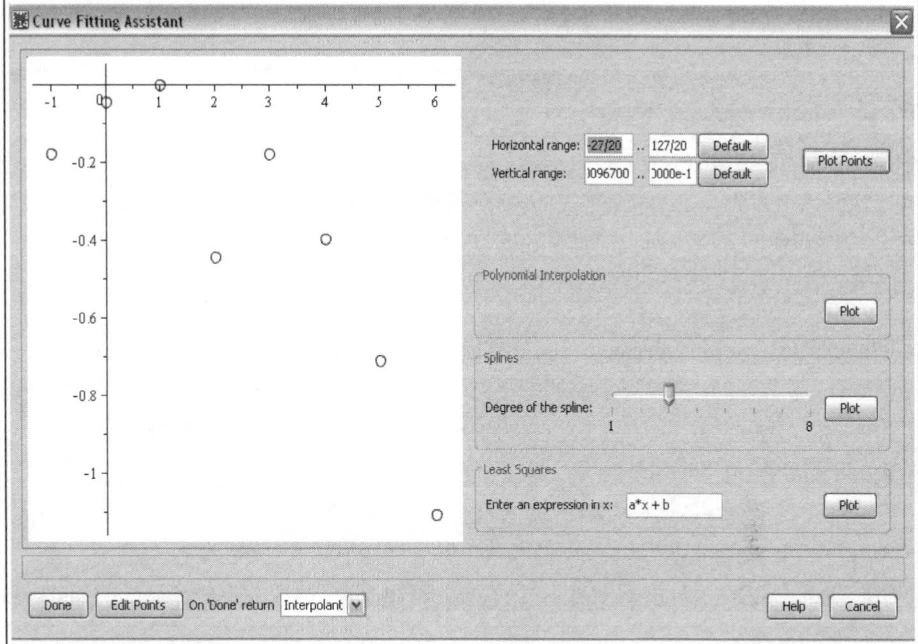
4. In this dialog, you can plot the data and several types of interpolations, including **Polynomial**, **Spline**, and **Least Squares**. For example, click the **Plot** button in the **Polynomial Interpolation** section. The polynomial is plotted with the data, and the interpolating function is displayed below.	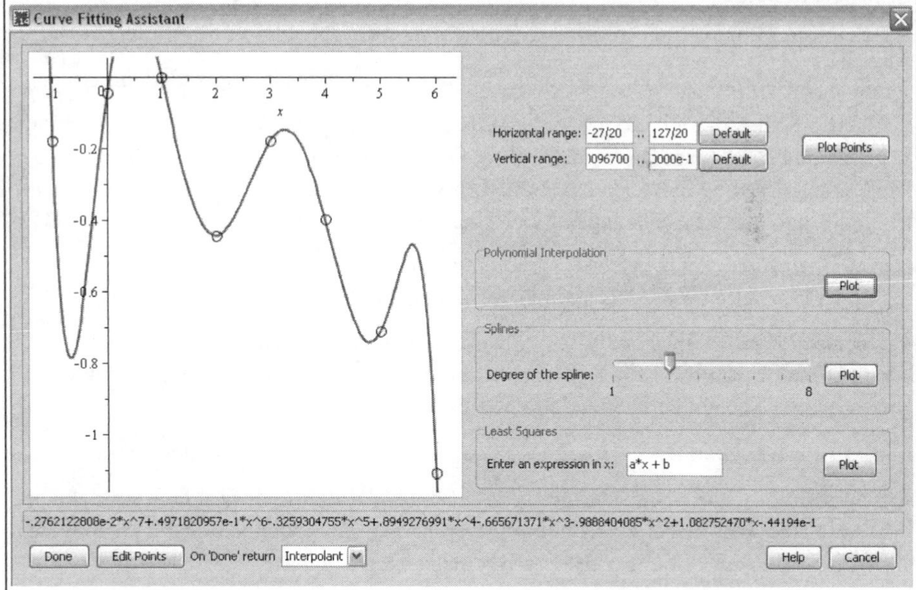
5. You can choose to return either the interpolating function or the plot to your	$$2.182341270 \, 10^{-9} x^7 - 4.027388889 \, 10^{-8} x^6 + 2.735838887 \, 10^{-7} x^5 - 7.985305551 \, 10^{-7} x^4$$ $$+ 7.52701389 \, 10^{-7} x^3 - 0.04419366118 x^2 + 0.08838747155 x - 0.0441940000$$

Action	Result in Document
document. When finished, click **Done**.	

Descriptions of Assistants

The remaining assistants are described below. Some of the assistants are interfaces to package commands. For more information on package commands, see *Package Commands (page 944)*.

- **Back-Solver** - an interface that allows you to take a mathematical formula, involving multiple parameters, enter values for all but one of the parameters and solve for the remaining value. You can also plot the behavior of the formula as one of the parameters change.

- **Curve Fitting** - an interface to commands in the **CurveFitting** package. Data points can be entered as independent and dependent values, and interpolated with polynomials, rational functions, or splines.

- **Data Analysis** - an interface to the data analysis commands in the **Statistics** package.

- **Equation Manipulator** - an interface for interactively performing a sequence of operations on an equation. You can group terms, apply an operation to both sides of the equation, complete the square, and so on.

- **Import Data** - an interface to read data from an external file into Maple.

- **Installer Builder** - an interface to the **InstallerBuilder** package in which you can create installers for your Maple toolboxes.

    For information on toolboxes, go to **http://www.maplesoft.com/developers/index.aspx**.

- **Library Browser** - an interface to manipulate the libraries in a specified directory.

- **Maplet Builder** - an interface to the **Maplets** package. The **Maplets** package contains commands for creating and displaying Maplet applications (point-and-click interfaces). Using the Maplet Builder, you can define the layout of a Maplet, drag-and-drop elements (visual and functional components of Maplets), set actions associated with elements, and directly run a Maplet application. The Maplet Builder is available in the Standard interface only.

- **ODE Analyzer** - an interface to obtain numeric or symbolic solutions to a single ordinary differential equation (ODE) or a system of ODEs and plot a solution of the result.

- **Optimization** - an interface to the solver commands in the **Optimization** package. The **Optimization** package is a collection of commands for numerically solving optimization problems, which involves finding the minimum or maximum of an objective function possibly subject to constraints.

- **Plot Builder** - an interface for creating two and three-dimensional plots, animations, and interactive plots.

- **Scientific Constants** - an interface to over 20 000 values of physical constants and properties of chemical elements. All of these constants come with the corresponding unit and, if applicable, with the uncertainty or error, that is, how precisely the value of this constant is known.

- **Special Functions** - an interface to the properties of over 200 special functions, including the Hypergeometric, Bessel, Mathieu, Heun and Legendre families of functions.

- **Units Calculator** - an interface to convert between 500 units of measurement.

- **Worksheet Migration** - an interface to convert worksheets from Classic Maple (.mws files) to Standard Maple (.mw files)

- **CAD Link** - an interface to explore the properties of models from supported CAD applications (available on Microsoft Windows only)

Tutors

Maple provides over 40 interactive tutors to aid in the learning of

- Precalculus

- Calculus

- Multivariate Calculus

- Vector Calculus

- Differential Equations

- Linear Algebra

- Complex Variables

These tutors are easily accessible in the **Tools** menu by selecting **Tutors**. See **Figure 34.6**.

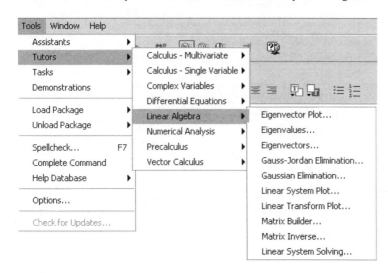

Figure 34.6: Accessing Tutors from the Tools Menu

Some of the tutors can also be accessed through the **Student** package. The Differential Equations tutor, **DE Plots**, is accessible through the **DEtools** package. For a definition of the term *package*, see *Package Commands (page 944)*.

The **Student** package is a collection of subpackages designed to assist with the teaching and learning of standard undergraduate mathematics. The subpackages contain many commands for displaying functions, computations, and theorems in various ways, and include support for stepping through important computations.

The **interactive** commands help you explore concepts and solve problems using a point-and-click interface. These commands launch tutors that provide a graphical interface to some of the visualization and computation commands described above. See for an example of one of the tutors.

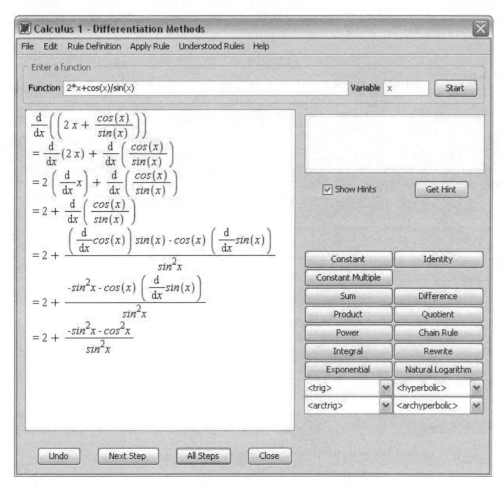

Figure 34.7: Calculus - Single Variable → Differentiation Methods Tutor

Demonstrations

Maple provides Demonstrations that offer interactive, entertaining ways to explore precalculus concepts. The demonstrations are accessible in the **Tools** menu by selecting **Demonstrations**.

For more information on the tutors, demonstrations, and related resources for mathematics education, refer to page 200 of the **Maple 15 User Manual**.

Context Menus

A context menu is a dynamically generated menu of actions that are applicable for the region upon which it is invoked. Context menus allow you to perform calculations and manipulations on expressions without using Maple syntax. To display a context menu, right-click an object, expression, or region. Context menus are available for many input regions, including:

- **expressions** to perform calculations, manipulations, or plotting
- **plot regions** to apply plot options and manipulate the plot
- **tables** to modify the table properties
- **palette regions** to add or remove palettes and palette regions
- **text regions** to add annotations and format text
- **spreadsheets** to manipulate the spreadsheet

When performing calculations or manipulations on an expression, a self-documenting arrow or equal sign connects the input and output, indicating the action that took place. See Figures 34.8 and 34.9 for two examples of context menus.

$$x^2 + 2x + 1 \overset{\text{factor}}{=} (x + 1)^2$$

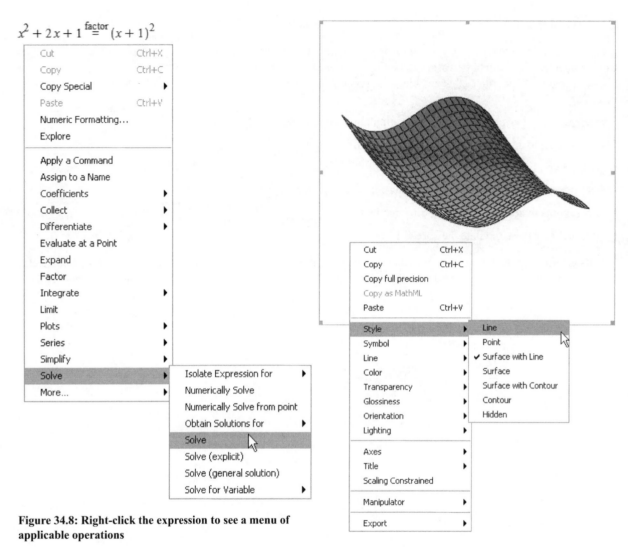

Figure 34.8: Right-click the expression to see a menu of applicable operations

Figure 34.9: Right-click the plot to see a menu of plot options

Task Templates

Task templates help you perform specific tasks in Maple, such as:

- performing a mathematical computation such as solving an equation symbolically or numerically, or determining the Taylor approximation of a function of one variable
- constructing a Maple object such as a function
- creating a document such as an application

Each task contains a description along with a collection of content that you can insert directly into your document. Content consists of 2-D mathematics, commands, embedded components (for example, buttons), and plots. You specify the parameters of your problem and then execute the commands in the document. See **Figure 34.10** for an example of a Task Template.

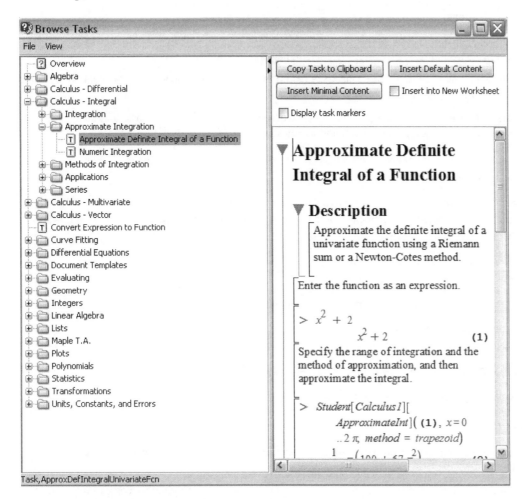

Figure 34.10: Browse Tasks Dialog

Previewing Tasks

To preview Maple tasks,

• From the **Tools** menu, select **Tasks**, and then **Browse**. The **Browse Tasks** dialog opens and displays the list of tasks.

The tasks are sorted by subject to help you quickly find the desired task. In the **Browse Tasks** dialog, you can view tasks without inserting them into your document.

Inserting a Task into the Document

To insert a task into your document,

1. Select the **Insert into New Worksheet** check box to insert the task into a new document.

2. Click one of the insert buttons.

-   Click the **Insert Default Content** button. Maple inserts the *default content*. The default content level is set using the **Options** dialog. For instructions, see the **usingtasks** help page.

-   Click the **Insert Minimal Content** button. Maple inserts only the commands and embedded components, for example, a button to launch the related assistant or tutor.

-   Click the **Copy Task to Clipboard** button. Place the cursor where you want to insert the task, and then paste the task. Maple inserts the default content. Use this method to quickly insert a task multiple times.

Note: You can view the history of previously inserted tasks. From the **Tools** menu, select **Tasks.** Previously selected task names are displayed below the **Browse** menu item.

Before inserting a task, Maple checks whether the task variables have assigned values in your document. If any task variable is assigned, the **Task Variables** dialog opens to allow you to modify the names. Maple uses the edited variable names for all variable instances in the inserted task.

By default, the **Task Variables** dialog is displayed only if there is a naming conflict. You can set it to display every time you insert a task.

To specify that the Task Variables dialog be displayed every time you insert a task:

1. From the **Tools** menu, select **Options**.

2. Click the **Display** tab.

3. In the **Show task variables on insert** drop-down list, select **Always**.

4. Click **Apply to Session** or **Apply Globally**, as necessary.

Updating Parameters and Executing the Commands

In inserted Task Templates, parameters are marked as placeholders (in purple text) or specified using sliders or other embedded components.

1. Specify values for the parameters in placeholders or using graphical interface components. You can move to the next placeholder by pressing **Tab**.

2. Execute all commands in the task by:

-   Placing the cursor in the first task command, and then pressing **Enter** repeatedly to execute each command.

-   Selecting all the template commands, and then clicking the execute toolbar icon .

3. If the template contains a button that computes the result, click it.

For more information on task templates, refer to the **tasks** help page.

Exploration Assistant

The Exploration Assistant allows you to interactively make parameter changes to expressions and view the result. The assistant can be used with almost any Maple expression or command that has at least one variable or parameter.

To launch the Exploration Assistant:

1. Enter an expression or command.

2. Right-click (**Control**-click, Macintosh) the expression or command. From the context menu, select **Explore**.

3. The **Explore** parameter selection dialog appears, where you can select the parameters to explore and the range for each parameter.

If you enter integer ranges, only integer values are allowed for parameters. To allow floating-point values, enter floating-point ranges.

Select **skip** for any of the parameters to leave that parameter as a variable.

4. Click **Explore** to continue to the **Exploration Assistant**. The assistant opens in a new document. You can use the slider or sliders to vary the parameters and see your changes as the expression output is updated.

5. Once you are finished interacting with the assistant, you can copy and paste the results into your document, or save the interactive document for later use.

Example 8 - Use the Exploration Assistant to Explore a Plot

In this example, we will explore how the plot of $\dfrac{\sin(ax) - b\cos(x)}{x}$ changes as we vary the parameters a and b.

Action	Result in Document
1. Enter the plot command shown.	$plot\left(\dfrac{\sin(ax) - b\cos(x)}{x}, x = 1..10 \right)$
2. Right-click (**Control**-click for Macintosh) the expression and select **Explore**.	$plot\left(\dfrac{\sin(a\,x) - b\,\cos(x)}{x}, x = 1..10 \right)$ Cut Ctrl+X Copy Ctrl+C Copy full precision Copy as MathML Paste Ctrl+V Evaluate Evaluate and Display Inline Ctrl+= Explore Apply a Command Assign to a Name Collect ▶

Action	Result in Document
3. In the Explore parameter selection dialog, set the ranges **a = 0..10.0** and **b = -5.0..5.0**. Select **floating-point computation**.	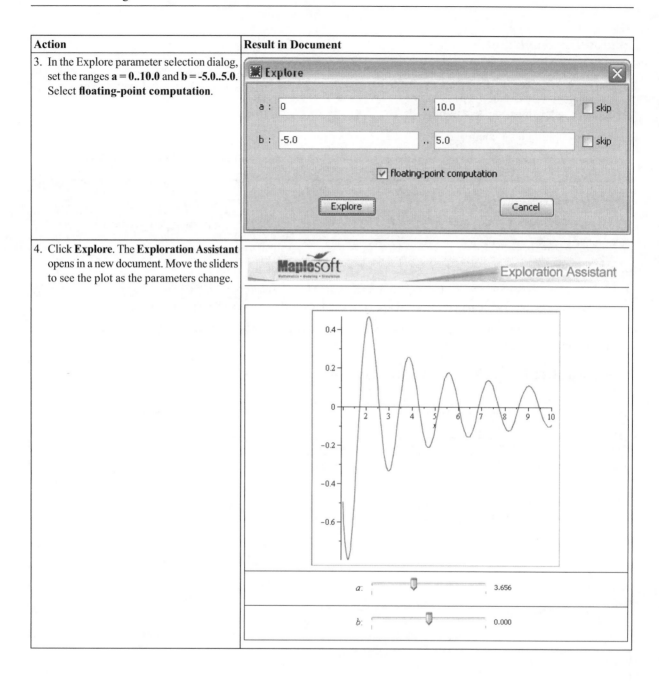
4. Click **Explore**. The **Exploration Assistant** opens in a new document. Move the sliders to see the plot as the parameters change.	

34.5 Commands

Even though Maple comes with many features to solve problems and manipulate results without entering any commands, you may find that you prefer greater control and flexibility by using the set of commands and programming language that Maple offers.

The Maple Library

Commands are contained in the Maple library, which is divided into two groups: the*main library* and *packages.*

The main library contains the most frequently used Maple commands.

Packages contain related commands for performing tasks from disciplines such as Student Calculus, Statistics, or Differential Geometry. For example, the **Optimization** package contains commands for numerically solving optimization problems.

For details on top-level and package commands, see *Commands (page 974).*

Entering Commands

If you want to interact with Maple using commands, simply enter the command using 2-D math. Notice that commands and variable names display in italics. Maple commands are constructed in a format similar to *command*(*arguments*), based on the command you are using.

For example, to factor an expression, enter:

$factor\left(x^2 + 2x + 1\right)$

$$(x + 1)^2$$

To differentiate an expression, enter:

$diff\left(\sin(x), x\right)$

$$\cos(x)$$

To integrate an expression on the interval $[0, 2\pi]$, enter:

$int\left(2x + \cos(x), x = 0 .. 2\pi\right)$

$$4\pi^2$$

To plot an expression, enter:

$$plot\left(\sin(x)\, x^2, x = -10\,..10\right)$$

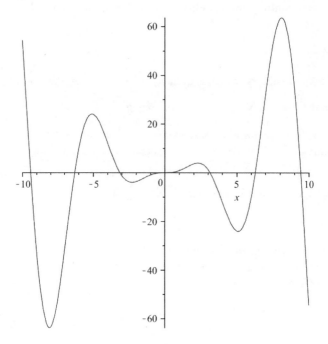

For a list of the top commands in Maple, see *Top Commands (page 976)*.

Package Commands

There are two ways to access commands within a package, using the long form of the package command or the short form.

Long Form of Accessing Package Commands:

The long form specifies both the package and command names using the syntax *package*[*command*](*arguments*).

$$LinearAlgebra[\,RandomMatrix\,](2)$$

$$\begin{bmatrix} 44 & -31 \\ 92 & 67 \end{bmatrix}$$

Short Form of Accessing Package Commands:

The short form makes all of the commands in the package available using the **with** command, *with(package)*. If you are using a number of commands in a package, loading the entire package is recommended. When you execute the **with** command, a list of all commands in the package displays. To suppress the display of all command names, end the *with(package)* command with a colon. Alternatively, you can load packages through the **Tools** menu, by selecting **Load Package**, and then the package name.

with(*Optimization*)

[*ImportMPS, Interactive, LPSolve, LSSolve, Maximize, Minimize, NLPSolve, QPSolve*]

After loading a package, you can use the short-form names, that is, the command names, without the package name.

$LSSolve([x-2, x-6, x-9])$

$$[12.3333333333333322, [x=5.66666666666666696]]$$

For a list of the top packages in Maple, see *Top Packages (page 977)*.

Command Completion

To help with syntax and reduce the amount of typing when entering Maple commands, you can use *command completion*. Command completion displays a list of all Maple packages, commands, and functions that match the entered text. If there are multiple ways to call a command, then the command completion list contains each one, with appropriate placeholders.

To use command completion:

1. Begin entering a command or package name.

2. Select **Tools → Complete Command** or use the shortcut key **Esc** (refer to the Preface of the **Maple 15 User Manual**). If there is a unique completion, it is inserted. Otherwise, a list of possible matches is displayed.

3. Select the correct completion from the list.

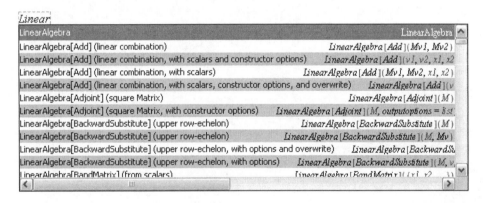

4. Some inserted commands have placeholders, denoted by purple text. The first placeholder is highlighted after you insert it into the document. Replace it with your parameter, then move to the next placeholder by pressing the **Tab** key.

Equation Labels

Equation labels help to save time entering expressions by referencing Maple output. See **Figure 34.11**.

By default, equation labels are displayed. If equation labels are not displayed,

1. From the **Tools** menu, select **Options**, and click the **Display** tab. Ensure that the **Show equation labels** check box is selected.

2. From the **Format** menu, select **Equation Labels**. Ensure that both **Execution Group** and **Worksheet** are selected.

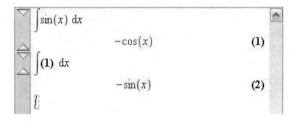

Figure 34.11: Equation Label

To apply equation labels:

1. Enter an expression and press **Enter**. Note that the equation label is displayed to the right of the answer in the document.

2. In a new execution group, enter another expression that will reference the output of the previous execution group.

3. From the **Insert** menu, select **Label**. Alternatively, press **Ctrl+L** (**Command**+L, for Macintosh) to open the **Insert Label** dialog. Enter the label number in the **Insert Label** dialog and click **OK**. The item is now a label. See **Figure 34.12**.

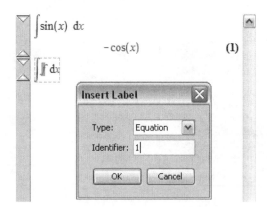

Figure 34.12: Inserting an Equation Label

4. Press **Enter** to obtain the result.

To change the format of equation labels:

- Select **Format** → **Equation Labels** → **Label Display**. In the **Format Labels** dialog, select one of the numbering schemes.

- Optionally, enter an appropriate numbering prefix.

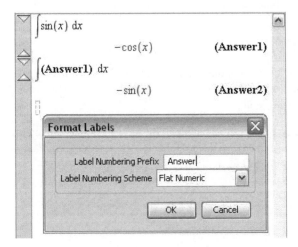

Figure 34.13: Format Labels Dialog: Adding a Prefix

The **Label Reference** menu item allows you to switch between the label name and its reference content. Place the cursor on the referenced equation label and select **Format** → **Equation Labels** → **Label Reference**.

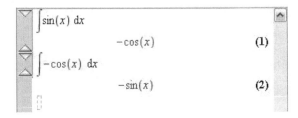

Figure 34.14: Label Reference

The label is associated with the last output within an execution group.

You cannot apply equation labels to the following:

- Error, warning, and information messages

- Tables, images, plots, sketches, or spreadsheets

Document Blocks

In Document mode, content is created as a series of document blocks. Document blocks allow you to hide the syntax used to perform calculations, which in turn lets you focus on the concept presented instead of the command used to manipulate or solve the problem. You can also create document blocks in Worksheet mode to perform the same function. Document blocks are typically collapsed to hide the Maple code, but these regions can also be expanded to reveal this code.

To create a document block:

From the **Format** menu, select **Create Document Block**. If text or math in one or more execution groups is selected, then a document block is created that contains those execution groups. If not, a new document block is created after the current execution group. For more information, see the next example.

Document block regions are identified using markers that are located in a vertical bar along the left pane of the document. See **Figure 34.15**. In addition to document block boundaries, these markers (icons) indicate the presence of hidden attributes in the document such as annotations, bookmarks, and numeric formatting.

To activate markers:

From the **View** menu, select **Markers**. See **Figure 34.15**.

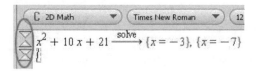

Figure 34.15: Document Block Markers

To view code in a document block:

1. Place the cursor in a document block to be expanded.

2. From the **View** menu, select **Expand Document Block**.

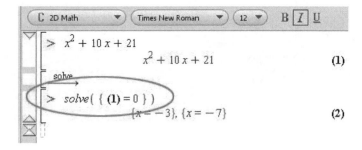

Figure 34.16: Expanded Document Block

With the Document Block expanded, you can see the Maple command that was used to perform this calculation. In **Figure 34.16**, the *solve* command was used.

Also notice a red prompt (**>**) before the original expression and the *solve* command. Entering commands outside of a document block region is done at this input region. To insert an input region, click the ▯**>** button in the toolbar menu.

In **Figure 34.16**, an equation label was used to refer to the expression. For more information, see *Equation Labels (page 946)*.

To collapse a Document Block:

• With your cursor inside the document block, select **View → Collapse Document Block**.

You can use this process of expanding document blocks to begin learning Maple commands.

Changing the Display:

You can specify which parts of the input and output are displayed when the document block is collapsed. For each execution group in the block, you can choose to display either the input or the output.

• Place the cursor in the execution group.

• From the **View** menu, select **Toggle Input/Output Display**.

Also, you can choose to display output either inline or centered on a new line.

• From the **View** menu, select **Inline Document Output**.

Example 9 - Creating a Document Block in Worksheet Mode

In Worksheet mode, you can create the content using commands, and then use a document block to choose how much information to display.

Enter the following sentence using text and 2-D Math input and output:

The answer to $\int \sin(x)\,dx$ is $-\cos(x)$.

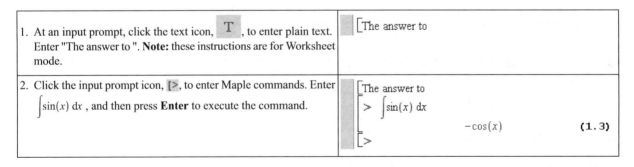

1. At an input prompt, click the text icon, **T** , to enter plain text. Enter "The answer to ". **Note:** these instructions are for Worksheet mode.	▯[The answer to
2. Click the input prompt icon, ▯**>**, to enter Maple commands. Enter $\int \sin(x)\,dx$, and then press **Enter** to execute the command.	▯[The answer to > $\int \sin(x)\,dx$ $\qquad -\cos(x)$ **(1.3)** >

3. Again, click the text icon to insert the rest of the text, "is", and then enter another input prompt icon. Make sure to put spaces around all of the text, so the sentence displays properly.	The answer to > $\int \sin(x)\, dx$ $\qquad -\cos(x)$ **(1.3)** is >
4. To display the same output again, use the **value** command and an equation label. This allows you to insert text between the input and output of a single command: there are really two commands. Enter and execute the command, as shown.	The answer to > $\int \sin(x)\, dx$ $\qquad -\cos(x)$ **(1.3)** is > $value(\,(1.3)\,)$ $\qquad -\cos(x)$ **(1.4)** >
5. To finish the sentence, click the text icon in the last execution group and enter a period.	The answer to > $\int \sin(x)\, dx$ $\qquad -\cos(x)$ **(1.3)** is > $value(\,(1.3)\,)$ $\qquad -\cos(x)$ **(1.4)** .
6. Select the entire sentence, then from the **Format** menu, select, **Create Document Block**. By default, only the text and output remains visible, and output is centered on a new line.	The answer to $\qquad -\cos(x)$ **(1.3)** is $\qquad -\cos(x)$ **(1.4)** .
7. To display the text and output on one line, place the cursor in the document block. From the **View** menu, select **Inline Document Output**.	The answer to $-\cos(x)$ is $-\cos(x)$.
8. To display input instead of output for the first expression, place the cursor in the first expression. From the **View** menu, select **Toggle Input/Output Display**. Only the first region displays input.	The answer to $\int \sin(x)\, dx$ is $-\cos(x)$.

34.6 The Maple Help System

The Maple program provides a custom help system consisting of almost 5000 reference pages. The help system is a convenient resource for determining the syntax of Maple commands and for learning about Maple features.

Accessing the Help System

There are several ways to access the Maple help system:

- From the **Help** menu, select **Maple Help**

- Click 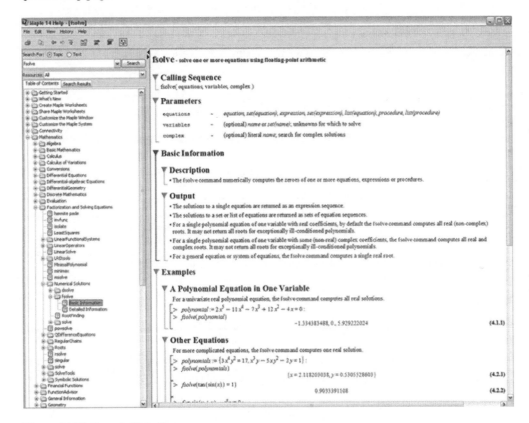 in the toolbar

To get help on a specific word:

- In a document, place the insertion point in a word for which you want to obtain help. From the **Help** menu, select **Help on ....** Alternatively, press **F2** (**Control** + **?**, for Macintosh) to access context-sensitive help.

- In a document, execute the command **?topic**, for example, enter **?LinearAlgebra** and press **Enter**

The Maple help system opens in a separate window with two panes. The left pane contains the Help Navigator where you initiate searches and browse the table of contents, and the right pane displays the final search result, such as a specific help page.

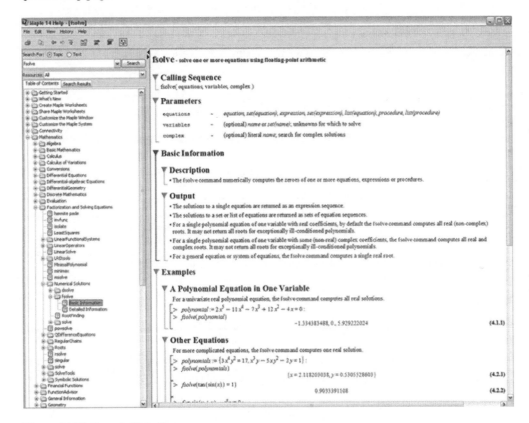

Figure 34.17: Sample Help Page

Every help page in Maple lists the command's calling sequence, parameters, and a description, with examples of the command at the end of the page. Some help pages also contain hyperlinks to related help pages and hyperlinks to dictionary definitions. Hyperlinks to help pages display in green, while hyperlinks to dictionary definitions display in dark red.

Using the Help Navigator

The Help Navigator contains a field for topic or text-based searches. The **Table of Contents** tab provides a structured list of all topics in the help system.

To search the help system:

1. In the left pane, enter a string in the search field.

2. By default, a topic search is performed. To perform a text search, select the **Text** radio button.

3. Enter the term and click **Search**.

- **Topic** searches reveal a list of matching topics sorted by the precision of the match.

- **Text** searches reveal a list of topics based on keyword frequency.

- You can search all of the help system or specific Resources such as Help Pages, Tasks, Tutorials, and Manuals by selecting the **Resources** drop-down menu.

Search results are displayed as a list in the **Search Results** tab of the left pane. Click the **Table of Contents** tab to view a structured list of all topics in the help system.

To display potential matches in the right pane, click a topic preceded by an icon. **Table 34.9** describes the different icons.

Table 34.9: Help Page Icons

Icon	Description
📁	A folder icon in the **Table of Contents** tab indicates that a topic can be expanded into subtopics.
[?]	Question mark icon indicates a help page and displays the associated help page in the right pane when selected.
[WS]	WS icon indicates an example worksheet. Example worksheets open in a new tab in the Maple document.
[D]	**D** icon indicates a definition and displays the associated dictionary definition in the right pane when selected.
[T]	**T** icon indicates a Task template and displays the associated Task Template in the right pane when selected.
[M]	**M** icon indicates a manual. Manuals open in a new tab in the Maple document.

Viewing Help Pages as Documents

In the help system, examples are not executable.

The Maple help system allows you to open help pages as documents that you can execute.

To open a help page as a document or worksheet:

• With the help page displayed in the right pane of the help system, from the **View** menu, select **Open Page as Worksheet.** A new worksheet tab opens and displays the help page as an executable document.

	Alternatively, in the help system toolbar, click the *open current help page in a worksheet window* icon.

Viewing Examples in 2-D Math

You can choose to view the examples in most help pages in either 1-D Math (Maple input) or 2-D Math mode. The default is 1-D Math.

To change the math mode:

In the Maple help system:

• From the **View** menu, select or clear the **Display Examples with 2D math** check box.

• Click the **2-D Math** icon, $\frac{X^2}{X^2}$.

Note: Some input in help pages displays as 1-D Math, no matter which option you have chosen. This is for Maple procedures and other code that is best input in 1-D Math. For more information, see the **helpnavigator** help page.

Copying Examples

Instead of opening the entire page as a document, you can copy the **Examples** section only.

To copy examples:

1. With the help page displayed in the right pane of the help system, from the **Edit** menu, select **Copy Examples.**

2. Close or minimize the Help Navigator and return to your document.

3. In your document, place the cursor at the location where you want to paste the examples.

4. From the **Edit** menu, select **Paste**. The **Examples** section of the help page is inserted as executable content in your document.

34.7 Available Resources

Your work with Maple is supported by numerous resources.

Resources Available through the Maple Help System

Help Pages

Use the help system to find information about a specific topic, command, package, or feature. For more information, see *The Maple Help System (page 950)*.

Dictionary

More than 5000 mathematical and engineering terms with over 300 figures and plots.

1. From the **Help** menu, select **Maple Help**.

2. Enter a search term. Dictionary entries that match your query are displayed in the left pane with a ⒟ icon.

Tutorials and the Maple Portal

The **Maple Portal** includes material designed for all Maple users, from new users to users who want more advanced tutorials. The Maple Portal also includes specific sections for students, math educators, and engineers. The Maple Portal includes:

- How Do I... topics that give quick answers to essential questions

- Tutorials that provide an overview of topics from getting started to plotting, data manipulation, and interactive application development

- Navigation to portals with specialized information for students, math educators, and engineers

Access the portal from the **Help** menu (**Help → Manuals, Resources, and More → Maple Portal**).

Applications and Example Worksheets

Applications

Sample applications demonstrate how Maple can be used to find and document a solution to a specific problem. Some applications allow for input or contain animations that you can run; however, their primary use is for demonstrations. Topics include DC Motor Control Design, Digital Filter Design, Frequency Domain System Identification, Harmonic Oscillator, Image Processing, and Radiator Design with CAD Systems.

Examples

Example worksheets are executable documents covering topics that demonstrate syntax or invoke a user interface to make complex problems easy to solve and visualize. You can copy and modify the examples as needed. Topics include Algebra, Calculus, Connectivity, Discrete Mathematics, General Numerics and Symbolics, and Integral Transforms.

- From the **Help** menu, select **Manuals, Resources, and more**, and then **Applications and Examples**.

Manuals

You can access all of Maple's manuals from within Maple, including the *Maple Programming Guide* and this manual. You can execute examples, copy content into other documents, and search the contents using the Maple Help System.

- From the **Help** menu, select **Manuals, Resources, and more** and then **Manuals**.

Task Templates

Set of commands with placeholders that you can use to quickly perform a task. For details, see *Task Templates (page 938)*.

- From the **Tools** menu, select **Tasks**, and then **Browse**.

Maple Tour and Quick Resources

Maple Tour

The **Maple Tour** consists of interactive sessions on several of the following topics: Ten Minute Tour, Numeric and Symbolic Computations, Matrix Computations, Differential Equations, Statistics, Programming and Code Generation, Units and Tolerances, and Education Assessment with Maple T.A.

- From the **Help** menu, select **Take a Tour of Maple**.

Quick Help and Quick References

The Quick Help dialog is a list of key commands and concepts.

- From the **Help** menu, select **Quick Help**. Alternatively, press **F1**. For additional information, click an item in the Quick Help.

The Quick Reference is a table of commands and information for new users that opens in a new window. It contains hyperlinks to help pages for more information.

- From the **Help** menu, select **Quick Reference**. Alternatively, press **Ctrl** + **F2** (**Command** + **F2**, for Macintosh).

Web Site Resources

Welcome Center

A Maple web site offering all of Maplesoft's key user resources in one central location. In the Welcome Center, you can view sample applications, participate in user forums, access exclusive premium content, and listen to podcasts. You can also access our support services, view training videos, download user manuals, and more.

http://www.maplesoft.com/welcome

Student Help Center

The Student Help Center offers a Maple student forum, online math Oracles, training videos, and a math homework resource guide.

http://www.maplesoft.com/studentcenter)

Teacher Resource Center

The Teacher Resource Center is designed to ensure you get the most out of your Maple teaching experience. It provides sample applications, course material, training videos, white papers, e-books, podcasts, and tips.

http://www.maplesoft.com/teachercenter

Application Center

Maple web site resource for free applications related to mathematics, education, science, engineering, computer science, statistics and data analysis, finance, communications, and graphics. Many applications are available in translations (French, Spanish, and German).

You can also search for Education and Research PowerTools, which provide free course curricula and are available as add-on Maple packages and courses. PowerTools are developed by experts in their fields to help users configure Maple for research in specific application areas.

http://www.maplesoft.com/applications

Training

Maplesoft offers a comprehensive set of complementary training materials. From complete training videos to recorded training seminars to downloadable documentation, you have many options to get familiar with Maplesoft products. In addition, whether you are an expert or someone who is considering a new license purchase, a custom training session that is right for you and/or your organization can be created.

http://www.maplesoft.com/support/training

MaplePrimes

A web community dedicated to sharing experiences, techniques, and opinions about Maple and related products, as well as general interest topics in math and computing.

http://www.mapleprimes.com

Online Help

All of Maple's help pages are available online.

http://www.maplesoft.com/support/help

Technical Support

A Maple web site containing FAQs, downloads and service packs, links to discussion groups, and a form for requesting technical support.

http://www.maplesoft.com/support

For a complete list of resources, refer to the **MapleResources** help page.

35 Document Mode

Using the Maple software, you can create powerful interactive documents. You can visualize and animate problems in two and three dimensions. You can solve complex problems with simple point-and-click interfaces or easy-to-modify interactive documents. You can also devise custom solutions using the Maple programming language. While you work, you can document your process, providing text descriptions.

35.1 In This Chapter

Section	Topics
Introduction (page 957)	• Comparison of Document and Worksheet Modes
Entering Expressions (page 958) - Overview of tools for creating complex mathematical expressions	• Palettes • Symbol Names • Mathematical Functions
Evaluating Expressions (page 961) - How to evaluate expressions	• Displaying the Value Inline • Displaying the Value on the Following Line
Editing Expressions and Updating Output (page 962) - How to update expressions and regenerate results	• Updating a Single Computation • Updating a Group of Computations • Updating All Computations in a Document
Performing Computations (page 962)- Overview of tools for performing computations and solving problems	• Computing with Palettes • Context Menus • Assistants and Tutors

35.2 Introduction

Maple has two modes: *Document* mode and *Worksheet* mode.

Document mode is designed for quickly performing calculations. You can enter a mathematical expression, and then evaluate, manipulate, solve, or plot it with a few keystrokes or mouse clicks. This chapter provides an overview of Document mode.

Document mode sample:

Find the value of the derivative of $\ln(x^2 + 1)$ at $x = 4$.

$$\ln(x^2 + 1) \xrightarrow{\text{differentiate w.r.t. x}} \frac{2x}{x^2 + 1} \xrightarrow{\text{evaluate at point}} \frac{8}{17}$$

Integrate $\sin\left(\dfrac{1}{x}\right)$ over the interval $[0, \pi]$.

$$\int_0^{\pi} \sin\left(\frac{1}{x}\right) \, dx \;=\; \sin\left(\frac{1}{\pi}\right) \pi - \mathrm{Ci}\left(\frac{1}{\pi}\right)$$

Worksheet mode is designed for interactive use through commands and programming using the Maple language. The Worksheet mode supports the features available in Document mode described in this chapter. For information on using Worksheet mode, see Chapter 36, *Worksheet Mode (page 971)*. **Note**: To enter a Maple input prompt while in Document mode, click ▷ in the Maple toolbar.

Important: In any Maple document, you can use Document mode and Worksheet mode.

Interactive document features include:

- Embedded graphical interface components, like buttons, sliders, and check boxes
- Automatic execution of marked regions when a file is opened
- Tables
- Character and paragraph formatting styles
- Hyperlinks

These features are described in Chapter 7 of the **Maple 15 User Manual**.

Note: This chapter and Chapter 34 were created using Document mode. All of the other chapters were created using Worksheet mode.

35.3 Entering Expressions

Chapter 34 provided an introduction to entering simple expressions in 2-D Math (see *Entering Expressions (page 917)*). It is also easy to enter mathematical expressions, such as:

- Piecewise-continuous functions: $|x| = \begin{cases} -x & x < 0 \\ 0 & x = 0 \\ x & 0 < x \end{cases}$

- Limits: $\delta(x) = \lim_{\epsilon \to 0} \epsilon |x|^{\epsilon - 1}$

- Continued fractions: $\sqrt{2} = 1 + \cfrac{1}{2 + \cfrac{1}{2 + \cfrac{1}{2 + \cdots}}}$

and more complex expressions.

Mathematical expressions can contain the following objects.

- Numbers: integers, rational numbers, complex numbers, floating-point values, finite field elements, i , ∞ , ...

- Operators: $+,\ \ -,\ \ !,\ /,\ \cdot,\ \ \int,\ \ \lim\limits_{x \to a},\ \ \dfrac{\partial}{\partial x},\ \ ...$

- Constants: $\pi, e,\ \ ...$

- Mathematical functions: $\sin(x),\ \ \cos\!\left(\dfrac{\pi}{3}\right),\ \ \Gamma(2),\ \ ...$

- Names (variables): $x, y, z, \alpha, \beta,\ \ ...$

- Data structures: sets, lists, Arrays, Vectors, Matrices, ...

Maple contains over a thousand symbols. For some numbers, operators, and names, you can press the corresponding key, for example, **9**, **=**, **>**, or **x**. Most symbols are not available on the keyboard, but you can insert them easily using two methods, palettes and symbol names.

Example 1 - Enter a Partial Derivative

To insert a symbol, you can use palettes or symbol names.

Enter the partial derivative $\dfrac{\partial}{\partial t} e^{-t^2}$ using palettes.

Action	Result in Document
1. In the **Expression** palette, click the partial differentiation item $\dfrac{\partial}{\partial x}f$. Maple inserts the partial derivative. The variable placeholder is selected.	$\dfrac{\partial}{\partial x}f$
2. Enter **t**, and then press **Tab**. The expression placeholder is selected.	$\dfrac{\partial}{\partial t}f$
3. Enter e^{-t^2} . **Note:** To enter the exponential e, use the expression palette or command completion.	$\dfrac{\partial}{\partial t}e^{-t^2}$

To evaluate the integral and display the result inline, press **Ctrl+= (Command+=**, for Macintosh) or **Enter**. For more information, see *Computing with Palettes (page 963)*.

You can enter any expression using symbol names and the symbol completion list.

Action	Result in Document
1. Begin typing the name of the symbol, **diff**, and press the symbol completion key (refer to the Preface of the **Maple 15 User Manual**).	*diff* diff .... diff diff (inline partial) .... $\frac{\partial}{\partial x}$ diff (inline) .... $\frac{d}{dx}$ diff@@ .... diff@@ diff_table (function and derivatives) .... *PDEtools[diff_table](expr)* diff_table (representation of function and derivatives) .... *DETools[diff_table](expr)* diffalg .... diffalg diffop2de (differential operator) .... *DETools[diffop2de](oper, y)*
2. Select the partial differentiation item, diff (inline partial) $\frac{\partial}{\partial x}$	$\frac{\partial}{\partial x}$
3. Replace the placeholder with **t**. Use the right arrow to move out of the denominator. Enter e^{-t^2} as in the previous example.	$\frac{\partial}{\partial t} e^{-t^2}$

Example 2 - Define a Mathematical Function

Define the function *twice*, which doubles its input.

Action	Result in Document
1. In the **Expression** palette, click the single variable function definition item, $f := a \rightarrow y$.	$f := a \rightarrow y$
2. Replace the placeholder **f** with the function name, *twice*. Press **Tab** to move to the next placeholder.	$twice := a \rightarrow y$
3. Replace the parameter placeholder, **a**, with the independent variable x. Press **Tab**.	$twice := x \rightarrow y$
4. Replace the output placeholder, **y**, with the desired output, $2x$.	$twice := x \rightarrow 2x$ $x \rightarrow 2x$

$twice(1342) = 2684$

$twice(y - z) = 2y - 2z$

Note: To insert the right arrow symbol $\rightarrow$, you can also enter the characters -> in Math mode. In this case, symbol completion is automatic.

Important: The expression $2x$ is different from the function $x \rightarrow 2x$.

For more information on functions, refer to page 344 of the **Maple 15 User Manual**.

35.4 Evaluating Expressions

To evaluate a mathematical expression, place the cursor in the expression and press **Ctrl + = (Command + =**, for Macintosh). That is, *press and hold* the **Ctrl** (or **Command**) key, and then press the equal sign (=) key.

To the right of the expression, Maple inserts an equal sign and then the value of the expression.

$$\frac{2}{9} + \frac{7}{11} = \frac{85}{99}$$

You can replace the inserted equal sign with text or mathematical content.

To replace the equal sign:

1. Select the equal sign. Press **Delete**.

2. Enter the replacement text or mathematical content.

For example, you can replace the equal sign with the text "is equal to".

$$\frac{2}{9} + \frac{7}{11} \text{ is equal to } \frac{85}{99}$$

In mathematical content, pressing **Enter** evaluates the expression and displays it centered on the following line. The cursor moves to a new line below the output.

$$\frac{2}{9} + \frac{7}{11}$$

$$\frac{85}{99} \tag{35.1}$$

By default, Maple labels output that is generated by pressing **Enter**. For information on equation labels, see *Equation Labels (page 988)*. In this manual, labels are generally not displayed.

In text, pressing **Enter** inserts a line break.

You can use the basic algebraic operators, such as $+$ and $-$, with most expressions, including polynomials—refer to page 152 of the **Maple 15 User Manual**—and matrices and vectors—refer to page 170 of the **Maple 15 User Manual**.

$$\left(2x^2 - x + 1\right) - \left(x^2 + 2x + 12\right) = x^2 - 3x - 11$$

$$3 \cdot \begin{bmatrix} -4 & 8 & 99 \\ 27 & 69 & 29 \end{bmatrix} = \begin{bmatrix} -12 & 24 & 297 \\ 81 & 207 & 87 \end{bmatrix}$$

35.5 Editing Expressions and Updating Output

One important feature of Maple is that your documents are *live*. That is, you can edit expressions and quickly recalculate results.

To update one computation:

1. Edit the expression.

2. Press **Ctrl** + = (**Command** + =, for Macintosh) or **Enter**.

The result is updated.

To update a group of computations:

1. Edit the expressions.

2. Select all edited expressions and the results to recalculate.

3. Click the Execute toolbar icon ⚡.

All selected results are updated.

To update all output in a Maple document:

- Click the Execute All toolbar icon ⚡⚡⚡.

All results in the document are updated.

35.6 Performing Computations

Using the Document mode, you can access the power of the advanced Maple mathematical engine without learning Maple syntax. In addition to solving problems, you can also easily plot expressions.

The primary tools for syntax-free computation are:

- Palettes
- Context menus
- Assistants and tutors

Note: The Document mode is designed for quick calculations, but it also supports Maple commands. For information on commands, see *Commands (page 974)* in Chapter 36, *Worksheet Mode (page 971)*.

Important: In Document mode, you can execute a statement *only if* you enter it in Math mode. To use a Maple command, you must enter it in Math mode.

Computing with Palettes

As discussed in *Entering Expressions (page 958)*, some palettes contain mathematical operations.

To perform a computation using a palette mathematical operation:

1. In a palette that contains operators, such as the **Expression** palette, click an operator item.

2. In the inserted item, specify values in the placeholders.

3. To execute the operation and display the result, press **Ctrl+=** (**Command+=**, for Macintosh) or **Enter**.

For example, to evaluate $\dfrac{\partial}{\partial t}e^{-t^2}$ **inline:**

1. Using the **Expression** palette, enter the partial derivative. See *Example 1 - Enter a Partial Derivative (page 959)*.

2. Press **Ctrl+=** (**Command+=**, for Macintosh).

$$\frac{\partial}{\partial t}e^{-t^2} = -2\,t\,e^{-t^2}$$

Context Menus

A *context menu* is a pop-up menu that lists the operations and actions you can perform on a particular expression. See **Figure 35.1**.

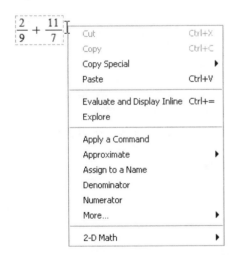

Figure 35.1: Context Menu

To display the context menu for an expression:

• Right-click (**Control**-click, for Macintosh) the expression.

The context menu is displayed beside the mouse pointer.

You can evaluate expressions using context menus. The **Evaluate and Display Inline** operation (see **Figure 35.1**) is equivalent to pressing **Ctrl+=** (**Command+=**, for Macintosh). That is, it inserts an equal sign (=) and then the value of the expression.

Alternatively, press **Enter** to evaluate the expression and display the result centered on the following line.

For more information on evaluation, see *Evaluating Expressions (page 961)*.

From the context menu, you can also select operations different from evaluation. To the right of the expression, Maple inserts a right arrow symbol ($\rightarrow$) and then the result.

For example, use the **Approximate** operation to approximate a fraction: $\dfrac{2}{3} \xrightarrow{\text{at 10 digits}} 0.6666666667$

You can perform a sequence of operations by repeatedly using context menus. For example, to compute the derivative of $\cos(x^2)$, use the **Differentiate** operation on the expression, and then to evaluate the result at a point, use the **Evaluate at a Point** operation on the output and enter 10:

$$\cos(x^2) \xrightarrow{\text{differentiate w.r.t. x}} -2\sin(x^2)\,x \xrightarrow{\text{evaluate at point}} -20\sin(100)$$

The following subsections provide detailed instructions on performing a few of the numerous operations available using context menus. Figures in the subsections show related context menus or palettes.

Approximating the Value of an Expression

To approximate a fraction numerically:

1. Enter a fraction.
2. Display the context menu. See **Figure 35.2**.
3. From the context menu, select **Approximate**, and then the number of significant digits to use: **5, 10, 20, 50**, or **100**.

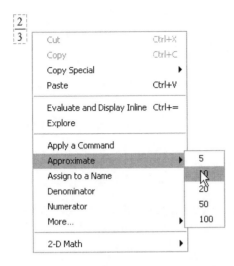

Figure 35.2: Approximating the Value of a Fraction

$$\frac{2}{3} \xrightarrow{\text{at 10 digits}} 0.6666666667$$

You can replace the inserted right arrow with text or mathematical content.

To replace the right arrow (→):

1. Select the arrow and text. Press **Delete**.

2. Enter the replacement text or mathematical content.

Note: To replace the right arrow with text, you must first press **F5** to switch to Text mode.

For example, you can replace the arrow with the text "is approximately equal to" or the symbol ≈.

$$\frac{2}{3} \text{ is approximately equal to } 0.6666666667$$

$$\frac{2}{3} \approx 0.6666666667$$

Solving an Equation

You can find an exact (*symbolic*) solution or an approximate (*numeric*) solution of an equation. For more information on symbolic and numeric computations, refer to page 104 of the **Maple 15 User Manual**.

To solve an equation:

1. Enter an equation.

2. Display the context menu. See **Figure 35.3**.

3. From the context menu, select **Solve** or **Numerically Solve** in the **Solve** menu item.

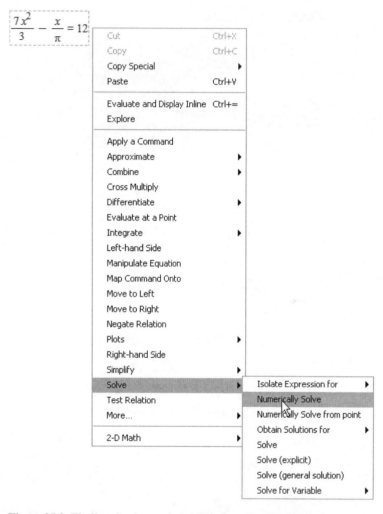

Figure 35.3: Finding the Approximate Solution to an Equation

$$\frac{7x^2}{3} - \frac{x}{\pi} = 12 \xrightarrow{\text{solve}} \left\{ x = \frac{3}{14} \frac{1 + \sqrt{1 + 112\pi^2}}{\pi} \right\}, \left\{ x = -\frac{3}{14} \frac{-1 + \sqrt{1 + 112\pi^2}}{\pi} \right\}$$

$$\frac{7x^2}{3} - \frac{x}{\pi} = 12 \xrightarrow{\text{solve}} -2.200603126, 2.337021648$$

For more information on solving equations, including solving inequations, differential equations, and other types of equations, refer to page 113 of the **Maple 15 User Manual**.

Using Units

You can create expressions with units. To specify a unit for an expression, use the **Units** palettes. The **Units (FPS)** palette (**Figure 35.4**) contains important units from the foot-pound-second (FPS) system of units used in the United States. The **Units (SI)** palette (**Figure 35.5**) contains important units from the international system (SI) of units.

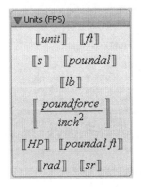

Figure 35.4: FPS Units Palette

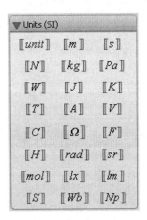

Figure 35.5: SI Units Palette

To insert an expression with a unit:

1. Enter the expression.

2. In a unit palette, click a unit symbol.

Note: To include a reciprocal unit, divide by the unit.

To evaluate an expression that contains units:

1. Enter the expression using the units palettes to insert units.

2. Right-click (**Control**-click, for Macintosh) the expression.

3. From the context menu, select **Units** and then **Simplify**.

For example, compute the electric current passing through a wire that conducts 590 coulombs in 2.9 seconds.

$$\frac{590[\![C]\!]}{2.9[\![s]\!]} \xrightarrow{\text{simplify units}} 203.4482759\,[\![A]\!]$$

For more information on using units, refer to page 130 of the **Maple 15 User Manual**.

Assistants and Tutors

Assistants and tutors provide point-and-click interfaces with buttons, text input regions, and sliders. For details on assistants and tutors, see *Point-and-Click Interaction (page 929)*.

Assistants and tutors can be launched from the **Tools** menu or the context menu for an expression. For example, you can use the **Linear System Solving** tutor to solve a linear system, specified by a matrix or a set of equations.

Example 3 - Using a Context Menu to Open the Linear System Solving Tutor

Use the **Linear System Solving** tutor to solve the following system of linear equations, written in matrix form:

$$\begin{bmatrix} 1 & 3 & 0 & -2 & -1 \\ 4 & 2 & -1 & 5 & 7 \\ 0 & -3 & 5 & 4 & -7 \\ 1 & -1 & 3 & 6 & 5 \end{bmatrix}$$

Action	Result in Document
1. In a new document block, create the matrix or set of linear equations to be solved.	$\begin{bmatrix} 1 & 3 & 0 & -2 & -1 \\ 4 & 2 & -1 & 5 & 7 \\ 0 & -3 & 5 & 4 & -7 \\ 1 & -1 & 3 & 6 & 5 \end{bmatrix}$
2. Load the **Student[LinearAlgebra]** package. From the **Tools** menu, select **Load Package → Student Linear Algebra**. This makes the tutors in that package available. For details, see *Package Commands (page 944)*.	Loading **Student:-LinearAlgebra**
3. Right-click the matrix and select **Tutors → Linear Algebra → Linear System Solving...**. The **Linear System Solving** dialog appears, where you can choose the solving method. **Gaussian Elimination** reduces the matrix to row-echelon form, then performs back-substitution to solve the system. **Gauss Jordan Elimination** reduces the matrix to reduced row-echelon form, where the equations are already solved. For this example, choose **Gaussian Elimination**.	

Action	Result in Document
4. The **Gaussian Elimination** dialog opens. You can specify the Gaussian elimination step-by-step, or you can use the **Next Step** or **All Steps** buttons to have Maple perform the steps for you. 5. Once the matrix is in row-echelon (upper-triangular) form, click the **Solve System** button to move to the next step.	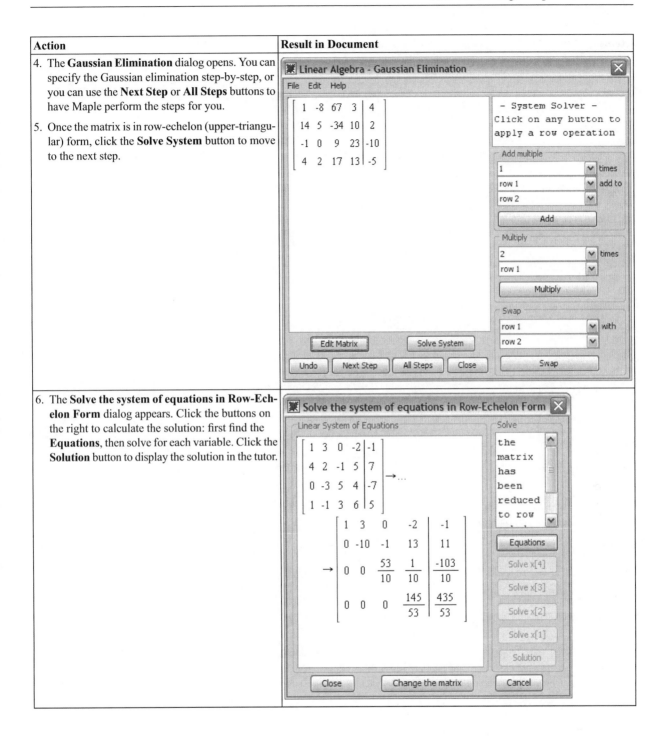
6. The **Solve the system of equations in Row-Echelon Form** dialog appears. Click the buttons on the right to calculate the solution: first find the **Equations**, then solve for each variable. Click the **Solution** button to display the solution in the tutor.	

Action	Result in Document
7. Click the **Close** button to return the solution to your document.	$\begin{bmatrix} 1 & 3 & 0 & -2 & -1 \\ 4 & 2 & -1 & 5 & 7 \\ 0 & -3 & 5 & 4 & -7 \\ 1 & -1 & 3 & 6 & 5 \end{bmatrix} \xrightarrow{\text{linear solve tutor}} \begin{bmatrix} -4 \\ 3 \\ -2 \\ 3 \end{bmatrix}$

For more information on linear systems and matrices, refer to page 160 of the **Maple 15 User Manual**.

36 Worksheet Mode

The *Worksheet* mode of the Standard Worksheet interface is designed for:

- Interactive use through Maple commands, which offers advanced functionality and customized control not available using context menus or other syntax-free methods

- Programming using the powerful Maple language

Using Worksheet mode, you have access to all of the Maple features described in Chapter 34, and most of those described in Chapter 35, including:

- Math and Text modes

- Palettes

- Context menus

- Assistants and tutors

For information on these features, see Chapter 34, *Getting Started (page 901)* and Chapter 35, *Document Mode (page 957)*.

Note: Using a document block, you can use all Document mode features in Worksheet mode. For information on document blocks, see *Document Blocks (page 948)*.

Note: This chapter and the following chapters were created using Worksheet mode.

36.1 In This Chapter

Section	Topics
Input Prompt (page 972) - Where you enter input	• The Input Prompt (>)
	• Suppressing Output
	• 2-D and 1-D Math Input
	• Input Separators
Commands (page 974) - Thousands of routines for performing computations and other operations	• The Maple Library
	• Top-Level Commands
	• Package Commands
	• Lists of Common Commands and Packages
Palettes (page 979) - Items that you can insert by clicking or dragging	• Using Palettes
Context Menus (page 980)- Pop-up menus of common operations	• Using Context Menus
Assistants and Tutors (page 982)- Graphical interfaces with buttons and sliders	• Launching Assistants and Tutors

Section	Topics
Task Templates (page 983) - Sets of commands with placeholders that you can insert and use to perform a task	• Viewing Task Templates • Inserting a Task Template • Performing the Task
Text Regions (page 985) - Areas in the document in which you can enter text	• Inserting a Text Region • Formatting Text
Names (page 985) - References to the expressions you assign to them	• Assigning to Names • Unassigning Names • Valid Names
Equation Labels (page 988) - Automatically generated labels that you can use to refer to expressions	• Displaying Equation Labels • Referring to a Previous Result • Execution Groups with Multiple Outputs • Label Numbering Schemes • Features of Equation Labels

36.2 Input Prompt

In Worksheet mode, you enter input at the Maple *input prompt* (>). The default mode for input is Math mode (*2-D Math*).

To evaluate input:

• Press **Enter**.

Maple displays the result (output) below the input.

For example, to find the value of $\sin^3\left(\dfrac{\pi}{3}\right)$, enter the expression, and then press **Enter**.

$$> \sin^3\left(\frac{\pi}{3}\right)$$

$$\frac{3}{8}\sqrt{3} \tag{36.1}$$

For example, compute the sum of two fractions.

$$> \frac{2}{9} + \frac{7}{11}$$

$$\frac{85}{99} \tag{36.2}$$

Suppressing Output

To suppress the output, enter a colon (**:**) at the end of the input.

$$> \frac{2}{9} + \frac{7}{11} :$$

A set of Maple input and its output are referred to as an *execution group*.

1-D Math Input

You can also insert input using Text mode (*1-D Math*). The input is entered as a one-dimensional sequence of characters. 1-D Math input is red.

To enter input using 1-D Math:

- At the input prompt, press **F5** or click the **Text** button in the toolbar, Text Math , to switch from 2-D Math to 1-D Math.

```
> 123^2 - 29857/120;
```

$$\frac{1785623}{120}$$

Important: 1-D Math input must end with a semicolon or colon. If you use a semicolon, Maple displays the output; if you use a colon, Maple suppresses the output.

```
> 123^2 - 29857/120:
```

To set the default input mode to 1-D Math:

1. From the **Tools** menu, select **Options**. The **Options** dialog is displayed.

2. On the **Display** tab, in the **Input display** drop-down list, select **Maple Notation**.

3. Click **Apply to Session** (to set for only the current session) or **Apply Globally** (to set for all Maple sessions).

To convert 2-D Math input to 1-D Math input:

1. Select the 2-D Math input.

2. From the **Format** menu, select **Convert To**, and then **1-D Math Input**.

Important: In Document mode, you can execute a statement *only if* you enter it in Math mode.

Input Separators

In 1-D and 2-D Math input, you can use a semicolon or colon to separate multiple inputs in the same input line.

> $\sqrt{4.4}$; tan(3.2)

$$2.097617696$$

$$0.05847385446$$

If you do not specify a semicolon or colon, Maple interprets it as a single input. This can either give unexpected results, as below, or an error.

> $\sqrt{4.4}$ tan(3.2)

$$0.1226557919$$

36.3 Commands

Maple contains a large set of commands and a powerful programming language. Most Maple commands are written using the Maple programming language.

You can enter commands using 1-D or 2-D Math. You must use 1-D Math input when programming in Maple. Chapter 9 of the **Maple 15 User Manual** provides an introduction to Maple programming.

To learn how to use Maple commands, see the appropriate help page, or use task templates. For more information, see *The Maple Help System (page 950)* and *Task Templates (page 983)*.

The Maple Library

Maple's commands are contained in the Maple library. There are two types of commands: *top-level commands* and *package commands*.

• The top-level commands are the most frequently used Maple commands.

- Packages contain related specialized commands in areas such as calculus, linear algebra, vector calculus, and code generation.

For a complete list of packages and commands, refer to the **index** help pages. To access the index overview help page, enter **?index**, and then press **Enter**. For information on the Maple Help System, see *The Maple Help System (page 950)*.

Top-Level Commands

To use a top-level command, enter its name followed by parentheses **(( ))** containing any parameters. This is referred to as a *calling sequence* for the command.

```
command(arguments)
```

Note: In 1-D Math input, include a semicolon or colon at the end of the calling sequence.

For example, to differentiate an expression, use the **diff** command. The required parameters are the expression to differentiate, which must be specified first, and the independent variable.

> $diff(\tan(x) \sin(x), x)$

$$\left(1 + \tan(x)^2\right) \sin(x) + \tan(x) \cos(x)$$

For a complete list of functions (commands that implement mathematical functions), such as **BesselI** and **AiryAi**, available in the library, refer to the **initialfunctions** help page.

> $\dfrac{\text{BesselI}(0.1, 1)}{\text{AiryAi}(2.2)}$

$$47.53037086$$

For detailed information on the properties of a function, use the **FunctionAdvisor** command.

> $FunctionAdvisor('definition', \text{BesselI})$

$$\left[\text{BesselI}(a, z) = \frac{z^a \, \text{hypergeom}\left([\ ], [1 + a], \frac{1}{4} z^2 \right)}{\Gamma(1 + a) \, 2^a}, \text{with no restrictions on } (a, z) \right]$$

For detailed information on how to use a function in Maple, refer to its help page.

For example:

> *?Bessel*

Note: In 1-D and 2-D Math input, when accessing a help page using **?**, you do not need to include a trailing semicolon or colon.

Top Commands

Here are a few of the most frequently used Maple commands. A complete list of top-level commands is available at **Help → Manuals, Resources, and more → List of Commands**.

Table 36.1: Top Commands

Command Name	Description
plot and **plot3d**	Create a two-dimensional and three-dimensional plot of functions.
solve	Solve one or more equations or inequalities for their unknowns.
fsolve	Solve one or more equations using floating-point arithmetic.
eval	Evaluate an expression at a given point.
evalf	Numerically evaluate expressions.
dsolve	Solve ordinary differential equations (ODEs).
int	Compute an indefinite or definite integral.
diff	Compute an ordinary or partial derivative, as the context dictates.
limit	Calculate the limiting value of a function.
sum	For symbolic summation. It is used to compute a closed form for an indefinite or definite sum.
assume/is	Set variable properties and relationships between variables. Similar functionality is provided by the **assuming** command.
assuming	Compute the value of an expression under assumptions.
simplify	Apply simplification rules to an expression.
factor	Factor a polynomial.
expand	Distribute products over sums.
normal	Normalize a rational expression.
convert	Convert an expression to a different type or form.
type	Type-checking command. In many contexts, it is not necessary to know the exact value of an expression; it suffices to know that an expression belongs to a broad class, or group, of expressions that share some common properties. These classes or groups are known as *types*.
series	Generalized series expansion.
map	Apply a procedure to each operand of an expression.

Package Commands

To use a package command, the calling sequence must include the package name, and the command name enclosed in square brackets (**[ ]**).

```
package[command](arguments)
```

If you are frequently using the commands in a package, load the package.

To load a package:

• Use the **with** command, specifying the package as an argument.

The **with** command displays a list of the package commands loaded (unless you suppress the output by entering a colon at the end of the calling sequence).

After loading a package, you can use the short form names of its commands. That is, you can enter the commands without specifying the package name.

For example, use the **NLPSolve** command from the **Optimization** package to find a local minimum of an expression and the value of the independent variable at which the minimum occurs.

$> \; Optimization[NLPSolve]\left(\dfrac{\sin(x)}{x}, x = 1 \,..15 \right)$

$$[-0.0913252028230576718, [x = 10.9041216700744900]]$$

$> \; with(Optimization);$

$$[ImportMPS, Interactive, LPSolve, LSSolve, Maximize, Minimize, NLPSolve, QPSolve]$$

$> \; NLPSolve\left(\dfrac{\sin(x)}{x}, x = 1 \,..15 \right)$

$$[-0.0913252028230576718, [x = 10.9041216700744900]]$$

For more information on optimization, refer to page 190 of the **Maple 15 User Manual**.

To unload a package:

- Use the **unwith** command, specifying the package as an argument.

$> \; unwith(Optimization)$

Alternatively, use the **restart** command. The restart command clears Maple's internal memory. The effects include unassigning all names and unloading all packages. For more information, refer to the **restart** help page.

Note: To execute the examples in this manual, you may be required to use the **unassign** or **restart** command between examples.

Some packages contain commands that have the same name as a top-level command. For example, the **plots** package contains a **changecoords** command. Maple also contains a top-level **changecoords** command.

$> \; with(plots):$

After the plots package is loaded, the name **changecoords** refers to the **plots[changecoords]** command. To use the top-level **changecoords** command, unload the package or use the restart command. (For alternative methods of accessing the top-level command, see the **rebound** help page.)

Top Packages

Here are a few of the most frequently used Maple packages. A complete list of **packages** is available in the Maple help system at **Help → Manuals, Resources, and more → List of Packages**.

Table 36.2: Top Packages

Package Name	Description
CodeGeneration	The **Code Generation** package is a collection of commands and subpackages that enable the translation of Maple code to other programming languages, such as C, C#, Fortran, MATLAB®, Visual Basic®, and Java™.
LinearAlgebra	The **Linear Algebra** package contains commands to construct and manipulate Matrices and Vectors, and solve linear algebra problems. **LinearAlgebra** routines operate on three principal data structures: Matrices, Vectors, and scalars.
Optimization	The **Optimization** package is a collection of commands for numerically solving optimization problems, which involve finding the minimum or maximum of an objective function possibly subject to constraints.
Physics	The **Physics** package implements computational representations and related operations for most of the objects used in mathematical physics computations.
RealDomain	The **Real Domain** package provides an environment in which Maple assumes that the basic underlying number system is the field of real numbers instead of the complex number field.
ScientificConstants	The **Scientific Constants** package provides access to the values of various physical constants, for example, the velocity of light and the atomic weight of sodium. This package provides the units for each of the constant values, allowing for greater understanding of an equation. The package also provides units-matching for error checking of the solution.
ScientificErrorAnalysis	The **Scientific Error Analysis** package provides representation and construction of numerical quantities that have a central value and an associated uncertainty (or error), which is a measure of the degree of precision to which the quantity's value is known. Various first-order calculations of error analysis can be performed with these quantities.
Statistics	The **Statistics** package is a collection of tools for mathematical statistics and data analysis. The package supports a wide range of common statistical tasks such as quantitative and graphical data analysis, simulation, and curve fitting.
Student	The **Student** package is a collection of subpackages designed to assist with teaching and learning standard undergraduate mathematics. The many commands display functions, computations, and theorems in various ways, including stepping through important computations. The **Student** package contains the following subpackages: • **Calculus1** - single-variable calculus • **LinearAlgebra** - linear algebra • **MultivariateCalculus** - multivariate calculus • **NumericalAnalysis** - numerical analysis • **Precalculus** - precalculus • **VectorCalculus** - multivariate vector calculus

Package Name	Description
Units	The **Units** package contains commands for unit conversion and provides environments for performing calculations with units. It accepts approximately 300 distinct unit names (for example, meters and grams) and over 550 units with various contexts (for example, standard miles and U.S. survey miles). Maple also contains two **Units** palettes that allow you to enter the unit for an expression quickly.
VectorCalculus	The **Vector Calculus** package is a collection of commands that perform multivariate and vector calculus operations. A large set of predefined orthogonal coordinate systems is available. All computations in the package can be performed in any of these coordinate systems. It contains a facility for adding a custom but orthogonal coordinate system and using that new coordinate system for your computations.

36.4 Palettes

Palettes are collections of related items that you can insert by clicking or dragging. For example, see **Figure 36.1**.

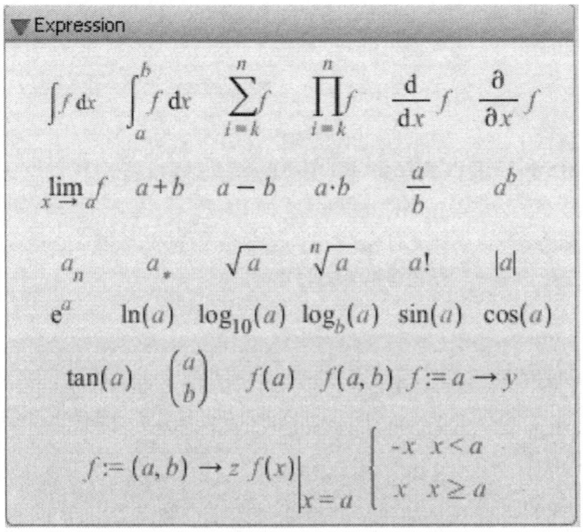

Figure 36.1: Expression Palette

You can use palettes to enter input.

For example, evaluate a definite integral using the definite integration item $\int_a^b f\, dx$ in the **Expression** palette.

In 2-D Math, clicking the definite integration item inserts:

$$> \int_a^b f\, dx$$

1. Enter values in the placeholders. To move to the next placeholder, press **Tab**. **Note:** If pressing the **Tab** key inserts a tab, click the Tab icon ⇥ in the toolbar.
2. evaluate the integral, press **Enter**.

$$> \int_0^1 \tanh(x)\ dx$$

$$-\ln(2) + \ln\!\left(e^{-1} + e\right)$$

In 1-D Math, clicking the definite integration item inserts the corresponding command calling sequence.

```
> int(f,x=a..b);
```

Specify the problem values (using the **Tab** to move to the next placeholder), and then press **Enter**.

```
> int(tanh(x), x = 0..1);
```

$$-\ln(2) + \ln\!\left(e^{-1} + e\right)$$

Note: Some palette items cannot be inserted into 1-D Math because they are not defined in the Maple language. When the cursor is in 1-D Math input, unavailable palette items are dimmed.

For more information on viewing and using palettes, see *Palettes (page 919)* in Chapter 34.

36.5 Context Menus

A *context menu* is a pop-up menu that lists the operations and actions you can perform on a particular expression. See **Figure 36.2**.

> 946929

Figure 36.2: Integer Context Menu

In Worksheet mode, you can use context menus to perform operations on 2-D Math and output.

To use a context menu:

1. Right-click (**Control**-click, for Macintosh) the expression. The context menu is displayed.

2. From the context menu, select an operation.

Maple inserts a new execution group containing:

• The calling sequence that performs the operation

• The result of the operation

Example - Using Context Menus

Determine the rational expression (fraction) that approximates the floating-point number $0.3463678 + 1.7643$.

Action	Result in Document
1. Enter and execute the expression.	> $0.3463678 + 1.7643$ 2.1106678 (36.3)
2. Right-click (**Control-click**, for Macintosh) the output floating-point number.	2.1106678 Cut Ctrl+X Copy Ctrl+C Copy Special ▶ Paste Ctrl+V Numeric Formatting… Explore Apply a Command Assign to a Name Next Float Previous Float Conversions ▶ Continued Fraction Integer Functions ▶ Exact Rational Units ▶ Rational
3. From the context menu, select **Conversions → Rational**. The inserted calling sequence includes an equation label reference to the number you are converting.	> $convert(\,(\mathbf{3.3}),\,'rational'\,)$ $$\frac{32270}{15289}$$

Notice that an equation label reference has been used. For information on equation labels and equation label references, see *Equation Labels (page 988)*.

For more information on context menus, see *Context Menus (page 963)* in Chapter 35.

36.6 Assistants and Tutors

Assistants and tutors provide point-and-click interfaces with buttons, text input regions, and sliders. See **Figure 36.3**.

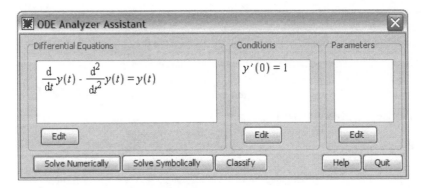

Figure 36.3: ODE Analyzer Assistant

Launching an Assistant or Tutor

To launch an assistant or tutor:

1. Open the **Tools** menu.

2. Select **Assistants** or **Tutors**.

3. Navigate to and select one of the assistants or tutors.

For more information on assistants and tutors, see *Assistants (page 929)* in Chapter 34.

36.7 Task Templates

Maple can solve a diverse set of problems. The task template facility helps you quickly find and use the commands required to perform common tasks.

After inserting a task template, specify the parameters of your problem in the placeholders, and then execute the commands, or click a button.

The **Task Browser (Figure 36.4)** organizes task templates by subject.

To launch the Task Browser:

• From the **Tools** menu, select **Tasks**, and then **Browse**.

You can also browse the task templates in the Table of Contents of the Maple Help System.

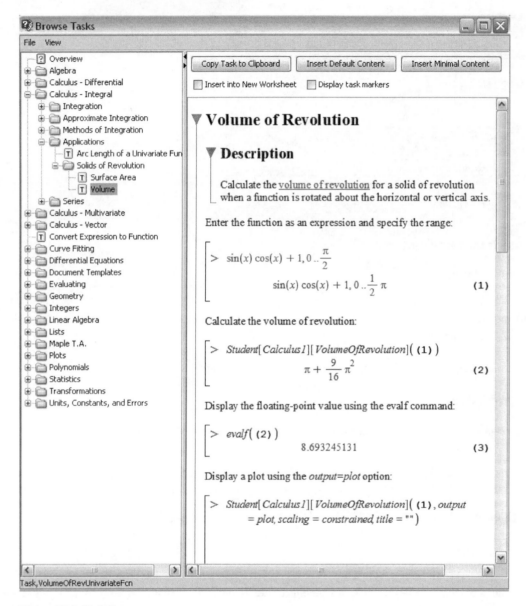

Figure 36.4: Task Browser

For details on inserting and using task templates, see *Task Templates (page 938)*. You can also create your own task templates for performing common tasks. For details, refer to the **creatingtasks** help page.

36.8 Text Regions

To add descriptive text in Worksheet mode, use a *text region*.

To insert a text region:

* In the toolbar, click the Text region icon T.

The default mode in a text region is Text mode.

In a text region, you can:

* Enter text with inline mathematical content by switching between Text and Math modes. To toggle between Text mode and Math mode, press **F5** or click the Math and Text toolbar icons, Text Math.
  Note: The mathematical content in a text region is not evaluated. To enter mathematical content that is evaluated, enter it at an *Input Prompt (page 972)*.

* Insert any palette item. Palette items are inserted in Math mode (2-D Math). **Note**: After you insert a palette item, you must press **F5** or click the toolbar icon to return to Text mode.

You can format text in a text region. Features include:

* Character styles
* Paragraph styles
* Sections and subsections
* Tables

For more information on formatting documents, refer to Chapter 7 of the **Maple 15 User Manual**.

36.9 Names

Instead of re-entering an expression every time you need it, you can assign it to a *name* or add an *equation label* to it. Then you can quickly refer to the expression using the name or an equation label reference. For information on labels, see the following section, *Equation Labels (page 988)*.

Note: Through the Variable Manager you can manage the top-level assigned variables currently active in your Maple Session. For more information about the Variable Manager, see the **Variable Manager** help page.

Assigning to Names

You can assign any Maple expression to a name: numeric values, data structures, procedures (a type of Maple program), and other Maple objects.

Initially, the value of a name is itself.

> *a*

$$a$$

The assignment operator (**:=**) associates an expression with a name.

> *a* := π

$$a := \pi$$

Recall that you can enter π using the following two methods.

• Use the **Common Symbols** palette
• In 2-D Math enter *pi*, and then press the symbol completion shortcut key. See *Shortcuts for Entering Mathematical Expressions (page 906)*.

When Maple evaluates an expression that contains a name, it replaces the name with its value. For example:

> cos(*a*)

$$-1$$

For information on Maple evaluation rules, refer to page 359 of the **Maple 15 User Manual**.

Mathematical Functions

To define a function, assign it to a name.

For example, define a function that computes the cube of its argument.

> *cube* := *x* → *x*³ :

For information on creating functions, see *Example 2 - Define a Mathematical Function (page 960)*.

> *cube*(3); *cube*(1.666)

$$27$$

$$4.624076296$$

Note: To insert the right arrow, enter the characters ->. In 2-D Math, Maple replaces -> with the right arrow symbol →. In 1-D Math, the characters are not replaced.

For example, define a function that squares its argument.

```
> square := x -> x^2:
> square(32);
```

$$1024$$

For more information on functions, refer to page 344 of the **Maple 15 User Manual**.

Protected Names

Protected names are valid names that are predefined or reserved.

If you attempt to assign to a protected name, Maple returns an error.

```
> sin := 2
```

```
Error, attempting to assign to `sin` which is protected
```

For more information, refer to the **type/protected** and **protect** help pages.

Unassigning Names

The **unassign** command resets the value of a name to itself. **Note:** You must enclose the name in right single quotes (' ').

```
> unassign( 'a' )
> a
```

$$a$$

Right single quotes (*unevaluation quotes*) prevent Maple from evaluating the name. For more information on unevaluation quotes, refer to page 366 of the **Maple 15 User Manual**.or refer to the **uneval** help page.

Also refer to page 368 of the **Maple 15 User Manual**.

Unassigning all names:

The **restart** command clears Maple's internal memory. The effects include unassigning all names. For more information, refer to the **restart** help page.

Note: To execute the examples in this manual, you may be required to use the **unassign** or **restart** command between examples.

Valid Names

A Maple name must be one of the following.

- A sequence of alphanumeric and underscore (_) characters that begins with an alphabetical character. **Note:** To enter an underscore character in 2-D Math, enter a backslash character followed by an underscore character, that is, _.

- A sequence of characters enclosed in left single quotes (` `).

Important: Do not begin a name with an underscore character. Maple reserves names that begin with an underscore for use by the Maple library.

Examples of valid names:

- **a**
- **a1**
- **polynomial**
- **polynomial1_divided_by_polynomial2**
- **`2a`**
- **`x y`**

36.10 Equation Labels

Maple marks the output of each execution group with a unique equation label.

Note: The equation label is displayed to the right of the output.

> $\int \sin(x)\ dx$

$$-\cos(x) \tag{36.4}$$

Using equation labels, you can refer to the result in other computations.

> $\int (3.4)\ dx$

$$-\sin(x) \tag{36.5}$$

Displaying Equation Labels

Important: By default, equation labels are displayed. If equation label display is turned off, complete **both** of the following operations.

- From the **Format** menu, select **Equation Labels**, and then ensure that **Worksheet** is selected.

- In the **Options** dialog (**Tools→Options**), on the **Display** tab, ensure that **Show equation labels** is selected.

Referring to a Previous Result

Instead of re-entering previous results in computations, you can use equation label references. Each time you need to refer to a previous result, insert an equation label reference.

To insert an equation label reference:

• From the **Insert** menu, select **Label**. (Alternatively, press **Ctrl+L**; **Command+L**, Macintosh.)

• In the **Insert Label** dialog (see **Figure 36.5**), enter the label value, and then click **OK**.

Figure 36.5: Insert Label Dialog

Maple inserts the reference.

For example:

To integrate the product of (36.4) and (36.5):

Action	Result in Document
1. In the **Expression** palette, click the indefinite integration item $\int f \, dx$. The item is inserted and the integrand placeholder is highlighted.	$> \int \blacksquare \, dx$
2. Press **Ctrl+L** (**Command+L**, for Macintosh). 3. In the **Insert Label** dialog, enter **3.4**. Click **OK**.	$> \int f \, dx$
4. Press *. 5. Press **Ctrl+L** (**Command+L**, for Macintosh). 6. In the **Insert Label** dialog, enter **3.4**. Click **OK**.	$> \int (3.4) \cdot (3.5) \, dx$

Action	Result in Document
7. To move to the variable of integration placeholder, press **Tab**.	$> \int (3.4) \cdot (3.5)\, dx$
8. Enter **x**.	
9. To evaluate the integral, press **Enter**.	$-\dfrac{1}{2}\cos(x)^2$ (36.6)

Execution Groups with Multiple Outputs

An equation label is associated with the *last output* within an execution group.

$$> \left(\frac{2}{3.5}\right)^2 ; \cos\left(\frac{\pi}{6}\right)$$

$$0.3265306122$$

$$\frac{1}{2}\sqrt{3} \tag{36.7}$$

$$> (3.7)^2$$

$$\frac{3}{4} \tag{36.8}$$

Label Numbering Schemes

You can number equation labels in two ways:

- **Flat** - Each label is a single number, for example, 1, 2, or 3.
- **Sections** - Each label is numbered according to the section in which it occurs. For example, 2.1 is the first equation in the second section, and 1.3.2 is the second equation in the third subsection of the first section.

To change the equation label numbering scheme:

- From the **Format** menu, select **Equation Labels** → **Label Display**. In the **Format Labels** dialog (Figure 36.6), select one of the formats.
- Optionally, enter a prefix.

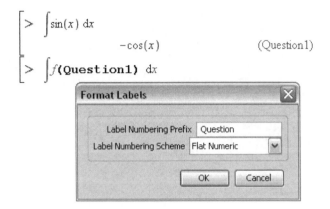

$$> \int \sin(x)\, dx$$

$$-\cos(x) \qquad\qquad (\text{Question1})$$

$$> \int f(\textbf{Question1})\, dx$$

Figure 36.6: Format Labels Dialog: Adding a Prefix

Features of Equation Labels

Although equation labels are not descriptive names, labels offer other important features.

- Each label is unique, whereas a name may be inadvertently assigned more than once for different purposes.
- Maple labels the output values sequentially. If you remove or insert an output, Maple automatically re-numbers all equation labels and updates the label references.
- If you change the equation label format (see *Label Numbering Schemes (page 990)*), Maple automatically updates all equation labels and label references.

For information on assigning to, using, and unassigning names, see *Names (page 985)*.

For more information on equation labels, refer to the **equationlabel** help page.

The following chapters describe how to use Maple to perform tasks such as solving equations, producing plots and animations, and creating mathematical documents. The chapters were created using Worksheet mode. Except where noted, all features are available in both Worksheet mode and Document mode.

36.11 Maple 15 User Manual

These three chapters are an excerpt of the **Maple 15 User Manual**. You can download the entire **Maple 15 User Manual** from the Maplesoft website, **http://www.maplesoft.com/documentation_center**.

Copyright

Maplesoft, Maple, Maplet, Maple T.A., and MapleCloud are all trademarks of Waterloo Maple Inc.

without notice and does not represent a commitment on the part of the vendor. The software described in this document is furnished under a license agreement and may be used or copied only in accordance with the agreement. It is against the law to copy the software on any medium except as specifically allowed in the agreement.

37 Examples

37.1 Calculus of a Single Variable

Problem 1 - Implicit Differentiation

Obtain $y'(x)$ by applying implicit differentiation to $3x^2 - 5xy + 7y^2 = 9$.

• Type the equation defining $y(x)$ implicitly. • Context Menu: Differentiate $>$ Implicitly In the resulting dialog, shown below, set y as the dependent variable, and x as the independent variable, then click OK. 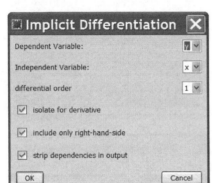	$3x^2 - 5xy + 7y^2 = 9 \; ; \; \xrightarrow{\text{implicit differentiation}} \; \dfrac{-6x + 5y}{-5x + 14y}$
• Alternatively, use the **implicitdiff** command.	$implicitdiff\left(3x^2 - 5xy + 7y^2 = 9, y, x\right) = \dfrac{-6x + 5y}{-5x + 14y}$

Problem 2 - Optimization

Minimize the area of the triangle formed in the first quadrant by the tangent to $y = \cos(x)$.

• At the point $(x, y) = (a, \cos(a))$, obtain the equation of the tangent line. It's slope is $-\cos(a)$.	$Student:\text{-}Precalculus:\text{-}Line(-\sin(a), [a, \cos(a)])[1]$ $y = -\sin(a)\,x + \cos(a) + \sin(a)\,a$
• Context Menu: Right-hand Side	$\xrightarrow{\text{right hand side}}$ $-\sin(a)\,x + \cos(a) + \sin(a)\,a \qquad (37.1)$
• Context Menu: Conversions $>$ Equate to 0	$\xrightarrow{\text{equate to 0}}$ $-\sin(a)\,x + \cos(a) + \sin(a)\,a = 0$

• Context Menu: Solve $>$ Obtain Solutions for $> x$ This gives the *x*-intercept on the tangent line.	$\xrightarrow{\text{solutions for x}}$ $$\frac{\cos(a) + \sin(a)\,a}{\sin(a)} \qquad (37.2)$$
• Expression palette: evaluate the right-hand side of the the tangent line equation at $x = 0$. This gives the *y*-intercept on the tangent line.	$\left.\mathbf{(4.1)}\right|_{x=0}$ $$\cos(a) + \sin(a)\,a \qquad (37.3)$$
• The area of the triangle is half the product of the *x*- and *y*-intercepts.	$$\frac{\mathbf{(4.2)}\cdot\mathbf{(4.3)}}{2}$$ $$\frac{1}{2}\,\frac{(\cos(a) + \sin(a)\,a)^2}{\sin(a)} \qquad (37.4)$$
• Context Menu: Plot Builder Set $0 \leq a \leq \pi/2$ Options: Range from/to: 0 to 10	$\rightarrow$
• Reference the area expression by its equation label. Press the Enter key. • Context Menu: Differentiate $>$ With Respect To $> a$ • Context Menu: Simplify $>$ Trig • Context Menu: Solve $>$ Numerically Solve	$\mathbf{(4.4)}$ $$\frac{1}{2}\,\frac{(\cos(a) + \sin(a)\,a)^2}{\sin(a)}$$ $\xrightarrow{\text{differentiate w.r.t. a}}$ $$\frac{(\cos(a) + \sin(a)\,a)\cos(a)\,a}{\sin(a)} - \frac{1}{2}\,\frac{(\cos(a) + \sin(a)\,a)^2\cos(a)}{\sin(a)^2}$$ $\overset{\text{simplify trig}}{=}$ $$-\frac{1}{2}\,\frac{(\cos(a)^2 - a^2 + a^2\cos(a)^2)\cos(a)}{\sin(a)^2}$$ $\xrightarrow{\text{solve}}$ $$0.8603335890 \qquad (37.5)$$

Expression palette: evaluation template $>$ evaluate the area at the critical value	$(4.4)\big|_{a = (4.5)}$
	1.122192676

Problem 3 - Constrained Optimization

A Norman window consists of a rectangle surmounted by a semicircle. The rectangle will contain clear glass; the semicircle, tinted glass letting in 20% of the light admitted by clear glass. If the perimeter of the window is 8, find the dimensions that admit the maximum amount of light.

Let the height of the rectangle be x and the width be $2\,y$. Let L be a measure of the total light admitted.

Define L, and let P be the perimeter of the window.	$L := \dfrac{1}{5}\left(\dfrac{\pi}{2}y^2\right) + 2xy :$ $P := 2x + 2y + \pi y :$

Solve this constrained optimization problem with the method of Lagrange multipliers, implemented in the Student *Multivariate-Calculus* package with the **LagrangeMultiplers** command. It returns the x- and y-coordinates of any extreme points found.

Student:-MultivariateCalculus:-LagrangeMultipliers$(L, [P - 8], [x, y])$

$$\left[\frac{8\,(2\pi + 5)}{9\pi + 20},\ \frac{40}{9\pi + 20}\right] \tag{37.6}$$

Expression palette: evaluation template Evaluate L at the critical point.	$L\big|_{x = (4.6)[1],\, y = (4.6)[2]}$
	$$\frac{160\pi}{(9\pi + 20)^2} + \frac{640\,(2\pi + 5)}{(9\pi + 20)^2} \tag{37.7}$$
Context Menu: Simplify $>$ Simplify	simplify
	$$\frac{160}{9\pi + 20} \tag{37.8}$$

Problem 4 - Taylor Polynomial

Obtain the third-degree Taylor polynomial for e^x, expanding about $x = 0$.

• Enter e^x, selecting the exponential "e" from a palette (Constants and Symbols or Common Symbols). • Context Menu: Series $>$ x In the resulting dialog (below), set Series order to 4 and check to Remove order term.	$e^x \xrightarrow{\text{series in x}} 1 + x + \dfrac{1}{2}x^2 + \dfrac{1}{6}x^3$

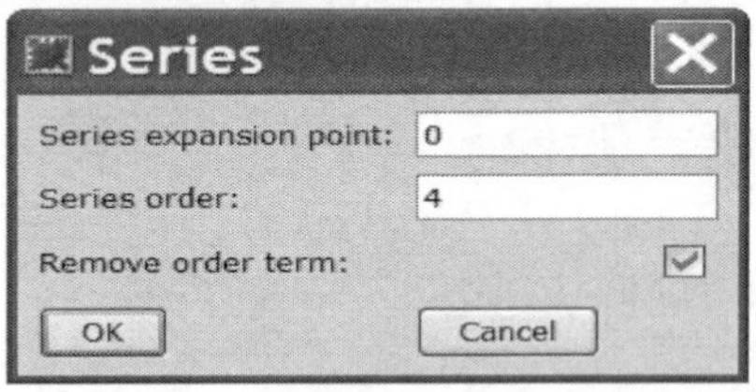

Alternatively, use the Taylor Approximation tutor in the Tools > Tutors > Calculus - Single Variable menu. This interactive tool will provide both the Taylor polynomial and its graph.

Problem 5 - Taylor Series

Obtain the complete series expansion of $\arctan(x)$, expanding about $x = 0$.

• Type the function $\arctan(x)$. • Context Menu: Series > Formal Power Series	$\arctan(x) \xrightarrow{\text{formal series}} \sum_{k=0}^{\infty} \frac{(-1)^k x^{2k+1}}{2k+1}$
• Alternatively, use the command shown to the right.	$convert(\arctan(x), FormalPowerSeries)$

Problem 6 - Numeric Integration

Evaluate (numerically) the definite integral $\displaystyle\int_0^1 \frac{\sin(x^3)}{\sqrt{1 + \cos(x^5)}}\, dx$.

• Expression palette: definite integral template • Context Menu: 2-D Math > Convert To > Inert Form • Context Menu: Approximate > 10	$\displaystyle\int_0^1 \frac{\sin(x^3)}{\sqrt{1 + \cos(x^5)}}\, dx \xrightarrow{\text{at 10 digits}} 0.1713186159$
• Alternatively, use the **Int** command to set the inert form of the integral, then apply the **evalf** command to obtain a numeric evaluation.	$q := Int\left(\dfrac{\sin(x^3)}{\sqrt{1 + \cos(x^5)}}, x = 0..1\right): \;\; = \; 0.1713186159$ $evalf(q) = 0.1713186159$

The integral sign and the "d" in dx are in black in the "active" form of the integral, but gray in the "inert" or unevaluated form.

Problem 7 - Volume of Revolution

Using the method of disks, obtain the volume of the solid of revolution formed when the region bounded by $y = \sin(x)$, $0 \leq x \leq \pi$, and the x-axis is rotated about the x-axis.

The Volume of Revolution tutor (Tools > Tutors > Calculus - Single Variable) will interactively provide information such as seen below. On the left, there is a figure of the solid so generated; on the right, a sketch of the solid segmented into ten disks; in the center, the integral whose value is the volume.

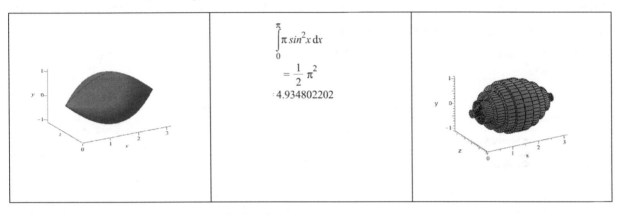

$$\int_0^\pi \pi \sin^2 x \, dx$$

$$= \frac{1}{2} \pi^2$$

$$\doteq 4.934802202$$

37.2 Calculus of Several Variables

Problem 8 - Plane through Three Points

Obtain an equation for the plane containing the points $(1, 2, 3)$, $(5, -1, 7)$, $(3, 8, -2)$.

Let **A**, **B**, **C**, respectively be vectors from the origin to the given points A, B, C. Then $\mathbf{V}_1 = \mathbf{C} - \mathbf{A} = 2\,\mathbf{i} + 6\,\mathbf{j} - 5\,\mathbf{k}$ and $\mathbf{V}_2 = \mathbf{C} - \mathbf{B} = -2\,\mathbf{i} + 9\,\mathbf{j} - 9\,\mathbf{k}$, respectively vectors from C to A, and C to B, are in the plane. A normal to the plane is $\mathbf{N} = \mathbf{V}_1 \times \mathbf{V}_2 = -9\,\mathbf{i} + 28\,\mathbf{j} + 30\,\mathbf{k}$, and the vector equation of the plane is given by $(\mathbf{R} - \mathbf{R}_0) \cdot \mathbf{N} = 0$, where $\mathbf{R} = x\,\mathbf{i} + y\,\mathbf{j} + z\,\mathbf{k}$ and $\mathbf{R}_0$ is any point in the plane.

• Tools > Load Package: Linear Algebra	Loading LinearAlgebra
• Define the vectors A, B, C.	$\mathbf{A}, \mathbf{B}, \mathbf{C} := \langle 1, 2, 3 \rangle, \langle 5, -1, 7 \rangle, \langle 3, 8, -2 \rangle :$
• Define the vectors V_1 and V_2.	$\mathbf{V}_1, \mathbf{V}_2 := \mathbf{C} - \mathbf{A}, \mathbf{C} - \mathbf{B} :$
• Obtain the normal $\mathbf{N} = \mathbf{V}_1 \times \mathbf{V}_2 :$	$\mathbf{N} := \mathbf{V}_1 \times \mathbf{V}_2 :$

• Implement $\left(\mathbf{R}-\mathbf{R}_0\right)\cdot\mathbf{N}=0$, with $\mathbf{R}_0=\mathbf{A}$.	$(\langle x,y,z\rangle-\mathbf{A})\cdot\mathbf{N}=0$ $-9x-137+28y+30z=0$

Problem 9 - Distance from a Point to a Plane

Calculate the distance from $P:(1,2,3)$ to the plane $3x-5y+7z=9$.

A normal to the plane is $\mathbf{N}=3\,\mathbf{i}-5\,\mathbf{j}+7\,\mathbf{k}$. If Q is any point in the plane, and $\mathbf{V}$ is the vector from Q to P, then the distance of P to the plane is the length of the projection of $\mathbf{V}$ onto $\mathbf{N}$, namely, $\mathbf{V}\cdot\mathbf{V}/\|\mathbf{N}\|$, where $\|\mathbf{N}\|$ is he length of $\mathbf{N}$. There is no loss in generality by taking Q as $(3,0,0)$.

• Tools > Load Package: Linear Algebra	Loading LinearAlgebra
• Define $\mathbf{N}$, and the "position" vectors $\mathbf{P}$ and $\mathbf{Q}$.	$\mathbf{P},\mathbf{Q},\mathbf{N}:=\langle 1,2,3\rangle,\langle 3,0,0\rangle,\langle 3,-5,7\rangle$:
• Obtain $\mathbf{V}$ as the vector from P to Q.	$\mathbf{V}:=\mathbf{P}-\mathbf{Q}$:
• Calculate the length of the projection of $\mathbf{V}$ onto $\mathbf{N}$.	$\mathbf{V}\cdot\mathbf{N}/\|\mathbf{N}\|\;=\;\dfrac{5}{7}$

Problem 10 - Lagrange Multiplier Method

Compute the extreme values of $f(x,y)=xy$ subject to the constraint $x^2+4y^2=8$.

Tools > Tasks > Browse: Calculus - Multivariate > Optimization > Lagrange Multiplier Method
The Lagrange Multiplier task template, shown to the right, and whose location in Maple is given above, provides interactive access to the **LagrangeMultipliers** command whose syntax is given below.   The table at the bottom of the template contains four solutions, one in each column. For each such solution, the Lagrange multiplier is denoted by λ_1 , and the value of the objective function at the extreme point, by f . The command below will also produce this solution. 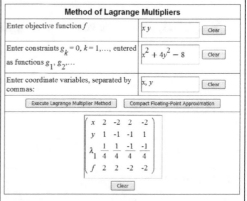
$Student\text{:-}MultivariateCalculus\text{:-}LagrangeMultipliers\left(xy,\left[x^2+4y^2-8\right],[x,y],output=detailed\right)$

The Lagrange multiplier method can also be implemented from first principles:

$$F := xy + \lambda\left(x^2 + 4y^2 - 8\right) :$$

$$solve\left(\left\{\frac{\partial}{\partial x}\,F = 0,\ \frac{\partial}{\partial y}\,F = 0,\ \frac{\partial}{\partial \lambda}\,F = 0\right\},\ \{x, y, \lambda\}\right)$$

$$\left\{x = 2, y = -1, \lambda = \frac{1}{4}\right\}, \left\{x = -2, y = 1, \lambda = \frac{1}{4}\right\}, \left\{x = 2, y = 1, \lambda = -\frac{1}{4}\right\}, \left\{x = -2, y = -1, \lambda = -\frac{1}{4}\right\}$$

Problem 11 - Center of Mass (Discrete)

Determine the center of mass of three objects whose masses are 3, 5, 4, located at the points $(0, 0, 0)$, $(1, 1, 1)$, $(3, 7, 6)$, respectively.

Use the **CenterOfMass** command from the Student *Precalculus* package:

$$Student{:}\text{-}Precalculus{:}\text{-}CenterOfMass([[0, 0, 0], 3], [[1, 1, 1], 5], [[3, 7, 6], 4])$$

$$\left[\frac{17}{12},\ \frac{11}{4},\ \frac{29}{12}\right]$$

Problem 12 - Center of Mass (Continuous)

A solid occupies the region $R = \left\{(x, y, z) : x + y - 1 \le z \le 5 - x^2 - 2y^2, x^2 \le y < -\sqrt{x}, 0 \le x \le 1\right\}$. Find its center of mass if its density is $\rho = z^2$.

Use the CenterOfMass command from the Student MultivariateCalculus package. It can provide the inert integrals that define the center of mass, or the actual coordinates $(\overline{x}, \overline{y}, \overline{z})$ of the center of mass.

$Student{:}\text{-}MultivariateCalculus{:}\text{-}CenterOfMass\left(z^2, z = x + y - 1 .. 5 - x^2 - 2y^2, y = x^2 .. \sqrt{x}, x = 0 .. 1, output = integral\right)$

$$\frac{\displaystyle\int_0^1 \int_{x^2}^{\sqrt{x}} \int_{x+y-1}^{5-x^2-2y^2} xz^2\, dz\, dy\, dx}{\displaystyle\int_0^1 \int_{x^2}^{\sqrt{x}} \int_{x+y-1}^{5-x^2-2y^2} z^2\, dz\, dy\, dx},\ \frac{\displaystyle\int_0^1 \int_{x^2}^{\sqrt{x}} \int_{x+y-1}^{5-x^2-2y^2} yz^2\, dz\, dy\, dx}{\displaystyle\int_0^1 \int_{x^2}^{\sqrt{x}} \int_{x+y-1}^{5-x^2-2y^2} z^2\, dz\, dy\, dx},\ \frac{\displaystyle\int_0^1 \int_{x^2}^{\sqrt{x}} \int_{x+y-1}^{5-x^2-2y^2} z^3\, dz\, dy\, dx}{\displaystyle\int_0^1 \int_{x^2}^{\sqrt{x}} \int_{x+y-1}^{5-x^2-2y^2} z^2\, dz\, dy\, dx}$$

$Student{:}\text{-}MultivariateCalculus{:}\text{-}CenterOfMass\left(z^2, z = x + y - 1 .. 5 - x^2 - 2y^2, y = x^2 .. \sqrt{x}, x = 0 .. 1\right)$

$$\frac{30088816}{82588397},\ \frac{119056003}{330353588},\ \frac{52695901851}{15691795430}$$

Problem 13 - Volume by Multiple Integration

Compute the volume of the first-octant region bounded by the cylinder $x^2 + z^2 = 1$, and the plane $y = x$. (The corresponding solid would be the scrap cut off from a piece of quarter-round molding when its "left end" is mitered. Think of the fence on the saw as the y-axis, and the traverse direction as the x-axis.)

- An unevaluated integral is formed with the **Int** command; an integral written with the **int** command evaluates immediately. Originally, Maple required iteration of the command, but now, giving a list of ranges in either the **Int** or **int** commands will generate iterated integrals. The order of the ranges in the list is the order of the *differentials*, that is, the order in which the integrals are evaluated. (Recall that this order is the reverse of the order in which the integral signs are written.)

$$Int\left(1, \left[z = 0 .. \sqrt{1 - x^2}, y = 0 .. x, x = 0 .. 1\right]\right) = \int_0^1 \int_0^x \int_0^{\sqrt{1 - x^2}} 1 \, dz \, dy \, dx = \frac{1}{3}$$

• Use the **Int** command and a list of ranges.	$int\left(1, \left[z = 0 .. \sqrt{1 - x^2}, y = 0 .. x, x = 0 .. 1\right]\right) = \dfrac{1}{3}$
• Iterate the **int** command.	$int\left(int\left(int\left(1, z = 0 .. \sqrt{1 - x^2}\right), y = 0 .. x\right), x = 0 .. 1\right) = \dfrac{1}{3}$
• Expression palette: definite integral template Iterate the templates See note below.	$\int_0^1 \int_0^x \int_0^{\sqrt{1 - x^2}} 1 \, dz \, dy \, dx = \dfrac{1}{3}$

- After the first (leftmost or "outer") integral template is inserted, fill in the fields for the limits, using the Tab key to move from field to field. When the integrand field is selected, again click on the definite integral template in the Expression palette. A new integral template is inserted, but the auto-selected field is the integrand. Use Shift+Tab to move through the fields in the reverse order. It takes two such actions to select the lower-limit field of this second template. If a third integral is needed, repeat the procedure.

We also recommend the task template

  Tools > Tasks > Browse: Calculus - Multivariate > Integration > Visualizing Regions of Integration > Cartesian 3-D

which provides for an iterated triple integral in any of the six possible orders, computes the value of the integral, and draws the region over which the integration takes place. There are similar templates for double integration in Cartesian and polar coordinates, and triple integration in spherical, and cylindrical coordinates.

37.3 Vector Calculus

Problem 14 - Frenet-Serret Formalism

Obtain **T, N, B**, the unit tangent, principal normal, and binormal vectors along the helix $x = \cos(t)$, $y = \sin(t)$, $z = t/3$. In addition, obtain the curvature and torsion of the curve.

The Space Curves tutor (Tools > Tutors > Vector Calculus) or the **TNBFrame** command can be used to obtain the graph and vectors displayed below. The curvature and torsion can also be obtained with the tutor, as well as with the specialized **Curvature** and **Torsion** commands. All the Frenet objects are also available in the Context Menu, once the *VectorCalculus* package has been loaded.

$VectorCalculus{:}\text{-}TNBFrame(\,\langle\cos(t),\sin(t),t/3\rangle,\hat{t}\,)$

$$\begin{bmatrix} -\dfrac{3}{10}\sqrt{10}\,\sin(t) \\[2mm] \dfrac{3}{10}\sqrt{10}\,\cos(t) \\[2mm] \dfrac{1}{10}\sqrt{10} \end{bmatrix}, \begin{bmatrix} -\cos(t) \\ -\sin(t) \\ 0 \end{bmatrix}, \begin{bmatrix} \dfrac{1}{10}\sqrt{10}\,\sin(t) \\[2mm] -\dfrac{1}{10}\sqrt{10}\,\cos(t) \\[2mm] \dfrac{3}{10}\sqrt{10} \end{bmatrix}$$

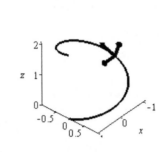

$simplify(VectorCalculus{:}\text{-}Curvature(\,\langle\cos(t),\sin(t),t/3\rangle,t\,)) = \dfrac{9}{10}$

$simplify(VectorCalculus{:}\text{-}Torsion(\,\langle\cos(t),\sin(t),t/3\rangle,t\,)) = \dfrac{3}{10}$

Problem 15 - Line Integration

Obtain the line integral of the tangential component of the vector field $\mathbf{F}=xy\mathbf{i}+(x-y)\mathbf{j}$ along the polygonal path connecting the points $(1,3),(2,5),(4,-1)$.

• Tools > Load Package: Vector Calculus	Loading VectorCalculus
• Define the vector field **F**.	$\mathbf{F} := VectorField(\langle xy, x-y\rangle, cartesian[x,y])$:
• Form a sequence of nodes along the path.	$L := \langle 1,3\rangle, \langle 2,5\rangle, \langle 4,-1\rangle$:

• Apply the **LineInt** command. With the optional parameter "inert" the unevaluated integral is written. From this, one can deduce the parametrization used along each of the line segments in the path. To evaluate the inert form of the line integral, use the "Evaluate (from inert)" option in the Context Menu.

$LineInt(\mathbf{F}, LineSegments(L), inert)$

$$\int_0^1 ((1+t)(3+2t)-4-2t)\,dt + \int_0^1 (2(2+2t)(5-6t)+18-48t)\,dt$$

• Obtain the value of the line integral.	$LineInt(\mathbf{F}, LineSegments(L)) = \dfrac{31}{6}$

Problem 16 - Surface Flux

Obtain the flux of the vector field $\mathbf{F}=yz\mathbf{i}+xz\mathbf{j}+xy^2\mathbf{k}$ through that part of the surface $z=1-2x^2-3y^2$

inside the cylinder whose cross-section in the xy-plane is the triangle with vertices $(1,2),(5,7),(4,5)$.

• Tools > Load Package: Vector Calculus	Loading VectorCalculus
• Define the vector field **F**.	$\mathbf{F} := VectorField(\langle yz, xz, xy^2 \rangle, cartesian[x, y, z])$:
• Form a list of the vertices of the triangle.	$T := \langle 1, 2 \rangle, \langle 5, 7 \rangle, \langle 4, 5 \rangle$:
• Define the surface as a "position" vector.	$S := \langle x, y, 1 - 2x^2 - 3y^2 \rangle$:

• Apply the **Flux** command, including the optional parameter "inert" so the unevaluated surface integral is displayed. (There are two double integrals because the domain is a scalene triangle.) Note the parametrization of the edges of the triangle. To evaluate the inert form of the line integral, use the "Evaluate (from inert)" option in the Context Menu.

$Flux(\mathbf{F}, Surface(S, [x, y] = Triangle(T)), inert)$
$$\int_1^4 \int_{1+x}^{\frac{3}{4} + \frac{5}{4}x} \left(10y\left(1 - 2x^2 - 3y^2\right)x + xy^2\right) dy\, dx + \int_4^5 \int_{-3+2x}^{\frac{3}{4} + \frac{5}{4}x} \left(10y\left(1 - 2x^2 - 3y^2\right)x + xy^2\right) dy\, dx$$

• Obtain the value of the flux.	$Flux(\mathbf{F}, Surface(S, [x, y] = Triangle(T))) = -\dfrac{132592}{5}$

See also the task template
Tools > Tasks > Browse: Vector Calculus > Integration > Flux > 3-D > Through a Surface Defined over a Triangle
that provides for the evaluation of flux through a surface defined over a triangular domain.

Problem 17 - Understanding Divergence

Show that the divergence of the vector field $\mathbf{F} = ax\mathbf{i} + by\mathbf{j} + cz\mathbf{k}$ is the limiting ratio of the surface flux to the enclosed volume. (For the surface, use the sphere with center (u, v, w) and radius ρ .)

• Tools > Load Package: Vector Calculus	Loading VectorCalculus
• Define the vector field **F**.	$\mathbf{F} := VectorField(\langle ax, by, cz \rangle, cartesian[x, y, z])$:

• Use the **Flux** command to compute the flux of **F** through the sphere, and assign this flux to the name f via Context Menu: Assign to a Name.

$Flux(\mathbf{F}, Sphere(\langle u, v, w \rangle, \rho)) = \dfrac{4}{3}\rho^3 b\pi + \dfrac{4}{3}\rho^3 a\pi + \dfrac{4}{3}\rho^3 c\pi \xrightarrow{\text{assign to a name}} f$

• Divide the flux by the enclosed volume. • Context Menu: Simplify > Simplify	$\dfrac{f}{\frac{4}{3}\pi\rho^3} \xrightarrow{\text{simplify}} b + a + c$
• Using templates from the Common Symbols palette, compute the divergence of **F**.	$\nabla \cdot \mathbf{F} = b + a + c$
• Alternatively, use the **Divergence** command.	$Divergence(\mathbf{F}) = b + a + c$

Problem 18 - Evolute of a Plane Curve

The *evolute* of a plane curve C (called the *involute*) is defined as the locus of the centers of curvature of C. If C is described in radius-vector form by $\mathbf{R}(p)$, then the evolute is given in vector form by $\mathbf{R} + r\mathbf{N}$, where, along C, $\mathbf{N}$ is the (unit) principal normal and r is the radius of curvature.

Find and graph the evolute of the ellipse defined parametrically by $x(p) = 2\cos(p), y(p) = \sin(p)$.

• Tools > Load Package: Vector Calculus	Loading VectorCalculus
• Implement the position-vector form of C.	$\mathbf{R} := PositionVector([2\cos(p), \sin(p)])$:
• Obtain r, the radius of curvature of $\mathbf{R}$.	$r := simplify(RadiusOfCurvature(R, p))$ assuming *real* $$\frac{1}{2}\left(-3\cos(p)^2 + 4\right)^{3/2}$$
• Obtain the (unit) principal normal $\mathbf{N}$.	$\mathbf{N} := simplify(Normalize(PrincipalNormal(\mathbf{R}, p)))$ assuming *real* $$\begin{bmatrix} -\dfrac{\cos(p)}{\sqrt{-3\cos(p)^2 + 4}} \\[2ex] -\dfrac{2\sin(p)}{\sqrt{-3\cos(p)^2 + 4}} \end{bmatrix}$$
• Implement the position-vector form of the evolute $V = \mathbf{R} + r\mathbf{N}$.	$\mathbf{V} := simplify(PositionVector(convert(\mathbf{R} + r\mathbf{N}, list)))$ $$\begin{bmatrix} \dfrac{3}{2}\cos(p)^3 \\[2ex] -3\sin(p)^3 \end{bmatrix}$$

- To obtain the graph on the right:

$g_1 := PlotPositionVector(R, p = 0..2\pi) :$
$g_2 := PlotPositionVector(V, p = 0..2\pi) :$
$plots[display](g_1, g_2, scaling = constrained)$

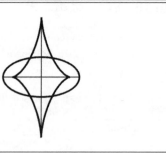

37.4 Differential Equations

Problem 19 - Direction Field

Obtain a direction field for $y' = x^2 - 2y - y^2$, and include solutions through the points along the y-axis.

The **DEplot** command in the *DEtools* package will draw both the arrows of a direction field, and solution curves through specified initial points. In the implementation below, colors have been set to black. The derivative in the differential equation can be denoted with an apostrophe, or with the prime symbol from the Punctuation palette.

$inits := [[0, .2], [0, .4], [0, .6], [0, .8], [0, 1]] :$
$DEtools[DEplot](y' = x^2 - 2y - y^2, y(x), x = 0..1, y = 0..1, inits, linecolor = black, color = black)$

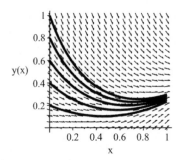

Problem 20 - Derivation of Newton's Law of Heating/Cooling

Formulate and solve the differential equation that models Newton's law of heating/cooling.

Newton's law of heat transfer postulates that the rate of change of temperature of a body is directly proportional to the temperature gradient (temperature difference) between the body and its surroundings. Of course, the assumption is that the temperature of the surroundings, thought of as a heat sink, does not change during the heat transfer process. Thus, the differential equation for the temperature $u(t)$ is $u'(t) = k\left(U_s - u(t)\right)$, where U_s is the (constant) temperature of the surroundings.

• Enter the differential equation.	$q := u'(t) = k\left(U_s - u(t)\right)$:
• Use the **dsolve** command to obtain the general solution. Maple uses _C1_ for the arbitrary constant of integration the solution process introduces.	$dsolve(q, u(t))$ $u(t) = U_s + e^{-kt}\_C1$
Solve the initial value problem in which the initial temperature $u(0)$ is given as U_0.	$dsolve\left(\{q, u(0) = U_0\}, u(t)\right)$ $u(t) = U_s + e^{-kt}\left(U_0 - U_s\right)$

It is convenient to think of the general solution as $u(t) = U_s + A\,e^{-kt}$, and to use this even when initial data is known.

The Context Menu for a differential equation will have two relevant options, namely, "Solve DE" and "Solve DE Interactively." The first option will return the general solution; the second, will launch the ODE Analyzer Assistant in which the equation or the related initial value problem can be solved (and graphed) interactively.

Problem 21 - Application of Newton's Law of Heating/Cooling

A medical examiner arrives at the scene of a homicide where the room temperature is 68F (20C) and finds the temperature of the deceased is 90F (32. $\overline{2}$ C). Twenty minutes later, the body has a temperature of 88F (31. $\overline{1}$ C). When was the murder committed?

• Write the equation $u(t) = ...$ Context Menu: Assign Function	$u(t) = 68 + A\,e^{-kt} \xrightarrow{\text{assign as function}} u$
• Write the three equations shown to the right. Context Menu: Solve > Solve	$u(x) = 98.6, u(0) = 90, u(20) = 88 \xrightarrow{\text{solve}}$ $\{A = 22., k = 0.004765508990, x = -69.23868075\}$

Note the use of the Fahrenheit scale in our calculations, and the use of 98.6F as the "normal" body temperature of a human. By taking the $t = 0$ as the time the ME arrived on the scene, we can take the time of death as the unknown x. Since the last temperature is taken 20 minutes after arrival, the solution for x is in minutes. The minus sign means that the death occurred 69.24 minutes *earlier*.

Conversions between temperatures in different scales are easily made with the Units Calculator Assistant, available from the Tools menu.

Problem 22 - Logistic Growth

A species undergoes logistic growth, governed by the formula $y(t) = \dfrac{y_0 c}{y_0 + (c - y_0) e^{-at}}$

> Observation yields the data points $(t, y(t)) = (1, 1300), (3, 1870), (4, 2070)$. Determine the carrying capacity c, the initial population y_0, and the rate constant a, if it is known that $a > 0$.

The logistic "formula" is a solution of the differential equation

$\dfrac{y'}{y} = \dfrac{a}{c}(c - y)$, which "says" that the rate of change of a population per unit of population is proportional to the difference between the limiting population c and the actual population y. The constant a is the intrinsic growth rate, and the limiting population c is the carrying capacity. Applications involving this model amount to data fitting, that is, to solving three equations in the three unknowns y_0, a, c.

• Type the equation $P(t) = \ldots$ Context Menu: Assign Function	$P(t) = \dfrac{y_0 c}{y_0 + (c - y_0) e^{-at}} \xrightarrow{\text{assign as function}} P$

- Write the three equations that express the observed data. Press the Enter key.
- Context Menu: Solve > Numerically Solve from point > $a = 0.1, c = 500, y_0 = 500$

$P(1) = 1300, P(3) = 1870, P(4) = 2070$

$$\frac{y_0 c}{y_0 + (c - y_0) e^{-a}} = 1300, \quad \frac{y_0 c}{y_0 + (c - y_0) e^{-3a}} = 1870, \quad \frac{y_0 c}{y_0 + (c - y_0) e^{-4a}} = 2070$$

$\xrightarrow{\text{solve}}$

$$\{a = 0.5236436096, c = 2450.909203, y_0 = 982.5017593\}$$

When writing the logistic function, be sure to use Maple's exponential "e" by selecting it from either the Constants and Symbols palette or the Common Symbols palette. The numerical solver is a form of Newton's method, so initial values have to be supplied for the iteration. Assuming that the growth rate is a small number, and that the carrying capacity and initial populations have to be in the hundreds, the choices used above are not mysterious.

Problem 23 - The Driven Damped Oscillator

> If a unit mass is attached to a spring that hangs vertically from a fixed support, and is constrained to move only vertically, its motion can be described by the differential equation $y'' + by' + ky = f(t)$, where $y(t)$ measures displacement (positive upward) from an equilibrium position, $f(t)$ is a "driving force," k is a measure of the stiffness of the spring, and b is a damping coefficient for damping assumed to be proportional to the velocity of the motion of the mass. If $b = 4$, $k = 13$, and $f(t) = 3\sin(t)$, and the mass is initially raised one unit and released, solve for the motion as a function of time.

Write the initial value problem and launch the ODE Analyzer Assistant from the Context Menu.

$$y''(t) + 4y'(t) + 13y(t) = 3\sin(t), y(0) = 1, y'(0) = 0 \xrightarrow{\text{solve DE interactively}}$$

The option "Solve DE Interactively" launches the Assistant, as per the following figure.

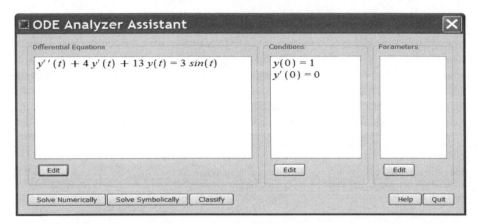

Clicking the "Solve Symbolically" button opens the dialog shown below. The "Solve" and "Plot" buttons have been clicked, the "Show Maple commands" checkbox has been selected, and the "Plot Options" dialog has been used to extend the *t*-axis from the default 10 to 15, better to show that after the initial descent, the motion of the mass is controlled in "steady-state" by the sinusoidal driving term.

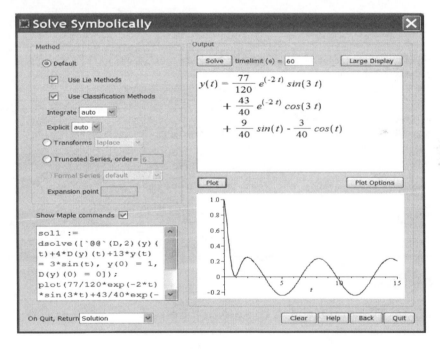

Problem 24 - Numeric Solutions

Obtain a numeric solution of the initial value problem $x^2 y'' + \cos(x) y' - y = 2, y(1) = 1, y'(1) = -1$.

The solution could be obtained as in Problem 23 by launching the ODE Analyzer Assistant and selecting the numeric option instead of the symbolic. However, the following solution will demonstrate additional tools available in Maple for the numeric solution of differential equations.

$Q := dsolve\left(\{x^2 y'' + \cos(x) y' - y = 2, y(1) = 1, y'(1) = -1\}, y(x), numeric\right)$:

• Maple's **dsolve** command defaults to a symbolic solution except when the option *numeric* is included. This form of the command produces a procedure Q that when invoked, generates the numeric data. The **odeplot** command is designed to take the output from this procedure and draw a graph of the solution.	$plots[odeplot](Q, x = 1..3, color = black)$

$T := dsolve\left(\{x^2 y'' + \cos(x) y' - y = 2, y(1) = 1, y'(1) = -1\}, y(x), numeric, output = listprocedure\right)$

$$\left[x = \mathbf{proc}(x) \; ... \; \mathbf{end\ proc}, y(x) = \mathbf{proc}(x) \; ... \; \mathbf{end\ proc}, \frac{d}{dx} y(x) = \mathbf{proc}(x) \; ... \; \mathbf{end\ proc} \right]$$

• From the list of procedures, select the right-hand side of the second one. The procedure assigned to Y then numerically generates values of the solution $y(x)$.	$Y := rhs(T[2])$:
• The function Y and any expression containing it can be graphed. When graphing functions (instead of expressions), give the function *name*, and the range without indicating the independent variable.	$plot([Y, Y^2], 1..3, color = black)$

37.5 Linear Algebra

Problem 25 - Linear Equations with a Unique Solution

Solve the equations $x + y + z = 1, 2x - 3y + 5z = 7, 3x + 5y - 9z = 11$.

$Eq := [x + y + z = 1, 2x - 3y + 5z = 7, 3x + 5y - 9z = 11]:$	
• Apply the **solve** command. When Maple can deduce the unknowns, it is not necessary to state them explicitly. • Alternatively, Context Menu: Solve > Solve	$solve(Eq)$ $$\left\{ x = \frac{94}{27}, y = -\frac{14}{9}, z = -\frac{25}{27} \right\}$$

Matrix Formulation

• Tools > Load Package: Linear Algebra	Loading LinearAlgebra
• Apply the **GenerateMatrix** command to produce the augmented matrix for the system. This functionality is also available through the Context Menu option Generate Matrix > Augmented.	$M := GenerateMatrix(Eq, [x, y, z], augmented)$ $$\begin{bmatrix} 1 & 1 & 1 & 1 \\ 2 & -3 & 5 & 7 \\ 3 & 5 & -9 & 11 \end{bmatrix}$$ $\xrightarrow{\text{reduced row echelon form}}$
• Context Menu: Solvers and Forms > Row Echelon Form > Reduced • The **ReducedRowEchelonForm** command applied directly to M would yield the same result.	$$\begin{bmatrix} 1 & 0 & 0 & \frac{94}{27} \\ 0 & 1 & 0 & -\frac{14}{9} \\ 0 & 0 & 1 & -\frac{25}{27} \end{bmatrix}$$
• Alternatively, apply the **LinearSolve** command, which returns the solution as a column vector.	$LinearSolve(M)$ $$\begin{bmatrix} \frac{94}{27} \\ -\frac{14}{9} \\ -\frac{25}{27} \end{bmatrix}$$

Problem 26 - Linear Equations with Multiple Solutions

Solve the equations $x + 2y + 3z = 5, 5x - 29y + 15z = 13, 3x - 7y + 9z = 11$.

$Eq := [x + 2y + 3z = 5, 5x - 29y + 15z = 13, 3x - 7y + 9z = 11]:$	
• The **solve** command or Context Menu: Solve gives the solution with z as a free variable, so that $x = x(z), y = y(z), z = z$.	$solve(Eq)$ $$\left\{ x = \frac{57}{13} - 3z, y = \frac{4}{13}, z = z \right\}$$

Matrix Formulation

• Tools > Load Package: Linear Algebra	Loading LinearAlgebra
• To formulate the equations as $A\mathbf{x} = \mathbf{b}$, apply the **GenerateMatrix** command, or use Context Menu option Generate Matrix > Matrix-Vector pair.	$A, b := GenerateMatrix(Eq, [x, y, z])$ $$\begin{bmatrix} 1 & 2 & 3 \\ 5 & -29 & 15 \\ 3 & -7 & 9 \end{bmatrix}, \begin{bmatrix} 5 \\ 13 \\ 11 \end{bmatrix}$$
• Apply the **LinearSolve** command, indicating that the free variable should have base-name s. The solution could be written in the form $$\begin{bmatrix} 57/13 \\ 4/13 \\ 0 \end{bmatrix} + s_3 \begin{bmatrix} -3 \\ 0 \\ 1 \end{bmatrix}$$	$LinearSolve(A, b, free = s)$ $$\begin{bmatrix} \dfrac{57}{13} - 3s_3 \\ \dfrac{4}{13} \\ s_3 \end{bmatrix}$$
• Any multiple of the vector $-3\mathbf{i} + \mathbf{k}$ is in the null space of A, that is, A maps such vectors to the zero vector.	$A.\langle -3, 0, 1 \rangle = \begin{bmatrix} 0 \\ 0 \\ 0 \end{bmatrix}$
• The **NullSpace** command produces a basis for this subspace of $\mathbb{R}^3$.	$NullSpace(A) = \left\{ \begin{bmatrix} -3 \\ 0 \\ 1 \end{bmatrix} \right\}$
• The equations are consistent, but not independent. That's why there are multiple solutions. The reduced row echelon form for such a system will contain at least one row of all zeros.	$ReducedRowEchelonForm(\langle A|b \rangle) = \begin{bmatrix} 1 & 0 & 3 & \dfrac{57}{13} \\ 0 & 1 & 0 & \dfrac{4}{13} \\ 0 & 0 & 0 & 0 \end{bmatrix}$
• The rows of A are not independent, so its determinant (also in the Context Menu) is zero.	$Determinant(A) = 0$

Problem 27 - Linear Equations with No Solution

If A and $\mathbf{b}$ are as defined to the right, show that the equations $A\mathbf{x} = \mathbf{b}$ are inconsistent, and hence have no solution. Find a least-squares solution, then find the least-squares solution of minimal length.	$A = \begin{bmatrix} -6 & -11 & 2 & 0 \\ -3 & 5 & 1 & 7 \\ 6 & 5 & -2 & -4 \\ 0 & 3 & 0 & 2 \\ 3 & -8 & -1 & -9 \end{bmatrix}, \mathbf{b} = \begin{bmatrix} 1 \\ 2 \\ -1 \\ 1 \\ 1 \end{bmatrix}$

• Tools > Load Package: Linear Algebra	Loading LinearAlgebra

$A := Matrix([[-6, -11, 2, 0], [-3, 5, 1, 7], [6, 5, -2, -4], [0, 3, 0, 2], [3, -8, -1, -9]])$:
$\mathbf{b} := \langle 1, 2, -1, 1, 1 \rangle : M := \langle A|\mathbf{b} \rangle$:

• Obtain the reduced row echelon form of the augmented matrix M. The zero in the last column of the third row corresponds to an equation of the form $0 = 1$, indicating that the system is inconsistent. Hence, there is no solution.	$ReducedRowEchelonForm(M)$ $$\begin{bmatrix} 1 & 0 & -\dfrac{1}{3} & -\dfrac{11}{9} & 0 \\ 0 & 1 & 0 & \dfrac{2}{3} & 0 \\ 0 & 0 & 0 & 0 & 1 \\ 0 & 0 & 0 & 0 & 0 \\ 0 & 0 & 0 & 0 & 0 \end{bmatrix}$$

A least-squares solution is one that minimizes the norm of the vector $A\mathbf{x} - \mathbf{b}$. (If this minimum is zero, then $\mathbf{x}$ is an exact solution, but no such exact solution exists.) Equivalently, write and minimize by the techniques of calculus, $F(x, y, z, w) = \|A\mathbf{x} - \mathbf{b}\|^2$, the square of the norm. (The Euclidean norm, the square root of the sum of the squares of the components, is called the 2-norm because it uses 2s. In the calculation below, the subscript "2" on the norm braces forces Maple to compute the *Euclidean* norm.)

$F := simplify\left(\|A.\langle x, y, z, w \rangle - \mathbf{b}\|_2^2 \right)$ assuming *real*

$8 - 22w + 30x + 22y - 10z + 90x^2 + 114xy - 60xz + 244y^2 - 38yz + 10z^2 - 144xw + 186yw + 48zw + 150w^2$

• Set the partial derivatives equal to zero and solve. The resulting vector is on the right, below.

$S := solve\left(\left\{ \dfrac{\mathrm{d}}{\mathrm{d}x} F = 0, \dfrac{\mathrm{d}}{\mathrm{d}y} F = 0, \dfrac{\mathrm{d}}{\mathrm{d}z} F = 0, \dfrac{\mathrm{d}}{\mathrm{d}w} F = 0 \right\} \right)$

$\left\{ w = -\dfrac{5}{462} - \dfrac{3}{2} y, x = x, y = y, z = \dfrac{81}{154} + 3x + \dfrac{11}{2} y \right\}$

$eval(\langle x, y, z, w \rangle, S)$

$$\begin{bmatrix} x \\ y \\ \dfrac{81}{154} + 3x + \dfrac{11}{2} y \\ -\dfrac{5}{462} - \dfrac{3}{2} y \end{bmatrix}$$

• This solution is immediately obtained with the **LeastSquares** command. Because the reduced row echelon form of the augmented matrix contained two rows of zeros, there are two free parameters in the solution. These are designated by c_1 and c_2. The solution decomposes into $\mathbf{X} = \mathbf{v}_0 + c_1\,\mathbf{v}_1 + c_2\,\mathbf{v}_2$, where the vectors $\mathbf{v}_0, \mathbf{v}_1, \mathbf{v}_2$ are defined below.	$\mathbf{X} := LeastSquares(A, \mathbf{b}, free = c)$ $$\begin{bmatrix} c_1 \\ c_2 \\ 3\,c_1 + \dfrac{11}{2}\,c_2 + \dfrac{81}{154} \\ -\dfrac{3}{2}\,c_2 - \dfrac{5}{462} \end{bmatrix}$$
$\mathbf{v}_0 := eval\big(\mathbf{X}, [\,c_1 = 0, c_2 = 0\,]\big)$: $\mathbf{v}_1 := eval\big(\mathbf{X}, [\,c_1 = 1, c_2 = 0\,]\big) - \mathbf{v}_0$: $\mathbf{v}_2 := eval\big(\mathbf{X}, [\,c_1 = 0, c_2 = 1\,]\big) - \mathbf{v}_0$:	$\mathbf{v}_0, \mathbf{v}_1, \mathbf{v}_2$ $$\begin{bmatrix} 0 \\ 0 \\ \dfrac{81}{154} \\ -\dfrac{5}{462} \end{bmatrix}, \begin{bmatrix} 1 \\ 0 \\ 3 \\ 0 \end{bmatrix}, \begin{bmatrix} 0 \\ 1 \\ \dfrac{11}{2} \\ -\dfrac{3}{2} \end{bmatrix}$$

The vectors $\mathbf{v}_1$ and $\mathbf{v}_2$ span the null space of A, and $\mathbf{v}_0$ contains components along these vectors.

• The null space of A is the set of all vectors $\mathbf{x}$ for which $A\mathbf{x} = \mathbf{0}$. Since $\mathbf{v}_1$ and $\mathbf{v}_2$ are null vectors by the calculations to the right, and the dimension of the null space is known to be 2, these two vectors span the null space.	$A\,\mathbf{v}_1, A\,\mathbf{v}_2$ $$\begin{bmatrix} 0 \\ 0 \\ 0 \\ 0 \\ 0 \end{bmatrix}, \begin{bmatrix} 0 \\ 0 \\ 0 \\ 0 \\ 0 \end{bmatrix}$$
• Since $\mathbf{u} \cdot \mathbf{v} = \|\mathbf{u}\|\,\|\mathbf{v}\|\cos(\theta)$, $\mathbf{u}$ has a component along $\mathbf{v}$ whenever the dot product is nonzero.	$\mathbf{v}_0 \cdot \mathbf{v}_1 = \dfrac{243}{154}$ $\quad \mathbf{v}_0 \cdot \mathbf{v}_1 = \dfrac{243}{154} = \dfrac{32}{11}$ $\mathbf{v}_0 \cdot \mathbf{v}_2 = \dfrac{32}{11}$

• To remove from $\mathbf{v}_0$ its null-space component, we first find this component by projecting $\mathbf{v}_0$ onto the null space, then subtracting this component from $\mathbf{v}_0$.	$C := \langle \mathbf{v}_1 \| \mathbf{v}_2 \rangle :$ $P := C \cdot \left(C^{\%T} \cdot C \right)^{-1} \cdot C^{\%T} :$ $\mathbf{v}_0 - P \cdot \mathbf{v}_0$
• A matrix that projects a vector onto the space spanned by other vectors is $P = C \left(C^T C \right)^{-1} C^T$, where C is a matrix whose columns are the spanning vectors, C^T is the transpose of C, and $\left(C^T C \right)^{-1}$ is the matrix inverse of $C^T C$. (In Maple, %T denotes transpose; and the period, noncommutative multiplication.) • The vector $\mathbf{v}_0 - P\mathbf{v}_0$ is the vector $\mathbf{v}_0$ with its null-space component removed.	$\begin{bmatrix} -\dfrac{1497}{19327} \\ -\dfrac{941}{19327} \\ \dfrac{499}{19327} \\ \dfrac{3607}{57981} \end{bmatrix}$

The vector $\mathbf{v}_0 - P\mathbf{v}_0$ is the least-squares solution of minimal length. To see this, minimize the norm of the least-squares solution $\mathbf{X}$. As earlier, it is equivalent to minimize the square of the norm.

• Let f be the square of the length of the least-squares solution $\mathbf{X}$.	$f := simplify\left(\|\mathbf{X}\|_2^2 \right)$ assuming $real$ $10\, c_1^2 + \dfrac{67}{2}\, c_2^2 + 33\, c_1\, c_2 + \dfrac{243}{77}\, c_1 + \dfrac{64}{11}\, c_2 + \dfrac{29537}{106722}$
• Minimize f by the techniques of calculus - set the derivatives equal to zero and solve for the parameters.	$Sol := solve\left(\left\{ \dfrac{d}{d c_1} f = 0, \dfrac{d}{d c_2} f = 0 \right\} \right)$ $\left\{ c_1 = -\dfrac{1497}{19327}, c_2 = -\dfrac{941}{19327} \right\}$
• Evaluate the least-squares solution $\mathbf{X}$ for the parameters found in the minimization step. This vector is the same as $\mathbf{v}_0$ with its null-space component removed, as a visual inspection will show.	$eval(\mathbf{X}, Sol)$ $\begin{bmatrix} -\dfrac{1497}{19327} \\ -\dfrac{941}{19327} \\ \dfrac{499}{19327} \\ \dfrac{3607}{57981} \end{bmatrix}$

The matrix A is not square, so does not have an inverse in the ordinary sense of a matrix inverse. However, it is possible to define a pseudo-inverse A^+ such that $A^+ \mathbf{b}$ is the minimal-length least-squares solution, typically called $\mathbf{X}^+$. The pseudoinverse can be obtained by the **MatrixInverse** command, or by invoking the Context Menu.

$A^+ := MatrixInverse(A, method = pseudo):$
$A^+, A^+ .\mathbf{b}$

$$
\begin{bmatrix}
-\dfrac{579}{19327} & -\dfrac{321}{19327} & \dfrac{597}{19327} & -\dfrac{9}{19327} & \dfrac{30}{1757} \\[2mm]
\dfrac{790}{19327} & \dfrac{263}{19327} & \dfrac{414}{19327} & \dfrac{188}{19327} & \dfrac{41}{1757} \\[2mm]
\dfrac{193}{19327} & \dfrac{107}{19327} & -\dfrac{199}{19327} & \dfrac{3}{19327} & -\dfrac{10}{1757} \\[2mm]
\dfrac{181}{19327} & \dfrac{1703}{57981} & -\dfrac{1361}{57981} & \dfrac{409}{57981} & \dfrac{64}{1757}
\end{bmatrix}
\begin{bmatrix}
-\dfrac{1497}{19327} \\[2mm]
-\dfrac{941}{19327} \\[2mm]
\dfrac{499}{19327} \\[2mm]
\dfrac{3607}{57981}
\end{bmatrix}
$$

Problem 28 - Eigenpairs

Obtain the eigenpairs for the matrices $A = \begin{bmatrix} -6 & -36 \\ 2 & 11 \end{bmatrix}$ and $B = \begin{bmatrix} -1 & -3 & 5 \\ 8 & -4 & -8 \\ 9 & -6 & 4 \end{bmatrix}$.

Tools > Load Package: Linear Algebra	Loading LinearAlgebra
• Context Menu: Eigenvalues, etc > Eigenvectors The eigenvalues are the numbers in the vector; the columns of the returned matrix are the corresponding eigenvectors.	$\begin{bmatrix} -6 & -36 \\ 2 & 11 \end{bmatrix} \xrightarrow{\text{eigenvectors}} \begin{bmatrix} 3 \\ 2 \end{bmatrix}, \begin{bmatrix} -4 & -\dfrac{9}{2} \\ 1 & 1 \end{bmatrix}$
• Context Menu: Eigenvalues, etc > Characteristic Polynomial	$\begin{bmatrix} -6 & -36 \\ 2 & 11 \end{bmatrix} \xrightarrow{\text{characteristic polynomial}} 6 + \lambda^2 - 5\lambda$
• Obtain the characteristic polynomial from first principles. The zeros of this polynomial are the eigenvalues.	$Determinant\left(\begin{bmatrix} -6 & -36 \\ 2 & 11 \end{bmatrix} - \lambda \begin{bmatrix} 1 & 0 \\ 0 & 1 \end{bmatrix}\right) = 6 + \lambda^2 - 5\lambda$

Calculating exact eigenvalues requires solving the characteristic equation, the roots of which can often be exceedingly cumbersome expressions, even for a cubic equation. Hence, it is advisable to compute the eigenpairs for B numerically.

• If at least one entry of the matrix is a floating-point (decimal) number, the calculation of the eigenpairs is done numerically.	$B_f := \begin{bmatrix} -1. & -3 & 5 \\ 8 & -4 & -8 \\ 9 & -6 & 4 \end{bmatrix} : v, V := Eigenvectors(B_f):$ $simplify(v);$ $simplify(V)$
• The return of the **Eigenvectors** command consists of a vector of eigenvalues, and a matrix whose columns are the corresponding eigenvectors. The software used for these numeric calculations returns all the floats as complex numbers. If the float is real, it will have 0.I added to it. The **simplify** command converts these to real numbers.	$\begin{bmatrix} -6.632158983 \\ -4.638914131 \\ 10.27107311 \end{bmatrix}$

$$\begin{bmatrix} -0.1151570861 & -0.2708121542 & 0.4456677231 \\ -0.9036592170 & -0.8995817031 & -0.2344757306 \\ -0.4124789268 & -0.3426565869 & 0.8639452600 \end{bmatrix}$$

The Eigenvector Plot tutor (Tools > Tutors > Linear Algebra) will draw unit vectors **u**, and the vectors A**u** for a given matrix A. Vectors **u** for which **u** and A**u** are collinear are eigenvectors. The Eigenvalues and Eigenvectors tutors step through the calculation of eigenpairs. The most convenient way to access these tutors is through the Context Menu for the matrix A, provided the Student *LinearAlgebra* package has first been loaded.

37.6 Statics

Problem 29

As per the figure to the right, a sphere of mass 50 kg is supported at the origin by three cables fastened to the points A, B, and C. Find the tension in each cable.

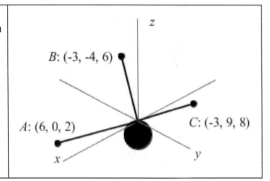

Mathematical Solution

If $\mathbf{u}_a$, $\mathbf{u}_b$, and $\mathbf{u}_c$ are respectively unit vectors from the origin to the points A, B, and C, and T_a, T_b, T_c are the magnitudes of the tensions in the cables to these points, then the equilibrium condition

$T_a\mathbf{u}_a + T_b\mathbf{u}_b + T_c\mathbf{u}_c + \mathbf{w} = \mathbf{0}$, where $\mathbf{w} = -50\,g\,\mathbf{k}$ is

the force of gravity acting on the sphere, must hold.

$$\frac{3}{\sqrt{10}}T_a - \frac{3}{\sqrt{61}}T_b - \frac{3}{\sqrt{154}}T_c = 0$$

$$-\frac{4}{\sqrt{61}}T_b + \frac{9}{\sqrt{154}}T_c = 0$$

$$\frac{1}{\sqrt{10}}T_a + \frac{6}{\sqrt{61}}T_b + \frac{4}{77\sqrt{154}}T_c = 490.5$$

This gives rise to the three equations above, whose solution is $T_a = 203.68$, $T_b = 348.27$, $T_c = 245.94$.

Maple Solution

• Tools > Load Package: Student Linear Algebra	Loading Student:-LinearAlgebra

• Define position vectors to points A, B, C.	$\mathbf{A}, \mathbf{B}, \mathbf{C} := \langle 6, 0, 2 \rangle, \langle -3, -4, 6 \rangle, \langle -3, 9, 8 \rangle :$
• Define unit vectors along $\mathbf{A}$, $\mathbf{B}$, $\mathbf{C}$.	$\mathbf{u}_a, \mathbf{u}_b, \mathbf{u}_c := (Normalize{\sim}([A, B, C]))[\ ] :$
• Define $\mathbf{w}$ and a zero vector.	$\mathbf{w}, \mathbf{ZERO} := \langle 0, 0, -50 \cdot 9.81 \rangle, \langle 0, 0, 0 \rangle :$
• Equate components on the two sides of the equilibrium equation, then solve the resulting equations.	$Eq := Equate\left(T_a \mathbf{u}_a + T_b \mathbf{u}_b + T_c \mathbf{u}_c + \mathbf{w}, \mathbf{ZERO} \right) :$

fsolve(*Eq*)

$$\{ T_a = 203.6794292, \ T_b = 348.2661333, \ T_c = 245.9371685 \}$$

Maple note: The tilde operator maps the **Normalize** command onto the members of the list. The empty list brackets at the end change the resulting list to a sequence so that the multiple assignment can be made.

Problem 30

In the figure to the right, collars at A and B slide (without friction) on smooth rods whose ends are at the coordinates (in meters) shown. The collars are connected by a cable that is 2 m in length. If collars A and B, weighing 13 and 10 kg, respectively, are in equilibrium, determine their positions on the rods, the tension in the cable, and the normal forces.	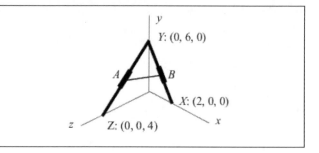

Mathematical Solution

The free-body diagram to the right shows three forces acting on the collars: the normal forces $\mathbf{N}_a$, $\mathbf{N}_b$ exerted by the rods; the weights $\mathbf{W}_a$, $\mathbf{W}_b$; and the tensile force $\mathbf{T}$ exerted by the cable.

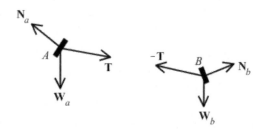

Equilibrium implies the two equations

$$\mathbf{W}_a + \mathbf{N}_a + \mathbf{T} = \mathbf{0} \ \text{ and } \ \mathbf{W}_b + \mathbf{N}_b - \mathbf{T} = \mathbf{0}$$

Because of the constraint exerted by a rod, it takes only one parameter to locate a collar along the rod. If $\mathbf{XY}$ and $\mathbf{ZY}$ are respectively vectors from X and Z to Y, then points on the lines from X to Y and Z to Y are respectively given by $\mathbf{X} + b \mathbf{XY}$, and $\mathbf{Z} + a \mathbf{ZY}$., where $) \le a, b \le 1$. The vectors $\mathbf{W}_a$ and $\mathbf{W}_b$ are respectively $-13 \, g \mathbf{j}$ and $-10 \, g \mathbf{j}$, where $g = 9.81$ is the gravitational constant. A vector from A to B is $\mathbf{AB} = (\mathbf{X} + b \mathbf{XY}) - (\mathbf{Z} + a \mathbf{ZY})$ and this vector must have length 2, so we have the constraint $\|\mathbf{AB}\| = 2$. The normal forces $\mathbf{N}_a$, $\mathbf{N}_b$ are perpendicular to the rods, so $\mathbf{N}_a \cdot \mathbf{ZY} = 0 = \mathbf{N}_b \cdot \mathbf{XY}$.

The normal forces can be eliminated from the equilibrium equations by dotting these equations with the vectors $\mathbf{ZY}$ and $\mathbf{XY}$, respectively. It T is the magnitude of the tension in the cable, then the equilibrium equations become

$$\mathbf{ZY} \cdot \left(\mathbf{W}_a + T\,\mathbf{AB}/2 \right) = 0 \ \text{ and } \ \mathbf{XY} \cdot \left(\mathbf{W}_b - T\,\mathbf{AB}/2 \right) = 0$$

These two equations, and the constraint on the length of $\mathbf{AB}$, are solved simultaneously for $a = 0.5695120134$, $b = 0.5166793969$, $T = 306.9416523$. This locates A at $(0, 3.42, 1.72)$; and B at $(0.97, 3.10, 0)$. Finally,

$$\mathbf{N}_a = - \left(\mathbf{W}_a + T\,\mathbf{AB}/2 \right) = -148.35\,\mathbf{i} + 176.18\,\mathbf{j} + 264.27\,\mathbf{k} \ \Rightarrow \ \|\mathbf{N}_a\| = 350.55$$

$$\mathbf{N}_b = - \left(\mathbf{W}_b - T\,\mathbf{AB}/2 \right) = 148.35\,\mathbf{i} + 49.45\,\mathbf{j} - 264.27\,\mathbf{k} \ \Rightarrow \ \|\mathbf{N}_b\| = 307.07$$

Maple Solution

• Tools > Load Package: Student Linear Algebra	Loading Student:-LinearAlgebra
• Define the position vectors $\mathbf{X}$, $\mathbf{Y}$, $\mathbf{Z}$.	$\mathbf{X, Y, Z} := \langle 2, 0, 0 \rangle, \langle 0, 6, 0 \rangle, \langle 0, 0, 4 \rangle;$ $$\begin{bmatrix} 2 \\ 0 \\ 0 \end{bmatrix}, \begin{bmatrix} 0 \\ 6 \\ 0 \end{bmatrix}, \begin{bmatrix} 0 \\ 0 \\ 4 \end{bmatrix}$$
• Define the vectors $\mathbf{ZY}$ and $\mathbf{XY}$.	$\mathbf{ZY, XY} := \mathbf{Y} - \mathbf{Z}, \mathbf{Y} - \mathbf{X}$ $$\begin{bmatrix} 0 \\ 6 \\ -4 \end{bmatrix}, \begin{bmatrix} -2 \\ 6 \\ 0 \end{bmatrix}$$
• Define the position vectors $\mathbf{A}$, and $\mathbf{B}$, and the vector $\mathbf{AB}$ from $\mathbf{A}$ to $\mathbf{B}$.	$\mathbf{A, B, AB} := \mathbf{Z} + a\,\mathbf{ZY}, \mathbf{X} + b\,\mathbf{XY}, \mathbf{B} - \mathbf{A}$ $$\begin{bmatrix} 0 \\ 6\,a \\ 4 - 4\,a \end{bmatrix}, \begin{bmatrix} 2 - 2\,b \\ 6\,b \\ 0 \end{bmatrix}, B - A$$

• Define the vectors $\mathbf{W}_a$ and $\mathbf{W}_b$.	$\mathbf{W}_a, \mathbf{W}_b := \langle 0, -13\,g, 0 \rangle, \langle 0, -10\,g, 0 \rangle$
	$$\begin{bmatrix} 0 \\ -13\,g \\ 0 \end{bmatrix}, \begin{bmatrix} 0 \\ -10\,g \\ 0 \end{bmatrix}$$

• Write the three governing equations for the parameters a, b, and T.

$expand\left(\mathbf{ZY} \cdot \left(\mathbf{W}_a + T\,\mathbf{AB}/2\right)\right) = 0$

$$-78\,g + 18\,T\,b - 26\,T\,a + 8\,T = 0 \tag{37.9}$$

$expand\left(\mathbf{XY} \cdot \left(\mathbf{W}_b - T\,\mathbf{AB}/2\right)\right) = 0$

$$2\,T - 20\,T\,b - 60\,g + 18\,T\,a = 0 \tag{37.10}$$

$\|\mathbf{AB}\|^2 = 2^2$

$$20 - 8\,b + 40\,b^2 - 72\,b\,a + 52\,a^2 - 32\,a = 4 \tag{37.11}$$

• Solve for a, b, and T. There are two solutions, only one of which locates the collars along the rods.

$S := solve(\{(\mathbf{4.9}), (\mathbf{4.10}), (\mathbf{4.11})\}, \{a, b, T\}, Explicit):$
$S_1 ; S_2$

$$\left\{ T = -\frac{3}{7}\,g\sqrt{5330}, a = 1 + \frac{22}{3731}\sqrt{5330}, b = 1 + \frac{19}{2870}\sqrt{5330} \right\}$$

$$\left\{ T = \frac{3}{7}\,g\sqrt{5330}, a = 1 - \frac{22}{3731}\sqrt{5330}, b = 1 - \frac{19}{2870}\sqrt{5330} \right\}$$

• Into the "correct" solution substitute the value for g, the gravitational constant. Note the value of T.	$SS := evalf\left(S_2 \Big|_{g=9.81} \right)$
	$\{T = 306.9416522, a = 0.5695120135, b = 0.5166793969\}$

| • Obtain the positions of collars A and B. | $[A, B]\Big|_{SS} = \begin{bmatrix} \begin{bmatrix} 0 \\ 3.417072081 \\ 1.721951946 \end{bmatrix}, \begin{bmatrix} 0.966641206 \\ 3.100076381 \\ 0 \end{bmatrix} \end{bmatrix}$ |

• Obtain the vectors $\mathbf{N}_a$ and $\mathbf{N}_b$.

$\mathbf{N}_a := -\left(\mathbf{W}_a + T\mathbf{AB}/2\right)\Big|_{SS\,\cup\,\{g\,=\,9.81\}} \quad : \mathbf{N}_b := -\left(\mathbf{W}_b - T\mathbf{AB}/2\right)\Big|_{SS\,\cup\,\{g\,=\,9.81\}} \quad :$ $\mathbf{N}_a, \mathbf{N}_b$ $$\begin{bmatrix} -148.3512244 \\ 176.1795920 \\ 264.2693876 \end{bmatrix}, \begin{bmatrix} 148.3512244 \\ 49.45040805 \\ -264.2693876 \end{bmatrix}$$	
Obtain the magnitudes of the normal forces $\mathbf{N}_a$ and $\mathbf{N}_b$.	$\|\mathbf{N}_a\| = 350.5504867$ $\|\mathbf{N}_b\| = 307.0695977$

Appendix: Answers to Quick Quiz and selected Further Study questions

Chapter 1

1. (a) iv, (b) iv, (c) i, (d) ii, (e) i, (f) ii, (g) ii, (h) ii, (i) iv, (j) i.

Chapter 2

1. (a) ii, (b) v, (c) i, (d) ii, (e) iv, (f) ii, (g) ii, (h) ii, (i) iv, (j) iv.

Chapter 3

1. (a) iii, (b) ii, (c) i, (d) iii, (e) iii, (f) iii, (g) iv, (h) iii, (i) ii, (j) iv.

Chapter 4

1. (a) iv, (b) i, (c) iii, (d) iv, (e) ii, (f) i, (g) iv, (h) i, (i) ii. (j) iii.

Chapter 5

1. (a) iii, (b) i, (c) iii, (d) ii, (e) iv, (f) iii, (g) i, (h) v, (i) iv, (j) iii.

Chapter 6

1. (a) iv, (b) ii, (c) ii, (d) ii, (e) iii, (f) ii, (g) iii, (h) iv, (i) iv, (j) ii.

Chapter 7

1. (a) iii, (b) iv, (c) i, (d) ii, (e) ii, (f) i, (g) v, (h) iii, (i) ii, (j) i.

Chapter 8

1. (a) i, (b) ii, (c) iv, (d) iii, (e) iii, (f) iii, (g) iii, (h) iv, (i) i, (j) ii.

2. Part of the fault tree is shown below.

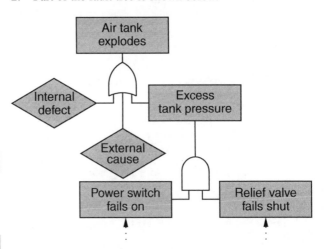

Chapter 9

1. (a) ii, (b) iii, (c) iv, (d) iv, (e) iii, (f) ii, (g) iii, (h) ii, (i) iv, (j) iii.

Chapter 10

1. (a) i, (b) ii, (c) v, (d) ii, (e) i, (f) iv, (g) iii, (h) i, (i) iv, (j) iv.

2.   From the given formula, $I = My/\sigma$; therefore, the dimensions of I are

$$\frac{[F][L] \times [L]}{[F]/[L]^2} = [L]^4,$$

that is, the dimensions of I are length to the fourth power. This parameter is a shape factor that determines how beams of different cross-section resist bending. It is called the area moment of inertia of the beam section and is calculated as $\int y^2 \, dA$, where the integral is over the area of the beam cross-section.

3.   From Newton's second law, $f = ma$, the mass is $m = (100 \, \text{lb})/(32.17 \, \text{ft/sec}^2) = 3.11$ slug. Mass is unaffected by gravity and is identical on the Moon, where its weight will be

$$3.11 \, \text{slug} \times 1.62 \frac{m}{s^2} \times \frac{1 \, \text{ft}}{0.3048 \, \text{m}} = 16.5 \, \text{lb}.$$

4.   The units of miles per gallon are length/volume $=$ length^{-2}, whereas the units of litres per 100 km are volume/length $=$ length^2, so to convert a figure given in miles per gallon, we invert it and multiply by

$$1 \frac{\text{gallon}}{\text{mile}} \times \frac{1 \, \text{mile}}{1.609 \, \text{km}} \times \frac{3.785 \times 10^{-3} \, \text{m}^3}{1 \, \text{gallon}}$$

$$\times \frac{1 \, \text{litre}}{10^{-3} \, \text{m}^3} \times \frac{100 \, \text{km}}{100 \, \text{km}} = \frac{378.5 \, \text{litre}}{1.609 \times 100 \, \text{km}}$$

$$= 235.2 \frac{\text{litre}}{100 \, \text{km}}.$$

5.   Energy is power $\times$ time, so the energy converted to heat is

$$(10^2 \times 200) \, \text{W} \times 3 \, \text{min} \times \frac{60 \, \text{s}}{1 \, \text{min}} = 3.6 \, \text{MJ}$$

$$= 3.6 \times 10^6 \, \text{N} \cdot \text{m} \times \frac{1 \, \text{lb}}{4.448 \, \text{N}} \times \frac{1 \, \text{ft}}{0.3048 \, \text{m}}$$

$$= 2.66 \times 10^6 \, \text{ft} \cdot \text{lb}.$$

6.   The dimensional equation is

$$(\text{dimensions of } T) = (\text{dimensions of } \ell)^a$$
$$\times (\text{dimensions of } g)^b (\text{dimensions of } m)^c,$$

or, substituting,

$$[T] = [L]^a \times ([L]/[T]^2)^b \times [M]^c$$

from which we see that $c = 0$ to eliminate the dimension of mass [M], $b = -0.5$ to make [T] a factor, and $a = -b$ to eliminate [L]. Thus the period T is proportional to $\ell^{0.5} g^{-0.5} m^0 = \sqrt{\ell/g}$. In fact, from a detailed analysis, it turns out that $T = 2\pi \sqrt{\ell/g}$.

Chapter 11

1.   (a) iv, (b) ii, (c) i, (d) iii, (e) iii, (f) iv, (g) iii, (h) ii, (i) iii, (j) i.

6.   With the operands expressed to the same power of 10, the computation is as follows, where the trailing zeros in $3100 (= 0.3100 \times 10^4)$ are shown as possibly not significant.

2.840 2	$\times 10^4$	
1.30	$\times 10^4$	
$-0.31(00?)$	$\times 10^4$	
0.003 289 734	$\times 10^4$	
3.833 489 734	$\times 10^4$	(computed exactly)
3.83	$\times 10^4$	(rounded)

The trailing zeros in 0.3100×10^4 are less significant than the trailing zero of 1.30×10^4 and are dropped. The fourth operand has seven significant digits and is the most precise but contributes nothing to the rounded result.